# Antennas Mastered

**by Peter Dodd, G3LDO**

**Compiled and edited by**

**Steve Telenius-Lowe, PJ4DX**

**Radio Society of Great Britain**

Published by the Radio Society of Great Britain, 3 Abbey Court, Fraser Road, Priory Business Park, Bedford MK44 3WH. Tel: 01234 832700. Web: www.rsgb.org

Published 2014

Reprinted 2015 & 2017



ISBN: 9781 9101 9303 7

Compiled by: Steve Telenius-Lowe, PJ4DX
Cover design: Kevin Williams, M6CYB
Production: Mark Allgar, M1MPA

Printed in Great Britain by Hobbs the Printers Ltd. of Totton, Hampshire

*Publisher's Note:*
The opinions expressed in this book are those of the authors and are not necessarily those of the Radio Society of Great Britain. Whilst the information presented is believed to be correct, the publishers and their agents cannot accept responsibility for consequences arising from any inaccuracies or omissions.

# Contents

# Foreword

This book is mainly a compendium of reprinted articles from the 'Antennas' column of *RadCom* from the period January 2002 until December 2013. It follows a tradition of such publications: a previous similar book on the subject was Pat Hawker's *Antenna Topics*, containing the cuttings from 'Technical Topics' during the period from 1958 to 1999.

I mentioned in the 'Antennas' column at an early date that: "The main purpose of this column is to address problems readers may have installing and adjusting antennas from suburban sites that may be regarded as a challenge; although any antenna subject that is considered to be of interest to readers will be discussed or described".

Also contained within these pages are several articles that I have written for *RadCom*, the first of these being a method of modelling HF antennas using VHF antennas written in December 1972; long before computer modelling was available to amateurs. Antenna theory is covered rather indirectly by describing the construction and use of RF measuring equipment and their uses. 'The User Friendly Smith Chart' is one of these examples you will find within this book.

Unlike most technical books, where the material is organised into subject chapters, here the subjects are discussed in the date order they were written. These discussions were often determined by readers' feedback and questions. However, a comprehensive Index is provided to allow the reader to access any specific subject.

Some of the pages carry a numbered note ("Note [x]"), which refer to information in the 'Notes' section. These refer to comments by readers and additional information that has emerged since the particular article was originally written as well as any corrections. Because the original material was printed in colour, photo captions that refer to colour are given additional explanations in these notes where it is considered necessary.

***Peter Dodd, G3LDO***
***July 2014***

**PETER DODD, G3LDO**
*37 The Ridings, East Preston, West Sussex, BN16 2TW*

WELCOME to the 'Antennas' column. As you are all aware, the single most critical item determining the performance of an amateur radio station is the antenna. The main purpose of the column is to address problems readers may have installing and adjusting antennas from suburban sites that may be regarded as a challenge; although any antenna subject that is considered to be of interest to readers will be discussed or described.

## MOXON RECTANGLE

THE YAGI antenna is probably the most effective way of obtaining gain and directivity. However, the 10m + 'wingspan' of a conventional Yagi for 20m can be a problem for many locations and many attempts have been made to make a more compact antenna. These include using loading coils or by simply bending the elements.

With antennas there is very little that is actually new and a two-element Yagi with bent elements certainly falls into this category. A configuration, where the elements of a two-element beam were bent so that the 'wingspan' was halved, was first suggested by John Reinartz, W1QP, way back in October 1937. Burton Simson, W8CPC, constructed such an antenna [1], the elements of which were supported on a wooden frame. This allowed the element ends to be folded towards each other. The 14MHz antenna was constructed from 1/4in copper tubing with brass tuning rods that fitted snugly into the ends of the elements for tuning.

A wire edition of the W1QP / W8CPC two-element antenna was described in 1973 by VK2ABQ [2]. In this configuration the tips of the parasitic and driven elements support each other in the horizontal plane. The insulators are constructed so that the tips of the elements are 6mm (1/4in) apart.

Les Moxon, G6XN, did a lot of experimental work with the two-element Yagi with bent elements [3], particularly in optimising the element spacing. However, some of these structures are complex and difficult to reproduce. A simplified, although slightly larger structure, was devised by L B Cebik, W4RNL (see WWW. below). This he named the Moxon Rectangle, and it is shown in **Fig 1**.

The remarkable characteristic of this arrangement is its very high front-to-back ratio. It also has a feed impedance close to 50Ω. The dimensions for the Moxon rectangle for 40 to 10 metres are given in **Table 1**. The dimensions are not perfect scaling because the length-to-wire-diameter ratio changes for each band.

The antenna has a feedpoint impedance between about 56 and 58Ω, a close match to the standard amateur 50Ω coaxial cable. Free space gain and front-to-back ratio are consistent for all the models, averaging 5.8dBi and greater than 30dB in free space, respectively.

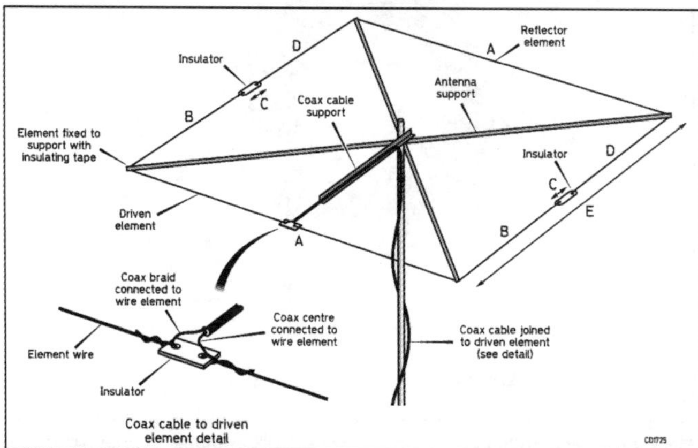


**Fig 1: Perspective view of the Moxon Rectangle showing the general construction. The element supports can be made from weather treated cane or fibreglass.**

| Freq MHz | A | B | C | D | E | A+B+B | A+D+D |
|---|---|---|---|---|---|---|---|
| | Dimensions, metres (*mm) | | | | | | |
| 29.50 | 3.79 | 0.59 | 125* | 0.74 | 1.45 | 4.97 | 5.27 |
| 24.94 | 4.33 | 0.67 | 140* | 0.84 | 1.66 | 5.67 | 6.0 |
| 21.20 | 5.00 | 0.80 | 158* | 0.99 | 1.95 | 6.6 | 6.98 |
| 18.12 | 5.96 | 0.94 | 180* | 1.16 | 2.28 | 7.84 | 8.28 |
| 14.17 | 7.62 | 1.22 | 219* | 1.48 | 2.92 | 10.06 | 10.58 |
| 10.12 | 10.66 | 1.71 | 305* | 2.07 | 4.08 | 14.08 | 14.8 |
| 7.15 | 15.10 | 2.75 | 405* | 2.93 | 5.73 | 20.6 | 20.96 |

**Table 1: Dimensions for the W4RNL-designed Moxon Rectangle beam. Refer to Fig 1 for dimensions A to E. These dimensions have been calculated using *EZNEC* for a non-critical design to give a free-space gain around 5.8dBi and a front-to-back ratio greater than 30dB. The elements are constructed from 1.6mm diameter copper wire. A+B+B is the driven element total length and A+D+D is the reflector total length. Remember to add additional wire for fixing the elements to the insulators.**

In *Backyard Antennas* [4], I stated that the Moxon Rectangle could be made into a multi-band antenna by simply interlacing the elements for the different bands on a common support structure. This was based on the diagram shown in Fig 12.11 of [3]. VK2ABQ [2] also describes this method of multibanding his antenna.

Some time after [4] was published I decided to build a *multiband* Moxon Rectangle and ran into some difficulties. I had previously built a multiband Double-D antenna (another antenna with bent elements, see [4]), which worked fine, so I had not expected any problems. No amount of playing with element lengths resolved the problem. I found I was not alone with this difficulty. From the L B Cebik, W4RNL, web site I found the following regarding this antenna: "I have had a number of inquiries into multi-banding the Moxon Rectangle. The compact antenna seems to beg for nesting. However, to the present time, I have had no success in developing a workable model of the antenna for any HF band combination in the nested configuration. In Moxon's book, *HF Antennas for All Locations*, G6XN notes a detuning system that he uses with his wire version. However, the wire spacing required by the system makes for a bad model. Consequently, I cannot say whether or not the system would work with aluminium rectangles, each of which has been optimised for its band."

W4RNL describes a number of solutions to multibanding the Moxon Rectangle but none of these is simple. I feel that the reason that, while multibanding works fine for the VK2ABQ and the Double-D, the parasitic element / driven element coupling on the Moxon rectangle is much more critical and is more easily disturbed by antenna elements of adjacent bands.

The antenna would probably work as a multi-band antenna if the element supports, shown in Fig 1, are set 90 degrees to each other; so that the antenna is a square rather than a rectangle. This arrangement would only work provided that the bands are an approximate octave apart (14, 21, 28 or 10, 18, 24MHz). The element lengths shown in Table 1 (A+B+B and A+D+D) are a good starting point. The driven elements can all be connected together and fed with one feeder.

I should point out, from the experiments that I have done, that the Moxon Rectangle is an excellent single-band antenna.

I would be pleased to hear from any readers who have built a multi-band antenna similar to those described above.

## FURTHER READING

[1] 'Concentrated Directional Antennas for Transmission and Reception', *QST* October 1937, John Reinartz, W1QP and Burton Simson W8CPC.

[2] 'VK2ABQ Antenna', Fred Caton, VK2ABQ, *Electronics Australia*, October 1973.

[3] *HF Antennas for all Locations*, 1984 Edn, Les Moxon, G6XN, RSGB.

[4] *Backyard Antennas*, Peter Dodd, G3LDO, RSGB. ♦

WWW.

**Peter Dodd, G3LDO: www.g3ldo.co.uk**
**L B Cebik, W4RNL: http//www.cebik.com/**

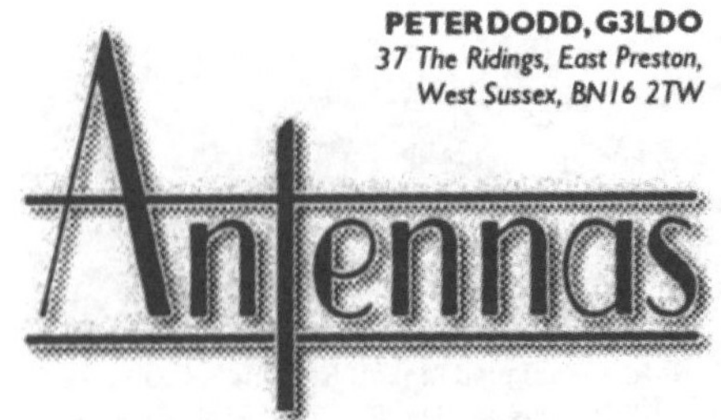


**PETER DODD, G3LDO**
*37 The Ridings, East Preston, West Sussex, BN16 2TW*

RADIO AMATEURS, unlike most commercial stations, normally use the same antenna for HF transmitting and receiving. While this is good practice on the upper frequency bands when using a beam antenna, it may not be the best solution on the lower bands. Vertical and loop antennas close to the house are liable to pick up electrical interference together with television line and switched-mode PSU noise. There are low-noise antennas for the LF bands, such as the Beverage; however, this antenna needs to be at least one-wavelength long on its lowest operating frequency, which rules it out for most suburban gardens.

Another solution to reducing receiver noise is to use a small loop antenna, orientated so that the null is in the direction of the QRM source.

The latest weapon in the QRM battle is the 'EWE' antenna, which was first described by Floyd Koonz, WA2WVL [1, 2]. The general configuration of the antenna is shown in **Fig 1**.

Stewart Cameron, GM4UTP, suffered QRM from a neighbour's television set. In the course of seeking a solution he came across the EWE antenna. [3]. GM4UTP notes "I cannot recommend it highly enough as a receiving antenna. It has put paid to the Bush TV EMC problems. The noise level is cut by two-thirds on a noisy 80m band and the signal-to-noise level has been improved by one S-point."

Provided that the antenna is electrically small it will produce a directivity pattern similar to that shown in **Fig 2**. The GM4UTP EWE antenna for the 3.7MHz band has a total length of 12.08m; 3m vertical (L1) at each end with 6.08m horizontal (L2). The antenna is terminated with a 600Ω non-inductive resister (carbon or metal film) at one end to ground connection. The diagrams shown in Fig 2 are for the GM4UTP antenna.

A similar antenna has been constructed by Jim Smith, VK9NS [4]. His antenna is designed for 160m; the length of L1 is 3.1m (10.1ft) and L2, 21m (68.9ft). The lengths were chosen so that they are supported with the poles of his 40m four-square array. I should mention that Jim has four EWE antennas that can be switched to provide 360 degrees of coverage. The antennas are terminated using with two 2.2k resistors in parallel (1.1k). He also uses a pre-amplifier to overcome the loss of the EWE antenna.

Laurie Mayhead, G3AQC, also uses the EWE antenna to good effect on 136kHz. On the south coast of the UK there is considerable interference from the Loran station at Lessay in

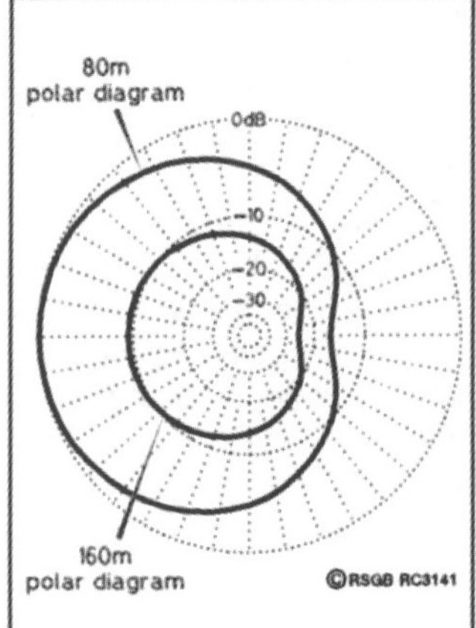


**Fig 2: Polar diagrams for the EWE antenna at 80m and 160m. The zero dB scale is around -22dBi. The polar diagram is remarkably similar over a wide range of frequencies with an increase in gain and loss of directivity as the frequency is increased.**

northern France, which is less than 100km away from Laurie's QTH. Spectral lines from this station seriously degraded reception when he uses his large omni-directional inverted-L transmitting antenna on receive.

By using an EWE antenna G3AQC is able to orientate the antenna with the null in the direction of Lessay and he reports that a deep null can be obtained by adjusting the values of the terminating resistor. A variable capacitor in series with the terminating resistor has also proved beneficial in this respect. His antenna is orientated NE / SW with its maximum response towards northern Europe and Scandinavia. Signals have been received on 136kHz from OH1TN at 579. The G3AQC EWE antenna dimensions are L1 6.1m (20ft) and L2 106m (350ft). This antenna has a front-to-back ratio of over 13dB. When the dimensions of this antenna are scaled into the 160m band they are L1 just 460mm and L2 8m!

The EWE antenna is reported to have a feed impedance of between 600 and 2000Ω. Most of the antennas I looked at were about 800 -jX400. Matching is not all that critical on receive and the standard method seems to be to use a 3:1 transformer, which gives a 9:1 impedance ratio, ie 450Ω to 50Ω or 75Ω to 675Ω.

The transformer can be wound on a toroid core as shown in **Fig 3** using enamelled covered wire or even thin plastic covered wire, which allows colour coding. VK9NS wound his transformer on a short length of ferrite rod.

## FURTHER READING

[1] 'Is this EWE for You', Floyd Koonz, WA2WVL, *QST*, February 1995.

[2] 'More EWEs for you', Floyd Koonz, WA2WVL, *QST*, January 1996.

[3] *Antenna Toolkit* (pages 83 to 86), Joe Carr. Available from RSGB Sales, price £21.24 (members) inc free CD-ROM.

[4] 'EWE "four" me', James Smith, VK9NS, *The ARRL Antenna Compendium, Vol 5*. Available from RSGB Sales, price £15.29 (members). ♦

WWW.
www.g3ldo.co.uk

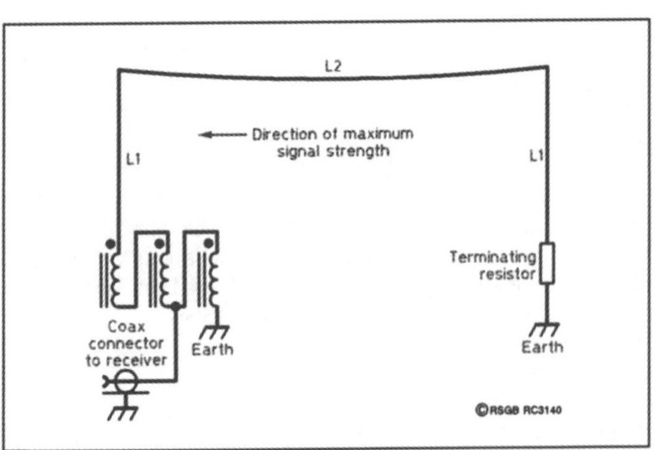


**Fig 1: The EWE antenna. The terminating resistor value is not critical and any value from 700 to 2000Ω seems to work although different values affect the front-to-back ratio but not the gain. For dimensions L1 and L2 see text. Maximum directivity is away from the termination.**

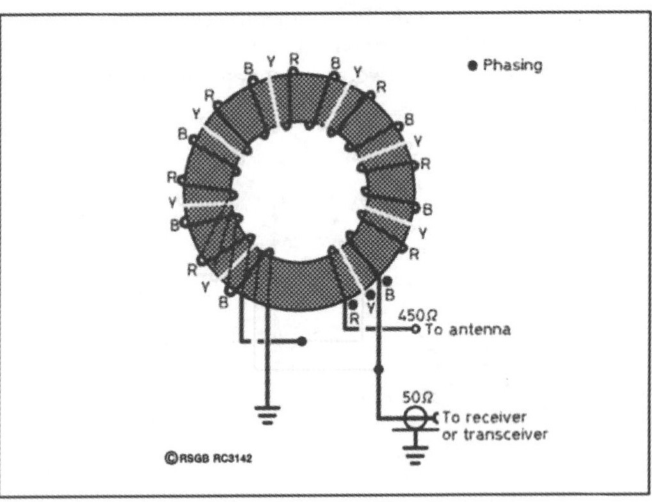


**Fig 3: Suitable matching transformer for the EWE antenna. In practice around 12 turns trifilar-wound on a T50 core are required. The wires are shown colour-coded to clarify the connections.**

See Note [1]

**PETER DODD, G3LDO**
*37 The Ridings, East Preston, West Sussex, BN16 2TW*

THE MOXON Rectangle antenna, described in the January 'Antenna' column [1], created a lot of interest. As Ryan Pike, G5CL noted, "the appeal of this antenna is that it very simple to build and does not take up that much room. I should imagine many new Novices [now Intermediate - *Ed*] and Foundation Licence holders have been glad to get the 'low-down' on it, as home construction should be easy".

Dave Hulatt, G4WFQ, constructed a 10m-band Moxon Rectangle from some light multi-stranded insulated house wiring, using the dimensions quoted in [1]. The wire elements are supported using white plastic 12mm tubing, with holes drilled for the elements. The driven element is fed directly with RG239 coax. He erected the antenna in the loft of his house and the results were excellent. The Moxon out-performed the ground plane verticals and a G5RV by an average of three S-points.

G4WFQ's antenna is fixed so that it beams west. During the 2002 ARRL 'RTTY Round-Up' contest, he made 155 QSOs (working 40 states and 9 Canadian provinces) on the 10 metre band. He remarked that had he had additional similar antennas for 15 and 20 metres he could have put in a really big score. G4WFQ also commented that this is the first beam antenna he has had at his present QTH and had forgotten what it was like to have an antenna with gain.

Tony Box, G0HAD, described his experiences with a multiband VK2ABQ beam back in 1993. The overall size of this structure was 20 x 12ft and this was (as Les Moxon, G6XN, suggested in [2]) the optimum size. In view of the difficulties I had described with multibanding [1] I decided to investigate further.

The original VK2ABQ antenna is a square structure, see **Fig 1**. The driven element and the reflector are a quarter wavelength apart although the tips the elements support each other using insulators. These insulators are constructed so that the tips of the elements are 6mm (1/4in) apart and, according to the original description [3], capacitive end (voltage) couples the driven element to the reflector, as opposed to the coupling that occurs on a Yagi. The gap between the tips of the elements is described as 'not critical'. Multiband versions of this antenna were constructed without any known difficulty.

G6XN [2] changed the structure from a square to a rectangle, thereby reducing the centre section spacing of the elements from 0.25 wavelength spacing to 0.17 wavelength spacing. This resulted in improved gain and directivity, see **Fig 2**.

C B Cebik, W4RNL [4], reduced the element spacing further to 0.14 wavelength and obtained yet more gain and improved directivity. This antenna he called the Moxon Rectangle and was the one I described in [1]. The downside of this higher performance is the problem of multibanding.

Going back to G0HAD's description, he says, ". . . as the result of a packet request I was recommended to contact Les Ward, G4XGC, at Blandford, who was a recognised expert on these antennas. I was invited down to view Les's aerial farm and after a short demonstration, I was 'hooked'. By experiment it was found that the gaps between the tips of the elements needed to be a lot larger than published [2] and I followed Les Ward's suggestion of 22in for 20m, 15in for 15m and 10in for 10m, which seemed to work well. It certainly outperformed the previous commercial mini beam . . . I can't remember ever having any problems that could be put down to interaction between the bands, although I remember reading about such a possibility."

It would appear that if you want a multiband beam, the original G6XN antenna gives the best compromise between performance and multibanding.

Lack of space precludes constructional details although I hope to include this in a later column. Details on the construction of this antenna are given in [2] and [4]. Details of the construction of my single-band W4RNL Moxon Rectangle are described in [5].

I have been asked how to work out the length of the support (cane or fibreglass rod) structure required. It is simply the length, squared, plus the width, squared which gives the length of the support (squared). For example, if we wanted a support for a 20m W4RNL antenna:

$$\sqrt{7.62^2 + 2.92^2} = \sqrt{66.59} = 8.16m$$

This is the total length of the diagonal so you would halve that figure for the length of each support:

*8.16/2 = 4.08m (approx 13.4ft).*

## FURTHER READING

[1] 'Antennas', *RadCom*, January 2002.
[2] *HF Antennas for all Locations*, L A Moxon, G6XN.
[3] 'VK2ABQ Antenna', Fred Caton, VK2ABQ, *Electronics Australia*, October 1973.
[4] www.cebik.com/
[5] 'The Moxon Rectangle Revisited', Peter Dodd, G3LDO, *Practical Wireless*, June 2000. ♦

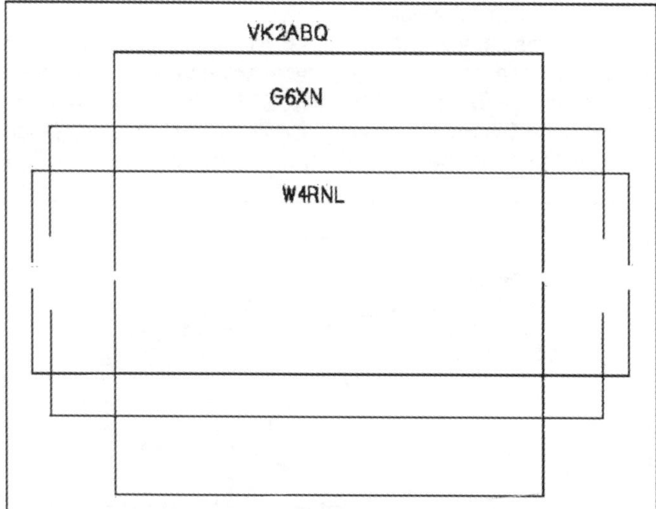


**Fig 1: The original VK2ABQ antenna structure compared with the G6XN and the W4RNL. The G6XN has a centre section spacing of the elements of around 0.17 wavelength spacing, while the W4RNL has element spacing reduced further to 0.14 wavelength.**

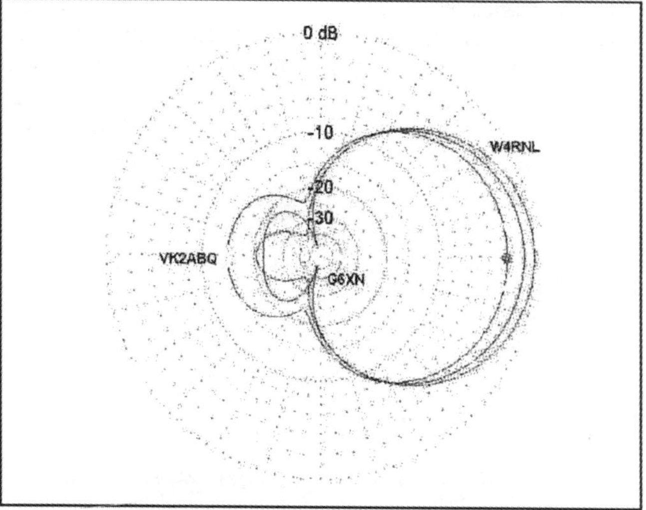


**Fig 2: Free-space antenna computer model (using *EZNEC*) showing the relative performances of the VK2ABQ antenna compared with the G6XN and the W4RNL. The calculated gain is 3.77dBi, 5.26dBi and 6.11dBi for the VK2ABQ, G6XN and W4RNL antennas respectively. Although the W4RNL gives the best performance as a single-band antenna, experience shows that problems occur if any attempt is made to construct a multiband model.**

**PETER DODD, G3LDO**
*37 The Ridings, East Preston, West Sussex, BN16 2TW*

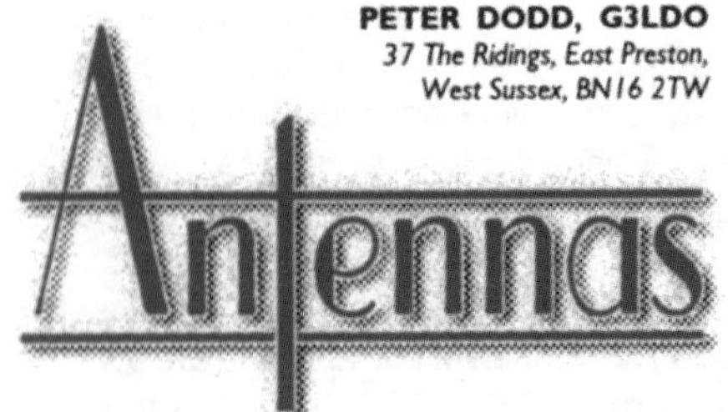


**The GM4UTP multiband antenna showing the inverted-V configuration. The antenna also supports a single quad element for 10 metres.**

IF YOU DO NOT have an ATU and you wish to operate on all bands, you need a multiband antenna that presents a near to 50Ω feed impedance on all bands. The G5RV is often the first antenna to come to mind, but an ATU is essential when using this antenna with a transceiver having a solid-state PA.

One solution is to use several dipoles fed in parallel from the same feed line. The length of each separate dipole is a half wavelength for each band so that each dipole presents a good impedance match to the feed line on the band for which it is intended and a poor match on all the others.

However, placing several dipoles in parallel can present some mechanical problems and there can be considerable interaction if the ends of the dipoles are spaced too close together. The ends of the dipoles must be arranged so they are far apart as practical. The only multiband dipole that I have used [1] is the example shown in **Fig 1**.

The multi-element structure is supported by the lowest-frequency dipole. Each dipole in the parallel-fed combination may be supported from different directions if different directions of radiation are desired and the space is available. This also has the advantage of placing the ends of the dipoles some distance apart. The ends of the lowest frequency dipole can be bent to fit into an available area if necessary, but the length will have to be increased slightly above the normal dipole length to get the lowest SWR.

## TWO OTHER SOLUTIONS

IF MORE THAN three parallel dipoles are used, using the construction method shown in Fig 1, the structure becomes complicated and difficult to manage. One solution is to use the G3BDQ 10-way ribbon cable arrangement, which is described and illustrated in [2]. This cable is 13mm wide and only 1.3mm thick and each of its conductors is made from 14 x 0.13mm tinned copper strands.

The cable can be obtained in complete lengths of up to 50m and a multiband antenna can made from a 40m section. The antenna is constructed by cutting away the unwanted parts of the cable. For this antenna to work, around 20% of each end of each higher frequency dipole is arranged so that it hangs down and away from the next supporting lower-frequency element.

This antenna, in common with other multiband arrangements, uses the inverted-V configuration with a single pole to support the centre insulator and coaxial cable feeder. Even so, the ribbon cable antenna will require some support because the weight of all the elements is carried by the lowest-frequency dipole. G3BDQ used 1mm diameter nylon cord, which was stitched into the multi-way ribbon cable with a packing needle using 500mm long 'stitches'.

Stewart, GM4UTP, uses a more rugged parallel dipole design. This arrangement uses the lowest frequency dipole to support the higher-frequency dipoles using spacing insulators made from 11mm plastic electrical conduit. The construction is shown in **Fig 2** and in the photo. The 24MHz dipole is not shown in Fig 2, but if included the element length each side of the centre insulator is 2.84 metres.

The antenna is configured as an inverted-V with the weight of the centre insulator and the 1:1 balun mounted on a 10m high aluminium scaffold pole. Low centre-band SWRs are possible if some time is spent tuning each dipole. This can be achieved by arranging the ends of the elements so that they are clear of their support insulators by about 200mm. The dipole lengths can be reduced or increased by folding back the end and securing with plastic tape.

The resonances of these dipoles can be interactive - when you adjust one it affects the resonance of the others, so be prepared to have to re-resonate elements.

A similar arrangement is described by K0GPD [3]. In this design all the spacer insulators are made the same length and a nylon cord is run from the end of the highest frequency dipole to the end of the multi-wire sections of the antenna to improve mechanical stability.

## REFERENCES

[1] *Backyard Antennas*, Peter Dodd, G3LDO (available from RSGB Sales).

[2] *Practical Wire Antennas*, John D Heys, G3BDQ (out of print).

[3] 'A Great 10 Through 40 Portable Antenna', Edward L Henry, K0GDP, *The ARRL Antenna Compendium, Volume 1* (available from RSGB Sales). ♦

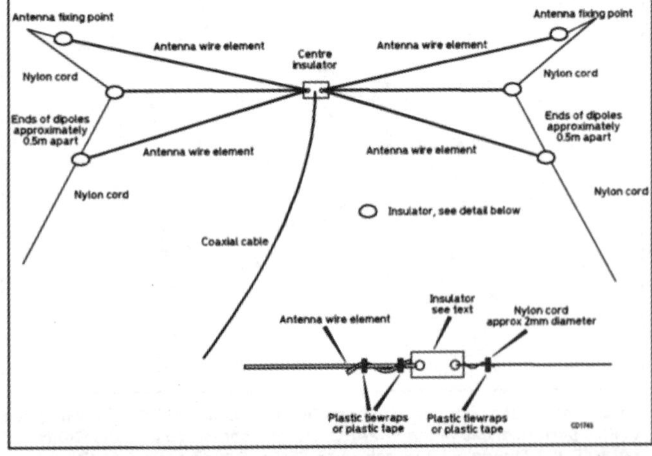


**Fig 1: Dipoles can be connected in parallel using a common coax feeder. Interaction can be minimised by keeping 500mm spacing or more between the ends of the wires. Each dipole end support should be adjusted to keep all the dipoles reasonably tight, which keeps them looking tidy and prevents them from getting tangled when they blow around in the wind.**

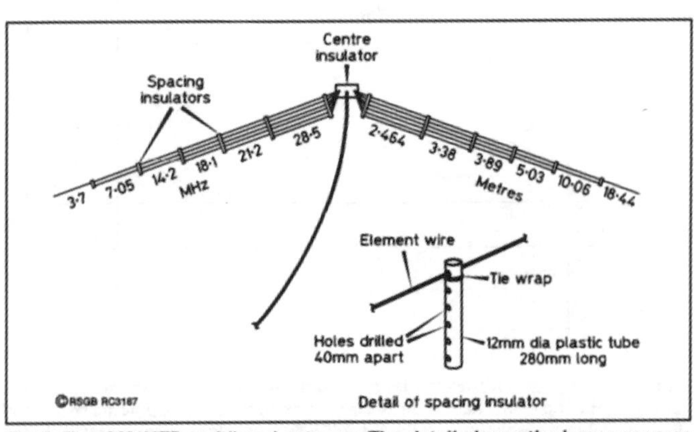


**Fig 2: The GM4UTP multiband antenna. The detail shows the larger spacers to accommodate six wires. The outer spacers are progressively shorter with holes drilled for five, four, three and two wires respectively.**

**PETER DODD, G3LDO**
*37 The Ridings, East Preston, West Sussex, BN16 2TW*
*E-mail: g3ldo@ukonline.co.uk*

**On the right, plastic-covered aluminium tube to be used as a durable alternative to cane for horticultural purposes. It even has annular ridges that make it look like cane. To the left is plastic-coated *real* cane.**

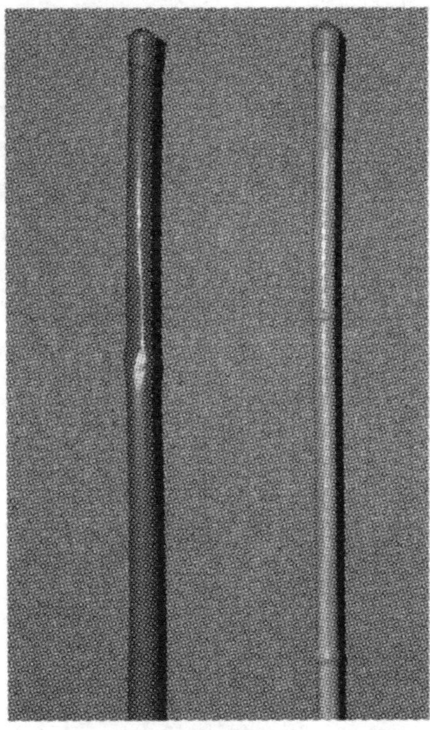

PETER Martinez, G3PLX, e-mailed me with some interesting facts about the EWE antenna [1] of which I was unaware. He says: "Your item on the EWE antenna was most interesting. I had never heard of it before under this name, but recognised it immediately. If you scale it right down in size to a few millimetres high and a few centimetres long, it's the sensor element in one of the classic SWR bridge designs. It's therefore possible to think of such an SWR bridge as being a directional antenna rather than a directional power sensor - it's just DFing the electromagnetic field within the coaxial cable in which it's placed! The plug-in sensors of the well-known Bird Thruline power meter is one of these, so it's really a tiny DF antenna that you poke into the line to see which way the energy is 'radiating' inside the line.

"If you scale it up it becomes a proper Beverage antenna. At an intermediate size you can make it square and balanced rather than build it over a groundplane, and have the resistor halfway along the back edge and the feedpoint halfway along the front edge. You could probably therefore improve the performance, particularly the front / back ratio, by adding a counterpoise wire between the two earth-points as shown in Fig 1 [1]. You can replace the resistor with a second feedpoint and bring a second feeder back into the shack, via a matching transformer of course, and then swap the resistor and the receiver between the two feeders to reverse the direction."

G3PLX adds: "If you do the maths, the required value of the resistor (and indeed the feed impedance, which is the same), is equal to the characteristic impedance of the wire above the ground. You can therefore make this lower by having more wires in parallel. If, instead of a wire you had a flat plate of width D and placed it at a height of D above the ground, the characteristic impedance becomes equal to that of free-space, namely 377Ω. From this you can see that practical versions of this antenna are always going to be rather high impedance.

"I recently saw this same principle used in a set of field-strength measuring antennas made by R&S. The Radiocommunications Agency field engineers have recently been issued with them. They are square loops made of broad flat sheet. Incidentally, because the directivity depends on the electric field and the magnetic field being in a specific amplitude ratio (the magic 377Ω number again), these antennas will only give a sharp null in the far field where this ratio holds true. I note reports from various people who suggest that loops are much better at rejecting local QRM than whips, which might mean that local QRM is predominantly E-field. If this is the norm, then I doubt if an EWE antenna could ever be very effective in nulling-out local QRM, and the same imbalance would apply if the local QRM field was predominantly magnetic."

## MOXON RECTANGLE MATERIAL

"HELLO DEAR, I've bought you a present - could you help me unload the car?" XYL Erica had been on a retail therapy session at a local garden centre. Amongst the hanging basket construction kits, flower pots, potting compost and other miscellaneous bits was my present, a bundle of green canes. These turned out to be 8ft (2.4m) canes coated in green plastic. Cane is often suggested as a material for any antenna that uses non-conducting wire element support structures, such as a quad or a Moxon Rectangle. While cane is cheap, lightweight and strong, its main disadvantage is that it is affected by weather unless adequately protected. On the face of it plastic-covered cane will overcome this disadvantage.

But beware. Some years ago I constructed a Double-D antenna [2] using what I thought was plastic-covered cane. I found it impossible to tune the antenna for either low SWR or directivity. I later discovered that the material was plastic-covered aluminium tube. The antenna performance (and my sanity) was restored when cane element supports were substituted.

As you can see from the photo there is very little visible difference between the two types of material. However, there are several clues. Plastic-covered cane is very rarely perfectly straight and the diameter tapers along its length. Plastic-covered tube *is* straight, has a constant diameter and gives a metallic sound when dropped on a hard surface.

The plastic-covered tube, shown in the photo, has languished in my antenna material junk pile for many years in all weathers and shows hardly any sign of deterioration except that it has become lighter in colour. This implies that the plastic-covered cane should make a durable wire element support.

I am constructing a Moxon Rectangle using this material and will give details of how it worked out in a later 'Antennas' column.

I have also included some construction and information on this antenna on my website (see WWW. below). Other references to this antenna are to be found at [3] and [4].

Plastic-coated bamboo canes were available in two of the many garden centres in my locality and from what I can gather they are imported from China. My canes were obtained from Country Fayre, Littlehampton Road, Ferring, West Sussex BN12 6PN (who regret they have no facilities for shipping canes). They were priced at £2.50 for a bundle of five canes, 8ft long. A rather more posh emporium, less than a mile away from my source, is selling the identical product for £4.99. Before you buy, inspect the canes to ensure that there is no damage to the plastic coating and that the end caps are securely in place.

## REFERENCES

[1] 'Antennas', *RadCom* January 2002.

[2] *The Antenna Experimenter's Guide* by Peter Dodd, G3LDO (RSGB).

[3] 'A Superbeam Experience on 24MHz', Vic Westmoreland, G3HKQ, *Practical Wireless* October 1996.

[4] 'The VK2ABQ Antenna Revisited', Vic Westmoreland, G3HKQ, *Practical Wireless* August 2000.

**WWW.**

**Peter Dodd, G3LDO** www.g3ldo.co.uk

PETER DODD, G3LDO
37 The Ridings, East Preston,
West Sussex, BN16 2TW

The plastic tube centre insulator for the GB2CPM multiband dipole

I WORK AS a part-time volunteer at Amberley industrial museum near Arundel. This museum [1] has an excellent vintage radio exhibition and GB2CPM is an operational amateur station associated with this exhibition. The existing G5RV antenna developed a fault so this seemed a good opportunity to test the multiband dipole described in the April edition of 'Antennas'. There was a spare coax feeder to the existing mast but no materials to hand such as insulators and antenna wire. A considerable amount of construction work had been undertaken during the winter months and I found some high-pressure blue plastic water pipe that seemed to fit the bill. This pipe is very tough and light and was used to make the centre insulator, end insulators and all the spacers.

For the antenna elements I used scrap telephone wire - the material that is used to make a telephone connection between a nearby distribution pole and a house. This material is excellent for antennas and comprises two plastic insulated copper-clad steel wires. The two insulated wires can be pulled apart to make a single wire but his must be done under tension otherwise it gets into a messy tangle.

The GB2CPM multiband dipole, configured as an inverted-V on the 7, 10, 14 and 18MHz bands and each dipole can be tuned without any noticeable interaction. All the other operators are very pleased with it.

## THE CFA ANTENNA

I HAVE BEEN asked if the Crossed Field Antenna (CFA) is a solution to operating from a very restricted QTH. I have never used one of these antennas, however, the CFA was reviewed in the May *RadCom* by Steve Nichols, G0KYA. The 40m version was the only one that performed well; however, this was fixed near the top of a 6m high mast and fed via 14m of coax. This begs the question of how would this compare with simple antenna comprising 14m of wire fixed to a 6m mast? Furthermore, I have no difficulty working EU and DX stations when operating mobile with an antenna 1.4m long.

The CFA theory represents a radical departure from conventional antenna theory. Progress in science evolves by new theories being independently tested to reproduce original claims, and for this to happen full details of any apparatus must be made available. With the CFA antenna this has not been done and I understand G0KYA was allowed to proceed with the review on condition that he did not reveal details of the new feed arrangements within the CFL which are the subject of a new patent. Several years ago I attended a lecture on the CFA antenna. It involved a lot of Maxwell equations and Poynting vectors and seemed to me more an exercise in obfuscation rather than elucidation.

You might like to consider the following, which is based on concepts we all understand. What follows is an edited extract from [2] by John Stanley, K4ERO, a broadcast engineering consultant. Empty space is a medium through which energy can be transmitted and any small volume of space can be considered as a multi-port network. As such, it has zero gain and no attenuation. Furthermore, it is perfectly linear and does not have a low power threshold or a saturation level. The implications of this linearity is that space can provide a medium through which any number of EM waves can propagate without mutual interaction. Light from the sun, radio waves and heat waves can all simultaneously pass through the square metre of space without interaction. A simple experimental demonstration of this is simply to cross two beams of light from two flashlights. Each beam passes through the other with no effects whatsoever. (So much for the Star Wars light-sabre duels!)

If there were interactions, as opposed to simple vector addition, we would be unable to send radio signals when the medium was saturated with sunlight. Also, just as a saturated amplifier produces intermodulation products, all of the light frequencies present in sunlight would mix together to produce a multitude of lower frequencies that would fill up the radio spectrum with noise.

The ability of space to contain a seemingly infinite number of EM waves also applies to electric and magnetic fields, which are not coupled as they are in the case of an EM wave. Furthermore, linearity guarantees that any combination of E and H fields may be contained in a given volume with no interaction whatsoever.

Any voltage or current pattern in a linear network is additive to any other voltage or current pattern, a phenomenon known as Superposition Theorem. NEC antenna analysis and other analysis related to antennas depend utterly on the validity of superposition. NEC, for example, calculates the net effect of many small current elements, each one producing an E field at a distant point. The sum of all these fields is the net field. The fact that NEC does work for so many types of antennas seems further proof of the validity of the superposition theory and, therefore, of the linearity of space. Since virtually all of EM theory uses superposition as a basis of its analysis, we cannot even imagine its falsity without overthrowing the whole of the theory.

EM radiation is produced directly by the acceleration of charge (RF currents) [3], and not through the production of E and H fields. Near fields are a parasitic effect, not an intermediate step in EM wave production. The theory of the CFA antenna suggests that the E and the H fields are generated separately and then combine in space to produce the EM wave, in other words, an interaction. This is not simple vector addition and such an E and H field metamorphosis in space would violate the principle of superposition. ♦

**WWW.**

[1] Amberley Museum:
www.amberleymuseum.co.uk
[2] John Stanley, K4ERO
http://members.aol.com/jnrstanley/mainpres.htm
[3] Peter Dodd, G3LDO (Radiation from an antenna)
**www.g3ldo.co.uk**

**PETER DODD, G3LDO**
*37 The Ridings, East Preston, West Sussex, BN16 2TW*

I RECEIVED a further e-mail from Peter Martinez, G3PLX, regarding the EWE antenna discussed in May 'Antennas'. He writes "Imagine a 1 metre cube which is metallised on the top and bottom surfaces. Between the centre of one edge of the top face and the corresponding point on the bottom face, connect a 377Ω resistor. A signal generator is then connected to the centres of the opposite faces, which is set to give an output of 1V. Now, stand in the centre of the cube with an E-field and an H-field probe. The E field here is clearly 1 volt per metre. Because of the presence of the 377Ω resistor at one edge, you can work out the current (=1 / 377A) flowing 'around' you and deduce the H field, which is exactly in the 377Ω ratio. It follows that the field at the centre of the cube is a true free-space TEM field (transverse electromagnetic field). Furthermore, it is also everywhere else (since it gets everywhere else by radiating from the centre). This antenna has no near field region. What I have described is known in the trade as a TEM cell and is used for EMC immunity measurements, but it is a crossed field antenna in that it intrinsically generates E and H in the 'right' ratio."

However, it is not a transmitting antenna. It has a calculated gain of around -15dBi on 28MHz and -50dBi on 3.5MHz.

## W4RNL

AN E-MAIL has been received from L B Cebik, W4RNL, who designed the Moxon rectangle, described in the March 'Antennas'. He writes: "I thought I might add some quick notes about my design aims. Initially, I strove for versions of the antenna with the best performance combined with a 50Ω feedpoint impedance for direct feed (with the usual choke for suppression of currents on the braid of the coax). This work culminated in a *GW BASIC* utility for designing rectangles with only two input variables - the element diameter and the design frequency (which I usually recommend to be about 1/3 up from the bottom of the desired band, given the manner in which performance and SWR curves go). This program is included in *HAMCALC* by VE3ERP, and a model-by-equation model for NEC-Win Plus is available at the NSI web site [1]. The benefit of the equation-based model is that one can run the emergent model and obtain a full profile of projected performance. The relevant item describing the program is at my site [2].

"I have used VHF and UHF Moxon rectangles as well as HF varieties. Vertically, their null is an almost ideal direction finder for 'foxhunts'. Or we can use three at equal angles and poll them for a repeater receiving antenna. Pointed straight up, we can turnstile a pair for a pattern with a broad dome of very nearly even gain above about 30° elevation. To simplify turnstiling, I redeveloped the design program, striving for about 95Ω feedpoint impedance (RG-62 becomes the phaseline and the result is a direct 50Ω feed from the turnstile array). The article shows the revised regression-based values for the equation-based model, which one can also plug into the *GW BASIC* program in place of the values for 50Ω versions, see [3]. As your March column shows, there is slightly less peak forward gain in the squarer 95Ω rectangle but, in satellite use, the dome is equal to the 50Ω version. However, the program itself is perfectly general (in both 50Ω and 95Ω versions), yielding buildable designs from very thin wire to quite fat tubing from the AM broadcast band through to 900MHz or so - where we should be using PCB construction."

## THE 'EFA' ANTENNA

IF YOU ARE a 160m or 80m operator, with an average-size garden, the EFA (Elevated Feed Antenna) described by Colin Draper, G3TSK, may be of interest to you. The layout is shown in **Fig 1**. It has a feedpoint at resonance of around 50Ω for a fair portion of the bands, so an ATU is not required.

The antenna is fed against earth, so a good RF earth is required for efficient operation. It also has a single buried insulated counterpoise. High voltages can be generated at the ends of the ground wire, (even with modest power levels), so the wire is insulated and taped at the end.

The antenna can be used with just the RF earth and no counterpoise, but the minimum SWR is about 1.4:1.

The loading coil is wound on a 21.5mm diameter round former, 254mm long. The windings consist of 292 turns of 21 or 22SWG enamelled copper wire (close wound), occupying a length of 240mm for the main body of the coil, with four turns at the high end occupying 10mm and three turns at the low end (nearest to the feedpoint) occupying 6mm. The winding is covered with shellac and the former and coil are then wrapped with 'stretch rubber tape' layered to give protection against the weather. The measured inductance using a home-brew inductance meter was approximately 150μH.

The EFA is adjusted for resonance using a dip meter coupled into a two-turn link at the feed point, altering the lengths shown in Fig 1. ♦

## WWW.

[1] NEC Win Plus www.nittany-scientific.com
[2] Equation-based model www.cebik.com/moxgen.html
[3] Use of [2] www.cebik.com/ms2.html

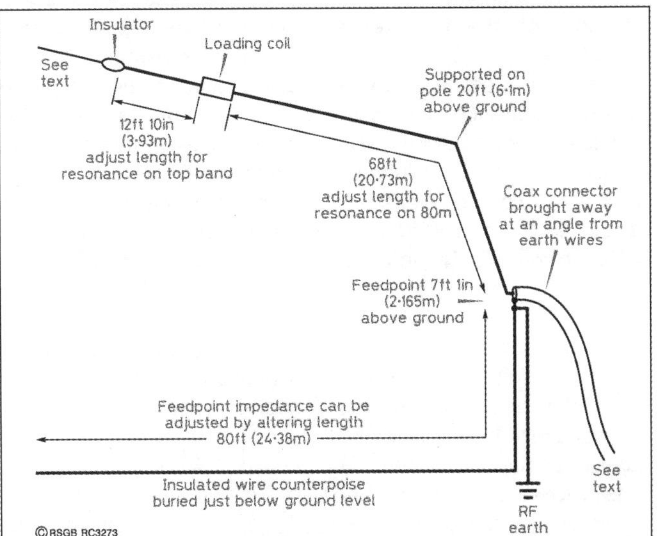


**Fig 1: The EFA antenna. The antenna feeder is coiled several times at ground level to choke off any antenna current that may be present on the feeder.**

**PETER DODD, G3LDO**
*37 The Ridings, East Preston, West Sussex, BN16 2TW*

MOST home-made beam antennas are constructed from designs published in amateur radio publications. Once the beam is constructed it is raised to its operating position, and provided the SWR is reasonable, and the antenna exhibits some directional properties, it is assumed that it is working correctly. In many cases this is true but there must always be the nagging doubt about its performance. Could be improved? Keen DXers and contest operators spend a lot of time optimising their beam antennas. This month, inspired by correspondence with Louis Thomas, GW4ZXG, regarding his quad, we will look at methods of doing this.

The dimensions of the driven element only affect the feed impedance and have little effect on the gain or directivity of the beam. For this reason, and because this column is limited to one page, I will only be considering a two-element quad and the tuning of the reflector.

The GW4ZXG antenna is a home-brew two-element two-band quad designed to operate on 10 and 15m. It uses short boom 'spider' construction with an element spacing of approximately 0.13λ for both antennas. It is mounted diamond pattern on an Altron telescopic tiltover tower with the boom approximately 40ft above ground. The mast can be tilted over so the antenna elements are easily accessible. In this way the reflector on each antenna can be resonated using a GDO, but the resonance changes when the antenna is raised to the operating height. A much better solution is to resonate the reflector at its operating height.

## THE GW4ZXG REMOTE TUNER

THIS IS A really neat idea, see **Fig 1**. It comprises tuning stubs of stiff copper wire about 0.84m (30in) long with 50mm (2in) spacing. A sprung metal paper (bulldog) clip is drilled and threaded on to the stub to form a sliding shorting bar. The stub is connected to the reflector element at the bottom of the 'diamond'. The ends of the stubs are taped to the fibreglass arm to hold them in a firm vertical position and a small simple pulley system using a small china 'egg' insulator is fixed to the arm just above the end of the stub. The clip is fixed, as shown in Fig 1, to a long nylon cord so that it may be slid up or down the stub whilst the antenna is at full working height and the operator is at ground level. GW4ZXG designed this stub for his diamond configuration antenna, with the tuning stub fixed to the lower reflector element support. With a conventional quad configuration, or any wire beam antenna such as the Moxon rectangle, a special stub support would have to be constructed.

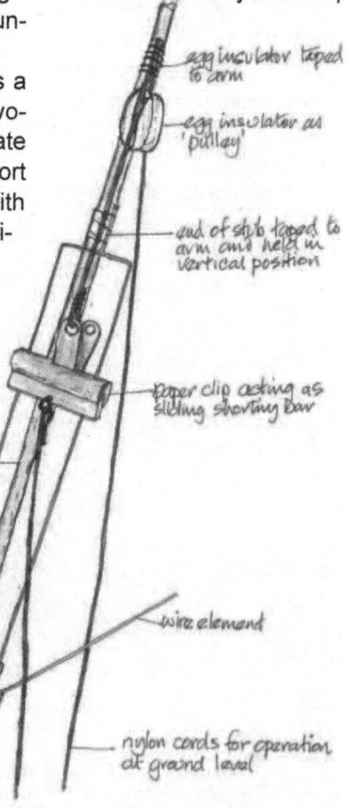

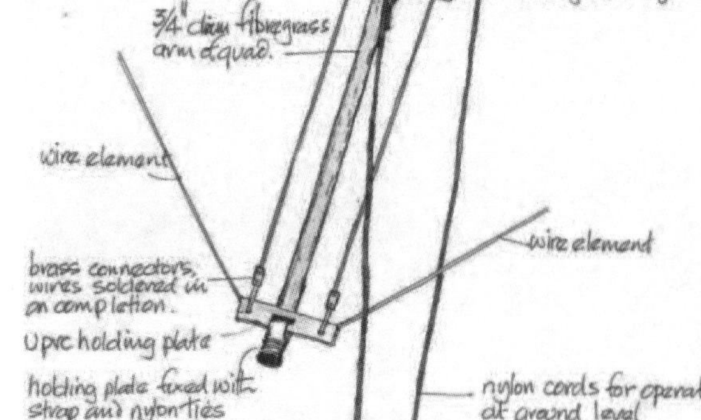


Fig 1: Remote quad tuner with bulldog clip remote controlled tuning slider, designed and drawn by GW4ZXG.

See Note [2]

Fig 2: Polar diagrams of a two-element quad from 21.0 to 21.45MHz. This is a free-space diagram, however, real ground azimuth diagrams plotted at very low angles of radiation are very similar.

## MEASUREMENTS

ANTENNA TUNING can be monitored in several ways, as described in [1]. You can use the transmitter, set to low power, connected to the antenna and use a remote antenna and field strength meter (FSM) to measure the signal strength as the antenna is tuned and rotated. The other option is to use a remote transmitter or signal generator and measure the signal strength on the transceiver S-meter.

GW4ZXG uses the remote receiver approach. This comprises a Kenwood DM-81 GDO switched to the FSM function with a link-coupled half-wave dipole, which is located about 200m from the antenna under test (AUT). A twin cable is run back to a remote meter on the operator's bench at the base of the tower. This allows the stub to be adjusted for minimum signal with the reflector of the AUT positioned nearest to the FSM. The process is repeated for the reflector element of the other band. The process is then repeated to minimise the effects of interaction of the interlaced antennas. The bulldog clip on the remote tuner of each antenna is then removed and replaced with stiff copper wire soldered in position. The FSM should be located in the far field. If you do not have the space a mobile FSM installation can be used.

The S-meter method of measurement is less sensitive because the S-meter has a log scale and it is very difficult to see small changes in signal strength as you make the parasitic element adjustments. Most FSMs use a linear (or near linear) scale so it is much easier to see these variations in signal strength.

Would it be better to tune the antenna for maximum gain or maximum 'front to back' because these two points do not coincide in frequency? Computer analysis, see **Fig 2**, indicates that if a two-element quad is tuned for maximum 'front to back' ratio at the high frequency end of the band it will have slightly greater gain at the expense of reduced 'front to back' on the lower frequencies. With an optimised beam using director(s), maximum front to back occurs at a lower frequency than maximum gain.

I always think that a beam with good directivity somehow seems better.

## REFERENCES

[1] *Backyard Antennas*, Peter Dodd, G3LDO. Available from RSGB Sales. ♦

**PETER DODD, G3LDO**
*37 The Ridings, East Preston, West Sussex, BN16 2TW*

I HAVE received various comments about the '50/50 Jubilee' competition [see 'Antennas' July 2002 - Ed]. While in general it is regarded as a good idea, at least one writer was unhappy about the 'competitive' nature of the project. I guess it might have been a better idea to call it an experiment. The operating aspect is really the only measure of antenna effectiveness. Most contest operators spend a lot of time honing their antenna systems for maximum performance and this can only be done with experimental operation. If you have any interest in the project at all then you should participate. Some suitable ways of using your 50ft wire are described below. I would be interested in hearing of your solution.

## TYPES OF 50/50 ANTENNA

THE SIMPLEST way of using your 50ft length of wire would be to make an inverted-L with a 10 to 30 ft vertical section (depending on where the shack is located) and the balance of the length being used for the top section. This antenna is fed using an ATU located close to the transmitter. A good RF earth is also required. If you have an upstairs shack, an artificial earth may be necessary and methods of feeding this antenna are described in [1]. The disadvantage of this antenna is that the vertical section is located close to the house wiring and electrical gadgets and there is a high probability of electrical interference. For some reason this type of antenna is a total failure at my QTH; the house seems to be a RF black hole that only generates electrical interference. On the other hand, Dave Sergeant, G3YMC, finds this type of antenna (65ft) at 30ft high very good and over a period of 50 days worked 311 stations in 79 DXCC countries using an Elecraft K2 running 5W. This would be a good achievement using a multiband beam!

The other method is to feed the inverted-L antenna remotely at a point located as far from the house as practicable to reduce electrical interference. To avoid high transmission line losses the ATU should be located at the feedpoint. With modern automatic ATUs the system can be quite simple. If you can't afford an automatic ATU, there are cheaper solutions, also described in [1]. Again a good RF earth should be used and a set of radials buried in the ground are effective. This method of end feeding an antenna works at my QTH so it would appear that the performance of the inverted-L is very much affected by its environment.

The 50ft length of wire centre fed with home made twin-line feeder. In the foreground is a PA0SE coax balun. This arrangement was replaced with 450Ω ladder line all the way back to the outside of the shack, with a short length of coax through the wall to the ATU.

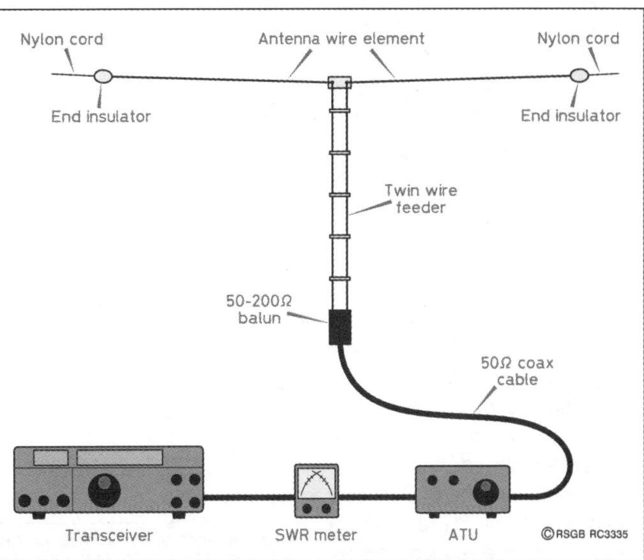


**Fig 1: The 'Comudipole' arrangement. This allows the use of low-loss twin feeder to be used in conjunction with coax cable. The coax cable section is used in order to negotiate areas where the use of twin feeder is not practical, such as in a conduit with other cables or in metal ducting in apartments. The coax section should be kept as short as possible to minimise losses.**

Because most electrical interference appears to be vertically polarised it might be better to use a horizontal antenna if you have the space.

Multiband dipoles do not have to be any specific length - after all if you want to operate on several bands a wire antenna cannot be resonant on all of them. Furthermore, the choice of a non-resonant length of wire avoids wild impedance values on some bands. My choice is to feed the 50ft of wire in the centre using balanced twin wire feeder. I decided to try the 'Comudipole' feed system [1] [2], which is shown in **Fig 1**. This method locates the balun unit, normally located inside the ATU, at some remote point so that coax can be used for the problem area of entry into the shack. Because a length of coax (24m) running from my shack to the garden already existed it seemed a good idea to use this. The 50ft dipole was fed with open wire feeder, using a PA0SE coax cable balun [1] to couple it to the existing coax feeder.

The antenna loaded on all bands using an MFJ Versa-Tuner V in the shack. On the 7MHz and 10MHz bands the performance was reasonable, but on the higher frequencies it was rather disappointing. I should have known better. With a multiband antenna like this high SWRs are common. With a 25m length of coax these high SWRs can cause losses of around 6 to 10dB at the higher frequencies. The graphs shown in G3SEK's *In Practice* column [3] illustrate this. Replacing the existing coax cable with 450Ω ladder line made a significant predictable improvement to the higher HF band performance of my 50ft centre-fed antenna. It does make you wonder about those G5RVs that you hear about that are fed with long lengths of RG58 and with reports of low SWRs on all bands!

There is rather a nice transmission line Windows software package that comes with *The ARRL Antenna Book* [4]. All you have to do is enter the transmission line type and length, together with measured impedance values, and up it pops with the calculated line loss plus a lot of other interesting information.

## REFERENCES

[1] *Backyard Antennas*, Peter Dodd, G3LDO.

[2] *Electron*, December 1992. Reported in 'Technical Topics' *RadCom* July 1984.

[3] Losses from High SWR, G3SEK, 'In Practice' *RadCom*, March 2002.

[4] TLW Transmission Line Program for Windows, by N6BV, *The ARRL Antenna Book*, 19th edition. ♦

**PETER DODD, G3LDO**
*37 The Ridings, East Preston, West Sussex, BN16 2TW*

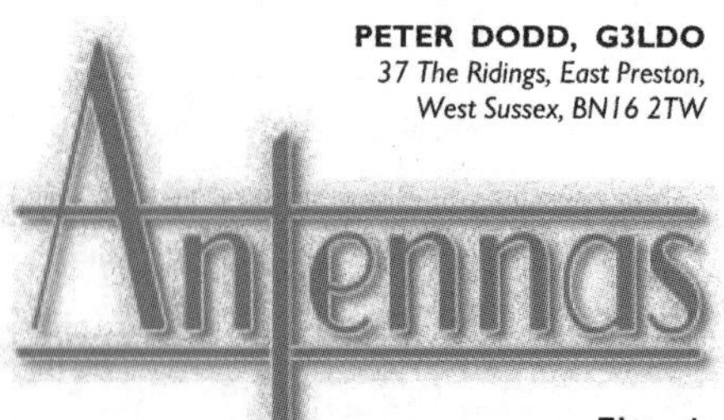


FROM MY mail I understand many of you are using one or other of those devices that Gerd Janzen, DF6SJ, refers to as an 'Active Standing Wave Ratio Meter'; a battery powered, comprehensive antenna measuring instrument all in one box. Gert has devoted a book [1] to a whole range of RF measurements for which one of these instruments can be used. Most manufacturers of these devices call them 'Antenna Analysers'.

## ANTENNA ANALYSERS

THE TWO MAIN suppliers of commercial antenna analysers are Autek [2] and MFJ [3]. I have the RF1 from Autek (1.2 to 35MHz) and the MFJ-249 (1.8 to 170MHz) from MFJ. These instruments do a fine job of measuring SWR but if you are into antenna experimenting it is useful to measure R ± j impedance. This impedance can be extracted from readings of SWR and Z from the RF1 and converted to R ± j using *TLW* program described in the September 'Antennas' column. However, as you are aware, the impedance at the antenna will not be the same as that measured at the other end of any feeder connected to the antenna, due to the transmission line transform effect. This impedance transformation is shown projected on a Smith Chart in **Fig 1**. Halfway round the chart equals 0.25 or quarter wavelength, while a full rotation equals 0.5 or halfwavelength.

There are two ways to find out what the real antenna impedance is:

1. Measure the electrical length of the feeder and use a transmission line calculator, such as the Smith Chart or the *TLW* program (or similar) to find the antenna impedance.

2. Measure the impedance of the antenna using a halfwave, or a multiple of a half wavelength, See Note [3] of coaxial. I use this method quite a lot but you have to bear in mind that, because the cable is resonant, it can result in antenna currents on the cable, which can give inconsistent impedance measurement results. However, antenna currents can be minimised using an RF current choke. Remember that the cable is a half wavelength long on one frequency only.

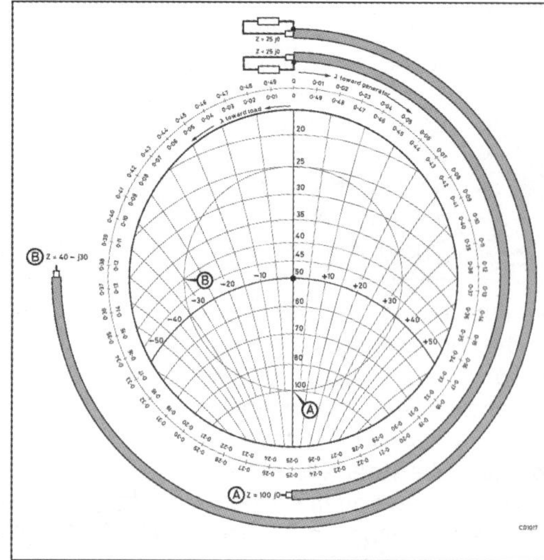


**Fig 1: Two lengths of 50Ω coaxial feeder are shown superimposed around the circumference of a Smith chart; one a quarter-wave long and the other 3/8-wavelength. Both lengths are connected to a load having an impedance of 25 +j0. The quarter wavelength line (0.25) gives a measured impedance of 100 +j0 at the other end while the 3/8λ section (0.375) gives an impedance of 40-j30. A halfwave length of coaxial would transform the impedance back to 25 j0.**

I have just acquired an Autek VA1. This remarkable little instrument has additional facilities compared with the RF1. It can measure R ± j, and its polar equivalent. Furthermore it can measure equivalent parallel resistance and reactance and even the transform action of a length of feeder.

My interest is the measurement of impedance so I was interested in how the good the VA1 was in this respect. One method is to use a set of accurate dummy loads. Assuming a 50Ω system, dummy loads for 50Ω, 25Ω and 100Ω are useful. However, these dummy loads only measure the resistive component of impedance. How would you go about measuring the reactive component?

A novel approach, first described by W N Carron [4], uses the impedance transform effect illustrated in Fig 1. A length of coaxial cable is used with a resistive load which will produce an SWR of around 1.5:1 to 2:1. The impedance is plotted over a range of frequencies, which has the effect of changing the electrical length of the test feeder. The physical length of the test feeder is not critical because the accuracy of the instrument will be apparent by any deviation from the SWR contour when the results are plotted on an impedance diagram. I made a test using my prized HP 4085A vector impedance meter and the Autek VA1, the results of which are shown in **Fig 2.**

While neither of the plots look ideal you have to remember that this is a sensitive test. Both instruments are accurate enough to enable one to devise a suitable matching network for an antenna. There may be errors due to the measuring technique. I feel that it would be more accurate to use a Cartesian projection for plotting R ± j, which is shown automated in [5]. Plots on a Smith chart projection are only necessary if you need to calculate impedance transforms, which are much more easily done on a computer these days. You can find a suitable Cartesian chart for impedance instrument checking on my website [6].

## REFERENCES

[1] *RF Measurements with an Active Standing Wave Ratio Meter*, Gerd Janzen, DF6SJ. DARC Verlag GmbH, Baunatal. ISBN 3-88692-023.

[2] Autek RF1 and VA1, available Eastcom, tel: 01692 650077. www.cqcqcq.com

[3] MFJ 249, 259B and 269, available Waters & Stanton, tel: 01702 206835 / 204956. www.wsplc.com.

[4] 'The Hybrid Junction Admittance Bridge', W N Carron, *Antenna Compendium Vol 3*, ARRL, 1992.

[5] *The Antenna Experimenter's Guide, Second Edition*, Peter Dodd, G3LDO, RSGB. Available from RSGB Sales.

[6] **www.g3ldo.co.uk**

♦

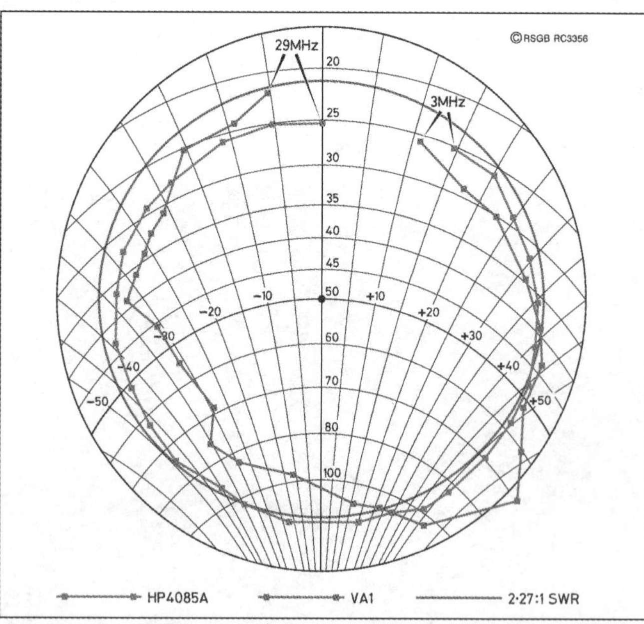


**Fig 2: Results of an impedance plot of a 22Ω resistor made via a length of coaxial cable over a frequency range 3 to 29MHz. The blue circle is the calculated 2.27:1 SWR produced by a 22Ω resistor. Ideally, the impedance plot should follow this circle with a slight spiralling towards the centre due to coax cable loss. The red and green plots are of the HP4085A and the VA1 respectively.**

**PETER DODD, G3LDO**
*37 The Ridings, East Preston,
West Sussex, BN16 2TW*

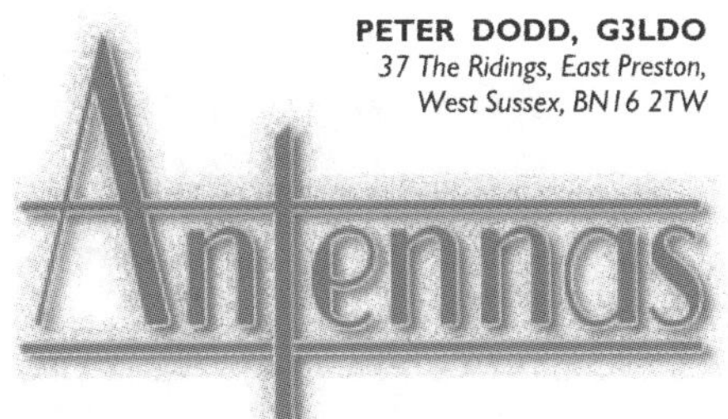


CONTINUING the experimental and measuring theme of last month's 'Antennas' column we will have a look at making polar diagrams of beam antennas. This can be done quite simply at VHF by energising the beam antenna with a QRP transmitter and using a dipole antenna and field strength meter (FSM) to measure the field strength as the beam antenna is rotated. Furthermore, HF beam antennas can be modelled using VHF antennas as described in [1].

## POLAR DIAGRAM USING A COMPUTER

POLAR DIAGRAM plotting, described above, can be automated using a computer. This method takes much of the work out of manual method of plotting polar diagrams and speeds up the process considerably.

Storage of data and the application of functions for normalisation and conversion from linear to log scales etc, are tasks amenable to computerisation. Additionally, very complex polar diagrams can be plotted that would otherwise be difficult using the manual method.

All my early work was done using a BBC computer. All that had to be done was to connect the DC output from the FSM, to the A/D converter, which was an integral part of that computer and addressable in BBC BASIC. The idea was not new and a polar diagram-plotting program, written by G4IJE and G3NOX, was first described in [2].

The program was later modified to run on the more widely used IBM compatible computer but an external ADC was required, see [1].

## WINDOWS SOFTWARE

A POLAR PLOT program, written to run on Windows 95/98/NT4 and Windows 2000, has been written by Bob Freeth, G4HFQ, and is obtainable from his website, see WWW below. This system circumvents the requirement for an ADC interface. Instead, a sound card with a line-in or microphone input is used, which is connected to the audio output of the receiver.

The volume of a beat note, in the SSB or CW mode of a plain unmodulated carrier has good correlation with the RF input level, provided the receiver is operated in a linear manner. This is best achieved by simply reducing the RF gain (most receivers with no RF gain control are unsuitable for this application). Modulated tones in AM or FM cannot be used, particularly FM, which is inherently designed to maintain audio level regardless of the RF input level.

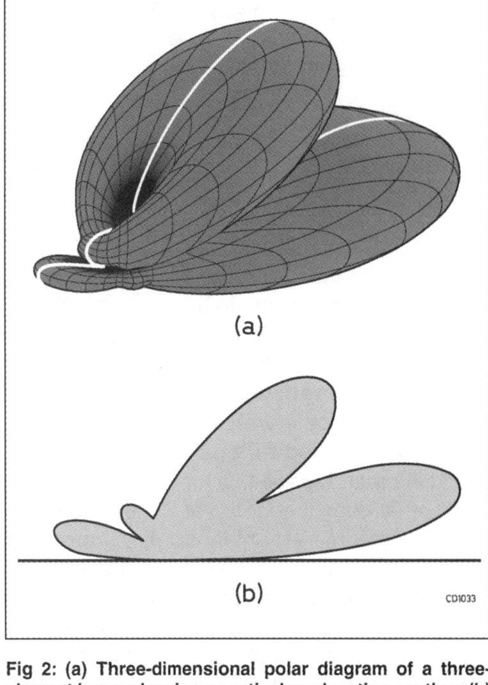


**Fig 2: (a) Three-dimensional polar diagram of a three-element beam showing a vertical or elevation section. (b) Radiation pattern through this section. This result was obtained using the *EZNEC* antenna analysis software.**

Although I used this technique in the past, for modelling HF antennas using VHF antennas on my garden antenna test range, by using the G4HFQ software it is possible to measure the performance of a full size HF beam. An example of an HF beam plot is shown in **Fig 1**. This antenna is a modified version of the commercial five-band MQ2 beam and Fig 1 illustrates the polar diagram on 10m. The measurement was made by energising a short dipole, located around three wavelengths from the beam, via an ATU with a signal generator. The beam antenna was then rotated and the measurements made using the G4HFQ software.

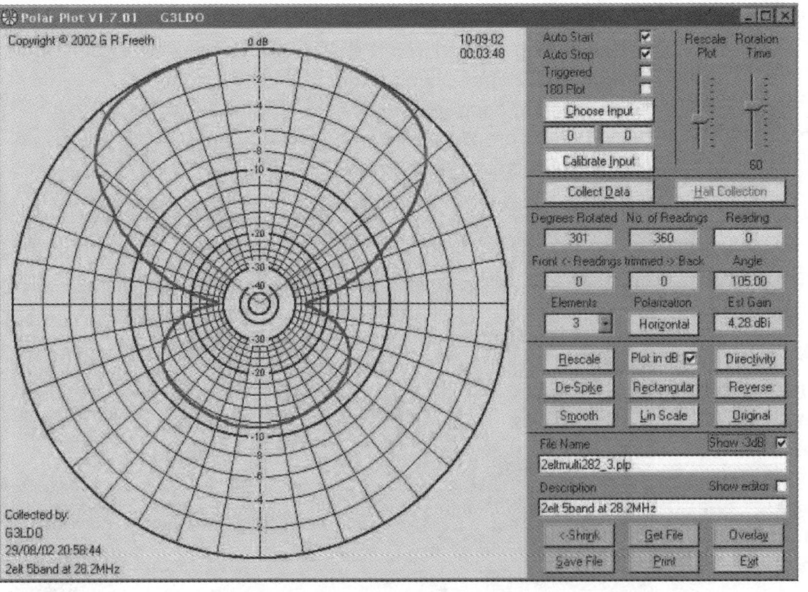


**Fig 1: Polar diagram of a modified MQ2 beam on 28MHz. The main lobe looks slightly squashed, possibly due to non-linearity in the receiver settings, although the 10dB F/B was what I was expected. The plot is done using a scale originated by the ARRL called a log periodic scale. The setting boxes to the right illustrate the range of processing that is available with this application.**

Many operators check their antenna with other locals and these ground wave tests are quite useful. I once described in an article how I did this and was taken to task by a reader. He regarded such measurements as unreliable and the point he made is illustrated in **Fig 2**. Most polar diagrams shown in antenna books are obtained through mathematical modelling. This indicates that the field strength of a practical antenna would only be a fraction of the main lobe. In fact, if you ask a modelling software program, such as *EZNEC*, to make an azimuth measurement at zero degrees elevation it will reject the measurement attempt with a message to say that the signal strength will be zero. In the real world the situation is far more complex. The polar diagram of the antenna shown in Fig 1 was made of a beam antenna 10m high yet the short dipole energised with a signal generator was only 4m high. The measured F/B of 10dB was what I expected from experience of using the antenna for several years.

## REFERENCES

[1] *The Antenna Experimenter's Guide (second edition),* by Peter Dodd, G3LDO, RSGB.

[2] 'VHF/UHF', Ken Willis, G8VR, *RadCom*, Jan 1987. ♦

WWW.

Polar Plot software www.bob.freeth.dial.pipex.com/polarplot

**PETER DODD, G3LDO**
*37 The Ridings, East Preston, West Sussex, BN16 2TW*

HAVE YOU ever noticed that in many locations the shack seems to be in the wrong place, relative to the antennas? In my case the shack is located in a bedroom at the front of the house while the antennas are located in the garden at the rear. My solution for yet another coax feeder to yet another experimental antenna was to drill yet another hole in the window frame and drape the cable with the rest - including a rotator control cable and an LF transmitter remote control cable - along the side of the house. Early this year I received an ultimatum from the management - tidy it all up or else.

## THE MULTI CABLE TIDY

TO ROUTE THE CABLE from the shack to the outside of the house a hole was made in the wall and a piece of plastic tubing fitted as shown in **Fig 1** and described in [1] and [2]. The next problem was to find a tidy way to route the cables from the front of the house to the back. The solution came in the form of two lengths of square section plastic tubing.

1 - Pilot hole here
2 - Mark outline of large hole
3 - Drill more holes
4 - Remove brick plug and open out hole to size
©RSGB RC1937

**Fig 1: How to make a 40mm hole through a brick wall for inserting plastic tube conduit to carry coax and other cables from the shack to the outside of the house.**

This material is available in a colour that closely matched the brickwork of the house, and with the matching wall clamps it was easy to fix to the wall. This was fitted so that one end was adjacent to the plastic pipe fitted into the wall and the other at the part of the wall nearest the garden. All the cables were then run through the wall aperture and plastic tubing, as shown in the photograph below right, resulting in a much tidier look to the side of the house and Brownie points for your columnist. A length of hard-drawn copper wire is included with the cable bundle to make it easier to draw through a new cable.

## THE COAX CABLE HORROR SHOW

WHILE MAKING THE changes to the coax cable feeders described above I noticed that one section of coax was behaving in a rather peculiar fashion. My method of testing coax is to connect the remote end to the MFJ VersaTuner V switched to the dummy load. The crossed meters of the SWR indicator are calibrated to read power so any loss is obvious. The section of coax in question indicated that the loss was low but the SWR at the transceiver was high, rather than the loss being fairly high and the SWR low as you might normally expect.

I replaced the coax and the measurements were normal. I examined the old length (of uncertain pedigree) and found although the centre conductor was nice shiny copper the braiding was a different matter. The braiding on this coax length comprised fairly open braiding over solid copper foil. The outer sheath appeared to have migrated through the braiding causing it to be a nasty dull black colour although the foil still seemed quite shiny, as shown in the photograph above.

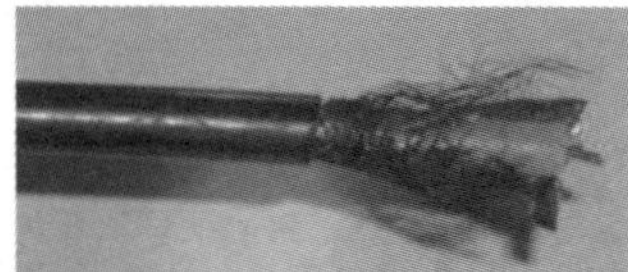

**The rogue coax length. The centre conductor is nice shiny copper although the braiding is a dull black colour.**

I had a similar problem on my mobile installation a couple of months ago where the antenna would not load and the antenna resonance was nowhere to be seen. I tested the coax with a meter together with the ground connection and this seemed OK. I replaced the coax, which was only about 3m long, and the problem disappeared. A post mortem on the coax length gave no clues as to where the problem lay. The moral is that if you have an antenna that is behaving strangely, check the coax. Always test that bargain length that you got from a rally before you press it into service.

## REFERENCES

[1] 'In Practice', Ian White, G3SEK, *RadCom*, November 1998.

[2] *The Antenna Experimenter's Guide (2nd edition)*, Peter Dodd, G3LDO, RSGB.

[3] Go to *Google* 'Advanced Search' and type in "PL-259 plugs". ♦

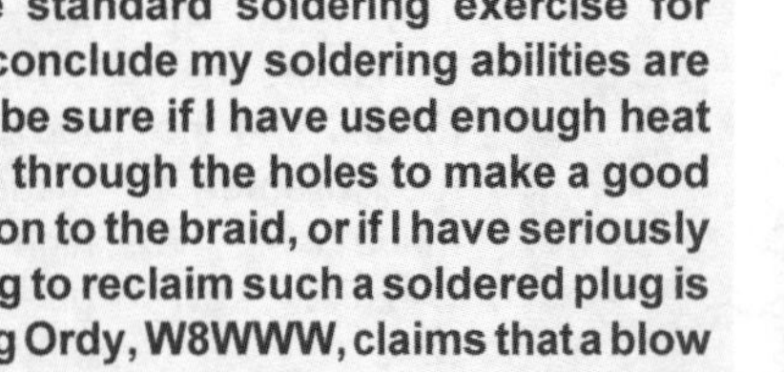

## FITTING PL259 PLUGS

**AS PART OF THE coax cable reorganisation described above I had to fit PL259 plugs to the RG-213 cable. I find the recommended way of doing this a pig of a job. Yes, I know that it is, or was, the standard soldering exercise for Novices so I can only conclude my soldering abilities are below par. I can never be sure if I have used enough heat to make the solder run through the holes to make a good dry-joint-free connection to the braid, or if I have seriously cooked the coax. Trying to reclaim such a soldered plug is a messy business. Greg Ordy, W8WWW, claims that a blow torch is better for the job although this is only part of the story, see [3].**

**My solution is to make up the end of the cable as recommended but make a loose pigtail of the braid and fold it back over the coax sheath. The cable is then screwed into the plug and the centre connection soldered. The protruding braid is then cropped so that there is approximately 5mm folded back over the body of the plug. The braid can be soldered to the plug, a much easier task than soldering through the holes and the soldered joint can be inspected for a good solder flow.**

**PL259 plugs are occasionally available with clamp nuts and pressure sleeves (as fitted to N-type plugs), which is a much better solution.**

**The arrangement for routing coax and other cables from inside the shack at the front of the house to the rear. There is plenty of room for future additional cables. The yellow cable is a safety earth wire connected to ground.**

**PETER DODD, G3LDO**
*37 The Ridings, East Preston, West Sussex, BN16 2TW*

IN THE November 2002 'Antennas' column I described a method of plotting the polar diagram of an antenna using a computer. I said that all my early work was done using a BBC computer, and although the idea was not mine the original had been written by G4IJE and G3NOX [1].

I received a letter from Tom Lawless, GM6JOD, stating that he had written such a program for the BBC computer and that it had been published in 1984 [2], predating [1] by three or four years. Tom sent me a copy of this article, which includes a computer listing and an interface circuit for connecting the receiver S-meter signal to the BBC computer ADC input. The listing has only 60 lines of code; BBC BASIC was a nice tool for small computation programs in amateur radio.

## MULTIBANDING THE MOXON RECTANGLE

SOME MONTHS AGO I asked if any of you had built a successful *multiband* Moxon rectangle or VK2ABQ beam. To those of you who replied, my thanks. It would appear those of you who built the design by G6XN were satisfied with the results. The photo shows the antenna built by Reg Gibbs, GM3SVE, who has built several similar antennas over the years, starting with the square VK2ABQ arrangement while the latest was the G6XN design. He reports a gain of approximately 4dBd and a front-to-back better than 25dB.

This antenna is for the 10, 15 and 20m bands. During assembly and test some interaction between the bands was evident and was overcome by adjusting the highest-frequency elements first.

## A HYBRID TRIBAND MOXON-YAGI

W4RNL HAS AN excellent website about antennas (see WWW below) and the quotes below are from this source. He received a number of notes enquiring if parasitic elements might be added to a 20-metre Moxon (the close-spaced W4RNL design) to produce a triband beam. The addition of a 10 metre director and a 15 metre reflector yields some forward gain, but there are large excursions of feedpoint impedance, precluding the direct connection of coax.

He goes on to say "These initial steps into developing a tri-band antenna around a 20 metre Moxon tend to stop short of something truly satisfactory. What is required for easy use is a system that permits a 50Ω feed for each band. The result will be more elements, but not a major increase in the footprint over and above the initial addition of a reflector and director.

"To develop a beam of this order, one might well adapt some of the principles underlying the Force 12 C3. This popular antenna uses a 2-element 20 metre driver-reflector Yagi at its core. It also places a 15 metre driver-reflector combination behind the 20 metre driver. The two drivers are close enough to permit open-sleeve coupling. Ahead of the 20 metre driver are three 10 metre elements - a driver (also open-sleeve coupled to the 20 metre driver) and two directors. The furthest director provides the essential pattern shaping function, while the closely-spaced first director functions much like the added director on the NW3Z/WA3FET OWA designs: it helps form a wider band feedpoint impedance than a single director could provide. Performance remains essentially the same as a two-element driver-director Yagi, but over a larger portion of the band.

"It is possible to replace the 20 metre elements with a Moxon rectangle and obtain triband performance on a 16ft boom. **Fig 1** shows the general outline. For this exercise, the 20 metre elements were set at 1in diameter, the 15 metre elements at 0.75in diameter, and the 10 metre elements at 0.5in diameter. Since the design uses open-sleeve coupling, a single feedpoint suffices for all bands.

"The antenna was designed using *MININEC* (AO 6.5), since the close spacing of the drivers produces excess gain estimates in NEC-2. The error is an especially large overestimation of gain on 10 metres. Hence, *MININEC* is the core of choice for this exercise. On 20 metres, the Moxon rectangle performs normally, with a typical Moxon rectangle pattern. On 15 metres the pattern is that of a two element driver-reflector while on 10m again it is a typical two-element Yagi pattern, with a slightly better front-to-back ratio due to the use of directors.

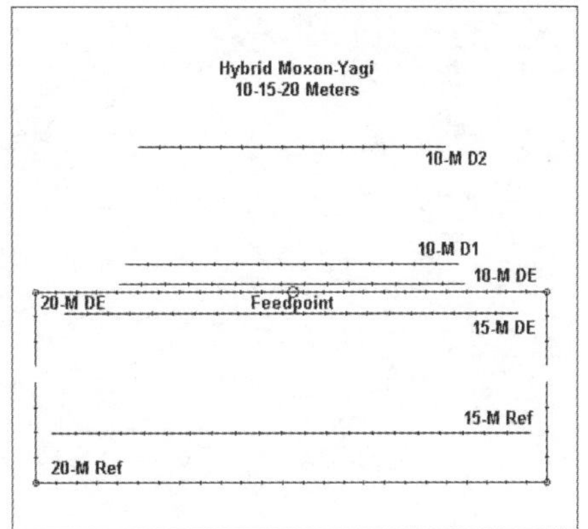


**Fig 1: *MININEC* (AO 6.5) model of the W4RNL hybrid tri-band Moxon-Yagi.**

**The three-band G6XN antenna by GM3SVE. The top mast section is aluminium scaffolding pole fixed to the top of a 40ft Tennamast via a rotator. The fibreglass rods are fixed to the mast using 2in aluminium angle.**

"Undoubtedly, one can improve on this hybrid design. Indeed, the requirement for adjusting element lengths and spacings to account for element diameter taper schedules would enforce an exploration of possible improvements. As with all models of open-sleeve coupling, considerable adjustment may be needed in the slaved drivers to achieve the correct impedance and bandwidth. Moreover, although home construction of single antennas for personal use requires no special attention to any legalities, any other use of the non-Moxon-rectangle techniques noted in the design should involve consultation with Force 12 to ensure compliance with any proprietary or patent rights held by that company".

So I was interested to see a description in W8FX's column in *CQ* magazine [3] on what appears to be a commercial application of the computer designed multiband antenna described by W4RNL above. The antenna is manufactured by a German company called Optibeam and antenna model is the OB6-3M. A full description and photo of the antenna can be found on their website. It appears to have a shorter boom length that the design by W4RNL.

## REFERENCES

[1] 'VHF/UHF' column, Ken Willis, G8VR, *RadCom* Jan 1987.

[2] 'Polar Plotting', by B P Hainey and Tom Lawless, *Computing in Radio,* autumn 1984.

[3] 'What's New', Karl T Thurber, W8FX, *CQ Amateur Radio*, October 2002. ♦

WWW.
W4RNL antennas: www.cebik.com/radio.html

**PETER DODD, G3LDO**
*37 The Ridings, East Preston, West Sussex, BN16 2TW*

IN THE JULY 2002 'Antennas' column I mentioned that I am often asked, usually by those who live in restricted locations, if certain commercial antenna products will solve their antenna problems. I said that in many cases a simple wire antenna, suitably placed and suitably fed, will outperform them even in the most restricted of locations. I proposed an experiment in the form of a competition to construct the cheapest of all antennas - a 50ft piece of wire.

## THE '50-50' COMPETITION

THE OBJECTIVE WAS to see how many stations could be worked using the 50ft wire, over a period of 50 days between 1 September and 20 October 2002.

The antenna wire could be any diameter up to 2mm and fed at any point using any length of feeder, but the feeder must not be part of the radiating system. The antenna could be re-orientated during the test period as part of the experimental process. The full details were given in the July 2002 'Antennas' column.

We had *two* winners! Their comments on antenna construction and operating illustrate the points I was trying to make so well that they have been included in this double-length 'Antennas' column.

## PETER COLE, G3JFS

G3JFS MADE 1248 QSOs with 139 countries to make 173,472 points under the competition rules. All contacts were made using a 50ft end-fed wire hung from trees at the bottom of his garden. The antenna, used for quick band hopping, is tuned by an SGC SG-230 Smartuner situated in a garden shed. About 60ft of buried low-loss 50Ω coax and control wires are used between the shed and the upstairs shack. The first 30ft of the antenna wire slopes northwards from the shed to about 25ft and the remainder slopes W to E up to 30ft. The earth system uses quite a lot of wire buried in the ground as well as fence wires on two sides of the garden.

G3JFS used an Icom IC-706 for QRP operation (5 watts) and an FT-990 and FT-1000 (100 watts) using CW, SSB, RTTY and PSK31. The total number of contacts was enhanced by casual operating in the large number of contests during the period of the test. However, a lot of the contacts were 'proper' QSOs of 10 - 30mins.

G3JFS goes on to say. "Like you I have been asked many times for advice on what antenna to use. My usual recommendations for a restricted site are:
"1. Put up the longest bit of wire you can and centre feed it with open wire line.
2. Put up a half-wave dipole for one of the HF bands and find out what you can do with it.
3. As a last resort use an end-fed wire on the lines of the W3EDP, preferably with quarter-wave counterpoise wires for the bands of interest.

"Invariably this advice is ignored in preference for a G5RV or a trap vertical because the man in the shop or the hyped up adverts recommended them! When G5RV devised his antenna it was meant to be a good performer on 20m and adequate for inter-G contacts on 80m. At that time we had no WARC bands, no 15m band and 10m was still dead (in fact I am not even sure if the band was available - I was 11 at the time!) 20m was the main DX band and 80m the 'wafflers' band. Few people could afford a beam (homebrew of course!) Coax was not in common use but 80Ω balanced twin, or even twin lighting flex, was - and this gave a low SWR with the feed impedance of 90 - 100Ω of three half-waves on 20m whilst the mismatch on 80m was acceptable. Louis also emphasised that on other bands a full-length open wire feeder should be used with a balanced ATU. Then it was no longer a 'G5RV', but a doublet antenna which had been around for many, many years.

"My preference for a simple wire antenna is a doublet with provision to change its length on the higher bands to go from a multi-lobe to figure of eight pattern. On the low bands it can be used as a 'T' with the feeder strapped. The end-fed wire plus the Smartuner is generally weaker but is very convenient. The Smartuner is very expensive but the same results could be achieved with a relay switched, pre-tuned matching / tuning ATU."

The 139 countries worked by G3JFS include 9L1BTB Sierra Leone, 3XY6A Republic of Guinea, FR/PA3GIO/P Reunion Island, JT1CO Mongolia, C98DC Mozambique, XX9TEP Macao, JY9AX Jordan, HC8N Galapagos Islands, XV9DT Vietnam, ZL7C, Chatham Island, YA5T Afghanistan, plus many more - not bad for 50ft of wire. Just imagine what the sales blurb of simple multiband commercial antenna be likely to say if it had been used to work these DX stations!

## DES VANCE, GI3XZM

GI3XZM USED THE competition in a rather different way, by orientating the 50ft length of wire in many ways. He says, "In the process I have learned a bit, noticed a few things which seem to have been overlooked and had some fun. It was not a scientific exercise. I made an aerial, loaded it up and had a few contacts covering the appropriate bands, so that I could say, 'It seems to work', then took it down and started again . . . And again . . . I didn't try to run up a score or chase DX. It was more like shooting at the first thing that moved, then moving on. Everything did work. Some might say that I have only demonstrated the 'wet string principle' which states that almost anything will radiate if you load it up, but hopefully I did a bit better than that.

"Just for the record, the log shows that the rig was used on 26 days covering a total time of roughly 17 hours. In this time I had 90 QSOs covering 28 countries. Not an operating triumph!

However, I hope that you will find something useful in the following, which

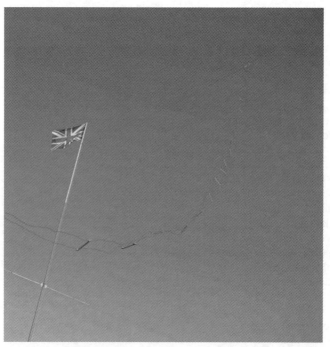

**G3LDO's own '50-50' antenna - a 50ft length of wire centre fed with home-made twin-line feeder. The green and white pole flying the union flag is part of a different antenna system.**

will help you nudge a few folk towards amateur, rather than cheque book, antennas."

The following is a brief description some of the antennas tried by GI3XZM.

**Dipole 50ft long, 30ft high, fed with open wire feeder.** This antenna was tried first simply because it is an obvious starting point. This is a very good antenna on the all bands from 40 to 10m although the routing of the open wire feeder might pose some problems is some locations. With an estimated radiation resistance on 80m of only about 2Ω and wire losses perhaps three times this (with 70ft of feeder) it is a poor choice for this band, but contacts were secured using 15W CW without difficulty. The antenna could be used as an end-fed T for 80 or 160m by connecting the feeders together and feeding against ground using an ATU (although this would have broken the competition rules as they were formulated). GI3XZM states that this would probably be his first choice in a small suburban garden. This is in line with the advice given by G3JFS above.

**50ft inverted L.** This is the simplest antenna of all but perfectly serviceable, given a good earth. On 80m, with radiation resistance of perhaps 12Ω, a good RF ground is essential since earth losses could far exceed this figure. Nevertheless, GI3XZM was pleased to work PY on 80m. His 'standard' ground system is described below. This is the type of antenna G3JFS used to contact 139 countries during the competition period.

**End-fed T.** the 'T' uses a 20ft top and a 28ft vertical and is designed for the 40, 30, 20m bands. It is fed with coax against buried radials via an ATU, which comprises a series capacitor on 40m while a parallel tuned circuit [tapped] is used on 30m. On 20m the antenna is nearly a half-wavelength long and is matched using a series inductor. A good DX antenna with a radiation resistance better than 30Ω on 40m, and higher on other bands.

GI3XZM tried five other antennas in all, although lack of space precludes their description here. His standard RF ground system comprises a number of 14SWG wires pushed into spade cuts in lawn. The 18SWG wire for antenna building was obtained from the mains transformer primary of a microwave oven, which provided over 200ft of wire. The insulators and spreaders are made from scrap Perspex from a shop signs maker.

## PETER DODD, G3LDO

WELL, I MIGHT as well put in my two pen'orth. I used a remotely-tuned 30ft x 20 ft inverted L with the MFJ Versa Tuner V (989C) ATU situated in the garden shed.

See Note [4]

This required a trip down the garden every time I wanted to change bands - not exactly operating convenience but it kept me fit! During my LF antenna experiments I tried various types of RF earthing systems. One of these is 50 square feet of chicken wire laid out on the lawn during the spring (about four years ago) and allowing the worms to bury it over the following couple of months. This works better than earth rods on the higher frequency bands.

I also tried the centre-fed antenna, which I found the best for the higher frequency bands (confirming the results described above). This arrangement is described in 'Antennas', September 2002. I operated on most days between 1 and 28 September and made 108 contacts with 53 countries.

## COMPARING ATUs

DOUG HARRIS, GW3NDR, has been comparing several ATUs and thought we might be interested in the results. They were all tested with a centre-fed wire about 80ft long and fed with slotted feeder some 20ft long and about 28ft above the ground. The balanced output of the ATU was measured using a twin meter version of the RF meter, see Fig 10.11 of [1]. The input to the ATU was measured using a standard SWR bridge.

The tuners compared are listed below in order of efficiency:

'Homebrew', as in **Fig 1**
MFJ Versa Tuner V (989C)
SSM Z Match
MFJ Versa Tuner II
SGC SG239 Smartuner

With differing ease all the tuners were able to match the transceiver to the antenna although there was a 6dB

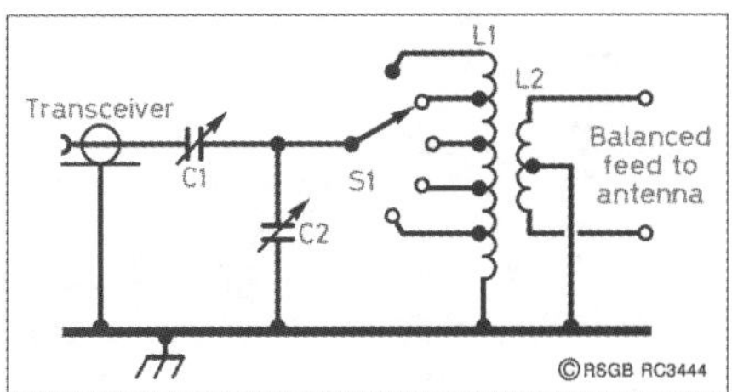


**Fig 1: C1 and C2 are unidirectional 300pF capacitors. The coil L1 and switch S1 is from an old valve rig PA pi-tank tuner. The coupling coil (no details on number of turns) is close wound to the cold end of the coil.**

difference in efficiency between the best and the worst (although it is not stated if this difference occurs on all bands). The ATU with the greatest losses was the SGC SG239 Smartuner, which often had a 2:1 SWR even after several attempts. The MFJ Versa Tuner II could be difficult to tune and was some 3dB down on the best. The SSM Z match was about 1 to 2dB down on the MFJ-989C and the homebrew tuner. The difference between the homebrew and the MFJ-989C was marginal, but the homebrew was just slightly better and was certainly easier to tune.

I looked at the circuit diagram of the SG239 and noticed it was designed specifically for an end-fed antenna and that there was no provision for a balanced feed, which exists on all the other tested ATUs. If the SG239 were connected directly to the test antenna described above without some balancing arrangement, it might explain its inferior performance.

The diagram of the homebrew ATU is shown in Fig 1, which GW3NDR describes as a half Z-match. Although he does not claim it to be original he hasn't seen it described elsewhere.

I have not tested this circuit but have included it in this column because, according to GW3NDR, it has a lot going for it. Firstly, it is so easy to make. There are a lot of old valve transmitters around (that one hasn't the heart to throw away) with pi-tank circuits that could be pressed into service in this ATU. It is claimed to be at least as good as the MFJ-989C although it probably wouldn't handle high power unless the pi circuit came from a linear. Finally, it is easy and not critical to tune.

GW3NDR notes that RF current meters are essential in monitoring the efficiency of ATUs.

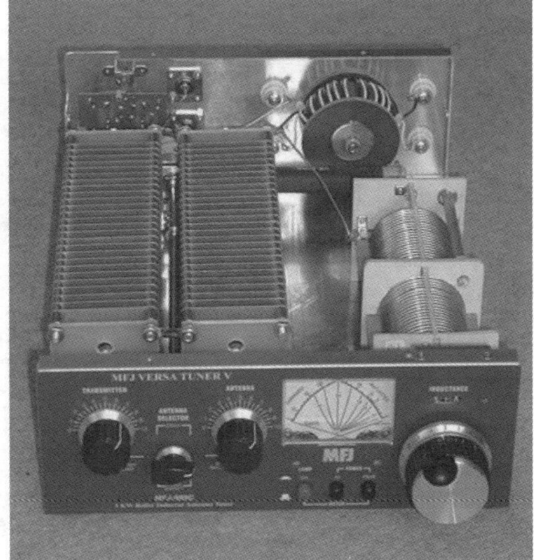


**MFJ Versa Tuner V (989C), which rated well on GW3NDR's efficiency test. Note that the components are quite chunky to handle high power, which may have contributed to good performance.**

## REFERENCE

[1] *Backyard Antennas*, Peter Dodd, G3LDO (RSGB Sales). ♦

**PETER DODD, G3LDO**
*37 The Ridings, East Preston, West Sussex, BN16 2TW*

IN THE December 2002 'Antennas' column I said that I found the recommended way of fixing PL-259 connectors to coaxial cable difficult and less than reliable. This is because you can never be sure if enough heat has been used to make the solder run through the holes to make a good, dry joint free, connection to the braid without 'cooking' the coax insulation.

The problem was further brought home when I tried to locate the fault on one of the VHF antenna feeders at GB2CPM. The symptom was an open feeder and the fault was eventually found to be at the shack end. All the connectors in the line are N-type with clamp nuts and pressure sleeves; with the exception of the one in the shack, which used a solder type connection.

The connector and a short length of feeder were cropped off and a new plug fitted. The old plug was disassembled, as shown in the photograph, to find out what had gone wrong. The cable had been made up perfectly with 1/4in (6mm) of braiding neatly trimmed and tinned. The prepared end had been screwed into the plug and the centre and braid soldered in the appropriate manner. In all probability the cable would have passed an initial continuity test; however, although the centre pin was soldered correctly the braid was not. Over a period of time a layer of corrosion had caused the braid / plug connection to become open circuit.

## OTHER SOLUTIONS

I HAVE RECEIVED further comments on this subject. Wyn Mainwaring, GW8AWT, says he has never soldered the outer braid of any type of coax plug that he has ever used in the light of work done at around 1000MHz by EMI research in 1949. He advises that the braid needs to be clean and corrosion / tarnish free. The strands are gently combed out with something that is both sharp yet smooth, such as the test probe of an Avo. These strands are then stroked back along the outer of the PVC skin. The end is made up so that there is 1/8in (3mm) length of inner insulating material clear of the braid and that the bared inner conductor is plenty long enough to poke well clear of the PL-259 when the coax is fitted. The coax is screwed into the PL-259 plug until the shoulder of inner conductor has become visible and the folded back braid has just come into view. Excess inner conductor is cropped and soldered to the PL-259 plug centre connector. The braid can then be cropped and grease or Vaseline worked into the solder holes and outer connection to make a water resistant joint.

Richard Brown, GW8JVM, gives similar advice, adding that the method also works with Pope H100 type cable where copper foil is used in the place of braid.

Walter Blanchard, G3JKV, notes "I agree with your piece on PL-259s. I gave up trying to solder through the holes years ago and did what you do. I found if you fold RG-213-type braid back on itself - *not* over the black PVC covering - it is thick enough to provide a good grip for the plug's internal screw thread. Also, you can screw the plug on right up to the end of the covering if you strip the right amount. If I think I might be taking the plug off again before long I don't solder the braid - just the inner - and that seems to do very well as long as it doesn't get wet. Soldering the outer braid can be a little tricky - some plugs don't take solder easily, and it has to be thin so the loose screwed attachment can slide back over it.

"Incidentally, there are PL-259s around that have a gold finish and are advertised as 'gold'. It's actually only a very thin plating and strips away easily from the muckite metal underneath so although it solders easily first time round the plating eventually gets pulled off by the solder and the connection is lost. Silver-plated PL-259s are far better if you can find them."

I find that whether you fold the coax braid back over the black PVC covering or not may depend on the coax type and diameter and the PL-259 connector.

Brian Armstrong, G3EDD, says, "I felt I had to comment on your section on coax cable and UHF series connectors. Perhaps I should explain that although long since retired, I worked in the Engineering Department at Pye Telecom in Cambridge all my working life, and one of my responsibilities for many years was the approval of VHF / UHF aerials and the coaxial components that went with them. Firstly, UHF (PL-259) series connectors should never be used outside a protected environment, and those that are used should be with pressure sleeve clamp, which is much easier to terminate. We always used N series for all external applications, again with pressure sleeve clamp.

"I think that the UHF series is awful [echoed by Richard Brown, GW8JVM, above] but then they are cheap and everywhere. One of my ex-engineers, now retired, who is licensed, always changes the PL-259 series connectors on any equipment he buys for N or BNC series, a bit of a drastic step maybe and one that I have done myself but not on a regular basis."

## PL-259 AVERSION

I FIND THE aversion to the PL-259 rather difficult to understand. I have used them for years and have been unable to detect any deterioration in performance at HF when compared with other types. I agree that at VHF and UHF it could be a different matter. It would be interesting to know if any research had been done to determine how much of an impedance 'bump' these plugs cause, and whether it is important.

Much of the early home brew equipment (and some commercial) used cheap domestic TV coax connectors. Eric Knowles, G2XK, used to put out the best signal from Europe on 28MHz in the early 1960s using such connectors together with television 75Ω coax.

The worst coaxial connector that I have ever come across is the old Pye clip-on type. In the RAF they were used on the coaxial connectors between units in airborne radar installations and were the cause of most equipment failures. ♦

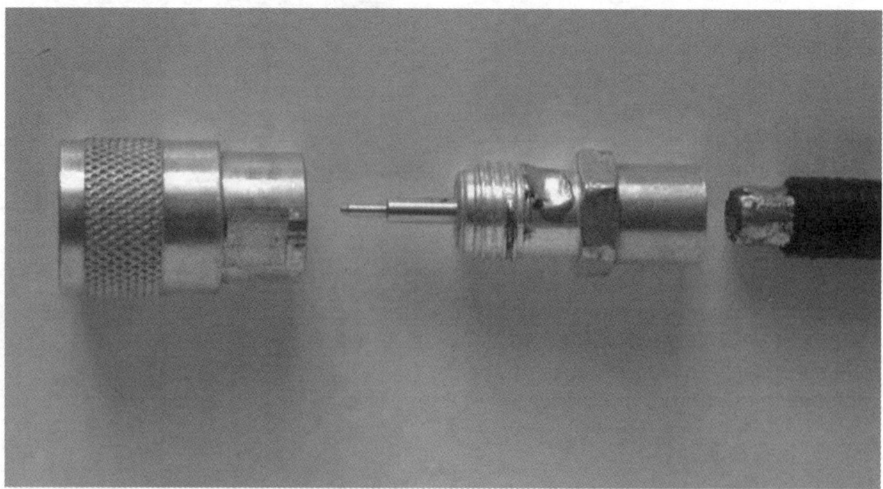

**N-type connector, using soldered outer braid arrangement, stripped down to determine why it had failed. The cable had been made up perfectly with 1/4in (6mm) of braiding neatly trimmed and tinned but the solder through the holes to the braid had not taken. The inner conductor, which was soldered correctly, is not shown.**

# ANTENNAS

I occasionally receive letters where the writer expresses the impossibility of operating on the lower frequency bands because of having a very small, or even no, garden in which to put up the ubiquitous G5RV. If you think about it, one of the most restricted sites you can have is a mobile one. Not only does the antenna have to be small but it also had to be fairly rugged. These sorts of restrictions do not stop radio amateurs operating /M.

With this in mind I tried my 'Texas Bugcatcher' mobile antenna as a fixed antenna by mounting it on a ledge above the bedroom window and using the central heating system as an RF ground. It worked fairly well on 80m, although the SWR bandwidth was rather narrow. This is understandable because on the lower HF bands a mobile antenna is small in terms of wavelength. If you are limited with space at your QTH and your interest is the lower frequencies what is the best antenna configuration?

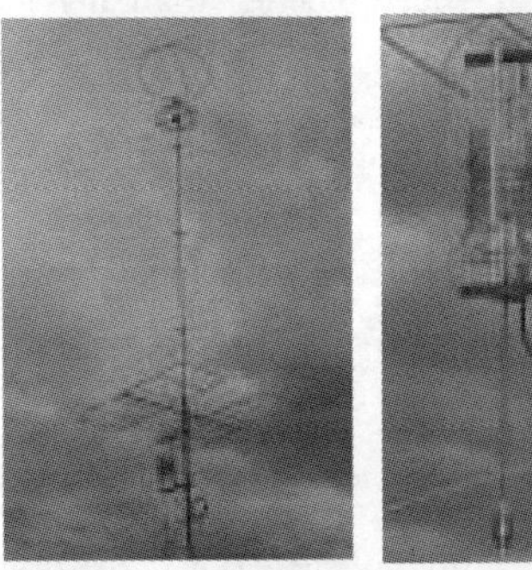

***(1) The top loading coil showing its construction and method of connecting to the top capacity section and the vertical radiator. This is actually the 40m version but the construction is the same as for the 80m version. (2) The 80m vertical, built by IK5PWN to the I5TGC design, with the 3.5m-long vertical radiator, a top capacity section, a top loading coil and two lower capacity frames. (3) The tuning and matching coil with 20 turns tapped at 15 turns. The two-turn coupling link can be moved up or down the coil former rods for optimum coupling adjustment. The remote tuning is achieved using an aluminium disk, which is moved along the axis of the coil by means of a threaded PVC rod, driven by a small motor and reduction gear. (4) The antennas of Cesare Tagliabue, I5TGC, on his rooftop in Florence.***

## THE I5TGC ANTENNAS

On 3 March 2000, I had a two-way QSO on 136kHz with Cesare Tagliabue, I5TGC. Later, I received a QSL card with a photo of his QTH and antenna. I was surprised to see that the antenna was confined to the roof area of his house, which is located in a suburban area of Florence. Cesare tells me that his 136kHz antenna is derived from earlier designs for the 40, 80 and 160m bands and he has kindly supplied me with diagrams, photos and notes. The most interesting aspect of these antennas is that (apart from the 136kHz version) they are vertical dipoles and do not require any RF grounding. From these designs I have selected information on the 80m antenna, which I trust you will find interesting. I hope to give further details of I5TGC's antennas in later 'Antennas' columns.

## VERTICAL DIPOLE FOR 3.5MHz

This antenna was originally designed and built in 1993 [1]. The example shown in photo 1 was built by IK5PWN and is made up using a 3.5m long vertical radiator, a top capacity spherical frame, a top loading coil and two lower capacity frames. A tuning and matching coil is used to tune the antenna and couple the antenna to the feeder.

The top capacity sphere comprises an open frame made from four 800mm diameter loops of aluminium tube. This is fixed to a short insulated section above the top loading coil. This coil has seven turns wound as a flat spiral with an inner diameter of 380mm and an outer one of 560mm as shown in photo 2. The outside of this coil is connected to the top capacity section and the inside to the vertical radiator.

The bottom end of the vertical radiator is connected to the bottom end of the tuning and matching coil, while the top end is connected to the two lower capacity frames, as shown in photo 1. Each of these frames is 600 x 1500mm and constructed from aluminium tube. The tuning and matching coil is 170mm in diameter and has 20 turns of 4mm aluminium wire spaced at 8mm (see photo 3). This is a greater inductance than required and coil taps are used for coarse tuning. The coil is coupled to the feeder with a two-turn link with a mechanical arrangement to allow for coupling adjustment.

The band of 3.5MHz is fairly wide, so the antennas has a remote tuning facility. This consists of an aluminium disk, which can move along the axis of the coil by means of a threaded PVC rod, driven by a small motor and reduction gear. Both coils are supported using 15mm diameter MOPLEN rods drilled with 4.5mm holes.

So how well does it work? An analysis of QSOs made by IK5PWN during the years 1993–96, using the I5TGC design, is shown in Table 1. This is an excellent way of assessing the performance of an antenna. IK5PWN has also built a 160m version – but that is another story.

## REFERENCE

[1] Described in *RadioRivista*, (official magazine of ARI, the Italian national amateur radio society), October 1996. ◆

| | |
|---|---|
| Total number of QSOs | 1261 |
| Number of stations | 1122 |
| Number of countries | 120 |
| Number of zones | 27 |
| Average signal reports | R4.95, S 9+2dB |
| Maximum signal reports | R5, S 9+40dB |
| Asia: AP, A4, A7, A9, DU, HL, JA, JY, OD, TA, UA9, UJ8, UM9, V8, XU, XY, ZC4, 4S, 4Z, 5B, 9K, 9V | |
| Average signal reports | R4.89, S6.87 |
| Maximum signal reports | R5, S9+10dB |
| Africa: C5, EL, J2, TU, 3V, 5N, 5T, 7X, 9G | |
| Average signal reports | R 4.9 S 8.26 |
| Maximum signal reports | R5 S9+20dB |
| Americas: CO, FG, FM, HH, HI, HJ, KP4, LU, PY, PZ, TI, VE, VP2, VP5, VP9, W, XE, YV, ZP, 8R, 9Y | |
| Average signal reports | R4.84, S7.56 |
| Maximum signal reports | R5, S9+20dB |
| Oceania: | VK, ZL |
| Average signal reports | R5, S7.25 |
| Maximum signal reports | R5, S9 |

Table 1: From the digital log of IK5PWN, the 80m band during the period from October 93 to January 1996. The signal reports indicate how DX stations received signals from IK5PWN and exclude Europe or meaningless contest reports.

# ANTENNAS

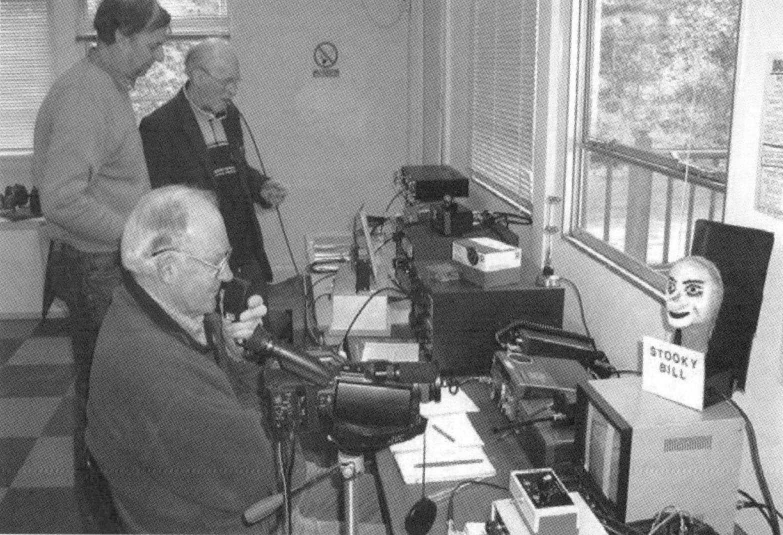


***Right:* TV shack at Amberley, with the video camera used to create the test card and 'Stooky Bill' images. 'Stooky Bill' was the ventriloquist's dummy used in the original Baird transmissions of 1928. In the foreground is Peter, G4JNU, on the SSB link, with Vic, G3SDQ, and Ted, G3GMZ, in the background.**

I don't often get the chance to play with 'big' antennas, so when the opportunity arose of being involved with making a big V-beam I accepted with alacrity. The Narrow Band Television Association was to make an attempt to transmit 40-line, mechanical scan television pictures from Amberley museum across the Atlantic. This was to commemorate the Baird transmission on 8 and 9 February 1928 (see 'RadCom News' April 2003).

The existing shack and antennas of the museum club station, GB2CPM, were unsuitable because of the lack of space. The Amberley museum authorities made a Portacabin available as a temporary home for the television equipment. A fairly high ERP was required to ensure the TV signals would get through, so a high gain antenna was required. The Amberley museum is located in what used to be a chalk quarry for the production of lime so most of the buildings, including the proposed Portacabin, are surrounded by chalk cliffs caused by years of quarrying activity. Fortunately, at this particular location within the museum, the ground is open to the northwest.

We had plenty of space, with a 30m-high sloping wall of chalk at the rear of the proposed antenna. A V-beam seemed an obvious choice. The apex of the antenna could be supported by the chalk cliff to the southeast and the ends of the wires supported by trees to the northwest.

**Fig 1**

***Fig 1:* Prediction of the performance of the V-beam using *EZNEC*. The antenna is bi-directional because it is not terminated. The rear lobe would probably be smaller than shown because of the presence of the chalk cliff, which could not be modelled.**

The distance from the antenna apex to the trees was over 350m so we needed a lot of wire. Fortunately Dave Rudram, the museum telephone and radio curator, had a good supply of twin drop telephone wire (as used between a house and a telephone pole). This material comprises twin steel copper-plated wire with a plastic insulation and is very strong. This was split to make the two wires of the V-beam.

We settled on a leg length of 120m, around six wavelengths a leg on 14MHz. An *EZNEC* model of this antenna, see **Fig 1**, with the ends of the elements some 60m apart gave us a calculated gain of 12.46dBi, or just over 10dBd. This is about the same as a five or six element monoband Yagi.

Feeding the antenna was a challenge. The V-beam is a balanced antenna, so 450Ω twin ladder line seemed the obvious choice. However, the transmission line also had to cross a road from the Portacabin. Coax cable, fixed under a wooden protector to prevent damage from vehicle wheels, was used for this part of the feeder run.

## BALANCED ATU

The solution was to use a balanced ATU located part of the way between the Portacabin and the antenna apex and located at the base of the chalk cliff. An ATU was built specially for the project by Ted Hardy, G3GMZ, a member of the Narrow Band Television Association. This unit covered the bands 14 to 21MHz and used breadboard construction as shown in the photograph. Because the ATU was to be situated outside it was built on to the lid of a plastic storage box; the box itself providing a weatherproof cover. The ATU was placed on a small wooden table to make it easier to connect and set up. The length of feeder from the ATU to the antenna apex was 50m.

Because I had already installed an antenna for 136kHz on the site and I knew where all the best fixing points were, I was elected to fix the apex of the antenna in position. Access to the top of the cliff is through a wood-covered hill at the back of the museum grounds. A wire, with a suitable weight, was thrown down from the top and the two wires and the feeder, pre-constructed to form the apex, were attached to the draw rope and raised into position. The ends of the wires, with suitable insulators, were then fixed to two trees. Although this sounds fairly simple it took three separate weekends to get the antenna into position.

## ANTENNA PERFORMANCE

The antenna was tested using the G3GMZ ATU on 14MHz using my mobile rig. Although the antenna loaded up without a problem the first tests were disappointing, not much better than my mobile antenna! Not only that, we were not working with the additional 40m of coax from the ATU to the Portacabin. In the event the antenna proved to be a winner: it was just that we were not used to fixed high-gain antenna. When the band opened up to the USA on the nose of our beam it was a different matter. Over several weekends trans-Atlantic tests were done using the television transmitting equipment. These indicated that the SSTV allocation on 21MHz would give superior results on the day. Predictions using *EZNEC* showed that the gain distribution was very similar to that in Fig 1, except that the main lobe was only 10° wide.

On the weekend of the test we were dismayed to find an SSB contest in full swing, with several heavyweights around the SSTV calling frequency. We needn't have worried. When we fired up with either the SSB communications link or the television transmission everyone else moved off.

Pictures were received Ed Gable, K2MP, at the Antique Wireless Association museum in the USA. You can see information on the AWA Museum at www.antiquewireless.org We wish to thank the Amberley Museum authorities for allowing us to use their site to conduct these historic television tests. ◆

# ANTENNAS

The debate on PL259/SO239 coax connectors continues to generate comment. Bryan Young, GW6TYO, sent the following (edited) e-mail exchange between W8JIT and K7FR that he found on the Internet:

To K7FR from W8JIT, responding to "...allow 0.1dB for the connectors at each end or 0.2dB total"; "I keep seeing this thing about connector loss everywhere I look. It's become accepted as fact in our community, but it's folklore. Here's an example why. With 0.1dB loss per connector, power loss in a PL259/SO239 combo would be about 35 watts at 1500W. Loss is concentrated in the centre pin and dielectric of the SO239 section, in an area less than one half-inch long. The PL259 section has almost no loss or impedance bump when properly installed. 35W of connector heat (with a 1500W transmitter), when concentrated in the inside of the SO239, would quickly make the connector so hot it would be untouchable. In a few minutes [it would] melt the solder connection and dielectric. If you doubt this, turn on a 35W lamp for a few minutes and touch the glass. Now imagine how hot the glass would be if it was all within a quarter inch of the filament. At 30MHz, the loss caused by a 239/259 combo is totally unimportant. One foot of 9913 cable has much more loss. Tom, W8JIT."

"Back in senior year at Washington State University we had to do a project in the measurements lab. Since there were two hams in the lab we decided to measure losses in coax connectors. We set up a calorimeter and measured $I^2R$ losses from DC to 2GHz for a PL259/SO239 combo, with the output increased in 100 watt steps until we observed a sharp up turn in losses. The results from my lab notes are shown in **Table 1**... Before this experiment I was paranoid about my connectors. Since then I have only been concerned with the quality of the assembly and water ingress. Gary, K7FR."

## LOADED VERTICALS

Des Vance, GI3XZM, while querying that the I5TGC antenna ['Antennas', *RadCom* April 2003] was a vertical dipole, was nevertheless inspired to try the following idea. All the lengths are given in imperial measurements (to convert feet to metres multiply by 0.3048 and inches to mm multiply by 25.4).

"I have often used a vertical about 5/16 or 1/3 wavelengths long, working against ground or elevated radials. A variable capacitor tunes out the extra length, giving 1/4-wave resonance and direct connection to coax. As is well known, this raises both the radiation resistance and the impedance (resistance) seen by the feeder. If the extra height arising from this arrangement is removed by using a top loading coil and capacity hat the radiation resistance is only slightly reduced. Could one optimise a vertical of limited height by 'stretching' the bottom until the maximum current point is half way up the permitted height and absorbing all the excess height in the top loading coil and capacity hat?

"Suppose one had a 20ft pole and wanted a vertical for 80 metres. Now we want the current maximum 10ft from the base so if we had a full 1/4-wave vertical, plus the 10ft, it would be, say, 66+10=76ft high which would resonate (with suitable earth) at about 3MHz. Suppose we top load the 20ft pole with inductance and capacitance until it resonates at 3MHz, then bring it up to 3.55MHz with a series capacitor we should have the current in the pole optimised.

**LOSSES MEASURED IN A PL259/SO239 CONNECTOR AT 1000 WATTS INTO A BIRD DUMMY LOAD** (SEE TEXT)

| f (MHz) | Loss (W) | dB |
|---|---|---|
| 0.1 | 1 | -0.00435 |
| 1 | 1.2 | -0.00521 |
| 10 | 1.3 | -0.00565 |
| 20 | 1.5 | -0.00652 |
| 30 | 1.8 | -0.00782 |
| 50 | 2.2 | -0.00957 |
| 100 | 2.6 | -0.01131 |
| 200 | 3.5 | -0.01523 |
| 400 | 7 | -0.03051 |
| 1000 | 15 | -0.06564 |
| 1500 | 28 | -0.12334 |
| 2000 | 100 | -0.45757* |

* CONNECTOR FAILED BEFORE CALORIMETER STABILISED

"I thought I would see if this idea might be easily implemented. I found a length of alloy tube in my heap about 13ft long, stood it in a jam jar on the lawn and guyed it with plastic rope as shown in **Fig 3**. With a one-turn link, see **Fig 1**, and the GDO I found this arrangement resonant at about 15.7MHz." The variable capacitor is shorted out to measure the antenna's natural frequency. The loop is replaced with a coaxial socket when used with a transceiver and the capacitor adjusted for minimum SWR.

"Top loading was added and the resonant frequency fell to 10.8MHz. The five-turn helical coil shown in **Fig 2** was inserted (another stab in the dark) and the resonant frequency became 6.4MHz." The top loading frame was made by supporting three 5ft garden canes fixed in holes in 1.5 x 1.5 inch timber, chamfered to fit the 50mm alloy pole. It has an inductive centre section with five helical turns 6in to 30in diameter, approximately 23ft wire total, and a capacitive outer section, with three broken loops connected in parallel. By including the variable capacitor the system was easily tuned to 7MHz.

"Not having a transmitter in working order I could not try my 40m vertical in the standard way. Undaunted, I drove off in the car, listening to the ground wave from the GDO. With an FRG7 [receiver] beside me and a length of hook-up wire tied to a garden cane taped to the door pillar I got a fair signal about 3 miles (5km) away. Since the input to the GDO is less than 5mW the output, with no matching, could hardly have exceed 1 or 2mW." ◆

*Fig 1: Base insulator and feed method for coupling a GDO.*

*Fig 2: Top loading frame.*

*Fig 3: General view of the GI3XZM antenna. Six 22SWG radials of similar length are pegged out on the lawn.*

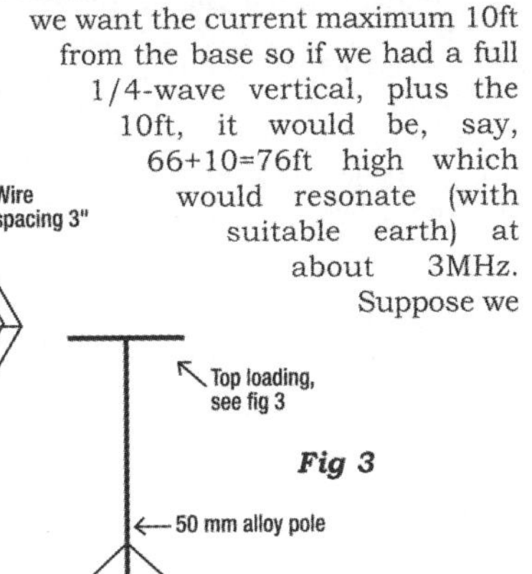


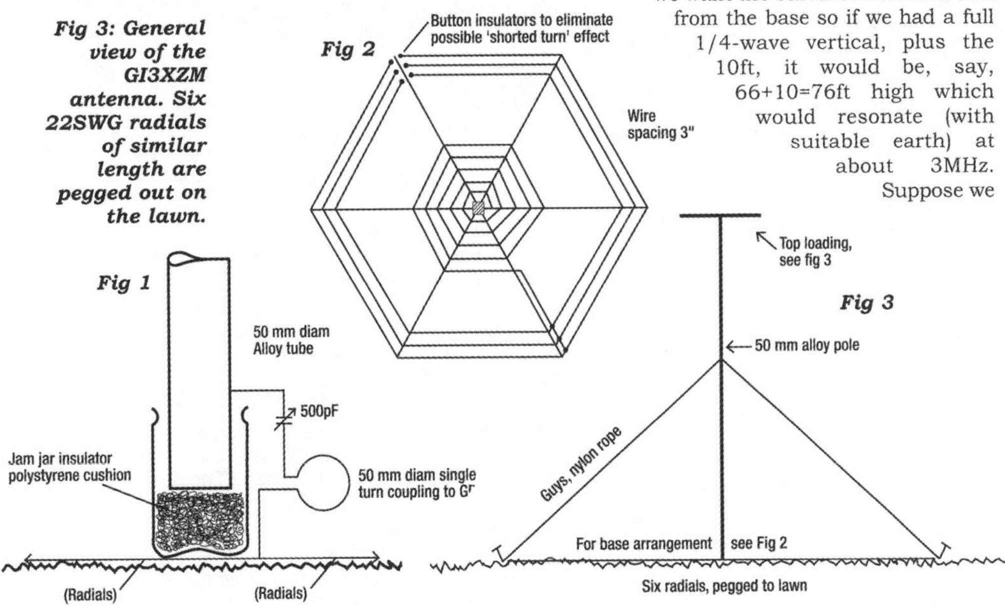

# ANTENNAS

In these days of solid-state transceivers, coax cable, and ATUs it can come as a surprise that in the early days the only way of feeding an antenna was to connect it directly to the transmitter. In my copy of the *Admiralty Handbook of Wireless Telegraphy* (1925) there is a circuit of a valve transmitter with the antenna is connected via taps on the PA tank circuit.

For this method of coupling to work efficiently the antenna had to present a fairly high impedance at the feedpoint and an end-fed half wave antenna would have been used. This practice was copied by radio amateurs and even as late as 1947, *The Radio Amateurs' Handbook* (ARRL) describes the method as 'direct excitation', when power is transferred directly from the source to the radiating antenna.

**Fig 1a**, shows the end of the antenna coupled directly to the transmitter tank circuit. The level of loading is achieved by connecting to the appropriate tap on the coil and a small capacitor is used to provide isolation. A preferred method is shown in **Fig 1b**, where a separate tuning circuit is used.

The disadvantages of this direct excitation were well known to amateurs, where the bringing the radiating antenna into the operating room had a close relationship with the house and electric wiring.

## THE ZEPP FEED

By the late 1920s the German airship, *Graf Zeppelin*, was making numerous successful intercontinental flights and an efficient wireless system was considered essential. Wireless communications with aircraft were effective, with the antenna system on the aircraft simply a long trailing wire with lead weights at the far end and fed directly as described above. However, this system was not considered safe for a hydrogen-filled airship because on some frequencies there would be a very high impedances (and high voltages) close to the surface of the airship. The German engineers therefore devised the tuned feeder system shown in **Fig 2**, which became known as the Zeppelin or Zepp antenna. The lengths of antenna and feeder are arranged so that on frequencies where the antenna (X in Fig 2) is approximately a half-wave long, the open wire balanced feeder length (Y in Fig 2) is a quarter wavelength. The quarter wavelength feeder transforms the high impedance, high voltage point to a low impedance, low voltage at the transmitter. At lower frequencies, where the antenna is closer to a quarter wave, the feeder is only 1/8th wavelength so the voltage on the antenna system where it is connected to the transmitter is still fairly low. Capacitors C1 and C2 could be adjusted so that the measured currents in both wires of the feeder are approximately equal.

For some reason the Zepp antenna became very popular with radio amateurs even though the environment restrictions and requirements that shaped the Zepp antenna did not apply to a ground station. It was even used as a feed system for the driven element in the early beam antennas. It is my contention that some antennas are the result of 'fashion' rather than good engineering practice.

A derivative of the Zepp was the so-called 'Double Extended Zepp', which comprised two halfwave lengths fed by the balanced feeder. Although this is an improvement, because it is now a balanced antenna fed from a balanced feed, it is really a rather long multi-band doublet and too directive to be of much general use on the higher frequency bands.

***The G3GMZ balanced ATU (see text).***

## ANTENNA TUNING UNIT

A wire antenna cannot be connected directly to the modern transceiver with a solid state 50Ω antenna connector. Some degree of impedance transformation is required that was done in early transmitters by the transmitter tank circuit and antenna link coupling circuit. An Antenna Tuning Unit (ATU) or 'tuner' is required, which can be thought of as putting the PA tank/antenna coupling circuits outside the transmitter. Nearly all ATUs on the market today are single-ended Pi or T network tuners that work nicely with coax lines or single wire antennas. These tuners can be used for balanced lines with a suitable balun at the output. If you want a truly balanced ATU you will probably have to make your own.

In the May edition of 'Antennas' I briefly described a balanced ATU built specially by Ted Hardy, G3GMZ, for use with the V-beam during the Narrow Band Television Association trans-Atlantic tests from Amberley museum. A photograph was referred to but was omitted due to lack of space, so is shown now. The ATU covers bands 14 to 21MHz. The coax coupling is achieved using swinging link coupling to the main coil. The band is selected using taps on the coil. Because the ATU was to be situated outside it was built on to the lid of a plastic storage box; the box itself providing a weatherproof cover. The waterproofing method could be used with any ATU, with the plastic box situated on a small wooden frame and the feeders routed through holes in the plastic base (lid). ◆

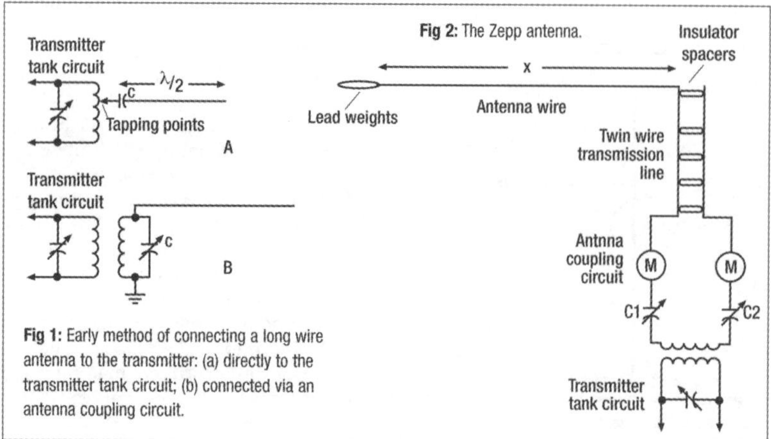


**Fig 1:** Early method of connecting a long wire antenna to the transmitter: (a) directly to the transmitter tank circuit; (b) connected via an antenna coupling circuit.

**Fig 2:** The Zepp antenna.

# Antennas

I decided to try to replicate the loaded vertical described by Des Vance, GI3XZM, in the June 'Antennas' column. You may recall that he used a length of aluminium tubing, which was resonant at about 15.7MHz. Top loading was added and the resonant frequency fell to 10.8MHz. By adding a five-turn helical coil the resonant frequency became 6.4MHz. By including the variable capacitor in series with the connection from the centre of the coax to the bottom of the pole the system was easily tuned to 7MHz.

My aluminium pole was a similar length but I used a simpler method of constructing the loading unit. It comprises a short off-cut from a square section of plastic ducting (as used to run coax cables along the side of the house) and two lengths of 1.2m (4ft) green plastic-covered canes from the garden centre (see photo). Holes are made in the plastic ducting for the plastic-covered canes which are held in place by black plastic tape. I used thin plastic-covered wire for the coil, also held in place with plastic tape.

I have an area of wire netting under the lawn so I used this as a counterpoise. The resonant frequency of my antenna was around 6.8MHz so I used a series variable capacitance at the feedpoint to bring the antenna into resonance. The SWR at 6.8MHz was around 1.1:1 and at 7.02MHz was 1.4:1. It looked good.

However, according to the antenna modelling program EZNEC, the feedpoint of a full-sized vertical fed against a good horizontal ground is around 45Ω (depending on the nature of the ground). With an electrically short loaded antenna the feedpoint is much lower and in my case should have been around 20Ω. The fact that it was nearer to 50Ω meant that there was additional series resistance, which in this case turned out to be earth resistance. Although the antenna had a nice low SWR it had a lot of loss. By adding radials, as described by GI3XZM, the feed impedance dropped to below 30Ω reducing the earth losses considerably - and the SWR shot up to 2:1. It just goes to show that a low SWR doesn't necessarily mean that the antenna is good. The characteristics of an antenna are often displayed using an SWR plot relative to frequency and as you can see this can sometimes be misleading.

A useful indication of antenna characteristics can be obtained using a plot of impedance relative to frequency, as shown **Fig 1**. This can be done using an SWR analyser, such as the MFJ-248 or one of the Autek instruments, such as the RF-1. This measurement should be done at the feedpoint of the antenna (which is not usually a problem with a vertical antenna) to avoid complicating things with transmission line impedance transformation effects.

*Top loading arrangement constructed from a square section of plastic ducting and two lengths of plastic-covered canes.*

Ideally the curve should pass through the zero reactance, 50Ω resistance intersection (SWR 1:1) at the frequency of interest and is usually achieved with a matching device such as a gamma match. The GI3XZM method is to use a variable series capacitor at the feedpoint to raise the impedance of the feedpoint and positioning the curve through the 1:1 SWR intersection at 7MHz.

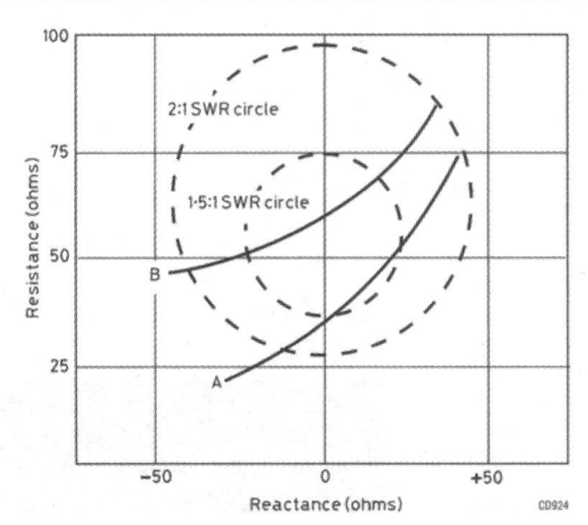


**Fig 1: Antenna impedance variations over a frequency range; A is for a vertical with a good radial system and B is my antenna with the chicken wire ground. The lowest frequencies are at the lower left of the curves.**

## EH / CFA ANTENNAS

You might find the URL www.eh-antenna.com headed 'Welcome to the Wonderful World of EH Antennas' interesting. It contains the following statement: "For more than 120 years all antennas have been Hertz antennas, except the Crossed Field Antenna. In the future all antennas will be EH Antennas. Fortunately, any antenna can be converted to an EH Antenna with a minimum of effort. We have filed an additional patent clarifying the scope of the original patent, extending its coverage such that any antenna can be converted to an EH Antenna and be under the umbrella of the patent."

John H Davis, KD4IDY, in an e-mail on the LF reflector, notes: "You should be careful how you construct your plain everyday 'Hertz' antenna or it may infringe a patent. Perhaps it would be too much to ask of our patent offices to require proof that an invention actually works. I wish we could at least return to the days when it was not possible to patent and re-patent techniques already known to the state of the art (in this case, electrically short verticals and dipoles), simply by virtue of sticking a new name on them or claiming a new theory of operation." ◆

**Many members may wish to try HF operation now that the Morse requirement for access to HF has been formally abolished in the UK. The author offers his thoughts on adding an HF antenna to your existing VHF/UHF antennas.**

*Fig 1*

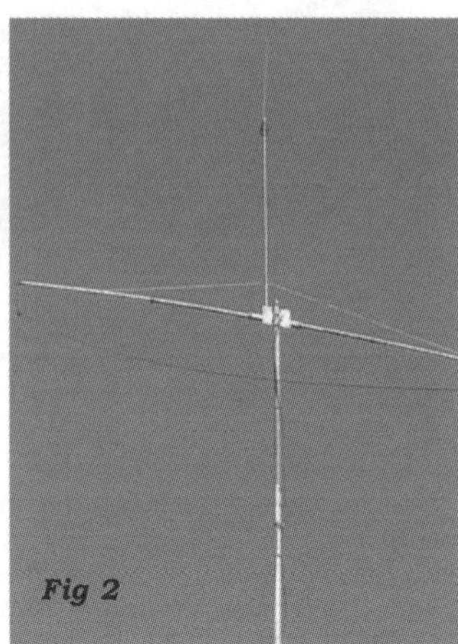

*Fig 2*

# Antennas

***Fig 1: Top of the LF antenna mast, showing method of fixing HF vertical. The counterpoise is connected directly to the support plate.***

***Fig 2: The 14MHz vertical fixed to the top of the LF antenna mast. The counterpoise can just be seen sloping away from the mast to the left.***

You may also wish to add another band to your existing single-band HF beam, so what might be the best approach? You could try fixing a dipole using the existing mast as a support, as described in [1], but the existing antenna system might not be suitable for such an arrangement. My antenna system is a case in point. I have a 14m (48ft) mast, which is currently supporting a 136kHz LF antenna and there is no room for any other wire antennas.

## ADDING AN HF VERTICAL

You could try a vertical mounted on the existing mast. The late G2XK fixed a 21MHz vertical above his 6-element 10m beam, which gave excellent results. In the past I have added a 14MHz vertical above an existing 21MHz metal quad and this also gave good results.

For a quarter-wave vertical to work, it has to be fed against a ground plane or radials. In both cases described above, the mass of the metal of the beams provided a suitable ground plane.

If the vertical were to be fitted to a mast supporting only a relatively small VHF antenna, would it still work? In the case of my LF antenna, the only metal at the top of the mast is a 3.5m length of aluminium tube that acts as a spreader for the two wires that make up the LF antenna; I was interested in seeing how a vertical would perform in this situation.

The method of fixing the vertical to the top of the mast is shown in **Fig 1**. Originally, there was a short stub mast, which was used to carry nylon bracing cords to prevent the spreaders drooping under the weight of the wire and insulators of the LF antenna. The stub mast was modified by insulating it from the spreader support plate using rubber insulating material and U-bolts. The top of the stub mast was modified so that the vertical element could be plugged in and the joint tightened using a hose clamp. The antenna is fed with 50Ω coax, the centre being connected to the vertical element and the braiding to the support plate.

## PERFORMANCE

Although the vertical was known to be a quarter-wave resonant at 14.1MHz, the antenna feed impedance, as indicated by the VSWR, was a long way off 50Ω. The problem was fixed by connecting a quarter-wave-long counterpoise wire directly to the support plate. The length of this wire could be shortened at the insulator (to increase the resonant frequency of the antenna) by folding some of the wire back along itself and fixing with insulating tape.

The 14MHz vertical fixed to the top of the LF antenna mast is shown in **Fig 2**. The top vertical element is only 2.5m long because, when the mast is folded over, that is the distance from the top of the mast to the end of the garden. The element is resonated using a centre-loading coil. Lack of space precludes a description of the loading coil, but it is described in [2].

The coax feeder to this antenna is rather long - some 60m - so it was important to get the VSWR down as low as possible to minimise signal loss.

First impressions indicated that the performance of this vertical was very similar to my two-element minibeam mounted on the chimney of the house at about 10m (30ft) high and fed with 20m of coax. The height of the vertical feed-point is 14m (48ft), but this height advantage is probably partially cancelled by the long feeder.

The DX performance of this vertical seemed quite good, having a slight advantage on long DX paths, although the noise level on the vertical was slightly higher.

## CONCLUSION

If you are mounting a vertical on a large existing metal structure, it should work well. Originally, I was of the impression that the mast itself would be sufficient but, in my case, this proved not to be true. The length (height) of the mast might be critical, but I was unable to test this.

If you mount an HF vertical above an existing small antenna, such as a VHF / UHF beam, the addition of a counterpoise seems to do the trick, and has the advantage that it can be used to adjust the antenna's resonant frequency. ◆

## REFERENCES

[1] ***Backyard Antennas,*** RSGB Sales
[2] ***The Amateur Radio Mobile Handbook,*** RSGB Sales

**Serious mobile DX operating is best done when the vehicle is not moving, in which case there are a lot more options for the types of antenna that can be used. The vehicle installation of Stefan Larsson, SM6FLL, is an example of just what can be done.**

*Left: The SM6FLL clip-on antenna mounting panel and matching/loading unit fixed to the vehicle using a bicycle carrier frame mounted on the tow-bar.*

*Below: A closer view of the clip-on antenna mounting panel and matching/loading unit.*

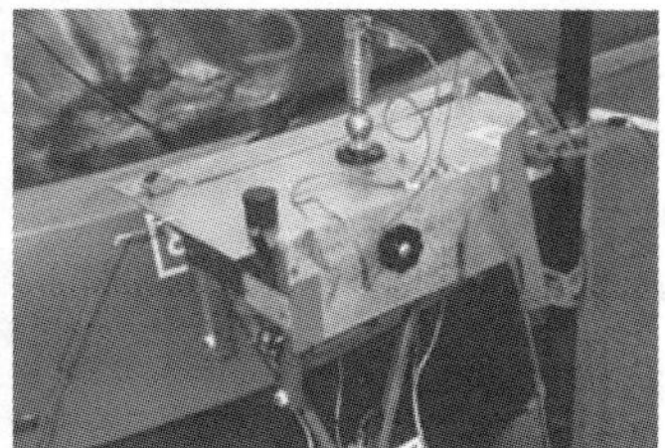

# Antennas

For those of us living in accommodation that presents difficulties for amateur radio operation, one solution is to operate mobile or portable. Generally, mobile antennas are less efficient than fixed station antennas because of the mechanical requirements of a mobile installation.

The SM6FLL installation allows a selection of relatively high-efficiency antennas for HF mobile or portable operation in the frequency range 1.8 to 50MHz. The installation is centred around a clip-on antenna mounting panel and matching/loading unit fixed to the rear of the vehicle. All this is built into a box, which is mounted on bicycle carrier frame that sits on a tow-bar ball. The assembly is held against the vehicle with bungee cords and cushioned from the vehicle body with two plastic balls. The method of fixing the antenna assembly to the vehicle is shown in the photographs.

There are several antenna structures that can be used with the mounting panel. One is the home-made mobile antenna, which screws into the sprung mounting base most clearly seen in the close-up. This mobile antenna is made from a 2.1m length of aluminium tubing with a capacity hat and telescopic extension at the top. No loading coils are used in the antenna structure and loading is achieved in the matching unit.

Two other arrangements make use of a long telescopic plastic fishing pole and the method of fixing is clearly shown in the photographs. The plastic pole can be used simply to support a wire up to 9m long to make a 5λ/8 vertical antenna on the highest frequency bands. The wire can be extended to 13m with the use of a small kite. For the lower frequency bands, a large kite is used where the lower end is secured to the bicycle support frame. In all cases, the wire is fed by simply clipping it on to the sprung mobile antenna base unit, as shown. The ground system can be improved using several radials connected to antenna mounting plate and held down at the extremities with tent pegs. One of the radials is terminated with a metal plate, which is submerged in the sea when operating from a coastal site. This type of counterpoise has been found to be very effective on 136kHz, so will probably also be effective on the lower HF bands.

## MATCHING/LOADING UNIT

The matching/loading unit, housed under the antenna mounting panel, comprises a roller-coaster variable inductor, with provision for adding an additional fixed inductor. A 250pF variable capacitance is used that can be connected either to the antenna or transmitter side of the inductor as shown in **Fig 1**. When the system is set up for mobile operation using the shorter mobile antenna, the variable capacitance is connected to the transmitter end. In this respect, the coil is being used as a variable base-loading inductor and the capacitance for transmitter impedance matching to the coil and antenna.

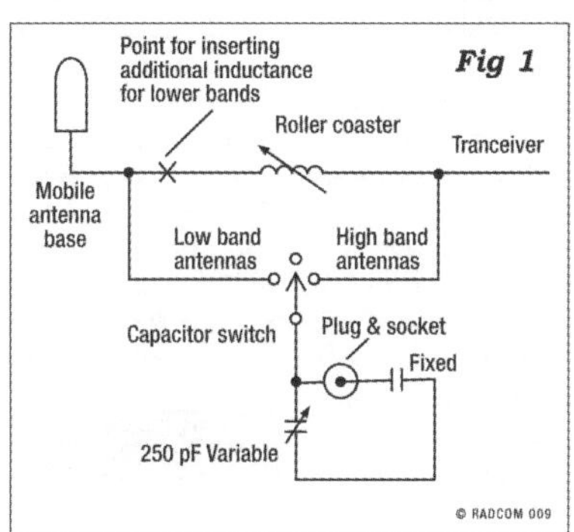


*Fig 1: Circuit diagram of the matching/loading unit. A fixed capacitor can be connected across the 250pF variable capacitor with a plug and socket arrangement if required.*

When the 250pF capacitor is switched to the antenna side of the variable inductor, the circuit becomes an L-section matching system and is used to match a range of varying impedances presented by all these experimental antennas. The capacitor can be switched out and the variable inductance set to zero for straight-through connection to a higher frequency resonant antenna.

## GENERAL

What is really interesting about SM6FLL's travelling antenna farm is the ingenuity used to obtain an improved antenna performance from a mobile/portable location. Too often our ideas are restricted by what antennas are commercially available. The rear-mounting antenna mounting panel and matching/loading unit provides an excellent arrangement for experimenting with all manner of antennas.

If you do intend to do a lot of mobile/portable work from a fixed location, remember the battery is not being charged. A voltmeter to measure the state of the battery is a useful accessory. I now use a separate sealed battery inside the vehicle, which is charged from the cigar lighter socket when the vehicle is in motion. ◆

# Antennas

## A design is offered here for those who like experimenting with small (or not-so-small) loops.

The conventional transmitting loop is a solution to HF operating from a site where there is insufficient room to erect a conventional wire antenna. It comprises a loop of large diameter tubing tuned by a substantial capacitor. The reason for this heavy engineering is the very high currents involved; these are typically 15 to 20amps through the loop element and capacitor when fed from a standard 100W transceiver. The efficiency of the loop antenna is the subject of much debate [1], and can be from 10% to 50% depending the coupling into nearby electromagnetic obstructions and other factors. A low insertion loss transformer/balun is also necessary to match to balanced loop to 50Ω coaxial cable.

### THE I5TGC LOOP ANTENNA

An alternative loop has been designed by Cesare Tagliabue, I5TGC. This antenna employs inductive rather than capacitive loading and the one about to be described operates on frequencies from 14 to 28MHz. The I5TGC antenna, shown in the photograph, actually comprises two loops set at 90° to each other in an 'X'-configuration to allow the selection of polarisation.

The electrical length (see **Fig 1**) of the loop is a half-wave at the lowest frequency (in this case, 14MHz.). This is made up from the lengths of the conductors A to B (1500mm), C (1500mm), two lengths of D (700mm), plus the inductive and capacitive loads. Details of the loop construction are shown in **Fig 2**. The diagrams are I5TGC's originals, and anyone interested in building the antenna can obtain the full-size diagrams (including the ATU and the loop switching mechanism) from me on receipt of an A4 or A5 SAE.

Other dimensions are:

Inductive load = 6 turns 235 mm. diameter.

Capacitive load = 1 ring 235 mm diameter.

Sections A, B are constructed from aluminium tubing 16/12mm diameter.

Section C is made from aluminium tubing 12/10mm diameter.

The coils and capacitive rings are aluminium tubing 6/4mm diameter and the coils are supported with MOPLEN rods, fixed to the coil ends and some intermediate turns.

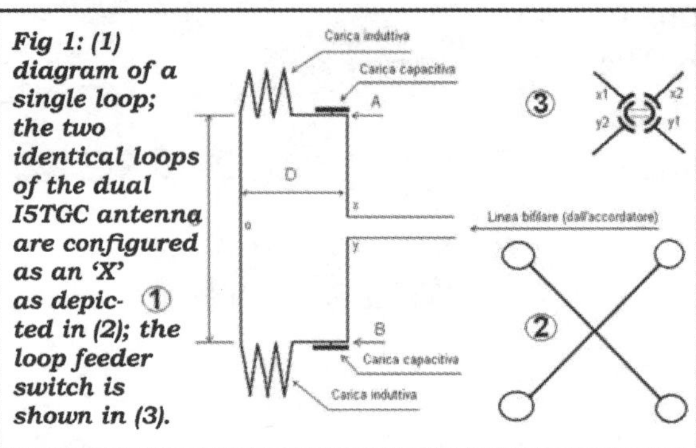


***Fig 1: (1) diagram of a single loop; the two identical loops of the dual I5TGC antenna are configured as an 'X' as depicted in (2); the loop feeder switch is shown in (3).***

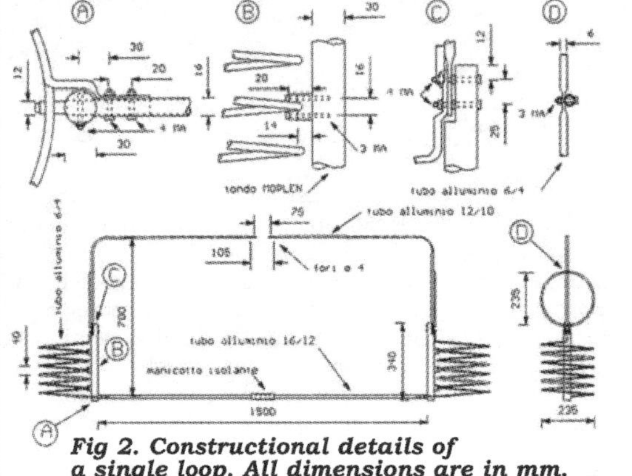


***Fig 2. Constructional details of a single loop. All dimensions are in mm.***

There is more than one way of looking at this antenna. On 14MHz you could think of it as a short loaded dipole, voltage-fed at the tips. On 28MHz it is more like a full-wave loop with a low-impedance feed. The main objective of this design is to increase of the efficiency, compared with a conventional loop, by increasing the radiation resistance.

As you can imagine, the feed impedance varies considerably over the design frequency range. This problem is solved by using a true balanced ATU and 450Ω balanced twin-wire feeder. The ATU used by I5TGC is situated relatively close to the antenna and is remotely-controlled from the shack. This arrangement allows the open-wire feeder to be relatively short to minimise losses caused by the high SWR. This arrangement also allows the crossed loop to operate on 10 and 7MHz. In this case, the antenna works more like a conventional loop with noticeable losses compared with the design frequency range.

As already stated, the feeder is connected to the extremities x, y, of one of the loops (Fig 1 part 1). Points x, y, of the other loop are connected to a switch, a diagram of which is shown in Fig 1 part 3. This switch allows the loop not directly connected to the feeder to be connected with 0° or 180° shift relative to the fed loop - or not fed at all. By this means, very quick variation of polarisation, horizontal, vertical, or oblique can be selected. The switch is remotely controlled by means of two nylon cords wound on a drum driven by a small motor. This antenna is fully insulated from the mast, constructed on a small boom of PVC high-pressure tubing.

***The I5TGC loop antenna in position.***

### OPERATION

I5TGC notes that the polarisation of most signals is elliptic, with horizontal and vertical polarisation at the same time. However, on some propagation paths, only one polarisation plane is present; in this case a switchable loop is a distinct advantage when working some DX stations.

This loop has proved to be an effective DX antenna, with countries such as VP8, BV, JW, and many others, being worked in pile-up situations.

This antenna was described in *RadioRivista*, the official magazine of the ARI (Italian Radio amateurs Association) in October 1996. The extent of the experimental antenna work done by I5TGC can be seen on his website, see below. ◆

**REFERENCE**

[1] This subject is covered in great detail in the new RSGB book International Antenna Collection, available from the RSGB Shop.

WEBSEARCH

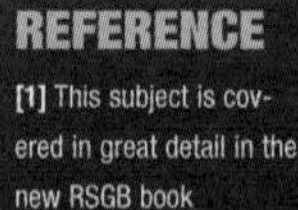

**I5TGC** **www.i5tgc.it**

# Antennas

## Using HF antennas on 136kHz

At this time of the year, you might like to try listening on our 136kHz band. Although there is very little activity during the week, on Sunday there are often some stations to be heard. You can use any existing long wire or dipole for the lower frequency bands. The long-wire antenna can be used as it would be for the lower HF bands, by connecting it to an ATU and feeding against a good RF ground. An HF dipole can also be used for LF by connecting both conductors of the feeder together and using the total antenna and feeder as a long wire fed against ground.

Amateur signals are very weak compared with the strong commercial and broadcast signals at LF. For this reason, you will need a receive ATU for LF, which comprises a loading coil and a method of matching to the receiver. The performance of modern receivers at LF varies considerably from model to model, so some signal amplification may also be required.

### A PORTABLE LF ATU

I have built an LF ATU, which is designed for portable operation with a small transceiver such as the FT-817 or IC-706 and an HF multiband centre-fed doublet antenna (although it can be used with a long wire). Not only does it provide the tuned circuits for loading and matching, but it also has a switching arrangement that allows the transceiver to be connected directly to the HF doublet or via the LF circuits.

The circuit is shown in **Fig 1**. When the antenna is switched to 'LF', the inner and the outer of the HF antenna coax feed are joined and connected to the LF loading circuit, the total HF ATU becoming part of the LF antenna; it is thus important that it is not connected to ground. When using a long-wire for HF, an RF earth for HF will be effective when made at the LF ATU.

Inductors at these frequencies are large. For transmitting, an inductor of around 3 to 4mH is required to load a suburban-sized antenna. Initially, I considered using a large inductance with taps but, for a portable LF ATU, there was not enough room for a large inductor. On receive, some capacitance loading can be used with some loss of efficiency and switching in appropriate values of capacitance is very easy.

### Inductor

The inductor is made from three short lengths of ferrite from an old transistor radio. In fact, it is one stick, 190mm long, cut into three sections. I found the best way of cutting a ferrite stick is to make a deep groove all round with a fine grindstone. The stick will then break very cleanly at the groove. The coil former is then finished off by binding the three lengths of ferrite together with plastic insulation tape. The coil is wound, initially single layer, using 26SWG or similar (0.5mm), wire. The earth end of the coil is connected to the ATU chassis and taps are provided every five turns to provide matching to a following receiver or preamplifier. The winding is continued along the length of the former, and a further layer of tape wound over the top two-thirds of the coil, clear of the matching taps. A further layer of wire is then wound over the tape.

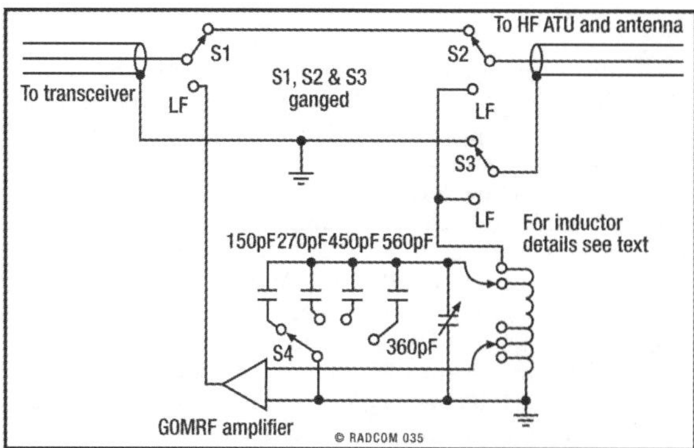


*Fig 1: Circuit diagram of the 136kHz ATU. Only one amplifier is shown, although two are used (see text). A tap on the earth end of the coil is selected for optimum matching. The +12V supply to the amplifier is not shown.*

### Preamplifier

This receiver ATU also has built-in pre-amplification. Most commercial amateur receivers have a relatively poor performance when tuned to the 136kHz LF band. The reason is that these receivers have an attenuator connected in the circuit below 1.8MHz to prevent overload from high-powered broadcast stations; this also reduces sensitivity on the 136kHz band. Dave Bowman, G0MRF, has produced a kit, based on an original design by Dave Pick, G3YXM, for a small 136kHz receive preamplifier. This amplifier gives around 13dB of gain at 136.5kHz, which overcomes the losses caused by the built-in attenuator. The G0MRF preamplifier has a built-in filter to reduce the effects of the very strong commercial and broadcast stations above and below the 136kHz band. The input/output of this amplifier is 50-75Θ.

Because my arrangement is to be used with the insensitive receiver of the IC-706, at 136kHz, with an inefficient antenna, I am using two G0MRF amplifiers in cascade to increase the gain to over 20dB.

*Left: Rear view of the 136kHz ATU. The 'chassis' and front panel is constructed from single-sided PCB material, a technique used by Tim Walford, G3PCJ, in the construction of some of his kits.*

### FURTHER INFORMATION

Full details of the G0MRF 136kHz LF pre-amplifier can be found on David's website.

A general discussion on the performance of receivers and transceivers at LF, giving the best and the worst, can be found in the LF section of my website. ◆

**WEBSEARCH**

| | |
|---|---|
| David Bowman, G0MRF | www.g0mrf.com |
| The author | www.g3ldo.co.uk |

# Antennas

**Beat the declining sunspot cycle with this small beam design for 40 metres.**

Although there are a few who are able to put up beam antennas for the lower frequencies, for most of us it is out of the question. Most designs for reducing the size of an antenna use loading coils. Other designs achieve a reduced turning circle by folding the ends of the elements.

In recent correspondence, Andy Göens, YS1AG/G5AYU, said "...several years ago in 'TT', Pat Hawker described a 'VK2ABQ Mini-Beam' ('TT', May 87). I made one, but it had a very low Q and, with the first heavy rain, the wooden frame bent and it looked like a dead octopus. Now I have made a different one, a parasitic Yagi, which is much easier to tame".

## THE YS1AG 40m TWO-ELEMENT BEAM

This design achieves a small element size by folding the ends of the elements back on themselves. The antenna is shown in **Fig 1** and, as you can, see the turning circle is only one third the size of a conventional 40m beam. But how does it perform? YS1AG claims "...on the air I have received consistent 2-3 S-unit reports over a local ham using a vertical. The front-to-back ratio is about 12dB. It is not the best antenna in the world, but it is much better than a dipole and very small indeed. The height of the antenna is only 14m until I can get a taller tower to obtain a lower angle of radiation."

Analysis of the antenna using *EZNEC3* indicates a maximum free-space gain of just over 4dBi and a front-to-back ratio of around 10dB, which agrees closely with the measured performance of the real antenna. Increasing the boom length from 0.078λ to 0.1λ results in an increase in gain to 5dBi and a front-to-back ratio of around 12dB. This would mean an increase of boom length from 3m (10.8ft) to 4.26m (14ft).

The feed impedance of such a small antenna is, as you might expect, very low, and *EZNEC* indicates a value of around 4 to 5Ω. The feed arrangement used by YS1AG utilises a gamma match, in which the gamma rod is 1.3m long made from 5 or 6mm OD tubing and spaced 180mm from the driven element. The series compensating capacitor comprises two tubes, one sliding inside the other to make up a variable capacitor with a maximum value of 180pF. A 100pF doorknob capacitor is connected in parallel to make up the required total capacitance. The measured SWR, using such an arrangement with 50Ω feeder, is 1.8:1 at 7MHz, less than 1.2:1 over the range 7.04 to 7.1MHz and 1.8:1 at 7.2MHz. For European use, the driven element could be tuned slightly lower.

## CONSTRUCTION

The centre supports for the antenna were constructed by welding four lengths of 20mm OD aluminium tubes to a centre ring made from a short length of larger diameter tube (the diameter selected to fit the boom). The construction is not unlike a quad 'spider' except that the angles are 60°/120° rather than 90°/90°. The 12mm diameter elements were fitted to the 20mm tube of the spider at the feed-point end using reducers machined from aluminium bar. The high-voltage ends are insulated from the spider using hardwood dowelling and reinforced with fibreglass.

For those of us without access to aluminium welding equipment or a lathe, I suggest a method of construction that uses one-metre lengths of aluminium angle stock. This material has two holes drilled in the centre to take a U-clamp, the size of which has been selected to fit the boom as shown in [1]. Two lengths of angle material are clamped to one end of the boom so that they form a 60°/120° spider. A further two lengths of angle are then clamped to the other end of the boom. When the angle sections are correctly aligned, the feed-point end of the elements can then be fixed to the angle material with hose clamps (the antenna experimenter's friend!). The high-voltage end of the elements can be supported using hardwood dowelling, which is fixed to the angle material. The wires forming the vertical part of the elements can be fixed to the ends of the 12mm elements using hose clamps.

I find that trying to waterproof a Gamma-match variable capacitor is difficult. I prefer to insert a temporary variable capacitor, make all the adjustments necessary to match the element to the feeder, then remove the capacitor. I then measure the capacitance of the setting of the variable capacitor and replace it with a fixed capacitor of the same value (you may need two or more capacitors in parallel to get the correct value). Fixed capacitors are normally inherently waterproof, although a coat of grease prevents degradation of the outside insulation of the capacitor due to prolonged exposure to our weather. ◆

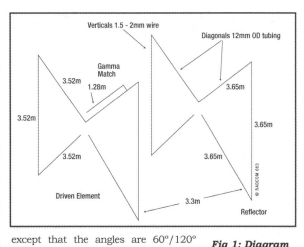

***Fig 1: Diagram of the YS1AG 40m minibeam.***

***Below left: The YS1AG beam in position.***

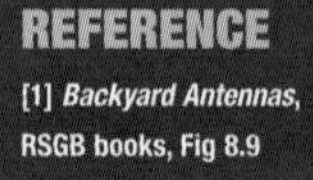
**REFERENCE**

[1] *Backyard Antennas*, RSGB books, Fig 8.9

# Antennas

**Are you plagued by failing connectors and leads? This month, Peter Dodd shows you how he makes up his leads and notes how reliable they are.**

In a recent re-arrangement of the shack, I found I needed a short length of coaxial cable with a PL-259 connector at each end. A rummage in my 'RF Connectors' box revealed a rather smart connector shown in the first photograph. When this was connected up I found that the rig didn't work. I checked out all the cables in the installation and found that my 'smart' coax connector had an open circuit braid. When the plastic sheath on the connector was removed it was found that the PL-259 plug relied on a crimp for connecting body of the plug to the cable outer braid; and it was this connection that had failed. The cable was consigned to the bin and replaced by one of my made-up ones - not so smart but much more reliable.

In the December 2002 'Antennas', I described the problems I had with soldering the body of the PL-259 plug to the coax braid. I proposed a solution where the braid was folded back over the coax sheath. The cable was then screwed into the into the plug and centre connection soldered. Any protruding braid was then cropped level with the PL-259 body.

Not all coax cables types of ostensibly the same type have the same outside diameter. The hodge-podge of coax cables that make up my station include RG-213 (OD 10.4mm), RG-8/U (OD 10.0mm), URM-67 (OD 10.5mm) and some cable of unknown pedigree with an OD of 9mm. Furthermore, not all PL-259 plugs have the same cable entry diameter. The internal diameter of most of my PL-259 plugs has an inside diameter of 11.4mm. This allows the type of connection of PL-259 to coax cable described above because the braid, folded back along the outer sheath, makes up the difference between the 10mm, or so, OD diameter of the cable and the plug. The other type of PL-529 plug I have in my collection has a cable entry diameter of 10mm. I found this out when I tried to fit one of these plugs to a length of URM-67 (OD 10.5mm). The larger diameter PL-259 cable entry plugs will take the RG-58c cable screw-in reducer, the other won't.

While looking through the 'RF Plugs & Sockets' box, I came across a couple of very good quality silver-plated PL-259 plugs labelled 'GE40032' as shown in the second photograph. The only reason they had not been pressed into service before is that they had a compression fitting for cable of around 6.5mm diameter cable, not compatible with the cables I had in use. When I removed the compression fitting gland, I found the plug's internal screw diameter was 11.6mm, excellent for making a connection to the URM-67 cable, using the method described later.

It has been suggested to me that a connector, where the braid is not soldered to the body of the plug, will eventually fail. I have found that connectors made up this way are very reliable provided the cable is a very tight fit to the plug. The cable is made up as shown in the third photograph, with the braid folded back along the coax sheath. Twist the strands of the inner conductor clockwise and tin (the clockwise twist prevents the inner conductor splaying out as cable is screwed into the plug). Often, the coax centre conductor treated this way will not fit inside the PL-259 centre pin. This can be fixed by scraping any excess solder off the coax centre conductor and running a suitable size twist drill through the centre pin of the plug before assembly.

For PL-259 connectors used externally, I smear the area around the cable centre insulator and the outer braid with grease before assembly. I also push grease into the holes that were originally designed for soldering the plug to the cable braid. I have never experienced a failure or a problem with this type of connector, even though I live close to the sea where the degree of atmospheric corrosion is higher than average.

## TESTING COAXIAL CABLE

You might be forgiven for asking why I have such a mixture of coaxial cables - why not chuck the lot away and buy a drum of new cable and get everything standardised. The answer is that, after all these years, I am still a bit of a radio junk kleptomaniac and have many hundreds of metres of coax cable and a large box of RF connectors. I see no problem using these cables and connectors, however, it is very important to test a length of cable before connecting it into an antenna installation (also important for new cable and plug installations).

This can be done using an RF power meter and dummy load (which are built in to some ATUs). First, measure the power at the transmitter then perform the measurement at the far end of the coax under test. The power loss can be converted into dBs and the test results compared with the published losses for the cable under test. This is done taking into account the length of the cable and the measurement frequency. ◆

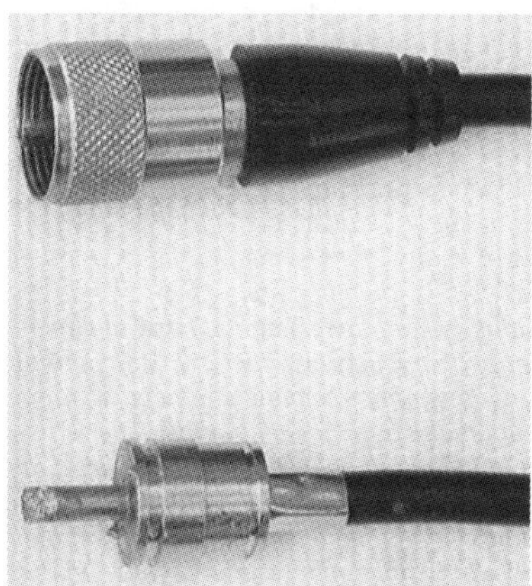

**_Top: Smart-looking coax connector with PL-259 plugs, but found to have a faulty crimp connection._**

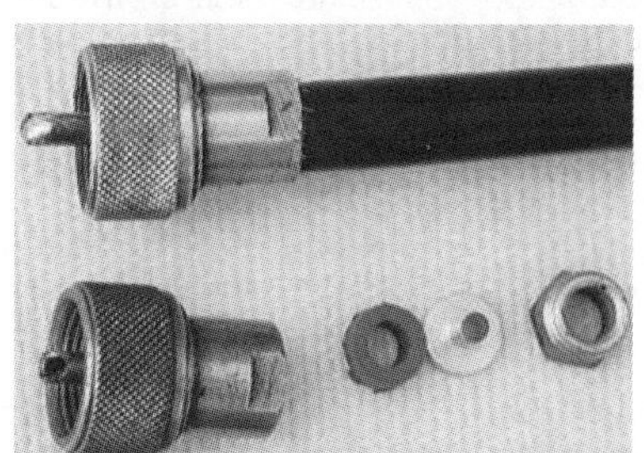

**_Middle: The GE40032 connector fitted to URM-67 coax cable (top) after removing the original cable glands shown below._**

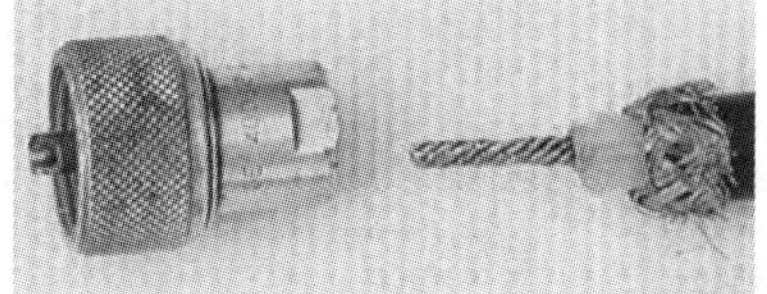

**_Bottom: Coax cable preparation prior to fitting to the plug. Note the clockwise twist in the centre conductor._**

**This month's subject is the balanced feed-line. *EZNEC 3.0* simulations show how things are supposed to be when the line is perfectly balanced, and how they are in practice, when the line is unbalanced by its environment, producing radiation of its own.**

# Antennas

I occasionally receive from readers antenna designs that have been found to work well. One of these is a design by Peter Nichols, M0RCS. It is a 66ft (20.12m) folded dipole configuration fed 16.5ft (5m) from one end using balanced feeder, but the antenna itself is inherently unbalanced. (This antenna is discussed in more detail below).

This had me thinking on just how important 'balance' was in a doublet antenna system.

Early amateur radio stations used open wire feeders coupled to the tank circuit of the transmitter in such a manner that the current in each of the wires of the feeder were equal and opposite. This ensured that only the antenna radiated but the feeder did not. Many operators went to a lot of trouble to ensure that the current in each of the feeder lines was equal by installing a current meter in each of the conductors of the feeder [1, 2]. They also provided methods of adjusting the coupling circuit for equal current. Additionally, there was a technique for further improving the balance on a transmission line. This involved transposing the positions of the feeder wires at regular intervals with the aid of a special spacer.

Most antenna books show the current distribution of antennas in their examples as though they were balanced. I have used antenna modelling software *EZNEC 3.0* to give some indication of current distribution on an antenna, my 50ft (15.25m) centre-fed special [3, 4] on several bands. In all the modelling illustrations the feedpoint is shown by a small circle. Currents are indicated by the red lines. Relative level is indicated by the distance of the red line from the antenna element.

The phase is indicated by the relationship between one red line and the other, as can be seen on the transmission line. *EZNEC 3.0* has current phase markers, but they proved to be a bit confusing on the printout. The transforming effect of the line can be seen on some illustrations - points of low current represent high impedance, conversely points of high current show low impedance.

At 7MHz, see **Fig 1**, the 50ft (15.25m) antenna is electrically short. The current distribution on the antenna is symmetrical, but an area of maximum current occurs in the feeders where the current in the lines is equal and opposite and therefore does not radiate. It does show that, for maximum efficiency, a multi-band doublet should be at least one half-wavelength long at the lowest operating band. It also shows that, in a restricted QTH, a short doublet will still work quite well.

On 14MHz, see **Fig 2**, the impedance at the centre of the antenna is fairly high and the SWR on the line will be very high. Notice that, again, the currents are still equal and opposite, so no radiation from the line takes place. On 21MHz, **Fig 3**, this short wire is quite a respectable DX antenna.

## ANTENNA WITH AN UNBALANCED FEED

The images of the current distribution on an antenna shown in Figs 1, 2 and 3 are theoretical and idealistic. In the real world, the antenna feed is rarely balanced. Nearly all commercial ATUs now use a T-match, which is an unbalanced antenna tuner. For this type of tuner to be used with twin feeder, some type of balun transformer must be incorporated as shown in the photograph. While a balun transformer provides a very simple solution for coupling a balanced feeder to an unbalanced tuning unit, it is not likely to be as effective in providing a properly-balanced feed. Furthermore, in an urban environment, there are usually lots of electromagnetic obstacles that further upset things.

So how much does a properly-balanced feed matter?

To try to find out I have again modelled the 50ft (15.25m) antenna, but fed in such a way that a degree of unbalance occurs in the feeder as shown in **Fig 4**. The amplitude of the currents on the feeder are unequal and, although it cannot be readily

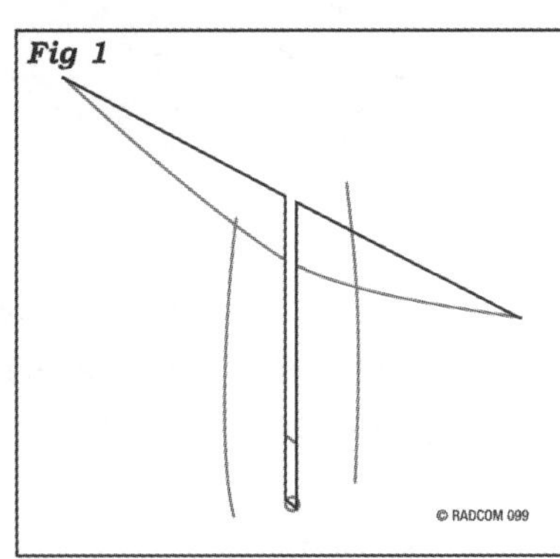


***Fig 1: Current distribution of a 50ft (15.25m) length of wire, 30ft (10m) high, centre-fed with balanced feeder on 7MHz. With moderately good ground, the gain of the antenna is 5.5dBi, with most of the radiation going vertically. A good NVIS antenna for working over a few 100km.***

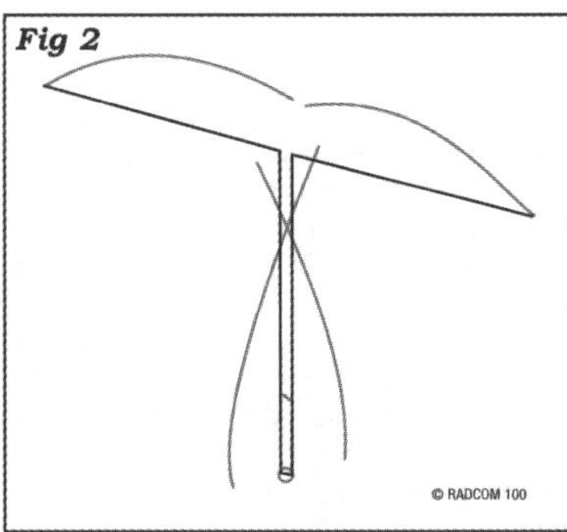


***Fig 2: Current distribution of a 50ft (15.25m) length of wire, 30ft (10m) high, centre-fed with balanced feeder on 14MHz. The centre of the antenna is a fairly high impedance, transformed to low by the transmission line to the feed-point. Maximum gain (6.5dBi) occurs at 40°.***

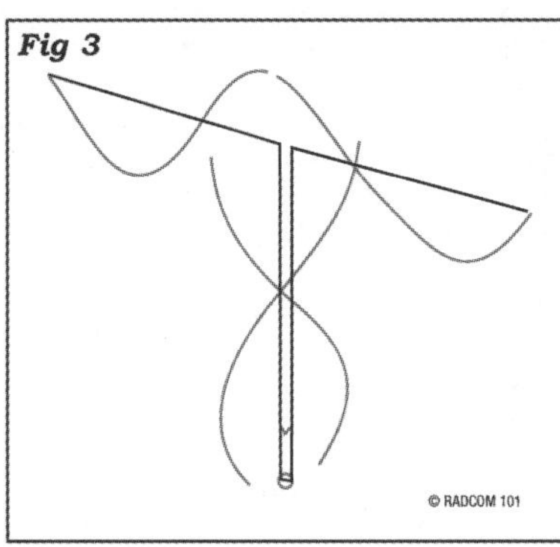


***Fig 3: Current distribution of a 50ft (15.25m) length of wire, 30ft (10m) high, centre-fed with balanced feeder on 21MHz. Maximum gain (nearly 10dBi) occurs at 26°.***

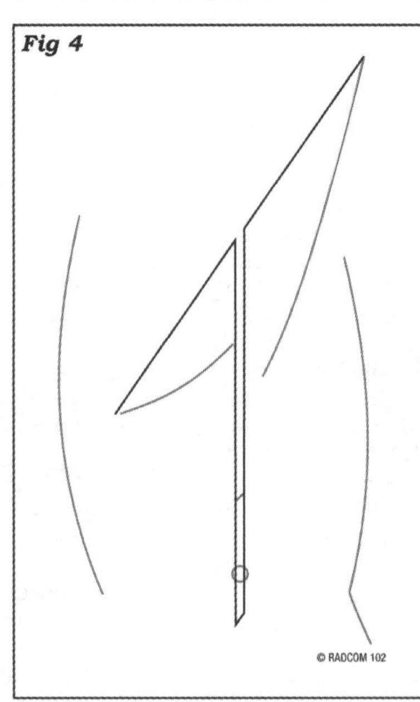


***Fig 4: The unbalanced feeder situation, implying that the feeder radiates. The current distributions on each section of the doublet are now not equal giving a small amount of distortion to the azimuth pattern.***

Fig 5

© RADCOM 103

***Fig 5: The amplitudes and phases of the 50ft (15.25m) antenna at 21MHz with an unbalanced feed.***

***The MFJ Versa Tuner V, MFJ-989C, which represents the most popular current design in ATUs. It is a single-ended (unbalanced) design, which has provision for connecting to twin-line feeder using a transformer balun.***

seen in the diagram, the phases of the feeder currents are not at 180° to each other; the amplitudes and phases on each leg of the doublet are also unequal. This same antenna shows some convoluted amplitudes and phases on 21MHz, see **Fig 5**, and probably represents what is happening with our antennas more accurately than the diagrams found in most antenna books.

It is obvious that there is a degree of radiation from an unbalanced antenna transmission line. This radiation can in some ways enhance the performance the doublet antenna. For example note the elevation polar plot of the balanced 50ft (15.25m) doublet antenna shown in **Fig 6**. The elevation plot of an unbalanced antenna is superimposed and shows a reduction in vertical gain and a slight increase in low-angle gain, making the antenna slightly more suitable for DX. The degree of unbalance in this case is not very great, having calculated current ratios of 1.3A and 1.6A on each of the feeder lines, respectively. The model implies that the characteristics of an antenna can be changed by altering the degree of current unbalance in the feeders. Has anyone ever noticed the characteristic?

However, the downside of an unbalanced line is that it radiates right down to the ATU in the shack, giving rise to possible BCI and TVI. Because of the reciprocal nature of antennas, the transmission line can also receive, increasing the risk of electrical QRM or a reduced signal-to-noise ratio on receive. If the level of RF in the shack is high, there is a chance of transmitter instability or RF burns from radio equipment when running high power. I recently tried feeding a balanced antenna from the single-ended coax port of an ATU and got quite a sharp RF 'bite' from the case of the ATU when running 100W.

## WHICH ANTENNA FOR YOU?

It is probable that the strictly balanced case derived from commercial practice where relative power was high and a small degree of unbalance resulted in high RF levels at the operating position. It could also result in power loss on long transmission line lengths. With lower power amateur transmissions some transmission line unbalance may not be a problem and there is a chance that it could be beneficial provided the transceiver is not located a long way from the antenna.

This brings me back to the M0RCS antenna introduced earlier and shown in **Fig 7**. It comprises a 66ft (20m) long folded dipole with the conventional centre break in the lower wire. However, instead of being fed at this break point it is fed half-way along one leg of the doublet. The obvious characteristic of this antenna is that it is unbalanced and the feeder will be working as an antenna element. It seems to work well for M0RCS. He faced the challenge of erecting an HF antenna within a confined space in terms of ground area and height. He goes on to say "A number of attempts at modifying existing designs failed to produce the desired performance, until I produced what I now refer to as the DOC66. The results were very satisfying with strong signal reports throughout the UK and on all bands from 40 to 15m tuned with a MFJ-934 Versa Tuner II". The antenna worked with reduced efficiency on 80m, and 10m was not open during the testing period. The antenna height is restricted to 16ft (4.9m) due to environmental considerations.

I tried modelling this antenna as shown in Fig 7. It took a lot of effort to effort to get the wires of the model in the right order and the right phase and even so I am not sure how good the model is. Even conventional multi-band doublets require careful modelling. For more on this subject, I recommend *Unfolding the Story of the Folded Dipole* by W4RNL, see [5]. ◆

Fig 6

0dB

-10

-20

-30

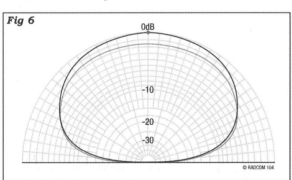

© RADCOM 104

***Fig 6: Elevation patterns of a 50ft (15.25m) length of wire, 30ft (10m) high comparing a balanced feed (black) with a partially-unbalanced feed (blue).***

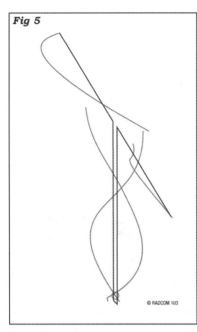

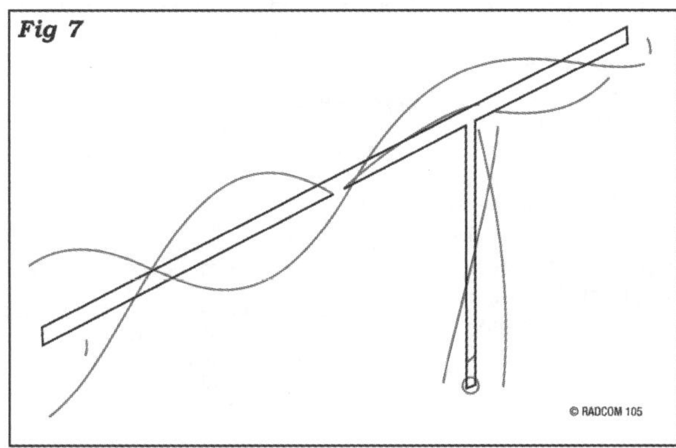


***Fig 7: The DOC66 antenna by Peter Nichols, M0RCS. The total length is 66ft (20.12m). The antenna is fed with balanced line 16.5ft (5m) from one end. Current distribution is shown at 21MHz.***

## REFERENCES

[1] 'A Balanced-Line ASTU', Ted Garrott, G0OUJ, *RadCom* July/August 1998

[2] *Backyard Antennas*, Peter Dodd, G3LDO.

[3] 'Antennas', *RadCom* July 2002.

[4] 'Antennas', *RadCom* February 2003.

[5] 'Unfolding the Story of the Folded Dipole', L B Cebik, W4RNL, www.cebik.com/fdpl.html

**Have you ever wondered about the calibration of your S-meter, or wondered how you could estimate the polar diagram of your antenna? G3LDO clarifies things for you.**

# Antennas

The normal way of checking out the new antenna that you have just bought or constructed is to just fire up the transceiver into it, having first determined that the VSWR is reasonably low. You then spend some time obtaining reports on both transmit and receive, where possible comparing it with some previous or existing antenna. Such methods are affected by fading, nevertheless, over a period of time, you can get quite a good statistical series of S-meter measurements. A more instant method of obtaining an idea of antenna performance is to use a Field Strength Meter (FSM) to make local field strength readings. A FSM can be used to:

- make comparative measurements of various antennas to assess relative gain;
- plot a polar diagram to record antenna directivity;
- enable a transmitter antenna to be tuned for maximum efficiency or gain;
- locate the source and measure the level of radio interference.

### THE COMMUNICATIONS RECEIVER AS AN FSM

While it is possible to make or buy a FSM, every radio shack has one in the form of a receiver or transceiver. On the face of it, the modern transceiver should make a good field strength meter. Many are small and portable and convenient to use. In practice, a receiver requires the RF gain to be turned to maximum for the S-meter to function correctly. Under these circumstances, the receiver is very sensitive and a variable attenuator may be necessary for adjusting the signal strengths so that they fall in a useful region of the S-meter range.

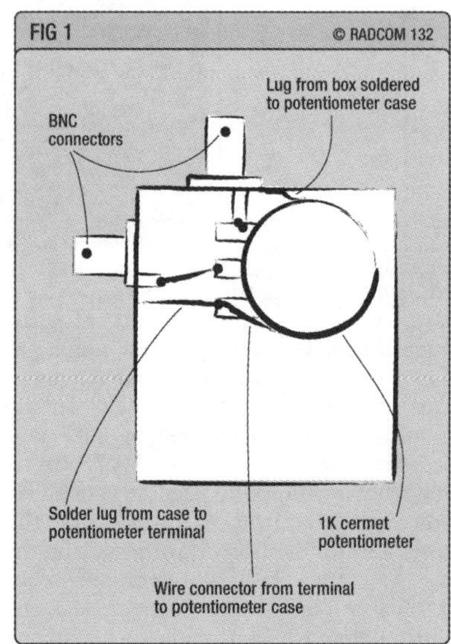


**Fig 1**
**A simple variable attenuator using a 1k cermet potentiometer.**

So just what is a useful range? We should not expect different receivers to give the same S-meter reading of a given signal level on a given frequency unless by coincidence. This is because the gain distribution of each receiver stage is different for a specified design and the S-meter is normally activated from the AGC line. Some years ago at least one receiver manufacturer attempted to standardise S-meter readings so that S9 was equivalent to 50μV and the signal level between each S-unit was 6dB, with the scale above S9 calibrated in dB relative to S9. Icom has got quite close to this standard. On the IC-7400, S9 is equivalent to 50μV and the signal level between every S unit is 3dB [1].

None of the S-meter linearity tests that I have made on any of my transceivers, using a signal generator, met this original specification, see the photograph. In general, the signal level between each S-point was around 1.5dB at the low S-point readings increasing to 3dB at the higher readings. In most cases, the dB marks at signal levels over S9 represented a true indication of signal level change. Many transceivers and receivers have S-meters comprising a bargraph indicator, which results in some loss in resolution, particularly noticeable at the high end of the scale. A conventional S-meter is preferred because of the higher resolution when measuring a change in signal strength.

**Test setup with a signal generator and a calibrated switched attenuator. The IC-737A uses a conventional S-meter while the IC-706 uses the bargraph type. Normally the receivers would be tested separately.**

### USING THE FSM

If you have installed a beam antenna, the most usual method checking out the beam pattern is to do some field strength tests with another local amateur who provides the test signal. The test is done by noting the S-meter reading when the beam is rotated, with the measurements being noted, with the beam stationary, every 10° or 20°. The transmitter power can be adjusted so that it fits into the most easily-read portion of the S-meter. Note that measurements made at the lower end of the S-meter scale may give an exaggerated idea of directivity for the reasons discussed above. If you do not have a friendly local amateur then the same test can be made using a mobile installation placed in the far field. I have found the test to be a particularly useful way of checking the relative performance of mobile antennas [2].

When performing these tests, you will probably find the receiver FSM is too sensitive with the RF gain at maximum. The answer is to use an attenuator. With a simple potentiometer variable attenuator, see **Fig 1,** you can adjust test transmission levels and FSM sensitivities appropriate to the measurements being performed. Note that the lower part of the S-meter scale is most sensitive to change in signal level. A calibrated step attenuator, shown in the photograph, is much more useful but lack of space precludes its description here. See [3] for full details of its use and many other aspects of antenna parameter measurements.

Note that if you use an attenuator with a transceiver, disconnect the microphone to prevent the attenuator being burned out by an accidental transmission. ♦

### REFERENCES

[1] Icom IC-7400 HF/VHF transceiver, reviewed by Peter Hart, G3SJX, *RadCom* October 2002. Note S-meter calibration on page 69.

[2] 'Computer-Modelling the HF Mobile Antenna', Peter Dodd, G3LDO. *The ARRL Antenna Compendium,* Vol 7. (also describes measurements).

[3] *The Antenna Experimenter's Guide*, 2nd ed, Peter Dodd, G3LDO. Note - updates to this book can be found on web.ukonline.co.uk/g3ldo

# Antennas

**This month, G3LDO concentrates on mobile antennas, and illustrates the results of computer modelling and practical field-strength tests for two makes of antenna**

**VQ4HX/M on a family outing in Kenya, circa 1961. The rig comprises an ex-army 19-set mounted into the dashboard of an old left-hand drive Armstrong Siddeley convertible. The set was powered by the original 12V dynamotor PSU and used the original variometer ATU to load a bumper-mounted whip antenna.**

One of the great challenges for antenna design is the mobile antenna. It has to be compact, preferably with multiband capability. When I was first licensed in 1957, mobile operation was very popular, particularly on 160m. Although commercial equipment was not available then (except for some ex military sets, see the photograph), it was relatively easy to build a 10W transmitter for this band, and the ground-wave coverage was in the region of 30miles (50km) even with what must have been rather inefficient antennas.

Modern vehicles present more of a challenge when it comes to installation of mobile equipment and antennas. However, now that radios are so small, there is usually a place where one can be installed and VHF antennas can be installed using a magmount. HF antennas are usually mounted at some low position on the vehicle so as to have maximum length (and highest radiation resistance and lowest losses) for a given overall height. Modern vehicles do not usually have the nice convenient bumpers for mounting HF antennas used by earlier generations of mobilers. If a shorter roof-mounted HF antenna is used, the losses would be greater, but the area of maximum radiation will higher from the ground.

My vehicle is fitted with a tow-bar, so it is quite easy to install one of the larger mobile antennas such as the Texas BugCatcher. A new antenna on the market is the motorised High Sierra Sidekick antenna. This antenna is only just over a metre long and uses an electric motor, controlled from a switch box from inside the vehicle to adjust the inductance of the loading coil. On the face of it, this seems the answer to the problems noted above and this month I will try to show how this antenna compares with the more traditional bumper-mounted version. I have an aluminium plate antenna rack which is fixed to the roof rack bars, which has a SO-239 socket for VHF antennas and a $^{3}/_{8}$in stud base for HF antennas. Initially, I planned to mount the Sidekick antenna on this base with tests to follow on a magmount later. The mobile test set up is shown in the second photograph.

Before conducting the tests, I would like to illustrate, using computer modelling, that the HF mobile installation on the higher frequencies is not omnidirectional. Directivity is affected by the position of the antenna, the size of the vehicle and the frequency of operation.

#### COMPUTER MODELLING

Before making the measurements on the two antennas, I made a computer model using *EZNEC3*. The vehicle is modelled using a wire grid of roughly the same dimensions as my estate car. This is now a standard way of modelling vehicles, originally described in [1] and expanded in [2] and [3].

A computer model of the High Sierra Sidekick antenna on the rear of my vehicle is shown in **Fig 1**. The vehicle structure and antenna currents are indicated by red and green lines respectively. The distance between the vehicle line and its associated current line is an indication of relative current flow. The circles and the squares on the antenna element are the feed-points and the loading coils, respectively. In fact, two loading inductors are used to try to model the fact that the real mobile coil is distributed along a proportion of the element length. Also shown is the fore and aft elevation section of the antenna polar diagram. This shows some directivity, which becomes more pronounced as the frequency is increased with the antenna mounted on the rear of the vehicle As you can see in Fig 1, there is a fairly high current in the metal structure of the vehicle near the base of the antenna element. It follows that, when an antenna is radiated against the body of the vehicle, the vehicle itself is part of the antenna system and radiates also.

The model predicts a maximum gain of -4dBi and a F/B directivity of 6dB on 18MHz. The Texas BugCatcher antenna was also modelled, predicting a maximum gain of -0.7dBi and a F/B directivity of 7dB. On 80m, the radiation pattern is almost omnidirectional on both antennas.

#### FIELD STRENGTH TESTS

It is always a good idea to check computer models with the real world if possible. From the space in the car park of a local supermarket I made some mobile field strength tests with Peter Craw, G3CCX, at his home, located about one mile away. With the vehicle facing G3CCX, and using the High Sierra Sidekick, a 10W

**Mobile antenna test arrangement. The unused antenna is removed during the actual test.**

**High Sierra Sidekick installation with improved earthing strip. Also shown are the power leads (with RF chokes) to the antenna motor.**

mobile carrier produced an S8 signal on G3CCX's Yaesu FT-1000MP. From the rear of the vehicle the signal strength was S6.8, a F/B directivity of S1.2. A rough calibration of the 1000MP gave 3dB per S point (in keeping with other rigs, see [4]) which, in turn, represents a F/B of around 4dB, fairly close to the computer model, see Fig 1.

The Texas BugCatcher gave S8.1 forward and S5.8 from the rear, a F/B directivity of S2.3. I was surprised how well the small High Sierra Sidekick performed relative to the Texas BugCatcher. There might have been factors affecting the performance of this antenna. For example, it was mounted on a tow-bar with no special RF connector to the vehicle body, although a resistance check showed that the resistance was very low.

**VSWR & MATCHING**

A mobile antenna is normally fed with 50Ω coaxial cable with the centre connected to the antenna and the braid to the vehicle body. However, the radiation resistance of the antenna will generally be lower than 50Ω and, for a given antenna size, depends on frequency. In practice, the feed impedance will include the RF resistance of the loading coil and the resistance losses, which are in series with the radiation resistance. The loss resistance, taken in total, is usually much greater than the radiation resistance, particularly at the lower frequencies. A low VSWR is no guarantee of a good performance. In fact it could possibly mean the opposite - that the loss resistance is high.

The easiest method of matching a mobile antenna to 50Ω feeder is simply by the addition of a shunt capacitor directly across the antenna feed-point. Exact values can be determined experimentally and will need to be switched for multiband operation. The way that this works can be seen by referring to **Fig 2**. The curve A represents the feed impedance of a Pro-Am antenna in the frequency range 3.55 to 3.65MHz. At the lower frequency, the impedance is about 10 - 50jΩ, while at the higher frequency it is 70 + 70jΩ. On no part of the curve is the VSWR better than 2:1. By increasing the inductance of the loading coil slightly and compensating with a capacitor across the feed-point, the curve can be shifted to B
to achieve an improved match at resonance. Other matching methods are described in [5].

While on the subject of resistance losses, it should be noted that a small antenna like the High Sierra Sidekick has a lower radiation resistance than the standard 8ft mobile antenna. It follows that the connection from the antenna base to the body of the vehicle should have the lowest RF resistance and inductance possible to obtain the best performance, particularly on the higher frequency bands. The handbook for this antenna has some interesting remarks about ground leads and recommends 25mm (1in) wide flat copper strap for vehicle ground leads.

Originally, my aluminium plate antenna rack was connected to the vehicle with a short 2mm diameter wire. After reading the Sidekick manual I changed the wire for 25mm close-woven braid (I didn't have any flat copper strip to hand). The installation is shown in the photograph, and the improvement in VSWR can be seen in **Fig 3**. I have yet to try a copper strap.

**GENERAL**

I was impressed with the High Sierra Sidekick antenna, which performed well considering how small it is. On 80m the losses are probably fairly high. This can be judged by comparative VSWR curves shown in **Fig 4**. The Texas BugCatcher required around 900pF of shunt capacitance to get this curve; without it the VSWR was above 3:1 at resonance. The Sidekick antenna required no shunt matching at all, which implies that the resistance losses are high on this band. However, for operating convenience, the Sidekick wins hands down. My thanks to Waters & Stanton for the loan of the High Sierra Sidekick antenna.

I have not mentioned magmounts in this column. The reason is that, from the experimental work done so far, I feel the subject needs a column to itself - a case of watch this space. ♦

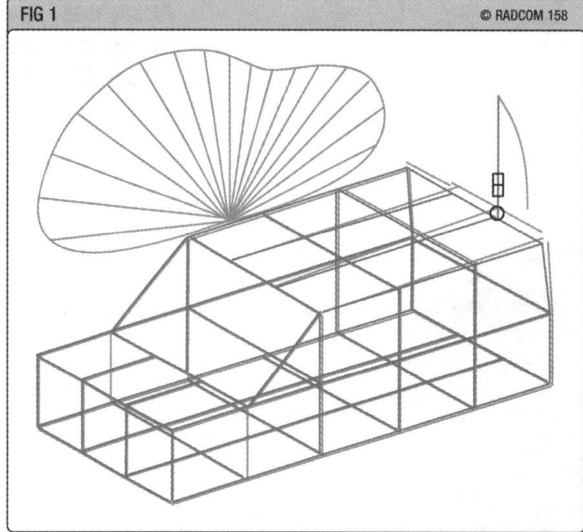

**Fig 1**
**Computer model of a HF mobile installation on 18MHz using the High Sierra Sidekick antenna. The model predicts a maximum gain of -4dBi and a F/B directivity of 6dB.**

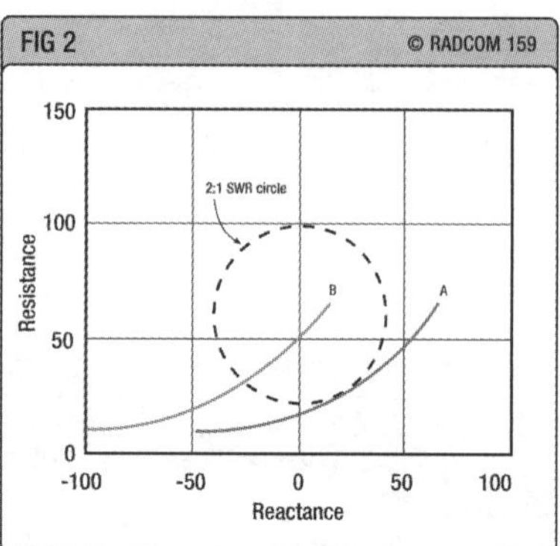


**Fig 2**
**Shifting of frequency/impedance curve using a shunt capacitance to obtain a 50Ω match.**

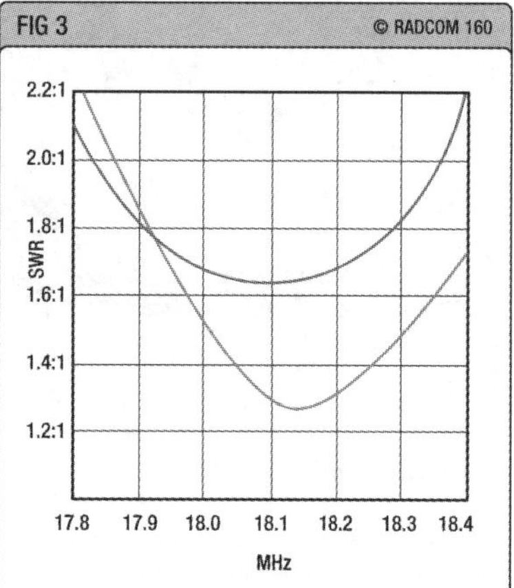


**Fig 3**
**VSWR curves of the High Sierra Sidekick on the 18MHz band. The lower VSWR resulted from changing the earthing connector from a 2mm solid wire to 25mm wide braid.**

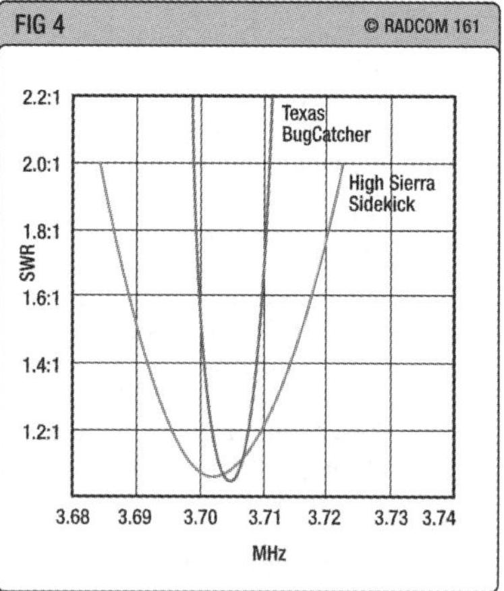


**Fig 4**
**Comparative VSWR curves of the Texas BugCatcher and the High Sierra Sidekick on 80m. The BugCatcher appears much more efficient, but the VSWR 2:1 bandwidth is limited to 12kHz for a particular setting.**

**REFERENCES**


[1] 'Short Coil-Loaded HF Mobile Antennas: An Update and Calculated Radiation Patterns', John Belrose, VE2CV, The ARRL Antenna Compendium, Vol 4.

[2] 'Computer Modelling the HF Mobile Antenna', Peter Dodd, G3LDO, The ARRL Antenna Compendium, Vol 7.

[3] 'Antenna Workshop', Peter Dodd, G3LDO, Practical Wireless, June 2002.

[4] 'Antennas', RadCom, April 2004.

[5] The Amateur Radio Mobile Handbook, Peter Dodd, G3LDO.

# Antennas

**G3LDO looks at the effect of the magmount on various types of HF mobile antenna, showing how the reactance of the mount affects the matching.**

The variable inductive loading of the High Sierra Sidekick shown with weather protection shield removed. The coil is moved in and out of the lower tube with a motor-driven lead screw.

The three-magnet type of magmount.

In the May 'Antennas' column, I discussed some aspects of mobile antennas and promised to give some information on magmounts, which use an antenna base with a magnet to fix the antenna to a horizontal flat surface of the ferrous metal vehicle body. They have the advantage of simplicity and require no special fixing arrangements, enabling them to be used with a vehicle on a temporary basis if necessary. The coax feeder is routed, either through the door seal (if you are using thin coax), or through a partly-opened window (if you are using thicker coax).

For larger HF antennas, the surface area contact between the vehicle body and magnetic base is insufficient to hold the antenna when travelling at any speed. You could use a much larger diameter magnetic base, but this is rather impractical. The solution is to use three or four magnets held together in a frame. This arrangement spreads the load over a much wider area than a single magmount and can be used to support larger HF mobile antennas. The most common multiple-magnet magmounts use three magnets. An example of one of these is the WMM-3401 series (now superseded by the W-300 series) made by Watson, and is shown in the photograph; it can support an average-size HF mobile antenna. It can also support a large antenna if operating from a stationary vehicle.

Because magmounts are not directly connected to the body of the vehicle and rely on capacitive coupling, the antenna tuning may be different from other methods of mounting the antenna. For example, the capacitance of the magmount shown in the photo is 400pF, which gives a series reactance of 14Ω at 28MHz and 110Ω at 3.6MHz. This aspect does not appear very often in amateur radio antenna literature.

Tests were carried out at 18MHz, where the capacitive reactance was 22Ω. I normally use a modified CB 'Firestik' antenna for this band, which gives a near 1:1 VSWR near resonance. When used with the magmount shown in the photo, the resonant frequency is shifted up about 200kHz but the VSWR remained low. However, when the magmount is used with the High Sierra 'Sidekick', shown in the photo and described in [1], the lowest VSWR obtainable was just under 2:1.

**GROUND CONNECTION**

The handbook on the Sidekick has some interesting comments on this subject. It recommends that a copper strip ground strap be used to connect the magmount to the metal body of the vehicle. It also says that braiding or wire is inadequate for this purpose. Originally, I used a 2mm wide copper strip, and close-woven braiding was then tried, which gave an improved VSWR performance, although I found no difference between the strip and the braid (although corrosion in the braid might affect its performance after a while). With the magmount grounded using the method described, the lowest VSWR obtainable was 1.6:1.

Such connections to the vehicle might be difficult to find and make. The method I used is to scrape away the paint just under the tailgate hinge. The antenna ground strap is then fixed to the vehicle with a self-tapping screw and a washer, protected against corrosion with a thin film of grease. If you don't like the idea of scraping paint off your vehicle, try a magnetic coupler. Lack of space precludes its description here but you will find it in [2], pp57/58.

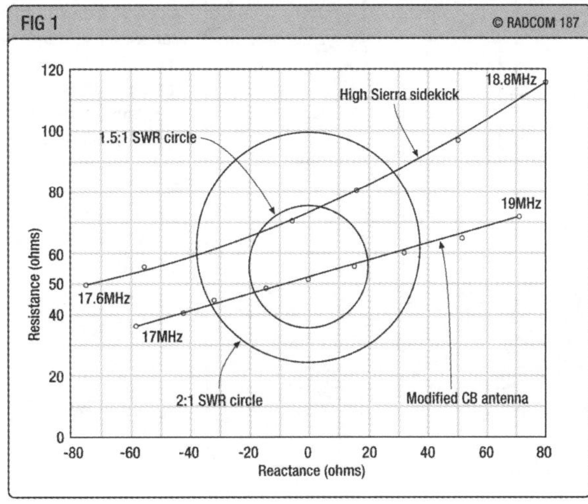


**Fig 1** Cartesian impedance plot of the modified CB antenna and the High Sierra Sidekick antenna, measured using a HP-4085 vector impedance meter.

**IMPEDANCE MATCHING**

I have described the High Sierra Sidekick because it seems to be one of the best HF multiband antenna solutions if you are using a magmount on a moving vehicle. The handbook on this antenna advises that a VSWR of 2:1 or better is satisfactory. It also advises the use of at least 15ft (4.6m) of coax between the transceiver and the antenna because short runs can affect the VSWR. It doesn't say why.

I found that the Sidekick antenna worked fine, provided that the VSWR level was not shutting down the transceiver power. The shunt capacitance matching method [1] didn't work; neither did [2] pp45/46, so I decided to try to find out why. A series of impedance measurements was made as described in [3], (which can tell you more than VSWR ever can) and the results are shown in **Fig 1**. This shows the impedance at resonance of the smaller antenna to be higher than the larger one. This higher impedance could be matched to give a VSWR of 1:1 using one of the inductive matching arrangements described in [2], pp46/47.

The construction of the variable loading of the High Sierra Sidekick is shown in the photograph. The high current portion of the antenna below the active part of the inductance is 360mm long and 50mm in diameter, and is ruggedly constructed.

My thanks to Waters & Stanton for the loan of the High Sierra Sidekick. The Watson magmount, described above, was also obtained from Waters & Stanton. ♦

**REFERENCES**

[1] RadCom May, 2004, 'Antennas'
[2] The Amateur Radio Mobile Handbook, Peter Dodd, G3LDO
[3] The Antenna Experimenter's Guide, Second Edition, Peter Dodd, G3LDO, Chapter 2.
Note: updates on [2] and [3] can be found on http://web.ukonline.co.uk/g3ldo

See Note [5]

# ANTENNAS

## This month, G3LDO gives details of how to measure the impedance of antennas, particularly the mobile type.

We are fortunate, down here in the Worthing area, to have one of those radio shops, namely GWM Radio, that sell ex-military and commercial equipment and all manner of RF components that you won't find in modern radio parts catalogues, see 'Web Search'. It has been the source of a lot of my RF test equipment over the years. Last week, while discussing with Simon, G0ELN, the proprietor, the merits of some home-brew RF test equipment that was being 'recycled', we got to talking about the noise bridge impedance-measuring instrument.

### MEASURING IMPEDANCE

Last month [1] I described how the feed impedance of the High Sierra Sidekick mobile antenna was measured to find what type of matching network would be required to reduce the VSWR. For this I used an HP4085 vector impedance meter. Prior to acquiring this instrument, I used home-brew impedance measuring instruments, one of which was the noise bridge. It was this instrument that was used to identify the problem of feeding the experimental double toroid antenna [2], see **Fig 1**.

All impedance measurement bridges measure the impedance presented to the *unknown* socket by adjusting a calibrated resistance and reactance (in practice, a variable resistor and capacitance) for a null in a detector. The impedance measurement has to be made on a spot frequency. The venerable General Radio 1606 Impedance Bridge used a signal generator as the source so a wide-band null detector could be used. The noise bridge uses a broad-band source (white noise) and a selective null detector (a selective receiver).

The reactance (X) scale is calibrated in ohms $X_C$ (-) or $X_L$ (+) at 1MHz, which has to be divided by frequency to get the true reactance reading. The impedance values can then be plotted on a chart as shown in Fig 1 or on a Smith Chart.

For many years, the balanced bridge was the most popular method of impedance measurement and commercial versions were also available.

If you are measuring the feed-point of an antenna, it follows that the measurement has to be made at the antenna. This means that method is limited to situations where there is access to the antenna *in situ*, which is fine for mobile antennas. Because the noise null detector (ie the receiver) also has to be within earshot, the measuring arrangement may be a trifle inconvenient 20 metres up a mast or on the roof of a house. The problem can be overcome by having the receiver located in the shack, with a small speaker, or a pair of headphones, connected to the output of the receiver via another feeder or a couple of wires from the rotator cable.

Antenna impedance can be measured via an electrical half-wavelength of feeder, which may be the only method available if the feed-point of the antenna is inaccessible.

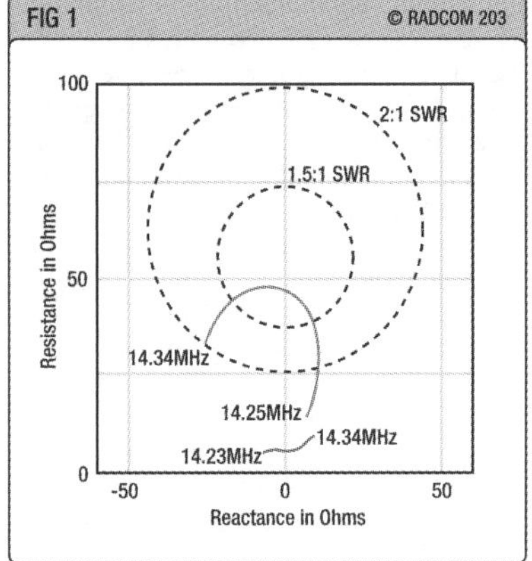


Fig 1 Impedance 'signatures' obtained by making a number of measurements over a range of frequencies on a double-toroid antenna. A direct connection is shown in red while a connection through a shunt matching arrangement is shown in green.

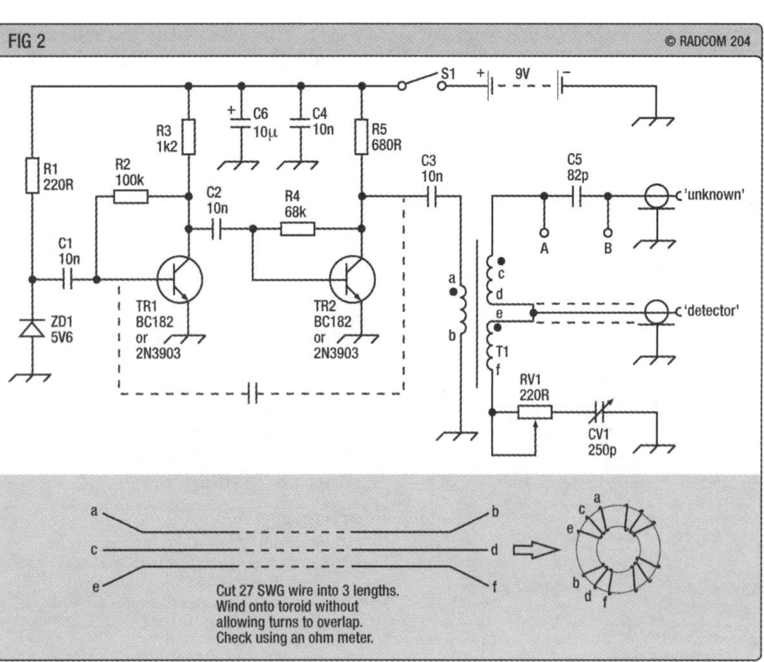


Fig 2 Circuit diagram of a noise bridge designed by G3ZOM.

### THE NOISE BRIDGE

The noise bridge comprises an integral noise source, which is fed to a balanced bridge. The unknown impedance is matched to a calibrated adjustable impedance bridge and the match indicated by a noise null in a receiver.

A circuit of a noise bridge is shown in **Fig 2**. ZD1 and R1 act as a noise source, which is then amplified by TR1 and TR2 and applied to the bridge circuit via a toroid transformer. The amplifier circuit can be modified by connecting a capacitor shown in dotted lines. This causes the amplifier to work as a multivibrator and the tone modulates the noise source.

When the values of RV1 and CV1 are equal to the 'unknown' at a specific frequency, the noise output to a receiver used as frequency-selective null detector is minimum, indicating that the bridge is balanced. The accuracy and the depth of the null depends mostly on the layout of the bridge network and the care taken in balancing the bridge.

Full details of the construction and calibration of this noise bridge can be found in [3].

The popularity of the noise bridge has been eclipsed by commercial instruments such as the MFJ-259 and the RF Analyst RF-1 but, to my mind, the RF bridge gives the best indication of actual impedance; and it is a good deal cheaper. ♦

### REFERENCES

[1] *RadCom* June, 2004, 'Antennas'
[2] 'Evolution of the G2AJV Toroidal Antenna', Peter Dodd, G3LDO, *RadCom* August 1994
[3] *The Antenna Experimenter's Guide*, 2nd edition, Peter Dodd, G3LDO.

| WEB SEARCH | |
|---|---|
| GWM Radio | www.gwmradio.co.uk |

See Note [6]

**G3LDO goes bicycle-mobile this month, and explains why some electrically-short antennas are better than others**

# Antennas

Some time ago I visited the planning department of our local council to discuss my antenna mast and the required size of my proposed antenna installation. During this discussion, the planning officer asked if antennas could be made smaller - after all electronic and communication equipment is now only a fraction of the size that it used to be. Why not smaller aerials?

Well, I did try to explain that the size of electronic components is determined by electronic component manufacturing processes whereas the length of the antenna element is related to the wavelength and the laws of physics. And although you can use inductors to load electrically-short antennas there is a penalty in terms of efficiency and bandwidth. Yes, I know that there is the Crossed-Field and EH antennas that claim to be able to circumvent the traditional antenna design restrictions, but you don't hear many on the bands even though they have been around for years.

### SIZE MATTERS

With the advent of smaller and smaller rigs there has been a renewed search for small antennas that match the portability of small rigs. Some designs use a whip with variable base-loading, such as the 'Miracle Whip', or the 'Wonder Wand', reviewed in [1]. These antennas use short whip antennas with variable base-loading. This type of loading has the advantage of being easy to adjust and the antenna can made of rugged copper-coated thin-wall steel tubing, as used in military installations. The disadvantage is that, for a given electrically-**small** antenna, it is the least efficient.

The current distribution of full quarter-wave vertical and two eighth-wavelength verticals, one using centre-loading and the other using base-loading, is illustrated in **Fig 1**. The relative radiation power density can be estimated by counting the number of small squares under the curves. This is a very simplified method of illustrating these relative antenna efficiencies and shows a big improvement in radiation power as the element length approaches a quarter wavelength. The counterpoise or ground also carries RF current, so it also will radiate, but this aspect is not shown in Fig 1. If you can use a full half-wavelength then that is even better because the maximum current point is raised at least quarter wavelength above the ground.

FIG 1 © RADCOM 209

Quarter wave vertical
$^1/_8$ th vertical
Centre loaded vertical
Loading coil
Antenna length in wavelengths
$^1/_4$
$^1/_8$
Full quarter wave
Centre loaded
Short vertical
Antenna current

**Fig 1**
**The current distribution of a full quarter-wave vertical and two λ/8 verticals, one using centre-loading and the other using base-loading.**

**The MP-1 antenna used for bicycle mobile, being tested for radiation efficiency with the FSM in the background. The MP-1 is being used here with a larger stainless steel whip rather than the 110cm telescopic whip provided.**

I was much taken with the description of the pedestrian mobile set up described by Tom Robinson, G0SBW [2, 3]. Tom uses big whip antennas in the range 13ft 8in (4.16m) to 18ft (5.48m) as an all-band verticals fed via automatic ATUs. On 10m these antennas are nearly half-wavelength long, while on 20m close to a quarter wave - an efficient antenna arrangement for the higher frequency bands.

### THE MP-1 PORTABLE ANTENNA

The use of large whip antennas is not practical for many situations. If you are taking your small rig, such as the FT-817, on vacation or on a business trip then an antenna that can be fitted inside a briefcase is obviously very useful. The 'Wander Wand' antenna described above is a solution; however, with a whip length of only 1.2m this equates to say around λ/16 on 20m. This doesn't result in a lot of squares under the 'short vertical' line in Fig 1.

A better solution is to use centre-loading, preferably with some way of varying the inductance. The MP-1 portable antenna does just this in the same manner as is used in the Sierra Sidekick described in [4], the only difference is that it is not motor-driven but operated manually. There is nothing new about the design of this antenna - the method was used in Webster Band-Spanner mobile antenna in the late 1950s [5]. The MP-1 comes with a telescopic whip, universal clamp with base mount, together with the all-important wire radials. I found the MP-1 very good for bicycle mobile. A bicycle frame appears to make a good RF ground on the higher LF bands.

My thanks to Waters & Stanton for the loan of the MP-1 portable antenna. ♦

### REFERENCES


[1] RadCom June 2004, page 29
[2] 'The Field trials of the IC-703', Tom Robinson, G0SBW, RadCom, October 2003
[3] 'HF Backpacking', Tom Robinson, G0SBW, RadCom, June 2004
[4] 'Antennas', RadCom, June 2004
[5] The Amateur Radio Mobile Handbook, Peter Dodd, G3LDO, p40.

# Antennas

## How to erect a visually low-impact delta loop for 7MHz and above

A mast is usually the main problem when trying to get neighbours to accept the installation of an HF antenna. Beams and their support masts can be quite intrusive and wire antennas normally require two supports, although the house can be one of them. One antenna I used for several years was a large delta loop with a chimney as the main support.

### A LOW-VISUAL-IMPACT MULTIBAND ANTENNA

As can be seen from the current discussion on loop antennas in *RadCom*, the efficiency of the small loop antenna improves with an increase in size. A loop larger than 0.25λ will lose its predominant 'magnetic' characteristic and become an 'electric' antenna of the quad or delta type. If a loop antenna in the form of an equilateral triangle is used, only one support is required, and if this support were a short mast fixed to the chimney, it can probably circumvent most planning restrictions.

The structure of the antenna is shown in **Fig 1** and it can be constructed with bare copper wire. You could use insulated wire for the entire loop, however lightweight wire and a lightweight support has a low visual impact. Using lightweight thin wire does not affect the antenna performance because the radiation resistance of a loop is fairly high.

The first experiments were carried out with the coax connected directly to the loop but the SWR was over 3:1. However, most literature puts the feed impedance of a loop greater than 100Ω, and models constructed in *EZNEC* confirm this. A 4:1 balun was fitted enabling the antenna to be fed directly with 50Ω coax that can be matched using the automatic ATU fitted to many modern transceivers. (This applies only to harmonic-related frequencies such as 7, 14, 21 and 28MHz).

On the 'WARC' bands, the impedances are rather wild and the best method of feeding is to use 450Ω-ladder feeder and an ATU. (I prefer this method of feeding for all bands).

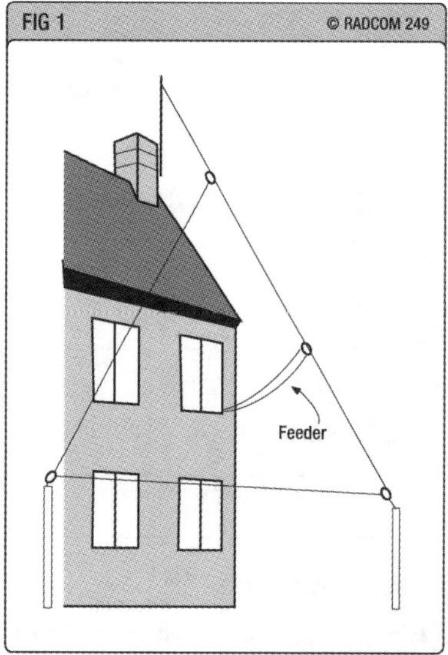


Fig 1
**Delta loop antenna one wavelength circumference on 7MHz, using a short stub mast on the chimney as a top support.**

Fig 2
**Comparison of elevation plots of the full wave delta loop, fed at the base and at the side.**

This antenna will give good results, even when the lowest leg of the triangle is only 0.6m from the ground.

The 7MHz characteristics of the antenna varied, depending at just which point the antenna was fed. For use as a NVIS antenna, the centre of the base of the triangle appears to be the optimum point and produces an elevation pattern as shown in **Fig 2**. For use as a DX antenna, the optimum feed point is just over one third up from the bottom on one of the vertical triangle sides as shown in Fig 1. These findings also apply to the 10MHz band. On the higher frequency bands, the lobes become very complicated, and the difference between the base and vertical feeds are less pronounced when it comes to working DX.

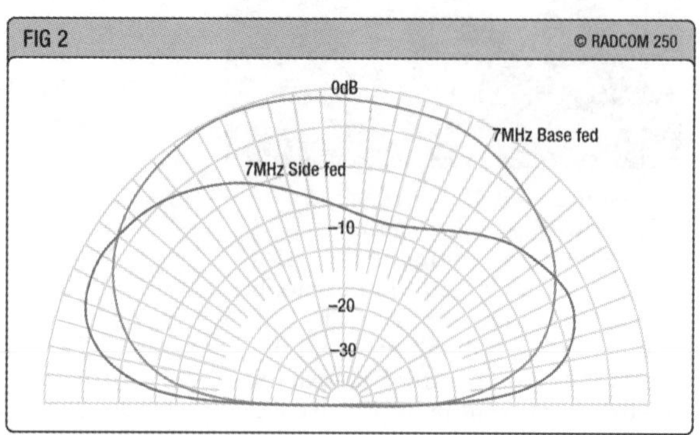


### CONSTRUCTION

Theoretically, the total length of the loop should be 140ft (42.8m), but my antenna was resonant with a total wire length of 120ft. This might have been due to the close proximity of the base to the ground, or the fact that insulated wire was used for the lower part of the loop, see below. The shape of the delta loop is not important. Fig 1 shows the corner insulators fixed to the ground with tent-peg-type fixtures, although trees and fences will also work as lower supports.

The apex support in the experimental model was a 2.5 metre length of scaffolding pole fixed to the chimney with a double TV lashing kit. The top of the chimney is about 9m above the ground. The pole gives the antenna enough height and a reasonable clearance above the roof. The apex of my loop was nearly 11 metres high.

As you can see, part of this antenna is close to the ground. This means there is a possible danger of someone receiving an RF burn if the antenna was touched when the transmitter is on. For this reason, wire with thick insulation was used for the lower half of the antenna. A loop antenna is not a high-*Q* device, so very high voltages, such as those found at the tips of a dipole, do not occur.

This antenna proved to be a good DX transmitting antenna on 7 and 10MHz. However, it did tend to pick up electrical noise from the house on receive. It could be used in conjunction with a smaller magnetic receiving loop, located in the electrically quietest part of the QTH, if electrical noise or QRM is a problem. This would normally require that the transceiver had provision for separate transmit and receive antenna connectors (rare). I have devised an antenna connector switch box, which I hope to describe in a future 'Antennas' column. ♦

# Antennas

In the July 'Antennas', I said that full constructional details of the G3ZOM noise bridge were available in [1], however this only applies to the second edition. The first edition describes the basic noise bridge from the then current ARRL *Antenna Handbook*. I also said that antenna impedance could be measured via an electrical half-wavelength of feeder, which may be the only method available if the feed-point of the antenna is inaccessible. I can see now that 'the only method' phrase is misleading. I received an e-mail to say that there was a spreadsheet available by G4JNH that allowed impedance to be measured over any length of feeder. The subject is interesting and is the basis for this month's 'Antennas'.

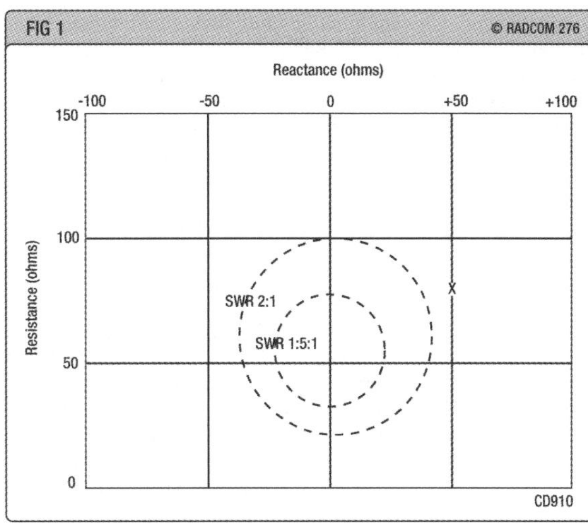


**Fig 1: Impedance Chart, with X showing an impedance of 75 + j50. The circles represent SWRs of 1.5:1 and 2:1 for 50w coaxial cable. Note that, on this projection, the SWR circles are not concentric as they are on the Smith Chart projection.**

### ANOTHER LOOK AT IMPEDANCE

The feed impedance of a resonant dipole antenna (for example) is purely resistive at resonance; at any other frequency there is always inductive or capacitive reactance present. The combination of resistance and reactance occurring in a series circuit is impedance (Z). The impedance of a circuit can be defined as the ratio of the driving voltage to the current it produces.

Because impedance is derived from resistance and reactance it is always expressed in two parts, Z = R + jX. An impedance having a resistance of 75Ω and a inductive reactance 50Ω is conventionally written as: Z = 75 +j50. For our consideration the 'j' part of impedance can simply be regarded as a convention for reactance, a '+j' indicating inductive reactance and a '-j' indicating capacitive reactance. When the antenna is at its resonant frequency, the +j and -j parts are equal and opposite so only the resistive part remains.

Impedance can be represented using a chart with Cartesian co-ordinates as shown in **Fig 1**. This method of plotting and recording the impedance characteristics of antennas is rather like a map Mercator projection, with the latitude and longitude of R and jX respectively plotted to define an impedance 'location'. Resonance, where the inductive and capacitive reactances in a tuned circuit or antenna element are equal and opposite, exists only on the zero reactance vertical line. The impedance measured at the end of a transmission line, with the other end connected to an antenna or a load, will rarely be the same as that antenna or load because of impedance transformation the transmission line.

There are two ways to find out what the real antenna impedance or load actually is.

- Measure the electrical length of the feeder and use a transmission line calculator, such as the Smith Chart or a computer program to find the antenna impedance.
- Measure the impedance of the antenna using an electrical half-wave, or a multiple of a half-wavelength, of coaxial cable.

### THE SMITH CHART

The traditional method of for calculating impedance transforms over a length of coaxial feeder is the by using a Smith Chart. This is a sort of slide rule and was invented by Phillip H. Smith and described as a Transmission-Line Calculator [2]. The Smith chart shown in **Fig 2** is an impedance map with a projection different from that shown in Fig 1, just as maps have different projections, such as the Mercator or Great Circle projections. The most obvious difference with the Smith chart is that all the co-ordinate lines are sections of a circle instead of being straight. The Smith chart, by convention, has the resistance scale decreasing towards the top. With this projection, the SWR circles are con-

**Fig 2: A simplified, restricted-range Smith Chart. An additional scale is added around the circumference, calibrated in electrical wavelength. Two lengths of coaxial cable are shown superimposed on the transmission line electrical length scale.**

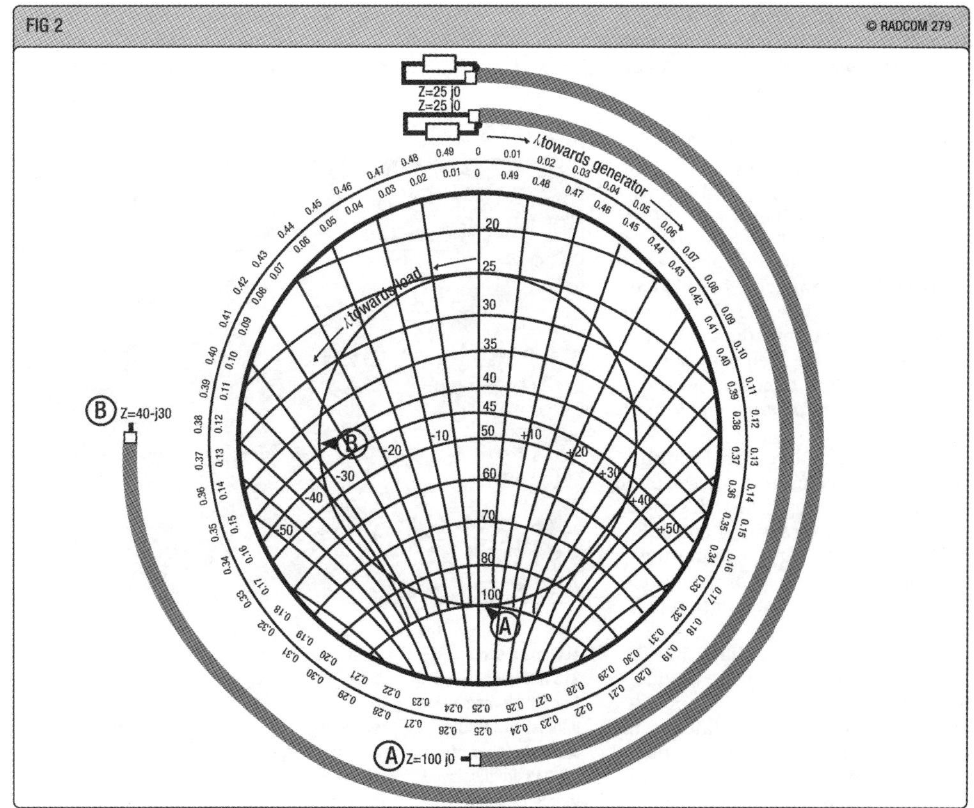

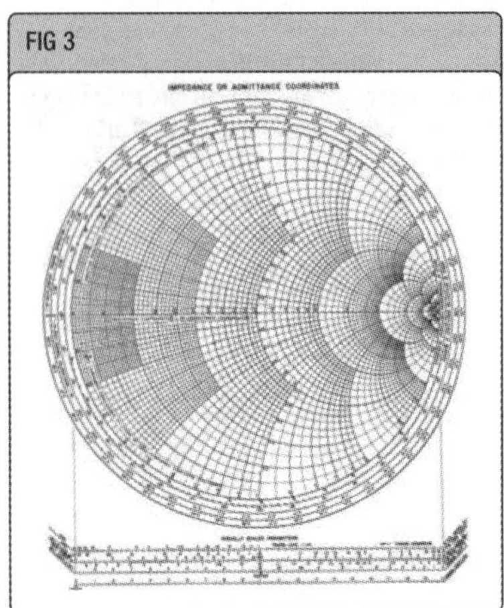


**Fig 3**
**A professional Smith Chart. Note the more modern convention – the chart is rotated 270° relative to that in Fig 2. This chart would have to be enlarged to 0.5m in diameter to be of any practical use.**

centric, centred on the 50Ω point, which is known as the prime centre.

Because the reflected impedance varies along the feeder, it follows that you need to know the electrical length of your coaxial feeder to the antenna. You can then calculate the transformation of impedance measured at the shack end of the coaxial feeder using a noise bridge or similar impedance-measuring bridge. You can also measure the electrical length of the feeder (length taking in to account the velocity factor) by terminating one end with a known load, such as a 100Ω resistor.

An additional scale is added around the circumference, calibrated in electrical wavelength. Halfway round the chart equals 0.25 or a quarter wavelength, while a full rotation equals 0.5 or a half wavelength. Two lengths of 50Ω coaxial feeder are shown superimposed around the circumference of a Smith chart in Fig 2, one length λ/4 long and the other 3λ/8 wavelength). Both lengths are connected to a load having an impedance of 25 + j0. The λ/4 length of line (0.25λ) gives a measured impedance of 100 + j0 at the other end, while the 3λ/8 section (0.375λ) gives an impedance of 40 + j30. It can also be seen from Fig 2 that a λ/2 length of coaxial would transform the impedance back to 25 + j0.

You can make a practical Smith chart calculator from the description and the charts in [1]. Also described are methods of measuring coaxial cable electrical length, calculating antenna impedance from measured impedance and the calculation of SWR.

The variation of the chart that I have just described is very simplified. By limiting its range of impedances and the number of lines in the chart it is very much easier to use than the professional Smith chart shown in **Fig 3**. This is achieved at the expense of some accuracy.

However, the chart shown in Fig 3 requires some skill and experience in its use. To complicate the issue further, most Smith charts are normalised so that they can be used at any impedance and not restricted to 50Ω, as is the one shown in Fig 2. This is achieved by assigning 1 to the prime centre and calling it 50; other values, for example, are 0.5 for 25Ω and 2 for 100Ω in a 50Ω system.

The chart is used with the cursor shown, using a range of calibrated 'radially-scaled parameters', the most common being SWR in amateur radio use. **Fig 4**. The cursor is attached to the chart so that the centre pivots on the centre of the chart. SWR for example is read from the centre to the marked measured impedance point. Other more common radially-scaled parameters are return loss and reflection coefficient, which are beyond the scope of this discussion.

## COMPUTER PROGRAMS

As in other fields of technical mathematics, the slide rule has been supplanted by the computer. One of the earliest programs was a computer simulation called *MicroSmith*, designed by Wes Howard, W7ZOI. This *DOS* program was originally written for the author's personal use in professional applications and was later modified for use by the engineering student and radio amateur.

There are many others. One of these, brought to my notice recently, is in a spreadsheet format designed

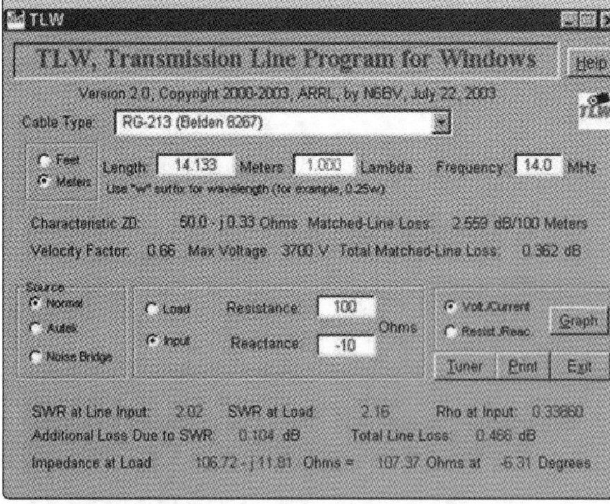


**Fig 4**
**TLW main screen. RG-213 has been selected from the transmission line list and all the characteristics of RG-213 are displayed four lines down.**

by G4JNH [3].

My favourite is *TLW* (*Transmission Line for Windows*) which comes bundled with a lot of other antenna software in [4] and is very simple to use. When the program is opened the main screen gives most of the information you need to know. All you have to do is specify the type of cable, the length of cable, the measurement frequency and the measured impedance. There is a library of 34 different types of transmission line plus a user defined transmission line to choose from and in **Fig 4** RG-213 has been selected.

From the measured impedance at the input *TLW* calculates the impedance at the load or antenna. I selected a value of 1.00λ for the length of the coax. The program calculates the length in metres or feet taking into account the velocity factor of RG-213. It also calculates the SWR. Note that the SWR is given for the input and the load; these are different due to the coax loss. *TLW* can also show impedance variation or voltage and current, along the coax length by selecting 'Graph' on the main screen as shown in **Fig 5**.

Theoretically, the impedance value is the same as the terminated value every half wavelength but, due to transmission line losses, there are small differences as can be seen in Figs 4 and 5. If you select a user-defined transmission line and insert a purely resistive transmission line characteristic impedance, a 1.0 velocity factor and zero line loss, you will see the terminated value occurring every half wavelength. ♦

## REFERENCES

[1] *The Antenna Experimenter's Guide*, **Second** Edition, Peter Dodd, G3LDO.

[2] 'Smith Radio Transmission-Line Calculator', Phillip H Smith, *Electronics*, January 1939.

[3] 'A Spreadsheet for Remote Antenna Impedance Measurement', Ron Barker, G4JNH, *QEX*, September/October 2001 and *QEX* July/August 2004.[4]
*The ARRL Antenna Book*, 20th Edition

[4] The ARRL Antenna Book, 20th Edition.

**Fig 5 Series resistance and reactance (impedance) along one wavelength of transmission line. Note that the impedance value is the same (nearly) as the terminated value every half wavelength.**

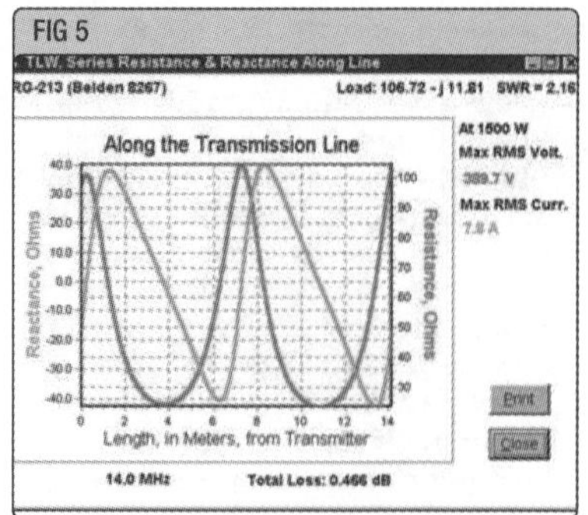

# Antennas

**G3LDO describes the construction of a simple antenna which he is using to track down interference**

The loop shown operating with a Yaesu FT-817.

I recently received an e-mail asking if I knew of a design for a loop antenna suitable for tracking down some electrical QRM. Apparently, this QRM manifests itself as a broad-band rasping sound, very much like a Morse spark transmitter and centred roughly within the low end of 14MHz. By chance I, together with other local radio amateurs, have also suffered from the same QRM, which was described in detail in [1].

One of the advantages of a small self-powered transceiver like the FT-817 is that it can be used as a field strength meter for detecting QRM. A small tunable antenna is required and suitable candidates include the Wonder Wand, reviewed in [2], and the Miracle Whip. I used my bicycle-mobile equipment described in [3] and, while this was fine for detecting patches of the QRM in the vicinity, it was not good enough for locating the actual source of the interference.

### LOOP PROBE ANTENNA

A small antenna with directivity was called for that could be used to locate or probe into less accessible QRM sources. The dimensions the loop that was constructed to were, to some extent, influenced by the size of the bits of 15mm OD copper tubing left over from a recent new kitchen installation. The loop had to tune the higher HF bands and the final 'design' comprised a square loop with outside dimensions 390mm and tuned with a broadcast receiver air-spaced dual-gang tuning capacitor of unknown pedigree. With one capacitor section of around 200pF, the loop easily covered all HF bands from 20 to 10m. The coax feed to the loop was shunt-coupled via a length of 2mm tinned copper wire.

The loop proved to be a sensitive receiving antenna and, while tuning up the antenna a couple of mornings ago, I received several VK3s and VK4s on 14MHz. The loop exhibited a conventional polar diagram pattern with approximately 20dB nulls.

### CONSTRUCTION

The loop is constructed using standard 15mm copper plumbing fittings. The support structure comprises a 140mm length of 15mm copper tubing with a plumbing T-piece which forms part of the loop as shown in the photograph. The lower part of the support tube was soldered to a 22mm pole via a 15mm to 22mm adapter to form the 'handle' of the loop probe. Using four 90° angle couplings and lengths of 15mm copper tubing, a square loop was constructed with a 20mm gap in the top section of the square.

Short lengths of 2mm tinned copper wire were soldered to the ends of the copper tubing at the gap in the loop to take the variable capacitor. A further length of 2mm tinned copper wire was soldered to the T-piece on the lower section of the loop to support the terminal block used to connect the coax feeder to the loop. All the soldering described here was done using a small propane blowtorch.

All plumbing connection surfaces must be cleaned with emery cloth or wire wool and smeared with flux. The joint is heated with a blowtorch until the applied solder runs freely and into the joint through capillary action. Most large DIY stores have leaflets on how to make good plumbing soldered joints.

The variable capacitor was soldered to the wire ends on the loop gap using a 60W soldering iron. The coax braid was joined to the T-connector via a connector block and the short length of 2mm wire previously soldered to the T-connector. This arrangement also served to support the coax connector at the loop. The centre of the coax is connected to the shunt wire via the connecting block.

### ADJUSTMENT

The only adjustment required is to match the coax feeder to the loop, and this is done by the usual method measuring the SWR using an MFJ-259 SWR Analyser. Obtaining a low SWR is not really necessary for an antenna that is to be used for receive-only, but if a good match is achievable without to much effort then it seemed sensible to go for it.

The best match was achieved using the shunt matching arrangement shown in the photograph. It comprises a short length of 2mm tinned copper wire whose connection to the copper tube element is made using a hose clamp; the position of this connection is selected at the point of minimum SWR. The spacing of the shunt connecting wire to the copper tube element also affected the SWR; the spacing in this case was 30mm. The minimum SWR was 1.2:1 on all bands, with 3:1 SWR bandwidths of 14.12MHz to 14.14MHz and 28.35MHz to 2850MHz.

### FINALLY

At the time of writing, I had still not identified the cause or source of the interference. The reason is that it radiates from some underground source which, in turn, is re-radiated by other services such as telephone lines and even water pipes. I am still working on it. Reports of the type of interference described earlier, in your area, would be much appreciated. ♦

### REFERENCES

[1] A 14MHz Mystery, 'EMC', *RadCom*, August 2004
[2] Miracle Whip reviewed, *RadCom*, June 2004
[3] 'Antennas', *RadCom*, August 2004

# Antennas

## More about 7MHz delta-loop antennas – how to configure and use them

In the September edition of 'Antennas' I described a delta full-wave loop for 7MHz, where the apex of the loop was supported by a small stub mast on the chimney of the house. Since that time, I moved the loop away from the house and it is now supported by an 18m high mast. The transmitting efficiency was changed very little by this move, but the receive performance, particularly on 7MHz, was much improved, because of the reduction of electrical interference. On the first night of operation on 7MHz, I heard stations from many parts of Latin America and worked a few of them.

If you have two supporting structures, say a mast and the chimney of a house, you could try inverting the loop. This arrangement is used by SM0DTK [1], with the base of the triangle 13.5m high and fed at the apex close to the ground. According to *EZNEC-4*, such an inverted loop would have a gain of around 5dBi over good ground, with a maximum angle of radiation of 50°, compared with my loop that has a maximum gain of only 1dBi but a maximum radiation of less that 30°. The sides of this triangle are 12.6m and the base is 16.9m.

SM0DTK has added another identical loop, located just over 5m away that is tuned with a 100pF capacitor via 4.85m of 450w ladder line so that it can act as a reflector or director. This gives an extra 3 or 4dB gain and a useful front-to-back ratio. The only disadvantage of this arrangement is that it requires four support structures (in SM0DTK's case, trees). It occurs to me that such an antenna could be scaled for the higher frequency bands with a loop spacing arrangement that requires only two support structures.

### THE COMUDIPOLE FEED ARRANGEMENT

I received an e-mail from ON6TJ, who uses the same type of single-support delta loop as described above. It is fed on one side, λ/4 down (on 7MHz) from the apex, using 450Ω ladder-line. This ladder-line does not go straight into the house; instead it is connected to the balanced side of a 4:1 balun located outside the house. The rest of the run into the house is made using coax cable. Such an arrangement, shown in **Fig 1,** is known as the 'comudipole'; it was first described in [2], but can also be found in [3]. The lengths of the coax and the twin feeder are not critical, although losses will be minimised by having as much of the total feeder length as possible being made up of twin feeder. I also use the comudipole feed method for my loop. In this case, the coax length is 6m and the 450ω ladder-line, 30m. The balun is a PA0SE wideband 4:1 coax type, as shown in the photograph, and is described in [2] and [4].

### WHY A 4:1 BALUN?

I was recently asked why the balun in an ATU should use a ratio of 4:1. Good question.

Most commercial ATUs use a T-match arrangement, which provides the best compromise between efficiency, simplicity and cost. However the T-match is an unbalanced antenna tuner, and some type of balun transformer must be incorporated if it is to be used successfully with balanced feeders. While a balun transformer provides a very simple solution for coupling a balanced feeder to an unbalanced tuning unit, it may not be as efficient as a properly-balanced ATU. Many published designs use a 4:1 balun on the assumption that most of the balanced impedances that will be encountered will be in the range 150 to 600w. The feed impedance of the full-wave loop discussed above is around 130w on 7MHz and 1300w on 10MHz (ignoring reactance). The unknown length of the feeder might mean that these impedance values could have a much wider range. In practice, the system seems to work, although some experimental pruning of the twin feeder might be necessary to ensure the antenna loads on all bands of interest.

The impedance range of the ATU can be increased by having a balun that can be switched from 4:1 to 1:1. If the balun is wound on a ferrite toroid core (as are all baluns in ATUs), it can easily be modified by replacing the two (bifilar) windings with three wires wound trifilar fashion. That is to say, three identical windings are wound on together. Lack of space precludes a description here, but full details of the construction of the G3TSO ATU can be found in [5] and [6]. ♦

FIG 1

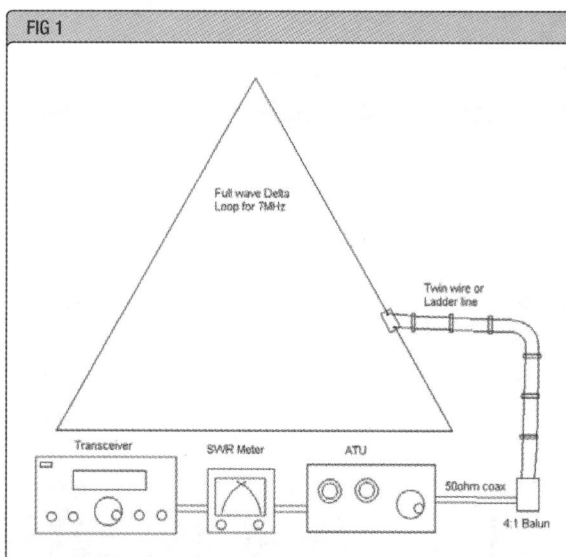

**Top: A 7MHz loop using the 'comudipole' feed arrangement. The coax cable from the balun is connected to the coax output socket of the ATU.**

**Left: The PA0SE wideband 4:1 coaxial balun. See 'The Comudipole Feed Arrangement'.**

### REFERENCES


[1] '2-Element Delta Loop for 40 metres', Martin Hedman, SM0DTK, *QTC.*

[2] 'Eurotek', Erwin David, G4LQI, *Radio Communication*, August 1992

[3] *Backyard Antennas*, pp26/27.

[4] *Backyard Antennas*, pp171/72.

[5] 'A General-Purpose Antenna Tuning Unit', M J Grierson, G3TSO, *Radio Communication*, August 1987.

[6] *Backyard Antennas*, pp45/46.[1] 2-Element Delta Loop for 40 metres', Martin Hedman, SM0DTK, *QTC*..

# Antennas

**This month, G3LDO describes things to be aware of when feeding balanced antennas (particularly short ones) with coaxial cable.**

For many years now I have used coaxial cable to feed a dipole antenna directly. The centre of the coax was connected to one leg of the dipole and the braid connected to the other. Antennas built this way seemed to work perfectly well, even though I was aware that connecting unbalanced feeder to a balanced antenna was, according to the text books, less than perfect.

In more recent years I have used a modified MQ-2 minibeam, the one shown on the front cover of [1]. This antenna is a small two-element beam antenna, which uses loading coils and capacitance 'spokes' to achieve multi-band operation. The driven element is split and fed directly with coax, as with the dipole described above. When SWR measurements were made on this antenna, it was found that, on some bands, the value of SWR changed if the length of the feeder was changed, or the shack end of the feeder was earthed. Common-mode currents, or antenna currents, were thought to be the problem.

In most previous discussions in this column regarding transmission lines, is has always been assumed that the two conductors carry equal and opposite currents (I1 and I2) throughout their length and consequently no radiation from the feeder takes place. In practice, this is very seldom the case. With coaxial cable, I1 flows on the inner conductor while I2 flows on the inside of the outer conductor. When this coax is connected to a balanced antenna all the I1 current flows on to its connected dipole element. The I2 on the inside of the inner conductor flows into the connected dipole element but part of I2 also flows down on to the outside of the coax outer conductor, which we can designate I3. Currents I1 and I3 are in phase and are the common-mode currents that can cause radiation from the coax.

Common-mode currents can also occur when the transmission line and the antenna arrangement is not symmetrical. In practice, most antenna arrangements are asymmetrical due to the number of electromagnetic obstructions to be found around an average suburban garden but, in most cases, they don't matter. In some cases, an antenna is designed so that the feeder is part of the radiating system as described in [2].

Common-mode currents seem worse on transmission line connected to small antennas, and this proved to be the case with my MQ-2. A current choke was originally made up a using a roll of RG-58 as a temporary stopgap. That was four years ago! and recently the antenna developed a high SWR, indicating trouble. The fault was found to be the 'temporary' current balun, which had succumbed to the ravages of years of coastal weather. I looked for a permanent solution that was in accord with the contents of my junk box.

### MAGNETIC CORE CURRENT BALUN

Magnetic-cored baluns employ ferrite or iron powder material to provide a high common-mode impedance over a wide frequency range. The discovery of a T200 toroid core in the junk box inspired me to try the current choke balun from [3].

The balun is constructed simply by winding 10 bifilar turns of 14 or 16SWG (2mm) enamelled copper wire on the core, which had previously been given a layer of PVC tape. The construction is shown in the photograph. Plastic insulated electrical wire would probably give just as good results and provide better insulation for outdoor use. The balun was fixed to a piece of insulating material using tie wraps before being fixed to the antenna as shown in the photograph. The balun unit was then coated in grease for weather protection.

Information on the construction of the current choke balun in [3] recommends an Amidon FT240-43 ferrite ring. My T200 seems to work fine, the common-mode current effect described earlier is not present and the SWR readings are now stable.

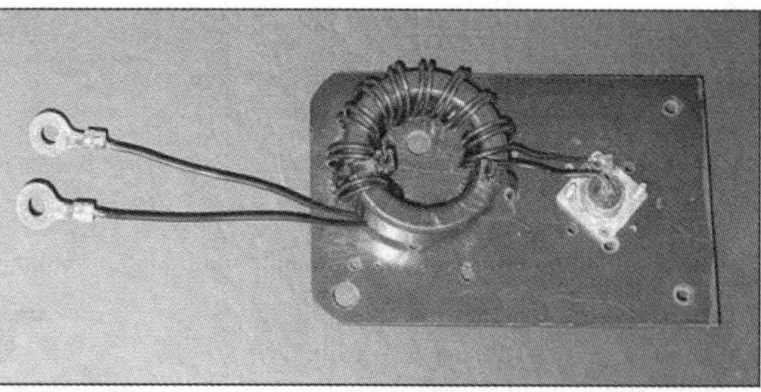

**The current balun with 10 bifilar turns of 14 or 16SWG (2mm) enamelled copper wire on a PVC tape layered T200 core.**

### FINALLY

In previous 'Antennas' columns, I described impedance measurement of an antenna. Because the impedance of a HF antenna varies with height, the only method of measuring the impedance of the antenna at its working height is to use a half-wavelength (or multiple) of feeder, which acts as a 1:1 transformer. However, a half-wavelength of feeder can have strong common-mode currents simply because it is resonant. This can have an adverse affect on the impedance measurements. The fix is to use the W2DU current balun comprising ferrite beads slipped over 300mm (1ft) of the feeder; described fully in [3]. ♦

### REFERENCES


[1] *Backyard Antennas*. The modified MQ-2 is also described on pp103 - 05.
[2] 'Antennas', *RadCom* March 2004.
[3] *The ARRL Antenna Handbook*, 20th edition, pp26.21 - 26.25.


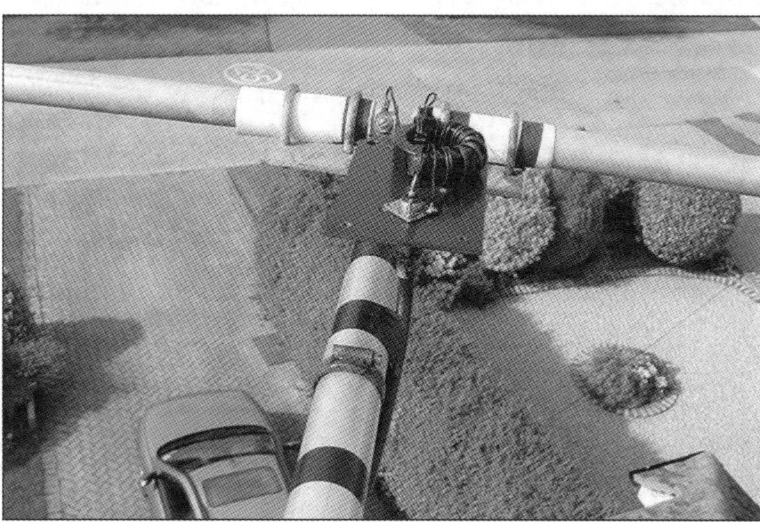

**Seagull's eye view of the current balun fixed to the feed-point of the modified MQ-2, before the protective grease coating was applied.**

# Antennas

**There are some situations where feeding an antenna with coax poses some mechanical problems. One of these is a dipole arrangement using a kite or a balloon as a support. Invariably the element to be fed has to be λ/4 long to present a low impedance to the coax feed. This requires some sort of radial or lower element, complicating the mechanics. Introducing the RFD (resonant feed-line dipole).**

This was described by AB2EZ in [1] and described as the RFD (resonant feed-line dipole). This arrangement, shown in **Fig 1**, shows the centre of the coax feed connected directly to end of the quarter-wave wire element and the braid left open-circuited. The coax braid currents are choked off λ/4 down from the feed-point by simply coiling the feeder into 13 turns.

According to AB2EZ, the method gives good results using 20m and 80m versions, with a SWR of better than 2:1 over the bands.

### A VHF RFD DESIGN

I received a description of a similar antenna for 2m from Peter Grant, G8HAR. For many years he had been using the traditional Slim Jim with good results.

G8HAR then tried an experimental RFD for 2m by simply removing quarter of a wavelength of braid from a length of coax feeder and making a small multi-turned loop of the feeder, quarter of a wavelength down from the point where the braid was removed. The antenna appeared to work well and this encouraged him to make a more permanent arrangement as shown in **Fig 2**.

The upper element is made from λ/4 of coax cable with the inner conductor and the braid soldered together with the centre of the feeder coax connected to this point. The feeder and the coax element are fixed to a plastic or wooden support using tie-wraps.

The coax choke is made by coiling the coax around the antenna support five and a half times and also fixed into place using tie-wraps.

The antenna is adjusted for minimum SWR by trimming the length of the top element and adjusting the position of the choke relative to the feed-point. When the adjustments are complete, the choke is fixed in place with the tie-wrap. The centre feed-point and the end of the elements should be then sealed with shrink-wrap.

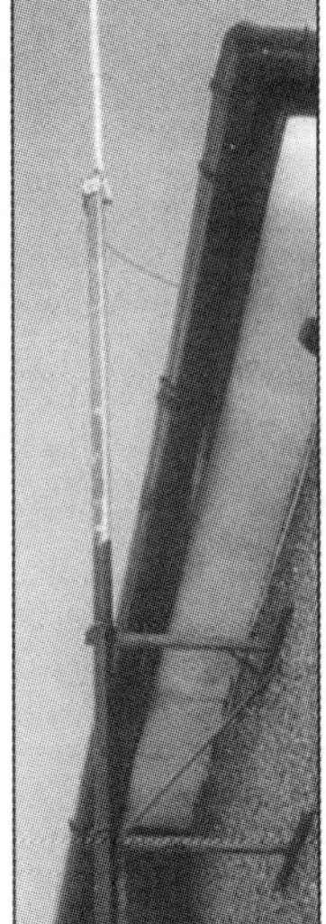

**The G8HAR RFD antenna, which is claimed to work as well as the Slim Jim antenna.**

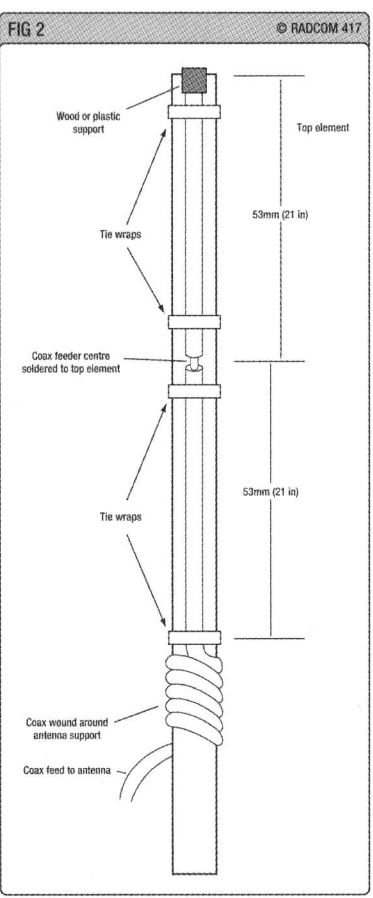


**Fig 1: The AB2EZ RFD half-wave dipole antenna for 80m [1].**

**Fig 2: The G8HAR RFD half-wave dipole antenna for 2m. After adjustment (see text) the SWR readings were 1.4:1 at 144MHz, 1.0:1 at 145MHz and 1.2:1 at 146MHz.**

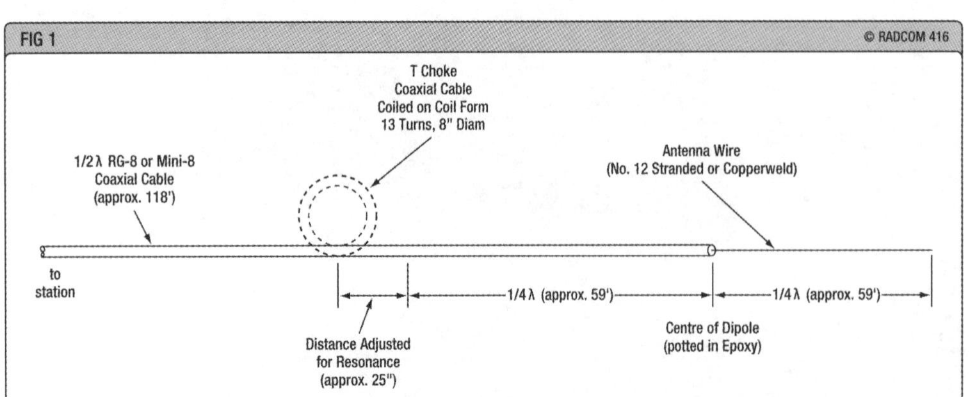


### FURTHER EXPERIMENTS

When I first received the description of the G8HAR RFD antenna, I felt unsure about it - it didn't seem right somehow and only decided to pursue the matter after coming across the antenna by AB2EZ [1]. This antenna does not feature in any other of the antenna books that I possess.

The normal method of feeding a coax centre-fed vertical is to use a bazooka λ/4 tube with the coax fed up the centre and the coax braid connected to the tube at the feed-point. I decided to make one of these RFD antennas for the 70MHz band. Pruning and adjustment resulted in a top element 0.93m while the distance from the feed-point to the choke was 1.2m. The choke comprised a single layer of the feeder wound on a 50mm (2in) cardboard tube and held in place using plastic clothes pegs. This arrangement made it easy to adjust the position of the coil on the feed-line and to also adjust the number of turns.

I am not so sure about this 'choke'. I found the number of turns as well as the position on the feeder had quite an affect on the resonant frequency of the antenna. Also, the position of the coil and the number of turns affected the feed-point impedance (measured using SWR). Could the turns be acting as a tuning coil similar to the arrangement that could be used to end-feed a half-wave dipole? Touching the coax above the 'choke' while making tests showed huge changes in SWR, while touching the coax below had no effect on the SWR so clearly the common-mode, or antenna currents, on the line were quite low.

My thoughts on using a kite- or balloon-supported antenna for 80m is that a single wire is much lighter than the lightest weight coax feeder. It might be better to use a single λ/2 wire with a simple parallel tuned circuit ATU at the base as described in [2]. ♦

### REFERENCES

[1] 'Experiments with a Balloon-Held Vertical Antenna', Stewart D Personick, AB2EZ. *ARRL Compendium,* Vol 7.

[2] *The Amateur Radio Mobile Handbook*, RSGB.

# Antennas

## G3LDO looks at different types of ATU, and their characteristics

The subject of ATU efficiency was discussed in 'Antennas', February 2003. Doug Harris, GW3NDR, described his results comparing several ATUs using a centre-fed wire about 80ft (24m) long and fed with slotted feeder some 20ft (6m) long and about 28ft (8.5m) above the ground. This was done by measuring the current in the twin feeder using a twin meter version of the RF meter while, at the same time, measuring the power into the ATU using a power/SWR meter. The tuners compared were listed below in order of efficiency.

- Home Brew ATU using a bal anced transformer output. Described as a half Z-match.
- MFJ Versa Tuner V (989C)
- SSM Z-Match
- MFJ Versa Tuner II
- SG-239 Smartuner

The MFJ-989C came out quite well in these tests. This ATU uses a T-network, which is the basis of most commercial units available today.

### THE T-NETWORK ANTENNA TUNER

The classic $\pi$-network can be used as the basis of an antenna tuning unit (ATU). It is a low-pass filter and is theoretically capable of matching any transmitter to any antenna impedance (resistive or reactive). However, in practice, the matching range is dependent on the component values. For the widest step-up and step-down transformations, the high-voltage variable capacitors need to have low minimum and very large maximum capacitance values, a very expensive and impractical solution.

Because modern solid-state transceivers include built-in low-pass filtering tailored to the individual bands, there is far less requirement for the harmonic attenuation previously provided by the ATU. This has led to greater use of the T-network, which can provide an acceptably wide range of impedance transformations without a requirement for large-value variable capacitors found in the $\pi$-network design.

However, the T-network has a reputation for low power-transfer efficiency on the higher frequencies at some impedance ratios. G3LNP describes [1] a simple method of overcoming some of these losses by allowing any T-network ATU, either home brew or commercial, to be switched to an inverted L-network (series C, parallel L) by modifying both capacitors with shorting switches to create the circuit shown in **Fig 1**.

**Fig 1: The series capacitor T-network, which forms the basis of most modern ATUs. The shorting switches across the capacitors allow the unit to be switched to an L-network, see text.**

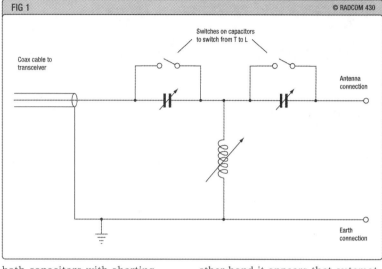

FIG 1 © RADCOM 430

Switches on capacitors to switch from T to L

Coax cable to transceiver

Antenna connection

Earth connection

### AUTOMATIC TUNERS

The SG-239 Smartuner fared less well in GW3NDR's tests. On the other hand it appears that automatic ATUs have been used by others with some success. You may recall a competition that was run during 2002, in the 'Antennas' column; to use a small 50ft (15m) length of wire and see how many countries and contacts could be made in 50 days. The winner was Peter Cole, G3JFS, who made 1248 contacts with 139 countries [2].

The simple wire doublet centre-fed with open wire line is G3JFS's antenna of choice but, for this competition, he used a 50ft (15m) end-fed wire hung from trees at the bottom of his garden. This antenna, tuned by a SG-230 Smartuner situated in a garden shed. The end-fed wire plus the Smartuner does not perform quite as well as the doublet but was very convenient.

The 139 countries worked by G3JFS included 9L1BTB Sierra Leone, FR/PA3GIO/P Reunion Island, 3XY6A Republic of Guinea, JT1CO Mongolia, C98DC Mozambique, XX9TEP Macao, JY9AX Jordan, HC8N Galapagos, XV9DT Galapagos Islands, ZL7C Chatham Island, YA5T Afghanistan, plus many more - not bad for 50ft of wire.

A few months ago I had a call from Dennis Ellis, M1BXO, who lives near me. He was experiencing heavy electrical QRM, and because of a peculiar type of QRM that is affecting radio amateurs in this area, I went to investigate. As it turned out, this particular QRM was not the problem - just a high level of electrical noise generally. M1BXO was using a SG-230 automatic tuner located inside the house, end feeding an 80ft (23m) length of wire against an earth system shared

**The antenna arrangement by M1BXO with the tuner outer weatherproof cover removed. The twists in the feeder improve antenna mechanical stability and can also improve feeder balance.**

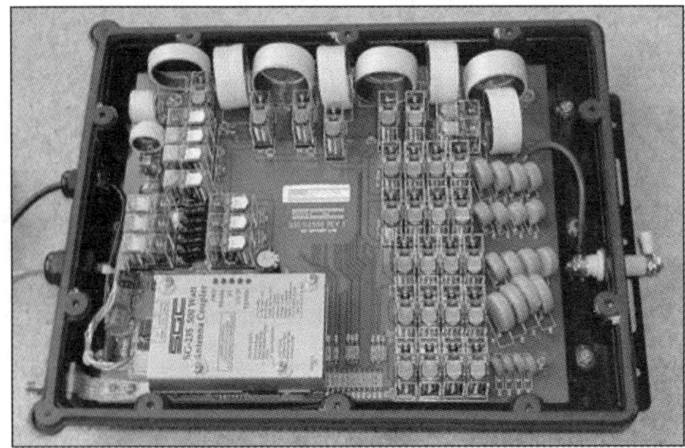

Internal view of the SG-235 automatic tuner.

with the electrical system. The antenna was an inverted-L with the vertical section against the wall of the house. Moving the ATU to the shed located at the end of a small garden was not an option because the shed was supplied with mains for power tools (source of noise) and there was no convenient area to install a counterpoise system.

I suggested a centre-fed doublet. The manual and [3] suggest placing the SG-230 at the feed-point, but this was impractical in this situation. The most convenient arrangement was to mount the SG-230 on the wall about 8ft (2m) high and feed the doublet via a short length of ladder line as shown in the photograph. This turned out to be a considerable improvement on the original installation.

## SG-235 AUTOMATIC TUNER

At around the same time, I received the offer of the loan of a SG-235 from Peter Craw, G3CCX, who also lives nearby. This is quite a robust unit is said to be capable of handling 500W and is obviously the big brother of the SG-230. I also borrowed the manual, which contained the circuit, a simplified version of which is shown in **Fig 2**. From this we can see that the SG-235 is a π-network, although if one of the banks of capacitors were switched out it would be an L-network.

Earlier, I mentioned the disadvantage of the π-network because it needed high-voltage, high-capacity variable capacitors. With switched fixed capacitors there is much less of a problem because it is possible to build fixed capacitors of any size and voltage working, within reason.

On the left hand side of Fig 2 are the capacitors associated with the low impedance 50Ω input from the transmitter. This bank of capacitors, with a total capacitance of over 6000pF, can be switched in or out (with a resolution of 100pF) with relay contacts. On the antenna side of the ATU, a total of nearly 400pF can be switched in with a resolution of 12.5pF. These capacitors are made up of groups of series / parallel capacitors to obtain a safe voltage working.

Additionally, these capacitors are switched using four sets of relay contacts in series for both switching voltage working and to reduce stray capacitance. The construction of the SG-235 is shown in the photograph. The π-section inductor (the section between the capacitor banks) is actually made up of eight inductors having a total inductance of 15.75μH and a switching resolution of 0.125μH. All this is fine for antennas longer than lambda/4, but what about short antennas, which present low and capacitively reactive impedances? This appears to be accommodated using four 4μH inductors (top right) that can be switched in or out to load a short antenna.

As with all automatic ATUs, tuning is accomplished using an RF head, which samples SWR and impedance on the feed-line and, in turn, operates the inductor and capacitor switching relays through a microprocessor using an embedded tuning algorithm.

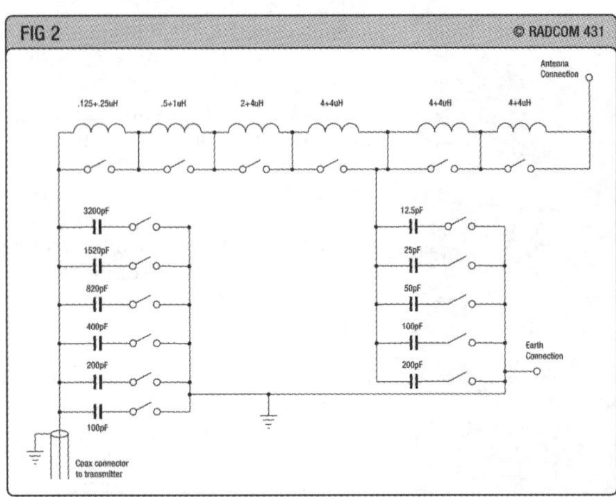


Fig 2: Simplified diagram of the SG-235. The p-section inductor (the section between the two capacitor banks) is actually made up of eight inductors, while the inductors (top right) are switched in for short antennas. Switching relays are controlled by a SWR/microprocessor circuit (not shown).

## GENERAL

Judging from the construction of the SG-235, these units appear to be very well-designed and constructed, although they are not cheap [note 1]. However, you can build one. The G3XJP PicATUne automatic ATU [4] is a simpler design employing a series-L – parallel-C – inverted-L network, see **Fig 3**. The antenna may need to be pruned lightly to avoid wild feed-point impedances.

All automatic antenna tuners appear to be designed for feeding end-fed antennas and there is no provision for feeding a balanced antenna via a length of twin feeder. This might have resulted in the inferior performance of the SG-239 described above. The MFJ-993 auto tuner has a balanced output, but I know nothing about this unit at the time of writing.

With the M1BXO installation, the doublet is fed by a short length of ladder-line, one conductor connected to the ATU antenna connection and the other to the ATU ground. Could a balun transformer be used on the antenna side of the ATU as is done on manual T-network ATUs?

David Knight, G3YNH [3], recommends not using a balanced transformer in this way, and to isolate the ATU using a current choke in the coaxial feed. However, commercial designs use transformer baluns in the outputs of their T-network ATUs. I have used the diminutive MFJ-901B with an IC-706 (100W), which gave excellent results. The 25mm OD ferrite was only slightly warm after hours of CW operation. ♦

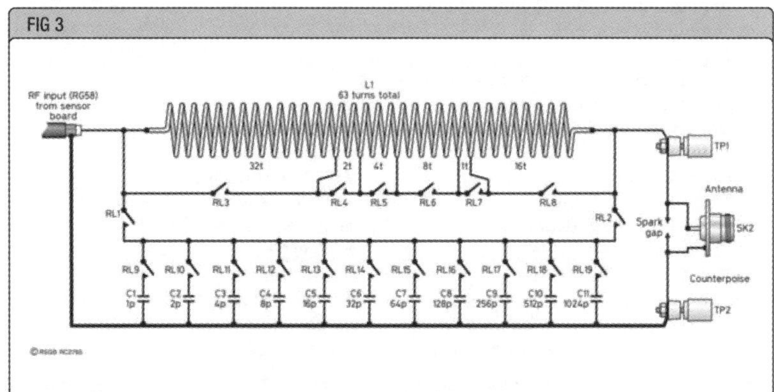


Fig 3: The switched L-matched section used in the G3XJP ATU. Each relay contact is, in fact, two normally-open contacts in series to increase breakdown voltage and to reduce capacitance across the contacts. Capacitor values C1 – C11 are nominal.

## REFERENCES


[1] 'Save Your Tuner for Two Pence', Tony Preedy, G3LNP, *RadCom* May 2000.

[2] 'Antennas', *RadCom* February 2003.

[3] *From Transmitter to Antenna*, David Knight, G3YNH, with contributions from Nigel Williams. Seven chapters including antenna coupling techniques and impedance matching. Appendix 1 gives a very good description of the SG-230 tuner. www.camera-sunderwater.co.uk/zbook

[4] 'PicATUne – the Intelligent ATU', Peter Rhodes, G3XJP, *RadCom* September, October, November, December 2000 and January 2001.


**Note 1:** The SGC automatic tuners described above can be obtained from Waters and Stanton. Check availability and prices on their web-site: www.wsplc.com.

# Antennas

**For those of us who spend all our lives on the HF bands, the subject of coaxial cable is hardly given a second thought. Just fit a PL-259 to one end and connect the other end to the antenna and away we go.**

All coaxial cable presents some attenuation to both the transmitted power being fed to the antenna and the received signal returning to the transceiver. But just how important is coax cable attenuation to the performance of a station and what are the properties of good coax?

## SERIOUS COAX

Electro-magnetic waves tend to propagate along the surface of conductors, rather than inside, due to the phenomenon of skin effect. Coaxial cable performance depends upon the conductivity and size of the outer surface of the inside conductor and the inner surface of the outer conductor.

The centre conductor of a coaxial cable may consist of either a single wire of the desired outer diameter, or a twisted bundle of smaller strands. Stranded-centre conductors improve cable flexibility, while solid centre conductors provide the greatest uniformity of outer diameter dimension, which contributes to stable electrical characteristics.

The outer conductor of coax cable should ideally be made from a solid conductive pipe, but this construction makes the cable difficult to bend. The flexibility and bend radius of such cables can be improved by corrugating the outer conductor; examples are shown in the photograph.

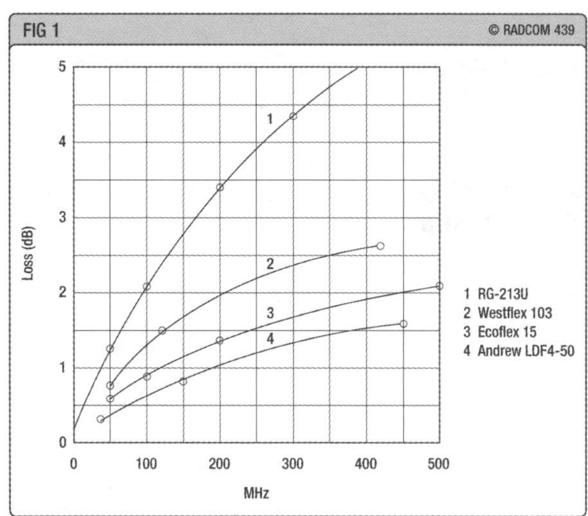


**Fig 1: Matched feeder attenuation for 30m of various feeders discussed in the text. Note the similarity between Ecoflex 15 and Andrew LDF4-50**

Nearly all of the popular flexible coaxial cables employ braided shields. These are not as effective electrically as solid outer conductors because gaps in the woven outer conductor permit some signal leakage, or radiation, from the cable, increasing the attenuation at higher frequencies. This effect can be minimised by adding a layer of copper foil under the braid, as is done in the Ecoflex cables.

The dielectric material that separates the outer conductor of a coaxial cable from its centre conductor determines the intensity of the electrostatic field between conductors and maintains the physical position of the inner conductor within the outer conductor. Common dielectric materials for coaxial cable in-clude polyethylene, polystyrene and Teflon®.

The least lossy dielectric material is a pure vacuum, which is totally impractical for use as a cable dielectric. However, the electromagnetic properties of air or gaseous nitrogen are very similar to a vacuum and can be used by mixing low-cost polyethylene with low-loss nitrogen. This is accomplished by bubbling nitrogen gas through molten polyethylene dielectric material before the polyethylene solidifies. This material is variously known as cellular polyethylene dielectric, foam dielectric, or polyfoam. It has half the dielectric losses of solid polyethylene at a modest increase in cost.

**From left to right, Ecoflex 15, with Andrew LDF4-50, LDF5-50 and LDF7-50 with the vinyl outer covers removed. (The latter may be impractical as a feeder for amateur use, but a short length, often available as an offcut, would make a nice magnetic loop antenna).**

**Partially-assembled N-connector used with Ecoflex 15 coax. Note that the centre pin is a tight push fit over the coax centre conductor.**

## LOW-LOSS COAX – IS IT WORTH IT?

The attenuation factors of various correctly-terminated coax cables are shown in Fig 1. These attenuation figures are for 30m (100ft) lengths and indicate that, for frequencies below 50MHz, there is not much to be gained by using expensive low-loss coax feeders. At VHF, and particularly UHF frequencies, it is a different matter. Good quality coax can really enhance a station's performance. On a typical UHF installation at least a 3dB increase should be possible by replacing RG-213 with, say, Ecoflex. If this doesn't sound much remember that generally the size a VHF/UHF antenna array has to be doubled to get 3dB gain.

One has to bear in mind the cost. Current prices for 'small quantities' (100m lengths) of LDF4-50 is apparently £2.50 per foot. That is around £8 per metre, although it can be obtained much more cheaply through surplus sources (try eBay). Ecoflex15, which has similar characteristics to LDF4-50 (see **Fig 1**), is £2.85 per metre up to 25m reducing to £2.65 per metre, 75 to 100m. (see facing page).

Interestingly, all connectors used on high-grade low-loss cable appear to be solderless. This applies to the N-type male and female connectors used with Ecoflex15, see the photograph. This connector proved to be very easy to fit.

## FINALLY

My thanks to Walter Blanchard, G3JKV, for samples and information about Andrew cable.

My thanks also to Terry Clayton, G0TKJ, of Diode Communications, for a sample of Ecoflex 15 coax and N-connectors. ♦

# Antennas

**The description of the RFD (resonant feed-line dipole) in February's 'Antennas' resulted in some informative and constructive mail and I was surprised at the amount of work some readers have done on this antenna**

John Heys, G3BDQ, says that he came across the RFD design in a small book called *Simple Low-Cost Wire Antennas for Radio Amateurs,* by Bill Orr, W6SAI and is described as a 'Cobra Vertical for 10 and 6 Metres'. This antenna uses a choke constructed by putting three turns of the feeder through a ferrite ring.

Neil Robertson, GM8EUG, also drew my attention to the W6SAI book, which describes the construction of the Cobra antenna; he also sent me a copy of the Cobra description. GM8EUG adds, "I have just been playing around with a similar design trying to get it to work on 15m. I was never able to get the SWR below 2:1; however (as you mentioned in your article) the choke seems to work as I could also touch the coax below the choke and the SWR did not change".

I find that I have a copy of *Simple Low-Cost Wire Antennas for Radio Amateurs,* and sure enough the Cobra antenna is described. I missed it because it was described as a 'Cobra' rather than a RFD.

Geoff Mackenzie-Kennedy, GM4ESD, says "Both the RFD-1 and RFD-2 antennas were the subjects of an article by James E Taylor, W2OZH, in *QST* August 1991. The article is also contained in ARRL's *More Wire Antenna Classics* - Volume 2. On 40m, one I tried as a vertical half-wave worked very well. One that I tried for 17m did not. Like yourself, I am not sure about the choke".

Bernard Spencer, G3SMW, has made Cobra antennas for 145MHz and for 14MHz. Also sometimes with traps to make them dual-band (eg 14/18MHz). He usually fixes it vertically on a fibre-glass telescopic mast, or sometimes horizontally from the house for HF.

### CHOKE DESIGN

G3SMW has things to say about the chokes in this application. "You mentioned choke problems, and indeed there are, not only for Cobras, but also for practically all coax-fed vertical antennas, including ground-plane antennas, J-poles, and those with a quarter-wave bazooka balun like the original 'Coaxial Dipole'.

"There are two effects, both distinctly undesirable, and they are not known to all manufacturers or amateurs, as I know from work and play. The worst one is an upwards tilt of the lobe in the elevation plane which should, of course, be horizontal for VHF/UHF antennas. This often results in the signal being between 3dB and 6dB less than it should be, and the user may not realise this. To eliminate this effect generally requires two 'chokes' on the feeder, one at the top near the base of the antenna, and the other about a quarter of a wavelength below it. Even if the top choke is perfect, the first half-wavelength of coax below it will usually have sufficient current induced on its outside from the antenna to cause this upward tilt (it does not require much, as can be seen if modelled in *EZNEC* etc). So the best place for the second choke is in the middle of this top half-wavelength of feeder ie a quarter-wavelength below the top choke, but the position and inductance of this second choke are not critical and it does not need to be a trap.

"For the top 'choke', which determines the length of the bottom half of the radiator, what is required is a high inductive reactance compared to the impedance at the end of the dipole, not always an easy thing to fabricate! A better way in principle (and practice) is to use the feeder coiled as a trap with a shunt capacitor, and tuned to the centre frequency of the antenna. This does not require a great deal of inductance, and the impedance will be very high at its resonant frequency. It is more tricky to make and adjust than just winding the coax into a coil of arbitrary inductance, but is better for defining the length and for reducing currents on the feeder.

"The second problem is that current on the outside of the coax feeder can be the cause of an unacceptable mismatch in the feeder. This may occur when there is only one choke, giving a disappointing match to the rig that changes as you run your hand along the coax."

G3BDQ also referred to an article he had written in *Practical Wireless* (August 1995) called 'The Slim Cobra'. By chance I had a copy of this magazine and the article, which describes the experimental work done by G3BDQ and G4SLU. Details of the construction of the G3BDQ Cobra antenna are shown in **Fig 1**.

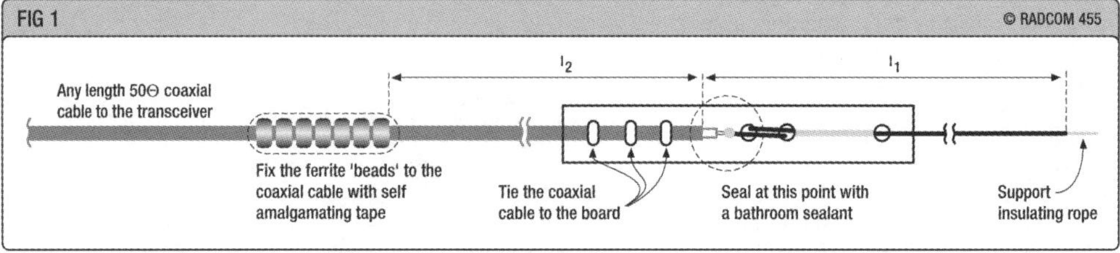


**Fig 1 Details of the Slim Cobra antenna by G3BDQ from Practical Wireless. The dimensions of l1 and l2, respectively, are 29MHz – 2.46m (2.66m); 28.1MHz – 2.54m (2.74m); 21.1MHz – 3.38m (3.65m); 18.1MHz – 3.95m (4.26m); 14.1MHz – 5.07m (5.47m); 10.1MHz – 7.07m (7.64m); 7.05MHz – 10.14m (10.95m).**

### OTHER COBRAS

Be aware that there are other antenna designs under the banner of Cobra. One of these is a balanced HF centre-fed dipole that uses what appears to be a linear loading arrangement and can be found on [1]. The other describes research into the microwave Coaxial Beam-Rotating Antenna (COBRA) [2]. ◆

WEB SEARCH

| | |
|---|---|
| [1] | www.hamuniverse.com/cobraantenna.html |
| [2] | www.vosssci.com |

# Antennas

**This month, G3LDO unravels some of the finer points of SWR - what it means and how it is measured**

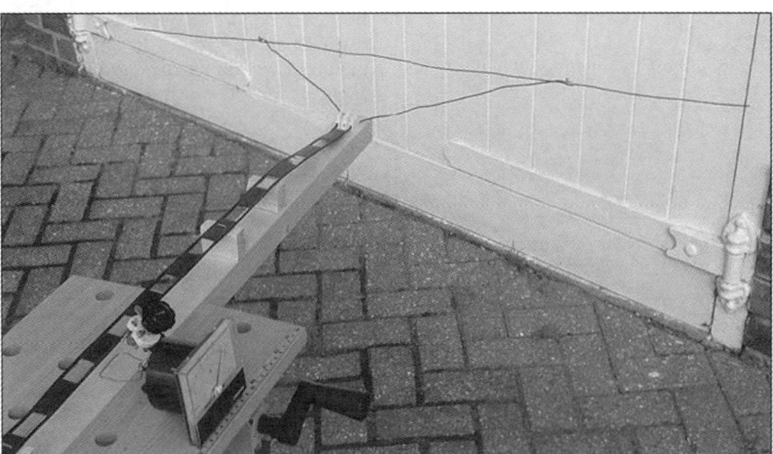
SWR test set-up.

When I first came to amateur radio back in 1955, most radio equipment was home-made and all radio equipment used valves. The most common method of matching the transmitter PA to the antenna via coaxial transmission line was the variable π-tank circuit as shown in **Fig 1**. This arrangement allowed the tuning and matching of quite a range of antenna impedances. Matching was achieved by first tuning the PA to resonance with C1, indicated by a sharp dip in the anode current. The value of C2 was then reduced causing the anode current dip to become less sharp at resonance as the loading was increased, and was set so the PA was operating at the correct rated anode current. The higher the feed impedance of the antenna and feeder the lower the value of C2. The dial of C2 could be calibrated using a number of dummy loads of different resistive values. At this stage I hadn't heard of the SWR meter.

### WHY SWR AND VSWR?

So at what stage did SWR become the important measure of transmission line impedance matching - and why VSWR, as seen in some amateur radio literature?

The 1947 edition of the ARRL *Radio Amateurs' Handbook* shows that open wire transmission line was used to connect the transmitter (and receiver) to the antenna on the HF bands, connected to the transmitter PA via a coupling coil. Matching was achieved by varying the distance between the antenna coupling coil and the PA tank circuit, while observing the PA anode current at resonance, as described above. Commercial radio used the same technique and used open wire transmission line supported, on wooden poles, to connect transmitters to antennas.

Because commercial station antennas were often located some distance from the transmitters, the business of adjusting any matching circuit at the antenna could be a problem if no method of monitoring the transmission line/antenna matching was available. The solution was to monitor SWR.

When a wave, travelling along a transmission line from the transmitter to the antenna (incident wave), encounters an impedance that is not the same as the impedance of the line, some of the wave is reflected (reflected wave). Whenever two sinusoidal waves of the same frequency propagate in opposite directions along the same transmission line, as occurs in any system exhibiting reflections, a static interference pattern is formed along the line, as illustrated in **Fig 2**.

For the purposes of quantifying reflection, we are interested in the amplitude of the maxima and minima. Standing Wave Ratio (SWR) is defined as the ratio of the voltage or current maximum to the voltage or current minimum along a transmission line.

### MEASURING ISWR

An interesting method of measuring SWR is described in [1]. It says: "The first step in matching the (antenna) array to the line is to energise the line and observe the stationary (SWR) wave. A suitable arrangement for this purpose is shown in **Fig 3**. It consists of a thermo-ammeter, reading 0-120mA, which is mounted in a loop circuit; this loop may be suspended from one of the conductors forming the transmission line. The size of the loop is suitable for an input into the line in the order of 1kW. The line is energised at a reduced input and the loop drawn along it, and the current reading observed, field glasses [binoculars] being of assistance in this process.

"The current maximum point nearest the array is then selected for particular observation and the power

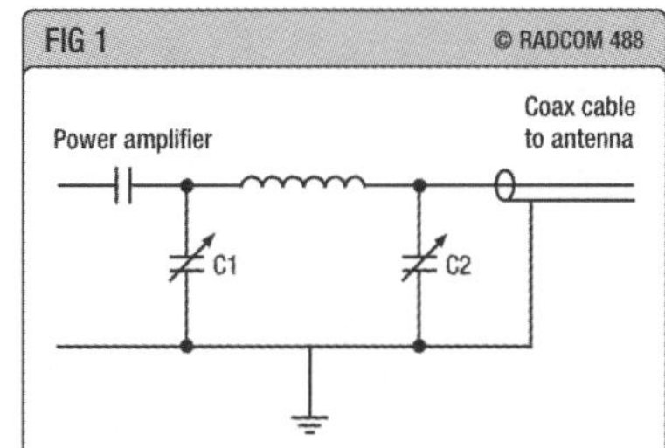


Fig 1
The π-tank circuit.

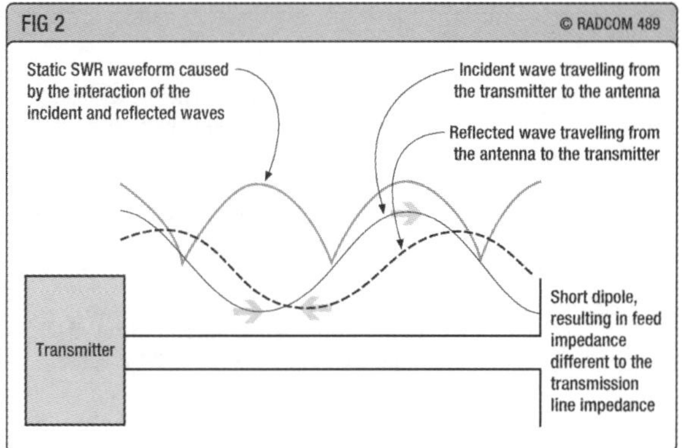


Fig 2
How a standing wave is created on a transmission line.

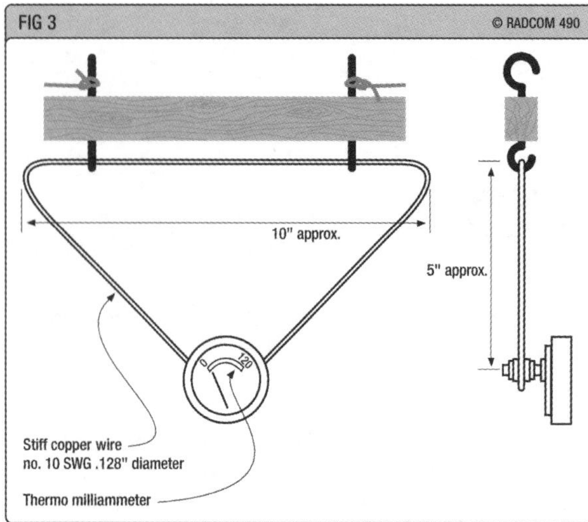


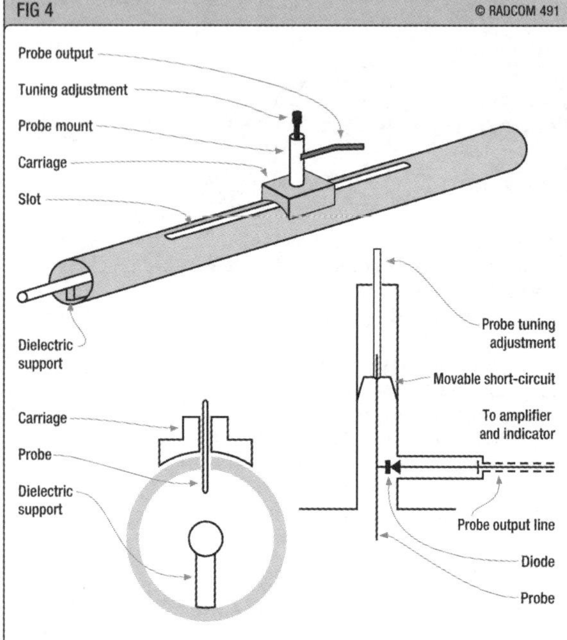


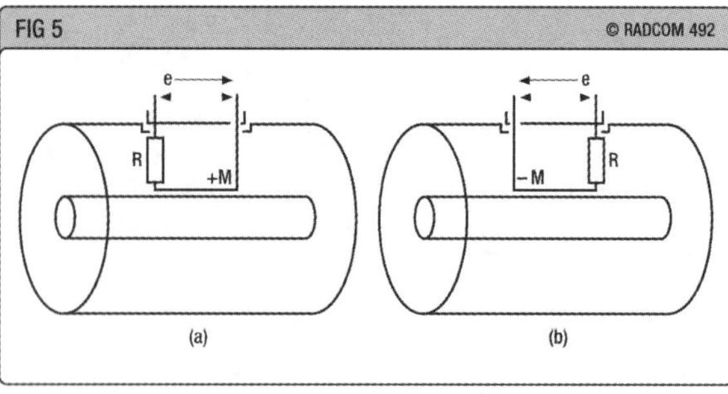


**Fig 3**
**Construction of an instrument for measuring current SWR on open wire transmission line.**

**Fig 4**
**Details of a slotted line type of standing wave detector for coaxial line.**

**Fig 5**
**The directional coupler sensing circuit. At (a) mutual coupling is positive, at (b), negative.**

increased until the ammeter gives nearly full scale deflection. The exact position on the line of the current measurement should be marked, and the actual scale reading, $I_{max}$, noted. The loop is then drawn along the line to the adjacent minimum, the current, $I_{min}$, being noted and the position marked".

The measurement method described above measures the current component of SWR and could be described as ISWR. I tried this method as shown in the photograph. The test setup comprised a length of 450Ω slotted line feeding a delta-matched dipole on the 2m band. The current probe consisted of a tuned single loop, a diode and a meter. This arrangement allowed SWR to be seen, but the test set up lacks the precision for any meaningful measurement. However, the dipole delta-match could be adjusted by placing the current probe at the maximum point and adjusting the dipole for minimum reading. An energising power of 0.5W from an FT-817 via a transformer balun was sufficient to make the measurement.

## MEASURING VSWR

The voltage component could be measured on a length of twin-line feeder, using a neon tube or a probe sensitive only to the voltage component. I have used such a method of measuring SWR on the waveguide of 3cm $H_2S$ radar while in the RAF many years ago. The test equipment comprised a small thin neon tube, with calibration marks on the side like a thermometer and was inserted into the slot of a short length of waveguide. When the transmitter was fired up the lower section of the neon tube was energised and glowed red, the height of the red glow in the tube varied as the tube was moved along the slot. The SWR (or VSWR in this case) was determined by comparing the maximum and minimum voltage levels.

A voltage probe for coax line is shown in **Fig 4**. In this case the instrument comprises a short wire probe, a coaxial resonant line and a diode. The voltage output is then measured on a sensitive electronic voltmeter.

## THE DIRECTIONAL COUPLER

From the descriptions of SWR so far, it can be seen that two measurements are required at two different positions on the transmission line, but the SWR meters in use these days are located in one position in the line. They use a device called a 'directional coupler', also known as a 'reflectometer'. It works because the current and voltage of the incident wave (see Fig 1) are in phase while the current and voltage of the reflected wave are 180 degrees out of phase.

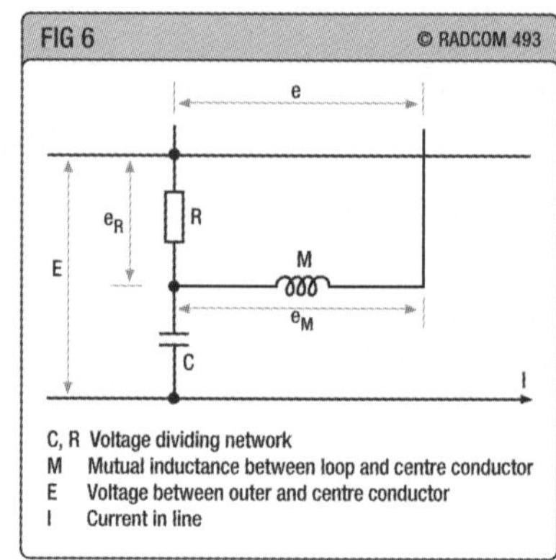


**Fig 6**
**Basic sensing circuit.**

A simplified diagram of a directional coupler is shown in **Fig 5**. It comprises a small length of coaxial cable with a small loop of wire inserted running parallel with the centre conductor, one end terminated in resistance, R. **Fig 6** shows the equivalent electrical circuit. C is the capacitance between the loop and the centre conductor, M the mutual inductance between the two and E is the voltage between the outer and the inner conductors. I is the current in the centre conductor.

The loop and the centre conductor can be considered as a transformer with the induced current in the loop converted to a voltage across R. This voltage is summed with E to produce a vector, *e*. These currents and voltages are the components of the incident wave. The directional coupler has two loops, each with its own measurement meter or a meter that can be switched between them (or one loop whose direction can be switched). When the second loop is switched in, the current vector is 180° out of phase from the first reading (while the voltage phase is the same as the first measurement). These currents and voltages are the components of the reflected wave. This description is rather simplistic and a more in-depth mathematical description is given in [2].

The ratio of voltage and current measurements will be affected by the load at the antenna connection of the directional coupler and is calibrated in terms of SWR, although it doesn't actually measure SWR as described earlier. It could also be calibrated as RF power or any of the Smith chart radially-scaled parameters such as return loss or reflection coefficient. It still doesn't answer the question of why some people talk about VSWR when they are using a directional-coupler-type instrument to measure transmission line mismatch. ♦

## REFERENCES

[1] *RAF Signal Manual,* Air Publication 1093. (1945).

[2] Reflectometers and directional power meters, M M Bibby, G3NJY, *RadCom* June 1968. Also in *HF Antenna Collection* (RSGB).

# Antennas

**G3LDO bemoans the fact that some types of computing don't appear as easy as they used to be, but he has found a way of running some of his early BASIC programs with more modern operating systems. He explains how.**

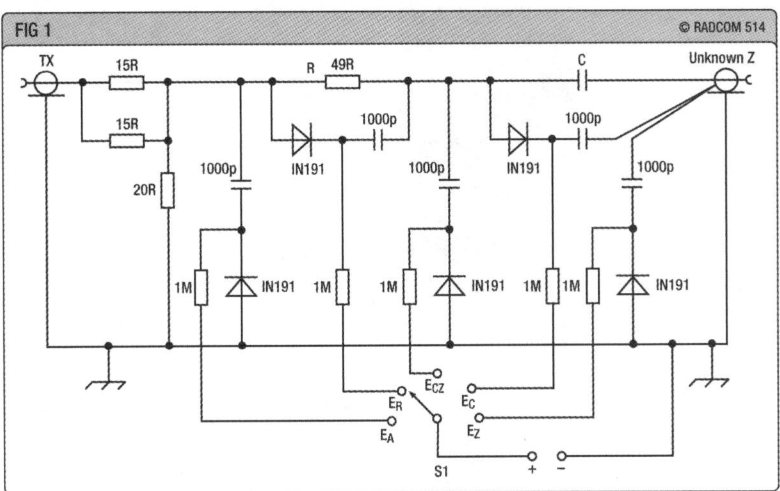


It is often convenient in the course of antenna construction or experimentation to make calculations of such things like the resonant length of a dipole or the length of wire necessary to make a quad loop. Most of these calculations are very simple and can be done on the back of a used envelope with a pencil; or more likely these days, with a digital calculator.

Some calculations are more complex, particularly if you wish to juggle with two or more of the variables. The answer to these types of problems seemed to met in the early days of Personal Computers when everyone seemed to have learned BASIC and was able to transcribe the formula found in antenna publications to something that was actually usable. Computers were being used for computing.

These days things are more complex. We now have PCs that have a far greater power than the early large mainframes. These PCs have applications that are wonderful for writing this column, for obtaining and editing photos and diagrams and communicating with the outside world.

But what about computing? *Windows 97* still allowed *DOS* programs to be used, so we were still able to use programs such as *GW-BASIC* and *Q-BASIC*, but this may not be the case with *Windows XP*.

One of the applications to be found on a modern PC is *Excel*. These spreadsheet programs are excellent for working out accounts and VAT returns. This is number crunching - is it not? I have seen Excel used in amateur radio articles to solve certain problems, but they are presented in a form of how they look and are used when the programming is completed. I have not seen a description of how the program was set up.

Recently, I tried to transcribe a program that I had originally written in *BASIC* to run on *Excel*.

After half an hour, I was aware of a large increase in blood pressure and after one hour I was feeling positively homicidal. Why should this be? I don't recall having this sort of problem with my early BBC computer!

It might be the additional complexity. It is so easy in software engineering to add extras *ad infinitum* to meet the marketing department's wish list; you then finish up with a package that has more bells and whistles than a troupe of Morris dancers. The same goes for many modern radios. Try operating an unfamiliar one of these without the instruction manual and see how far you get.

Now, back from the Grumpy Old Man digression, (as a >70 G3, I am privileged to be one of these) how can I use a modern PC to do amateur radio calculations?

While giving a talk at the Worthing Radio club some months ago, I was describing the three-meter method of measuring impedance. Unlike most impedance-measuring methods, which use calibrated resistance and reactance variables in the bridge, this method uses fixed variables as shown in **Fig 1**. It has the advantage of being very easy to construct, and is fairly accurate because it is easier to control stray reactances with small fixed components; it is self-calibrating. The 3M box is energised via a QRP transmitter source and the unknown Z is connected to the antenna or component under test. Although the instrument is called a three-meter measuring device, five voltage measurements are required to get an unambiguous impedance measurement.

The down side is that you need a sheet of graph paper to convert the voltage readings to impedance in the form of R ± jX, see **Fig 2**. This procedure was much simplified using a simple *BASIC* program written by the late Tom Lloyd, G3TML, and described in [1]. During this talk, I was bemoaning the difficulties of the modern computer in this context and the club computing guru, Matt Wilson, G8XIT, pointed me to a simple solution to be found on the Internet.

It is called *BBC BASIC for Windows* and is a version of the *BBC BASIC* programming language, which is fully integrated into the Microsoft *Windows* operating environment (*Windows 95/98/Me/NT4/2000/XP*). *BBC BASIC for Windows* can be obtained from **www.rtrussell.co.uk**. An evaluation version is available for free although the user's program and data is restricted to 8KB (quite large enough for the program shown in the screen-shot). The 'Compile' command, used for the creation of stand-alone executable files, is only available with the full version.

I was able to scan in some of my early *BBC BASIC* listings as text files and insert them into the program; they require just a little tweaking to get them going. The construction and use of the 3M box is covered in [1], although I will describe it in a later 'Antennas' column if there is enough interest. ♦

**Fig 1**
**Circuit diagram of the three-meter impedance meter.**

**Values for C**

| | |
|---|---|
| 3.5MHz | 1000pF |
| 7MHz | 560pF |
| 14MHz | 390pF |
| 21MHz | 180pF |
| 28MHz | 100pF |
| 50MHz | 49pF |
| 144MHz | 22pF |

**Fig 2**
**Graphic method of converting meter readings to R ± jX impedance.**

**Below:**
**Program for extracting R ± jX from meter readings. To simplify the program, $E_A$, $E_R$, $E_{CZ}$, $E_C$ and $E_Z$ have been assigned A, B, C, D and E, respectively. The inset shows an example of the display when 'Run' is selected.**

### REFERENCE

[1] *The Antenna Experimenter's Guide*, 2nd Edition, RSGB.

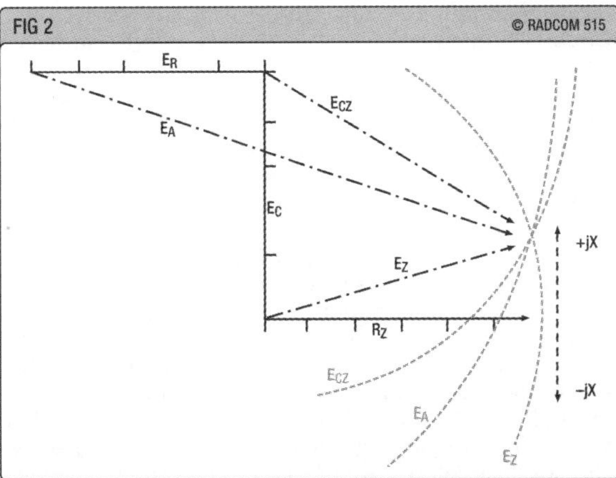

# Antennas

## G3LDO looks at his Double-D antenna, the VK2ABQ, the Moxon Rectangle, and modelling HF antennas at VHF

Sending and receiving material with images over the Internet and e-mail had been testing my patience of late, so last month I invested in broadband. While exploring antenna article sites on the Internet I came across *Rothammels Antenna Buch*, see [1]. This German antenna book comprises 42 chapters and is larger than the ARRL *Antenna Book*. To give an example of the scope of the book, the first five chapters cover: 1. Terms, fields, waves; 2. Propagation of electromagnetic waves; 3. Antenna forms; 4. Antenna characteristics; 5. Transmission lines. The best method of looking at this website if you don't understand German is to go via Google and use the translation facilities. The site contains a full contents list and index, plus some sample pages and other information.

Chapter 18, HF directional antennas (beams) has a sub-title, '18.1.4 Miniature Yagis', and under this sub-title I was surprised to find '18.1.4.3 G3LDO-Beam'. In references [2] and [3] it is called the 'Double-D Antenna'.

### MODELLING HF ANTENNAS AT VHF

The G3LDO or Double-D antenna configuration was conceived by mischance. When I first moved to my present QTH nearly 20 years ago I looked for a method of making a small compact beam to go on the chimney of this rather small house. The only configuration that I was aware of at the time that would fit the bill was a wire beam by VK2ABQ [4], the basic structure of which is shown in **Fig 1**. I didn't know how this antenna would perform and (this was before the days of computer modelling) so I made a VHF model. This technique had been used with some success to investigate the performance of other HF beams, and is described in [5].

The model was constructed with wire elements laid out on a wooden X-spreader with the element ends tried in various directions. The results were rather disappointing. It would give the gain of a two-element Yagi provided the elements were not folded too far back on themselves, or directly towards each other on the same plane as shown in Fig 1.

The VHF model indicated that the ends of the elements could be folded back towards the mast and down to an angle of 20° from the horizontal before the gain started to deteriorate. This resulted in a structure shown in **Fig 2**. The antenna proved to be a simple and stable mechanical arrangement and the HF model survived some very strong gales.

Since that time, antenna modelling programs such as *EZNEC* have shown the antenna configurations shown in Fig 1 do work quite well, even at VHF. So why did my VHF model fail in this regard? It is possibly that it was due to capacitive end-coupling. With VHF modelling, wavelengths, capacitances and inductances in the VHF scale model are reduced in proportion to the linear dimensions while gains and impedances are unchanged. However, the insulator supporting the ends of the elements represents a fixed capacitor, the reactance of which is frequency-dependent.

### THE MOXON RECTANGLE

The original VK2ABQ antenna is a square structure, see Fig 1. The driven element and the reflector are a quarter-wavelength apart, although the tips of the elements support each other using insulators. G6XN [6] changed the structure from a square to a rectangle, thereby reducing the centre section spacing of the elements from 0.25λ spacing to 0.17λ spacing. This resulted in improved gain and directivity. It also reduced the feed impedance from around 120Ω to 50Ω, thereby overcoming the need for a matching network. Multiband editions of these antennas can be made by nesting the elements.

C B Cebik, W4RNL, reduced the element spacing further to 0.14λ, and obtained yet more gain and improved directivity. The downside of this higher performance is that the design is more critical, the feed impedance is down to around 35Ω and multibanding can pose a challenge. This antenna was called the Moxon Rectangle.

The first documented account of a two-element Yagi with bent elements (that is what all the antennas described above are) was by John Reinartz, W1QP, and a model was constructed for 14MHz by Burton Simson, W8CPC. It was described in *QST*, October 1937 [7].

These antennas are also described in an earlier 'Antennas' column [8], and in [9]. ♦

**Front cover of the German antenna bible, '*Antennen Buch*'.**

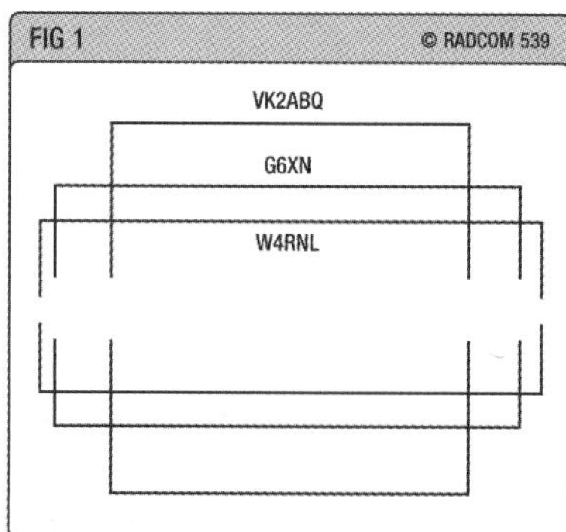


**Fig 1**
**The original VK2ABQ antenna structure compared with the G6XN and the W4RNL. The G6XN has a centre section spacing of the elements of around 0.17λ spacing, while the W4RNL has element spacing further to 0.14λ, the closer spacing gives a greater gain and front-to-back ratio.**

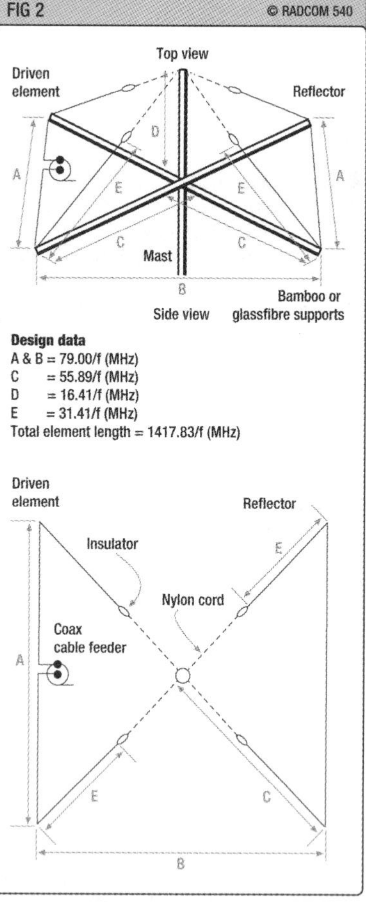


**Fig 2**
**The basic G3LDO Double-D wire antenna with approximate design data. Multiband versions of this antenna have been made by fixing nested elements to the existing support structure.**

### REFERENCES

[1] http://www.antennenbuch.de/antennenbuch.html
[2] 'Wire Beam Antennas and the Evolution of the Double-D', G3LDO, *Radio Communication*, June/July 1980. Also *QST* October 1984.
[3] 'Further Evolution of the Double-D', G3LDO, *Radio Communication*, April 1990.
[4] 'VK2ABQ Antenna', VK2ABQ, *Electronics*, Australia, October 1973.
[5] *The Antenna Experimenter's Guide*, G3LDO, 2nd edition.
[6] *HF Antenna for all Locations*, G6XN.
[7] 'Concentrated Directional Antennas for Transmission and Reception', W1QP & W8CPC, *QST* October 1937.
[8] 'Antennas', *RadCom*, March 2002.
[9] *Backyard Antennas*, G3LDO.

# Antennas

**G3LDO explains in detail the use of the three-meter method of impedance measurement**

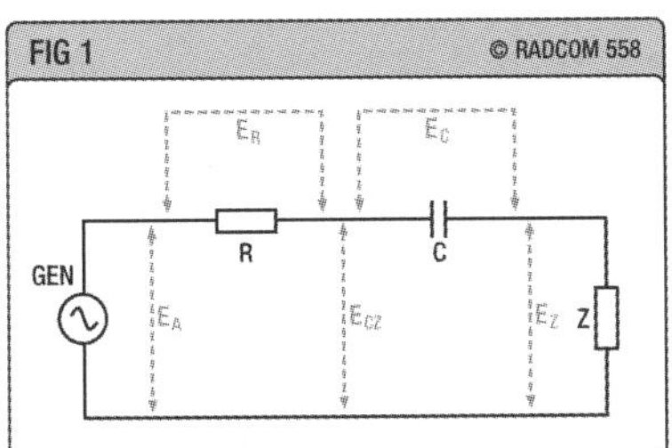


**Fig 1**
**Block diagram of 3M Z bridge showing the voltage measurement points.**

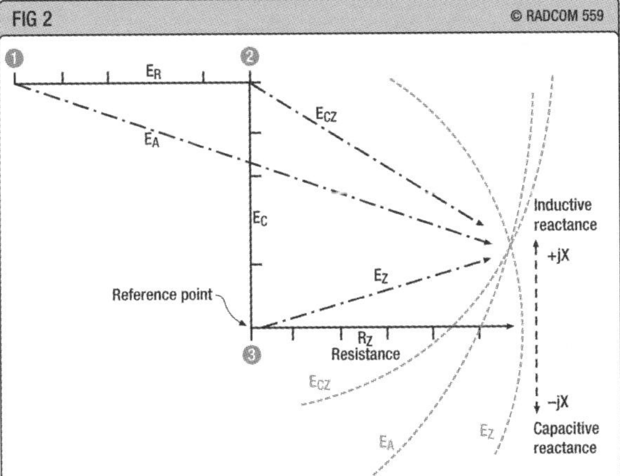


**Fig 2**
**Method of determining impedance from measured voltages.**

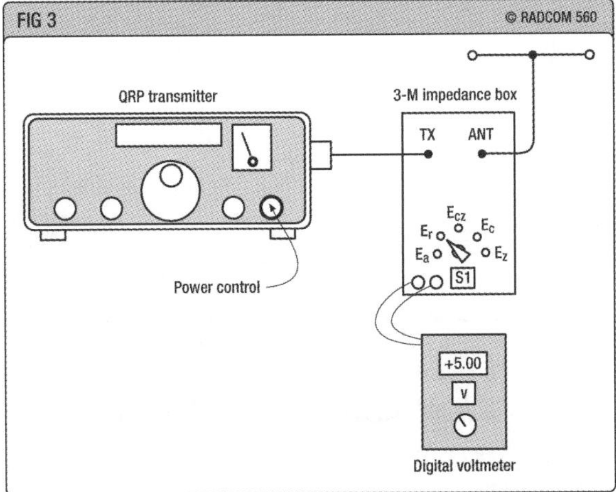


**Fig 3**
**Three-meter test bridge, transmitter and digital voltmeter connections for antenna impedance measurements.**

**My 3M impedance measurement bridge showing its simplicity. This model, built in 1970, is still going strong.**

The discussion on the three-meter impedance instrument and the *BASIC* program for converting the scalar voltage measurements to impedance created much interest. This method of measuring impedance was first described in [1] way back in 1965. I made my first three-meter instrument in 1970 and used it extensively using the prescribed method of converting the voltage readings to impedance with the graphic method described below. At the time, the only instrument for measuring impedance in use by amateurs (those not able to lay their hands on a commercial bridge) was the noise bridge, the design of which, in those days, allowed only the measurement of the resistive component of impedance. The three-meter instrument was also described in *RadCom* in 1987 [2].

I have been asked to give some information on how this method works. This is necessarily brief. The method compares the unknown impedance with a fixed standard impedance and the ratio is indicated by voltmeter readings. The fixed standard impedance comprises a resistor and capacitor as shown in **Fig 1**. Although called the three-meter method in [1], in actual fact two additional readings are required, making five in all. One of the additional readings allows in place calibration of the reference capacitor (line Ec in **Fig 2**) and the second permits several solutions for the unknown impedance, thus giving an indication of the random errors that may be present in the data.

An RF excitation voltage, at the measurement frequency, is applied to Z via R and C. The voltages across R and C are measured, together with the input voltage, Ea, the voltage across Z, and the voltage across Z, plus C. The excitation level is adjusted until Er = 5V, then all the other voltages are measured.

The RF voltages are measured using diode probes, selected by a switch. These probes measure peak volts and require a high impedance voltmeter; a digital voltmeter is ideal. The full circuit was shown in Fig 1 of July 'Antennas'. The impedance value can be derived from the voltage using a graphic method shown in Fig 2. Each voltage is plotted on graph paper using compasses and a ruler. Two of the voltages determine the reference points for the pivot points of the radii of three arcs the lengths of which are proportional to this voltage (vectors). Impedance is identified as the point where the three arcs intersect.

For greatest accuracy, the value of R and the value of C need to be appropriate to the ranges of impedance and frequency of the measurements being made. For example, most measurements are made using 50Ω impedance coaxial cable, on one or more of the amateur bands. R can be 50Ω and C to a reactance of 50Ω. In practice, a reactance value for C of between 25Ω and 100Ω will give reasonable results, although highest accuracy will result if the reactance of C is near to 50Ω.

A low-power transmitter with a variable power output can be used as an excitation source. It is very important that the harmonic output from the excitation source is kept as low as possible; if your results are inconclusive, this may be the cause

An attenuator is used at the input, so the transmitter is isolated from the variations of unknown impedance as the transmitter frequency is varied during a series of measurements.

Power stability of the excitation source is also important ie that Er remains constant while the other parameters are being measured.

**USING THE 3M Z BRIDGE**

Connect the unknown impedance, excitation source and digital voltmeter to the three-meter test bridge as shown in **Fig 3**.

- Set the switch to read Er.
- Set the transmitter to the lowest power level and switch on.
- Increase the power until the voltmeter reads 5V; record this on a note pad as 50.
- Note the voltages at the other switch positions, (12V being recorded as 120 and 6.3V as 63, etc); then check the stability of the transmitter power output by checking position Er again. The readings should be repeated if the excitation level has drifted more than about 0.1V.

The graphic method of extracting impedance from the voltage readings is as follows:

On a sheet of linear graph paper (refer to **Fig 2**) -

- Draw a horizontal line, the length of which is equal to Er.
- Draw a vertical line down from the right-hand side of line Er, the length of which is equal to Ec.
- Place the point of the compasses on (1) and draw an arc, the radius of which is equal to Ea. Repeat (2) and (3) for radius values Ecz and Ez respectively.
- Mark the point at which the arcs intersect. An exact intersection of all three arcs is not always possible due to the errors in the data.

A horizontal line from the reference point to the arc intersection gives the resistive value of impedance. A vertical displacement up or down from the resistive line gives the value of the inductive or capacitive reactance, respectively. If the arcs do not intersect, take the centre of the triangle (known as a cocked hat) formed by the non-intersecting arcs as the impedance point.

A special chart, shown in **Fig 4**, and available in [5], projects the plotted reading directly on to an impedance chart.

**COMPUTER PROGRAMS**

I bought my first computer, a BBC 'A' model (with its 16K of memory!), in 1984. It was obvious that the packaged *BASIC* language was capable of running a program, but I needed help to achieve this. The late Tom Lloyd, G3TML, came to my rescue with a mathematical solution that could be converted into a *BASIC* program and we published the results in *QEX*, in late 1987 [3]. There followed a lot of correspondence in subsequent issues of *QEX*, some pointing out errors and one suggestion that there was a more simple and rigorous solution than the trigonometrical approach. G3TML stuck to the trigonometrical method because it could indicate the inevitable measurement errors. His reasons for doing this are described in [3] and [4].

Later work, described in [5], [7] and [8], used Microsoft *GWBASIC* or *QBASIC* because of their more widespread use. These programs are slightly more complicated because neither supports the inverse sine function.

As a result of my described difficulties with *Excel* ('Antennas', July 2005) many of you sent programs and suggestions of other solutions too numerous to describe here, which I appreciate and found interesting. Dave Roberts, G8KBB, and Dave Murray, G8GTR, sent me *Excel* programs that gave the correct results. G8KBB notes "Attached is an *Excel* spreadsheet that does the same as the *BASIC* program. It is not particularly efficient - I just wanted to show a close correlation to the original. The main changes are to the lines 180 - 210 where I combined slightly and used the Excel IF construct and in the output routines that do not need to convert - you just ask Excel to format the cells appropriately". G8GTR's program contained a graphic similar to that shown in Fig 2.

All *BASIC* programs described in [4] and later were extended to assess errors, similar to placing a mark in the centre of a 'cocked hat' in the graphic method and producing an estimate of the errors. A further program was introduced to modify the data automatically in the event of a non-intersection as shown in **Table 1**. I also found it useful to save batches of measurements to a file so that they could be used to create impedance signatures of antennas as a table or in a graphical form. Impedance measurements of a length of mis-matched feeder is a useful method of impedance bridge calibration as shown in **Fig 5**.

I expect to have more details of the three-meter impedance-measuring method on my website [9] by the time this column appears. It will contain as much source code as I can get together. ♦

**REFERENCES**


[1] 'Measurement of R + jX', D Strandlund, W8CGD, *QST*, June 1965.
[2] 'Measurement of Antenna Resistance and Reactance', J Bazley, G3HCT, *Radio Communication*, June 1987.
[3] 'Measurement of Antenna Impedance', P Dodd, G3LDO & T Lloyd, G3TML, *QEX*, November 1987.
[4] *The Antenna Experimenter's Guide, 1st Edition*, P Dodd, G3LDO.
[5] *The Antenna Experimenter's Guide, 2nd Edition*, P Dodd, G3LDO, available from the RSGB Bookshop.
[6] 'Correspondence', *QEX*, August 1988.
[7] 'Measuring RF Impedance Using the Three-Meter Method and a Computer', P Dodd, G3LDO, *The ARRL Antenna Compendium, Vol 4.*
[8] 'More on the Three-Meter Impedance Measuring Bridge', P Dodd, G3LDO, *The ARRL Antenna Compendium, Vol 5.*
[9] www.g3ldo.co.uk


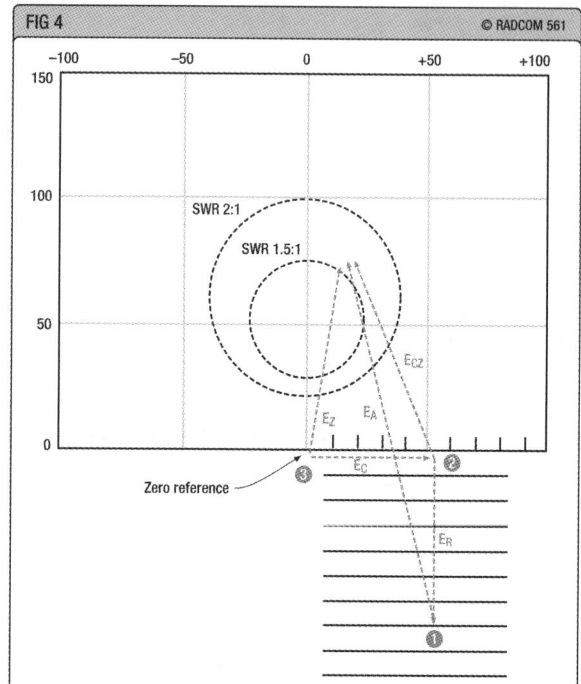


**Fig 4** A special chart allows the voltmeter readings to be plotted reading directly on an impedance chart. A full-size version is included in [5].

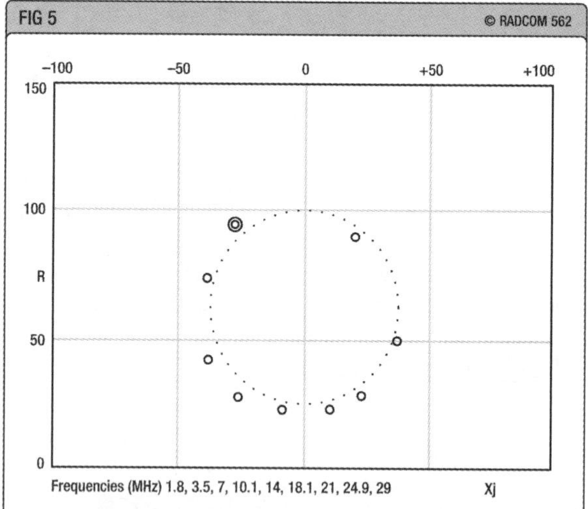


**Fig 5** Graphical measurements of a length of mis-matched feeder is a useful method of impedance bridge calibration

**Table 1** The print-out of a program which automatically modifies data in the event of a non-intersection.

**TABLE 1**

Ez (E) 56

If there is more than one line of data below then the data has been corrected.
Last line indicates corrected data used to determine impedance.

Ea (A) = 98 , Ecz (C) = 45 , Ec (D) = 50 , Ez (E) = 56
Ea (A) = 98 , Ecz (C) = 46 , Ec (D) = 50 , Ez (E) = 56
Ea (A) = 98 , Ecz (C) = 47 , Ec (D) = 50 , Ez (E) = 56
Ea (A) = 98 , Ecz (C) = 48 , Ec (D) = 50 , Ez (E) = 56

Solution
Resistance 46.4
Reactance +38.3

Errors
R = (+/-) 1.6
X = (+/-) 11.7
Go to Main <enu 1. Repeat this program 2. ?

# Antennas

## G3LDO looks at the Gamma Match, and discusses practical examples.

The driven element feed impedance of a multi-element Yagi is usually much lower than that of the coax feed, so some method of matching is required. My favourite beam antenna-to-coax feeder matching method is the gamma match. This is an unbalanced feed system and is well suited to plumber's delight construction, where all the metal parts are electrically and mechanically connected to the boom. The gamma match is popular for amateur arrays, particularly home-made arrangements. However, it is not popular with everyone. G6XN noted in [1] that a large increase in SWR bandwidth can be obtained by going from a gamma match to a balanced system. He went on to say that although no guidelines were available "...the author can do no more than invite the reader to share his misgivings about gamma matches".

I have also read (although not able to find a reference at the time of writing) that the asymmetrical feed causes some distortion of the polar diagram pattern. Perhaps some experimental work is in order. First of all, how does the gamma match work?

As you are aware, the impedance of a half-wave element is low at the centre and increases with distance from the centre. The gamma match comprises a short conductor, which is used to connect the centre of the coax to the correct impedance point along the antenna element. This short conductor has some inductive reactance, which is cancelled by installing a series capacitor, as shown in **Fig 1**.

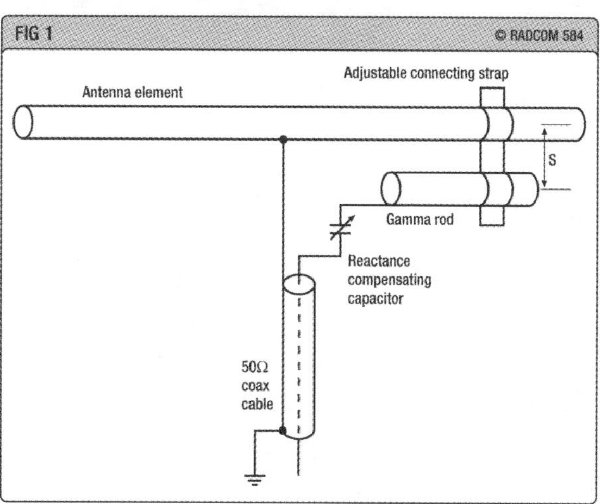


**Fig 1**
**Diagram of the gamma match. With this arrangement, the centre of the driven element does not require an insulator and can be connected directly to a metal boom (plumbers delight construction).**

Because of the many variable factors – driven-element length and diameter, gamma rod length and diameter, spacing between rod and driven element, and value of series capacitors – a number of combinations can provide the desired match. This, in turn, has given the gamma match a bad press regarding ease of adjustment and has resulted in the publication of some convoluted mathematical models and programs.

Taking the variables described above, the following should be considered:

- The feed impedance increases as the gamma rod is made longer and the connection to the element is moved away from the centre.
- The length of the gamma rod can be reduced for a given impedance match as the ratio of antenna element diameter to gamma rod diameter is increased.
- Gamma match adjustment is easier if the element is close to resonance.

It follows that the adjustment is much easier if some method of measuring impedance is to hand. For some years now, the instrument of choice has been the noise bridge. The adjustment has, ideally, to be made with the antenna *in situ*. While noise bridges are small, they require a receiver to detect the null. This problem has been overcome in the past using the receiver in the shack. The noise bridge can be connected to the antenna via the gamma match and the receiver is connected to the noise bridge via the antenna coax feed. The receiver speaker output is fed to the antenna adjustment point via a couple of disconnected leads from the rotator to a small speaker carried aloft for the purpose of listening to the noise null. These days you could use the diminutive FT-817 as a null detector.

There are also these nice little active SWR/impedance meters such as the MFJ-259/269 and the RX Vector Analyst models from Autek Research that make these sorts of measurement much easier.

Most publications recommend that the gamma rod is made from a thin metal tube, the diameter of which is $^1/_3$ to $^1/_6$ of the antenna element diameter. However, it is worth trying what is to hand and it is interesting to see just what you can get away with. For example, the arrangement shown in **Photo 1** uses 14SWG hard-drawn copper wire as the gamma rod to match a 50MHz two-element beam. The connection from the gamma rod to the antenna element is achieved using a hose clamp, which makes it very easy to adjust.

I also made a gamma match for a reference 144MHz dipole, see **Photo 2**, to be used in a series of comparative field strength measurements. The element was made from 14SWG hard-drawn copper wire (my favourite material for making VHF and UHF antennas). In this case, the gamma rod was the same diameter as the element, and a concentric trimmer capacitor was used for gamma rod reactance correction. No difficulties were experienced in obtaining a good match as shown on the MFJ-269 readings in Photo 2.

The traditional method of reactance correction is to use an air-spaced variable capacitor and enclose it in a weatherproof metal box. No matter how weatherproof you make the box,

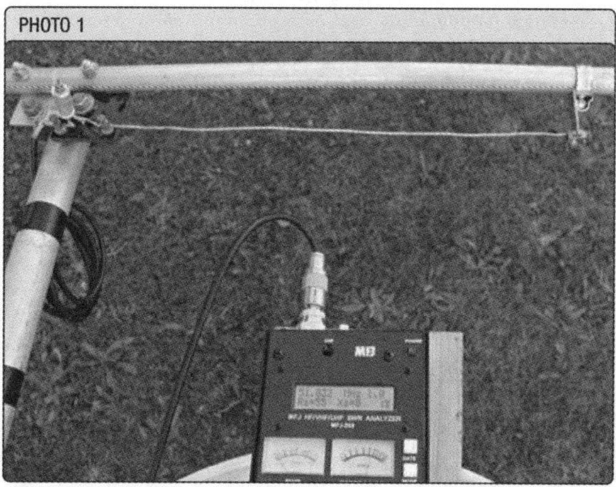


**Photo 1**
**Gamma match on a 50MHz two-element beam using 14SWG copper wire as the gamma rod. Gamma rod reactance is cancelled with a Philips variable trimmer capacitor. Note the low SWR reading on the MFJ.**

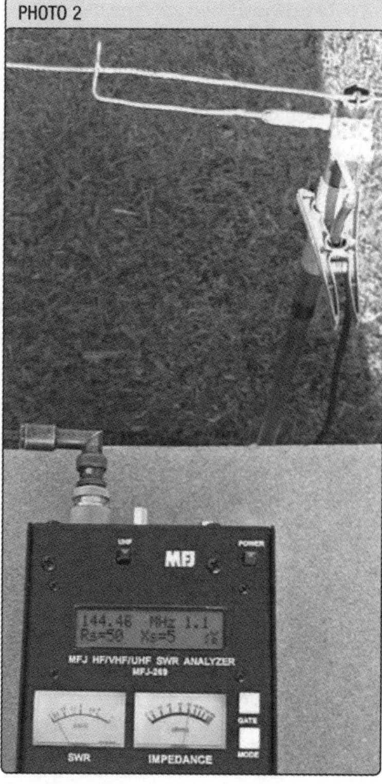


**Photo 2**
**144MHz dipole constructed from 14SWG copper wire and using a gamma rod of the same material. The centre of the dipole element is soldered to the copper tube mast. A concentric ('beehive') trimmer capacitor is used for gamma rod reactance correction.**

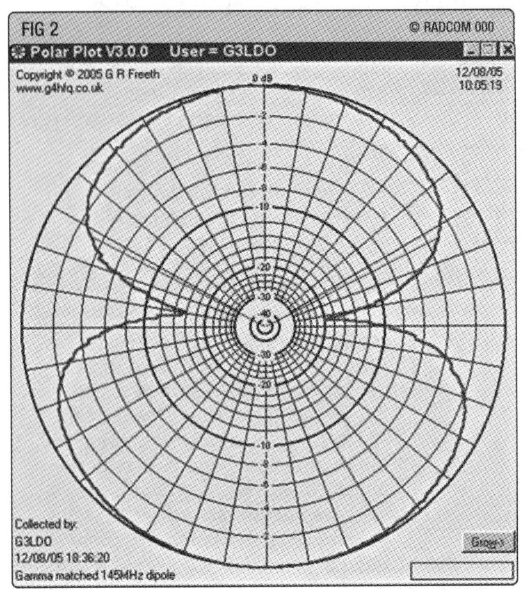


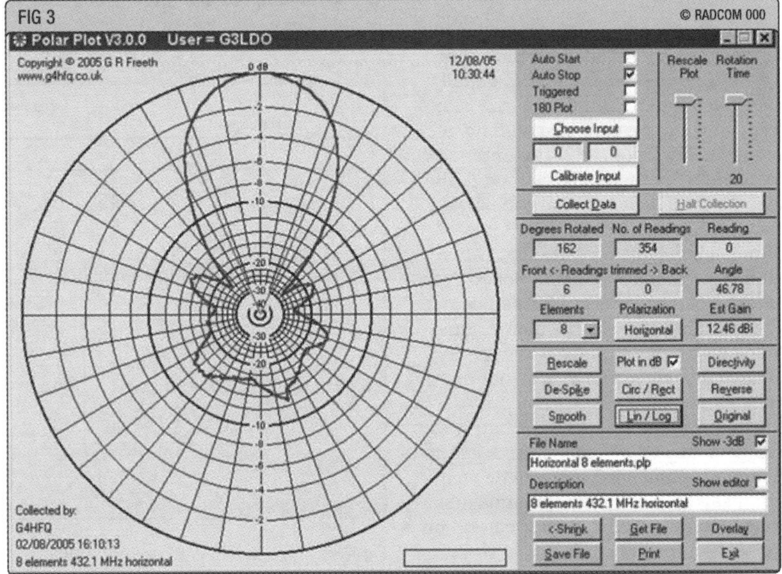


corrosion to the capacitor can still occur because of condensation. This problem can be overcome by using a fixed capacitor whose value is determined by experiment with a variable capacitor. The value of the variable capacitor is then measured and a silver mica (or similar) fixed capacitor (or several series/parallel combinations) substituted. This arrangement will handle 100W without breakdown and only requires a smear of grease to achieve weatherproofing.

All experimental evidence so far has not found that the gamma match causes a reduction of SWR bandwidth compared with other feed methods. SWR bandwidth becomes rather narrow when the element is part of a close-spaced Yagi. SWR bandwidth can be increased by using a larger diameter element.

**POLAR DIAGRAM SYMMETRY.**

In the November 2002 'Antennas', I described a method of plotting a polar diagram of an antenna using a computer and a program called *PolarPlot*, [2] written by Bob Freeth, G4HFQ.

The purpose of this program is to plot the polar diagram of a beam antenna using a signal source, such as a signal generator or QRP transmitter. The variation in signal strength as the antenna is rotated is measured and plotted using a receiver and a computer, using the *PolarPlot* program.

The volume of a beat note, in the SSB or CW mode of a plain un-modulated carrier has good correlation with the RF input level, provided the receiver is operated in a linear manner. The audio output of the receiver is then connected to the line-in socket of the computer's sound card.

In an ideal world measurement of antennas is undertaken using an antenna range, suitably equipped with a full set of laboratory test equipment. For the amateur, though, a more restricted set of equipment must suffice, as described below.

This seemed like a good method of checking to see if the gamma match introduces any asymmetry into a polar diagram. The 2m gamma-matched dipole, shown in Photo 2, was used as the Antenna Under Test (AUT) and energised using a Marconi TF2019A signal generator. The signal was monitored on another dipole located some four wave- lengths distance from the AUT, which in turn was connected to a FT-817.

The result of the plot is shown in **Fig 2**, and shows a degree a symmetry that would be expected using a conventionally-fed dipole.

G4HFQ, aided and abetted by G2HCG, has been experimenting with 430MHz Yagis using what can be best described as a half-folded dipole driven element. The type of feed was described by MW0OPS in [3], based on [4], in a design for a portable 2m VHF Yagi. This rather clever design, which uses a plastic tube as both the boom and element-carrying container, has the most lopsided feed arrangement I have yet to see. However, the polar diagram, shown in **Fig 3**, appears to be as good as any using other feed arrangements.

**MORE ABOUT *PolarPlot***

*PolarPlot* runs on a standard PC that has sound recording capability with a line-in or microphone socket. It has been tested on all flavours of *Windows* running on desktop machines and laptops.

It is now available to radio amateurs free of charge from G4HFQ's website [2].

**Fig 2: Polar diagram of the 144MHz dipole antenna shown in Photo 2.**

**Fig 3: Polar diagram of a multi-element 430MHz Yagi antenna constructed by G4HFQ, using the half-folded dipole driven element described in the text**

The *PolarPlot* relies upon the linearity of the receiving audio system for accuracy of plot and the measurement of gain. Whilst the linearity of the average sound card is generally quite good, the linearity of the receiver depends on how it is operated. At a minimum, the receiver must be capable of controlling the RF gain to such an extent as to be able to negate the operation of AGC.

If you can turn AGC off as well as control the RF gain then this is ideal. The AGC on the FT-817 receiver, used as described above, has several settings for the AGC; one of these is OFF. However the 'S' meter bar still works so I am not convinced that the AGC has been switched out. The RF control is very non-linear; however, with a bit of fiddling the receiver could be made to work in a linear manner.

If the sound card's linearity begins to degrade as the peak input level capability is approached (due to overload protection circuitry) the program can be instructed to treat a lower value on the linear part of the curve as peak input.

To measure the transmitting station's polar diagram, the receiving station's antenna remains stationary and the transmitting station's antenna rotates. To measure the receiving station's polar diagram the transmitting station's antenna remains stationary and the receiving station's antenna rotates. The control panel shown in Fig 3 gives some idea of the range of signal processing and scaling arrangements in the program. ♦

**REFERENCES**

[1] *HF Antennas for all Locations*, L A Moxon, G6XN.
[2] www.g4hfq.co.uk
[3] 'Antennas', *RadCom*, March 2005
[4] www.clarc.org

# Antennas

**Using the multiband doublet, centre-fed via a slotted-line and simple ATU ♦ *Excel* yields some of its secrets**

Earlier on this year, I volunteered support of an amateur radio station for the East Preston Festival. This entailed setting up an HF station and providing a temporary multiband HF antenna. My antenna of choice was the multiband doublet which, to my mind, provides the most flexible and practical solution. The main advantage of this antenna is that the doublet length is not at all critical, a major advantage when planning an antenna for a location that you have never seen. In practice, it seems that a 20m centre fed length works very well for all bands all HF bands 40m to 10m.

The antenna is best supported at the centre where the radiation is the greatest. Telescopic fibreglass poles are available, which were originally made for fishermen and (I think) called roach poles. These poles are very light and the one I used is called a Kenley Popular Telepole. It weighs only 500g and is only 1.2m long when telescoped and will open to a 6m long tapered pole when fully extended. (I took the top section out of mine because it was too thin and flexible, so it is probably now only 5m long when extended).

I used plastic clothes pegs as end insulators with holes drilled in them to fix the ends of the elements. The pegs also double as clips for fixing the ends of the antennas to small branches of trees or any other suitable fixture. The performance of the antenna is improved by placing it as high as possible such as on the roof of a building.

The doublet can be made from 2mm plastic covered insulated wire fed in the centre, using 300Ω slotted-line feeder. The centre insulator on my antenna comprises a terminal block using screw connectors. This is fixed to the top of the support pole with plastic tape as shown in the photograph.

You might ask why not use coaxial cable as used in most centre-fed antenna arrangements? The answer is that slotted-line is very convenient for running through gaps in doors or windows that might be encountered in a location not seen before. I would recommend using the black 300Ω slotted-line feeder rather than the lightweight clear plastic 300Ω line.

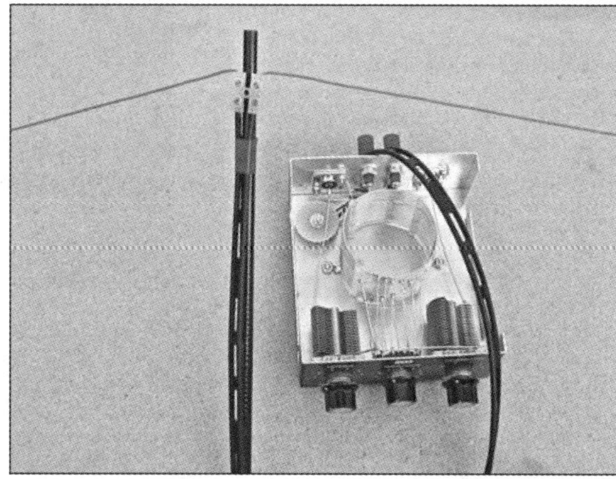

**Construction of the portable multi-band doublet, and the method of feeding usimg the MFJ-901B**

An essential item, when using such an antenna, is a suitable ATU with provision for feeding a balanced antenna. Originally I tried to make a small ATU that would handle 100W but found obtaining just the right sized components rather expensive and difficult to locate. I then found at [1] a suitably small moderately priced unit, the MFJ-901B, which is quite small (135 x 150 x 60mm) and weighs only 600g. As you can see from the photograph, in spite of its small size, it uses a large low-loss air-spaced inductor. The ATU is an unbalanced T-network and requires a balun to provide the necessary balance to feed this antenna. This balun can be seen in the top left hand side of the ATU and is a mere 25mm OD toroid and really does not look man enough for the job. Furthermore, this method of feeding balanced lines is not regarded with favour by some authorities.

In 2003 I operated from Marrakech as CN2PD [2]. I used the antenna and ATU described above and, after working through a pileup for over two hours, found that the balun was just slightly above ambient temperature so it obviously was not that inefficient.

#### HOW I LEARNED TO LOVE EXCEL

I briefly mentioned the amateur radio station for the East Preston Festival, which was to demonstrate amateur radio and was organised by Frank James, G0LOF. The venue for this event was the East Preston Conservative Hall.

After the amateur radio demonstration was over, the Conservative Hall, normally used for events such as flower arranging, keep fit classes or meetings of the various residents' associations, was transformed into what looked like mission control at Houston. Around 18 computers (plus an instructor's computer complete with a large projection screen) were all linked together via Ethernet to broadband Internet. This was the weekly meeting of the East Preston Silver Surfers Computer Club, also organised by Frank.

The reason for the strange title of this club is that a condition of membership is that you have to be over 55 years of age. In due course, the members showed up, mostly sporting a flash memory necklace containing homework or other bits of software.

The club runs courses mainly on applications and, for the last three weeks, the subject has been *Excel*, the very application I was having difficulties with, described in the July 'Antennas'. I now have a much greater understanding of *Excel* but am not yet at the stage where I could write a program to convert the 3-meter voltage readings into impedance... ♦

#### REFERENCES


[1] Obtainable from Waters & Stanton PLC, Tel: 01702 206 835.

[2] 'One-Man Holiday DXpeditions', *RadCom* July 2004.

# Antennas

**This month, Peter looks at the practical use of the tunable RF current meter, and explains why you needn't be too concerned that every metallic object in the house appears to be radiating!**

In a recent letter in 'The Last Word', Peter Ball, G3HQT, described how he had built the Tunable Magnetic Field Strength Meter, as described in *The Antenna Experimenter's Guide*.

By using this meter, he discovered that not only was there RF current on the antenna elements, but also on the outside of the coax feed. He also found RF current on the support post, leads from the transmitter, TV aerial, mains wiring, water pipes, the hot (water) tank, gas pipes, the sink draining board – in fact, every metallic object around the house. As the antenna appeared to be working OK he asked if he should worry about it.

This really emphasises the actual situation regarding an amateur radio antenna installation. Because many garden plots are small, much of the electrical and plumbing hardware is within the near field of the antenna. As long as the currents in these metal objects are relatively small compared to the current flowing in the antenna elements then they should not have much effect. If any one of the currents is much higher, due perhaps to the metal object being close to the resonant frequency of operation, then this might be cause some disturbance of antenna performance. Current may be flowing in telephone and power lines as well. All of these RF currents may have an influence on antenna patterns, or can be of significance in the case of RFI.

### TUNABLE CURRENT METER

The tunable current meter is simply a tuned circuit with a diode detector and a meter. This useful little instrument is truly a junk-box project where the main components can be salvaged from an old transistor radio. The main component is the variable air-spaced capacitor from an older transistor radio. The other component is the ferrite rod. The original windings are removed from the rod, although the cardboard coil former can be retained.

The instrument is built into an aluminium box. Any non-ferrous metal is suitable provided it shields the detector circuit from the electric field of the electromagnetic wave and does not impede the magnetic component of the wave. A slot is cut with a hacksaw across the top and filed smooth with a thin file. This slot is needed to prevent the box acting as a shorted turn.

The ferrite rod is supported by rubber grommets fitted in holes in the metal enclosure at the ends of the slot. This slot must be cut with a hacksaw from the front to the back of the box, and a thin file may be used to smooth the cut.

By chance, I had recently modified my tunable current meter described in *The Antenna Experimenter's Guide*. The original used 12 turns of thin insulated wire, wound on the ferrite rod and tapped four turns from the earthed end. This gave a frequency range of 5 – 18MHz when tuned with a 250pF (value guessed at) capacitor.

I needed a greater frequency coverage, so some sort of band-switching was necessary. The circuit shown in **Fig 1** is based on the design found in all recent editions of the *ARRL Antenna Book*. The coil windings and expected frequency coverage, when C1 is 140pF, are as follows.

- L1 30 turns, tapped 3 turns from earthed end. (1 to 8.5 MHz)
- L2 8 turns, tapped at 2 turns from earthed end. (5 to 20 MHz)
- L3 2 turns, tapped at 1 turn. (17 to 39MHz)

A larger value of C1, that might be found in an old transistor radio, will give a greater frequency range on each band. The characteristics of the ferrite rod will vary from one transistor radio to another and this will affect the frequency range.

### USING THE PROBE

The instrument is very useful for checking the current distribution in antenna elements. In measuring the current in a conductor, the ferrite rod should be kept at right angles to the conductor, and at a constant distance from it. It is also useful for measuring RF ground currents in radial systems. A buried radial may be located easily by sweeping the ground. Current division at junctions may be investigated. Areas of high current in existing radials may indicate where additional radials might be effective.

Stray currents in conductors not intended to be part of the antenna system can be investigated. As stated earlier it is not unusual to find RF currents in all metal structures and services around the house and most of these cannot be avoided. If you come across a conductor that is radiating a higher-than-average current, it may be possible to reduce the current by bonding or changing the physical length. I have even used this method for detecting electrical wiring and plumbing pipes embedded in the wall before drilling holes to put up a shelf, although I must warn that the technique may not be infallible. ♦

**The tunable current meter being used to measure the current in a buried radial. This instrument is built in a 100mm x 100mm x 65mm aluminium box. The tuning control and indicator is calibrated with just some of the amateur frequency bands.**

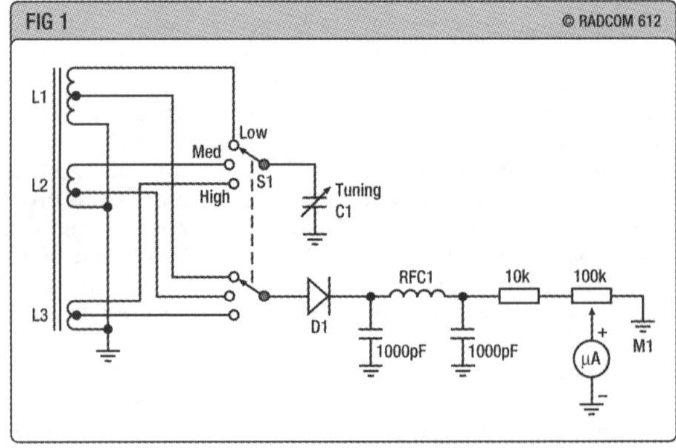


**Fig 1**
**Circuit diagram of the Tunable Magnetic Meter.**

# Feeding doublets

*This month, G3LDO looks at losses on twin-line and coaxial feeders.*

In 'Antennas', November 2005, I recommended the multiband doublet as the most flexible and practical solution for a portable antenna. The main advantage of this antenna is that the doublet length is not at all critical, a major advantage when planning an antenna for a location that you have never seen. I also noted that a 20m centre-fed length, supported in the centre using a collapsible telescopic fibreglass pole, worked very well for all bands 40m to 10m.

I suggested that the antenna be fed with black 300  slotted line twin feeder, on the grounds that it is very convenient for running through gaps in doors or windows that might be encountered in a location not seen before.

**FEEDER LINE LOSSES.** I received an e-mail from Brian Austin, G0GSF, commenting on this antenna and its feed arrangement. He says: "There's a much more important reason not to use coax and that's the very high SWR (easily > 10:1) likely to occur at some frequencies (which ones will depend on the antenna length). With coax, the increased line loss, over an above its inherent loss/m, can be very significant and will soon turn the transmitted signal into QRP or even QRPP, depending on what you started out with! Likewise, the receiver will sound very flat on those bands. By contrast, slotted line has a considerably lower intrinsic loss and a higher characteristic impedance than coax. The end result is that the SWR excursions tend to be smaller (because of the higher $Z_0$) and the increased loss due to the inevitable mismatch on some frequencies will be a lot less too.

"My 23m inverted-V, which is fed with 300  slotted line, is very poor on 80m. The receiver sounds as if there's 10dB of attenuation permanently in circuit; which there is because the feed-point resistance of the antenna is so low and the SWR so high that even the 'low-loss' line becomes increasingly lossy on that band and is made worse the longer the feed-line.

"So low-loss line is mandatory if the matching network sits at the transmitter end, which is where it usually is."

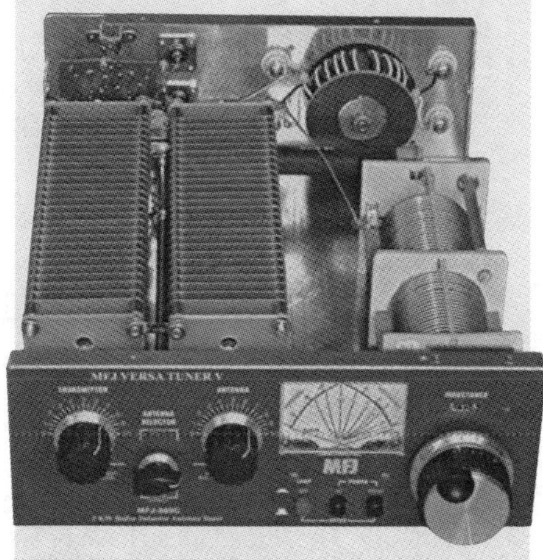

THE MFJ-989C HIGH-PASS T-NETWORK TUNER WITH A FERRITE-CORED BALUN FOR A TWIN FEEDER.

I was aware of the greater losses caused by using coax cable rather than slotted-line twin feeder and described a problem I had with a multiband doublet in [1]. This also referred to losses caused by SWR graphs in G3SEK's 'In Practice' column [2], which graphically illustrated this. I also described how replacing the existing 25m of coax cable with 450  ladder line made a significant predictable improvement to the higher HF band performance of my centre-fed multiband antenna.

However, I didn't think that the SWR problem would be significant when using a portable HF antenna with a short length of feeder (say 5m) and decided to use available software to make a few calculations. The centre feed impedance of the antenna was calculated using *EZNEC4*. The feeder losses were then calculated using *TLW* (*Transmission Line Calculator for* Windows) available on a CD with *The ARRL Antenna Handbook* [3].

My portable antenna was examined first, comparing 5m of RG-58 (taking the view that lightweight coax would be used on a portable antenna) and comparing it with 450  slotted twin feeder. Actually 300  slotted line was used with my portable antenna, but it is not included in the library of feeders in *TLW* and 400  was the nearest I could get. The results are shown in **Table 1**. The SWRs column represents the calculated SWRs at the antenna and at the ATU respectively, 11/9 for example. You can see that the greater the transmission line loss the greater the difference between these two SWR figures. Using slotted line, even on a short 5m length, gives an average increase on all bands of over 3dB in antenna gain compared to using coax.

If we now look at a more permanent installation of, say, a 22m inverted-V antenna fed with 15m, which is similar to

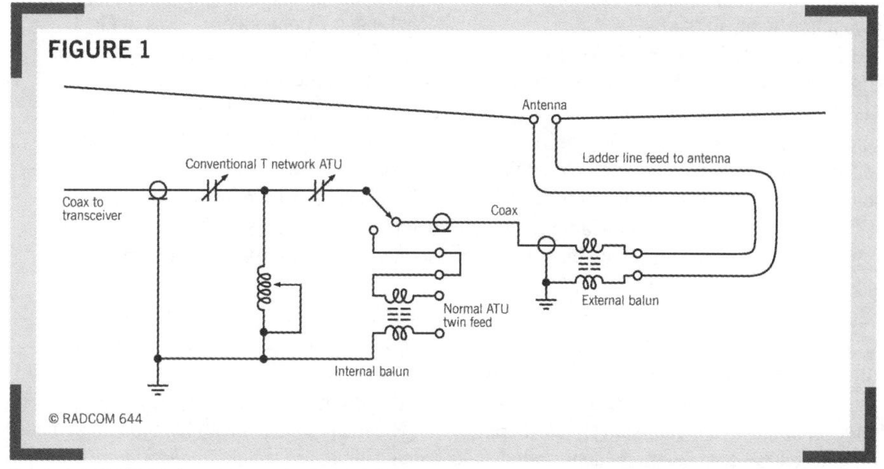


FIG 1: A CONVENTIONAL HIGH-PASS T-NETWORK TUNER WITH A BALUN FOR CONNECTING TO A TWIN FEEDER. WITH THIS 'COMUDIPOLE' ARRANGEMENT, THE INTERNAL BALUN CAN BE BYPASSED AND A SEPARATE BALUN PLACED OUTSIDE THE SHACK AND CONNECTED VIA A SHORT LENGTH OF COAX.

**TABLE 1**

Calculated losses on 5m of transmission line feeding a 22m-long inverted-V, comparing RG-58 with 450 slotted line.

| Band MHz | Centre Z R | ± j | RG-58 SWRs | RG-58 Loss dB | 450 slotted line SWRs | 450 slotted line Loss dB |
|---|---|---|---|---|---|---|
| 7.0 | 101 | +205 | 11/9 | 0.18 | 5.1/5 | 0.024 |
| 10.1 | 700 | +365 | 69/29 | 2.9 | 8.8/8.7 | 0.027 |
| 14.2 | 828 | -1820 | 94/30 | 5.5 | 12.3/12 | 0.123 |
| 18.1 | 107 | -264 | 15/11 | 1.8 | 5.46/5.41 | 0.066 |
| 21.2 | 200 | +488 | 16/29 | 2.8 | 5.28/5.22 | 0.051 |
| 25.0 | 1329 | +688 | 79/23 | 5.4 | 9.77/9.52 | 0.121 |
| 28.5 | 298 | -880 | 56/20 | 4.35 | 8.37/8.18 | 0.099 |

**TABLE 2**

Calculated losses on 15m of transmission line feeding a 22m-long inverted-V, comparing RG-213 with 450 slotted line. *The impedance at the ATU was 4.0 +j40 as calculated using TLW.

| Band MHz | Centre Z R | ± j | RG-58 SWRs | RG-58 Loss dB | 450 slotted line SWRs | 450 slotted line Loss dB |
|---|---|---|---|---|---|---|
| 3.6 | 12 | -810* | 600/44 | 14 | 148/106 | 2.1 |
| 7.0 | 101 | +205 | 11/8 | 1.2 | 5.1/5.0 | 0.065 |
| 10.1 | 700 | +365 | 68/19 | 5.5 | 8.8/8.4 | 0.162 |
| 14.2 | 828 | -1820 | 95/18 | 7.0 | 12/11.5 | 0.324 |
| 18.1 | 107 | -264 | 15/8 | 2.7 | 4.46/5.28 | 0.155 |
| 21.2 | 200 | +488 | 28/11 | 4.0 | 5.28/5.1 | 0.15 |
| 25.0 | 3829 | +688 | 79/13 | 7.8 | 9.77/7.88 | 0.34 |
| 28.5 | 298 | -880 | 72/12 | 6.7 | 8.3/7.8 | 0.30 |

**TABLE 3**

Calculated losses on 15m of coax feed to a G5RV antenna, comparing RG-213 and RG-58. The impedances have been calculated at the point were the coax feeder is connected to the twin tuned line.

| Band MHz | R ± j, tuned line end | | RG 213 SWRs | RG 213 Loss dB | RG58 SWRs | RG58 Loss dB |
|---|---|---|---|---|---|---|
| 3.6 | 25 | +260 | 64/27 | 3.1 | 64/21 | 3.4 |
| 7.0 | 202 | -444 | 24/14 | 2.3 | 24/10.8 | 3.7 |
| 10.1 | 337 | +966 | 65/19 | 5.2 | 65/13 | 6.2 |
| 14.2 | 104 | -4 | 2.1/1.9 | 0.6 | 2.1/1.8 | 0.8 |
| 18.1 | 322 | -706 | 37/12.8 | 4.8 | 37/9.5 | 5.8 |
| 21.2 | 235 | -684 | 44/12.8 | 5.3 | 44/9.3 | 6.9 |
| 25.0 | 177 | -131 | 5.5/4.2 | 1.4 | 5.5/3.7 | 1.9 |
| 28.5 | 1233 | -1215 | 49/11.6 | 6.1 | 49/8.5 | 7.6 |

the G0GSF's antenna, how do the transmission line losses compare? Using the transmission line shown in **Table 2**, we can expect an average increase in gain of around 5 or 6dB using slotted line rather than good quality RG-213. G0GSF noted that on 80m "The receiver sounds as if there's 10dB of attenuation permanently in circuit". From Table 2 the calculated value of the slotted line loss is just over 2dB, which isn't a high enough loss to be that noticeable on short skip 80m contacts. There could be another reason for the poor performance.

While the efficiency of an electrically quarter-wave short dipole is quite reasonable, being only about 1dB down on a full half-wave, the feed impedance is very low. In the example shown in Table 2 the reflected impedance at the ATU, for our 22m antenna with 15m of slotted line feeder, is 4.0 +j40 .

Very low impedances can be matched using the conventional high-pass T-network tuner, but settings are rather critical and the losses are very high. According to the ATU section of *TLW*, the losses are in the region of 5dB. The problem is made worse by the 4:1 impedance step-up balun at the output. According to *TLW*, a low-pass L-network is required to match this very low impedance to 50 . The problem can be avoided altogether by avoiding low impedance antennas where possible – this is achieved in practice by using a doublet that approximates a half-wavelength on the lowest frequency in use.

LOSSES ON THE G5RV ANTENNA. The G5RV antenna, which uses a section of twin-line transmission line as tuned line, normally uses a length of coax from the bottom of the transmission line to the shack. So how efficient is this arrangement?

The calculations, shown in **Table 3**, indicate that losses can be quite high on most bands, with the exception of 20 and 12m. These results also indicate that an ATU is essential if a G5RV is used as a multiband antenna. The figures in the SWR column again show the SWRs at the antenna and the ATU respectively. Note that the thin RG-58 coax, with its higher losses, gives a lower SWR at the ATU when compared with the better quality RG-213. It follows that if you have a nice low SWR measured in the shack *on all bands* there might be something wrong with the coax between the rig and the antenna.

A PRACTICAL METHOD OF USING TWIN FEEDER. Most commercial ATUs use a high-pass T-network as shown in **Fig 1**. Most of these tuners can be used with twin feeders by using an internal balun at the output of the tuner as shown in Fig 1, although this method of feeding twin lines is not regarded with favour by some authorities [4]. However, as mentioned in [5], I have used the small MFJ-901B with a 20m long doublet and a twin feed. The balun in this ATU is mere 25mm OD toroid and its temperature rose to just slightly above ambient temperature after several hours of 100W CW contest-type operation on various bands, so it is obviously not that inefficient.

The main problem with twin feeder can be routing it into the shack. The feeder must not be allowed to come in close contact with metal objects or bundled together with other feeders or conductors. A solution was described by PA2ABV [6] in which the balun, normally located inside the ATU, is placed in such a position that there is an RF obstacle-free path between it and the antenna. The ATU is connected to the balun with a short length of coax cable as shown in Fig 1. Such an arrangement was called the 'Comudipole'. The internal balun can be removed from the ATU and used externally or a separate balun can be constructed, which is very simple, see [7]. A balun wound on a T200 ferrite toroid can be waterproofed by simply smearing it in grease.

PA0SE describes a balun constructed with coax cable on a coil former [7], which is claimed to have a better performance over ferrite-cored baluns when handling the highly reactive impedances seen in Tables 1 and 2.

REFERENCES

[1] Antennas, *RadCom* September 2002.
[2] 'Losses from High SWR', G3SEK, 'In Practice' *RadCom*, March 2002.
[3] '*TLW* Transmission Line Program for *Windows*', by N6BV, The *ARRL Antenna Book*, 19th edition.
[4] *HF Antennas for all Locations*, L A Moxon, G6XN, 1984 edition, p54.
[5] 'Antennas', *RadCom* November 2005.
[6] *Electron*, December 1992, reported in 'Technical Topics' *RadCom*, July 1984.
[7] *Backyard Antennas*, G3LDO, RSGB.

# Balancing act

*Last month's column showed how feeder losses could be reduced considerably when twin line feeder was used rather than coax as tuned feeder fed multiband doublet. No other aspect of using twin line feeder was considered. Following on...*

THE MFJ-947 BALANCED TUNER. THE CHOKE BALUN AT THE INPUT, ON THE RIGHT, COMPRISES 50 FERRITE RINGS ON A LENGTH OF TEFLON RG-303. THE GANGED SETTING OF THE TWIN-T CAPACITORS IS ACHIEVED USING INSULATED GEARS, SHOWN ON THE LEFT. (SOURCE: MFJ)

A QUESTION OF BALANCE. By chance, in the same *RadCom*, GM3SEK's 'In Practice' noted that there was a widespread belief that twin-wire feed-line means balanced feed-line which, in turn, implies the antenna is balanced, which is rarely the case. By 'balanced' we mean that the transmitted power in each conductor of the feeder is equal and the current distribution over the whole length of the antenna is symmetrical.

In the earlier days of amateur radio, twin-wire feeder was the only practical feeder available and the design of the feed methods was influenced by commercial radio practice. Rugby, for example had a huge antenna farm of broadside arrays (later replaced by rhombics) on a several-hundred acre site. Some of these lines had to be as long as 1.5km, so they had to be good. Each twin wire line consisted of copper conductors, with one conductor placed 23cm from the other and supported 5m above ground. The supports consisted of wooden telephone-type poles with low capacity insulators and the feed-line conductors were under tension so did not require spacers.

With some 60 or 70 antennas, the feed-line system was somewhat complicated. On the main routes, the feeders were arranged fairly close together. It can be appreciated that such an arrangement requires that the feed-lines should be well balanced (equal RF current in each conductor) to prevent radiation loss and cross-talk (mutual interference between sets of lines). Using Rugby as an example is an extreme case, but the same problems affected smaller commercial and military point-to-point systems.

In a previous 'Antennas' [1], I described an instrument for measuring the current component of SWR on twin-line feeders. This instrument was described in [2] as part of a procedure for matching a long transmission line into a multi-dipole array. Although I didn't mention it at the time (because it wasn't relevant to the discussion), it had an interesting comment on transmission line balance.

"At this point (when the initial SWR measurements had been performed) it is advisable to change the ammeter over to the other conductor and verify that the currents along both lines are equal and that the maxima and minima are in the same positions on each line. If this is not so, the line and input termination should be examined with a view to the elimination of any out-of-balance effects, as it is hopeless to attempt to match an unbalanced line". (Stub matching being the method under discussion).

Even with the most symmetrical of layouts it is rare that the antenna system will be balanced and, as indicated above, the out-of-balance effects can be eliminated. How can this is be done and is it important in an amateur installation?

A BIT OF AMATEUR HISTORY. In early amateur transmitters, the twin feeder was connected to the transmitter output as shown in **Fig 1** [3]. There was often provision for balancing the transmission line currents, by adjusting coil tappings or capacitor values. Most of the ARRL antenna books I possess mention using two ammeters to check balance, but don't seem to attach much importance to it. Most of the interest in the earlier publications was focused on using the 'tuner unit' to reduce the level of harmonics produced by class-C power amplifiers as well as providing matching to the transmission line.

Balanced-feed antenna systems in amateur installations fell out of favour for many years because coaxial cable became cheap and plentiful and being so much more convenient when it came to routing a feeder to the antenna, particularly a rotary beam antenna. The $\pi$–tank PA circuit was able to cope with the range of impedances presented to the transmitter output by multiband antennas, such as the G5RV, in the pre-WARC days.

The advent of the solid state PA transmitter created a greater need for an ATU. Because modern solid-state transceivers include built-in low-pass filtering tailored to the individual bands, the requirement for the harmonic attenuation, previously provided by the ATU, is not as great.

This opened the way for much greater use of the T-network, which can provide an acceptably wide range of impedance transformations without a requirement for large-value variable capacitors. The price for this flexibility is that it can be quite lossy

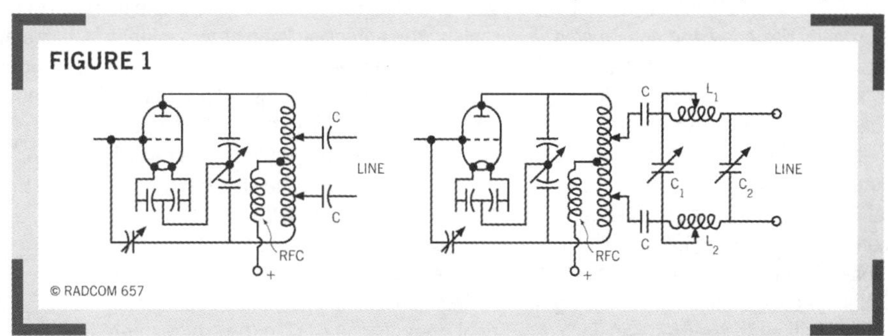


FIG 1: METHODS OF COUPLING A TRANSMITTER PA TO TWIN FEEDER. THE COIL TAPPING POINTS PROVIDE MATCHING AND BALANCE ADJUSTMENT. CAPACITORS C PROVIDE ISOLATION. (SOURCE: *THE RADIO AMATEUR'S HANDBOOK*, 1947 EDITION (ARRL)).

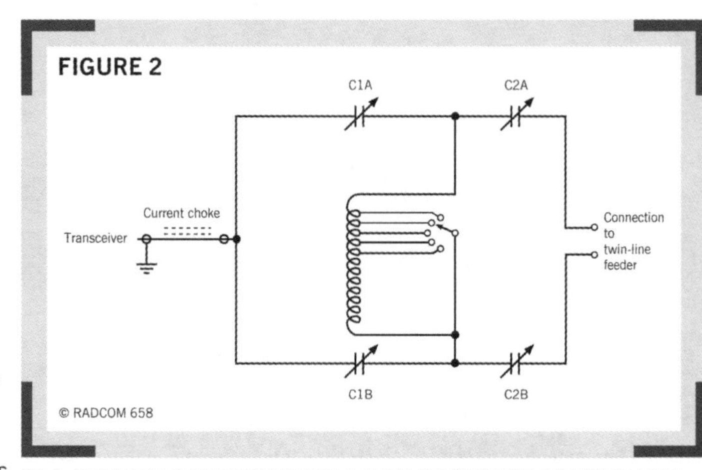


FIG 2: SIMPLIFIED CIRCUIT OF THE MFJ-947 BALANCED TUNER CIRCUIT. C1A/C1B ARE GANGED, AS ARE C2A/C2B.

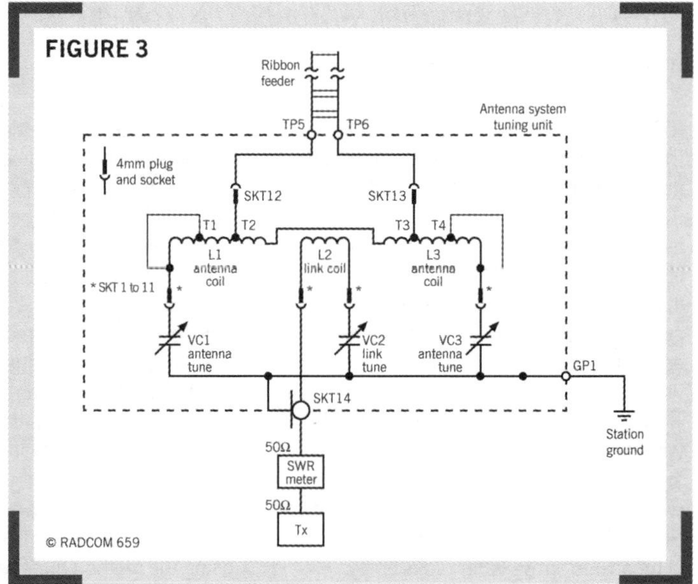


FIG 3: THE G0LMJ BALANCED-LINE FEEDER ATU. THIS USES PLUG-IN COILS, ONE FOR EACH BAND, WITH PROVISION FOR ADJUSTING THE COIL TAPS. A DUAL RF CURRENT METER IS USED TO MEASURE BALANCE AND MAXIMUM OUTPUT.

compared to other network types, particularly at the lower frequencies, whenever the load impedance is low. The T-match ATU has enjoyed considerable popularity in the USA, being described as the 'Transmatch'.

BACK TO THE BALANCED ATU. While the T-match, or Transmatch' has been the circuit of choice for most commercial ATUs (and quite a few home-made ones [4, 5]) over the last few years, it is an unbalanced or single-ended arrangement for coax cable transmission line.

Most of these units are fitted with a balun at the output so that they can be used to connect to twin-line feeder as shown in Fig 1 of [6]. However, this method is not approved by some authorities on the grounds that the ferrite core of such a balun would be saturated under some power and impedance values. The place for the balun is said to be at the input to the ATU, where the impedance value is near to 50Ω. The down side of this arrangement is that the variable inductance and capacitances have to be floated from the metal chassis of the ATU.

Nevertheless, because there has been a resurgence of interest in matching twin-line feeders to the transceiver, some manufacturers have produced the 'Balanced-Line ATU'. The most interesting is the MFJ-747 and the MFJ-976 [7]. These ATUs use a balanced T-network with a current choke at the input as shown in the photograph and **Fig 2**. The capacitors used on each side of the balanced-T are ganged together to maintain the balance when tuning.

The solution adopted by Linear Amp UK, as used in their 'True Balanced Line Antenna Tuner', appears to be a high-power version of the once-popular Z-match.

But are these arrangements truly balanced? According to W4RNL [8], nothing beats a properly designed and constructed link-coupled ATU for the most efficient transfer of power from a transmitter to twin-line feeder. The only two such commercial ATUs that were ever produced (many years ago) were the Johnson Matchbox and the Annecke. More recently is an interesting home constructed ATU by G0LMJ, which uses a link-coupled arrangement using plug-in coils, one for each band as shown in **Fig 3**. This design allows the currents in each of the conductors of the twin feeder to be equalised (balanced). For a full description of these ATUs see [5, 9].

IS TWIN LINE BALANCE IMPORTANT? Earlier, I described the need for balanced currents in the conductors of twin-line feeder in a situation where the feed-lines are very long. In the case of an amateur suburban environment the feeder length is relatively short, so how important is twin feeder balance in this situation?

In a previous 'Antennas' column [10], I used the computer simulation program *EZNEC* to model the effect of deliberately introducing unbalance into twin-line feeder connected to a doublet. The model showed that not only were the amplitudes of the currents on the feeder unequal, but that the phases of the feeder currents were not at 180° to each other. Also, the amplitudes and phases on each leg of the doublet itself were also unequal. In this situation, there is a degree of radiation from an unbalanced antenna transmission line.

It turned out that this can, in some cases, enhance the performance of the doublet antenna in the small suburban garden. This occurs because of the small amount of vertically-polarised radiation from the twin feeder. This, (according to the model) causes some reduction in vertical gain and a slight increase in low-angle gain, making the antenna slightly more suitable for DX. The degree of unbalance in this case was not very great, having calculated current ratios of 1.3A and 1.6A on each of the feeders lines respectively. The model implied that the antenna characteristics can be changed by altering the degree of current unbalance in the feeders, but I know of no-one who has ever noticed this effect.

Because an unbalanced line radiates right down to the ATU in the shack, there is a chance of possible BCI and TVI problems if the unbalance is high. Because of the reciprocal nature of antennas, the transmission line has the increasing risk of electrical QRM or a reduced signal-to-noise ratio on receive.

To conclude: I personally have not found using the popular T-match ATU with the balun at the output a problem on transmit, provided that the antenna feeder does not present a low impedance at the ATU on any band. In practice, this entails making the antenna near to half a wavelength long on the lowest frequency bands. I have yet to try an arrangement that has provision for balancing the currents on twin feeder. It would be interesting to see if it would reduce local electrical noise at this QTH.

REFERENCES.


[1] Antennas, RadCom, June 2005.
[2] RAF Signal Manual, Air Publications 1093, 1945.
[3] The ARRL The Radio Amateur's Handbook, 1947 edition.
[4] 'A General-Purpose Antenna Tuning Unit', M J Grierson, G3TSO, Radio Communication, January 1987.
[5] Backyard Antennas, G3LDO.
[6] 'Antennas', RadCom, January 2006.
[7] www.wsplc.com
[8] www.cebik.com
[9] 'A Balanced-Line ASTU', Ted Garrott, G0LMJ, RadCom July/August 1998.
[10] 'Antennas', RadCom, March 2004.

# Off-centre feeds

*Is the off-centre-fed dipole the solution to your problems?*

In the February 'Antennas', I discussed the pros and cons of a balanced feed and balanced antennas. This subject was also discussed previously in [1], noting that it is probable that the strictly balanced case derived from commercial practice where relative power was high and a small degree of unbalance resulted in high RF levels at the operating position. It could also result in power loss on long transmission-line lengths. With lower power amateur transmissions, some transmission-line unbalance may not be a problem, and there is a chance that it could be beneficial, provided the transceiver is not located a long way from the antenna. Also in [1], I described the he MORCS antenna, which comprises a 66ft (20m) folded dipole with the conventional centre break in the lower wire. However, instead of being fed at this break point it is fed halfway along one leg of the doublet.

The unbalanced nature of this antenna seemed to work well for MORCS. He noted: "A number of attempts at modifying existing designs failed to produce the desired performance until I evolved what I now refer to as the 'DOC66'.

**OFF-CENTRE-FED ANTENNAS.** It turns out that there is a lot more interest in the off-centre-fed antennas than I originally thought, and they have been the subject of much correspondence. Writing in [2], Roy O. Hill, Jr, W4PID, noted: "Thirty or 40 years ago, it was more or less generally accepted that the impedance of a half-wave antenna was about 4kΩ at the ends, about 72Ω at the centre, and that the impedance along the antenna could be accurately represented by a straight line on semi-log graph paper. Using these premises, I plotted the impedance along a half-wave 3.5MHz antenna on the graph of **Fig 1**. Then I added 7.0MHz and 14.0MHz plots for the same antenna.

"All three lines cross at two points at about the 280Ω impedance mark. These two points are $^1/_3$ of the way (within 0.1 percentage point as I measure it) from the ends of the antenna. The antenna can be fed with 300Ω line at either of the triple-crossing points and it will work on all three frequencies. You could miss the exact crossing point (or change the frequency) somewhat and still have an impedance of between 150 and 600Ω..."

Such an arrangement is called an Off-Centre-Fed Dipole (OCFD) and is useble if your transceiver has an internal auto ATU, but would be unsuitable for the WARC bands without a wide impedance matching range ATU. A current choke or balun is required at the antenna feed-point to prevent feed-line antenna currents.

In an article by Bill Wright, G0FAH [3], the OCFD was extended to cover 21MHz. This involved a length of ladder line as shown in **Fig 2**. The addition of the length of ladder line also has an effect on the performance of the antenna on other bands. The current imbalance on the line, caused by the asymmetrical feed, ensures that the ladder line radiates and modifies the radiation patterns of the antenna on other bands.

A further development of the OCFD is the Carolina Windom. The original Windom antenna, popular in the 1940s, comprised a wire element fed by a single wire 'feeder' approximately $^1/_3$ from the end. Such a configuration had to be fed against ground

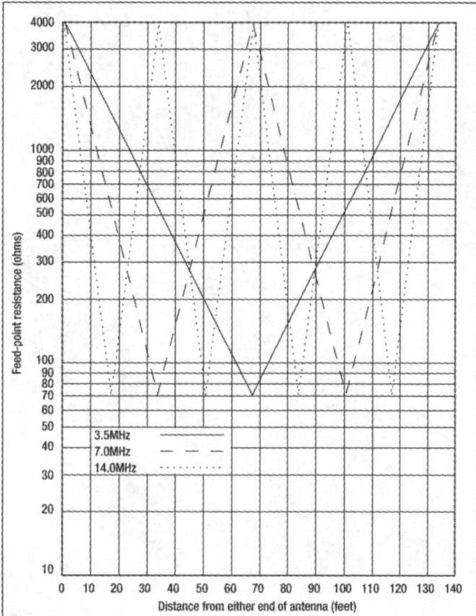


FIG 1: IMPEDANCE PLOT OF AN OCFD FOR 3.5, 7 AND 14MHz AS A FUNCTION OF THE FEED-POINT DISTANCE FROM EITHER END OF THE ANTENNA (FROM [2]).

FIG 2: THE G0FAH VERSION OF THE OCFD ANTENNA (FROM [3]). THE FEEDER LENGTH IS ANY ODD MULTIPLE OF 21MHz QUARTER-WAVELENGTH.

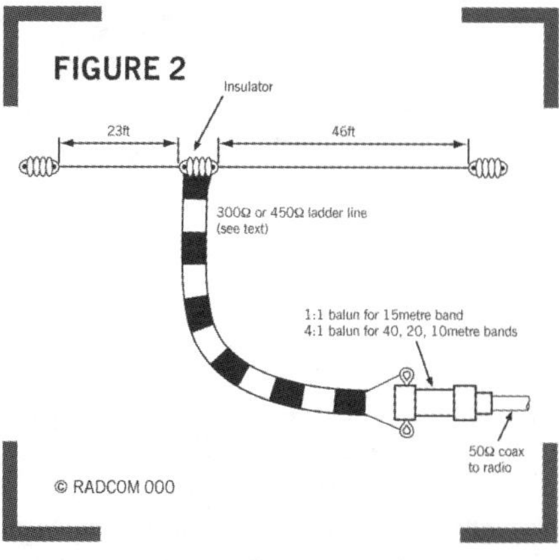


FIG 3: THE LAYOUT OF THE CAROLINA WINDOM (FROM [4]). THE MATCHING UNIT IS A VOLTAGE-TYPE BALUN TRANSFORMER, WHICH PURPOSELY DOES NOT ACT LIKE A COMMON-MODE CHOKE. THE LINE ISOLATOR IS A COMMON MODE CHOKE. AN ATU IS REQUIRED FOR THIS ANTENNA.

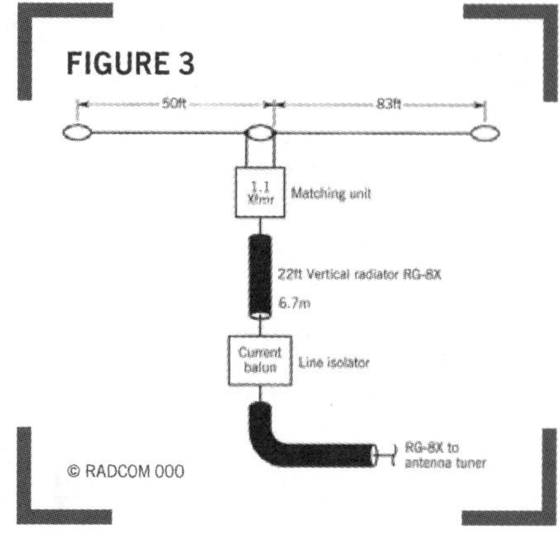


similar to an inverted-L antenna.

The Carolina Windom is also fed approximately $^1/_3$ from the end using RG-8 coax and the feeder is encouraged to radiate due to the position of the asymmetrical feed-point. By placing a current choke some distance from the feed-point, the length of the radiating section of the feeder can be preset as shown in **Fig 3**.

Several versions of the Carolina Windom are marketed by Radio Works [5]. They have coined a title for the radiating section of feeder and called it called 'VERT' (Vertically-Enhanced Radiation Technique).

I don't understand why this antenna could not just use 300Ω feeder for the vertical radiating section and have a combination of transformer and current choke at the end of the radiating section as shown in Fig 2. This would save a lot of weight at the centre, which can be a problem. No doubt someone will tell me.


REFERENCES.

[1] 'Antennas', *RadCom* March 2004.

[2] Roy O Hill Jr, W4PID, Technical Correspondence, *QST* October 1996.

[3] 'Four Bands, Off Center', Bill Wright, G0FAH, *QST* February 1996.

[4] *The ARRL Antenna Book*, 20th edition, page 7.8.

[5] *UK Radio Communications Equipment Guide, 2006*, Waters & Stanton PLC.

# The balanced ladder antenna

*Peter Dodd, G3LDO, looks at April Fool antenna designs, and the 'Strange Antenna Challenge'*

April is often the time of spoof articles, a tradition initiated by the *QST* article many years ago on the Harpits (or Cotley) ultra-stable VFO oscillator under the pseudonym of Larson E Rapp. The reaction to these is generally extreme; some regarding them as just good fun, others deeply offended and complain that the pages of the magazine could be better used to print more serious and useful material rather than this spoof rubbish.

But spoof articles can have a useful function provided they are reasonably well written. They can highlight popular misconceptions in a light-hearted and less didactic manner that may not be possible in traditional text books.

THE STRANGE ANTENNA CHALLENGE. Provided that RF current can be made to flow in a metal object, it is bound to radiate. In my early days of amateur radio I had been aware of one radio ham who had used his bed (they were mostly made of metal in those days) as an antenna, resonated against the water tap earth of a wash basin using an ATU.

By chance I came across the website for the KOS Kurt N. Sterba *Strange Antenna Challenge* hosted by Erik Weaver, NOEW [1]. In view of what I have said above you might be forgiven for regarding this as a spoof, but I would seriously suggest that you at least look at this site.

The idea of the challenge is simple. Construct an antenna from something that is not normally used as an antenna. Antenna materials used in previous challenges have included such items as metal folding chairs, shopping trolleys, chicken wire, fences, ladders and trucks

Antennas constructed of wire or metal pipe or tubing (normal antenna materials) are NOT permitted. Feeder is permitted but efforts must be made to prevent the feeder from radiating using current chokes or baluns if using coax, or a balanced feed if using twin feeder.

Inspired by this I 'constructed' an antenna from two step ladders and placed them on a garden table as shown in the photograph. The two ladders were fed as two elements of a dipole using a two-metre length of 400Ω ladder line feeder. The 'antenna' exhibited a broad resonance at about 23.5MHz with a feed impedance of around 12Ω at resonance. The antenna was tried on several bands and loaded on all HF bands, 10MHz and up. Using a diminutive MFJ-901B ATU (later I found the SEM Z-match worked better with this arrangement) and an IC-706MkI on CW, I was surprised how well it worked. Contacts were no more difficult than working with QRP (less than 5W) into a 'normal' multiband dipole antenna, 10m high. In just over an hour I made five contacts around Europe and, on average, my reports were about two S-points down on the ones I gave out.

TWO STEP LADDERS SET UP FOR THE *STRANGE ANTENNA CHALLENGE*

I then moved the antenna to the flat roof of the house extension, thereby increasing the height from 0.8m to 3.2m. The resonance was about the same and the feed impedance increased to 16Ω. This move improved the performance so that the average signal strength difference was less than one S-point. I even managed a couple of east-coast USA stations during the short test period.

COMMERCIAL ANTENNAS. I often get e-mails asking what do I think of such-and-such commercial antenna. Most of the time, I am not able to answer the question because I do not have any experience of the antenna under consideration. I sometimes find that an antenna's performance is indirectly proportional to the manufacturer's claims, so it is difficult for the buyer to know just what he is getting. However, some help is at hand. The eHam amateur radio website [2] has a review section, which you might find illuminating. The table below is from a review of HF portable (not mobile) antennas by KQ6XA. These antenna 'shoot-outs' are quite popular in the USA, particularly with homebrew VHF/UHF antennas. I wonder how my dual step-ladder antenna would fare in such a review?

| | **dB ±Ref** |
|---|---|
| Reference Vertical | 0.00 |
| KA5DVS 'PAC-12M' | -1.76 |
| SuperAntennas MP-1 | -1.88 |
| KA5DVS 'PAC-12' | -1.88 |
| SuperAntennas MP-2 | -1.94 |
| Webster Short Bandspanner | -3.92 |
| Diamond RHM5 | -3.95 |
| Waters & Stanton ATX Walkabout | -4.61 |
| KA5S Backpack Delta Loop | -4.82 |
| Outbacker Tri-Split | -5.03 |
| Outbacker Joey | -5.12 |
| Miracle Antenna Miracle Whip | -10.48 |
| Miracle Whip [no counterpoise] | -29.21 |

**Note:** The Reference Vertical was a quarter-wave whip and the estimated margin of error was ±0.3dB.

WEB SEARCH

[1] Strange Antenna Challenge www.n0ew.org/k0s
[2] eHam reviews www.eham.net/reviews

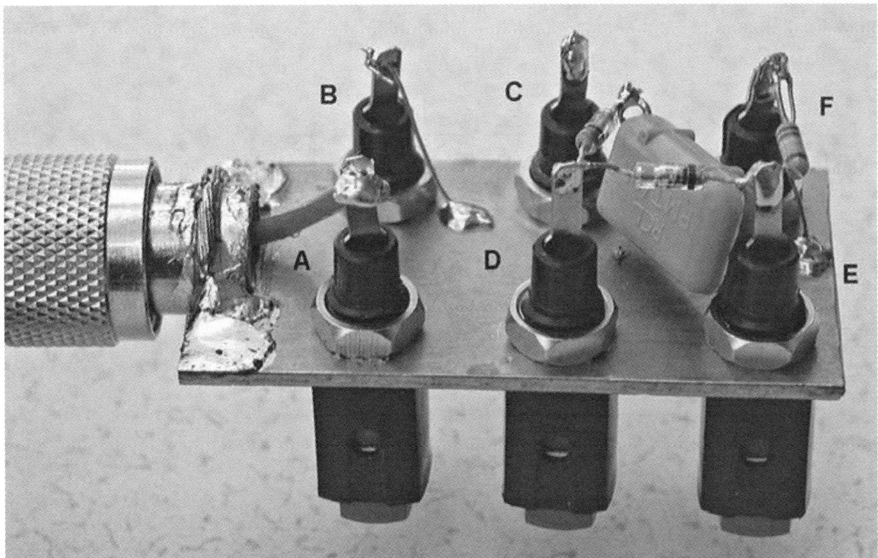


PHOTO 1: SHOWING THE CONSTRUCTION OF THE SWR ANALYSER TEST ADAPTER. THE LABELLING OF THE TERMINALS IS RATHER ARBITRARY, BUT THIS WAS RATHER AN EXPERIMENTAL SET UP. THE DIODE VOLTMETER COULD BE ARRANGED TO OCCUPY JUST TWO TERMINALS, THEREBY FREEING UP AN EXTRA TERMINAL FOR SUPPORTING COMPONENTS UNDER TEST.

# Using an SWR Analyser

*Your SWR Analyser has several more applications than just checking your antennas. Peter Dodd, G3LDO, explains some of these.*

THE ANALYSER. Antenna experimenting has become much easier since the introduction of what Gerd Janzen, DF6SJ, referred to as the 'Active Standing Wave Ratio Meter' [1] and is now generally known as the SWR Analyser. These instruments comprise wide-range tunable low-power RF generators, usually with a digital frequency readout. SWR and other RF parameters are measured with internal sensors.

The main suppliers of commercial SWR analysers are MFJ, Autek and Kuranishi. Their main purpose is to measure the SWR on a transmission line, normally connected to an antenna, at a specified frequency. They are normally fitted with a SO-239 socket so that they may be connected to a coax line fitted with a PL-259 plug. However, these instruments can be used for measuring parameters other than SWR. Other useful measurements and tests are:

- measuring the resonant frequency of a tuned circuit or trap;
- testing RF chokes;
- Testing RF transformers and baluns.

THE MFJ-259. An example of some these tests, taken from the MFJ-259 HF/VHF SWR Analyser Instruction manual, is shown in **Fig 1**. These instructions show several ways of measuring the resonant frequency of tuned circuits. The method shown in **Fig 1(a)** shows a parallel-tuned circuit, in series with a 50Ω resistor, connected to the 'Antenna' connector. The MFJ-259 is tuned for the highest SWR, which indicates the resonant frequency. This arrangement is works best with high-capacitance tuned circuits. The terminals indicated in the diagrams have been allocated letters A to F and these are described later.

For high-inductance tuned circuits the method shown in **Fig 1(b)** is preferred. Here, a series-tuned circuit is connected in series with a 50Ω resistor to the 'Antenna' connector. The MFJ-259 is tuned for the lowest SWR, which indicates the resonant frequency.

Resonance can also be indicated by using a diode detector and a high impedance voltmeter as shown in **Fig 1(c)**. In this case resonance is indicated by maximum voltage reading.

The diode detector can be used to measure the frequency characteristics of components such as RF chokes as shown in **Fig 1(d)**.

THE TEST ADAPTER. Connecting up the arrangements described above can be inconvenient and you will have to get the soldering iron out to jury rig the circuits shown in Fig 1. If you want to make lots of experiments that do not use a PL-259 as a connector then you will find a test adapter very useful. This idea is not new and was first described in [2].

The adapter is constructed from a small section of double-sided PCB board as shown in **Photo 1**. The size of the board is not critical and depends on what type of terminals you propose to use. The board shown in Photo 1 measures 35mm x 65mm and the connectors used are known as 'Quick Connect'. If your junk box does not contain six suitable terminals then Farnell [3] appears to offer the widest selection; the most common (and cheapest) being described as 'Panel Mounting Terminals'.

A notch, 12.7mm wide and 6mm deep is cut into the board to take the rear case of a PL-259 plug. An insulated lead is connected to the centre pin of the plug before the PL-259 case is soldered to the PCB board.

Six terminals are fitted to the board spaced about 14mm apart. The connection from the centre of the PL-259 is soldered to terminal A, while terminal B is connected to ground (the printed circuit board). The diode voltmeter is built around the terminals D, E and F. Terminal C is used as a support for components under test so is not connected.

The adapter can now be tested. Connect a wire link from A to D, the diode voltmeter. This is shown in Fig 1(d) but, in this case, the RF choke is replaced with the link. This arrangement is useful for testing the output of the SWR analyser or unknown diodes for their suitability for use as an RF diode detector. With the circuits shown in Fig 1(c) and Fig 1(d) the MFJ analyser output is around 800mV into a 10kΩ load while the Autek analyser output is about 500mV.

USING THE ADAPTOR. The simplest application of the adapter is just to use the terminals A and B, nearest the PL-259 socket as a convenient method of connecting a component or coax cable not fitted with a PL-259.

A 50Ω resistor can be used for calibrating the analyser, which should show an SWR of 1:1. A 100Ω, or 25Ω resistor, will give an SWR of 2:1 and so on.

I have found that this adapter is most useful for measuring the characteristics of a balun; one set up for testing is shown in **Photo 2**. The terminals provide a very convenient way of connecting a balun to the SWR analyser. You can try out various types of ferrite cores (often with unknown characteristics) and number of windings before coming up with a final design and fitting the necessary plug, connections and housing. The arrangement in Photo 2 shows the standard type of auto transformer arrangement, normally found on the output of most commercially-available ATUs. This type of balun is normally a 4:1 ratio transformer so, if loaded at the balanced output with a 200Ω resistor, it should reflect a 50Ω load (and an SWR of 1:1) at the unbalanced input.

The operating instructions of the MFJ-259 show this and also advise that the load be made of two 100Ω resistors in series. By using a grounded clip lead connected to the junction of the two resistors, there will an indication of balun balance – when the clip is attached there should be no change in the SWR reading.

The characteristics of a simple auto transformer balun, comprising 20 turns of plastic-covered wire bifilar-wound on a T-200 core, (shown in Photo 2) turned out to be surprisingly good. When loaded with a 220Ω resistor, the SWR was less than 1.3:1 over a frequency range of 8 to 26MHz and less than 1.5:1 over a frequency range of 4 to 32MHz.

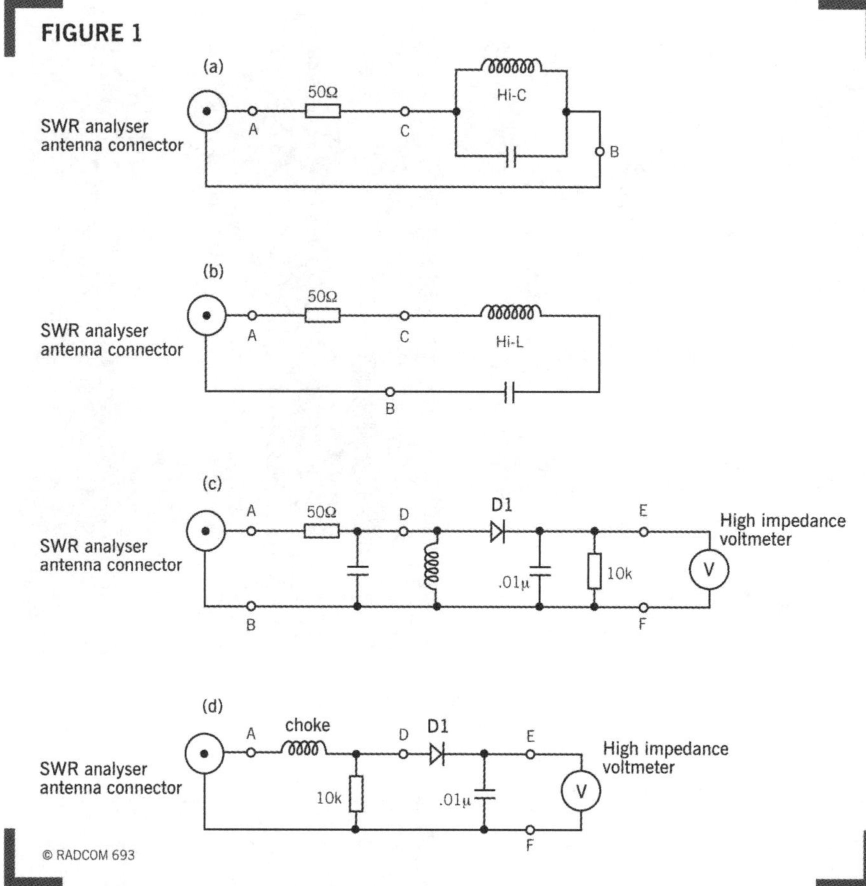


FIGURE 1: CIRCUITS FOR TESTING PASSIVE COMPONENTS AT RF FREQUENCIES. D1 IS AN OA91 OR NEAR EQUIVALENT, SUCH AS A OA90, 1N34 OR 1N191. IN CIRCUIT (D) THE CHOKE CAN BE REPLACED BY A WIRE LINK FOR TESTING THE OUTPUT OF THE SWR ANALYSER OR UNKNOWN DIODES FOR THEIR SUITABILITY FOR USE AS RF DIODE DETECTORS. TERMINALS B AND F ARE BOTH GROUNDED TO THE PCB BOARD.

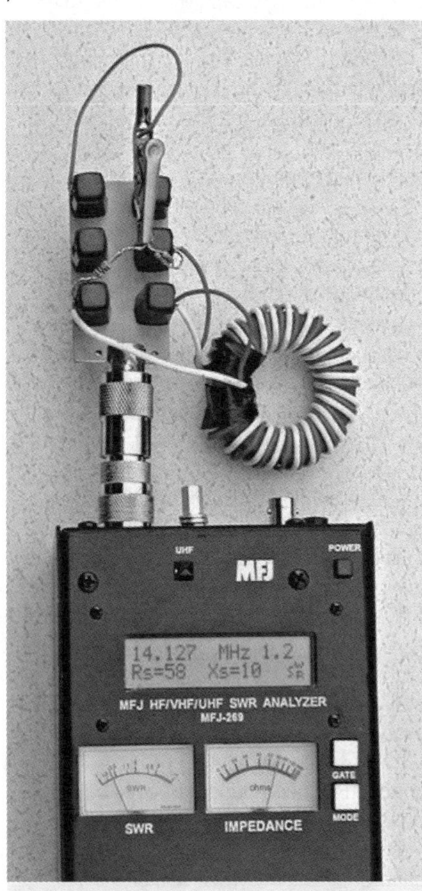


PHOTO 2: AN ARRANGEMENT FOR TESTING A 4:1 BALUN USING A MFJ-269 AND THE ADAPTER.

The adaptor can be used for checking the characteristics of an in-line coax high- or low-pass filter. The adaptor is set for reading the voltage output as described above, but with a 50Ω resistor across terminals A and B. The filter is then inserted in a coax connector from the analyser to the adapter. The voltages are recorded at various frequencies, which should then give some indication of the filter characteristics.

The adapter can be used with other analysers such as the Autek RF-1. The oscillator of the RF-IA covers 1.2 to 35MHz, rather less than the MFJ instrument of 1.8 to 170MHz. The main disadvantage of the RF1 is that can only display one parameter at a time so you have to keep togging between frequency and SWR during the tests. However, the RF-1 can measure capacitance and inductance (0 to 9999pF and 4 to 300μH, respectively). This enables capacitor and inductor values to be measured directly by connecting them to terminals A and B.

FINALLY. While on the subject of SWR analysers, I should mention the MFJ-269 and the Autek VA1. The measurement facilities have been extended considerably on these instruments compared with those mentioned earlier. The MFJ-269 comes with a 39-page manual which, in itself, is a good treatise on RF measurements. The MFJ instrument description and sales can be found at [4] and the Autek instrument sales and service at [5]. Also check out the reviews on [6].

REFERENCES

[1] RF Measurements with an Active Standing Wave Ratio Meter, ISBN 3-88692-023, by Gerd Janzen, DF6SJ. DARC Verlag GmbH, Baunatal.
[2] 'The Gadget – an SWR Analyzer Add-On', Fred Hauff, W3NZ, QST October 1996.
[3] Farnell – www.farnell.com.uk
[4] Waters & Stanton PLC – www.wsplc.com
[5] CQ Direct – www.cqcqcq.com
[6] Reviews – www.eham.net/reviews

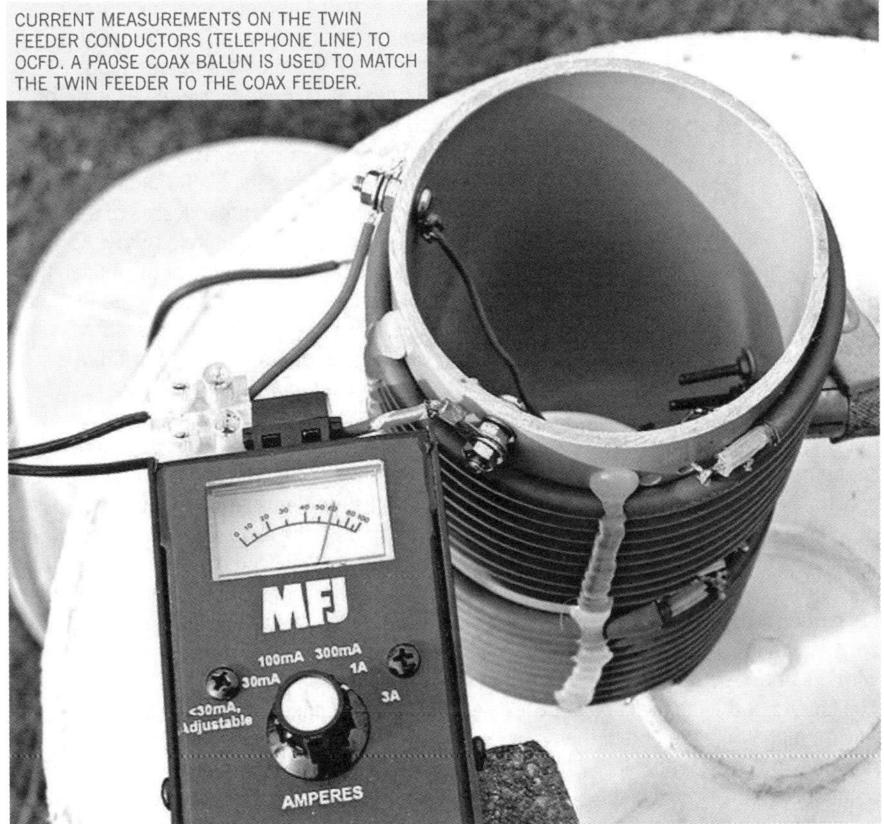


CURRENT MEASUREMENTS ON THE TWIN FEEDER CONDUCTORS (TELEPHONE LINE) TO OCFD. A PA0SE COAX BALUN IS USED TO MATCH THE TWIN FEEDER TO THE COAX FEEDER.

# Further discussion on the OCFD antenna

*Details for the Off-Centre-Fed Antenna (OCFD), described in [1], resulted in a lot of correspondence. Here, G3LDO airs your comments.*

FEEDBACK. Bob, 2M0KDZ, e-mailed me to say "I have one with similar top dimensions to the one in G0FAH's article in *QST*. It started life as a half-sized G5RV with a sloping top. I wasn't very happy with the performance, so I modified it to a half-sized Windom by adding 40ft (12m) to the bottom end and changing the feeder to 11ft (3.35m) of 300Ω ladder line. I added a home-brewed 4:1 current (Guanella) balun at the bottom of the feeder which acts both as an impedance converter and a choke balun. There's a 15m coax run from there to a Ten-Tec Model 229B ATU in the shack."

TABLE 1
**CALCULATED IMPEDANCES OF THE OCFD USING *EZNEC4*.**

| MHz | Impedance | R | ±j |
|---|---|---|---|
| 3.6 | 102 | + | 54 |
| 7.0 | 134 | – | 37 |
| 10.1 | 2614 | – | 225 |
| 14.0 | 113 | – | 98 |
| 18.1 | 217 | + | 126 |
| 21.2 | 842 | – | 419 |

John Bolton, G3FBN, wrote: "I read your article in the current issue of *RadCom* with great interest, as I have been using a version of the OCFD since around 1985. It is known as the FD-4 and was invented by DJ2KY in the 1970s; the data was first published in DARC *QTC* in 1974". John very kindly sent me a copy of the original DJ2KY article.

To recap, the OCFD is a multiband antenna, half a wavelength long on the lowest frequency, fed one-sixth of a wavelength from the end as shown in **Fig 1**. The article by DJ2KY makes interesting reading. As well as giving some history of the development of the FD4, it also gives a description of how the antenna works.

TABLE 2
**MEASURED CURRENTS ON THE OCFD TWIN FEEDER.**

| MHz | I, L1(mA) | I, L2(mA) |
|---|---|---|
| 3.6 | 320 | 280 |
| 7.0 | 90 | 220 |
| 10.1 | 450 | 500 |
| 14.2 | 330 | 280 |
| 18.1 | 430 | 480 |
| 21.2 | 90 | 120 |

The impedance of the feed-point of a λ/2 wire is low in the centre (high current) and high at the ends (near zero current). Generally, the impedance at the centre is around 60Ω and rises to 5000Ω at the ends. For a single band antenna, this would enable you to select a feed-point that would match any impedance of feeder that you might choose to use, and was shown in a graph, see Fig 1 of [1]. However the situation is different if you want to feed a multi-band antenna.

The diagram in **Fig 2** (based on a diagram in DJ2KY's article) shows the current distribution on a half-wavelength of wire on 80m superimposed on the current distribution on other higher frequency bands. The impedance is related to the current amplitude – the greater the current, the lower the impedance. It can be seen that the current amplitudes on some of the bands coincide at one-sixth of a wavelength from the end, a point that DJ2KY described as a 'Windom point'.

However, the current distributions shown in Fig 2 are idealistic, showing the current distributions in free space. In practice, these currents can have slightly different amplitudes and phases due to the proximity of the ground. Furthermore, amplitudes of the current variations along the antenna element may not be constant on the higher frequencies when the antenna is fed off-centre. Nevertheless, the impedances found at the λ/6 point are fairly close together on some bands and the free-space impedances of a half-wavelength of wire on 3.6MHz has been calculated using *EZNEC4* shown in **Table 1**.

When the antenna is modelled close to the ground, the impedances shown in Table 1 do change but, with the exception of 10 and 21MHz, are still within the range 100 to 200Ω.

Most OCFD builders are in general agreement regarding the position of the antenna feed-point; most of the differences relate to the feed arrangements. The FD-4 antenna was 42m (138ft) long fed at the 1/3 point. DJ2KY's article appears to have assumed that the feed-point impedance was 600Ω and used a 6:1 transformer balun arrangement to match it to a 60Ω coax feed-line.

G3FBN, in his letter says "My version varies only slightly from the original FD-4: the overall length is 139ft (42.37m) long, the short leg is 46ft 4in, (14.1m) the long leg is 92ft 8in (28.25m). I am feeding my version with 75Ω TV coaxial cable, via a home-brew 4:1 balun at the feed-point. The balun comprises 8 turns of 70Ω twin feeder tightly wrapped and taped to a length of 9mm ferrite rod, and all this is enclosed in a plastic 'T' electrical conduit, on which is mounted a PL-259 socket and suitable terminals for connecting the aerial wires. I am currently using a TS-2000 or a TS-570D both fitted with auto ATUs. I seldom need to use the main ATU, the SWR is within the range acceptable to both rigs. The bands covered are 3.5, 7, 14, 18, 24 and 28MHz, but the SWR is too high on 10 and 21MHz and I have alternative antennas for those bands."

G3GRO described his experiments with an OCFD antenna in the Crawley Amateur Radio Club Newsletter (he kindly sent me a copy). He says "For many years I had an 80m OCFD fed with 300Ω ribbon feeder via a home-made 6:1 ferrite transformer, nominally 139ft (42.37m) long and running in a straight line up at 40ft (12.2m) AGL. This worked very well on 40m and bands above, but the SWR at the band edges on 80m rose to around 2.5:1". He then goes on to describe a series of tests with different feed configurations of the antenna using 300Ω twin feeder fed via a commercial 6:1 transformer mounted at ground level. 50Ω coax was used to connect the transformer to the shack. The SWR results using this arrangement were variable and depended on the feeder length and grounding of the 50Ω coax outer etc, before it went into the house. With all these variables, it proved difficult to optimise the antenna length – nominally 41.5m overall.

G3GRO improved the SWR compromise by changing the antenna configuration: The ferrite transformer was placed at the feed-point of the antenna and fed with 50Ω coax more or less vertically downwards to ground level. At this point, a current choke was inserted into the feeder. It comprised a number of turns of RG-58U coax feeder wound on a powdered-iron toroid Type T240-15 (Red) about 60cm in diameter. The outer of the coax was connected to the earth system as before. Other members of the Crawley club, notably Lech, G3KAU, have also had success with this design of OCFD.

FIGURE 1: THE BASIC OCFD ANTENNA.

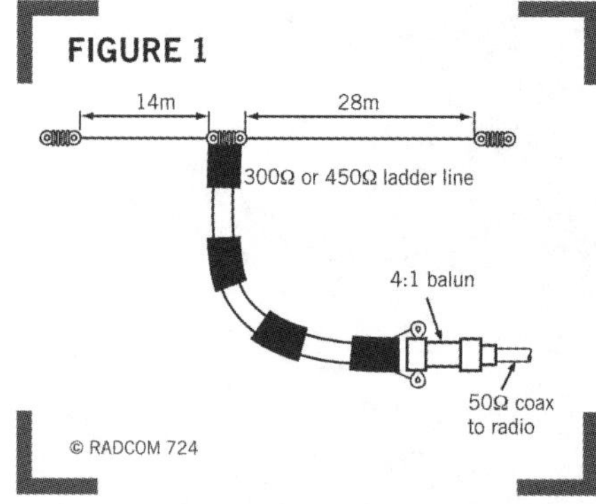


THE G3LDO OCFD. It would appear that, unlike the simple half-wave dipole, the configuration of the OCFD varies from constructor to constructor. Not wanting to be left out, I constructed an OCFD using a nominal 138ft (42m) top. Because my mast is about two-thirds of the way down the garden it finished up being a cross between an inverted-L and an inverted-V, with the apex about 48ft (14.6m) high. The far end of the long section is 28ft (8.5m) high while the end of the short section is 4m high. This placed the feed-point about 40ft (12m) high.

I originally fed the antenna with 450Ω ladder line, with a balun at ground level. I found that SWR measurements were all over the place unless I earthed outer braid of the coax feed to the shack at the point where it connects to the balun.

The 450Ω ladder line was then replaced with twin line telephone drop wire (this is the external wire used by BT to connect house telephones to the nearest telegraph pole). The conductors of this material are made from 1mm diameter hard drawn copper wire spaced at 3.3mm (centre to centre). A local radio amateur, Frank James, G0LOF, who gave me a length of this material, claims to have measured the impedance as 120Ω. The telephone wire feeder improved the SWR, although whether this was due to losses or a better overall match, I am unable to say. As regards the performance of the feeder, the relative conductor currents did not differ as much as expected and the measured values (see photo) are given in **Table 2**.

I have often advocated using a doublet fed with balanced feeder. This overcomes the losses caused by using coax, and was described in [2]. However, twin feeder can have its problems when routing a long length from the shack to the feed-point. An antenna whose feed impedance does not vary wildly from band to band has certain advantages and may be fed using coax with the internal ATU found in many transceivers.

I would encourage you to experiment with this antenna. Altering the overall length is quite easy. Moving the feed-point can be achieved by making one end longer and the other shorter. These variables can be made easier to adjust by making the top section longer than required and folding back the excess length at the end insulators back along the elements. The excess lengths can be temporarily held in place with clothes pegs while measurements are made.

REFERENCES
[1] 'Antennas', *RadCom* March 2006.
[2] 'Antennas', *RadCom* January 2006.

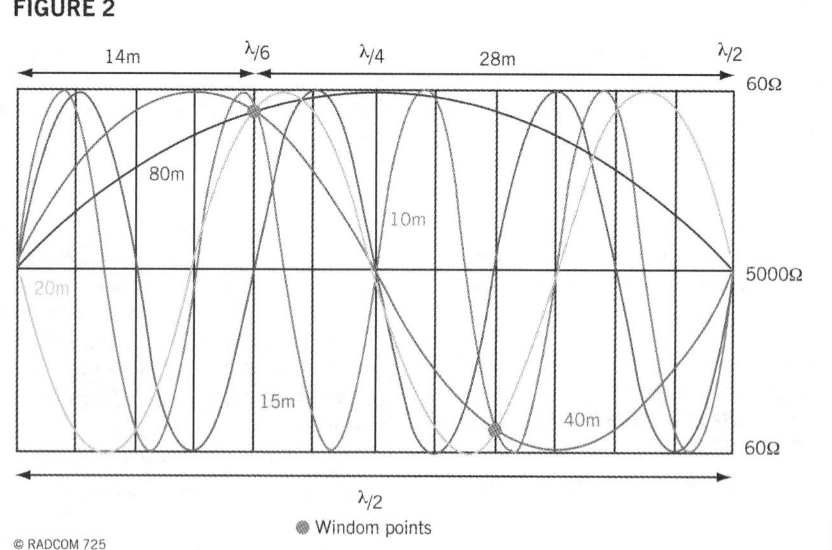


FIGURE 2: THE CURRENT DISTRIBUTION ON A HALF-WAVE LENGTH OF WIRE ON 80m SUPERIMPOSED ON THE CURRENT DISTRIBUTION ON OTHER HIGHER BANDS. IT CAN BE SEEN THAT THE CURRENT AMPLITUDES ON SOME OF THE BANDS COINCIDE AT L/6 FROM THE END, A POINT THAT DJ2KY DESCRIBED AS A 'WINDOM POINT'.

# More on RF measurement techniques

*Methods of measuring the inductance and capacitance of components used in the construction of ATUs, antenna traps and loading coils.*

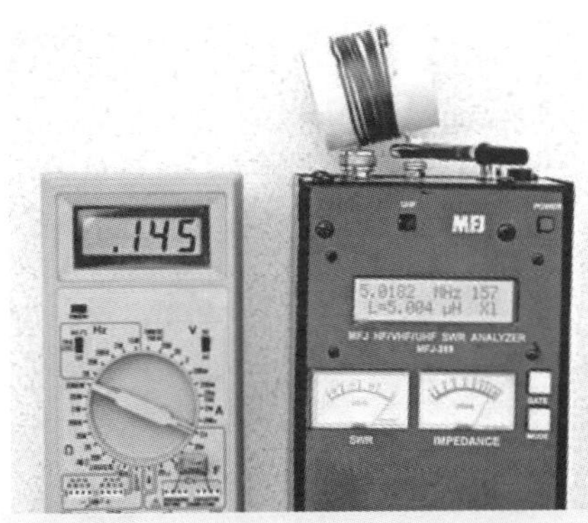

A CIRKIT TM-175 BEING USED TO MEASURE A 150pF CAPACITOR AND SHOWING 0.145nF. THE MFJ-269 IS MEASURING A 5µH INDUCTANCE.

RF MEASUREMENTS. The description of an adapter for connecting components to an MFJ-259 HF/VHF SWR Analyser so that their parameters can be measured [1] resulted in a couple of e-mails. These inspired me to extend the subject of measurements at RF (my pet hobbyhorse). While the MFJ-259/269 is normally used for measuring SWR, some of the other functions are not often mentioned, so let us look at a couple of these.

MEASURING CAPACITANCE AND INDUCTANCE. Now why should we want to measure capacitance and inductance?

The capacitance of a fixed capacitor is written on the side of the component (if you can understand the modern symbols) so you don't need to measure it. However, there are times when experimenting with antennas that you may well need to measure the value of an unmarked or variable capacitor. If you wanted to make a parallel capacitance shunt matching unit for a 3.7MHz mobile antenna, the best plan would be to use a 1000pF (a two-500pF ganged receiver capacitor, each capacitor in parallel). This is then connected across the feed-point of the antenna and adjusted for the lowest SWR. When the correct match has been obtained, the capacitance of the variable setting can be measured and the temporary variable replaced by a fixed capacitance of

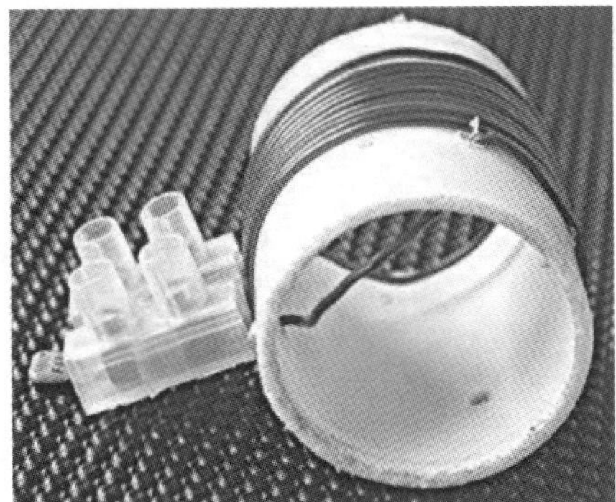
THE CONSTRUCTION OF A STANDARD INDUCTANCE WITH A HALF WINDING EACH SIDE OF THE COIL FOR TUNING.

equivalent value. The same can be done for Gamma matches on beam antennas.

It is often difficult to estimate the value of an inductor, so the ability to measure inductance is often useful when making up loading coils, ATU coils or antenna traps.

If you have a component-measuring bridge, like the Atlas Passive Component analyser (£79 available from [2]) for example, making these measurements is simple. If not, the simplest and cheapest method to measure capacitance is to use the capacitance-measuring facility often found on digital multimeters. The meter shown in the photograph has five ranges; 2n, 20n, 200n, 2µF and 20µF. This particular meter uses an internally-generated 500Hz, 100mV (pk-pk) semi-square wave in conjunction with a bridge and the meter to measure capacitance. Although the lowest capacitance ranges are calibrated in nF, the value of a capacitance in the pF range shows up quite well as shown in the photograph.

There are a few multimeters on the market that have the ability to measure inductance as well, such as the WG020, see [2], but these are just a bit more expensive starting at around £60.

For many years, I had a Marconi TF 1313A Universal Bridge. The capacitance measurement was from 0.1pF to 110µF in seven ranges and the inductance measurement from 0.1µH to 110H in seven ranges. Measurements could be made at 1kHz or 10kHz. A simplified diagram of the bridge arrangement is shown in **Fig 1**. As you can see, the bridge component switching arrangement is quite elaborate, but it could achieve measurement accuracies better than 0.1%

THE ANTENNA ANALYSERS. If you have one of these modern antenna analysers, such as the MFJ-259B, MFJ-269 or Autek RF-1, you can measure capacitance in pF or inductance in µH directly. I recently had an e-mail exchange with Maurice Murphy, G0CDQ, over some inconsistent measurements he found while using the MFJ-259B to measure the values of capacitors and inductors and felt that the subject warranted further investigation.

The MFJ-259B and MFJ-269 capacitance and inductance measurement techniques are the same. Starting with a 82pF capacitor and a 150pF capacitor (which measured 0.145nF on the TM-175 multimeter as shown in the first photograph) the MFJ-269 came up with the results shown in **Table 1**, while the Autek RF Analyst RF1 came up with the results shown in **Table 2**. All this goes to show that the measured capacitance varies with frequency, although the component value variations with an increase in frequency shown in Tables 1 and 2 are different. Nevertheless, the greatest accuracy on both instruments appears to occur at around 4 or 5MHz. So what do the manuals have to say about the subject?

The MFJ-259B and the MFJ-269 manuals state that "[these instruments] measure reactance and convert the reactance into capacitance (or inductance)...". It goes on to say about the 'Capacitance in pF' mode: "It measures capacitance in pF in whatever frequency you select on the display...". Then follows a note to say "It is normal for the reactance of a capacitor to vary with frequency. This effect occurs because series inductance in the leads and sometimes in the capacitor causes effective capacitance to change with frequency". And I thought it was a fundamental characteristic of capacitors, ie $X_c = 1/2\pi fC$!

The Autek RF-1 had nothing much to say about measuring C and L in the instructions – but see Ref [3], which discusses 'Measuring Coils and Capacitors' and 'Coils are Measured at RF Frequencies'.

I find some of these notes produced by the manufacturers of these instruments a bit confusing. You might find the item by Ian White, GM3SEK, [4] a lot clearer. My view is that these antenna analysers do a good job of measuring capacitance and inductance provided that the appropriate measuring frequency is selected as shown in Tables 1 and 2. You can calibrate your own instrument using close tolerance inductors or capacitors. Most of these lower-cost measuring instruments give adequate results provided you are aware of their limitations. Note that the adaptor, described in [1], added an extra 9pF to the measured value of capacitance.

THE DIP METER METHOD. The dip meter, normally used for measuring the resonance of a tuned circuit, can also be used for measuring capacitance and inductance. The dip meter measures the resonance of a tuned circuit so, provided you know the value of one of the components, you can obtain the unknown value of the other by simply measuring the frequency.

According to radio text books, the resonant frequency of a tuned circuit is obtained from the formula

$f = 1/2\pi\sqrt{(LC)}$,

in units of Hz, H and F

This formula is rather cumbersome for our purposes. A much simpler one (GM3SEK reminded me of it in a recent e-mail exchange) uses the magic number 25330.

$C = 25330/(f^2L)$ or $L = 25330/(f^2C)$.

The units used are the much more managable; MHz, μH and pF.

To find the value of an unknown inductor, connect the inductor in parallel with the reference 100pF capacitor. Measure the frequency of the tuned circuit using the dip oscillator. Note; you will get more accurate results if the frequency of the dip meter is monitored with a frequency counter. Assume the measured frequency is 8.2MHz. The value of the inductor is determined by:

$L = 25330 / (8.2 \times 8.2 \times 100) = 3.77\mu H$.

Similarly, the value of a capacitor can be obtained from our 5μH reference inductor, with a measured frequency of 7.1MHz by:

$C = 25330 / (7.1 \times 7.1 \times 5.0) = 100.5\mu F$.

An even simpler formula was proposed by Ed Chicken, G3BIK [5]. His method assigns a factor to the known reference capacitor or inductor, which is divided by the square of the frequency, to produce the value of the unknown in pF or μH. The factor for the 100pF capacitor is 253 and the 5μH inductor is 5054.

$L = 253 / f^2 = 253 / 8.2 / 8.2 = 3.76\mu H$.

Similarly, $C = 5054 / f = 5054 / 7.1 / 7.1 = 100pF$.

G3BIK supplied tables for a range of reference capacitors and inductors which are given in [5]. There is also a chart for determining the unknown values of *L* and *C* in [6].

TABLE 1

**MEASURED VALUES OF AN 82pF AND 150pF CAPACITOR AND A 5μH INDUCTANCE USING THE MFJ-269.**

| MHz | reference pF | measured pF | reference pF | measured pF | reference μH | measured μH |
|---|---|---|---|---|---|---|
| 2.0 | 82 | 66 | 150 | 135 | 5.0 | 4.778 |
| 3.0 | 82 | 78 | 150 | 145 | 5.0 | 4.286 |
| 4.0 | 82 | 81 | 150 | 149 | 5.0 | 4.894 |
| 5.0 | 82 | 82 | 150 | 151 | 5.0 | 4.979 |
| 6.0 | 82 | 83 | 150 | 153 | 5.0 | 5.094 |
| 7.0 | 82 | 83 | 150 | 154 | 5.0 | 5.226 |
| 8.0 | 82 | 83 | 150 | 156 | 5.0 | 5.349 |
| 9.0 | 82 | 84 | 150 | 158 | 5.0 | 5.570 |
| 10.0 | 82 | 84 | 150 | 159 | 5.0 | 5.839 |

TABLE 2

**MEASURED VALUES OF AN 82pF AND 150pF CAPACITOR AND A 5μH INDUCTANCE USING THE AUTEK RF ANALYST RF1.**

| MHz | reference pF | measured pF | reference pF | measured pF | reference μH | measured μH |
|---|---|---|---|---|---|---|
| 2.0 | 82 | 78 | 150 | 162 | 5.0 | 5.40 |
| 3.0 | 82 | 81 | 150 | 159 | 5.0 | 5.26 |
| 4.0 | 82 | 84 | 150 | 155 | 5.0 | 5.12 |
| 5.0 | 82 | 84 | 150 | 153 | 5.0 | 5.05 |
| 6.0 | 82 | 84 | 150 | 152 | 5.0 | 5.00 |
| 7.0 | 82 | 84 | 150 | 152 | 5.0 | 4.95 |
| 8.0 | 82 | 84 | 150 | 151 | 5.0 | 4.90 |
| 9.0 | 82 | 82 | 150 | 150 | 5.0 | 4.86 |
| 10.0 | 82 | 83 | 150 | 150 | 5.0 | 4.82 |

A REFERENCE TUNED CIRCUIT. A reference tuned circuit is shown in the photograph. The capacitor is a close tolerance 100pF silver mica and the 5μH inductor is made up with 10turns of 22SWG enamelled copper wire wound on a short length of 1.5in (40mm) diameter plastic waste pipe. Half-turn loops are included inside the pipe at each end of the coil so that the inductance can be varied by having the loop adding to or subtracting from the total inductance (variometer technique).

REFERENCES

[1] 'Antennas', *RadCom* March 2006.
[2] Maplin, **www.maplin.co.uk**
[3] *Some uses for the RF1, RF5 and VA1 Analysts.* **www.autekresearch.com**
[4] 'Can Inductance Vary With Frequency?', Ian White, GM3SEK, 'In Practice', *RadCom* November 2005.
[5] 'More From Your Dip Meter', Ed Chicken, G3BIK, *RadCom* May 2000.
[6] *The Antenna Experimenters Guide* (see chapter on measurement of resonance).

**FIGURE 1**

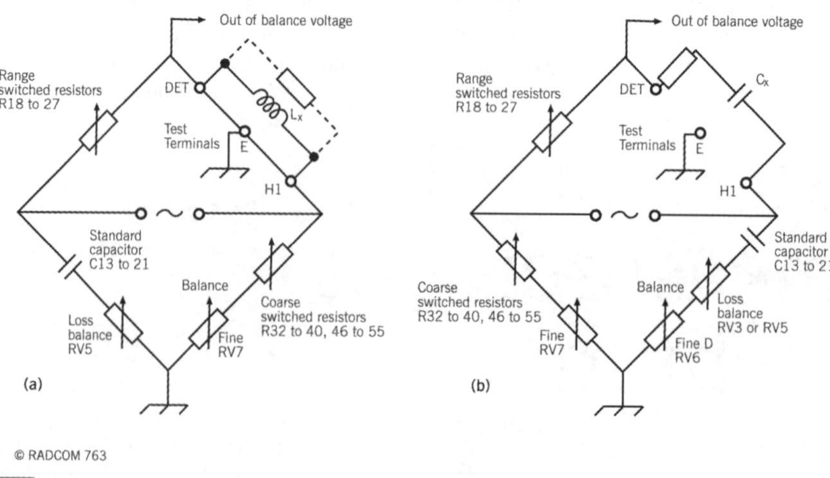


FIGURE 1: SIMPLIFIED DIAGRAMS OF THE BRIDGE ARRANGEMENTS USED TO MEASURE (A) INDUCTANCE AND (B) CAPACITANCE IN THE MARCONI TF-1313A UNIVERSAL BRIDGE.

# The radiating ladder

*Peter, G3LDO, enters the 'Strange Antenna Challenge' and reports on his findings.*

THE 'STRANGE ANTENNA CHALLENGE' AGAIN. In the April edition of 'Antennas', I described the KOS Kurt N Sterba 'Strange Antenna Challenge' hosted by Erik Weaver, NOEW [1]. To recap, the idea of this challenge is simple. Construct an antenna from something that is not normally used as an antenna. Materials used in previous challenges have included such items as metal folding chairs, shopping trolleys, chicken wire, fences, ladders and trucks.

Antennas constructed of wire, metal pipe or tubing (normal antenna materials) are *not* permitted. Feeder is permitted, but efforts must be made to prevent the feeder from radiating using current chokes or baluns if using coax, or a balanced feed if using twin feeder.

The 'event' date of this challenge was from 1600UTC on Saturday, 27 May 2006 until 0000UTC on Monday, 29 May 2006 so I decided to participate. My 'antenna' comprised two halves of an extension ladder, which were fed as two elements of a dipole using a four-metre length of 450Ω ladder line feeder. Originally I had one of the ladder sections on the flat roof of the house extension propped up at a near vertical position and against the roof of the house and fed against the other section lying on the flat roof. For some reason this arrangement did not work; the mutual interference with the television set was very severe and the antenna performance was very poor.

TWO LADDERS SET UP FOR THE STRANGE ANTENNA CHALLENGE.

The antenna was then laid out on the flat roof of the house extension so that it was about 10ft (3.2m) above the ground as shown in the photograph. The antenna was tried on several bands and loaded on all HF bands, 7MHz and up, when used with the diminutive MFJ-901B ATU.

So how did it work out? In its new location, the antenna worked much better and the mutual interference described above was no longer a problem (the new location was well clear of electrical and television antenna wiring). During intermittent operating sessions in the date slot described above, I made 19 contacts in 15 countries.

The Strange Antenna Challenge called for a fair amount of information exchange on the equipment, antennas and meaningful reports. With inter-state contacts in the USA this would be no problem. However, with inter-European contacts and operators not working in their native language, my description of my ladder antenna was often met with "¿que?" or its equivalent. There were also some stations working from obscure islands who gave the usual meaningless 59 or 599 reports.

Short skip contacts with Europe using 100W were fine, with the reports I received similar to those I gave out. DX was a different matter – I called quite a few DX stations but they could not hear me. The exception was John, N1FOJ, in New Hampshire. Now this station was using a big beam and 800W. My report was 55 and his 59, and I felt that this was an honest report because we discussed the strange antenna business.

The interesting aspect of this exercise is not *what* the antenna is but *where* it is. By moving the antenna from one location to another improved the performance no end. The lack of DX capability of this strange antenna was due to the fact it was a horizontal antenna only 10ft high. Placing it 30ft high would have made a large difference to its DX capability as shown in **Fig 1**.

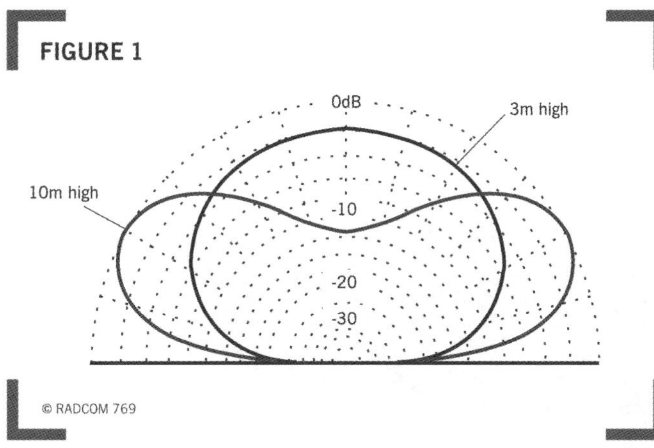


FIGURE 1: POLAR DIAGRAMS OF A SHORT DIPOLE (LADDER) AT 3m AND 10m, WHICH SHOWS A 6dB IMPROVEMENT AT 30°

MARITIME MOBILE ANTENNAS. When I wrote the *The Amateur Radio Mobile Handbook* [2] in 2001, I had to include a chapter on MM installations. Not having had any experience on this subject I sought information from G3AQC and others who owned boats. I visited several marinas along the south coast and found that, without exception, all the sailing boat HF installations used the backstay (with suitable insulators) as the antenna in conjunction with an automatic ATU. Large power boats fitted with HF radio used a large whip antenna, also with an ATU.

One of the most interesting contacts I had with the strange antenna weekend was with Mike, F/G4SKJ/MM, located off the coast of France. Mike had rigged an additional wooden mast at the stern of his boat and had strung a centre fed dipole from this mast to the main mast, which placed the antenna relatively clear of rigging. This made a significant improvement to the performance of the antenna compared with the original backstay arrangement. This additional mast had also been the support for a full sized 14MHz quad at one stage, which worked exceptionally well. That antenna on the high seas must have been a sight to behold!

REFERENCES

[1] The Strange Antenna Challenge www.n0ew.org/k0s

[2] *The Amateur Radio Mobile Handbook*, Peter Dodd, G3LDO, RSGB.

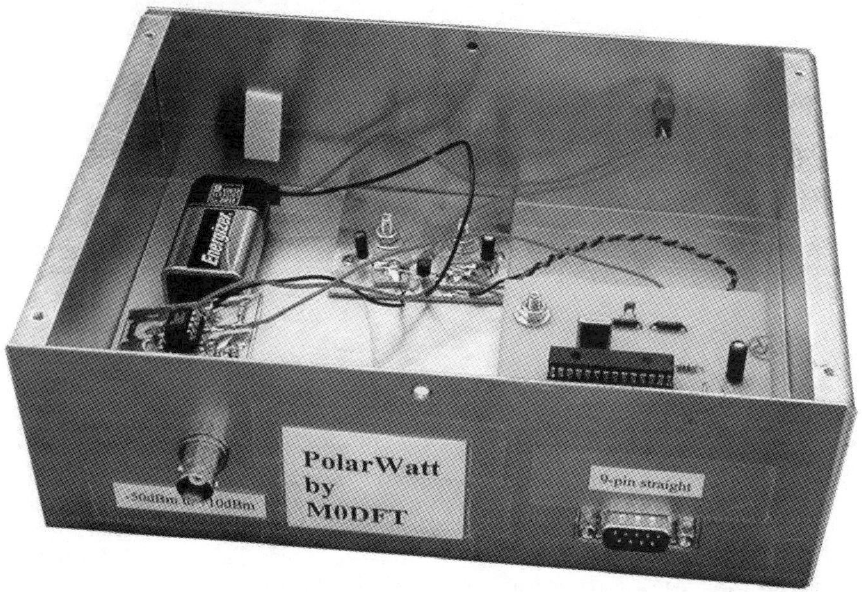


PHOTO 1: THE M0DFT POWER METER DESIGNED SPECIFICALLY FOR USE WITH POLARPLOT (AND NOW CALLED POLARWATT!). THIS DESIGN IS BASED ON ANALOG DEVICES AD8207 LOGARITHMIC AMPLIFIER INTEGRATED CIRCUIT.

# DIY polar diagrams

*PolarPlot provides an easy way to plot antenna polar diagrams.*

TRADITIONAL TESTING. The performance of an antenna is best described by plotting the relative field strengths around the antenna when energised using a transmitter. The time-honoured way of checking either a HF or VHF/UHF antenna installation is to enlist the help of a friendly local amateur to provide a transmitted signal. You can then take S meter readings at various beam headings while the antenna under test is being rotated and plot them on polar graph paper to produce a polar diagram. If you are really into playing with antennas then you can make up a VHF antenna test range as shown in the **Figure 1**. A method of constructing such an antenna range is described in [1].

POLARPLOT. In the November 2002 issue of Antennas (and also in [2]) I described methods of plotting the polar diagram of an antenna using a computer, in particular using a program called PolarPlot, by Bob Freeth, G4HFQ. PolarPlot allows the antenna field strength to be converted into a form that can be read by the computer and suitable software to display the results. Storage of data and the application of functions for normalisation and conversion from linear to log scales etc, are tasks amenable to computerisation. Additionally, very complex polar diagrams can be plotted that would otherwise be difficult using the manual method.

With PolarPlot, the signal level can be obtained in one of two ways:

**1.** Using a receiver as a field strength meter, whose audio output is fed into the line-in or microphone input of the computer soundcard. The volume of a beat note, in the SSB or CW, mode of a plain unmodulated carrier has good correlation with the RF input level, provided the receiver is operated in a linear manner. This is best achieved by simply reducing the RF gain. Most receivers with no control of RF gain are unsuitable for this application. With this arrangement a few mW is adequate as an energising signal; a stable signal generator is suitable. The advantage of this method is that it uses available equipment (Computer, soundcard and receiver). The disadvantage is that the linearity is restricted to around 30dB and the RF and AF levels have to be carefully set up. Best results will be achieved with a desktop PC that has a quality sound card fitted. Many of the on-the-motherboard sound systems tried generated some residual noise at very low levels that affected the depth of the recorded nulls.

**2.** Versions of PolarPlot V3.1 and later can be used with the signal strength acquired by an external RF milliwatt power meter. This gives a much better resolution to nulls below –30dB. Two examples of these meters, based on Analog Devices AD8207 logarithmic amplifier integrated circuit, have been designed and constructed by OZ2CPU and can be seen on [3]. David Bates, M0DFT, has also produced a design especially for PolarPlot, which excludes the LCD display and has a small range of commands to start/pause and stop the reading sequence. The M0DFT power meter is shown in **Photo 1**. By utilising the external wattmeter the need for a receiver connected to the soundcard is eliminated, together with the complexity of setting the AF and RF levels.

DISPLAYING THE RESULTS. The results are normally displayed on one of several polar scales, the most common in amateur radio today being the ARRL Log Co-ordinate scale. **Figure 2** shows the polar diagram of a dipole antenna plotted using this scale. A home made three-element beam is shown in **Figure 3**.

Sometimes the original collected readings are irregular for one reason or another, creating a ragged plot. This can be caused by noise on the signal, or wind blowing the antenna during the measurement. In an attempt to produce a smoother looking plot, a smoothing facility is provided. It must be stressed that the main objective should be to get a smooth plot in the first place, and that this facility should only be used if the plot is very ragged. The smoothing routine performs an averaging process on the point being plotted by summing its value with the immediately preceding and immediately succeeding points. This rather rudimentary

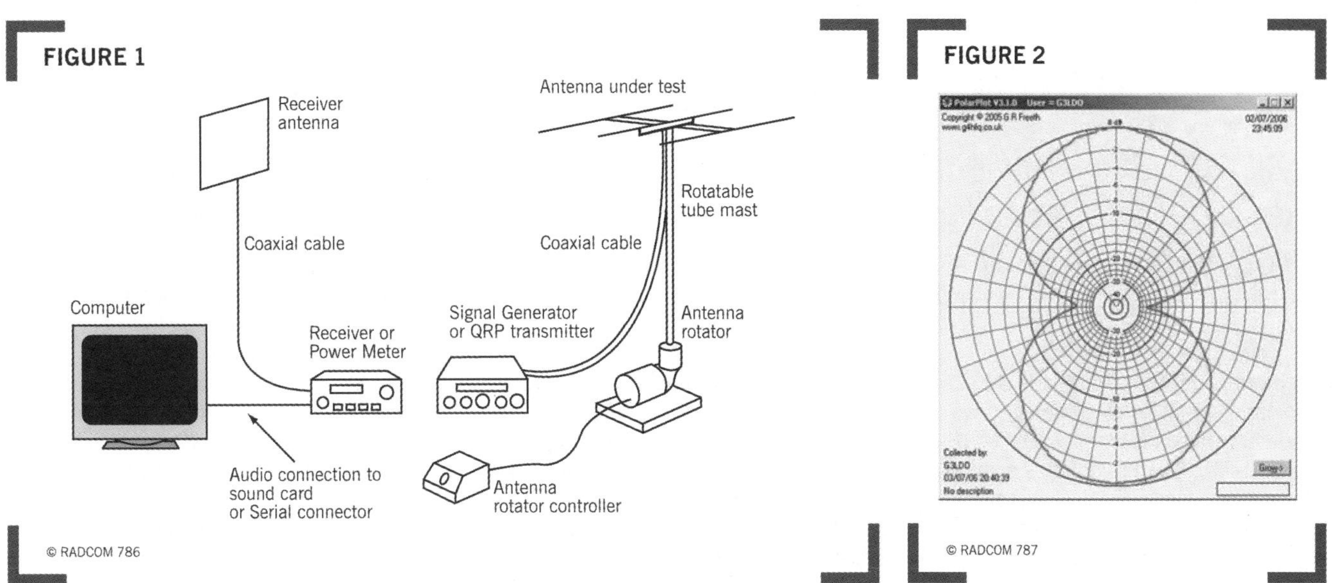


FIGURE 1: DIAGRAM OF THE COMPONENTS REQUIRED TO MAKE UP A VHF TEST RANGE. THE DISTANCE BETWEEN THE ANTENNA UNDER TEST AND THE RECEIVE ANTENNA SHOULD BE GREATER THAN 2.5 WAVELENGTHS.

FIGURE 2: POLAR DIAGRAM OF A DIPOLE ANTENNA PLOTTED USING THE ARRL LOG CO-ORDINATE SCALE.

process is performed twice, and the resulting averaged values are then plotted.

It is rare that you can get the maximum part of the main lobe to occur with the same orientation every time you make measurements. PolarPlot has a facility to rescale the plot so that the main lobe is made to equal 0dB while at the same time re-orientated to face 'north'. This facility has been applied to all the polar plots shown in **Figures 2, 3 and 4**. The four-element Tonna, see **Figure 4**, gives a similar pattern to the one supplied in their literature.

This updated version of PolarPlot is free and can be downloaded from the Internet, see [4]. It comes with full operating instructions, and can be run on all flavours of Windows. System requirements are not critical; I can run PolarPlot on anything from my Windows 98, HP 5700 Omnibook (166MHz 48MB RAM) to the Windows XP Toshiba Equium L10-30 (1.6GHz 500MB RAM).

REFERENCES

[1] *The Antenna Experiment's guide second edition.* Peter Dodd, G3LDO
[2] Antenna Workshop, Practical Wireless June 2006
[3] **www.webx.dk/oz2cpu/radios/milliwatt-dk.htm**
[4] **www.g4hfq.co.uk**

**FIGURE 3**

© RADCOM 788

FIGURE 3: POLAR DIAGRAM OF A HOME MADE, GAMMA MATCHED THREE-ELEMENT 144MHz YAGI ANTENNA PLOTTED USING THE ARRL LOG CO-ORDINATE SCALE.

**FIGURE 4**

© RADCOM 789

FIGURE 4: POLAR DIAGRAM OF A COMMERCIAL FOUR-ELEMENT TONNA 144MHz ANTENNA, WHICH GIVES A SIMILAR PATTERN TO THE ONE SUPPLIED IN THEIR LITERATURE. THE SETTING BOXES TO THE RIGHT ILLUSTRATE THE RANGE OF PROCESSING THAT IS AVAILABLE WITH POLARPLOT.

# The plot thickens…

*It's all very well simulating an antenna and believing the results, but what counts is how it performs in the real world. Peter Dodd investigates the correlation between EZNEC and reality with the help of PolarPlot and a homebrew VHF Quad.*

**Last month** I described methods of plotting the polar diagram of an antenna using a computer using a program called PolarPlot, by Bob Freeth, G4HFQ [1]. This month I will describe how I used PolarPlot to further investigate the properties of the well-known Quad antenna.

The proven antenna analysis programs such as EZNEC can predict the gain and front-to-back ratio of the quad, as shown in Figure 1, which shows the effect of varying the size of the reflector. The length of the driven element has little or no effect on the directivity characteristics of the beam pattern, within limits. On the other hand the length of the parasitic element (the reflector in this case) has a marked effect on beam pattern. This means that different lengths of reflector can be simulated by making measurements at different frequencies. This is achieved using the frequency sweep on EZNEC at 144, 145 and 146MHz as shown in **Figure 1**. This simulation shows the effect of a short reflector (144MHz) and progressively longer reflectors when modelled at 145 and 146MHz.

PHOTO 1: EXPERIMENTAL 2M QUAD ANTENNA

However, feed impedance, and hence the SWR, is affected by the length of the driven element and the coupling between the driven element and the reflector. With EZNEC the calculated feed impedance can be seen by clicking 'ScrDat' after making a plot.

THE 144.5MHz QUAD. The photo shows a quad I constructed for 144.5MHz for measurements with PolarPlot. The elements were made from 1mm diameter single strand copper wire and supported with 8mm square section wood battens. The mast and boom were constructed from 15mm copper tubing with the element supports fixed to the boom with metal brackets and hose clamps (jubilee clips). This arrangement allowed for easy adjustment of the element spacing. The total element lengths were 2110mm for the reflector and 2028mm for driven element. The resonant frequency of the reflector is adjusted using a 100mm long variable stub. The coax feed was connected directly to the driven element.

RESULTS. The model quad was set so that the distance between the elements was 310mm (0.15 wavelengths) and the reflector stub was set at 30mm long. The measurement frequency was 144.67MHz. The first attempt at making measurement using PolarPlot produced a lop-sided pattern shown in the red trace of **Figure 2**.

The coax feed was connected directly to the driven element with a simple balun comprising three loops of the feeder through a ferrite ring. The feeder was routed up the mast, along the boom and down on to the driven element. In the end the simplest feed method turned out to be the best, with the 'balun' removed and the feeder routed via the mast to a point adjacent to the driven element as shown in the photo. This resulted in the more symmetrical purple trace shown in Figure 2.

The SWR of the model configured this way was 1.8:1 and the calculated gain was 7.2dBi. The effect of progressively increasing the reflector loop size is illustrated in the PolarPlot measurements shown in **Figure 3**. As the reflector stub is increased from 30mm (Figure 2) to 70mm (red trace) and 90mm (purple trace) the front-to-back ratio increases and the gain decreases.

OBSERVATIONS. You will have noticed that the gain figures in all the plots are quoted are in dBi. To calculate the gain of an antenna we need some sort of reference. For theoretical gain calculations (including antenna modelling programs), a hypothetical point source antenna has been devised which radiates equally in all directions and is known as an isotropic radiator. The power gain of an antenna in a given direction is expressed in decibels relative to an isotropic radiator, and in this context is referred as dBi. This was used in the free space (ie not affected by ground) mathematical model shown in Figure 1.

However, measurements performed with PolarPlot are on practical antennas and have to be at some height above ground. In the case of the measurements shown in Figures 2 and 3 the antenna is around 3/4 wavelengths high. The ground under the antenna acts as a reflector and produces ground gain. In the case of the measurements so far described, the receive antenna was place at an angle of around 25degrees to the quad, close to the main angle of radiation at the height specified.

In the past I have used a single half-wave dipole as the reference antenna because it is the simplest practical form of radiator, and is generally accepted as a basis for comparison. The radiation pattern of a dipole is not uniform and has a power gain of 2.15dbi. Gain measurement

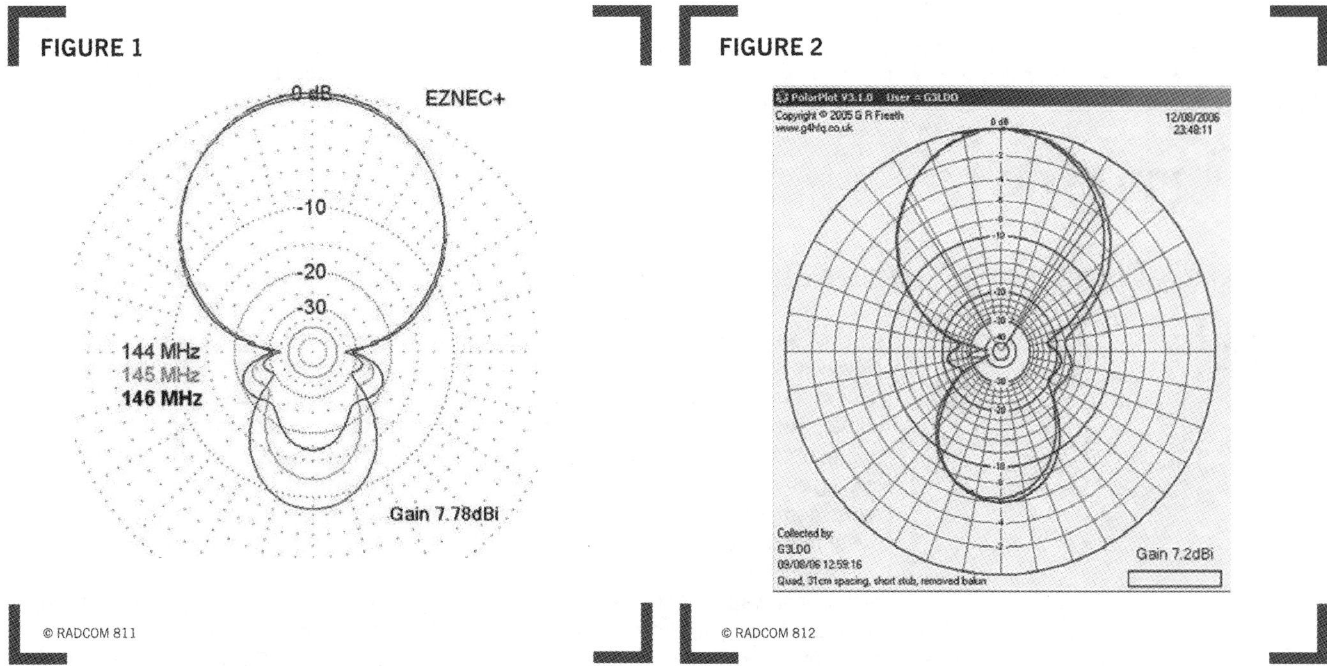


FIGURE 1: AZIMUTH POLAR DIAGRAMS OF A COMPUTER MODEL OF THE QUAD SHOWN IN PHOTO 1 USING EZNEC. VARIATION OF REFLECTOR LOOP DIAMETER IS SIMULATED USING SEPARATE PLOTS ON 144, 145 AND 146MHz AND OVERLAYING THEM.

FIGURE 2: TWO AZIMUTH POLAR DIAGRAMS OF THE QUAD SHOWN IN PHOTO 1, MEASURED USING POLAR PLOT. THE EFFECT OF THE FEED ARRANGEMENT IS SHOWN IN THE PLOT AND DISCUSSED IN TEXT.

figures, using the dipole radiator as a reference, are symbolised dBd. However, PolarPlot uses dBi. Bob Freeth, G4HFQ, in the PolarPlot user guide says: "There is a relationship between power gain and directive gain, the efficiency factor k, which is the ratio of the power radiated to the total input power. It is a number between 0 and 1, where 0 is totally inefficient and 1 is totally efficient. Thus the relationship between directive gain D and power gain G is: G = kD.

"If the antenna has no ohmic losses and therefore radiates all of the power delivered to is then k = 1 and G = D i.e. the power gain and directive gain are equal. PolarPlot measures the relative field strength E of signals delivered to the receiver and calculates relative power from these readings. The input power and antenna efficiency is not known by the program, and all estimates of gain are Directive Gain relative to an isotropic radiator ie dBi.

"The Directive Gain of the antenna is estimated in two ways: by measuring the half power beamwidth of the antenna, and by integration of the whole pattern's readings. The results are shown in dBi. As well as other factors the gain of an antenna is principally a function of horizontal and vertical beamwidth. Because the program is not aware of the full details of the antenna design, e.g. stacked array, quad, simple Yagi, element spacing etc and is simply reading the level of received signal of a given polarity, it can only provide an indication of gain.

"Nevertheless, comparison of several plots of the same antenna before and after changes are valid and can be useful in determining whether changes to design, operating height etc have had the desired effect. However, unless you have precise before and after measurements and can accurately determine input power, you will not see the power gain changes resulting from modifications to the feeder system (assuming the feeder is not an integral part of the radiating system!).

"For its calculations the program uses particular ratios between the horizontal and vertical beamwidths based on the number of elements. The difference between horizontal and vertical beamwidth is usually greatest with a 2 element beam, and decreases as the number of elements increases. When the number of elements is greater than 8 both beamwidths are, for practical purposes, the same.

"The ratios used have been determined by reviewing the EZNEC results of a number of antenna designs. A Yagi designed for optimum front/back ratio and a clean pattern will show a reading close to reality, but an antenna designed for maximum forward gain resulting in a pattern full of side and rear lobes will yield optimistic readings."

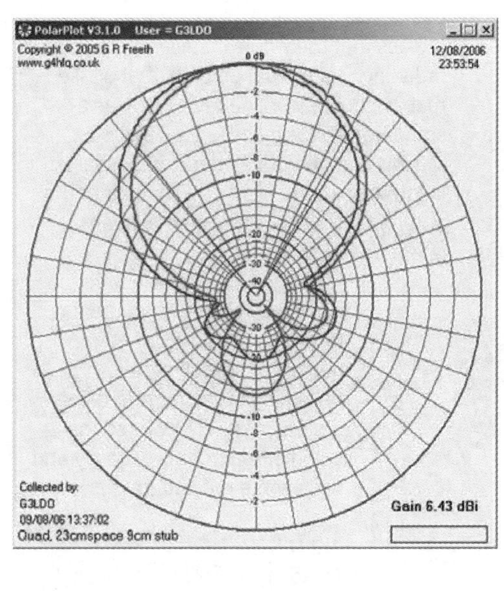


FIGURE 3: TWO ADDITIONAL MEASURED AZIMUTH POLAR DIAGRAMS USING POLAR PLOT. THE REFLECTOR STUB IS INCREASED FROM 30MM (FIG 2) TO 70MM (RED TRACE) AND 90MM (PURPLE TRACE).

REFERENCE

[1] *RadCom* September 2006 p 64

# Unconventional HF mobile

*Peter Dodd risks getting fitter through amateur radio*

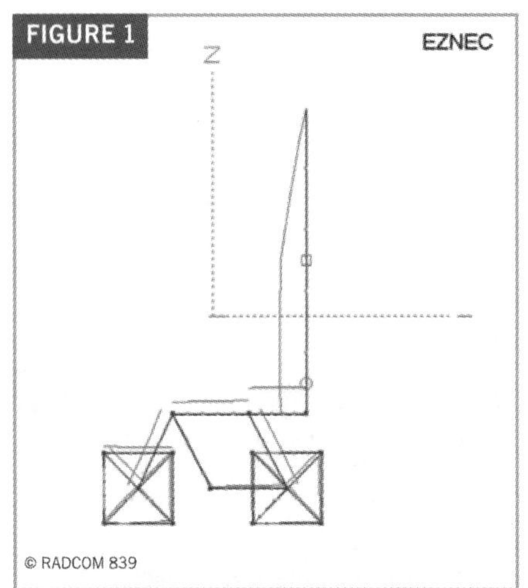


FIGURE 1: SIMPLE COMPUTER MODEL OF A BICYCLE MOBILE INSTALLATION 100mm ABOVE GROUND.

ADVICE GIVEN WITH GOOD INTENTIONS. My XYL suggested that I would benefit from some exercise and towed me along to her local sports centre. In there I found an array of contraptions which gave the place the ambience of a medieval torture chamber – the only machine that I felt confident enough to try was a sort of high tech exercise bike. After pedalling for some time I found the experience boring, gave up on the idea of the sports centre and bought a real bike.

BIKE MOBILE. I now combine my exercise with amateur radio. Bicycle mobile is not new to me – I have described this sort of activity before in [1], [2] and [3] (I haven't discussed VHF/UHF operation because this can be done simply by using a handheld). However, my original bicycle is rather a heavy mountain bike; the new one is compromise between a road bike and mountain bike and is more efficient for cycling on roads. Additionally, this one has more room for fitting accessories such as the antenna and a larger power supply.

I often wondered how efficient a bike mobile installation at HF really is. Generally the signals from my bike mobile are not as good as from my standard mobile installation in the car but this could be due to the QRP nature of bike mobile – it is difficult to run 100W from a bike due to power supply restrictions.

Modelling vehicles systems is now fairly well known as described in [4]. Using this technique I have attempted a crude model of a bicycle HF installation, which is shown in **Figure 1**. The bike structure and antenna currents are indicated by black and red lines respectively. The distance between the bike structure and its associated current line is an indication of relative current flow. The circle and the square on the antenna element represent the feedpoint and the loading coil respectively. This rough and ready model shows RF current in all parts of the bicycle as well as the antenna, which implies that the whole installation is radiating. The model predicts that a bike mobile should work nearly as well as a standard vehicle mobile, see **Figure 2**.

However, a mobile operator in a car is located inside the vehicle and clear of the antenna. This is not the case with an operator of a bike mobile, who is positioned close to the antenna no matter what arrangement is used. I do not know of any method of modelling the presence of the operator using a program like EZNEC3, so the only method open was to try and make some measurements.

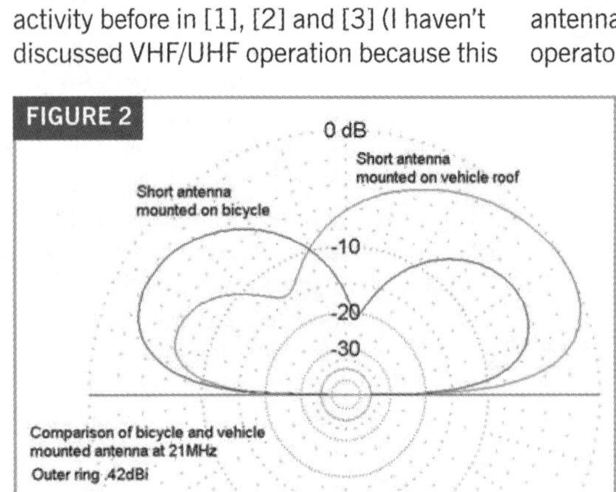


FIGURE 2: COMPARISON OF CAR AND BICYCLE MOBILE INSTALLATIONS AT 21MHz.

FIELD STRENGTH MEASUREMENTS. The signal strength measurements were done using the bicycle mobile shown in the photo. I used an MP-1 antenna; the variable inductance and telescopic whip make this antenna ideal for experimental work [5]. The antenna was energised using a FT-817 transceiver and the power output and SWR monitored using a Oskerblock SWR-300. The signal level was measured using a Heterodyne Voltmeter 2006 (Brüel & Kjaer) as a field strength meter (FSM).

Tests were carried out on the 14, 18 and 21MHz bands (my favourite HF mobile bands). The antenna was tuned for minimum SWR and the signal level measured on the FSM. I then sat on the bicycle and checked the SWR and field strength. This performance was repeated on all three bands. The difficulty of reading the signal level while sat on the bicycle was resolved by using binoculars...

To my surprise I found the presence of an operator close to the antenna appeared to make very little difference; just a slight increase in SWR on the higher frequency bands. There was a slight decrease in the field strength but not enough to quantify under the measurement conditions. These results may be explained if the mobile installation is considered as a total radiating entirety and not just radiation from the antenna itself.

BIKE MOBILE TEST SET-UP. FOR THE ACTUAL FIELD STRENGTH MEASUREMENTS THE FSM WAS LOCATED FURTHER FROM THE BICYCLE THAN SHOWN HERE.

REFERENCES

[1] *The Amateur Radio Mobile Handbook*, Peter Dodd, G3LDO. Note; updates to this book can be found on www.g3ldo.co.uk

[2] Antennas, *RadCom*, August 2004

[3] 'Antenna Workshop', *Practical Wireless*, June 2002

[4] 'Computer Modeling the HF Mobile Antenna', Peter Dodd, G3LDO, *The ARRL Antenna Compendium Vol 7*.

[5] MP-1 portable multiband antenna, available from Waters & Stanton

# We call it a Yagi, but...

*Peter Dodd traces the development of the now-familiar Yagi-Uda Array by contributors from around the world.*

TRACING THE HISTORY. Just over three years ago I was asked if I could write about the early development of the Yagi antenna. I was aware that the parasitic beam antenna was the result of research carried out at Tohoku Imperial University in Japan in the early 1920s. The main information source was from a paper written in English by Professor Hidetsugu Yagi when he visited the USA in 1928. This paper was published in the IRE journal under the heading 'Beam Transmission of Ultra Short Waves' **[1]**. I had hoped to describe how co-researcher Shintaro Uda came to discover the properties of the parasitic beam antenna.

EARLY ANTENNA WORK IN JAPAN. Uda had published a considerable amount of work, which appeared in a series of papers, published between 1926 and 1929 **[2]**. This work was, of course, published in Japanese. In spite of much effort I was unable to discover any information about the contents of these papers and decided instead to describe the evolution the parasitic beam in amateur radio **[3]** using amateur radio magazines as a source. However, from **[1]** and **[4]** I was aware that Uda's early antenna work concerned the measurement of the single-wire resonant loop radiation pattern and he observed and recorded the effect of ground. He also noted that nearby unconnected resonant loops caused changes in directivity, and from this a directional antenna was created. Could this have been the first quad antenna? Improved directivity was obtained when the loops were replaced with rods, then the driven element itself was replaced with a half-wave dipole. Some idea of Uda's experimental work was described by Yagi in [**1**].

"Suppose that a vertical antenna is radiating electromagnetic waves in all directions. If a straight oscillating system, whether it be a metal rod of finite length or an antenna with capacities at both ends and an inductance at the middle, is erected vertically in the field, the effect of this oscillator upon the wave will be as follows. If its natural frequency is equal to or lower than that of the incident wave, it will act as a 'wave reflector.' If, on the other hand, its natural frequency is higher than that of the incident wave, it will act as a 'wave director' ... a number of wave-directors may be arranged along the line of propagation.

"... The length of the directors must be accurately adjusted otherwise successful directing action will not be obtained. It has been found that the interval between the adjacent directors must be adjusted to a suitable value. The most advantageous value for this interval seems to be approximately 3/8 wavelength..."

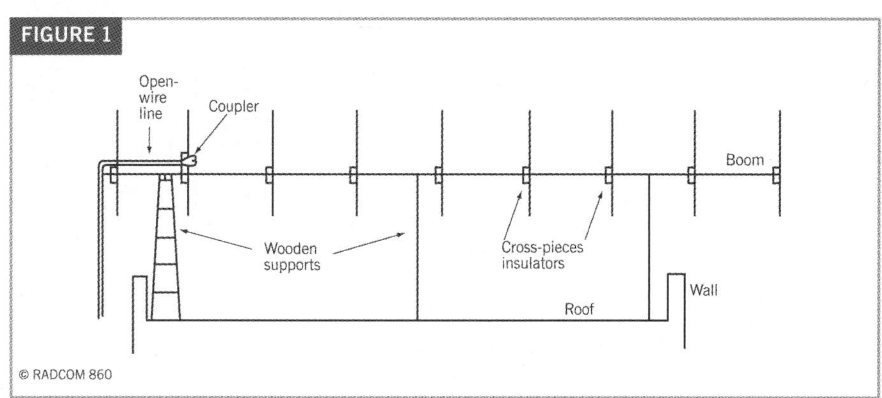


FIGURE 1: AN EXAMPLE OF ONE OF SHINTARO UDA'S EXPERIMENTAL ANTENNAS USING ONE REFLECTOR AND 7 DIRECTORS. THIS ANTENNA WAS MOUNTED ON THE ROOF OF TOHOKU UNIVERSITY FOR VERTICAL POLARISED 68MHz TRANSMISSION TESTS DURING 1927 AND 1928. SOURCE, *ANTENNAS (SECOND EDITION)* JOHN D. KRAUS.

FIGURE 2

EZNEC+

© RADCOM 861

FIGURE 2: AN EZNEC MODEL OF SHINTARO UDA'S ANTENNA SHOWN IN FIGURE 1. IT HAS A RESPECTABLE FREE-SPACE GAIN OF OVER 13dBi AND A FRONT-TO BACK OF 20dBi.

An example of one of Shintaro Uda's experimental antennas is shown in **Figure 1**. From this it can be seen that the director element spacings were quite wide. In common with the standardised design established by Uda, a model has been made using EZNEC4, with the reflector spaced at $\lambda/2.5$ and the directors $\lambda/3$ apart; the results are shown in **Figure 2**.

AMATEUR RADIO PARASITIC BEAM ANTENNAS. These were described in detail in [1]. A synopsis of these experiments is as follows:

In October 1928 the first documented use of a parasitic beam appeared in QST. It described the work of Mr. E. C. Crossett, 1CCZ, who built a beam antenna for the 28MHz. It was undertaken under the auspices of the ARRL Technical Development Program to explore the possibilities of long distance communication using the reflected signals from the ionosphere. The antenna system consisted a Yagi, with a driven element, three reflector wires and two director wires, and described as "arranged in the manner suggested by Uda and Yagi" [3].

One of the earliest designs of a practical amateur DX beam was built by John P.

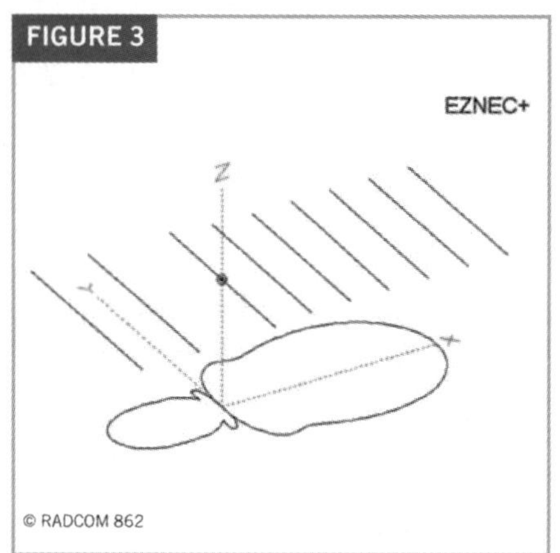


FIGURE 3: THE CALCULATED FREE-SPACE GAIN OF THE GM6RG'S 9 ELEMENT CLOSE-SPACED PARASITIC ANTENNA IS 10.46dBi.

Shanklin, W3CIJ, and described in QST in July 1934 **[5]**. This antenna comprised two 14MHz three-element wide spaced vertical yagis fed in phase.

In June 1938 **[6]** GM6RG described a high gain antenna for 28MHz comprising two vertical phased parasitic antennas, each comprising a driven element, reflector and three directors. The construction method he chose was the same as used by W3CIJ. This antenna was quite a monster. This large antenna did not live up to its expectations and behaved badly in stormy weather! The new design **[7]** used the original heavy top central lattice structure as a boom to support a nine element parasitic array using self-supporting tubular elements instead of wire elements. It comprised one driven element, six directors, and two reflectors, all at a height above ground of 48 feet.

WIDE/NARROW ELEMENT SPACING. When I wrote the article on beam antenna evolution **[3]** I was very puzzled as to the complete change of design in the later GM6RG design. Where had the design come from? It used 0.1λ spacing between the directors and two reflectors spaced at 0.2λ respectively. This new antenna had, according to EZNEC, over 10dBi gain, which must have been very impressive for those days although rather poor considering the size of the antenna. The antenna and polar pattern is shown in **Figure 3**.

The puzzle was solved for me by Pat Hawker, G3VA. After seeing my article Pat very kindly sent me a letter and two copies of articles from an amateur radio magazine called *RADIO*, a West Coast USA publication that existed in the 1930s and early 1940s. These magazines **[8, 9]** contained articles on the design and construction of two-element close spaced parasitic beams with an element spacing of just 0.1λ. They were inspired by the work of G. H. Brown who designed a close-spaced two-element parasitic vertical beam for MF broadcasting stations. A description of this work was published in January 1937 **[10]**. The work of G. H. Brown and W3CHO appeared in TT in 2003 **[11]**.

Modern empirical design **[12]** and computer analysis support the findings of Brown and W3CHO and most of the two and three element HF beam designs that followed used closer spacings, as can be seen in the design graphs shown in **Figure 4** and **Figure 5**.

The long parasitic beam by GM6RG appeared later than the published work of Brown and the *RADIO* articles so it is highly likely that the later GM6RG antenna was based on this work, although the additional reflector is a bit of a mystery. However, whereas the early HF antennas designs were very cumbersome because they extrapolated Uda's work on long parasitic beams to HF antennas with just a few elements, GM6RG's antenna was less that optimum for extrapolating W3CHO's spacings to a long parasitic beam. If the elements had been rearranged as in Uda's original design, using the same boom length, an extra 3dB gain would have been possible, similar to that shown in Figure 2.

Nevertheless, modern long Yagi designs use a mixture of close and wide spaced elements to obtain optimum performance.

REFERENCES

[1] 'Beam Transmission of Ultra Short Waves', Prof. Hidetsugu Yagi. *Proc*: IRE Vol 16 June 1928.

[2] 'On the Wireless Beam of Short Electric Waves'. S. Uda. A series of 11 papers published in the *Journal of the I.E.E (Japan)* from March 1926 until July 1929.

[3] 'Evolution of the Beam Antenna', Peter Dodd, G3LDO, *RadCom* July and August 2003

[4] 'Yagi: The Man and his Antenna', Robert H Welsh, N3RW, *QST* October 1993 1926

[5] 'A 14-Mc Rotary Beam Antenna for Transmitting and Receiving'. John P. Shanklin, W3CIJ, *QST* July 1934.

[6] 'A 28 Mc. Rotary Beam', Bryan Groom, GM6RG. *The T & R Bulletin*, June 1938.

[7] 'Rotatable Array Design', Bryan Groom, GM6RG. *The T & R Bulletin*, December 1938.

[8] 'The Compact Uni-directional Array', Walter Van.Roberts, W3CHO, *Radio* January 1938

[9] Practical Design of Close-Spaced Unidirectional Arrays, W. W. Smith W6BCX, *Radio* June 1938

[10] 'Directional Antennas', G. H. Brown, *Proc*: IRE Vol 25 January 1937

[11] 'Technical Topics', Pat Hawker, G3VA, *RadCom* October 2003

[12] *Beam Antenna Handbook*, 5th edition, Bill Orr, W6SAI

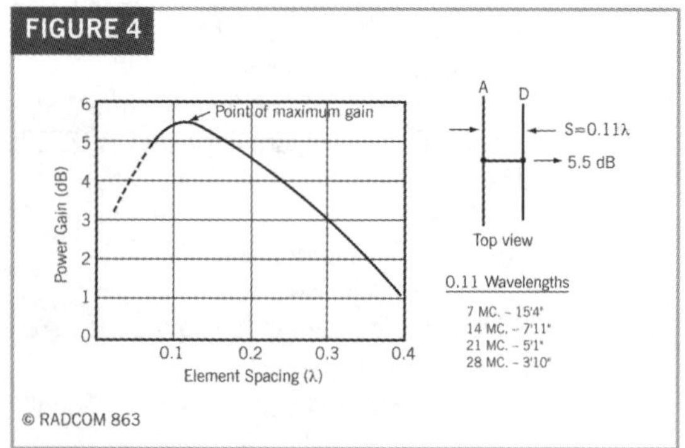


FIGURE 4: THE MAXIMUM POWER GAIN OF A TWO ELEMENT PARASITIC ARRAY USING A DIRECTOR ELEMENT OCCURS AT 0.11 WAVELENGTH. SOURCE, *BEAM ANTENNA BOOK (FIFTH EDITION)* BILL ORR, W6SAI

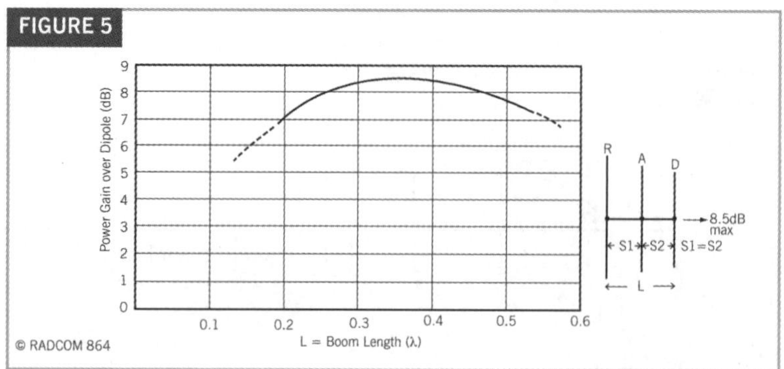


FIGURE 5: THE MAXIMUM POWER GAIN OF A THREE ELEMENT PARASITIC ARRAY OCCURS AT 0.17 WAVELENGTHS SPACING BETWEEN THE ELEMENTS, MAKING A TOTAL BOOM LENGTH OF 0.34 WAVELENGTHS. SOURCE, *BEAM ANTENNA BOOK (FIFTH EDITION)* BILL ORR, W6ASI

See Note [7]

PHOTO 1: A LARGE CARBON RESISTOR USED AS A DUMMY ANTENNA.

# Artificial aerials

*Sometimes you only need your transmitter to* ***think*** *it's talking to an aerial. Peter Dodd examines the role and construction of a dummy load.*

A DAY OUT. On Saturday 7 October 2006 I visited the G-QRP Convention in Rochdale, run by Rev George Dobbs, G3RJV. This is one of my favourite events, with lots of amateur radio components and radio bits; an event not dominated by commercial interests. One of the items that I bought during the visit was a dummy antenna kit, otherwise known as a dummy load.

AVOIDING INTERFERENCE. In the days when much of the transmitting equipment was home made, a dummy load ("artificial aerial") was an essential item. A resistive non-reactive load in place of the antenna was a great help when trying to adjust and neutralise a lively PA. Additionally, the rest of the amateur radio community was spared the rasps and squawks that accompanied this procedure if the antenna were to be used as a load.

Now that most transmitters in use today are commercially manufactured the business of adjusting a PA is no longer necessary. However, there are other transmitter adjustments, such as the microphone gain, speech processor (speech compression) or processor frequency shift that need to be done with the transmitter on. Judging by the number of whistling acts and larynx testing "Walloogh"s to be heard on the bands a lot of test transmissions are done using the antenna as a load. Life would be nicer if some of these tests were done using a dummy load.

A dummy antenna can be made simply by connecting a resistor to a PL-529 plug then connecting it to the antenna socket of your transceiver or transmitter. Because the resistor has to absorb all the transmitter power a simple 2W resistor is out of the question except for QRP work.

You can sometimes come across suitable large high wattage carbon resistors, usually at radio rallies. An example of such a resistor is shown in **Photo 1**. I use this load resistor for transmitter testing and it will handle the 1kW of RF power generated by a 136kHz transmitter for short periods. The value stamped on the side of the resistor is 66 ohms ± 20%. The measured value was 68.6 ohms. The impedances at 5, 15 and 30 MHz were R68 +j0, R70.4 +j15 and R73.6 +j31 respectively, measured on a HP4815A vector impedance meter. I suspect the inductive reactance was caused by the 250mm (10in) length of wire which was necessary to connect both ends of the resistor to the socket. The impedance increased to R107 +j147 at 100MHz, which made it rather unsuitable for 144MHz transmitter testing.

The resistor is 25mm (1in) in diameter. I guess that if the resistor were enclosed in a metal tube 500mm (2in) diameter of the same length, it would form a short coaxial section where the characteristic impedance would be maintained along the whole length of the resistor. Such a design can be found in [1].

A PRACTICAL DUMMY LOAD. If you don't have a large carbon resistor you can make one from a number of ordinary one or two watt resistors connected in series or parallel to make up a value of 50Ω. Which brings me back to the dummy load kit purchased at the G-QRP Convention from Dave Penny, G3PEN.

This kit comprises two pieces of double-sided PCB material, 95mm (3¾ in) square, 42 x 2.2k resistors (to be connected in parallel) and a SO-239 socket. There were no instructions with this kit so I tinned both boards and drilled a pattern of matching holes in them, with one large hole in the centre of the top board to take the SO-239 socket. The wires at one end of the resistors were then soldered into the one board, then the other end wires coaxed into holes in the other board, see **Photo 2**.

It occurred to me that it would have been easier if I had fixed the resistors on the outside of the board – I should have paid more attention when I bought the kit. Indeed this turned out to be the case. In an e-mail to me (after I had constructed my kit!) G3PEN said: "The resistors are placed along each edge of the PCB, fairly symmetrically, and each is soldered in place, trimming or turning the wires slightly if they would otherwise overlap on

PHOTO 2: THE G3PEN DUMMY LOAD UNDER SWR/FREQUENCY MEASUREMENT TESTS.

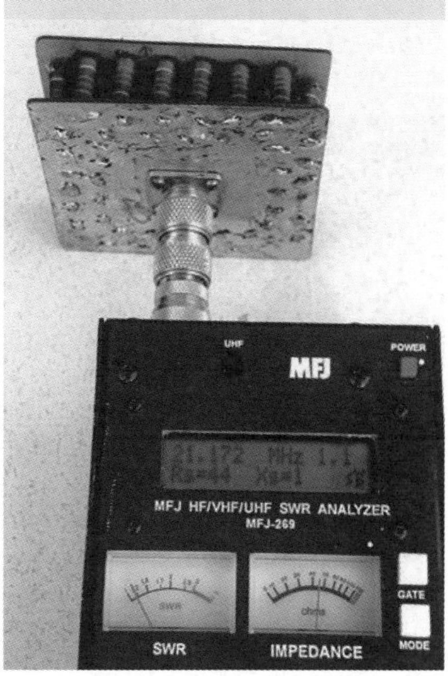

the PCB face. (I leave the wires as long as possible to aid heat conduction from the resistor to the PCB.) I did try notching the PCB at first, but found it wasn't really needed, and caused a lot more work! I did do some with holes, as you describe, but that was really too much effort altogether, even drilling in batches".

This dummy load handles the power from a standard 100W HF transceiver on all modes, becoming not uncomfortably warm after several minutes testing on CW and SSB. The impedance of this load was R49.5 +/-j0 on 5MHz, R44 +j4 on 30MHz and R25 +j43 on 100MHz. The SWR was very low on the HF bands and less than 1.5:1 on 50MHz. It could be used at 144 MHz but the SWR was over 2:1.

You will notice that the resistance component of this dummy antenna impedance decreases as the frequency is increased. So what is the frequency/impedance characteristic of each individual resistor?

CHARACTERISTICS OF RESISTORS. Carbon composition resistors, as shown in **Figure 1(a),** are often recommended for RF service. However, all resistors have some series inductance and a shunt capacitance. A 360Ω 1W of this type measured R363 -j25 at 3MHz and R339 -j78 at 70MHz. This resistor had more capacitive reactance than expected. A 20Ω carbon film resistor (5% tolerance) measured R20.5 +j0.5 at 3MHz, which moved to R20.5 +j18.4 at 70MHz. A similar resistor of 180Ω showed no change in reactance as the frequency was increased to 70MHz.

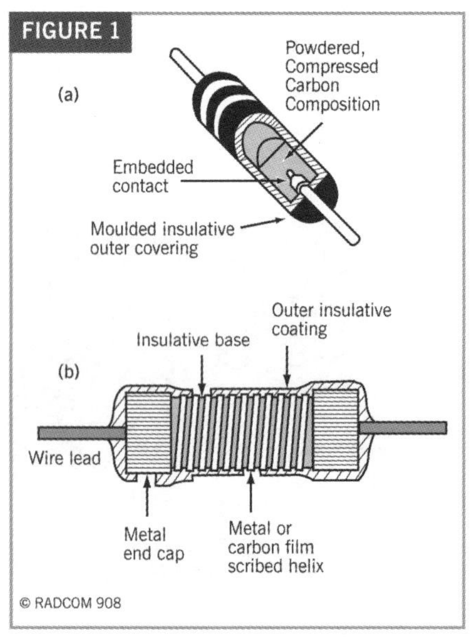

FIGURE 1: (A) A CARBON COMPOSITION RESISTOR. (B) A METAL OR CARBON FILM RESISTOR.

The construction of a metal or carbon film resistor is shown in **Figure 1(b).** The metal or carbon film is inscribed on the insulating base in the form of a helix, which might lead you to believe that such a resistor would be inductively reactive at RF. In the case of our 2.2kΩ resistors that made up the kit pack a resistor sample measured R2164 -j265 at 3MHz and R432 -j812 at 80MHz. However, when they were all connected in parallel to make up the dummy antenna it was only slightly inductively reactive up to 30MHz.

The resistive component of the impedance of the large carbon resistor described earlier remained fairly constant with frequency change. I also measured the frequency characteristics of a 60Ω wirewound resistor. There are numerous warnings in numerous publications about using these resistors at RF and you can see why. The resistor exhibited all the characteristics of an inductor, with a rapid increase in reactance as the frequency was increased.

These frequency characteristics are shown in **Figure 2**. The numbers along the curves indicate measurement frequency. The 2.2k film resistor and the 360Ω carbon resistor values have been 'normalised' to below 100Ω and ± j60 to enable the characteristics to be plotted along side the 50Ω dummy load and the 60Ω wire wound resistor.

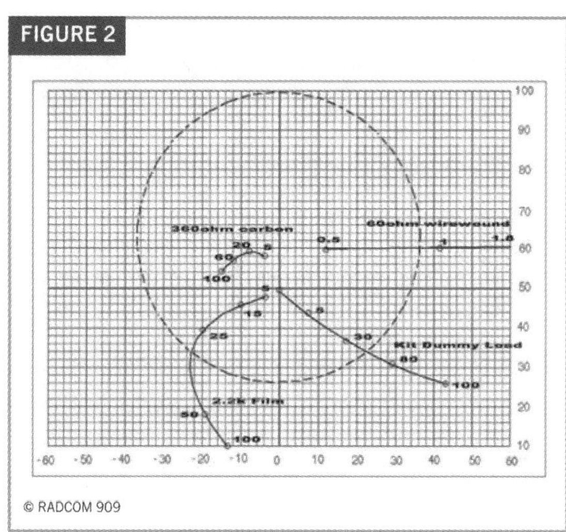

FIGURE 2: THE FREQUENCY CHARACTERISTICS OF SOME OF THE RESISTORS DESCRIBED IN THE TEXT. THE NUMBERS ALONG THE CURVES INDICATE MEASUREMENT FREQUENCY IN MHz.

Temperature characteristics are a further consideration. G3PEN says: "The resistors used in the kit are metal-oxide. These have slightly rounded ends to the body, whereas some kits use real carbon-rod resistors (same values), which have sharp edges to the body. The real difference comes in the heat characteristics. I have tested various metal-oxide types (various values of R, but all either 2W or 3W rating) by applying a variable DC supply to a specimen hanging in free air, raising the voltage gradually until the dissipation was at least 25W per item (some I took to 50W). At first they start smoking, and then go black, with all the paint catching alight and burning merrily. Eventually, they glow a deep cherry red. When allowed to cool down, each resistor has still measured within specification for resistance".

DUMMY LOAD RATINGS AND COMMERCIAL PRODUCTS. There is quite a range of dummy loads on the market at lots of different prices and specifications, see [2]. The power handling capacity is somewhat arbitrary but seems to mean how long the load can continue to handle a given power over a given time before overheating. The MFJ-250 had the load resistor immersed in a tin of oil. The Vectronics DL-2500 uses a cooling fan.

The G3PEN kit would handle 25W (maximum power available on AM) for over 3 minutes. At that time although it was hot, I wouldn't say it had overheated. The transceiver would not give a continuous 100W for testing but slow-keyed dashes were used and the kit dummy load handled this for over a minute without difficulty.

REFERENCES
[1] Super Dummy, *The ARRL Handbook 1993, chapter 34*
[2] *UK Radio Communications Equipment Guide 2006*, Waters & Stanton

# Rescuing old aerials

*When it comes to renovating aerial bits, Peter Dodd is in his element...*

**Photo 1**: Disassembly of a badly corroded joint on a VHF vertical antenna, showing a thick deposit of aluminium oxide within the joint.

**Photo 2**: The joint shown in Photo 1 after renovation. The facing surfaces of the joint have been cleaned, coated with a thin film of grease and reassembled with a new jubilee clip.

**Last month I described my visit to the** G-QRP Convention in Rochdale. In addition to the dummy load kit I also bought a couple of other treasures (the sort that the station manager calls 'junk'). One of these items was a 2m co-linear vertical antenna in a poor state of preservation. However, I am unable to resist acquiring old antennas just to see how they are constructed and in this case it also provided a subject for me to discuss: renovating an antenna and dealing with corrosion. So if the performance of your antenna has become less than optimum recently then the following may be pertinent.

RENOVATING AN ANTENNA. The upper join in the vertical section of this 2m antenna was held in place with a jubilee clip. This was seized solid with corrosion and I sheared the screw head off in an attempt to undo it. I also sheared two of the wing nuts that held the counterpoise rods in place; it didn't seem like a good start.

After sawing through the clip with a diagonal cut as shown in **Photo 1** I pulled the joint apart slightly. You can see a thick deposit of white powder on the facing surfaces of the aluminium tubes. This powder is aluminium oxide, and although it does conduct its performance at RF is much poorer than clean aluminium tubing, and it causes a reduction in antenna performance.

I cleaned the facing surfaces of the joint using emery paper, coated with a thin film of grease and reassembled it with a new jubilee clip. **Photo 2** shows the joint during assembly. The corroded wing nuts shown in Photo 1 were replaced with new nuts, bolts and washers. As I live about 400m from the beach on the south coast, the prevailing winds carry a fairly high salt content during stormy weather so antenna corrosion can be a problem. My solution is to coat all joints and junctions, U-bolts and jubilee clips with grease using an old toothbrush. The grease I use is nothing special and is labelled Duckhams LB10 Grease and it comes in a 500g tin: any similar grease can be used.

During the summer of 2006 I did some maintenance on my modified MQ2 on the chimney (this is the antenna shown on the front cover of, and described in, *Backyard Antennas*). The grease applied at the last maintenance (about three years earlier) had formed a sort of thick dark brown mess and didn't look very pretty. However all the U-bolts and jubilee clips that held the antenna and its mounting together were undone without difficulty. Furthermore, when the aluminium tubing joints were pulled apart the mating surfaces of the tubing were free from the sort of corrosion shown in Photo 1.

Aluminium forms its own protective oxide barrier, which prevents further corrosion providing it is undisturbed. For this reason I limit the grease treatment to the joints and fittings.

HOME MADE ANTENNA FITTINGS. The main difficulties encountered by newcomers (and some old-timers) to constructing a beam antenna is acquiring or constructing antenna fittings. This month I will describe the construction of boom element extensions and quad spiders that you can make without the use of any specialised tools. A hacksaw, a variety of screwdrivers, spanners, a selection of files and an electric drill are all that you'll need. Use protective gloves when sawing or drilling metal – some of the edges can be quite sharp.

The following are required to make antenna fittings:

- **Jubilee clips.** These are a real friend to the antenna experimenter. They can be used for joining different diameter sections of elements, joining sections of mast, joining wire to metal elements, joining quad spreaders to angle stock - the list is endless. They are readily available at all hardware, DIY and car part stores. When used as part of an outdoor antenna structure always coat it with a film of grease to prevent corrosion. Never use paint or varnish because this will make it impossible to remove and also make it unusable for further construction projects.

- **Exhaust pipe clamps.** Used to construct boom-to-mast and element-to-boom fittings. Also can also be used to fit angle stock to booms when constructing Quad spiders or X beam element supports. The clamp comprises a U-bolt and a metal former whose purpose is to fit a section of

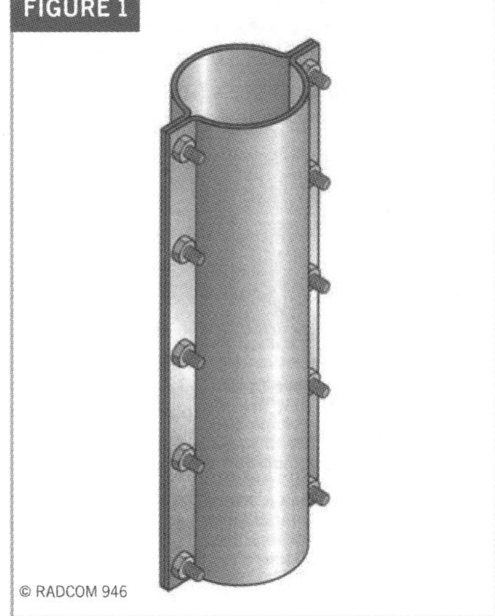


**Figure 1**: Two-piece steel sleeve used to join 1½ or 2 inch sections of tube together

tubing to a flat surface. They come in a range of sizes to fit tubing from 1 to 2½ inches (25mm to 64mm). Unfortunately there seems to be no standardisation of U-bolt thread types so you have to be careful not to lose the nuts in the grass while working on the antenna.

- **Aluminium tubing.** I have not had much luck locating a local supplier of aluminium tube. However, you can buy aluminium tubing from Waters & Stanton [1] from one inch to two inches (25mm to 51mm) diameter in ¼ inch (6mm) increments. On the other hand there are a couple of scrap metal merchants nearby from who I have bought metal tubing of all sorts over the years. The policy of some scrap metal dealers is to reduce tubing and pipes to short lengths when it arrives on site so as to make it more manageable. Others keep long lengths because they consider it as a more marketable commodity. This is particularly true regarding aluminium scaffold pole. Scaffold pole appears to be 1⅞ inches (48mm) outside diameter rather than the 2 inches (51mm) outside diameter described above. Note that scaffold pole is heavy-duty stuff with a wall thickness of 4mm rather than 2mm for the 2 inch diameter tubing described above.

MAKING TUBING EXTENSIONS. If you need to extend a 2 inch mast or boom section then you can use two-piece sleeves or couplings obtainable from [1] and shown in **Figure 1**. Sleeves are also available to extend 1½ inch tube sections. I am not sure whether the 2 inch sleeve would be suitable for extending scaffold-tubing sections because this tubing diameter is less than 2 inches. You can make your own extension sleeves as shown in **Photo 3**. This is done with a short section of the same or similar (slightly larger) diameter tubing, which is sawn longitudinal down one side. The coupling slot is prised apart using screwdrivers and forced over one end of the section of tubing to be extended. The extension tube can then be forced into the other side of the coupling and the whole lot clamped together with jubilee clips. If the joint is required to handle torque then more than three jubilee clips may be required, or holes can be drilled through the joint and self tapping screws inserted to secure it.

**Photo 3**: Home made extension sleeves for 2 inch and 1 inch tubing. The middle jubilee clip on the 1 inch join has been removed so that the junction may be seen more clearly.

**Photo 4**: A quad spider constructed from angle section aluminium stock, fixed to the boom using exhaust pipe clamps.

QUAD SPIDERS. A device to hold the spreaders of a quad to the boom, known as a spider, is often regarded as difficult structure to build. There are commercial quad spiders that use aluminium castings but they are rather expensive. My solution is the arrangement shown in **Photo 4**. Exhaust pipe clamps are used fix angle section aluminium to the boom. The cane or fibre glass spreaders can then be fixed to the angle section using jubilee clips. The same construction can be used to make spreaders for horizontal wire antennas such as the Moxon rectangle. This structure is very strong and lightweight.

There is another method of fixing spreaders to the boom and that is to use shelf angle supports (brackets). The shelf brackets that I tried out are 250 x 300mm and have "max weight 32kg" marked on the label. They are made of 1mm thick mild steel and each bracket weighs only 180g. They are fixed to the boom using jubilee clips as shown in **Photo 5**. Note that only two, rather than four are shown to illustrate more clearly the method of fixing.

This brings me to a further spider construction. The boomless quad uses an arrangement that allows optimum spacing of all elements of a multi-band quad. Not only do the four quad spreaders have to be fixed at 90° to each other, but they also have to be pitched about 22° away from the supporting mast. This makes for a more complex arrangement of spider that normally requires a casting or some welding to achieve the required shape. Using the shelf bracket arrangement shown in Photo 5 it occurs to me that the appropriate angle could be achieved by placing appropriate sized wooden wedges under the brackets where they are fixed to the boom. This is in the 'idea' stage at the moment – watch this space.

THE D2T ANTENNA. I get e-mails from people asking me if the D2T antenna is really as good as quoted in a catalogue. The quote goes "The antenna was reviewed by Peter Dodd, G3LDO... he describes how it achieved excellent results on all bands (1.5 to 200MHz!)". Well, I never said anything of the sort. The review, and others, of this antenna can be found on [2]. Note that the contact results given in the review were in published 1999 when the sunspot cycle was much higher than now.

REFERENCE
[1] Radio Communications Equipment Guide 2007, page 162, Waters & Stanton
[2] www.antenna.it/world.htm

**Photo 5**: Quad spider constructed from shelf brackets. Note that only two, rather than four are shown to illustrate more clearly the method of fixing.

# Deeply dippy

*Don't overlook the dip oscillator, says Peter Dodd.*

THE DIP OSCILLATOR. Recently I have been using a dip oscillator to set up the reflector parasitic element (and stub) of a quad antenna. For the newcomer I will describe this instrument and its uses, as it seems to fallen out of favour and is not described in amateur radio literature much these days.

The dip oscillator is an instrument capable of measuring the resonant frequency of tuned circuits and antenna elements, a very useful item for experimenting with antennas. The main attribute of the dip oscillator is that a direct connection with the tuned circuit being measured is unnecessary. At the time when the instrument was constructed using a valve as the active element it was a known as a grid dip oscillator (GDO), and although these instruments now use a bi-polar transistors or FET as the active element they are still better known as GDOs.

TYPES OF GDO. The GDO works on the principle that RF power from a calibrated tuneable oscillator is absorbed by a close-coupled resonant circuit when it and the oscillator are tuned to the same frequency. This results in some oscillator energy loss and an indication of this loss can be used to indicate the tuned circuit resonance. There are several ways this energy loss can be seen:

- By measuring the level of base, gate or grid voltage, which is proportional to the peak-to-peak level of the oscillator waveform. The early vacuum tube or valve instruments used this method by using a meter in the grid circuit to measure grid current; hence Grid Dip Oscillator. An example of this type of circuit is shown in **Figure 1.**
- By measuring the DC current through the active element (i.e. FET) of the oscillator. This current varies with the peak-to-peak level of the oscillator waveform. The circuit shown in **Figure 2** measures the total current through the FET. The variation of current as the GDO detects resonance is only a small part of the total current through the FET. The dip is enhanced by offsetting the meter using a potentiometer in a bleeder network. This is set so that the meter reads about 75% FSD when the instrument is not coupled to a load. The circuit in Figure 2 is based on two very similar designs published in *QST*, Technical Correspondence **[1] [2].**
- By using a diode to measure the peak-to peak oscillator voltage. This method is the most popular with solid state designs. Early designs suffered from the disadvantage that if the oscillator waveform amplitude fell below the conduction level of the diode all indication disappeared. Later designs use Schottky barrier diodes, or some bias, so that the problem is minimised. The GDO design **[3] [4]** by A.T. Bailey, G3WPO, shown in **Photo 1,** uses the diode detection method in conjunction with a push-pull Kaliatron oscillator circuit covering 0.8 to 215MHz in six ranges. This GDO was the best of the solid state designs tried, particularly at VHF.

GDO PERFORMANCE. A good GDO should possess the following features:

- Good sensitivity. Some indication of sensitivity can be checked by squeezing the coil of the GDO between the thumb and forefinger and noting the meter deflection; this should dip to at least 50% of the maximum reading. The GDO should also be capable of measuring resonance of a high C tuned circuit at a distance of 60 to 70mm (2-3in). I use a parallel tuned circuit, comprising a 5mH inductor with a 100 pF capacitance, as a standard, see **[5]** for a description of this procedure.
- Large frequency dial with smooth reduction gear tuning. The GDO could have an internal frequency counter instead of the dial but this would increase the complexity of the instrument. Provision for connection of the GDO to a frequency counter is probably a better arrangement, which would make the quality of the frequency dial less of an issue.
- Meter large enough to see the dip clearly. An audio indication of a dip is also useful and is used in the G3WPO design.
- Be self contained, no power leads.

MEASURING ANTENNA ELEMENT RESONANCE. One authority describes the method of measuring the resonance of a driven element by coupling it to the GDO via a length of feeder and a coupling loop **[6]**. This simply will not work because the resonances of the feeder will be included in the element measurements, as described in **[7]**.

I tried measuring resonances on my multi-band two-element antenna and

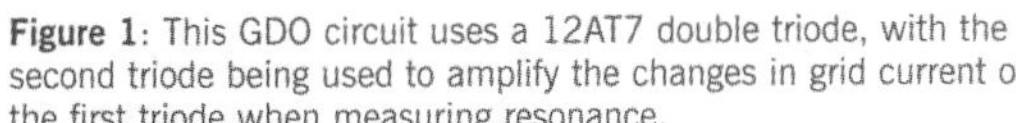

**Figure 1**: This GDO circuit uses a 12AT7 double triode, with the second triode being used to amplify the changes in grid current of the first triode when measuring resonance.

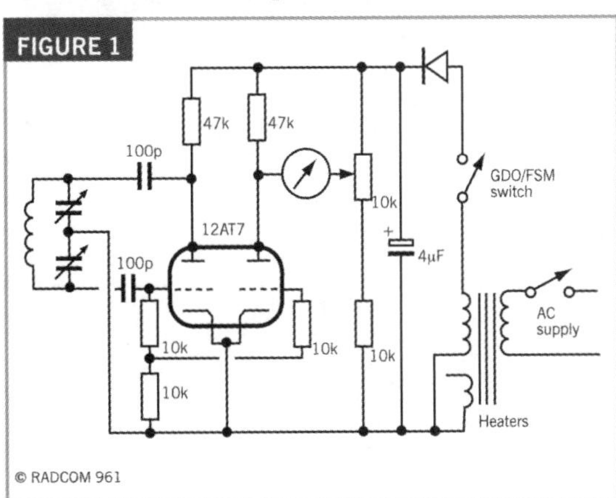


**Figure 2**: Circuit of an FET GDO which detects resonance by measuring the variation in DC current through the FET.

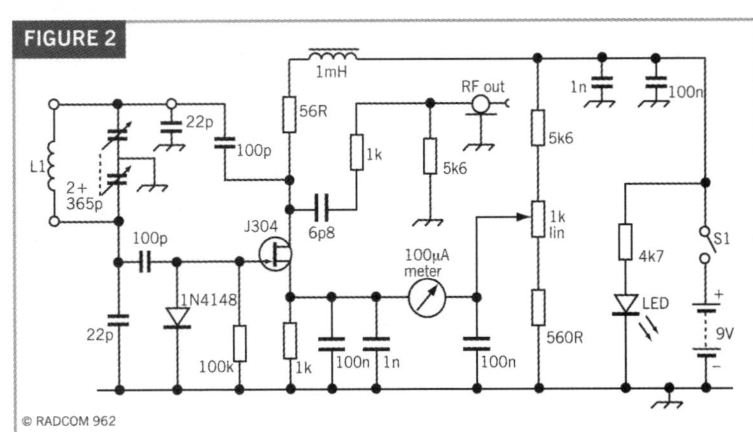

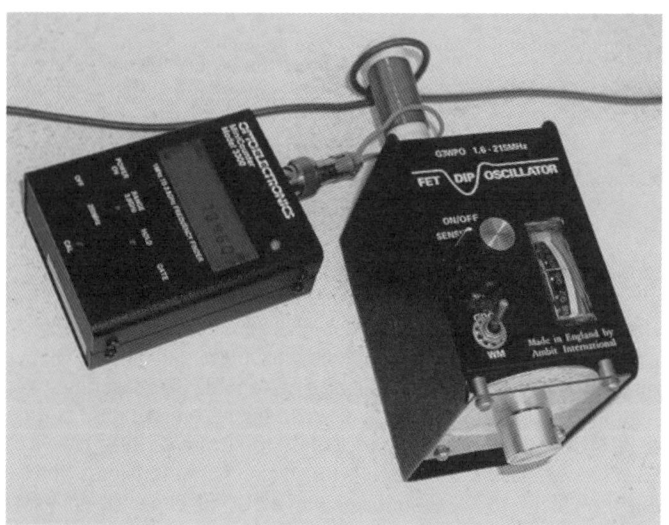


**Photo 1**: GDO coupled into a wire antenna element. The frequency dial of this GDO is very small and difficult to read but when used with a frequency counter, as shown, this limitation is circumvented.

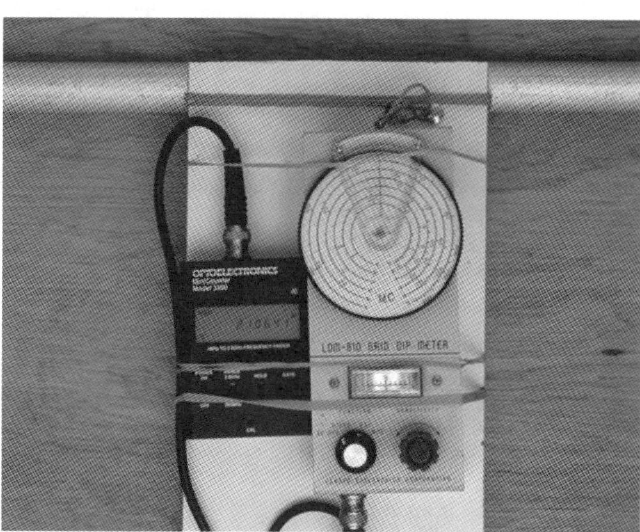


**Photo 2**: The G3LDO MK5 antenna element resonance measuring kit, for measuring tubular antenna elements.

obtained a set of resonance measurements that suggested I was looking at the parasitic reflector resonances, with an extra strong dip at 22MHz. I then increased the length of the feeder and the frequency of all the resonance points shifted, with a very large dip at 21.7MHz; so it was obvious that the feeder resonance played a part.

The best way of measuring a driven element via a length of feeder is to use a SWR meter. This begs the question of why use a GDO. As stated earlier, the main advantage of a dip meter is that it doesn't have to have a direct connection to the resonant circuit (antenna element) under test. This makes it particularly useful in determining the resonance of parasitic elements or for measuring the resonant point of a large single turn lower HF band loop whose frequency is difficult to determine in other ways. If it is used to measure driven element resonance then the feeder should be disconnected and the centre insulating section shorted out.

Antenna elements are measured by coupling the coil to current point (the centre of a half-wave antenna) of the element and varying the frequency of the GDO until a dip in the meter is seen. If your GDO lacks sensitivity, additional coupling to the element can be achieved by forming a small loop in the wire element. The GDO can then be coupled to the element as shown in Photo 1. All GDOs that I have tested will couple into an element modified in this way.

GDO/ELEMENT COUPLING. Coupling to tubular elements is more difficult because the coupling between a small diameter coil and a tubular element is very loose and you can hardly bend a tubular element into a loop. If a dip cannot be obtained in the normal way then a different type of coil is required to improve coupling. I tried using a GDO with a large diameter, coat hanger shaped, one-loop coil proposed by G6XN **[7]**.

Although the coat-hanger shaped coil worked very well on the high HF and lower VHF bands a coil design for the lower frequencies posed a problem; how to wind a multi-turn on a large diameter former with a flat side. The final practical design is shown in **Photo 2**. The coil is wound on a short board, 100mm wide and 14mm thick. The coil is shown in Photo 2 and comprises three turns of 16SWG plastic insulated wire, which allows the oscillator to be tuned from 14 to 34MHz. This arrangement uses a home brew GDO built into a defunct LM810 case, using the circuit shown in Figure 2. The coils plug into an FT283 crystal socket, which is a very convenient arrangement for plugging in the coil wire ends. An additional single turn loop is used to couple the coil to the frequency counter if provision on your GDO, as shown in Fig 2, does not exist. The coupling of this pick-up coil to the main winding can be adjusted with respect to the main winding until just enough energy is available to operate the frequency counter.

The board provides a platform for the GDO, frequency counter and even a note pad. The flat sided coil couples into any antenna element, with the board providing a stable point to rest the measuring kit against the element while measurements are being made.

TRANSMISSION LINE RESONANCE MEASUREMENT. It is very useful to be able to measure the resonant length of a length of coaxial cable. Sometimes we wish to avoid half-wave resonant lengths of transmission line to reduce the effects of antenna currents on the line, or we might need resonant lengths to make a coaxial balun or a phasing network for a directional array or for circular polarised yagi. Resonance can be measured by shorting one end of the feeder and fitting a small wire loop to the other end so that the GDO can be coupled to it. I use a PL259 socket with a coupling loop soldered to it, which plugs into the connector at the end of the feeder.

If you want to know the length of a feeder in an existing installation then look for a series of resonances using the higher frequency coils of the GDO. The frequency difference between these resonances is the lowest resonant frequency of the feeder. For example: on the coaxial cable from my shack to the antenna on the roof, using the GDO with high HF frequency coil, I measured resonances at 47.24, 35.4 and 23.7MHz.

The differences between these figures are 11.84 and 11.7. I then plugged in the GDO coil covering the appropriate range and measured the lowest resonant frequency at 11.76MHz, which is the *electrical*, not the physical wavelength. The physical length of feeder can be calculated by:

Length in metres = (150 x *TLVF*) / *LRF*
or Length in feet = (487.5 x *TLVF*) / *LRF*
where
*LRF* = lowest resonant frequency
*TLVF* = transmission line velocity factor (typically 0.6 to 0.8, but check for your specific cable).

Further descriptions of the uses of the GDO can be found in **[5]** and **[7]**.


REFERENCES

[1] "Technical Correspondence", W1CER, *QST*, November 1971

[2]"Technical Correspondence" by Peter Lumb G3IRM, *QST* June 1972,

[3] "A FET dip oscillator for 1.6-215MHz with Tone Dip Feature" by A.L. Bailey G3WPO. *Radcom* November 1981.

[4] "The G3WPO FET dip oscillator Mk2", by A.L. Bailey G3WPO *Radcom* April 1987.

[5] *The Antenna Experimenter's Guide, second edition*, Peter Dodd, G3LDO, RSGB

[6] *Antenna Toolkit*, Joe Carr, K4IPV

[7] *HF Antennas for all Locations*, L.A. Moxon, G6XN

# The Counterpoise

*The secret of success when using an end fed wire antenna.*

END FED ANTENNAS. The end-fed antenna is simple, cheap, and easy to erect; suits many house and garden layouts and is equally amenable to base or portable operation. There are two aspects of the end-fed antenna which need to be considered. The first is the matching the transmitter to the range of impedances encountered at the end of wire antenna on the different bands, and the other is an effective and efficient RF earth or ground.

A good RF earth at the transceiver in the shack is very important when using an end fed wire antenna. The penalty for not having a good RF earth is that the outside of the radio equipment can be at a high RF potential. Furthermore, the microphone, key or headset leads are also 'hot' with RF so you get RF feedback and BCI problems. Additionally, the IC circuits of modern communications equipment (keying or microphone circuits) are easily damaged in these circumstances.

THE CENTRE FED DIPOLE. Let us consider the simple half-wave dipole. Looking at it from the point at which it is fed, the centre of the coax is connected to one wire and the braiding to the other, as shown in **Figure 1**. Each wire is a quarter wavelength long and both wires radiate equally. The arrangement is good for only one band, although additional wires could be added as shown to make a multiband dipole.

Supposing the dipole is now orientated so that it is vertical with the right hand wire uppermost. This wire, which is connected to the centre of the coax could now be considered as the 'antenna' and the other wire, connected to the coax braiding, as the 'counterpoise'. The current in both wires is still equal provided they are both quarter of a wavelength long. Note that the transceiver is earthed. This is included for electrical safety reasons and may not be a good RF earth.

THE RESONANT COUNTERPOISE. Suppose we now dispense with the coax feeder and connect the 'antenna' wire to the centre pin of the antenna socket of the transceiver in the shack (via the SWR meter), as shown in **Figure 2**. Where is the 'counterpoise' to be connected now? In the case of the dipole it is connected to the braid of the coax as shown in **Figure 1**. In this case it can be connected to the outside connector of the coax socket. A more practical connection point would be the ground connector of the transceiver, which will be at the same RF potential as the outside of the coax socket.

This arrangement will work only provided that the 'antenna' and the 'counterpoise' are resonant at the frequency in use as with the case of the dipole described above. A multiband antenna could be made up of wires in parallel as shown in Figure 1.

Any conductor carrying an RF current will radiate. A counterpoise is part of the antenna transmitting and receiving antenna and radiates on transmit so some consideration should be given to where it is placed. Just putting the counterpoise under the shack carpet may not be such a good idea.

For multiband use, instead of multiple wires, a more practical solution is to use a long wire that is quarter of a wavelength long on the lowest frequency in use. This sort of antenna is often referred to as a 'Long Wire' or 'Random wire antenna'. This antenna is connected to the transceiver via an ATU. This device, when correctly tuned, presents a low impedance to the transceiver antenna socket. The multiband counterpoise problem can be solved by connecting quarter-wave radials, one for each band in parallel, to the transceiver and ATU earth connector. Then run the free ends away from the transceiver, preferably outside the shack.

Such an arrangement will require some experimenting to find the best position for the radials. They can be bent or even folded but the length may have to be altered to maintain resonance. The radials are best located outside the house in the horizontal plane to reduce coupling into the

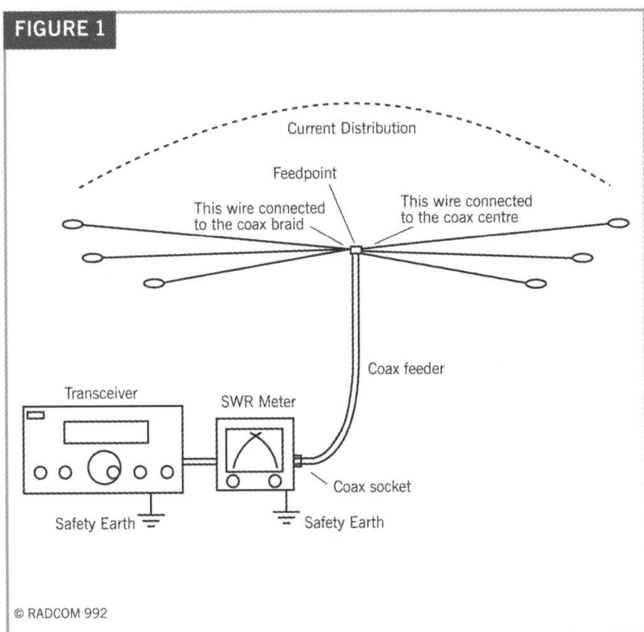


Figure 1: Simple dipole showing the RF current distribution. The safety earth is provided for electrical safety rather than as an RF ground.

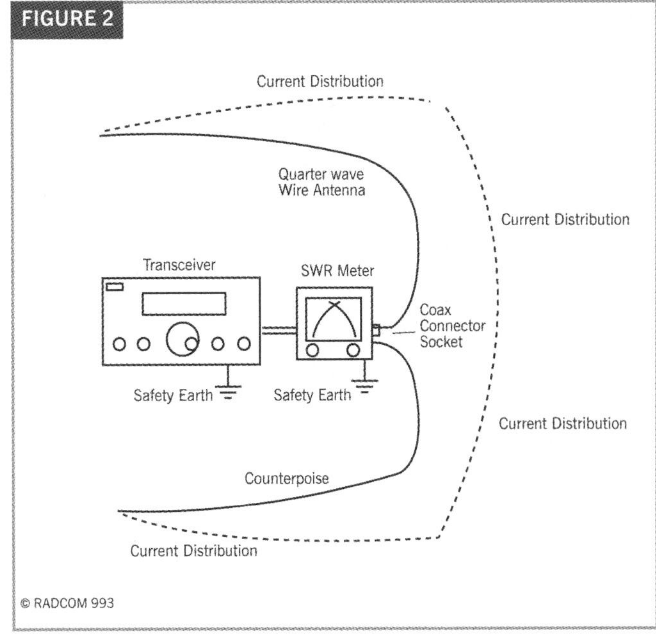


Figure 2: A resonant quarter wave end fed wire and a counterpoise.

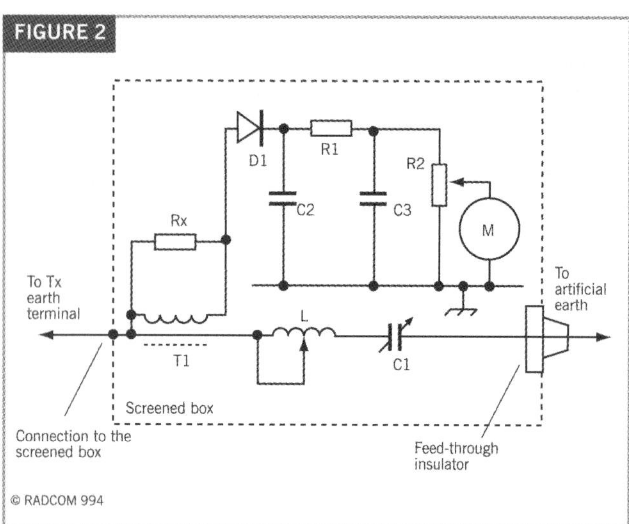


**Figure 3**: SM6AQR's earth lead tuner. T1 =Amidon T-50-43 ferrite toroid. The primary is simply the earth lead through the toroid centre; secondary = 20t small gauge enamelled wire. L = 28$\mu$H rollercoaster or multi-tapped coil with 10-position switch; see text. C1 = 200pF or more air variable, >1mm spacing, insulated from panel and case. C2, C3 = l0nF ceramic. Dl = AA119; R1 = 1k$\Omega$; R2 = 10k$\Omega$ pot, Rx see text. M = 100$\mu$A or less.

electrical wiring. If the radial(s) are used indoors (say round the skirting board), use wire with thick insulation with additional several layers of insulating tape at the ends. The RF voltage at the ends can be fairly high when the transmitter is on.

The best way to check resonance of a radial is to connect it to the transceiver earth, make a loop in the radial and use a dip meter to check resonance. If such an instrument is unavailable then apply a low power transmission. With a series RF current meter and adjust the radial length for maximum current.

EARTH LEAD TUNER. Alternatively, one single length radial can be tuned to place a very low RF potential at the transceiver on any band by inserting a LC series tuning circuit between the transmitter and the radial (just like the ATU for the antenna). Such a units are commercially available, the MFJ 931 **[1]** is an example. These units are normally described as an Artificial Ground. In addition to the LC circuit these devices usually have a through-current RF indicator which helps tuning the radial or earth lead to resonance (maximum current).

Alternatively, you can make one yourself. The unit designed by SM6AQR **[2] [3]** and shown in **Figure 3** uses a 200-300pF air spaced tuning capacitor with at least 1mm plate spacing; the capacitor and its shaft must be insulated from the tuner cabinet. The inductor is a 28$\mu$H roller coaster. Alternatively, a multi-tapped fixed coil with as many taps as possible could be used.

The tuning indicator consists of a current transformer, rectifier, smoothing filter, sensitivity potentiometer and DC microammeter. The 'primary' of the current transformer is the artificial earth lead itself; it simply passes through the centre of the ferrite toroid T1, onto which a secondary of 20 turns of thin enamelled wire has been wound. Rx, the resistor across the T1 secondary, should be non-inductive and between 22 and 100$\Omega$; it is selected such that a convenient meter deflection can be set with the sensitivity control R2 on each required frequency and for the RF power used.

Just as important as setting up the ATU, the earth lead or counterpoise tuner should be adjusted on low power. The approximate settings for each band can be recorded and fine tuned on high power.

REAL EARTH. All this messing around with radials seems to be a lot of trouble – would it not be possible to use a connection to earth, say a ground stake, outside the shack window? Well, it depends.

The counterpoise, described above, presents a low impedance at the frequency in use so the RF current on transmit is high. Provided that our ground stake arrangement will handle this then it is fine.

In practice a good RF earth connection is hard to find and is only practicable from a ground floor shack. The problem with the 'earth stake' is that ground has resistance and the lead connecting the earth stake radio has reactance. This ground resistance is in series with the radiation resistance of the antenna so it is important to get the ground resistance as low as possible if you want an efficient end-fed antenna.

Many ways have been tried to reduce the ground resistance. In general, the more copper you can bury in the ground the better. I found that an old copper water tank made a very good earth for the lower HF bands, when connected to the radio with thick short copper wire.

Low band DXers tend to use buried multiple radials; lots of wires radiating out from the earth connection. The rule seems to be is the more wires the better, see **[4]**. The length of the wires will be restricted in many restricted QTHs but nevertheless they will contribute to lowering the RF ground resistance.

If you operate from an upstairs shack, engineering a low-impedance earth connection at ground level using the method described above will probably be a waste of time. The reason for this is that the distance up to the shack is a significant fraction of a wavelength on the higher HF bands and above. G(M)3SEK **[5]** makes the point that at frequencies where this length is near one or three quarter wavelengths, the earth connector will act as a RF insulator, which is just the opposite of what is wanted, see **Figure 4(a)**. This is bound to happen in one or more of our nine HF bands.

On the other hand, if the lead resonates as a half-wave, (a situation that is likely to arise on any band above 10MHz), it will may act as a good RF earth. However, it also has a high-voltage point halfway down which may couple RF into the house wiring, see **Figure 4(b)**, because electrical wiring within the wall of a house is generally perpendicular. In other words although an earth wire from the radio in an upstairs shack to an earth stake will provide a safety earth its usefulness as an RF earth is unpredictable.

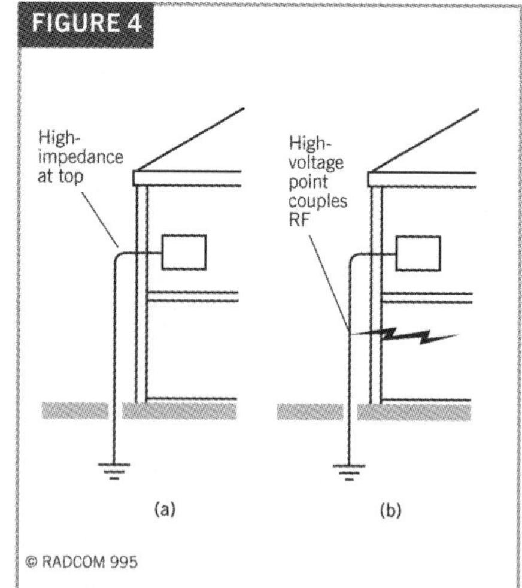


**Figure 4**: Why RF ground leads from upstairs seldom work. (a) Ground lead with quarter-wave resonance (or odd multiple) is ineffective; very little current will flow into it. (b) Ground lead with half-wave resonance (or multiples) will have high-voltage points, which couple RF into house wiring.

REFERENCES

[1] Available from Waters & Stanton plc
[2] 'Eurotek' *Radio Communication* September 1993
[3] *Backyard Antennas*, Peter Dodd, G3LDO, RSGB
[4] 'Portable ground plane system', Ron Bennett, G4DIY, *RadCom* December 2006
[5] 'In Practice' *Radio Communication* May 1994

# Go forth and radiate

*The summer season is a good time to go mobile or portable, a good way to escape the general racket caused by SMPSUs and other QRM. Mobile operation is an excellent way of experimenting with compact and miniature antennas.*

**Photo 1**: The G3LDO Mk 1 experimental DDRR antenna. The far end of the element is supported by a plastic block, which could be slid along the element to alter its height above the roof of the car.

**Photo 2**: Bird's eye view of the DDRR roof rack antenna. The element overlap provides capacity for tuning the antenna rather than capacity to ground.

THE DDRR ANTENNA. I was recently in e-mail with Peter Saul, G8EUX, who was interested in the mathematical analysis of the DDRR. DDRR is short for 'Directional Discontinuity Ring Radiator' although I am not sure what the this actually means. The *QST* version of the DDRR is described in the earlier editions of *The ARRL Antenna Book* **[1]**, see **Figure 1**, but not included in the later editions. I just considered the DDRR antenna as a short vertical section, with the rest of a quarter wavelength formed into a horizontal loop.

Tom Francis, NM1Q, writing in QST **[2]** gave a short history of this antenna. "The DDRR was designed by J. M. Boyer for shipboard operation at very low frequencies. Basically, the DDRR is a quarter wave, end-fed antenna, grounded at one end and shaped as a single-turn coil. (Mr. Boyer described his antenna design in the January 1963 issue of *Electronics* as a 'hula-hoop' antenna.) The DDRR requires a counterpoise (ground plane) for effective operation.

"The antenna was described to Amateur Radio operators in the June 1970 issue of 73 Magazine by W. E. English, W6WYQ. This article illustrated the problems confronted in building an HF version of the DDRR and how these problems were overcome. After numerous requests for a ground-mounted version, English wrote an article for the December 1971 issue of QST, in which he described a 40-meter DDRR as 'an apartment dweller's dream...'".

It attracted the interest of W2WAM, who wrote a mathematical analysis of the DDRR antenna, see **[3]** (it is also included in **[4]**). This analysis detailed the shortcomings of the DDRR and suggested ways of increasing efficiency. He concluded that increasing the vertical height could improve the efficiency appreciably.

MOBILE DDRR. Like many other mobile operators I have used a luggage rack as a platform for HF and VHF over the years. I decided to see if the luggage rack itself could be used as an antenna. The most likely candidate for the basis of the design was the DDRR antenna.

A 14MHz mobile version of the DDRR antenna was constructed from 2mm copper tubing. Instead of using a circular horizontal section my design used a rectangle configuration. There were two reasons for this approach: firstly, a square or rectangle can be made up using straight sections of tubing, with the ends joined using 90 degree angle joints. Secondly, a rectangular configuration looks more like a roof rack, and if constructed well enough can even be *used* as a roof rack (although

FIGURE 1

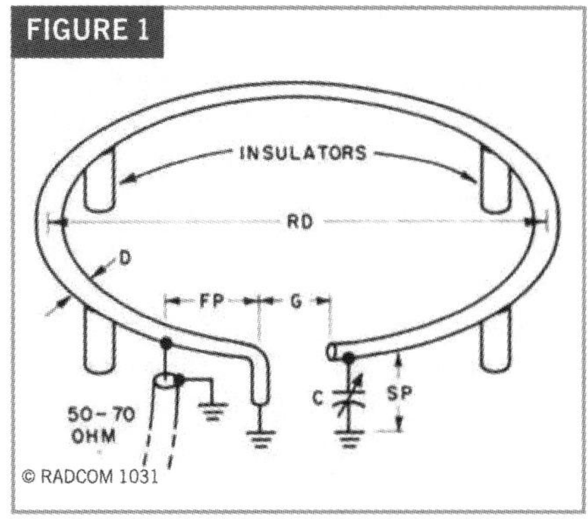


**Figure 1**: The DDRR antenna as shown in the 14th edition of the ARRL Antenna Handbook.

not as a transmitting antenna at the same time!) The Mk. 1 mobile DDRR antenna is illustrated in **Photo 1.**

A more robust version was constructed and fixed to the roof of the car by a bar roof rack – the sort used to transport ladders or timber – and is illustrated in **Photo 2**. As well as supporting the DDRR antenna, this rack also provides facilities to mount more conventional antennas. After reading W2WAM's mathematical analysis I increased the vertical height to 250mm (10in), which was as high as practicable if the antenna was to masquerade as a roofrack. Details of how to construct this antenna are given in **[5]** and **[2]**. The antenna is shunt fed by tapping the feed-line centre up from the ground end of the element as shown in **Photo 3**.

The traditional DDRR is tuned with capacitance to ground as shown in **Figure 1**. My variation uses capacitance provided by overlapping the top end of the element with the lowest part of the horizontal section. The capacitance is adjusted by sliding the top end of the element along the tube-to-wall fittings, thereby adjusting the overlap as shown in **Photo 2**. These fittings offer just enough friction to retain the element in the desired position. Calibration marks are used so that the overlap position can be set at any frequency within the tuneable range.

This antenna proved to be a very useful single band antenna for 14MHz. I didn't have to worry about removing it when parked for fear that it might get vandalised or stolen, after all it looks just like a luggage rack. Furthermore I could drive into low roofed multi-storey car parks without having to remove it.

In April 'Antennas' I noted that with an end fed vertical the current in the counterpoise is equal to the current in the antenna. The mobile antenna is no exception and in this case the counterpoise is the vehicle metal body. This is illustrated in the computer model of a mobile DDRR antenna shown in **Figure 2**. The black lines represent the antenna element and the vehicle body. The red lines show current distribution and the model shows RF current in the vehicle body as well as the antenna when the transmitter in on.

RF current in the antenna and counterpoise is indirectly proportional to the radiation resistance. The DDRR antenna has a very low radiation resistance so the current induced into the vehicle body and vehicle wiring can be very high when using a standard 100W transceiver. It is this RF current in the vehicle body that can affect the running of modern cars that use microprocessor controlled engine management systems. Having said that I have not personally experienced any problems of RF transmission interference with vehicle performance, even with the DDRR antenna.

**Photo 3**: The feed end of the mobile DDRR antenna. The lower end of the element is connected to the bodywork of the car with tinned copper braiding, together with the braiding of the feeder coaxial cable. The centre of the coaxial cable is connected with a wire to an adjustable point (shunt feed) on the antenna element.

You may find the detailed notes on the subject from Icom **[6]** useful for testing a modern vehicle with any sort amateur radio installation and antenna. An edited extract is given in the sidebar.

FINALLY. Extensive computer modelling and measurement **[7]** indicates that maximum current in the vehicle body occurs near the base and feedpoint of the antenna as you might expect. This means that the traditional method of mounting the antenna on the rear of the vehicle is best for reducing the possibility of EMC. A current choke near the antenna feedpoint might also be advisable to reduce the chance of RF being routed inside the vehicle by currents on the feeder braid.

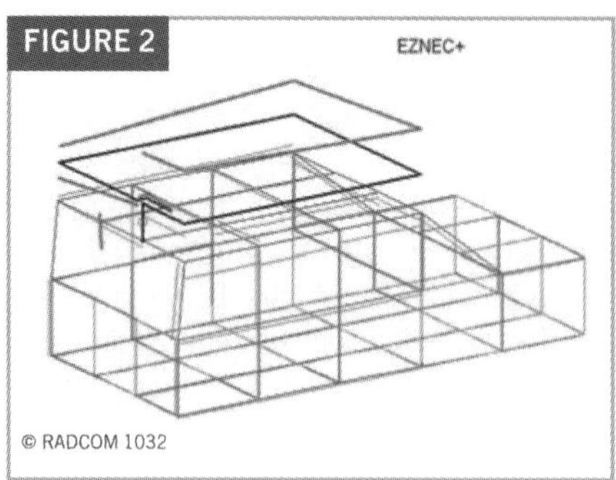


**Figure 2**: Computer model of a DDRR antenna fixed to an estate car with the feedpoint set at the rear of the vehicle. The DDRR antenna and its associated RF current distribution have been emphasised for clarity.

### MOBILE RADIO & THE DDRR

Mobile operation is an excellent way of experimenting with compact and unusual antennas, the mobile DDRR antenna is an example. But it is essential to ensure that your experiments do not compromise the operation of the vehicle. Here are some typical notes on things to check.

**Initial Checks**

Switch on transceiver and check that it and the antenna functions correctly (Low SWR). Switch on ignition (but not engine) and check that all instruments, warning light displays are normal. Now transmit and verify that displays are unaffected, then repeat the test in all operating bands. If the transceiver is multimode, then repeat the test with all modes.

In each case use the maximum RF power. If there is ANY disturbance of the vehicle instrumentation then stop and identify the source of the problem before continuing. Repositioning the antenna and power leads is the sort of action that might solve the problem. If the above tests have been completed successfully proceed to Static Checks.

**Static Checks**

Start the engine of the vehicle and repeat all the tests described in the Initial Checks. Check that there is no disturbance of the engine control or engine speed. Switch on the vehicle lights, indicators, etc. while transmitting. Check that no unintended flashing or indication occurs. If the above tests are proceed to Mobile Checks.

**Mobile Checks**

Find a road free of traffic. Start the vehicle and while moving slowly operate the transmitter. Check that brakes, etc. all operate as normal. Repeat using bands, modes, etc. as applicable to your transceiver.

If all is OK, then increase to normal driving speed and repeat the tests. If there is any unexpected reaction from the vehicle (accelerator, transmission, steering or other in-car electronic device) then stop transmitting immediately. If these tests are satisfactory perform a braking test at normal speed while transmitting.

REFERENCES

[1] *The ARRL Antenna Handbook*, 17th Edition
[2] 'The Mobile Roof-Rack Antenna', Peter Dodd, G3LDO, QST, November 1988
[3] 'A study of the DDRR Antenna', Robert B. Dome, W2WAM, QST July 1972
[4] *The Antenna Experimenter's Guide*, 2nd Edition, Peter Dodd G3LDO, RSGB publication
[5] *The Amateur Radio Mobile Handbook*, Peter Dodd, G3LDO. RSGB publication
[6] *Guide to Installing Mobile Transceivers in Vehicles*. Icom document A-62081-1EU
[7] 'Computer modeling the HF Mobile Antenna', Peter Dodd, G3LDO, *The ARRL Antenna Compendium, Vol 7*

# Feedback

*Peter Dodd responds to readers' correspondence.*

**Photo 1**: In spite of its small size the design of this the MFJ-901B ATU uses a 2.5in (64mm) diameter air-spaced coil and is well constructed.

SMALL ANTENNA TUNING UNITS. With many commercial transceivers now less than the size of a shoebox and SMPSUs capable of providing 12V at 20amps even smaller, it might be worth while looking at small antenna tuning units. In 2003 I went on vacation in Marrakech and took some radio equipment with me. I did try to make a small ATU that would handle 100W but obtaining just the right sized components was difficult and expensive. I found a suitable small, moderately priced unit, the MFJ-901B, which measured 5¼in (132mm) x 2¼in (57mm) x 5¼in (146mm) and weighed only 600gm.

In spite of its small size the design of this ATU uses a 2.5in (64mm) diameter air-spaced coil and is well constructed, see **Photo 1**. Used with a centre-fed 20m wire antenna it worked very well and handled 100 watts of CW from the IC-706 without difficulty. The 25mm diameter transformer balun was slightly warm after a couple of hours of pile-up type operation.

Not every one has been as lucky with small MFJ ATU's. I had an email exchange with John Patrick McDonald, PG8PGC, (G8PJC) on the subject of end fed antennas. He says "Thanks very much for your article on the counterpoise in April *RadCom*, it will help others like me understand how it works and why it is a better option than an earth spike if you are not on the ground floor. As I mentioned in my earlier emails I am surprised that the material in your article is not basic bread and butter information available in all the getting started type literature for amateur radio.

"I said I would keep you posted on my random wire project and the story so far is: I received my MFJ 931 and MFJ 1610 random wire turner from W&S. The turner would not tune on the higher frequencies. I found the fault as you can see in the attached picture (**Photo 2**). The combined inductor/tap switch body frame was bent and the wiper arm contact got mangled after one rotation.

"The MFJ 1610 was replaced but unfortunately the replacement was also faulty. Again the rotary switch was the problem but this time due to the contact wafer, to which the inductor is soldered, not being crimped firmly to the switch frame. This results in intermittent contact on part of the arc of travel (The slightest touch of the inductor lifts the inductor wafer away from the contact arm)."

Because the heavy ferrite inductor arrangement is mainly supported by the switch in the MFJ 1610 it indicates a possible design flaw, which can result in damage to the switch if the unit is dropped (as can happen during shipping). This is in contrast to the MFJ-901B, which I feel is very well designed and could stand any amount of bumps."

LIGHTNING PROTECTION. It has been pointed out to me that the subject of lightning protection has not been covered in any of the publications that I have been responsible for **[1] [2]**, except to say that the antenna system and equipment in the shack should be well grounded or earthed. (I have also been taken to task for not mentioning PME but I will come back to this in a later 'Antennas').

I must confess to being rather paranoid about lightning; I go round the house and shack disconnecting rigs, TV sets and telephones at the slightest showing of an electrical storm. And for good reason. I experienced my house and antenna being hit by a particularly devastating lightning bolt when I was in Sierra Leone in the 1960s.The mast was a solid 60ft steel mast supporting a 14MHz all-metal quad. The antenna suffered no damage due to its construction. However, the house electricity, which was supplied via overhead wires, picked up enough energy to blow all the electrical components such as the fuse boxes and the meter off the wall.

Two houses within two miles of this QTH have required extensive repairs to the roof after lightning strikes, which has not eased my paranoia. An interesting side affect of the last lightning strike is that several parked cars near the house had to be towed away because the EMP (electro magnetic pulse) from the lightning zapped their engine management systems!

It is, however, always a good idea to keep these things in perspective. Alan Martindale, G3MYA, in a very good article on the characteristics of thunderstorms **[3] [4]** produced some interesting facts and figures on thunderstorm activity in the UK. He noted: "In assessing the need for protection from electrical storms, the following information may help to make up your mind – or, conversely, it may only serve to confuse you even further! By scientific observation it has been established that, on a nationwide basis, there are 10 days in the year when there are thunderstorms in the vicinity of any one place. They need not be directly overhead, only within clearly audible range. Of course this is an average which is subject to differences in location and counts from year to year, but these figures have been calculated over a long period and from a large variety of locations. My own recollection seems to differ quite substantially from this, but then mine is subjective while the quoted figures are objective.

"Allowing for the fact that not all storms are overhead and that most storms consist of more than one storm centre, it is calculated that 10 storm centres pass directly overhead in any one year (on average!). However, seasonal variations, preferred storm paths and other stray phenomena could double this figure, so we will assess the risk on the basis of 20 storm centres passing overhead per year.

"In the UK and similar temperate regions, each storm centre produces about 20 or 30 strokes during its average life of 30 to 60 min. Of these strokes, less than half (about 40%) are cloud to ground strokes, and of these groundstrokes about 95% are negative type.

"Each storm centre covers a ground area of about $4km^2$. If the storm centre were to remain perfectly stationary during its active life, it would produce 2.5 ground strokes/ square kilometre, but on average a storm centre travels across the ground at a speed of 50km/h so its ground strokes are distributed over an area of $100km^2$. This gives an average of 0.1 ground strokes/storm centre/square kilometre. Multiply this by 20 storm centres/year and this leaves us with two ground strokes/square kilometre/ year.

Photo 2: Damaged MFJ 1610 ATU. The relatively heavy ferrite inductor arrangement is mainly supported by the switch. This has resulted in damage to the switch, perhaps due to the unit being dropped during shipping.

"Now let us take a look at an average domestic property of about 20 x 50m or an area of $1{,}000m^2$. One thousand such properties would fit into $1km^2$, which means that the chances of a direct strike on a single property works out at once every 500 years! We all know what happens to averages and statistics, but I think it is wise to try and get the whole thing into perspective.

"Of course, radio amateurs do tend to tempt providence a bit by putting things up high in the sky with good electrical connections to a point not too dissimilar from earth potential – this must increase the risk of a strike on our property, to the relief of our neighbours! If, in our quest for better radio communications, we do put up such electrically attractive devices, it is in our own interest to do something to protect them."

As G3MYA mentioned, one of the best lightning protection items may already exist at your QTH and that is your metal antenna mast. Ideally it should be in the centre of your property and be 5m higher than any other part of the installation. To increase the mast's effectiveness as a lightning conductor it should have a short length of copper rod not less than $25mm^2$, with a sharp point on the top and very securely fitted to the mast with an excellent electrical connection, and fully protected against corrosion. All joints on the mast should also have a good electrical connections. G3MYA also recommends that the base of the mast should be connected to an earth rod of 0.5in galvanised pipe or, better still, hardened copper rod or 'T' section earth rod. A mast so described will provide a cone of protection for all equipment within a radius of 20m or a circle 130ft across.

What has so far been discussed is protection to the house and shack from a direct strike. Most electrical storms pass us by without causing the damage so far discussed but the EMP generated by all types of lightning stroke cause 'spikes' that can seriously damage the health of solid-state devices in the front-ends of receiving equipment. An antenna selector switch, which allows all the antennas to be earthed, is probably a wise investment. Additionally, disconnect all the antenna connections from rigs when you go on vacation. I will write more about EMP transient suppression in a later 'Antennas'.

CORROSION AND WEATHER PROTECTION'. The method I suggested of protecting antenna components from corrosion using a coating of grease in the February 2007 column resulted in some feedback. Dick Biddulph, MOCGN, wrote "In your Feb 2007 column, you suggest that greasing is best or threaded components exposed to the weather. I have found that lanolin is better than ordinary grease. I dissolve lanolin in natural turpentine to make a thick solution and apply that to the threads. It lasts better that grease - in fact threads so treated are still moveable after 12 years without further treatment. I got my lanolin from Boots as 'Hydrous lanolin' and ignored the water in the solution. I only used natural turpentine because I don't like the smell of white spirit so I don't know if the latter would work".

Trevor Beamond noted "I was interested in your piece in Feb 2007 *RadCom* and your use of grease as corrosion protection. The recommendation for car battery terminals is not to use grease because of the conductive lithium stearate, which it contains and can give galvanic corrosion. The recommendations I have seen is to use petroleum jelly (Vaseline), this can be thinned with white spirit if necessary to give a thin surface coat. I use Waxoyl since this is already thinned (a least in warm weather) and dries to a hardish wax which is OK to handle. It seems to be effective in keeping nuts and bolts free to undo after long periods. I keep a little pot in the house to routinely dose fixings for outside use such as lights or electric fence energisers which I am asked to repair on occasions".

REFERENCES

[1] *Backyard Antennas*, Peter Dodd, G3LDO, RSGB
[2] *Radio Communications Handbook*, Chapters 13, 14 and 15. RSGB
[3] Lightning, Alan Martindale, G3MYA, *RadCom*, January 1984
[4] Lightning, Alan Martindale, G3MYA, *HF Antenna Collection*, Erwin David G4LQI

# Testing, testing...

*Antenna analyzers can tell you a lot about antenna parameters but can they tell you how well your beam is working?*

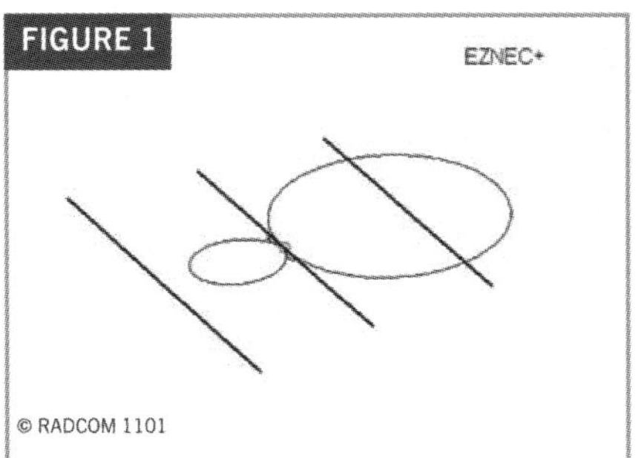


**Figure 1**: A free space computer model of a 28MHz three-element Yagi. The elements are spaced at 0.19 wavelength and the driven element is 0.46 wavelengths long. The gain of this antenna is 8.54dBi with the radiation pattern superimposed on the antenna model.

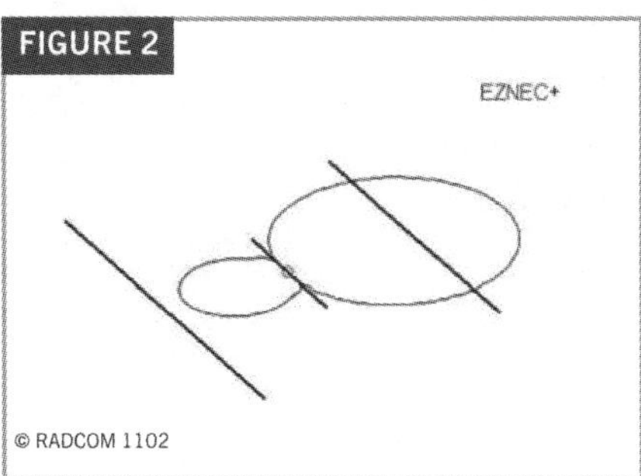


**Figure 2**: Computer model showing the same antenna as in Figure 1 but with the driven element length reduced to 0.2 wavelengths. The radiation pattern has changed very little and the gain is 8.49dBi.

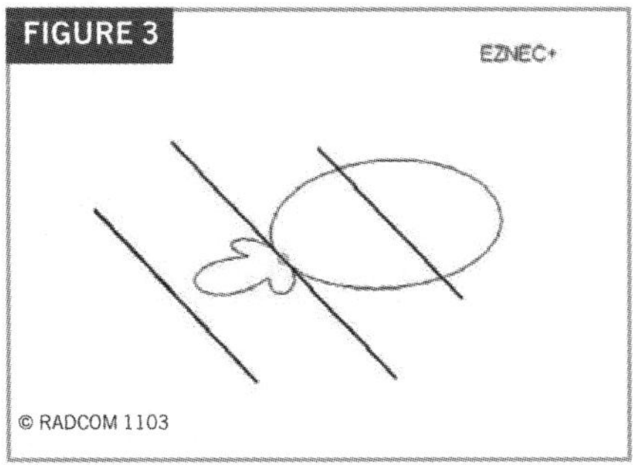


**Figure 3**: Computer model showing the same antenna as in Figure 1 but with the driven element length increased to 0.7 wavelengths. The gain is increased slightly to 8.6dBi.

A VERSATILE INSTRUMENT. One of the most significant changes to the way we measure some of the characteristics of antennas in the last few years has been the availability of low cost antenna analysers. This type of instrument was originally referred to as an 'Active Standing Wave Ratio Meter' by Gerd Janzen, DF6SJ, described in **[1]**. Probably the best known of these instruments is the MFJ249, 259 & 269 series. The MFJ269 was extensively reviewed **[2]** and described technically **[3]** by Ian White, G(M)3SEK.

In brief the MFJ 269 is used mostly to measure the SWR on an antenna transmission line at a specified frequency. It can also be used to:

- Measure the feedpoint resistance of an antenna
- Test and tune stubs and transmission lines
- Determine the velocity factor of transmission line
- Adjust an antenna tuner
- Determine the characteristic impedance of transmission line
- Test RF transformers
- Test RF chokes.

The signal source used by the instrument can also be used as a signal generator in the frequency range from 1.8MHz to 170MHz. The frequency counter (10Hz to 170MHz), used to monitor the signal source, can also be used as a frequency counter to measure the frequency of other oscillator sources. All in all quite a comprehensive instrument. Although it is fine for monitoring the matching of the feeder to the antenna, what it will not do is measure the performance of the antenna.

THE YAGI ANTENNA. Stuart Lindsay, G0KDS, in a recent email exchange, described the construction of a five element monoband Yagi for 28MHz. The driven element (the starting point of the construction) posed a problem because the available data on the length were inconsistent. The driven element was constructed using 3/4in and 5/8in tubing, split in the centre and fed directly with 50ohm coax. The other end of the feeder was connected to an MFJ269 and the length of the driven element adjusted until resonance fell into the lower end of the 28MHz band. The best SWR obtainable was 1.3:1, which was quite acceptable but adding the extra parasitic elements gave "very poor results".

It is not generally realised that the driven element length has very little effect on the performance of a parasitic beam. In the computer model shown in **Figure 1** we have a free space model of a 28MHz three-element Yagi. The elements are spaced at 0.19 wavelength and the driven element is 0.46 wavelengths long. The gain of this antenna is 8.54dBi (the radiation pattern superimposed on the model) and the feed impedance is 25ohms (minimum SWR 2:1) at 28.5MHz.

Using the same parasitic elements and spacings as in Figure 1 I reduced the driven element length in the model to a mere 0.2 wavelengths as shown in **Figure 2**. The radiation pattern had changed very little and the gain was 8.49dBi. By increasing the driven element length to 0.7 wavelengths, see **Figure 3**, the gain increased slightly to 8.6dBi.

So why all this fuss about driven element length? Well, it is about matching to the feeder. The extremes of driven element length present some wild feedpoint impedances, as you might expect. For example, the short driven element shown in Figure 2 has a feed impedance of R28 –j492, which gives an SWR of greater than 100:1, while the long driven element shown in Figure 3 and impedance of R140 +j500 (SWR of 38:1).

Clearly, trying to find a matching network that will match these sorts of impedances would be a problem and it is much easier to use a driven element that is near to 0.5 wavelength long, although with a gamma match this length is not that critical.

In general it is better in the first instance to construct a Yagi from an existing design (my favourite is **[4]**) and then tweak it for best performance. Whatever type of matching is used it is preferable that it is variable because any adjustment of the length or spacing of the parasitic elements will affect the feed impedance and hence the SWR.

MATCHING THE DRIVEN ELEMENT. The driven element feed impedance of a multi-element Yagi is usually lower than the coax feed so some method of matching is usually required. My favourite beam antenna to coax feeder matching method is the Gamma match. This matching method was described is in detail in **[5, 6]** and some this information is repeated below.

The Gamma match is an unbalanced feed system and is well suited to plumber's delight construction, where all the metal parts are electrically and mechanically connected to the boom. This is a preferred mechanical arrangement for home brew arrangements.

As you are aware the impedance of a halfwave element is low at the centre and increases with distance from the centre. The gamma match comprises a short conductor, which is used to connect the centre of the coax to the correct impedance point along the antenna element. This short conductor has some inductive reactance, which is cancelled by installing a series capacitor as shown in **Photo 1**.

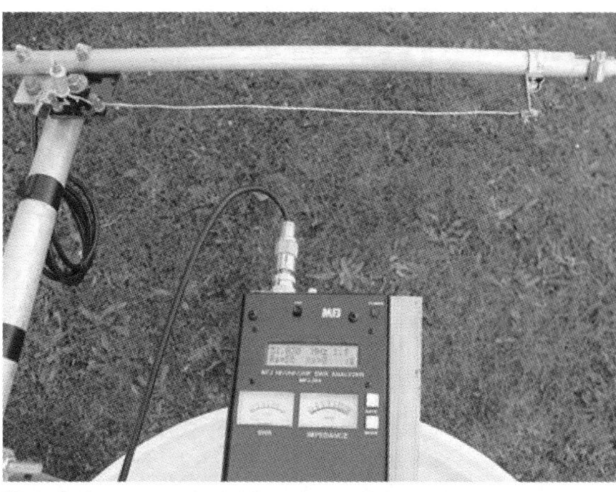

**Photo 1**: Gamma matched driven element being adjusted using an MFJ269. Although this shows a 50MHz model the setup for 28MHz would be very similar.

Because of the many variable factors – driven-element length and diameter, gamma rod length and diameter, spacing between rod and driven element, and value of series capacitors – a number of combinations can provide the desired match. This in turn has given the gamma match a bad press regarding ease of adjustment and has resulted in the publication of some convoluted mathematical models and programs. I find adjustment of this match is relatively easy bearing in mind the following:

- The feed impedance increases as the gamma rod is made longer and the connection to the element is moved away from the centre.
- The length of the gamma rod can be reduced for a given impedance match as the ratio of antenna element diameter to gamma rod diameter is increased.
- Gamma match adjustment is easier if the element is close to resonance.

It follows that the adjustment is much easier if some convenient method of measuring impedance or SWR is to hand and this is where the MFJ-259/269 type of instrument comes into its own.

Most publications recommend that the gamma rod is made from a thin metal tube whose diameter is $1/3$ to $1/6$th of the antenna element diameter. However, it is worth trying what is to hand and it is interesting to see just what you can get away with. For example the arrangement shown in **Photo 1** uses 14SWG hard drawn copper wire as the gamma rod to match a 50MHz two-element beam. The connection from the gamma rod to the antenna element is achieved using a hose clamp, which makes it very easy to adjust.

The traditional method of reactance correction is to use an air-spaced variable capacitor and enclose it in a weatherproof metal box. No matter how weatherproof you make the box, corrosion to the capacitor can still occur because of condensation. This problem can be overcome by using a fixed capacitor whose value is determined by experiment using a variable capacitor. The value of the variable capacitor is then measured and a silver mica (or similar) fixed capacitor (or several series/parallel combinations) substituted. This arrangement will handle 100W without breakdown and only requires a smear of grease to achieve weatherproofing.

**BEAM ANTENNA OPTIMISATION.** Optimising the antenna is achieved by altering the lengths of the parasitic elements for the best radiation pattern. Many HF DX operators spend a considerable amount of effort optimising their beam antennas. Elements made of different diameter telescoped tubes clamped with Jubilee clips (hose clamps) are easy to adjust. Length adjustment is achieved by loosening the clamp and sliding the tube to the required length. It is a good idea to make a mark on one of the tubes to provide a reference in case you find it necessary to return to this point during the adjustments.

Adjusting a HF antenna *in situ* is only possible if the antenna is mounted on top of a flat roof or on a fixed tower with a working platform at the top of it, with the antenna element lengths and feeder matching adjustments easily accessible.

**ADJUSTING AN HF ANTENNA ON A FOLD-OVER MAST.** Clearly the ideal arrangement described above is only available to a few. The next best thing is a fold-over mast. Fold the mast over so that the antenna reflector element is nearest the ground (but well clear of the ground), with the beam pointing upwards. The driven element matching system (gamma match), or length adjustment, should then be accessible using stepladders. Adjust the driven element as described above.

Raise the antenna and check the performance (described later).

Repeat these adjustments as often as is necessary to optimise the antenna.

If the antenna has director element(s), lower the mast so that these elements are nearest the ground. Adjust the length(s) and raise the antenna and check the performance. When the parasitic element adjustments are complete readjust the driven element feeder matching.

All stages of antenna adjustment should be documented, including element lengths and any change in performance. This is useful to enable you to follow the trends in change of performance and makes it easier to return to the previous settings.

If you do not have a fold over mast then you may have to accept that optimising may be impractical without a considerable amount of work. In this case the best you can do is to adjust the matching with the antenna as high as possible on some sort of jury mast before placing the antenna in position.

**GROUND-WAVE TESTS WITH ANOTHER STATION.** One of the most frequently used and reliable methods of testing an antenna is with another station some distance away, say 2 to 3km (1 to 2 miles).

Ground wave tests are particularly useful for obtaining beam antenna gain comparison and directivity data. Tests can be done at a closer range using low transmitter power or with an attenuator fitted into the antenna feeder of the receiver. The receiver RF gain must be set at maximum for the S meter to function correctly.

Tests can also be performed using a HF mobile as the other station. The main advantage of using a mobile is that it can be sited at a distance that is more compatible with transmitter power and the antenna under test.

REFERENCES

[1] *The Antenna Experimenter's Guide, 2nd Edition*, Peter Dodd, G3LDO, RSGB publication
[2] MFJ-269 HF/VHF/UHF SWR Analyser, reviewed by Ian White, G3SEK, Radcom May 2000.
[3] SWR Analysers, a technical background, 'In Practice', Ian White, G3SEK, *Radcom* May 2000.
[4] Beam Antenna Handbook, Bill Orr, W6SAI
[5] Antennas, *RadCom* October 2005
[6] Re-examining the gamma match, *RadCom* September 2006

# Analysing the analysers

*Just how good are the new VNA Antenna Analysers?*

AUTEK VA1 ANTENNA ANALYSER. In the early part of August 2002 I acquired an Autek VA1 antenna analyser. In addition to measuring the usual SWR this instrument was quoted of being able to measure the two components of impedance R ± j impedance (Cartesian co-ordinates R ± j and polar co-ordinates, magnitude and phase). Over the last 10 years my main impedance measuring instrument has been the HP4085A vector impedance meter and in October Antennas I described a method of checking the accuracy of these instruments.

An obvious method is to use a set of accurate dummy loads. Assuming a 50Ω system, dummy loads for 50Ω, 25Ω and 100Ω would be useful but these would only measure the resistive component of impedance. How would you go about measuring the reactive component?

One method is to use the impedance transform effect of transmission line described by W. N. Carron **[1]**. A length of coaxial cable terminated with a resistance greater or less than its characteristic impedance is used as the test load. The actual impedance presented to the instrument test connection depends on the value of the resistor and the electrical length of the coax cable as illustrated in **Figure 1.**

Instead of changing the length of the coax every time a measurement is made the measurements can be made over a range of frequencies; each change in frequency has the effect of changing the electrical length of the coax. Each impedance measurement can then be plotted on a Smith chart. Provided the instrument is reasonably accurate these plotted points on the chart should form a rough circle centred on the 50Ω prime centre. This circle is the SWR contour and shows that the SWR is the same over the whole length of a mismatched line. Actually this isn't quite true, there is a slight change over frequency and line length due to losses but I will come to this later.

The accuracy of the instrument under test will be apparent by any deviation from the SWR contour. Test results plotted on Smith chart shown in **Figure 2** are for an HP4085A vector impedance meter (red) and the Autek VA1 (green).

While neither of the plots look ideal you have to remember that this is a sensitive test. Both instruments are accurate enough to enable one to devise a suitable matching network for an antenna.

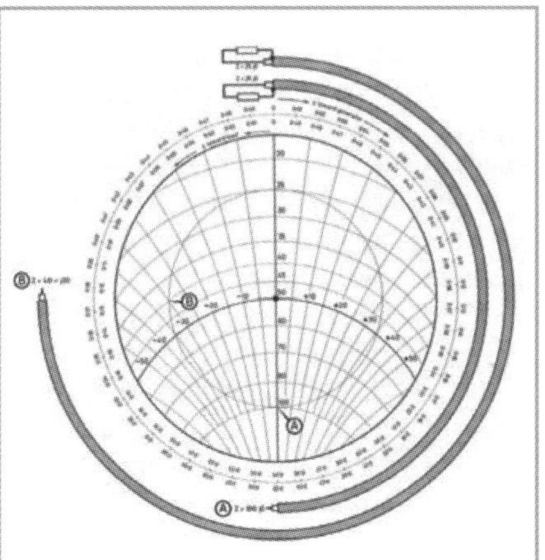

**Figure 1**: Two lengths of 50Ω coaxial feeder are shown superimposed around the circumference of a Smith chart; one length quarter wave long and the other 3/8 wavelength. Both lengths are connected to a load having an impedance of 25+j0. The quarter wave length of line (0.25) gives a measured impedance of 100+j0 at the other end while the 3/8 section (0.375) gives an impedance of 40-j30. A halfwave length of coaxial would transform the impedance back to 25 j0.

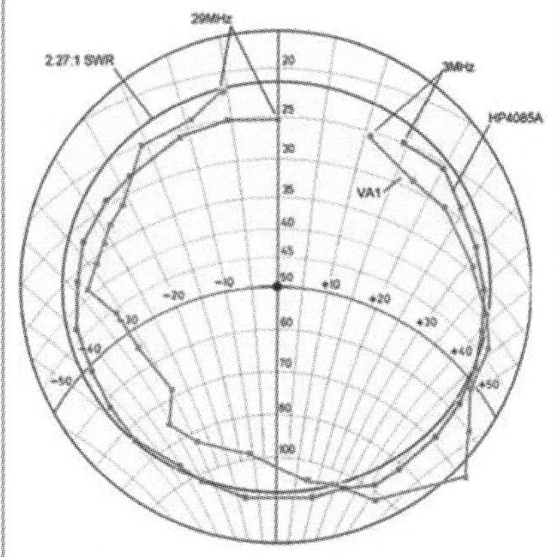


**Figure 2**: Results of an impedance plot of a 22 resistor made via a length of coaxial cable over a frequency range 3 to 29MHz. The blue circle is the calculated 2.27:1 SWR produced by a 22 resistor. Ideally, the impedance plot should follow this circle with a slight spiralling towards the centre due to coax cable loss. The red and green plots are of the HP4085A and the VA1 respectively.

ENTER THE VNAs. A new generation of analysers have now become available; the low cost Vector Impedance Analysers (VNAs) although they have been around for some time now (the first I heard of them was in TT September 2004). The construction of N2PK VNA was described by G(M)3SEK **[2]** and is a home brew project. The lack of availability of some of the required components outside the USA meant that only a small group of dedicated constructors actually built them.

Vector Impedance Analysers have now become commercially available and the AIM4170, designed by Bob Clunn, W5BIG, was reviewed in last months *RadCom* **[3].**

Additionally there is the miniVNA from Mini Radio Solutions. This instrument is based on a design by IW3HEV, details of which can be found at **[4]**.

In the meantime I had bought an AIM4170. This unit communicates with the PC using a RS232 serial link and it seemed to work with any flavour of Windows from Windows 95 onwards. It worked with my old Compaq Armada 750, which is used for various other radio measurement applications such as PolarPlot.

The first item I looked at after the unit was calibrated was the SWR characteristics of my multi-band minibeam – the one shown on the front cover of *Backyard Antennas* **[5]**. When you first switch on the AIM4170 there is an overwhelming number of parameters displayed and it is best to switch off the ones that are not needed.

The dips in SWR shown in **Figure 3** coincide with the higher amateur bands where you would expect to find them. What I hadn't noticed before was the decrease in off-resonance SWR with an increase in frequency. This improvement in SWR is an indication of transmission line losses. So far so good, the results looked quite promising. But how accurate are they?

CALIBRATION AND ACCURACY. The AIM4170 VNA is calibrated first using a shorted terminal then an open one. The calibration procedure is then completed using a 200Ω resistor. Several tests with

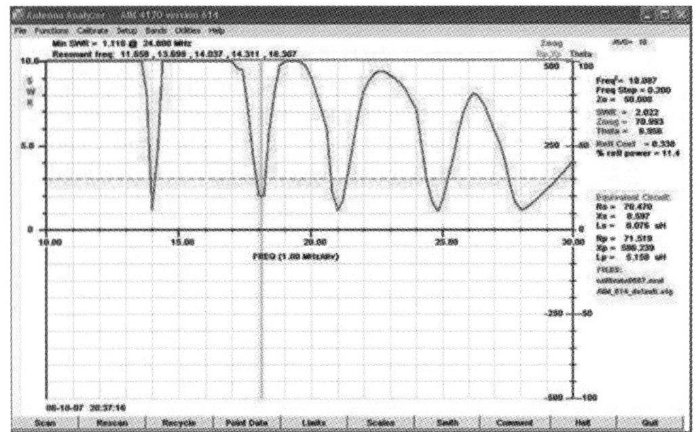

**Figure 3**: A SWR plot of my 5-band two-element beam using the AIM4170 VNA. Only the SWR parameter switched on. Note the reduction in SWR at off-resonance as the frequency is increased indicating transmission line losses. The parameters at the vertical green line marker are displayed on the right.

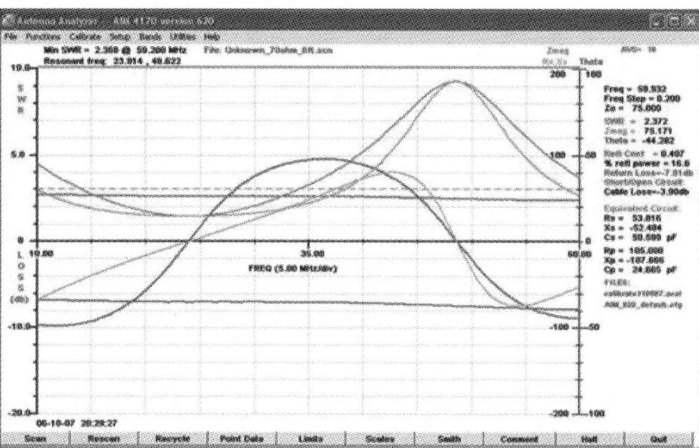

**Figure 4**: Results of an impedance plot of a 200Ω resistor made via a length of coaxial cable over a frequency range 10 to 60MHz using the AIM4170 VNA. This main display, shows impedances, reflection coefficient, return loss and SWR.

various lengths of coax and termination resistors were tried.

The results of a test obtained by measuring a 200Ω resistor (one that came with the calibration pack) over a two metre length of coax cable is shown in **Figure 4** and **Figure 5**. The main display, showing the impedances, reflection coefficent, return loss and SWR, is shown in Figure 4. A Smith chart of the same measurement is shown in Figure 5. The green circle is SWR 3:1 marker. It can be seen that the actual plot (shown in red) is a smooth circle that spirals in towards the centre as the frequency is increased and is caused by coax cable loss.

What is interesting is how smooth and close to the SWR circle this plot is, showing the impedance errors to be very small and an improvement compared with the measurements in Figure 2. However Figure 2 has a limited range, which magnifies the errors, while Figure 5 shows the whole universe of impedance values.

This measurement procedure didn't originally go to plan. When I made the first plot of the coax with the 200Ω termination I found that the SWR plot was sinusoidal with frequency on the main display. On the Smith chart the plotted SWR circle was displaced to the right of the prime centre as shown in **Figure 6.**

An email to Jay Terleski of Array Solutions resolved the problem – had I checked the coax impedance Zo? Examination of the test coax showed that it was RG59. A more sensible display resulted when the Zo was changed to 72Ω as shown in Figure 5.

I would like to make a couple of other comments about the Smith charts described here. The examples shown in Figure 1 and Figure 2 have the line of zero reactance in the vertical plane. This has

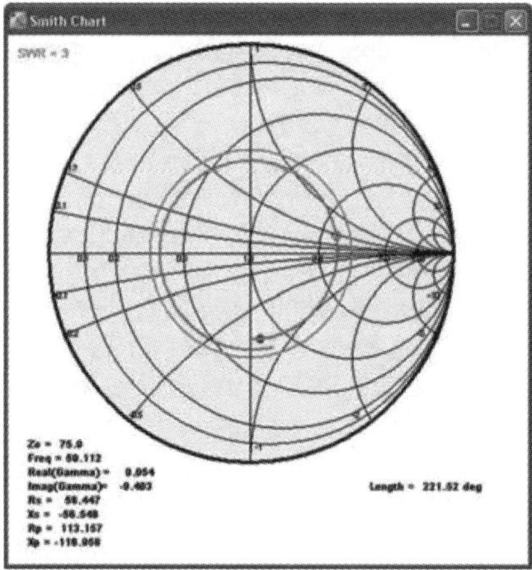

**Figure 5**: A Smith chart of the same measurement is shown in Figure 4. The green circle is SWR 3:1 marker. It can be seen that the actual plot (shown in red) is a smooth circle that tends to spiral towards the centre as the frequency is increased and is caused by coax cable loss.

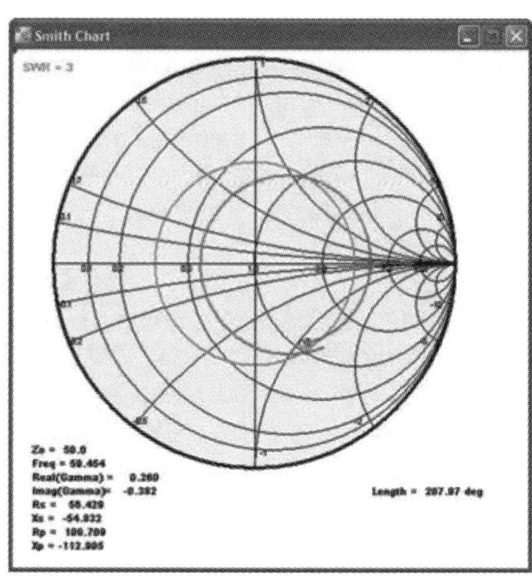

**Figure 6**: A Smith chart of the same measurement is shown in Figure 5 but with an incorrect setting of Zo. The actual plot is shifted to the right relative to the green SWR marker and the prime centre.

been the convention in most UK literature **[6]** and earlier American literature **[7]** but it has been more common in more recent publications and software to display the line of zero reactance in the horizontal plane, as shown in Figure 4.

The charts shown in Figure 1 and Figure 2, are designed to plot impedances relative only to 50Ω, i.e. the prime centre is 50Ω. On the other hand in Figure 4 the prime centre is shown as 1.0. The values assigned to the lines on the chart represent a ratio with respect to the prime centre. All this might seem a bit convoluted but the advantage of this arrangement is that the chart can be used for any value of transmission line impedance and not just 50Ω.

Plotting values on this sort of chart would normally require a fair amount of skill and experience but in the case of the Smith display on the AIM4170 the values are simply read out by placing a cursor on the appropriate point on the SWR plot.

I didn't understand what the 'gamma' shown in the bottom right hand corner of Figure 5 and 6 meant. In an email exchange with Bob Clunn, W5BIG, it appears that the Reflection Coefficient is sometimes represented by 'rho' and sometimes by 'gamma'.

If the AIM4170 VNA is anything to go by I am impressed by the accuracy and usability of these instruments. At this time I have only had time to scratch the surface of discovering what they are capable of.


REFERENCES

[1] The Hybrid Junction Admittance Bridge',W N Carron, *Antenna Compendium Vol 3* ARRL 1992.

[2] In Practice, *RadCom* October 2004

[3] *RadCom* July 2007

[4] www.miniradiosolutions.com/

[5] *Backyard Antennas*, G3LDO, RSGB Book Sales.

[6] *HF Antennas for all Locations*, L. A. Moxon G6XN, RSGB Book Sales

[7] *The ARRL Antenna Book, 13th Edition* (1974)

# Antennas

*A letter from America*

**Photo1**: The N3LJS pickup truck sporting a High Sierra 1500

**Photo 2**: A general view of the K8PJ mobile antenna installation

**Photo 3**: Close up of the base and fold-over mechanism of the K8PJ mobile antenna

SIZE MATTERS FOR HF ANTENNA EFFICIENCY. When I was first licensed in 1956 mobile operation was very popular, particularly on 160m. It was relatively easy to build a 10W transmitter for this band and the ground wave coverage from a vehicle could be up to 30 miles (50km), even with what must have been rather inefficient antennas. To get an 8 or 9ft (2.5m) whip to resonate required a fair amount of inductance and a mobile whip was quite a chunky device. A mobile rally car park with the forest of HF antennas used to be quite a sight.

While compiling information for the Amateur Radio Mobile book in the year 2000 I went to a couple of radio rallies to obtain some photographic examples of HF mobile antennas. I was disappointed – there was hardly an HF mobile antenna to be seen. I wasn't sure why this should be; perhaps there wasn't as much interest in HF mobiling as I though or perhaps they were removed to prevent them being stolen.

A possible factor is that modern vehicles present more of a challenge when it comes to installation of mobile equipment and antennas. They do not usually have the nice convenient bumpers for mounting HF antennas used by earlier generations of mobilers, consequently mobile HF antennas have generally been downsized, with VHF/UHF becoming the bands of choice for mobile operation.

On the other hand it was obvious that the mobile situation in the USA is alive and kicking, with a considerable interest in HF mobiling, if the number of HF antennas fitted to vehicles in the various car parks at Dayton was anything to go by. This is possibly because the area of coverage for a mobile operation is much greater in the USA. Some of the antenna installations to be seen were quite impressive with most of them constructed using the motor driven variable inductance – the so called 'screwdriver' antenna because the first one used an electric screwdriver motor and gearing. Most of them were commercial designs as shown in **Photo 1** with the N3LJS pickup truck sporting a High Sierra 1500.

The disadvantage of antennas fixed to the rear of 4x4s and estate cars (mine is a case in point) is that the antenna obstructs the rear door. The arrangement used by K8PJ uses what looks like an extension of the tow bar to support a large 'screwdriver' type antenna. It also has a fold over mechanism to allow the tailgate door to be opened. A general view of the K8PJ mobile antenna installation is shown in **Photo 2** and a close up of the fold-over mechanism is shown in **Photo 3**.

To my mind the star of the show was the mobile antenna installation of N8DM. For the size of the antenna relative to the size of the vehicle the antenna shown in **Photo 4** it takes first prize. I have never seen a mobile antenna this size before and it is probably home made. However there are such a wide variety of mobile antennas available in the USA I cannot be sure of this. The approximately 8ft long mast section of the antenna appears to be made with 4inch (100mm) diameter tubing. The coil fits into the tube using the conventional 'screwdriver' driven coil and the whole lot is protected with a plastic cover. The large diameter mast means that a larger diameter low loss high Q coil can be used, which has a larger coil diameter than the well known Texas Bugcatcher.

The top section of the antenna appears to be a five foot stainless steel whip with a six-spoke capacity hat, making the total antenna height around 16ft – a truly impressive mobile antenna. A close up of the antenna base, feed, control and earthing system is shown in **Photo 5**.

HI-Q-ANTENNAS. On my wanderings around the Hamvention site I came across a selection of very impressive HF mobile antennas as shown in **Photo 6**. These turned out to be antennas manufactured by Charlie Gyenes, W6HIQ, of Hi-Q-Antennas.

I was curious as to how such seemingly high Q coils could be of any practical value in a mobile installation. When I discussed mobile antenna efficiency in an earlier 'Antennas' **[1]** I noted that on 80m the Texas Bugcatcher very efficient but

**Photo 6**: A display of the W6HIQ Hi-Q mobile antennas

required around 900pF of shunt capacitance to obtain a reasonable match (implying a low radiation resistance). In addition the 2:1 SWR bandwidth was only 12kHz as shown in **Figure 1**. The coils shown in Photo 6 have a greater diameter than the Texas Bugcatcher so would seemingly have a higher efficiency, greater Q and narrower SWR bandwidth. This might have implied a lack of operating convenience because the antenna would be very critical and would have to be readjusted every few kHz of a QSY.

However, the tuning appears to have a degree of precision if the details on W6HIQ's website **[2]** are to be believed. The antenna coil and tuning mechanism is housed on the inside of the coil in an internally threaded extruded Lexan (polycarbonate) tubing. The coil is tuned with a silver plated beryllium copper "D" shaped contactor, which is in constant contact with two turns of the loading coil under 8lb of preset pressure. The contactor is driven by a planetary gearhead 12 or 24 VDC motor (depending on the model) that tunes the antenna from 10-160m in one minute.

The antenna length does not change with different frequency settings as it does on the screwdriver antenna. The moving parts are isolated from the weather although most screwdriver antennas have a plastic housing to protect the coil. The outside of the coils and protective covers of all mobile antennas need to be cleaned regularly to minimise losses.

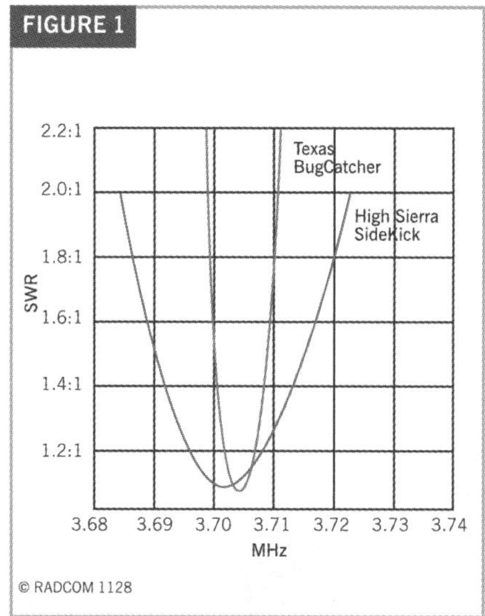


**Figure 1**: Comparative SWR curves of the high Q Texas Bugcatcher and small low Q High Sierra Sidekick on 80m

**Figure 2**: An advertisement for the Webster Band Spanner mobile antenna, June 1962

NOTHING NEW UNDER THE SUN. The concept of the sliding contacts on an infinitely variable loading coil is not new. Furthermore having the contacts on the inside of the coil is also not new. The advertisement shown in **Figure 2** is of the Webster Band Spanner mobile antenna and comes from the inside cover of QTC, the journal of the Radio Society of East Africa, June 1962. The resemblance is clear although the Webster antenna is not motor driven. The concept of a variable contact inside the coil has the advantage that the coil diameter is not determined by the lower mast section, as is the case with the screwdriver antenna design.

NUMBER PLATES AND CALL SIGNS. You can see on the photos that many US amateurs have vehicle number plate call signs. I did a check on the internet and found that registering a number plate as an amateur callsign in the USA cost from $3.00 to $30.00 depending on which state the plate was registered. I checked to see how much it would cost to register G3LDO here as a number plate. I was quoted £410!

**Photo 4**: A general view of the N8DM mobile antenna installation

**Photo 5**: A close up of the view of the antenna base, feed, control and earthing system of the N8DM mobile antenna

REFERENCES
[1] 'Antennas', *RadCom*, May 2004
[2] www.hiqantennas.com

# The Multiband Quad

*Simple methods of feeding this versatile aerial*

**TABLE 1**: Multi-band quad gamma dimensions using 14SWG copper wire

| Band | L inches (mm) | S inches (mm) | C pF |
|---|---|---|---|
| 14MHz | 35 (890) | 2.0 (50) | 100 |
| 21MHz | 27 (685) | 1.5 (38) | 75 |
| 28MHz | 18 (457) | 1.0 (25) | 50 |

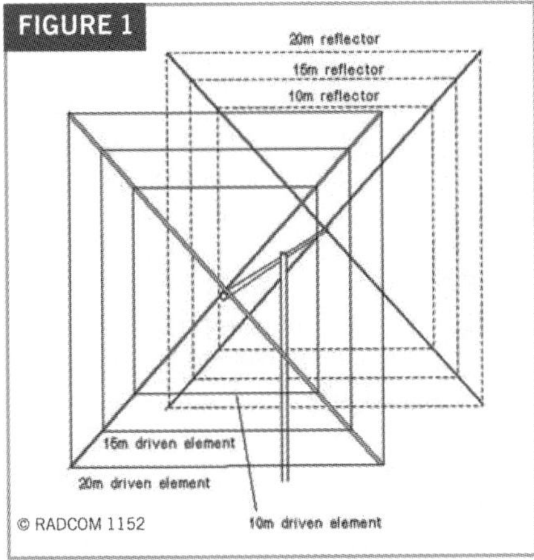


**Figure 1**: A traditional three-band cubical quad

NESTED QUADS. The advantage of the quad antenna is that it can be made into a high performance multi-band antenna by nesting quad loops for the different bands on a common support structure as shown in **Figure 1**. The total area is no larger than that required by the largest beam of the group – normally a 14MHz beam for upper HF applications. The arrangement shown is for a three-band quad, but how do you feed it?

My first real DX antenna was a two-band quad for 21 and 28MHz in 1959. This antenna was fed with a single length of 75Ω television coax with the driven elements connected in parallel. In those days I didn't have an SWR meter and only indication of matching was the transmitter Pi output loading capacitor dial calibrated in ohms. Each antenna loaded without any problem and the directional characteristics on each band were very satisfactory.

Because this antenna was so successful I had formed the opinion that for a multiband quad all one had to do was connect all the driven elements in parallel and use a single feeder. This assumption, according to W4RNL, is incorrect if any one of the elements on the antenna is harmonically related to one of the others. On a three-band quad for 14, 21 and 28MHz for example, when the antenna is energised on 28MHz the 14MHz element also presents a near matching impedance to the feeder, being a two-wavelength loop on that band. The effect of this is to damage the desirable quad directivity pattern on 28MHz. It is probable that this is the reason most multiband quads that I have seen use a separate feeder for each band.

To feed five bands would need quite a lot of coax cable. Because of this some quad builders have opted for a single feed arrangements and what follows are possible solutions that do not involve electro-mechanical devices at the antenna to effect band switching.

MULTIPLE GAMMA MATCH. A method of feeding a three-band quad with a single feeder is described in the quad antenna book by W6SAI **[1]**. I have never seen this method implemented so the following is an edited description of it.

The use of separate gamma matching devices (one for each quad) allows a relative degree of isolation to be achieved between the antennas while permitting them to be excited from a single transmission line.

The assembly of the Tri-Gamma matching system is shown in **Figure 2**. The heart of the device is a short length of open wire transmission line seen running between the centre points of the three driven loops of the multi-band quad.

The individual gamma devices are made of 14SWG solid copper wire and a small

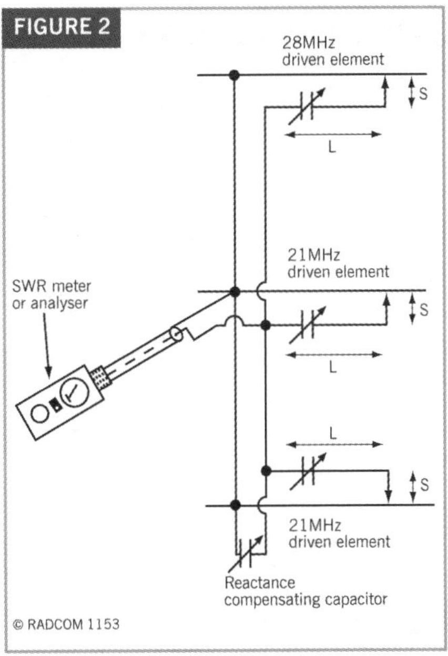


**Figure 2**: Multi-gamma matching arrangement for a three-band quad (after *All About Cubical Quad Antennas*, by W6SAI)

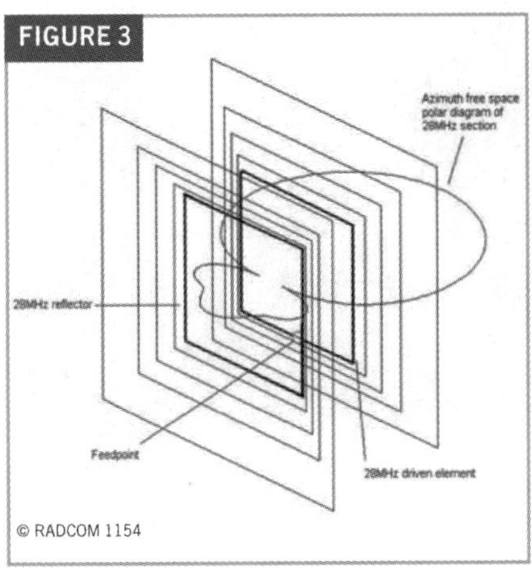


**Figure 3**: Computer model by W4RNL of a five-band quad using a boomless spider element support. The 28MHz band elements, which are energised, are shown in bold for clarity.

variable capacitor. The wire length and spacing to the quad loop are set to the preliminary dimensions given in **Table 1** and **Figure 2**. The open wire line section may be made 300Ω ladder line.

The adjustments of the Tri-Gamma tend to interact, as is true of any multiband matching system. In general, the length of the gamma wire determines the impedance transformation required and the gamma capacitor is used compensate for the inductive characteristics of the gamma conductor.

Additional compensation is required for the detuning action of the unused gammas. The 14 and 21MHz gammas tend to upset the 28MHz adjustment; the 21 and 28MHz gammas upset the 14MHz adjustment; and so on. Fortunately, the reactance capacitor at the 14MHz loop position is used to counteract the effects of detuning introduced by the multiple gamma devices.

The 28MHz, 21MHz and 14MHz gamma capacitors and gamma lengths are adjusted in turn for minimum SWR indication.

The reactance capacitor is then adjusted to enhance the SWR null.

The 15 and 28MHz bands are rechecked for minimum SWR, which may have risen after adjustment of the reactance capacitor.

The 14MHz gamma section has the greatest detuning effect upon the assembly. Exact adjustment of the 28MHz and

**Photo 1**: A commercial aluminium 'spider' casting for a boomless quad. This item was obtained at a radio club junk sale and is of unknown pedigree.

**Photo 2**: The G3LDO two-band cubical quad for the 18 and 21MHz bands. The feeder is fixed to a plastic pipe insulated support to hold it clear of the mast so that so that the quad and the feeder can be used as a low frequency antenna fed against ground.

**Photo 3**: The feed arrangement of the 18 and 21MHz quad.

21MHz gammas may be carried out with little interaction as long as the 14MHz gamma capacitor is set at minimum capacitance. As soon as the 14MHz gamma capacitor is brought into play, however, an intolerable detuning action is noticed on the 10 and 21MHz sections unless the reactance capacitor is used to compensate for the ill effects of the 14MHz gamma section. The experimenter can easily tell if the adjustments are getting out of line, as it seems that the SWR improves as the gamma lengths are shortened. If the gamma lengths are much less than shown in **Table 1**, it is a good indication that the reactance capacitor setting is incorrect.

Once the correct value of capacitances have been determined by adjustment, the capacitors may be removed, measured on a bridge, and fixed capacitors of the correct value substituted in their places. The main advantage of fixed capacitances is that they very much lighter than variable ones.

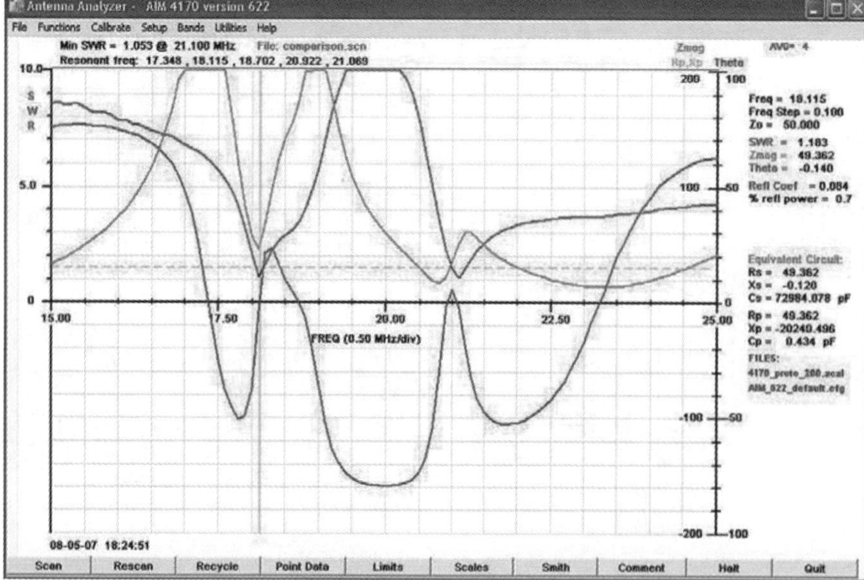


**Photo 4**: Analysis of the 18 and 21MHz quad using the AIM 4170 analyser. The more familiar SWR plot is shown in red. The impedance is shown in polar form (Zmag and theta) but the more familiar R±jX equivalent at the blue frequency cursor setting is displayed on the right.

Furthermore fixed capacitors do not need weatherproof enclosures.

IS THERE AN EASIER WAY? Earlier, I mentioned my 21 and 28MHz antenna that worked by simply paralleling the driven elements. How would such an arrangement work for an 18 and 21MHz quad I was considering?

One of the difficulties of the multiband arrangement shown in Figure 1 is that the spacing between the driven element and the reflector for each band is a compromise. This does not have a great deal of effect on the directive properties of each individual band but the feed impedances will vary quite a bit with these different spacings.

One solution for obtaining element spacing between the driver and the reflector that is constant in terms of wavelengths on each band (and a constant feed impedance on the various bands) is to use boomless construction. This involves the use of a spider, which is one of those 8-legged hubs that hold all of the supports for a multi-band 2-element beam, see **Photo 1**.

W4RNL **[2]** constructed a computer model of a five-band quad using the 'spider' configuration. The model shown in **Figure 3** has just the 28MHz band energised and it predicts that the performance on each individual band can be as good as a single band quad.

I constructed my proposed 18 and 21MHz multi-band antenna with the driven elements connected in parallel. It didn't work! I then tried connecting the two driven elements via a length of 300Ω ladder line feeder and this did work. The antenna is shown in **Photo 2** and the feed arrangement shown in **Photo 3**.

An analysis of the feeder matching on the 18 and 21MHz bands is shown in **Photo 4**. The AIM 4170 used to make this plot has the feeder characteristics taken into account so the impedances shown represent the impedance at the feedpoint of the antenna.

STOP PRESS. I have now added 14MHz elements to the quad. It is fed using an extension of the 300-ladder line and I am pleased to say that it matches very well. Furthermore, it does not disturb the matching of the 18 and 24MHz elements although at this time the directivity has yet to be optimised. Time and space prevent further description in this column but, as they say, watch this space.

REFERENCES

**[1]** *All about cubical quad antennas*, Bill Orr, W6SAI and Stuart Cowan, W2LX

**[2]** www.cebik.com

See Note [8]

# Multibanding the Quad Antenna

*In October's Antennas column Peter Dodd described how he had added 14MHz elements to an existing 18 and 21MHz quad. He continues the story with a description of how it worked out.*

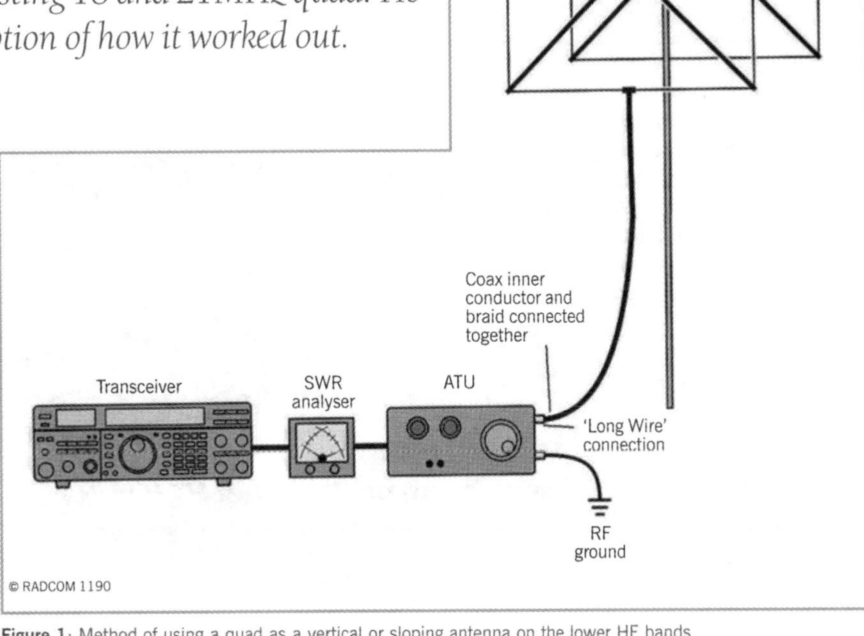


**Figure 1**: Method of using a quad as a vertical or sloping antenna on the lower HF bands

ADDING THE 14MHz ELEMENTS. The support structure for this quad consists of a boomless aluminium spider and fibreglass spreaders. These spreaders were originally used in the quad arrangements constructed by the late Al Slater, G3FXB; he used conventional quad spiders because his quad was multi-element beam.

The spreaders are 90 degrees to the horizontal on a conventional quad. With my boomless arrangement I found that the spreaders were too short because of the angle they presented to the horizontal. I felt that I could make up the deficiency on the reflector by using a large stub constructed from 60cm of 300Ω ladder line.

The driven element was connected to the tips of the spreaders with the hope that some method of matching could be devised. I started be feeding it from the 18/21MHz elements using ladder line as shown in **Photo 1**. In the event I was pleasantly surprised to find the lowest SWR occurred in the upper part of the 14MHz band (2:1 SWR bandwidth 14.15MHz to 14.6MHz). Perhaps the ladder feed was acting as a loading stub. The SWR on the higher frequency bands was not noticeably affected.

Directional tests using a local noise source indicated that while the front to back ratio was good on the upper section of the 14MHz band it was poor in the CW section. The reflector stub was increased to 1m in length, which improved the directional properties in the lower part of the band. Also, adding the reflector stub moved the SWR 2:1 bandwidth down the band to 14.0-14.24MHz due to mutual coupling between the reflector and the driven element. The driven element was then shortened by 10cm, which moved the 2:1 SWR bandwidth to 14.03-14.4MHz.

A scan of this multiband quad antenna is shown in **Photo 2**. If you compare this plot with the 18/21MHz band quad in Photo 4 of the October edition you can see that the two higher band SWR bandwidths are hardly affected. The one most notable characteristic of the plot shown in Photo 2 (compared with photo 4 in October) is that the out of band impedances are not so wild. Hmm.

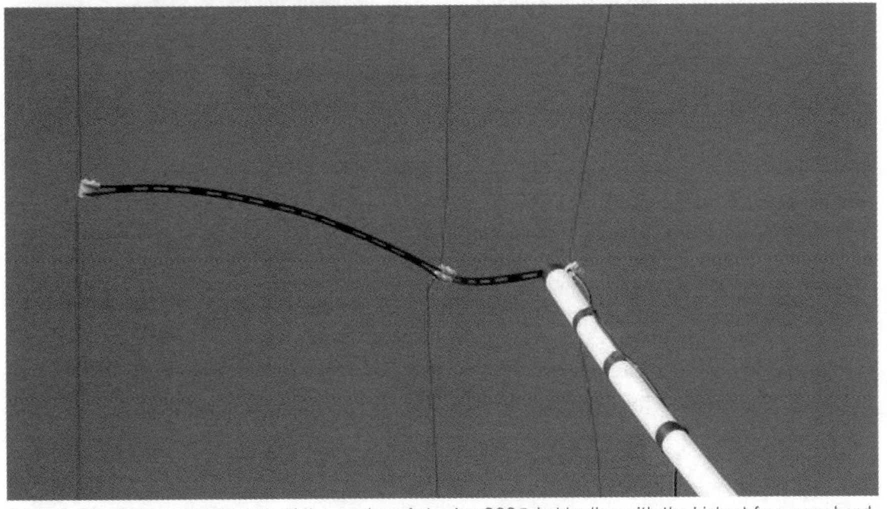

**Photo 1**: The three separate bands of the quad are fed using 300Ω ladder line with the highest frequency band nearest to the coax termination. Nylon terminal block screw connectors are used as insulators and for fixing the ladder line to the elements.

PRACTICAL CONSIDERATIONS. No matter how carefully you follow an antenna construction plan with regard to dimensions you will be lucky if you get it right first time. It is no surprise that top DXer stations perform well because their owners spend considerable time and effort honing their antennas for maximum performance.

Changing the length of metal elements of a Yagi presents no problem if a sensible method of telescoping the tubing and clamping is used. Quads present a different problem. You might think that wire elements are easily altered – after all, adding or snipping out a length of wire couldn't be simpler.

The problem is the points where the element is attached to the supports. If you add or remove some of the wire from an element then, unless the changes are very minor, the points where the elements fix to the supports will also change. When making these changes is difficult to gauge the correct distance along the support from the centre and if these distances are unequal the quad will look lopsided. A certain amount of asymmetry can be tolerated but with a multiband quad these asymmetries can look a mess.

One way around the problem is to use a temporary fixing to of the element to the support, which can be easily adjusted until the antenna functions correctly and the structure looks right. You can use plastic clothes pegs provided that the support diameter is no larger than around 20mm. My favourite temporary clip was bought from one of those emporiums that appear to sell everything. These clips are called mini-clamps and came on a shrink wrapped card – eight for £1! The method of temporarily fixing the elements to the support is shown in **Photo 3**.

When the quad is working satisfactorily the clips can be replaced with your favourite method of fixing the element to the supports. I just fix the elements to the supports using plastic tape because most of my antenna structures experimental and temporary. This method works fine with plastic insulated wire. If you are using plain copper wire for the elements then they need to be fixed to the supports using plastic tubing as insulation.

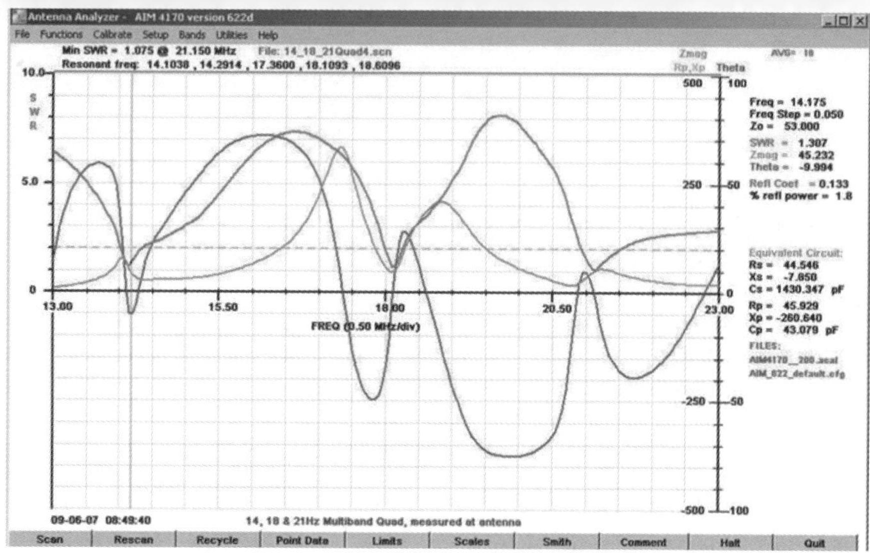


**Photo 2**: Analysis of the 14, 18 and 21MHz quad using the AIM 4170 analyser. The more familiar SWR plot is shown in red. The impedance at the blue frequency cursor setting is shown in polar form, Zmag and Theta. The more familiar R±jX equivalent is also shown labelled Rs and Xs respectivel.

**Photo 3**: A method of temporarily fixing a quad element to the spreaders during the tuning and adjusting phase.

**Photo 4**: The G3LDO three-band cubical quad for the 14, 18 and 21MHz bands. The feeder is fixed to a plastic pipe insulating support to hold it clear of the mast so that so that the quad and the feeder can be used as a low frequency antenna fed against ground (see text).

THE LOWER HF BANDS. The HF quad as described can also be used on the lower HF frequency bands and even at 150kHz. I first used this method in the late 1950s where a 21 and 28MHz quad was used on 1.8MHz. The quad and the feeder itself is used as wire antenna fed against earth using an ATU and is connected as shown in **Figure 1**.

Obviously, the method will only work if the feedpoint is relatively close to the quad. Also the feeder will have to be arranged so that it is well clear of the metal structures such as the boom or mast. **Photo 4** shows how this can be achieved with feeder fixed to a plastic pipe insulated support, which holds the feeder clear of the mast.

The shack at my QTH is located some distance from the antenna and the RG213 feeder takes a long, convoluted route along the side of the house and along the inside of a hedge where it is connected to a length of RG58A/U to feed the quad. Clearly, this arrangement would be of little use as a long wire antenna. In this case the solution is to use a nearby shed as a remote ATU house, as shown in **Photo 5**. In my case the distance from the shed to the antenna mast is about the same as the mast height so the RG58 section of the coax feeder forms a 45 degree sloping antenna on the lower frequencies. The quad elements form a considerable top load and the antenna performs quite well on 1.8 and 3.5MHz.

By using coax connectors the feeder can be switched to the quad directly or via the ATU. An automatic ATU would be a much more convenient arrangement but in the meantime the manual one helps keep me fit when I want to change bands.

The performance of this antenna is dictated by the quality of the RF earth connection and at this QTH it performs as well as any other wire antenna that I have tried. The antenna performance on 150kHz will be the subject of a future 'Antennas' column.

**Photo 5**: Corner of the garden shed taken over as an ATU house. The MFJ-989c is used for bands 1.8 to 10MHz. The coil shown below is an experimental resonating and matching arrangement for 150kHz.

# Antennas

*If you want to optimise your HF beam antenna you don't need several acres of real estate to make a test range*

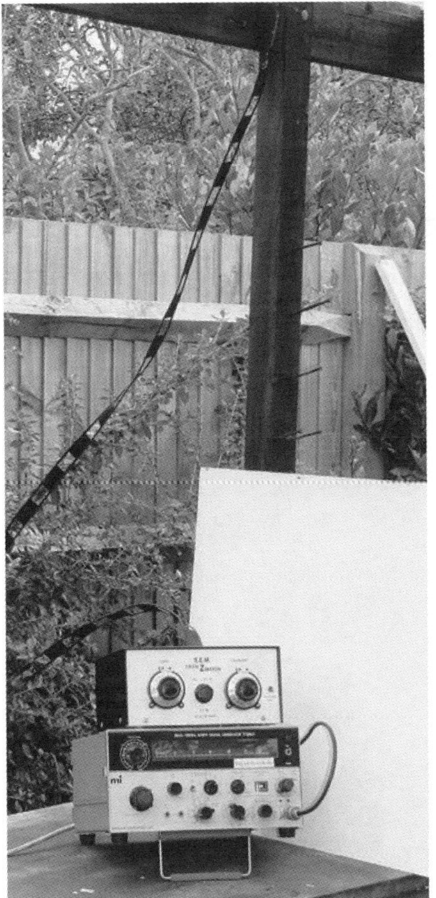

**Photo 1**: Signal generator, ATU and short dipole used to provide a test signal for beam directivity measurements

SWR ISN'T EVERYTHING. In a previous Antennas **[1]** I noted that a low SWR did not necessarily mean that the antenna is performing well. You could have a good SWR but the antenna or feeder could be very lossy or the antenna badly located, or that the parasitic elements of a beam antenna are not the correct length. It is the parasitic element(s) that really determine a beam antenna's performance.

I have also recently described a multiband quad for 14, 18 and 21MHz **[2]**. I understand that there can be adverse effects on the directivity patterns on some bands of nested quads so I needed to make some directivity pattern measurements.

FAR FIELD GROUND-WAVE TESTS. One of the most frequently used and reliable methods of testing an antenna is with ground wave tests with another station some distance away, say 2 to 3km (1 to 2 miles). With your receiver connected to the antenna under test (AUT) the signal strength of the local station can be monitored as the AUT is rotated. These signal levels can be plotted against antenna direction to provide a fairly comprehensive directivity pattern. Better still you can computerise the procedure using Polar Plot as described in **[3]**.

The disadvantage of this method is that the other station's transmitter will have to radiate a fairly large signal, which can cause QRM to other users. A further disadvantage of this method is that the procedure for making the measurements is a bit cumbersome with another station being involved. It would be more advantageous to have access to both the AUT and the signal source and antenna, particularly if you are making constant adjustments to the antenna in an effort to obtain maximum performance.

I had the impression that field strength measurements (and antenna directivity patterns) could only be done in the far field, as described above. See also the ARRL Antenna book **[4]**. I have spent many happy hours plotting polar diagrams of VHF antennas where access to the far field was not a problem; this is described in detail in **[5]**.

In the past I had, at my previous QTH, made similar HF antenna measurements using a signal generator with a short antenna as signal source located in the loft of the house. The AUT was located at the end of the garden about two and a half wavelengths and the polar plots were very successful.

NEAR FIELD TESTS. What I am about to propose now is something different. As stated earlier I needed to measure the directivity patterns of my multiband quad for 14, 18 and 21MHz and to be able to do a bit of 'tweaking' and see if the patterns improved. The quad is located on a mast in the middle of the garden so a far field antenna range was out of the question if I wanted control of the AUT and the signal source.

The arrangement finally decided on is shown in **Figure 1**, and although specifically shown as a method of measuring the directional performance of a quad I see no reason why it should not be used to estimate the performance of any beam antenna.

The AUT is fixed to a 14m high mast, which does not have a rotator. The whole mast is rotated manually and is described in **[6]**. The field strength meter comprises a FT-990, which has a very good S-meter, and an attenuator.

The signal source is provided by a signal generator and an antenna. The signal source antenna is a horizontally polarized short dipole about 3m long and 2.4m high. It is fed in the centre with balanced slotted line and matched to the signal generator with a balanced ATU. The length and height of the signal source antenna is quite arbitrary and was determined more by convenience than any technical considerations.

Because of the relative heights and distances between the AUT and the signal source antenna the measurement angle was just over 30° below the horizontal axis of the AUT. So how would this rather unconventional test range perform?

The quad had been in use only a few weeks before the measurements (or perhaps I should say the assessment of the antenna range) so I had some idea of how the quad was performing. I also have this strange QRM on 14MHz radiating from a telephone pole some 150m to the SW of my antenna. Although this is a confounded nuisance it is useful for measuring antenna directivity on 14MHz. Because the reflector of my multiband 14, 18 and 21MHz quad is a bit short on 14MHz (at the present time) the F:B on 14.02MHz is non existent while at the top of the band it is quite good. On the 18 and 21MHz bands it 'seemed OK'.

Because the mast is rotated manually I limited the readings to front-to-back ratio measurements only. I did have a quick look for side nulls as the AUT was rotated but didn't see any. The initial F:B results were:

| | |
|---|---|
| 14.02MHz | 0dB |
| 14.27MHz | 13dB |
| 18.1MHz | 8dB |
| 21.04MHz | 14dB |
| 21.33MHz | 23dB |

The 18.1MHz reading was rather poor and there was an indication of an improvement as the frequency was altered from 18.06 to 18.16MHz. I added an extra 200mm to the 18MHz quad reflector and measured new F:B as 19dB.

Because the distance between the AUT and the source antenna is so small the

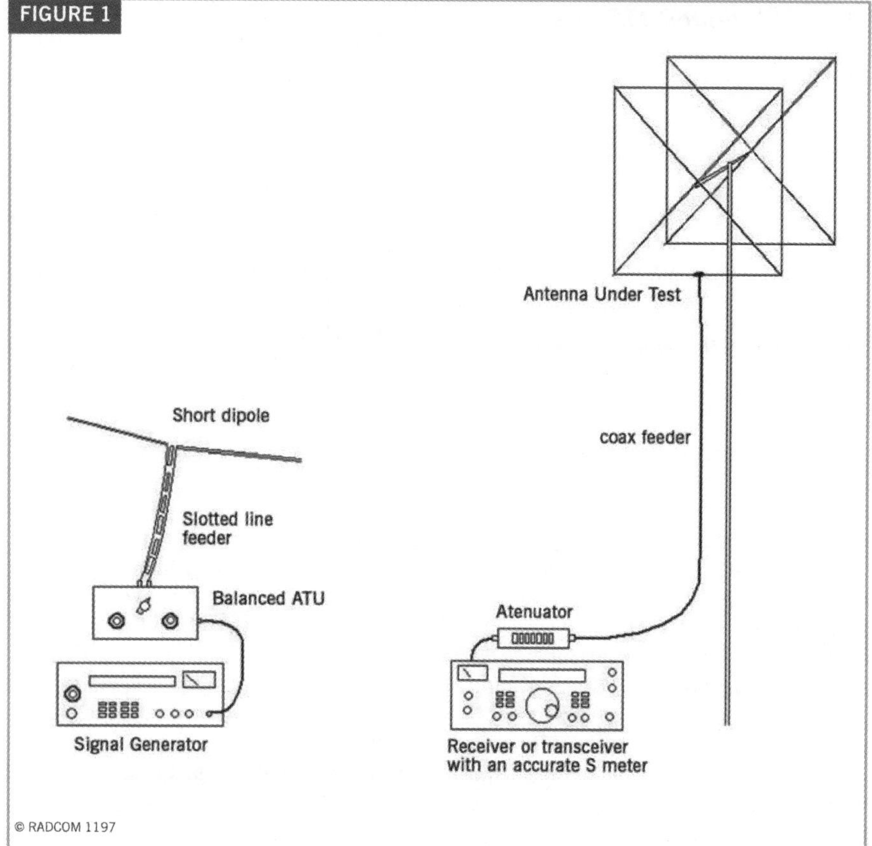

Figure 1: Test arrangement for measuring the directive properties of a beam antenna in the near field

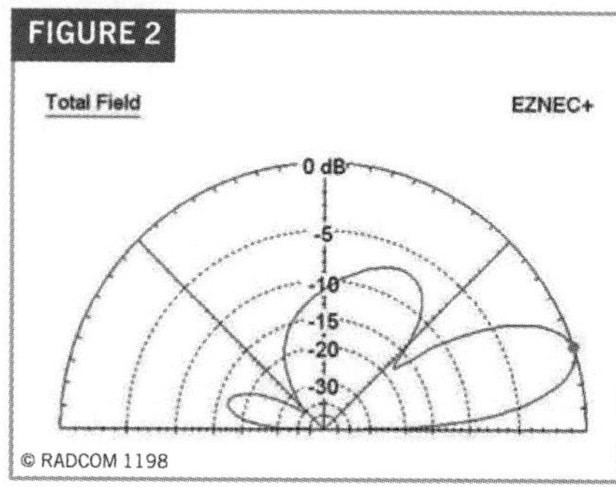

Figure 2: Elevation diagram of an 18MHz antenna 14m high

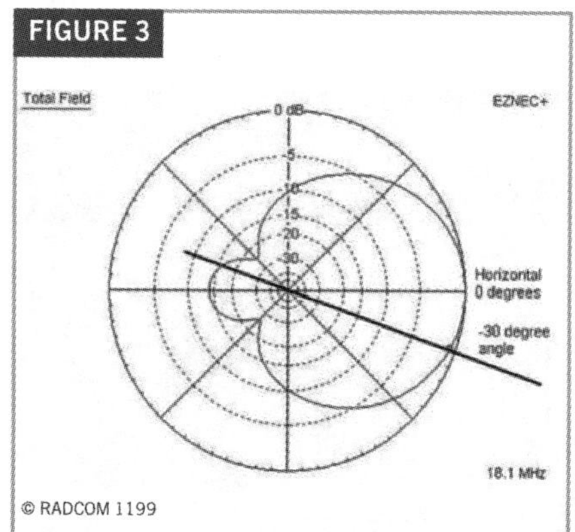

Figure 3: Free space elevation diagram of an 18MHz antenna with calculated angle of 0 and –30°

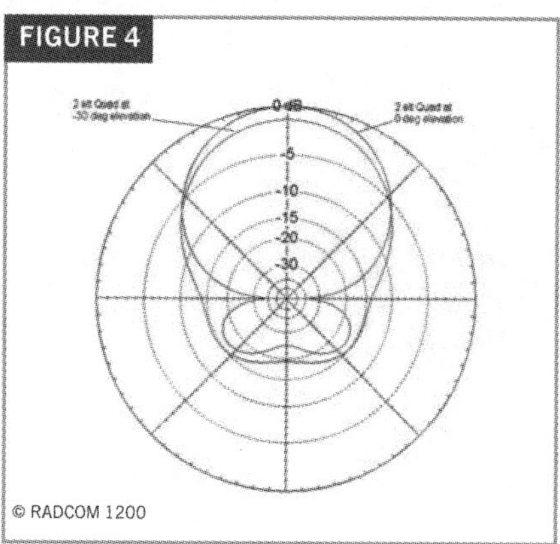

Figure 4: Azimuth free space diagrams of an 18MHz quad calculated at 0° elevation and –30° elevation

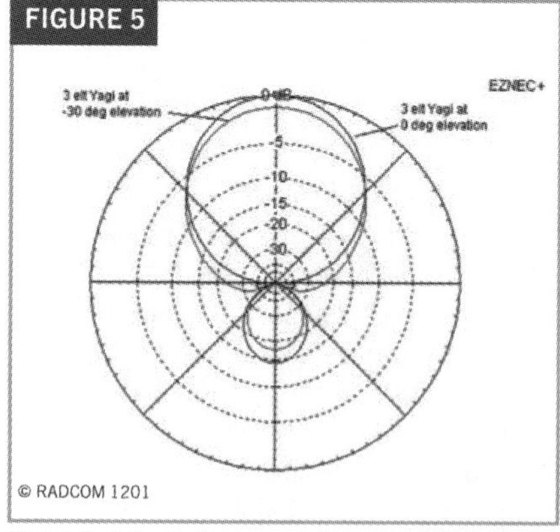

Figure 5: Azimuth free space diagrams of 3-ele Yagi calculated at 0° elevation and –30° elevation

output from the signal generator is quite adequate. The ATU control settings were recorded for each band, set up before each test using an MFJ-269.

For the S meter on the receiver to operate correctly the RF gain must be set to maximum. This causes the S meter reading to bounce around on the noise and signals and a variable attenuator is necessary: on 14MHz I had to insert 20dB of attenuation to calm things down. On 18 and 21MHz things were much quieter. More information on using a receiver as a field strength meter is described in **[7]**.

If you are using an older signal generator best results are obtained with the signal generator, set to AM and the modulator switched on, and with the receiver is also switched to AM. This makes the test arrangement less susceptible to drift.

OTHER CONSIDERATIONS. Ideally, these measurements should be made in the far field. Additionally they should be made at the angle of maximum radiation. A model of the elevation plot of my 18MHz quad is shown in **Figure 2** and as you can see the angle of maximum radiation is 18°. The distance between the AUT and the source would be 2.5 wavelengths, which works out at about 42m (137ft) on 18MHz. To intercept the maximum angle of radiation the signal source antenna would have to be 27m (88ft) high.

In practice a signal generated by a local amateur seems to work well although in this case the elevation measurement angle is 0°. The signal strength is well down on the maximum angle but that doesn't seem to matter. According to the model in Figure 2 there is no signal at 0° elevation but in practice this is not the case. (This is the difference between modelling and the real world).

The elevation polar diagram model shown in Figure 2 is the result of interaction between direct radiation from the antenna and earth reflection. In the near field the wavefront hasn't expanded enough be affected by the ground so we can make some sort measurement in the near field provided we know the limitations of doing so. A free-space elevation diagram of the same antenna is shown in **Figure 3**, with a line to show the measurement angle of –30°. From this diagram it doesn't look as though there is much difference between the –30° angle and the 0° angle. The difference is more apparent in **Figure 4**, which does show that there is a small difference in the measurements made at these two angles, with no nulls at –30°, as noted earlier.

FINALLY. While the near field measurement method described in this article is unsuitable for measuring gain, it is perfectly suited to maximizing the front-to-back ratio of beam antenna, which was what I wanted it for in the first place.

Would the method work with other beam antennas? According to EZNEC it certainly would with a Yagi antenna. The diagrams in **Figure 5** show that there is very little difference between 0° and –30°. Not only that but even the nulls are quite pronounced on the –30° plot.

REFERENCES

**[1]** Antennas, *RadCom* July 2007
**[2]** Antennas, *RadCom* Nov 2007
**[3]** Antennas, *RadCom* Nov 2002, Oct 2005, Sept 2006, Oct 2006.
**[4]** *The ARRL Antenna book*, 20th edition, pages 27-47 to 27-53.
**[5]** *The Antenna Experimenter's Guide, 2nd edition*, Peter Dodd, G3LDO, from RSGB
**[6]** *Backyard Antennas*, 2nd edition, Peter Dodd, G3LDO, from RSGB
**[7]** Antennas, *RadCom* April 2004

# Antennas

## The HexBeam: A lightweight multiband beam antenna that performs well and is easy to build

**Photo 1:** The multiband HexBeam as constructed by G3TXO

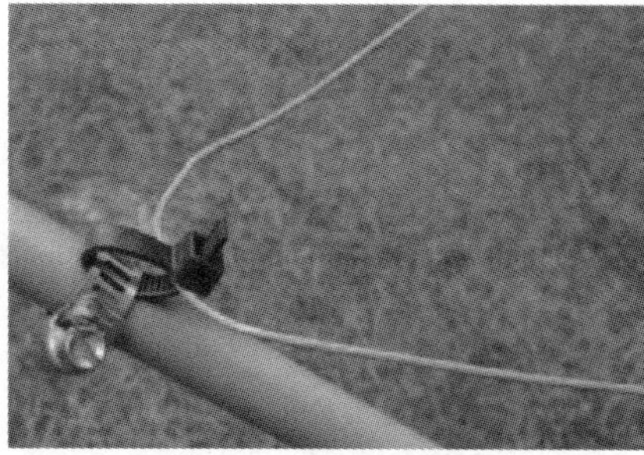
**Photo 3:** Method of fixing an uninsulated wire to the element support by K4KIO

**Photo 2:** Feed method for the multiband HexBeam by K4KIO

MULTIBAND MISUNDERSTANDINGS. From time to time, interest re emerges in some existing designs for compact beams. L B Cebik, W4RNL **[1]** notes: "the interest usually stems from the publication of some peak performance figures for a particular design rather than from the antenna's performance across an entire band. Consequently, misunderstandings of antenna potentials multiply endlessly". The situation is even more complex with multiband beams – particularly compact multiband beams.

THE HEXBEAM. One of these designs is the HexBeam. Steve Hunt, G3TXQ, who contacted me regarding his experiments on this antenna. He noted: "I've spent recent weeks doing more HexBeam experiments on a 10m test bed antenna. In particular I've looked at a method of extending the bandwidth, searched for the optimum Driver/Reflector tip spacing, and found a suitable Driver/Reflector ratio that lends itself to Beta matching. The results are presented in two new pages on my website" **[2] [3]**.

G3TXQ notes in his web page "I like the HexBeam - it's an innovative design, ..... although not a 'magic' antenna – (other designs beat it for gain, front-to-back ratio and bandwidth). However, if you want an antenna that can be multi-banded, exhibits useful gain and directivity, is very lightweight, has a small turning radius, and lends itself readily to 'Do It Yourself' construction, the HexBeam should be very high on your list of options". G3TXO's complete multiband HexBeam is shown in **Photo 1**.

Holger, DL7IO, on his website **[4]**, notes that the first time he came across the HexBeam was in the 80s in Great Britain where it was described as evolving from a M or X-beam. He was looking for a lightweight antenna for his DXpeditions and finally built a HexBeam around 1999 (I have not found any information on this beam in earlier literature).

The HexBeam is a parasitic two-element beam with the driver and reflector elements bent into a 'W' shape to conserve space, see **Figure 1**. A free space computer model is shown in **Figure 2**. It is usually constructed of wire elements strung onto a support structure of fibreglass spreaders. By 'bowing' the spreaders, the elements for several amateur bands can be accommodated on the same support structure and spaced apart in both the horizontal and vertical planes. This approach allows a multiband beam to be constructed with a turning radius about half that of the corresponding Yagi. The general layout of the multiband HexBeam is shown in **Figure 3** although this shows the horizontal spacing it does not show the vertical spacing, which can only be seen by studying Photo 1.

In a later e-mail G3TXO went on to say: "Leo Shoemaker, K4KIO, and I have co-operated on the content of our respective websites - we agreed that I would major on the theory and experimental work, while he covered practical constructional information. We found so much conflicting information on the Web that we decided to try to produce a definitive set of dimensions. The recommended dimensions on his site were a joint effort; they are well proven and are the result of many hours of EZNEC simulation followed by the construction of at least 6 'real' antennas. I have also provided individual builders with 40m and 30m wire dimensions, which have worked out well for them".

CONSTRUCTION. The very detailed description of how to construct a five band HexBeam, on Leo K4KIO's website **[5]**, is

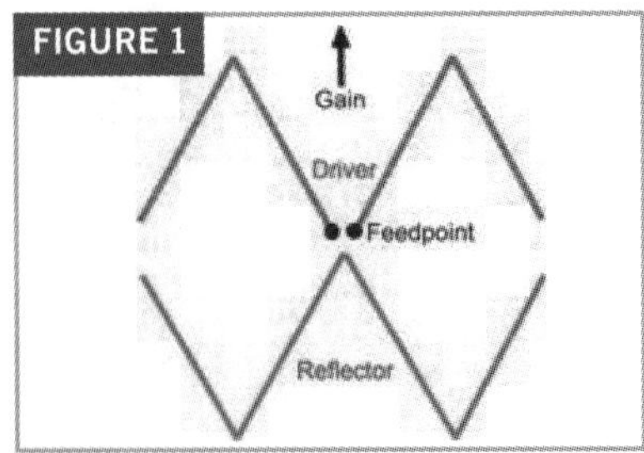


**Figure 1:** Basic configuration of a single band HexBeam.

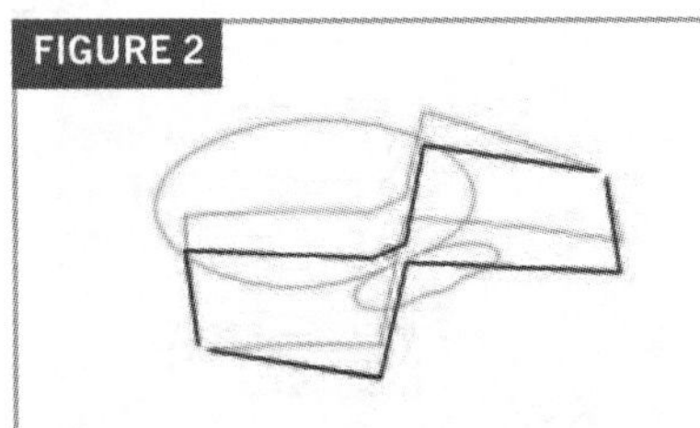


**Figure 2:** Computer model of a single band HexBeam showing the current distribution and an azimuth freespace polar diagram. The model predicts a free-space gain of 5.7dBi and a F/B of 24dB.

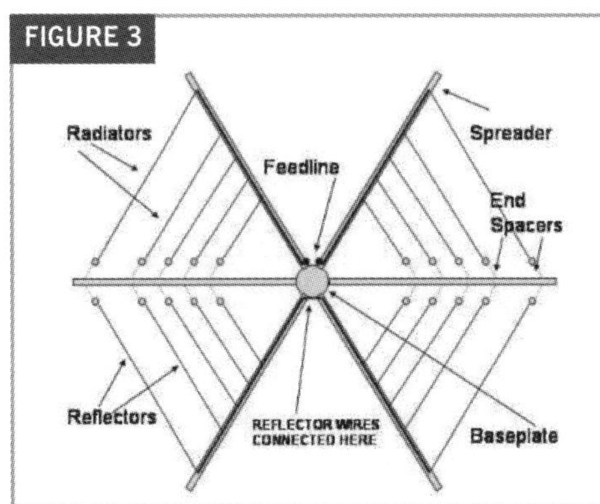


**Figure 3:** Top view of a five-band HexBeam

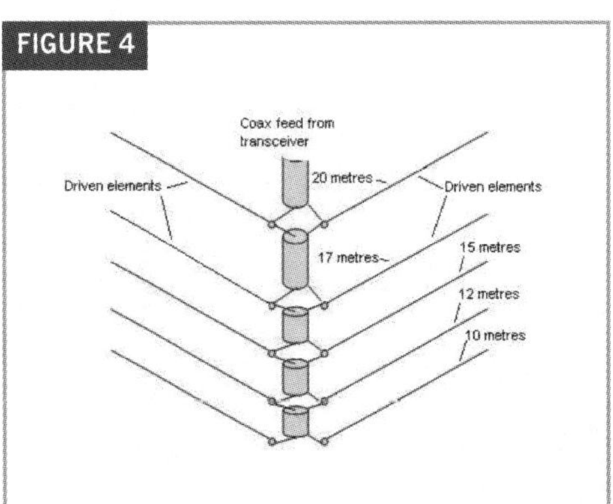


**Figure 4:** Feed line wiring configuration for a Multi-band HexBeam. 50 ohm coax is connected to the top of the HexBeam at the terminals for the 20m band. Note the transposition on alternate band connections.

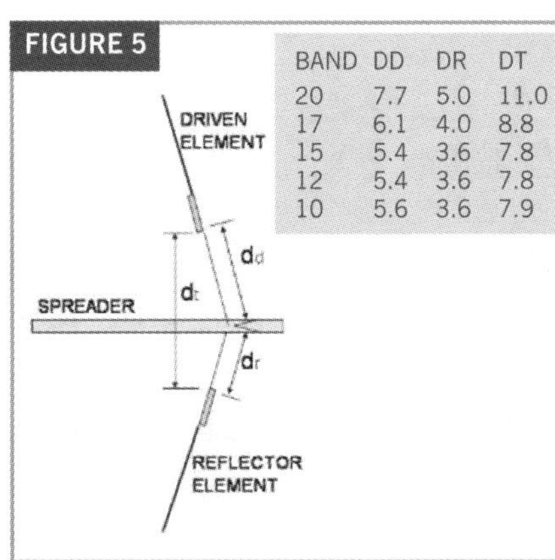

FIGURE 5
DRIVEN ELEMENT
SPREADER
REFLECTOR ELEMENT
BAND DD DR DT
20 7.7 5.0 11.0
17 6.1 4.0 8.8
15 5.4 3.6 7.8
12 5.4 3.6 7.8
10 5.6 3.6 7.9


**Figure 5:** Element end spacing dimensions in inches.

| Band | Freq | 1/2 Driver wire length | 1/2 Reflector wire length |
|---|---|---|---|
| 20 | 14.050 | 216.0 | 220.5 |
| 17 | 18.150 | 166.9 | 170.3 |
| 15 | 21.100 | 142.8 | 145.7 |
| 12 | 24.950 | 121.1 | 123.6 |
| 10 | 28.100 | 107.7 | 109.9 |

**Table 1a:** Element lengths optimised for the CW end of the band.

| Band | Freq | 1/2 Driver wire length | 1/2 Reflector wire length |
|---|---|---|---|
| 20 | 14.200 | 213.6 | 218.0 |
| 17 | 18.150 | 166.9 | 170.3 |
| 15 | 21.300 | 141.4 | 144.2 |
| 12 | 24.950 | 121.1 | 123.6 |
| 10 | 28.600 | 106.2 | 108.4 |

**Table 1b:** Element lengths optimised for the SSB section of the band.

| Band | Length |
|---|---|
| 20 metres | 42 inches |
| 17 metres | 20 inches |
| 15 metres | 14 inches |
| 12 metres | 10 inches |
| 10 metres | 6 inches |

**Table 2:** Distance of driven element feedpoint above the baseplate.

the most comprehensive constructional project I have ever seen. It includes many photos, with appropriate captions shown at every stage of construction. I don't propose to duplicate this (I wouldn't have nearly enough space in two pages) but to give a few details to whet the appetite for constructing this antenna. To my mind the K4KIO HexBeam is very well engineered.

The main construction task is building a centre hub to support the six fibreglass element support poles. This must also have provision for fixing an insulated vertical support for the multiband feed system and of course provision for mounting on a mast. Several solutions are described in the web pages shown in the References. Some builders have used canes but these don't take kindly to bowing as shown in Photo 1.

K4KIO specifies wire elements of 1.5mm diameter uninsulated copper and the lengths are shown in **Tables 1a** and **1b**. The dimensions are quoted in inches - those who prefer the metric system can multiply by 2.54 to get the equivalent in centimetres.

The method of feeding is interesting and is shown in **Figure 4**. When you hear about the problems of feeding multiband quads it comes as a surprise that the method of feeding the multiband Hexbeams is so simple. The practical implementation of the feed method is illustrated in **Photo 2**. The feedpoint height above the baseplate for each band is given in **Table 2**.

One interesting detail is shown in **Photo 3** as a method of providing an insulating fixing for an uninsulated wire element to a support. I will be modifying my quad so that it uses this type of fixing. A modification to this fixing will include a piece of plastic between the hose clamp and the fibreglass support to prevent damage to the support.

The spacing between the ends of the reflector and driven element ends are more critical when it comes to gain and front-to-back ratio performance. The data shown in **Figure 5** is by K4KIO.

FINALLY. On the face of it this antenna would appear to provide a solution for a beam antenna for those with restricted sites – that means most of us! The gain and F/B figures shown in the computer model in Figure 2 are quite astonishing although this performance is not maintained over the whole band. Furthermore, the measured performance on a multiband is down on that shown in Figure 2.

The mechanical data is also impressive. The K4KIO antenna data is:

| | |
|---|---|
| Freq bands | 10, 12, 15, 17, 20 |
| Weight | 20 lb |
| Diameter | 19.3 ft |
| Wind Surface Area | under 5 Sq ft |
| K factor | 192.5 ft lb |

The true value of an antenna is just how many people have built it and how much it is talked about. Just try typing 'HexBeam' into Google and see what you get. There is also a Yahoo special interest group at http://groups.yahoo.com/group/hex-beam/. Other HexBeam constructors not so far mentioned include G0TSM, EI7BA, 7Q7BP, W1GQL, WA2JJX, W2HIG, KC0MSX and N8XE and there are many more.

My only gripe with this antenna is that it looks like an umbrella that has blown inside out in a gale. Others might think differently – beauty lies in the eyes of the beholder.

REFERENCES

[1] http://www.cebik.com/wire/4.html
[2] http://www.karinya.net/g3txq/hexbeam/measurements_1/
[3] http://www.karinya.net/g3txq/hexbeam/broadband/
[4] http://dl7io.de/reflectedw
[5] http://www.leoshoemaker.com/hexbeambyk4kio/general.html

# More Adjustments & Measurements

## Adjusting quad directivity, plus a high tech GDO

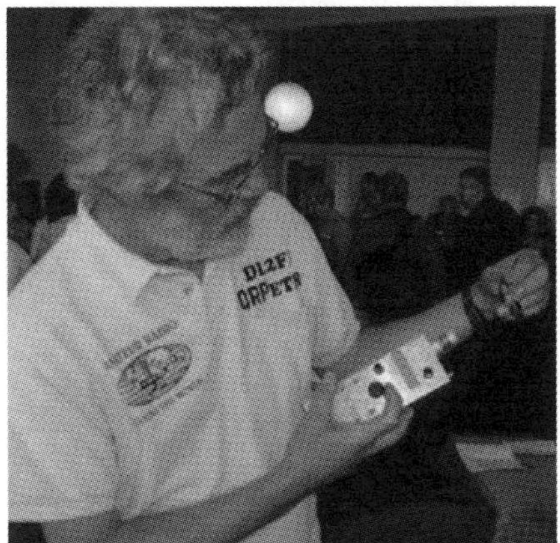

PHOTO 1: Peter Zenker, DL2FI, demonstrating the DiPiT GDO at the GQRP Convention in Rochdale.

**MAST PROBLEM.** In December's 'Antennas' I described a method of adjusting the directivity of a quad where a stub was used to tune the reflector. The difficulty in optimising the directivity is that the antenna has to be lowered for each stub adjustment, then raised again to perform the measurement. My counter weighted fold-over antenna mast can be raised and lowered in less than half a minute so I don't find this adjustment procedure too arduous. The standard commercial mast that telescopes down before folding over will take around 15 minutes to lower and the same amount of time to raise; this is more of hassle. In an early 'Antennas' **[1]** I described a method used by GW4ZXG that allows the quad reflector adjustment to be performed while the antenna is raised. It is such a good idea that it is well worth repeating.

**GW4ZXG REFLECTOR RESONANCE ADJUSTER.** This adjustment method, shown in **Figure 1** comprises tuning stubs of stiff copper wire about 0.84m (30in) long with 50mm (2in) spacing. A sprung metal paper (bulldog) clip is drilled and threaded onto the stub to form a sliding shorting bar.. The ends of the stubs are taped to the fibreglass arm to hold them in a firm vertical position and a simple pulley system using a small china 'egg' insulator is fixed to the arm just above the end of the stub. The clip is fixed to a long nylon cord so that it may be slid up or down the stub whilst the antenna is at full working height and the operator is at ground level.

From Figure 1 you will notice that the adjustable stub is vertical. This is because the GW4ZXG quad uses a diamond configuration. This is the same as the conventional quad shown in **Figure 2** but rotated through 45 degrees as shown in **Figure 3**. The lower and upper supports for the diamond quad are vertical. The feedpoint on the driven element and the tuning stub on the reflector is fixed to the lower element supports. With a conventional quad configuration, or any wire beam antenna such as the Moxon rectangle, a special stub support would have to be constructed.

I checked the performance of the conventional quad and the diamond and this is nearly the same, as shown in Figure 1 and Figure 2. The diamond quad sheds moisture more easily than the conventional quad and the element supports can also be used as a feeder and a stub support.

**THE DIP-OSCILLATOR (GDO) REVISITED.** The GDO (as you all probably know) is an instrument for measuring the resonance of a tuned circuit or antenna element without the instrument being connected directly to the element. It can also be used for measuring the resonant length of transmission line. The construction details of such an instrument appeared in the December edition of that excellent 'Homebrew' series **[2]**.

The GDO comprises a calibrated tuneable oscillator. Power is absorbed by a resonant circuit when it and the oscillator are tuned to the same frequency. Some indication of oscillator energy loss is required and with the instrument described in [2] this is done by measuring the level of gate voltage, which is proportional to the peak-to-peak level of the oscillator waveform. The early vacuum tube or valve instruments used this method by measuring the grid current; and were known as Grid Dip Oscillators (GDOs) for this reason.

I recently described a GDO in a previous 'Antennas' **[3]**. This circuit does not measure gate current directly; instead it measures the total current through the FET. This current is large compared with that flowing in a base or gate of a solid-state oscillator. However, the variation of current through resonance is only a small part of the total current through the FET. The dip is enhanced by offsetting the meter reading using a potentiometer in a bleeder network. This is set so that the meter reads about 75% FSD when the instrument is not coupled to a load.

A good GDO should possess the following features:

- Good sensitivity. To achieve good accuracy and avoid detuning of the GDO or the measured tuned circuit the GDO coil should always be coupled as loosely as possible. Unfortunately looser couplings result in a less defined dip so some compromise between coupling and dip is necessary. The higher the sensitivity of the GDO the less this compromise has to be. Some indication of sensitivity can be checked by

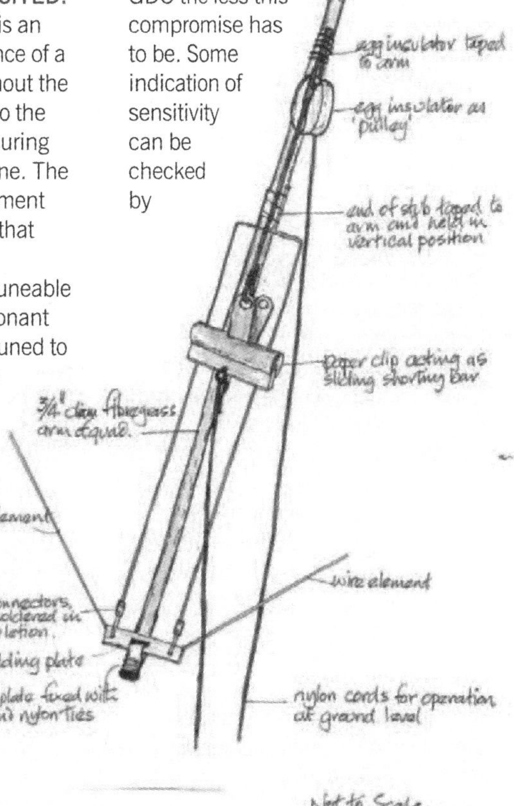


FIGURE 1: Sketch of the GW4ZXG remote quad reflector tuner with a bulldog clip remote controlled tuning slider.

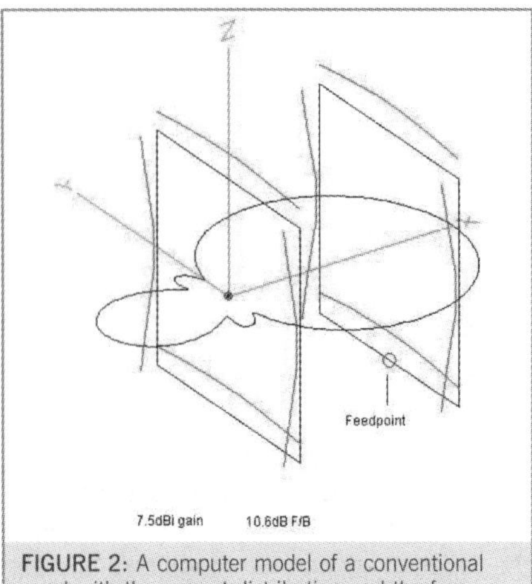

FIGURE 2: A computer model of a conventional quad with the current distribution and the free space polar diagram superimposed.

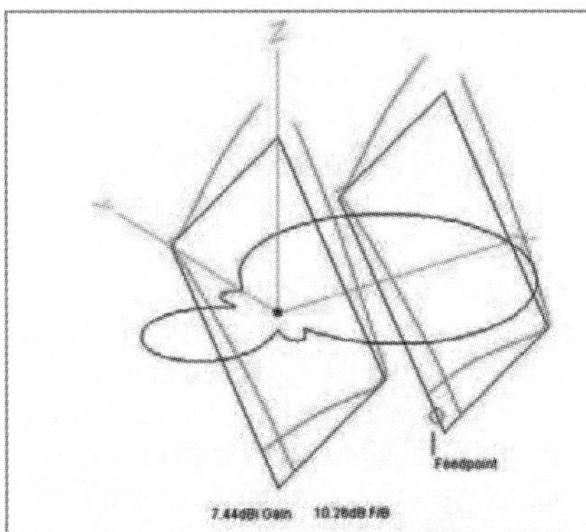

FIGURE 3: A computer model of a diamond quad with the current distribution and the free space polar diagram superimposed. The feedpoint is off-set to meet modelling constraints.

squeezing the coil of the GDO between the thumb and forefinger and noting the meter deflection; this should dip to at least 50% of the maximum reading. The GDO should also be capable of measuring resonance of a high C tuned circuit at a distance of 6 to 7cm (2-3in). I use a parallel tuned circuit, comprising a 5mH inductor with a 100pF capacitance, as a standard.

- Large frequency dial with smooth reduction gear tuning. The GDO could have a frequency counter instead of the dial but this would increase the complexity of the instrument. Provision for connection of the GDO to a frequency counter is probably a better arrangement. A broad frequency range together with a good frequency readout resolution is achieved in most Dip Meters with the use of plug in coils.
- Meter large enough to see the dip clearly. The layout of the instrument should allow the frequency readout and the dip indication to be visible at the same time. An audio indication of a dip has been used to some effect.

**DiPiT, THE ULTIMATE DIPMETER.** While at the GQRP Convention in Rochdale last October, I had the good fortune to meet Peter Zenker, DL2FI. Peter brought along several items of RF test equipment, which are built as kits by the German QRP Club. The one item that caught my eye was the high tech 'DipIt' GDO, designed by Peter Solf, DK1HE. By popular request of the club members this instrument was designed as a kit with the following specification:

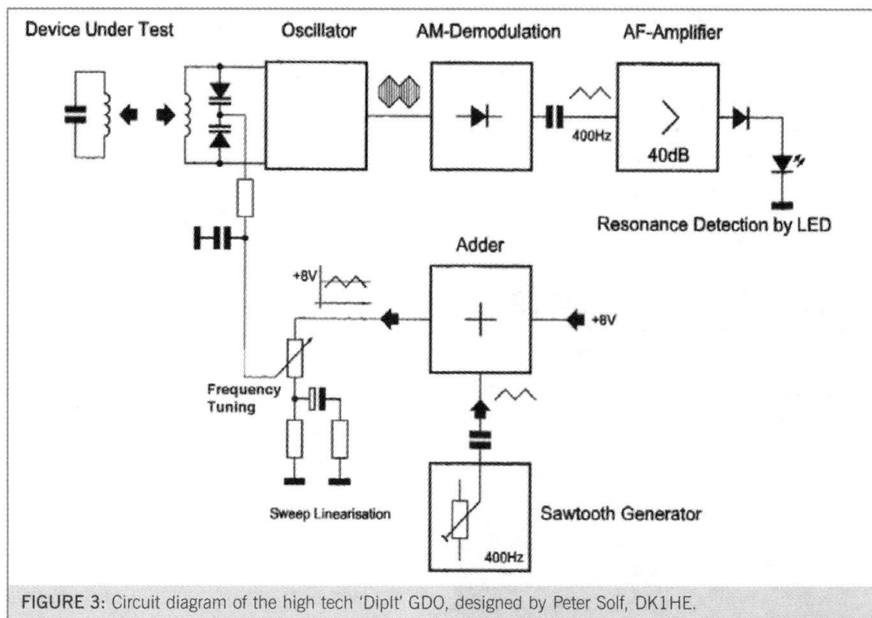

FIGURE 3: Circuit diagram of the high tech 'DipIt' GDO, designed by Peter Solf, DK1HE.

- Frequency range: 1 - 42MHz, divided into five bands by means of plug in coils. (It has a VHF/UHF option using a plug in oscillator)
- A 'sweep-frequency' method that produces exceptional sensitivity.
- A built in frequency counter.
- Resonance is indicated using a super bright light-emitting diode

Like other GDOs it can be used as an absorption frequency measurement using the built in frequency counter. It can also be used as a heterodyne frequency meter using an additional headphone output and BNC input (with attenuator). It can also produce an amplitude stable +7dBm generator output for peripheral attachments such as an antenna analyser.

The circuit of the DiPit is shown in **Figure 4**. Like all conventional GDOs it has an oscillator whose frequency is determine by the inductance of the plug-in coil and the parallel varactor diodes. That is where the similarities between the DiPit and the conventional GDO end.

The normal tuning voltage to the varactor, set by 10-turn potentiometer, has superimposed upon it a low amplitude balanced sawtooth voltage from the 400Hz sawtooth generator. This results in a balanced frequency modulation which sweeps the VFO around the selected mid frequency. The chosen frequency shift is approximately ±0.2% of the oscillator frequency setting.

When the instrument is coupled to a tuned circuit under test the oscillator frequency sweeps over the resonating curve of this tuned circuit. When the oscillator frequency and the tuned circuit under test resonant frequency are the same, some of the oscillator energy is absorbed by the test circuit, just as in a conventional GDO. In this case the loss of oscillator energy results in a greater modulation depth, which is detected by an AM demodulation circuit and amplified by a 40dB gain audio amplifier. The output of this amplifier is then fed to the resonance detector LED.

Because the demodulated 400Hz signal can be amplified almost to any level this GDO design offers a significantly higher sensitivity than the conventional GDOs described earlier. The tuned circuit under test can be measured using extremely loose coupling that enhances reading accuracy. (High quality PA tank tuned circuits can be dipped cleanly from a distance greater than 20cm). Coupling a GDO into antenna element is much easier with a sensitive instrument. A specially constructed coil, as described in [3], **[4]** and **[5]**, is necessary when coupling a dip oscillator to a tubular antenna element.

REFERENCES


[1] 'Antennas', RadCom August 2002
[2] 'Homebrew', RadCom December 2007.
[3] 'Antennas', RadCom March 2007.
[4] The Antenna Experimenters Guide, Peter Dodd, G3LDO, RSGB
[5] HF Antennas for all Locations, 2nd Edition, Les Moxon, G6XN, RSGB

# Antennas

## More on measuring the resonant frequency of antenna elements, and the Hexbeam revisited

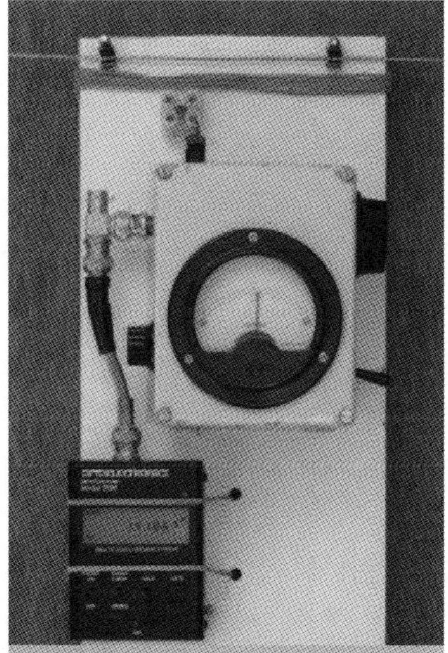
PHOTO 1: Element resonant frequency measuring unit MkVI shown measuring the frequency of an uninsulated wire antenna element.

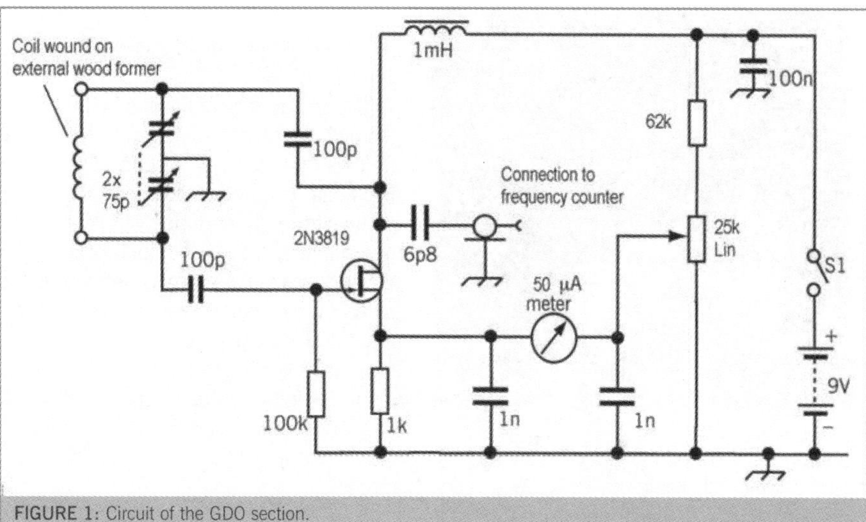

FIGURE 1: Circuit of the GDO section.

**TWANG!** I have been rebuilding the quad described in earlier columns. The original was constructed from some rather thin 20SWG plastic insulated wire because I had a lot of this material to hand. The wire seemed to work quite well but was not very robust and the elements broke several times during the winter storms. I am in the process of replacing this thin wire with 16SWG uninsulated wire, which by chance is the same diameter (1.5mm) as the original, taking into account the insulation.

There were two consequences of changing the design. The fixing to the element supports required to be insulated and the elements had to be made slightly longer than the original. This is because the velocity factor of insulated wire causes its resonant length to be slightly shorter compared with uninsulated wire of the same length.

I felt that my arrangement for measuring the resonant frequency of elements, described in [1] and [2], was inadequate. This, as you may recall, comprised a GDO with a modified coil to provide a closer coupling with the element. The existing GDO had rather a small meter so the dip was difficult to resolve. It is possible to couple a conventional GDO to a wire antenna element but a loop has to be made in the wire element, which is clearly impractical with uninsulated wire. A further difficulty was maintaining a constant coupling with the element while a measurement was being performed.

**MEASURING UNIT RE-DESIGN.** It occurred to me that the frequency dial of the original instrument was taking up a lot of space. The dial itself was calibrated with regard to plug-in coils and, in the element measuring arrangement, was meaningless because of its non-standard coil. Furthermore, because the unit was being used with a frequency counter, a frequency dial was not required.

A new design, with a large sensitive 50μA meter and the frequency control consigned to the side of the unit was constructed from junk box components and is shown in **Photo 1**. The circuit is a simplified version of the Colpitts circuit described in [3] and is shown in **Figure 1**. The layout is shown in **Photo 2** and, as you can see, it does not use any specialised components.

Unlike most traditional GDOs this circuit does not measure gate current directly. What it does do is to measure the total current through the FET. This current depends on the gate voltage, which in turn depends on the oscillation amplitude. However, the variation of current through resonance is only a small part of the total current through the FET. To enable this small variation to be seen the 50μA meter is offset using a potentiometer in a bleeder network. This is set so that the meter reads about 50% of full scale deflection when the instrument is not coupled to a load. If you find that adjusting the meter to this value is too critical for your liking, use a lower resistance potentiometer or/and a larger value of the 62k bleeder resistor.

The GDO is fixed to a piece of laminated chip board, 150mm wide by 15mm thick. A coil comprising five turns of 20SWG insulated wire is wound on to this board. This makes up a rectangular section coil that gives a very good coupling to a wire or tubular antenna element and has an inductance of around 3μH. With the capacitor used in this model it tunes from 12MHz to just over 22MHz, just enough to cover the 20, 17 and 15 metre bands used in my quad. The frequency range can be extended by shorting out coil turns.

For some reason, the sensitivity of this latest instrument was superior to the original. You may recall that I said that some indication of sensitivity can be obtained by squeezing the coil of the GDO between the thumb and forefinger and noting the meter deflection, which should dip to at least 50% of the maximum reading. On this latest

PHOTO 2: The layout of the GDO section of the element resonant frequency measuring unit, constructed from junk box components

TABLE 1: Hexbeam dimensions
(All dimensions in inches. To convert inches to cm multiply by 2.54)

| Band | 20m | 17m | 15m | 12m | 10m |
|---|---|---|---|---|---|
| Driver (half-length) | 218 | 169.5 | 144.5 | 121.7 | 106.8 |
| Reflector (total) | 412 | 321 | 274.4 | 232 | 204.4 |
| End spacing | 24 | 18.5 | 16 | 13.5 | 12 |
| Vertical spacing from 10m elements | 38 | 15 | 9 | 5 | 0 |

instrument the reading fell by 75% with this test. Additionally I said that the GDO should also be capable of measuring resonance of a high C tuned circuit at a distance of 6 to 7cm (2-3in). This instrument can detect a parallel tuned circuit comprising a 5mH inductor with a 100pF capacitance at 10cm (4in).

The problem of maintaining a constant coupling between a wire antenna element and the sensing coil was fixed by using small plastic cable wall clips as shown in Photo 1. The wire antenna element is placed inside these two inverted clips so that the distance between it and the coil is held constant, which makes the business of measuring the element resonance much simpler. Quad elements are not high Q but resonant dips of 30 to 40% of FSD were measured during the quad rebuild.

To measure the resonance of a tubular element the instrument coil is place on top of the element. A method of fixing the distance between the element and the coil is unnecessary in this case.

**THE HEXBEAM AGAIN.** In 'Antennas', Jan 2008, I described the HexBeam by Steve, G3TXQ. In **Figure 4** of that column the caption indicates that the feed to each band should be transposed although the diagram does not. G3TXQ e-mailed me so say that on no account should the feed be transposed and that all band driven elements are fed in phase.

G3TXQ has also described his latest experimental work to improve the performance of the HexBeam on his website **[4]**. An edited portion of this work is as follows:

"A consequence of the HexBeam's geometry is a relatively narrow performance bandwidth; typically the F/B exceeds 10dB over a band equivalent to only 1.4% of the centre frequency, and the SWR is above 2:1 for a significant proportion of this band. This narrow bandwidth is largely determined by the Q of the reflector, which I measured at about 30 for a 10m element constructed from 16SWG wire. Compare this with a linear dipole, which has a Q of about 10. If we can find a way of reducing this Q we should end up with a broader-band antenna.

"I spent many hours modelling reflectors and evaluating ideas on a 10m test-bed - you can see the detail on the Reflector Experiments page of my website **[4]**. I tried using thicker wire of various types, including two varieties of coaxial cable and 'caged' wires. I also tested alternative reflector shapes. Of all the ideas evaluated, by far the most effective and easiest to implement was to change the shape of the reflector as shown in **Figure 2**. Even when using relatively thin 16 wire this shape has a radiation resistance of 44 ohms and a Q of about 17. It requires an increase in turning radius of about 15%. Modelling a HexBeam with this geometry produced very encouraging results with a F/B >10dB and SWR <2:1 across all of the 20m, 17m, 15m and 12m bands, and approximately 1MHz of the 10m band (listening tests with DX stations indicate that the F/B could be as high as 30dB). The modelling suggested there was little to be gained by making the same change to the shape of the driver element; in fact, retaining the classic shape for the driver delivers a better match to 50 ohms and avoids a further increase in the turning radius.

"Construction and testing of a 10m monoband version of the new antenna confirmed the modelling results, and so a full 5-band test beam was constructed. The 20m, 17m and 15m results were immediately satisfactory, but it took some time to optimise the 12m and 10m performance; the proximity of these bands

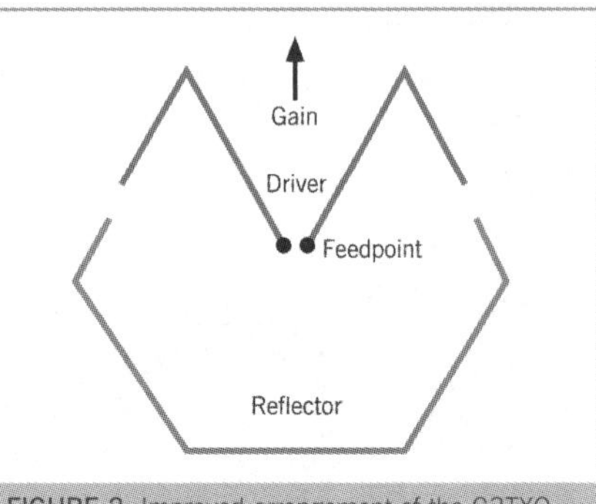


FIGURE 2: Improved arrangement of the G3TXQ HexBeam

often causes problematic interactions which are not always predicted by the modelling, and the final wire dimensions for these bands were a result of 'cut and try' on the testbed.

"The final dimensions using 16SWG bare copper wire are shown in **Table 1**. The band feedpoints are interconnected with 50 ohm coax, and the array is top-fed. This 5-band design requires a horizontal distance of about 130 inches from the centre post to the tips of the spreaders. If you are unable to accommodate this increased size, don't be tempted to stick to the classic shape for 20m and adopt the new shape for 17m through 10m: modelling shows that the 20m performance bandwidth suffers dramatically. This is probably due to the mid section of the 17m reflector providing an RF coupling path between the knees of the 20m reflector".

**OTHER FEEDBACK.** Brian Mitchell, G3HJK, came up with information on the boomless quad spider that I am currently using, shown in 'Antennas', Oct 2007. Apparently, they were made by Labgear, of Cambridge. This very strong-cast alloy unit, which will carry heavy weight military fibreglass spreaders.

REFERENCES

[1] 'Antennas', RadCom August 2002
[2] 'Antennas', RadCom March 2007.
[3] The Antenna Experimenters Guide, Peter Dodd, G3LDO, RSGB
[4] www.karinya.net/g3txq/hexbeam/reflector_expts/

# Antennas

## Low band success with HF antennas, waterproofing and Hexbeam history

PHOTO 1: The ATU used for 500kHz comprising a variometer coil and a matching transformer

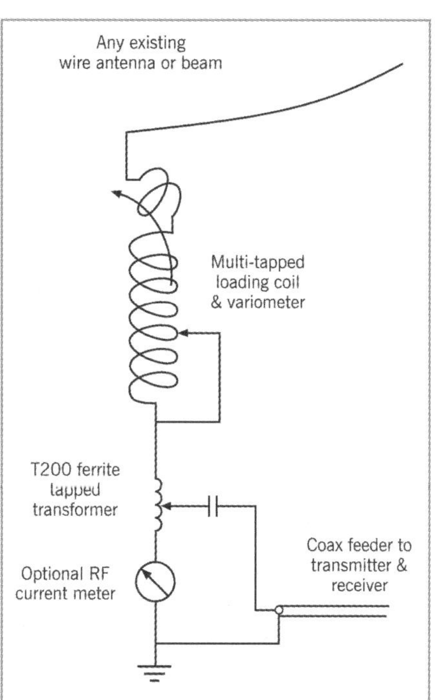


FIGURE 1: Circuit of an ATU for 500kHz. The loading coil has a built in variometer giving it a inductance variation of 260 to to 540$\mu$H. The matching transformer is wound on a T200 ferrite with a range of tappings. The coupling capacitor is 0.01$\mu$F.

PHOTO 2: Method of providing temporary weather protection to an outdoor coax connection

**THE LOWER HF BANDS.** I previously described a method of using an HF quad (or any other wire beam or antenna) designed for the higher HF bands on the lower HF bands, or even the LF bands **[1]**. I described it as using my quad on 150kHz. This was a mistake – I really meant 500kHz. At the time I hadn't tested this arrangement. Since then (at this time of low sunspot activity) I have used my unconventional set up on lower HF bands and on 500kHz. The following is how the tests worked out. All the QSOs were made using 100 watts of CW on HF and 20W of CW on 500kHz.

On 500kHz, the LF/quad antenna was tuned using the arrangement shown in **Figure 1** and **Photo 1**, and the characteristics of the tuner and antenna are shown in **Figure 2**. This antenna arrangement has a gain of about –20dBi. However this was not a problem with the restrictions in place at the time, which limited us to 100mW ERP. The antenna worked surprisingly well. Contacts around the UK were fairly comfortable and my second contact in the test was with GM4SLV in the Shetland Islands.

I also had contacts with GI3PDN and several cross-band contacts (3533kHz) with stations in Germany and France. The best DX was two way 500kHz QSO with OH1SLQ; my report was 319.

Matching the quad antenna system on the lower HF frequency bands was done using a MFJ 989C ATU. When using 100W on 1.8MHz I found that contacts around Europe were fairly comfortable but QSOs 'across the pond' were normally only readability 4. I did call an expedition station J5C only to get reprimanded for calling on his JA listening frequency (I had misinterpreted the listening instructions!). On 3.5MHz the situation was similar to those on 1.8MHz except that the DX reports were better. The antenna also gave reasonable results on the 7 and 10MHz bands.

The whole purpose of this exercise was to show that an electrically small antenna, suitably loaded and matched, was capable of working quite well. You can load or match a dipole or short wire antenna to become operational on the lower frequencies where QTH size restrictions preclude conventional resonant antennas. When using a coax fed HF antenna on the lower frequency bands, the coax itself is no longer a feeder but part of the radiating element and it is probably a good idea to have an arrangement that allows the coax inner and outer to be shorted together. If you are using a quad or a wire beam (such as the Hexbeam) ensure that the coax is well clear of the metal tower or mast.

**WATER PROOFING TEMPORARY COAX CONNECTORS.** The arrangement here for connecting the rig in the shack to the antennas is achieved by a coax run from the shack to a point two thirds down the garden. I then connect directly to the quad or via one or other ATUs in the garden shed. This means of course having the coax connecting arrangements at a point where they are open to the weather. Conventional coax cable weather proofing is not practical option so a temporary method of protection is shown in **Photo 2**. This consists of clipping the connection in a small plastic packet and supporting it upside down on a tree branch or in a hedge. I still coat the coax connectors with just the small film of grease to prevent corrosion but not enough to get my hands in a mess when reconnecting the coax connectors.

**PRECURSOR TO THE HEXBEAM.** Tom Morgan, G0CAJ/ZS1AFS, commenting on the Hexbeam descriptions in previous 'Antennas', noted that had I not mentioned the forerunner of this antenna by Ken Taylor, G4EEC. He called it the Bow Tie Antenna and it appeared in an old edition of Amateur Radio Techniques **[2]**. He goes on to say "It was certainly around well before 1984, when I became G0CAJ. I made this antenna as per the drawing in the book and it worked very well.

"Removing it to different locations for portable use was easy. It was made with carpet roll bamboos and an aluminium tube like those used in stretchers (and in my case, for an occasional boat bunk). The spacing between the ends of elements was not emphasised, but the precise dimensions of each part of the elements ensured this aspect".

Sure enough I found it in Amateur Radio Techniques. However, according to the description of this antenna it was first built by VK2ABQ. It is reproduced in **Figure 3**, which shows a design for a 14MHz model. It is built using wire elements supported on a light timber frame, which has a turning radius of 12ft. A front-to-back ratio in the order of 20dB with a forward gain of up to 6dBi is claimed for this antenna. The original source of this antenna is not given.

I modelled this antenna on EZNEC and found that the performance described above is very close to that claimed above. It would be nice to know how it was measured.

Ken Taylor, G4EEC, made a two-band bow-tie for 14 and 21MHz (shown in **Figure 4**) based on the VK2ABQ mono-band design. It was constructed using six varnished canes for spreaders clamped to the 2in x 1in timber fixed by V clamps of Dural sheet and rustless screws.

Note that the antennas were tuned using a GDO coupled to the driven elements with a single turn coil at Y. Resonance was adjusted by altering the amount of wire folded back with nylon ties. The wire size used was 18SWG, enamelled for the outer loop and insulated with PVC for the inner loop. At point X an egg insulator was used as an anchor point for the centre of the loop. Point Y is the feed point for the 50-ohm coaxial feeder (no balun was used). The length of the element for 14MHz was 33ft and gave an SWR bandwidth of 1.2:1 from 14.15 to 14.275MHz. On 21MHz the element length was 22ft 1in and gave an SWR bandwidth of 1.5:1 from 21.2 to 21.3MHz.

This antenna is shown for two bands. However, the support structure will not allow the antenna configuration to be maintained over a number of bands. This is where the Hexbeam stressed spoke arrangement comes into its own. Not only does it maintain an identical shape for each set of elements on each band but it allows each band set to be placed slightly above the other, which assists good multi-band performance.

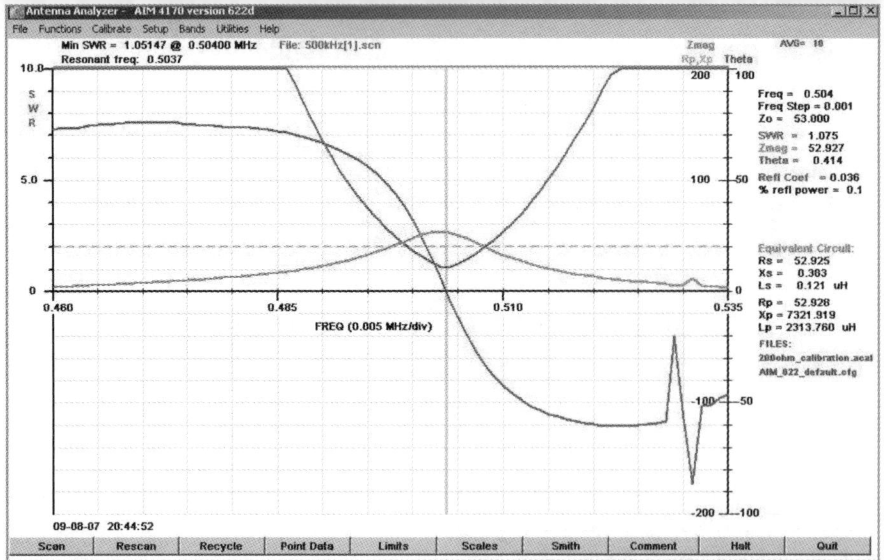


**FIGURE 2:** Analysis of the 500kHz antenna system using the AIM 4170. The resonant frequency is indicated by the lowest SWR at the green cursor. The impedance measured at the cursor is shown at the right hand side of the graph.

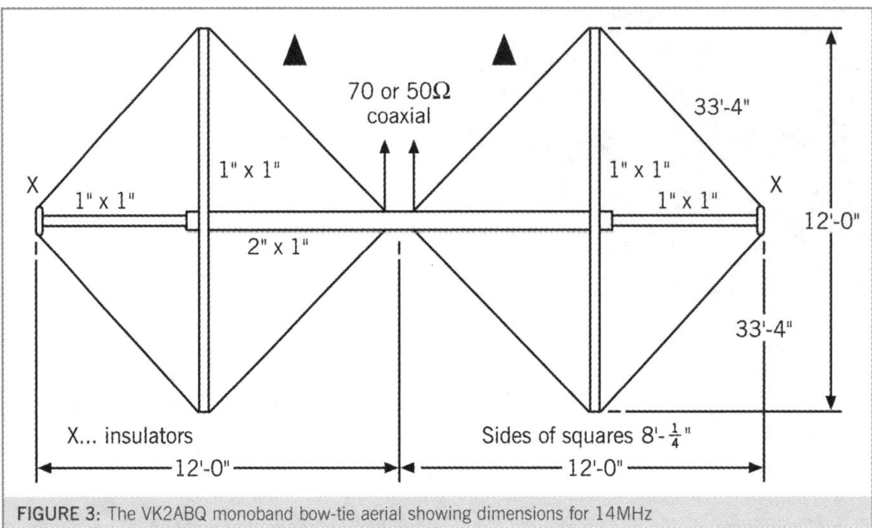


**FIGURE 3:** The VK2ABQ monoband bow-tie aerial showing dimensions for 14MHz

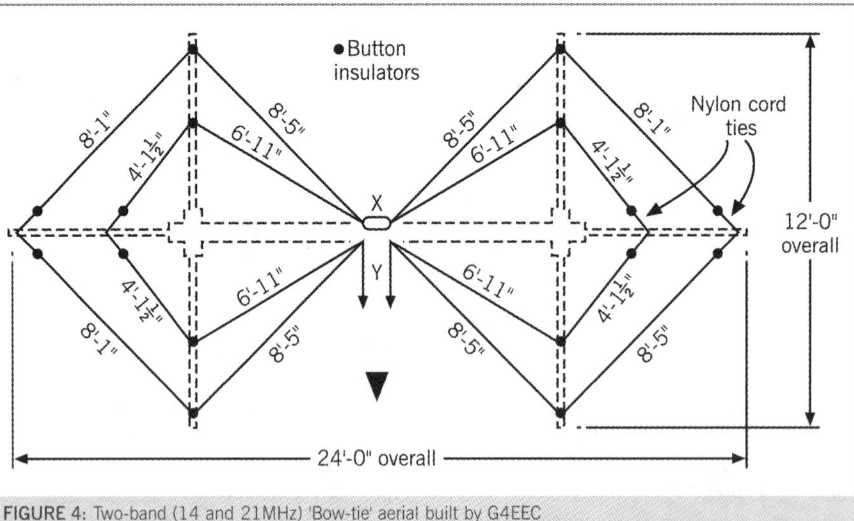


**FIGURE 4:** Two-band (14 and 21MHz) 'Bow-tie' aerial built by G4EEC


**REFERENCES**

[1] Antennas, *RadCom* December 2007, Figure 1

[2] *Amateur Radio Techniques* 7th edition, Pat Hawker G3VA, RSGB

# Antennas

## A simple but effective multiband antenna - and it's cheap, too

I get many requests for advice on the best type of HF multiband antenna to install and am often asked which commercial product I recommend. I have tried in the past to extol the virtues of a single length of copper wire as an antenna but I realise that perhaps in many cases it isn't so simple. So in this month's column I will consider the problem in more detail, especially in regard to feeding and matching a length of wire.

THE TWIN FEEDER TUNED DIPOLE. If you feed a length of wire in the centre you do not require a counterpoise or RF ground system. You can use a resonant dipole fed with coax but this is a single band arrangement. A better solution is to use what is known as the Tuned Doublet or Random-Length Dipole, shown in **Figure 1**. It is very simple, yet is a most effective and efficient antenna for multiband use.

The antenna is fed with open wire tuned feeders. This type of feeder or transmission line has the advantage of low loss even with a high SWR and long runs. You can use open wire feeder or any commercial 300 or 450ohm ladder-line. An ATU with a balanced feed is used to take care of the wide variations of feed impedance on the different bands.

If you haven't already got an ATU I strongly advise you get one. Unlike your latest radio, an ATU is a low tech bit of kit and will last a lifetime. The traditional T match with a balun at the output for balanced feeders is the most popular and is fine. They come in different prices depending on power handling requirements and whether or not it has a built in SWR meter (a useful feature).

Most information available **[1]** indicates that the Tuned Doublet should be at least half a wavelength long at the lowest frequency of use. However I have found that the doublet can be reduced to 3/8 wavelength on the lowest frequency, which still has an effectiveness greater than 98% relative to a half wave dipole, and impedance values which are reasonably easy to match. A 3/8 wavelength dipole at 3.5MHz is approximately 30m (100ft) long, which means that any length from 27m (90ft) to 30m will make an excellent radiator on all HF amateur bands from 80 to 10 metres, including the WARC bands.

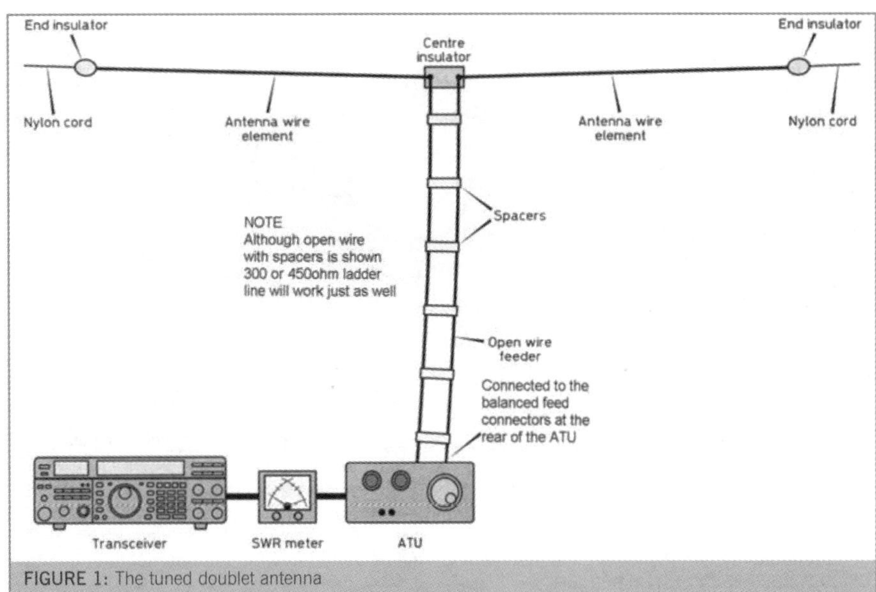


FIGURE 1: The tuned doublet antenna

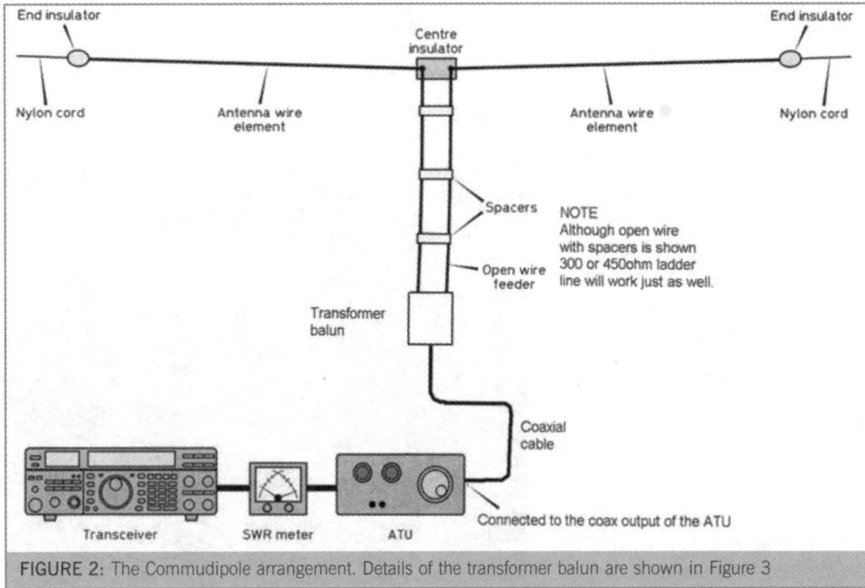


FIGURE 2: The Commudipole arrangement. Details of the transformer balun are shown in Figure 3

Loading difficulties can be overcome by selecting a different ratio on the balun (see below) or altering the length of the twin feeder.

If you don't have room for a 30m length of straight wire for operation on 80 metres, a 3 to 5m (10 to 16ft) portion of each end may be dropped vertically from each end support. There will be no significant change in radiation pattern on 80 and 40 metres. There will, however, be a minor change in polarisation in the radiation at higher frequencies, but the effect on propagation will be negligible. This antenna can also be supported using a single pole to form an inverted V although the ends should be fixed as high as possible.

If you are willing to forgo the 3.5MHz (80m) band, a centre fed wire half the length quoted above will work on all bands from 7 to 29MHz including the WARC bands. And remember, the dimensions of this antenna are not critical, unlike the resonant dipole or the G5RV.

While the open-wire tuned dipole is a very good antenna there are problems in many locations of bringing open wire feeder into the shack. This is because twin feeder must not be allowed to come close to metal objects such as metal window frames, guttering or flashing and particularly electrical wiring. Metal objects close to the line can cause the currents in the line to be unbalanced. On the other hand coax cable is fully screened and can be allowed close to metal objects but has greater losses. The solution, if you do not have a clear run from the antenna to the ATU, is to use part coax and part balanced feeder, a solution first described by Ton Verberne, PA2ABV, for apartment dwellers. Ton called his antenna feed arrangement, shown in **Figure 2**, the Comudipole.

All this arrangement does is to move the balun, normally located inside the ATU, to a place outside the ATU and the shack making a more convenient connecting point for open line feeder. It is connected to the coax output socket of the ATU. Although the position of the balun is not critical, the coax section should be kept as short as possible to keep the losses down. You don't have to remove the balun physically from your ATU! You can buy one, or make one as described below.

Many published and commercial T match ATU designs use a 4:1 transformer balun to provide a balanced input for impedances in the range 150 to 600ohms. However, under certain circumstances a low impedance is presented to the balun on some bands depending on the length of the antenna and the length of the feeder. It is very easy to expand the design of the balun to include a 1:1 ratio which can be selected from 4:1 by a selector switch or coax connector. This will expand the range of balanced inputs from about 45 to 600ohms without introducing any noticeable losses into the system.

**BALUN CONSTRUCTION.** The balun transformer is wound on a single Amidon T200-2 powdered-iron core, colour coded red. For sustained high-power operation, 400W plus, two such cores can be taped together by using plumbers' PTFE tape, which can also be used to provide an added layer of insulation between the core and the windings. T200-2 cores can be obtained from **[2]**. The design of the balun and the construction description below is by G3TSO.

"Balun construction is simple, but a little cumbersome; some 14 turns of 16SWG enamelled-copper wire have to be wound trifilar fashion onto the toroidal core. That is to say, three identical windings are wound on together. Care must be taken to ensure that the windings do not overlap or cross one another and that neither the core nor enamel covering is badly scratched during construction.

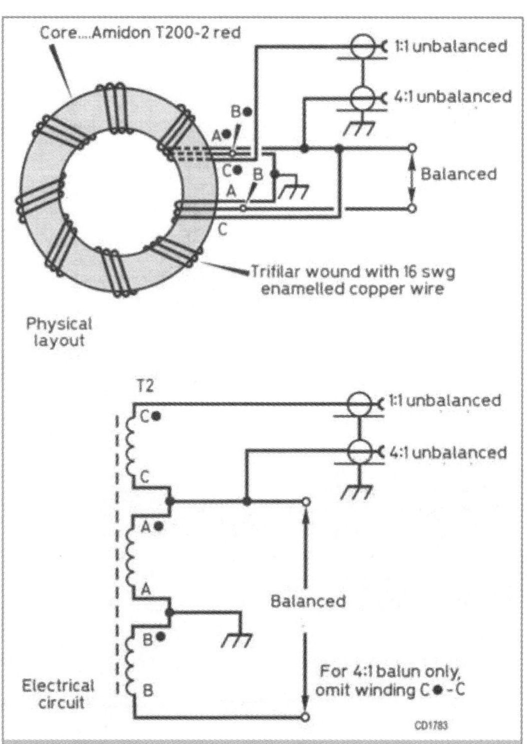

FIGURE 3: The balun transformer wound on a T200-2 core

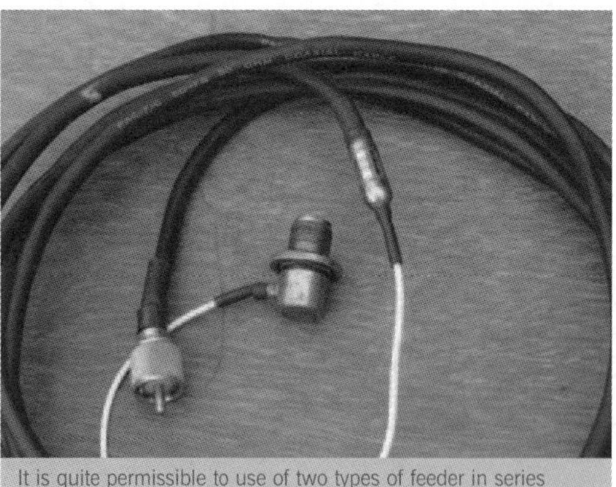
It is quite permissible to use of two types of feeder in series

"Fourteen turns will require approximately 97cm (38in) of 16 SWG (1.6mm) wire, so cut three equal lengths of 16SWG wire slightly longer than required and pass all three wires through the core until they have reached about halfway. This now becomes the centre of the winding and it is easier to wind from the centre to either end, rather than from one end to the other which involves passing long lengths of wire through the toroid. The T200 size core will accommodate 14 turns trifilar without any overlapping of the start and finish of the winding. Close spacing will occur at the inside of the core, and a regular spacing interval should be set up on the outside. A small gap should be left where the two ends of the winding come close together.

"Connection of the balun requires care and it is necessary to identify opposite ends of the same windings, which can be done with a continuity meter, with some form of tagging or colour coding being worthwhile. On the circuit diagram a dot is used to signify the same end for separate windings. It is essential that the various windings are correctly connected if the balun is to work properly. "

Details of how the balun transformer is wound and connected are shown in **Figure 3**. Construction of a 4:1 balun only is slightly simpler and only requires two (bifilar) windings.

**MIXED FEEDERS.** My multiband quad was originally fed with RG-213 coax to a spot near to the base of the mast. RG-58 lightweight cable was used for the final 12m or so. The reason for this was so that I could use the feeder and the quad as a vertical antenna for LF experiments and the lower HF bands (RG-213 was considered too heavy for this application).

This business of using lengths of coax feeder of different types is not unknown. The feeder shown in the photo is a solution to providing a feed to a mobile VHF antenna; low loss coax is used for the main feed and a short length of very thin feeder is used negotiate the tail gate door or window. The important thing about using mixed feeders is to use a coupling arrangement that does not produce an impedance bump.

**FOXED.** I decided to replace the RG-58 section of feeder with Mini-8 coax. This feeder is a compromise between the heavy RG-213 and RG-58 and looks quite robust. A couple of days later no signals could be heard on the antenna and the SWR was sky high. I inspected the antenna and found that my nice new Mini-8 had been cut at a point where it touched the ground. Surely this couldn't be the act of an antenna mast-hating neighbour. The following evening after repairing the coax I went down the garden to raise the antenna mast and met a fox carrying a short length of RG-58. I now ensure that the coax feeder is now well clear of the ground!

REFERENCES
[1] MFJ Versa Tuner V (MFJ-989C) instruction manual
[2] JAB Electronic Components www.jabdog.com

# Antennas

## Peter looks at Uda's early antenna experiments

**HISTORY OF THE YAGI.** Early in 2003 I was asked by the editor of RadCom if I could write something about the history of the Yagi antenna in response to a reader's question. No problem, I thought. This is probably the best-known antenna in amateur radio – all I would have to do is look it up on the internet. As it turned out there was precious little on the history of the subject in the public domain. The two main sources of information (not in the public domain) were **[1]**, (available in the RSGB library) and **[2]** available from the ARRL.

What I did find were articles, mainly in QST, regarding amateur radio work on this antenna during the 1930's, so I finished up writing about Yagi antenna history from an amateur radio perspective **[3]**.

PHOTO 1: Professor Hidetsugu Yagi.

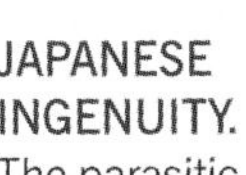

**JAPANESE INGENUITY.** The parasitic beam antenna was the result of research carried out at Tohoku Imperial University in Japan in the early 1920s. The research team was headed by Professor Hidetsugu Yagi, who by that time had considerable experience of radio engineering gained in Europe and the USA. Professor Yagi selected several students and co-researchers. Two of these were Shintaro Uda, who was to investigate the properties of antennas, and Kinjiro Okabe, who was carry out research on the magnetron This resulted in a number of papers on the subjects being published between 1926 and 1929. These papers were of course published in Japanese.

We are only aware of this work because in 1928, Professor Yagi visited the USA, giving speeches to the IRE members in New York City. He also contributed, to the IRE, a paper in English, called 'Beam Transmission of Ultra Short Waves **[1]**. This two-part paper, which is now regarded as a classic, described the development beam antenna and the generation of ultra-short waves using the split anode magnetron.

In an article in QST on Yagi **[4]**, N3RW stated that Uda's early antenna work concerned the measurement of the single-wire resonant loop radiation pattern and he observed and recorded the effect of ground. He also noted that nearby unconnected resonant loops caused changes in directivity, and from this a directional antenna was created. Improved directivity was obtained when the loops were replaced with rods, then the driven element itself was replaced with a half-wave dipole. If this is the case it would appear the quad was nearly discovered in 1926!

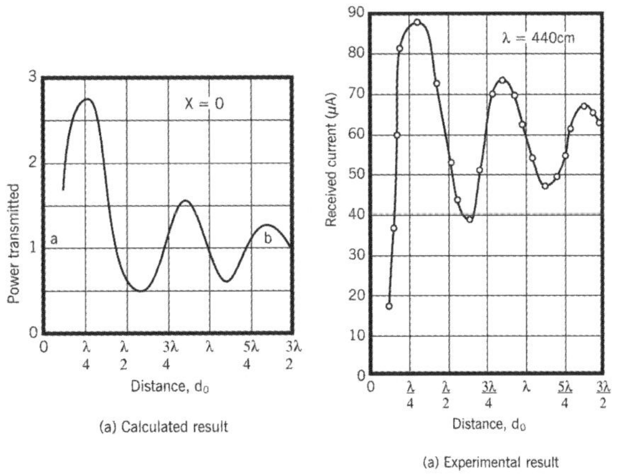

FIGURE 1: Graphs of (a) the calculated results and (b) the experimental results of placing a parasitic element (whose natural frequency is equal to that of the incident wave) at varying distances from the driven element.

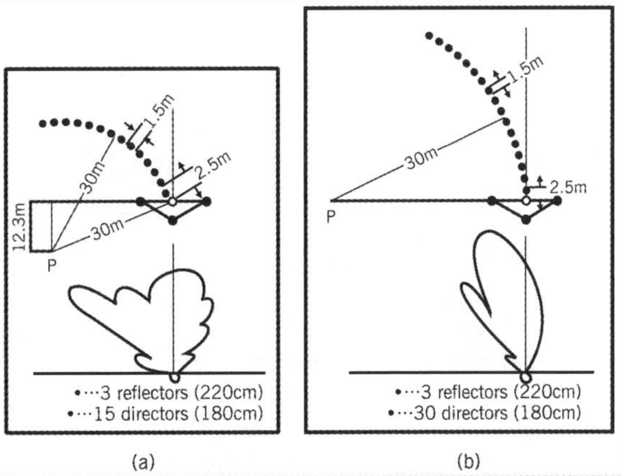

FIGURE 2: Measurements of experimental curved parasitic beams.

The antenna design went from a loop to a dipole configuration, and the now familiar 'Yagi' antenna, with the dipole and parasitic rods emerged.

Surely there was other information around. I understand from **[4]** that Professor Yagi's home and personal library, which included 30 years of research, was destroyed in the fire bombing of Tokyo in April 1945. This could explain the dearth of information. I did track down Yagi-Uda Antenna by Shintaro Uda and Yasuto Mushiake to AstroLogos Books of New York. They offer a service digitally scanning any one of 1520,000 books no longer in print and Yagi-Uda Antenna was one of them!

I duly ordered a copy. It proved to be a most comprehensive book (written in 1954) on the design of the Yagi with a very theoretical and mathematical grounding. But as a historical document it turned out to be a disappointment.

I was also aware from **[4]** of a book that did describe the historical work of Shintaro Uda **[5]**, but no one seemed to have a copy of this book, not even AstroLogos Books of New York. I eventually tracked down a copy at the Library of Congress in the USA but they don't lend books out or have a copying service. That seemed to be that.

**A VISIT TO AMERICA.** In May 2007 I visited an old friend Bert Weller, WD8KBW, in Columbus, Ohio. During my stay Bert had to go to his local library to renew or change some of his library books and I went along with him. During this visit I asked if the library was able to loan a book from the Library of Congress – yes they could. As a reference book I would only be allowed to examine it; borrowing was out of the question. Unfortunately, I had come to the end of my USA vacation before the book arrived. However, Bert was able to copy some pages of the book for me.

In the preface of the book **[5]** the author, Professor Shintaro Uda explains that it is a collection of his studies made at Tohoku University, Sendai, Japan, commencing 1926. The book consists of four chapters and one supplement as follows:

Chapter 1 Short Wave Projector
Chapter 2 Communication Tests on Decimeter Waves
Chapter 3 Metre Waves and their Practical Use
Chapter 4 Some Studies on Microwave Tubes
Supplement Microwave (2000MHz) Propagation Tests in India (1955 – 1958)

Because my main interest was the history of the Yagi-Uda antenna only Chapter 1 was relevant. This chapter describes the development of this antenna from 1925 to 1929 and is divided as follows:

- Induced Electromagnetic Force and Current
- Radiation Power
- Wave Reflector and Wave Director
- Effect of Reflector and Director on Sending Antenna
- Directing and Reflecting Actions of Metallic Sheet
- Composite Reflectors and Trigonal Reflector
- Wave Canal and Wave Projector
- Direction Control of the Beam and a Radio Beacon
- Horizontal antenna and the Effect of Earth
- Propagation Tests of a few Metre Waves around Sendai

The striking impression on reading this chapter is the amount of experimental work that was undertaken, and in this column I can only describe a fraction it. Once the effects of parasitic elements were noticed Uda derived expressions for parasitic rods and used them to produce graphs. These were then compared with experimental results as shown in **Figure 1**. A Mesny oscillator was used to produce the radiated signal and the authors stressed its ability to maintain a constant level of transmitted power during the measurements. The receiver comprised a half-wave dipole with a diode bridging the centre point; the measured voltage across the diode indicated the signal strength.

Sheets of metal were also tried as parasitic elements at 130MHz. Metal sheets of 10, 30 and 40cms wide with varying lengths from 50 to 180cm were placed 0.6m from a receiver dipole. Metal sheets shorter than 85cm functioned as directors while those longer than 110cm worked as a reflector. Sheets 40cm wide produced a

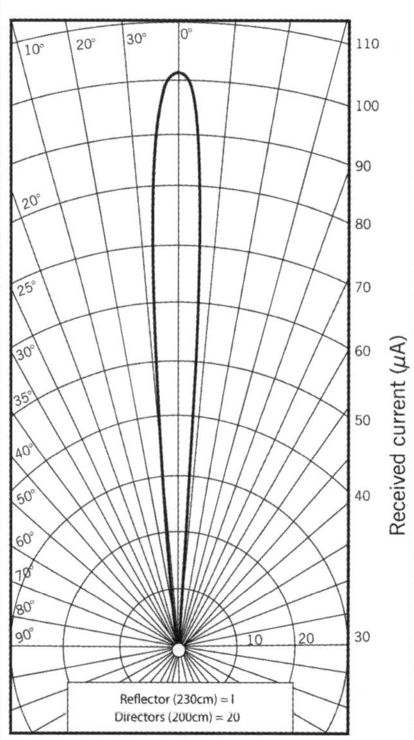


**FIGURE 3:** Polar diagram of a 22 element parasitic 'wave canal' measured by Uda. The diagram looks particularly sharp compared with modern measurements because of the restricted dynamic range of the diode receiver.

broader frequency response particularly as a reflector. Uda considered metallic sheet as a collection of rods of small diameter and most of his later antennas used multi element reflectors.

Other arrangements using two and three paralleled arrangements of up to 26 director elements were tried. These antennas were tested on 68MHz. The two paralleled antennas structure was 19.5m long and 1m wide while the three parallel structure was 3m wide and 13.5m long – quite large antennas! These complex structures exhibited a wider frequency bandwidth but very little extra gain compared with a single antenna.

Similar experiments were also made using aqueous solutions of salt or sulphuric acid. Glass tubes of varying lengths were filled with different concentrations of this electrolyte and placed near to a driven element in the same way as the rod elements. These did produce directive results but not as marked as with metal rods.

Uda also experimented with curved arrangements of directors. The one shown in **Figure 2**(b) must have been a monster with its 30 directors, 1.5m apart.

What is interesting about the description of these extensive experiments is that no attempt was made to cover up the tracks of experimental arrangements that did not give good results. This gives anyone researching the subject an insight into the creative process of the experiments. In the end Uda produced an in-depth analysis of the variables that controlled directivity such as parasitic element lengths, spacing and geometric arrangement of parasitic elements, and the effect of receiving antenna height and the effect of transmitting antenna height.

All this experimental work summed up by Professor Yagi during his visit to the USA **[1]** as:

"Suppose that a vertical antenna is radiating electromagnetic waves in all directions. If a straight oscillating system, whether it be a metal rod of finite length or an antenna with capacities at both ends and an inductance at the middle, is erected vertically in the field, the effect of this oscillator upon the wave will be as follows. If its natural frequency is equal to or lower than that of the incident wave, it will act as a 'wave reflector.' If, on the other hand, its natural frequency is higher than that of the incident wave, it will act as a 'wave director.' The field will converge upon this antenna, and radiation in a plane normal to it will be augmented. By utilising this wave-directing quality, a sharp beam may be produced.

"....... In front of the radiating antenna, a number of wave-directors may be arranged along the line of propagation. By properly adjusting the distance between the wave-directors and their natural frequencies, it is possible to transmit a larger part of the energy in the wave along the row of directors. Adjustment of the natural frequency of the directors is made by simply changing their length or by adjusting the inductance inserted at the middle of these elements. The larger number of directors the sharper the beam, which has been designated a 'wave canal'...and a field strength diagram of a wave canal with 21 directors is shown in **Figure 3**".

It is probable that all this experimental work was way before its time, which could explain why it was slow to be assimilated into general radio technology.

**REFERENCES**

[1] 'Beam Transmission of Ultra Short Waves', Prof. Hidetsugu Yagi. *Proc:* IRE Vol 16 June 1926
[2] 'Yagi: The Man and his Antenna', Robert H. Welsh, N3RW, *QST* October 1993
[3] ' Evolution of the Beam Antenna', Peter Dodd, G3LDO, *RadCom* July and August 2003
[4] 'On the Wireless Beam of Short Electric Waves'. S. Uda. *Journal of the J.I.E.E (Japan)* March 1926, pp. 273-282 910; April 1926 (II); July 1926 (III); January 1927 (IV); January 1927 (V); April 1927 (VI); June 1927 (VII); October 1927 (VIII); November 1927, pp. 1209-1219 (IX); April 1928 (X); July 1929 (XI).
[5] *Short Wave Projector – Historical Records of my Early Studies*, Shintaro Uda 1973

# Antennas

## Peter Dodd reveals an interesting broadband antenna

**W4RNL SK.** One of the amateur radio's most prolific writers of good quality antenna material, L B Cebik, W4RNL, is no longer with us. W4RNL was the Technical Editor for *antenneX Online Magazine* for 11 years. His speciality was antenna computer modelling and he produced two dozen books published by *antenneX* and the ARRL. Fortunately, his extensive website containing some 1000 modelling files using NEC and EZNEC is to be preserved by antenneX. Their stated goal is to preserve and protect LB's excellent works in this field and continue to make them available to help those who need it and educate those who seek to learn. To use this service you need to register at **[1]**.

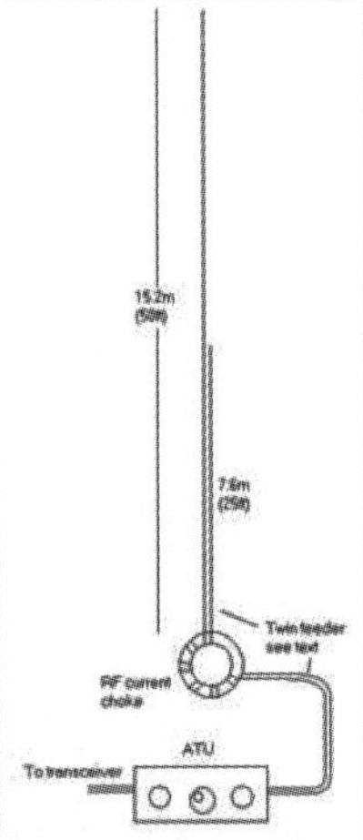

FIGURE 1: A single vertical 'no-counterpoise' multiband antenna attributed to K9ESE.

**THE NO-COUNTERPOISE VERTICAL.** The single vertical no-counterpoise antenna (as I understand by Jeff Imel, K9ESE) is an end fed, multi-band antenna that can cover a very wide frequency range. It will cover bands from 7 to 28MHz and its low angle of radiation characteristic makes for a good DX antenna. The antenna is shown in **Figure 1** and is made of a single length of insulated wire and the bottom section of twin feeder. The two conductors of the antenna are fed with a balanced tuner or via a balun and a standard ATU.

As this antenna is end fed, the problem of a centre feed point is circumvented and it can be conveniently supported from a tree or a tall building. Alternatively, the antenna can be wound helically around a fishing pole for support as shown in **Figure 2**. A half size version will cover 14 to 52MHz.

**THE M3KXZ ANTENNA.** Pete Millis, M3KXZ, has designed and built a two-element vertically phased array based using the no-counterpoise principle, which came about as he was looking for a simple solution to the problem of making a phased multi-band array for portable QRP use.

The 'no-counterpoise' antenna presents an easy to match impedance across a very broad range of frequencies, with the resistive and reactive components never rising above a few hundred ohms. If twin feed line is used, line losses resulting from high SWR will remain very small, especially when the line length is short (as in a typical portable type operation). He decided to see how a pair of vertical 'no-counterpoise' antennas would perform when used in a phased array.

FIGURE 2: 1:1 balun or RF choke at base of the antenna. The twin feeder is wound helically around a fishing pole to create a neat self supported structure.

M3KXZ notes, "Computer modelling with *EZNEC* indicated that performance with two 25ft 'no-counterpoise' antennas would be good for the range 20m through 6m when spaced at 3 metres apart, with an excellent bi-directional endfire pattern when fed 180° out of phase and an excellent broadside pattern when fed in phase on the higher frequencies, approaching omni-directional on 20m. Broadside directivity can be improved on the lower frequencies (20m) by increasing the distance between the elements, but this results in additional lobe formation on the higher bands. For the computer modelling, I simulated the array as two vertical 'no-counterpoise' antennas with an individual source at the base of each, and fed either in phase or 180° out of phase".

The construction of the antenna is shown in **Figure 3**. M3KXZ built his antenna out of twin speaker wire and used the same material to make the phasing lines on the grounds that it should have lower losses than coax considering the high SWR between the balun and the two verticals. The twin feed phasing lines are decoupled from the antennas using a simple 1:1 balun at the base of each antenna. The baluns are constructed by winding 8 turns of the phasing line around an FT114-43 toroid and are required because the antennas are unbalanced but the phasing lines need to be balanced.

The lead phasing lines are coupled to an unbalanced tuner via a 4:1 current balun and a short length of coax. The balun on each end of the phasing lines serves to help force the phasing lines to be balanced. Both phasing lines are attached to the 4:1 balun at the tuner end. When the antennas are fed such that A long and B long (see **Figure 3**) are both connected to one terminal on the 4:1 balun and A short and B short are both connected to the other, then the array is fed in phase. If the connections to one antenna are reversed, the array is fed 180° out of phase. A full description of this antenna can be found at **[2]**.

**INITIAL TESTS.** M3KXZ noted: "...tuning was easy on all bands 20 – 6m with the Elecraft T1 ATU. With the antennas in phase, I had S5 to S8 of noise on 20m thru 12m. With the antennas fed 180° out of phase the noise went down to S0 to S1 so it seems the noise source was broadside to the antennas. During a QSO on 12m with a Spanish station his signals were S5 to S8 with a high level of noise with the antennas fed in phase. With the antennas fed out of phase the station was S9 in S0 to S1 of noise; a massive improvement ... I then went into my shack and tuned to the same frequency (24.962MHz) using a 10m tall vertical which is fed against wire garden fence as counterpoise and tuned with an SG237; I couldn't hear the Spanish station at all, only S9 of noise".

**W4RNL ANALYSIS.** One of the last additions to W4RNL's website was his analysis of the M3KXZ antenna. What follows is just brief outline of this work but, hopefully, it will convey the essentials of this antenna. The full analysis at [1].

"The antenna is interesting in several respects. First, it uses a very simple structure and common materials. The second significant aspect of the antenna is its performance. A single element length covers a spread of bands, for example, 20 to 6m using a total length of 25ft. The normal limit for either a 1/4λ monopole or a 1/2λ dipole is about 2.5:1, which would suggest a cut-off of about 35 – 36MHz, if the original antenna is cut for 14MHz. Once a monopole exceeds about 5/8λ or a dipole exceeds 1-1/4λ the main radiation is no longer broadside to the wire. For a vertical antenna, the long lengths result in very high angle radiation, rather than the low angle radiation that we normally need. However, the M3KXZ antenna and array yield very usable patterns from 20 through to 6m. In addition, the gain of the antenna is close to the gain available from either vertical dipole/doublets or from elevated monopoles with radials on all bands.

"One consequence of the lower double-wire or transmission-line section is that the dominant radiation currents do not follow the patterns that they would in a straight dipole/doublet, whatever the feedpoint. Hence, M3KXZ has found essentially an antenna designer's grail or silver bullet: an arrangement of wires that extends the range of desirable pattern formation beyond its normal limits while sustaining good gain for an antenna of its type and leaving quite workable feedpoint impedance values.

"The M3KXZ antenna and array constitute an ingenious arrangement of element parts that achieves low-angle vertically polarized radiation over an extended operating bandwidth that common configurations cannot match. The 2-element version of the array offers some gain and pattern shaping for bi-directional operating. Even with improved materials designed for both RF service and durability through seasonal weather cycles, the antennas are inexpensive. Moreover, they a relatively short for a given frequency range, adding to their neighborhood acceptability.

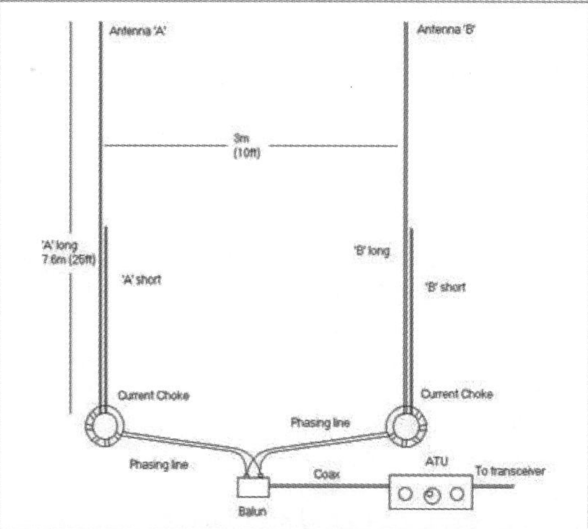


FIGURE 3: The 'no-counterpoise' antenna two element phased array for 20m through 6m. The 1:1 baluns consist of 8 turns of the phasing line (twin core speaker wire) on an FT114-43 toroid. The long and short antenna elements are 7.6m (25ft) and 3.8m (12.5ft) respectively.

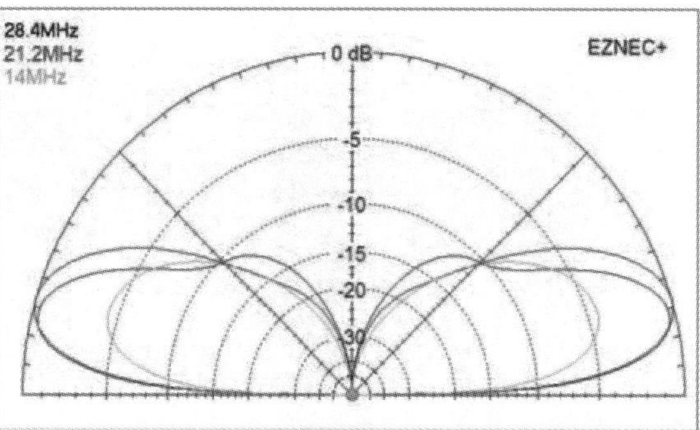


FIGURE 4: Elevation diagrams of the M3KXZ phased array for 14, 21 and 28MHz.

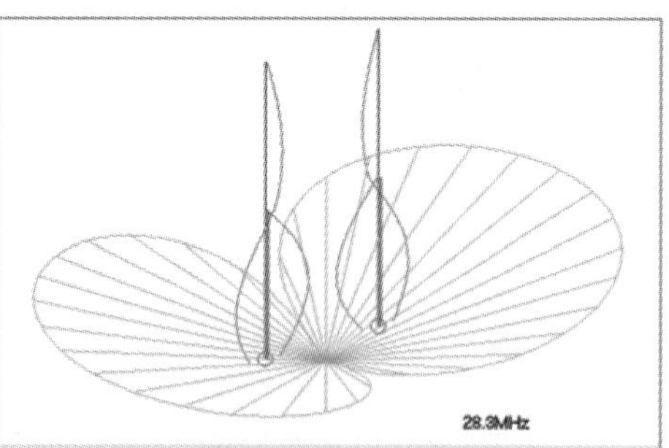


FIGURE 5: Three-dimensional diagram of the M3KXZ phased array on 28.3MHz showing the current amplitude and phases, together with an azimuth polar diagram, with the antennas connected 180° out of phase.

The challenges presented by the antenna and the array revolve around the matching and the feed system. Increased attention to these details may result in a very serviceable wide-band vertical array."

I modelled this antenna using EZNEC 5. The antenna appears to produce some very low angle radiation on all the upper HF bands. Comparison diagrams of the 14, 21 and 28MHz are shown in **Figure 4**. Three-dimensional diagram of the M3KXZ phased array on 28.3MHz is shown in **Figure 5**. The current amplitude and phases, together with an azimuth polar diagram, are shown with the antennas connected 180degrees out of phase. A comprehensive set of diagrams for this antenna can be found at [1].

**FEEDBACK.** The simple centre-fed multiband antenna I described in May 2008 *RadCom* brought a surprising amount of mail and e-mail. I have replied individually to most of this mail, however, there is one item that requires a more public airing. I described an arrangement known as the comudipole for feeding a centre-fed antenna with a balanced feeder. This arrangement places the balun, normally located inside the ATU, to some point outside the shack, thereby overcoming the problems of routing balanced feeder into the shack. I stated that Ton Verberne, PA2ABV, was the first to use this arrangement.

Dick Rollema, PAOSE, noted in an e-mail, "It was a surprise to see the 'comudipole' mentioned in your column of May 2008. The comudipole was not 'invented' by Ton Verberne, PA2ABV. I coined the title 'comudipole', which means 'coax fed multiband dipole'. See *Technical Topics* May 1993. The balun I used was inspired by the pre-match unit (PMU) described by Mike Underhill in his 1981 conference paper mentioned in *TT*. Ton Verberne, PA2ABV ... has moved to a smaller apartment building so the coax between the balun on the roof and the shack is much shorter than the 30m before the move."

Indeed this proved to be the case. This edition of *TT* gives the whole story and, in particular, PA2APV's implementation of the comudipole. If you don't keep all your back issues of *RadCom* you can find the *TT* story in **[3]**.


**REFERENCES**

[1] www.cebik.com/mm2/register.php
[2] www.outsideshack.com
[3] Technical Topics Scrapbook, 1990 to 1994, pages 205 and 206.

# Antennas

## Antennas and EMC considerations for HF mobile operation.

**OH, FOR THE QUIET LIFE.** The proliferation of domestic electronic devices into our homes has, in many cases, created a general noise level that makes operating from home rather difficult. On top of this, many modern houses are built on postage stamp plots and this poses a problem when it comes to erecting an antenna. Many of us try to circumvent these issues by operating /M. However, we don't necessarily leave all the electronic equipment problems behind.

David Write, G4BKE e-mailed me to say, "Just been looking at your *Amateur Radio Mobile Handbook* [1] again. For years I've been operating /M and /P, both VHF & HF, from our old Ford Fiesta diesel. That car had no electronics and no airbags. I used two boot mounts with Watson single-band whips for HF bands and a 2m/70cm whip of Italian make. But now we have a 'new' Ford Fiesta Ghia diesel with electronic everything and the dreaded air bags. The car came from Ford Direct, ie it was previously owned by Ford themselves. I have risked running 10W of RF on 2m using a magmount with my old whip. But I'm dead scared of setting off the airbags with say 100W of SSB on 40m. Have you any experience of operating /M and whether this can affect airbags?"

**INTERFERENCE TO VEHICLE ELECTRONICS.** When I wrote the *Amateur Radio Mobile Handbook* I investigated the problem of RF interference to electronic control systems, mainly because the possible safety aspects. Basically, the problem is caused by the possibility of RF energy being picked up in the wiring of the car and entering the logic of the control circuits. I was told that the effects can vary from specific faults, such as failure of door locks or erratic flashers, to complete failure of the engine control system, although I have never heard of anyone actually experiencing these problems. The best advice I could find was in [2] and [3], one of which read as follows:

"If you are going to install an amateur radio transceiver in a vehicle that you already own, which has an electronic engine control unit, then it is probably a good idea to commence with a temporary installation. Use a separate battery large enough to allow the transceiver to produce close on to full power output when transmitting. Otherwise, run fused power leads from the passenger compartment through an open window and under the bonnet directly to the battery, making sure that these power leads are located as far from any other cabling as possible. The transceiver can be placed on the seat and the antenna can be fixed to a magmount or attached to a tow bar if you have one.

**PHOTO 1:** The cobweb mobile antenna fixed to the roof rack of a van.

"With the vehicle stationary and the engine running, the following should be checked while the transmitter is being operated at its maximum power:

- "There is no apparent engine misfiring.
- "No warning lights flicker or come on.
- "The direction indicators flash at the normal rate.
- "The windscreen wipers operate normally.
- "There are no unwanted effects on other electronic systems, such as central locking or air bags.

"If any unwanted effects occur, it will be necessary to relocate the antenna and/or reduce transmitter power. It should be noted that not all possible adverse effects can be detected when the vehicle is stationary. For example, anti-lock braking, cruise control, automatic transmission, electric power assisted steering and so on can only be checked with the vehicle in motion. It is therefore advisable to test drive the vehicle in a suitable location, preferably off the public highway. If any effect such as engine misfiring is noted when the transmitter is operated, transmission should cease immediately."

Now, while all this may sound rather daunting, I should point out that there are many HF and VHF mobile operators on the road whose vehicles experience no adverse affects whatsoever. Vehicle electronic systems must have some degree of EMC protection – a vehicle that developed a failure every time it was near a high power broadcast station would hardly be good publicity.

The above check, "There are no unwanted effects on other electronic systems, such as central locking or air bags" doesn't seem all that satisfactory, to my mind. What is an unwanted effect on an air bag? Perhaps you might have some information on this matter. My vehicle maintenance handbook says that the air bag is deactivated when the ignition is switched off.

There is a lot of information on the subject on the web. Just type in "Code of practice for the installation of mobile radio equipment" into Google and see what you get. The police appear to have an EMC department to which they send any vehicles that are suspected of EMC problems.

**MOBILE ANTENNA LOCATION.** In 2001, I did a lot of research on mobile HF antennas, which was published in [1] and [4]. Most of this work involved computer modelling and some interesting facts emerged. One

PHOTO 2: The cobweb antenna unfolded and ready to be raised to the vertical position.

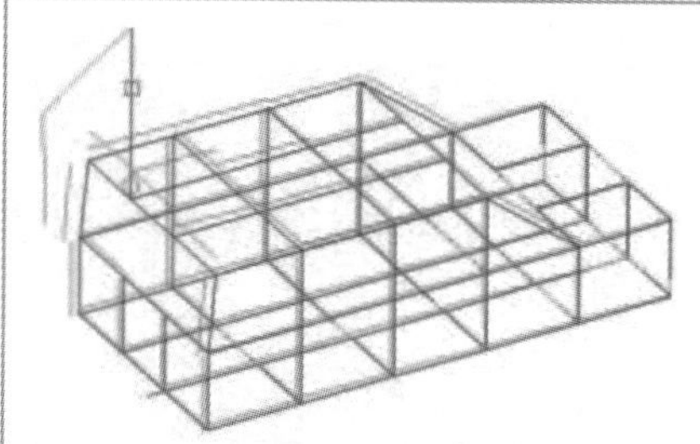
FIGURE 1: Computer model of an estate car or small van with a short loaded antenna mounted on the rear. The vehicle body is modelled as a grid. This grid and the antenna is shown in black. The current on the antenna and the vehicle is shown in red.

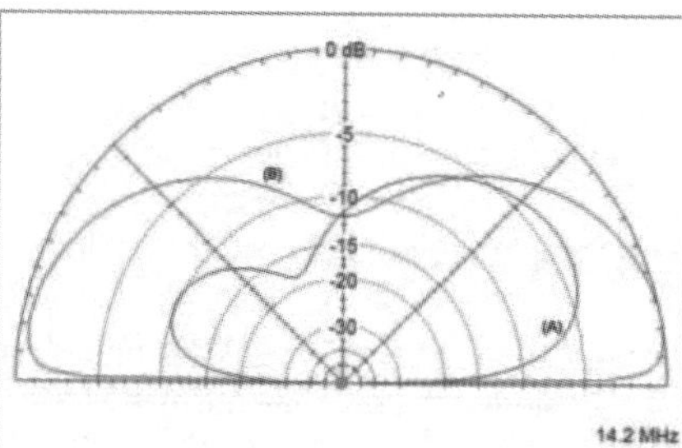

FIGURE 2: Computer prediction of the radiation pattern of a short loaded HF antenna on (A) normal ground and (B) near the sea.

question I sought answers for was which is the best place to locate the antenna. As it turned out, it didn't make a lot of difference. A computer model of a mobile installation is shown in **Figure 1**. It shows that there is considerable RF current flowing in the metalwork of the vehicle; just as much as is flowing in the antenna. This means that the vehicle radiates as part of the antenna system.

Furthermore, the current is greatest at the base or feedpoint of the antenna. Additionally the current flows on the outside of the metalwork, which is also a Faraday cage, giving some protection to the vehicle's electronics. It follows that the best place to locate a conventional mobile antenna is at the rear, which happens to be the most convenient place to put it. It is probably a good idea to fit a choke balun on the co-ax feeder to prevent RF currents entering the vehicle through the feeder.

I have also been in e-mail correspondence with Richard Bone, 2E0UOO, who has done some interesting mobile antenna experiments. He says, "My reason for getting in contact with you is for your comments on what has turned out to be a very good mobile antenna. The location where I live is not particular good for the installation of antennas, plus the noise level is quite high. This has forced me to go down the route of being 100% mobile. I originally operated on 20m with a Comet CHS14, which is a 0.9m loaded whip. This turned out to be hard work but I did achieve quite a few contacts with this arrangement.

"After studying lots of antenna documentation, I decided to build a portable cobweb, which would be easy to erect and collapse. After some basic tests and a few modifications the antenna was resonant on each band at the required frequency, so next I needed to find a place to work some DX. We have a stretch of road along the sea shore about two miles from my home (Meon Shore). One side is Titchfield Haven Nature Reserve and the other side is just the sea. The noise level is very low and it's a great place to just sit and talk on the radio."

The mobile setup using the cobweb is shown in **Photo 1** and the operating location in **Photo 2**.

**THE COBWEB ANTENNA.** The cobweb antenna was designed by G3TPW and is a commercial product. Details can be found at **[5]**. However, this antenna is amenable to home construction, an example of which can be found at G4ZFQ's website **[6]**.

The cobweb antenna is essentially parallel dipoles formed into a square. The effect of this is to make a very compact multi band antenna with no side nulls but this reduces the dipole feedpoint from 50Ω down to around 13Ω. Matching to 50Ω cable is achieved using twin wire as folded elements bringing the feedpoint up to just over 50Ω.

In the description of the antenna at [5] the gain is given as 7dBi! I checked the free space gain of a cobweb with EZNEC5 (zero copper losses) as 1.25dBi. A zero loss free space dipole gave 2.13dBi.

The 2E0UOO antenna has the added advantage that it can be folded like an umbrella for transportation to the operating site. My first reaction on seeing the 2E0UOO photos was what an ideal location it is for mobile or portable operating. Sea water is the most effective far field ground reflecting system you can have, particularly for vertical antennas. Parking places elevated above the sea are hard to find. Perhaps we could compile a list of such ideal operating sites. From **Photo 2**, it would appear that the antenna is around 25ft above sea water. In this case the antenna should be easily capable of producing the gain quoted in [5], due to ground reflection.

As regards the Comet CHS14, it isn't an antenna that I know anything about. If we assume that the loading coil is small and fairly lossy we should expect a gain of –2.5dBi. However, if this mobile setup is operated near to the sea as shown in Photo 2 then the gain may be as high as 1.25dBi as shown in **Figure 2**.

**REFERENCES**

[1] *Amateur Radio Mobile Handbook*, Peter Dodd, G3LDO
[2] RSGB EMC Committee Leaflet *EMC 06 Automotive EMC for Radio Amateurs*
[3] *Radio Telephone/Mobile Radio Installation Guidelines* issued by General Motors Corp. (USA)
[4] *'Computer Modelling the HF Mobile Antenna'*, Peter Dodd, G3LDO, *The ARRL Antenna Compendium*, Vol 7
[5] www.g3tpw.co.uk
[6] http://homepages.wightcable.net/~g4zfq/cobweb.htm

# Antennas

A new type of antenna tuner, the S-Match, is revealed.

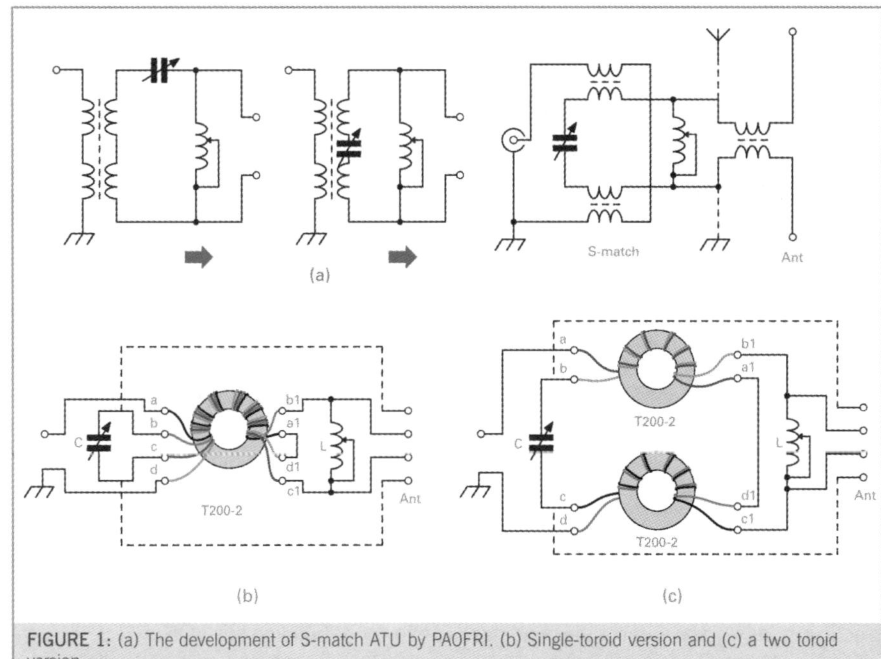


FIGURE 1: (a) The development of S-match ATU by PAOFRI. (b) Single-toroid version and (c) a two toroid version.

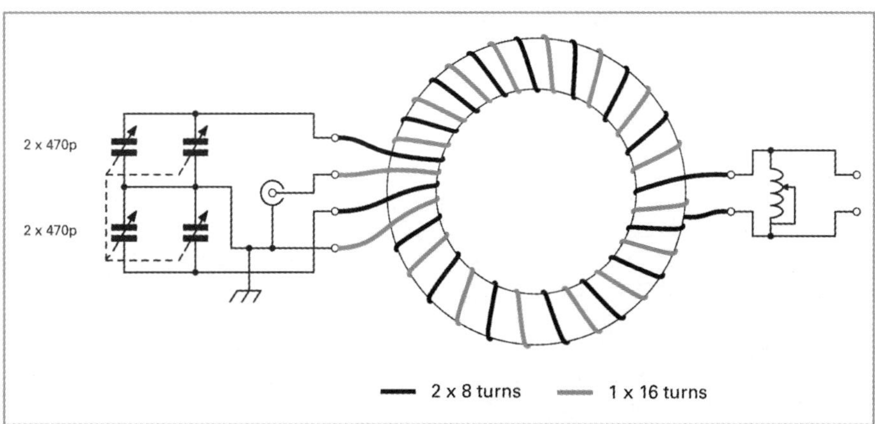


FIGURE 2: Single toroid S-match ATU. This circuit is very similar to Figure 1(b) but with a different capacitor tuning arrangement.

**ANTENNA TUNING UNITS AND THE PAOFRI S-MATCH.** In the February 2003 Antennas column, I mentioned the comparative efficiency measurements on several ATUs done by Doug Harris, GW3NDR. These ATUs were all tested with a centre fed wire about 24m (80ft) long and fed with slotted feeder some 6m (20ft) long and about 8.5m (28ft) above the ground. The balanced output of the ATU was measured using a RF current meter. The tuners compared were listed below in order of efficiency as follows:

Home Brew
MFJ Versa Tuner V (989C)
SSM Z Match
MFJ Versa Tuner 11
SG239 Smartuner

The home brew ATU was described by GW3NDR as a half Z-match. In view of its claimed efficiency, I will build and test one and I hope to report the results in a later 'Antennas'.

Recently, I made some comparative tests of the ATUs at the G3LDO QTH. The first was the SEM Zmatch; the second the tiny MFJ 901B; the third the large MFJ 989c and finally a home brew S-Match. (I will describe the S-Match later). The antenna used for the test is 20m long, 9m high at one end and 5m high at the other, fed roughly in the centre with 5m of 400Ω ladder line. It was originally erected as a temporary receiving antenna for 7MHz for some 500kHz/7MHz transatlantic cross-band tests.

The tests were carried out using 20W RF and the ATU tuned for minimum SWR. The outputs were measured using a MFJ-854 RF current meter, which is not a precision instrument and has a rather small meter. In addition to this, a selective wavemeter was used to measure the relative signal strengths but the signal strength readings were not very reliable, probably due to feeder radiation in the cases where the feeder currents were not balanced.

The results are listed in **Table 1** and are in broad agreement with the measurements done by GW3NDR with the order of efficiency as follows:

1) MFJ 989c
2) MFJ 901B
3) SEM TranZmatch
4) S-Match.

The MFJ 901B has a very small metal enclosure and a large air spaced coil. This means that the metal enclosure is close to the top and bottom of the coil and might be considered as a shorted turn. The cover was removed as part of the tests but only the 80m band was affected by the enclosure. The measured figure in Table 1 was with the top cover removed. When the cover was replaced the readings were reduced by around 15%. On the higher frequency bands the cover made no noticeable difference to the readings.

**THE PAOFRI S-MATCH.** The fashion for simple multiband antennas these days seems to be the tuned transmission line

PHOTO 1: The MFJ-974 balanced ATU.

PHOTO 2: The G3LDO version of the single toroid S-match ATU.

doublet or similar described in earlier 'Antennas'. In general, the most common type of ATU is the T match with a 4:1 transformer balun to feed twin-line transmission line. Commercial manufacturers are catering for this need by producing 'balanced' ATUs. The most common of these are the twin T as used in the MFJ- 974 shown in **Photo 1**. This arrangement requires that the input and output capacitors in each T-section have to be ganged together, which makes for a mechanically complex unit.

A simpler balanced ATU would be a more practical unit for home construction. You might like to consider the PAOFRI's S-Match symmetrical and universal ATU, which was described in **[1]**.

PAOFRI notes in his web page **[2]** that, "After an extensive research and experimenting I achieved the design of the Balanced Universal ATU System. To make it distinctive from other types of ATUs, I call my design S-Match©. The system is intended to accommodate balanced antenna systems transmitting on a very wide frequency spectrum, ranging from 160m to 10m. It is able to take proper care of impedances and associated reactances ranging from less than 20Ω and up to 3000Ω. Built with suitable components, it is able to transfer power of more than 1000W. This balanced antenna tuning unit has only three components: a capacitor, a roller inductor and a balun or RF transformer. The input circuits are isolated from the output circuits, resulting in a system which is suitable also for single-wire antennas and coax fed antennas".

The development of this ATU by PAOFRI is illustrated in Figure 1(a). Two practical versions are shown; the single-toroid version in Figure 1(b) and a two toroid version in Figure 1 (c).

**COMPONENTS.** The transformers are made with Amidon toroids. For transmitter powers of less than 400W use a T200-2 toroid. For higher power use two T200-2 units sandwiched together or a T200A-2. The T200A-2 toroid is a near substitute of two T200-2 units sandwiched together.

For Figure 1(b) use T200-2 with 2 x 8 bifilar turns with Teflon-covered wire or T200A-2 with 2x6 bifilar turns with Teflon-covered wire.

For Figure 1(c) each toroid is wound with 11 bifilar turns with Teflon-covered wire.

For 10 - 160m the L roller inductor should be greater than 20μH. C should be greater than 200pFwith a minimum capacitance of less than 15pF.

For both Figure 1(b) and (c), if any imbalance occurs, try interchanging connections to a and d. With some antenna systems a better efficiency may be achieved if the antenna is connected to the capacitor as shown by the dotted line in Figure 1 (b) and (c).

**THE G3LDO VERSION.** My version of the S-Match is shown in **Figure 2**, which is also from PAOFRI's website. It is similar to the single toroid version shown in Figure 1 but has a different capacitor tuning arrangement. The toroid comprises two stacked T200-2 cores with several layers of plastic insulation. The wire for the windings is stripped from heavy-duty electrical cable, which has the advantage of being colour coded – an important consideration when winding a relatively complicated transformer.

The construction is shown in **Photo 2**. The capacitor is a four-ganged unit with a maximum value of 223pF per section (12.5pF minimum). The roller-coaster inductor came from an ex-commercial automatic ATU. It has a maximum value of 50μH – rather more than needed for this project. As noted above 20μH would have been sufficient.

This inductor is interesting. Instead of a single roller contact running from one end of the coil to the other it has two separate coils with two separate roller contacts, which are connected together. The coils are counter wound so that as the coil is rotated the two contacts move closer together or further apart. I am not sure why this is done. It might be to overcome certain resonances when a coil is tapped along its length or it might be that you get twice the inductance change per revolution – perhaps a consideration in a motorised ATU, from whence this inductor came.

There is yet a further interesting feature of this inductor. Underneath the cylindrical capacitor (Photo 2) by one of the inductors is a wire resistance strip. This strip has a slider mechanically linked to one of the roller contacts, which was probably part of the feedback circuit of the motorised system. It occurred to me that this resistor, together with a DC supply (a 1.5V battery) and a digital voltmeter, would make a good inductor position indicator.

TABLE 1: ATU test results. L and R are left and right conductors of the antenna feeder currents in mA.

| 3.7MHz | L | R | Avg | Rating |
|---|---|---|---|---|
| TranZmatch | 58 | 52 | 55 | 1 |
| MFJ 901B | 26 | 26 | 26 | 4 |
| MFJ 989c | 28 | 28 | 28 | 3 |
| S-match | 32 | 28 | 30 | 2 |
| **7.05MHz** | | | | |
| TranZmatch | 28 | 10.6 | 19.3 | 2 |
| MFJ 901B | 27.3 | 11.3 | 19.3 | 2 |
| MFJ 989c | 26.6 | 35 | 30.8 | 1 |
| S-match | 22 | 11 | 16.5 | 4 |
| **14.2MHz** | | | | |
| TransZatch | 34 | 15 | 24.5 | 4 |
| MFJ 901B | 60 | 23 | 41 | 1 |
| MFJ 989c | 35 | 23 | 29 | 2 |
| S-Match | 15 | 40 | 27.5 | 3 |
| **21.2MHz** | | | | |
| TranZmatch | 16 | 15 | 15.5 | 4 |
| MFJ 901B | 16 | 17 | 16.5 | 2 |
| MFJ 989c | 23 | 17 | 20 | 1 |
| S-Match | 10 | 22 | 16 | 3 |

**PERFORMANCE.** According to Table 1 my S-Match was not as efficient as the others. However, I have to say that this was my first attempt at building this type of ATU. It proved very easy to tune, not the slightest bit critical, so that slow motion drives on the capacitor and inductance were not necessary. It loaded all bands from 1.8MHz to 21.3MHz with ease.

PAOFRI notes in [2]; "The efficiency is a little less than with a LC system using two capacitors and a one roller inductor or two roller inductors and one capacitor, but in practice, the difference is minimal". Some test results are described in **[3]**.

**FINALLY.** In some e-mail exchanges between Dick Rollema, PAOSE, on the subject of ATUs, he noted that the FRI-tuner is an interesting design. Frits Geerlings, PAOFRI, is a regular officer in the Dutch army. He is a keen experimenter as you can see on his website [2]. The lack of a theoretical description makes it difficult to judge whether designs are sound but judging by the favourable comments of several amateurs in [2] these ATUs appear to work OK.

#### REFERENCES


[1] TT, *RadCom* March 2003

[2] www.xs4all.nl/~paOfri/ATU/Smatch/smatcheng.htm (or just type 'smatcheng' into Google)

[3] www.xs4all.nl/%7EpaOfri/ATU/KlasseATU/classatu.htm

# Antennas

## Following a query about gain figures, Peter Dodd explains his antenna testing rationale.

TESTING ANTENNA SUGGESTIONS. I regularly receive material describing antennas or antenna accessories for which I am grateful. They provided grist for the column and enable readers to describe their experimental work and often invite me to make comments. The phased vertical [1] and the mobile CobWeb antennas [2] are such examples. Before publishing, I sometimes build the antenna to check its performance or try to find some endorsement from an authority. The phased vertical [1] and the analysis on this antenna by W4RNL [3] is an example.

The other method of checking an antennas performance is using an antenna modelling program. I use EZNEC, which is a program that I have used for many years. But I can't please everybody. Steve Webb, G3TPW, the designer of the CobWeb antenna e-mailed me to say:

".....you have made a comment about the CobWeb Antenna that could be most misleading to people who have not read my website. I presume that you fall into this category as on my site I quite clearly state that the gain of the CobWeb and a dipole are about 5dB over the gain of a dipole in free space, due to ground reflection. Anybody reading your comments would infer that you say that the gain of the CobWeb is lower than what I say it is. As I have been completely open and honest about the antenna performance I consider that you have done me a great injustice and have tried to group me with other antenna marketing hype types!

"As a professional Electromagnetics Engineer I always use dB over isotropic as then there is no way you can mislead people. If you do use comparison with a dipole you must state that the reference dipole is in the same position over ground as the antenna being tested. It is most misleading to quote the gain of your antenna over a dipole in free space as this will add 5dB to your gain figure and most people do not realise that! It is also most misleading to say you have calculated the gain of CobWeb in free space and then compare it with my gain figure, which is specifically including ground gain.

"The CobWeb does in fact perform much better than a dipole in many installations because of reduced near field coupling to trees, houses, telephone and TV cables and other antennas.

"I trust that you will re-do your calculations and this time include ground reflections and thus compare like with like and will 'right the wrong' in a future RadCom."

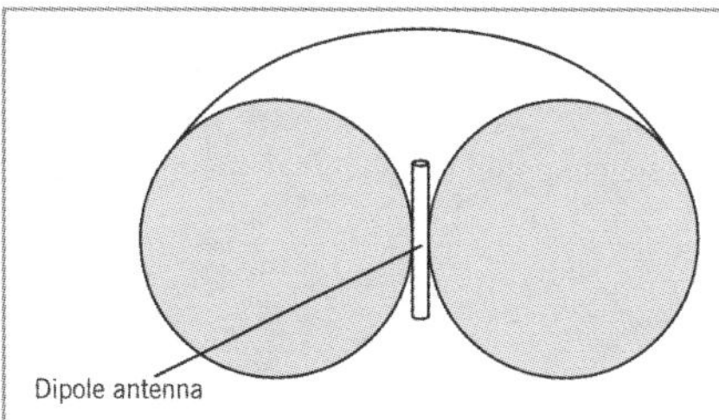


FIGURE 1: The three dimensional radiation pattern of a free-space dipole antenna is doughnut shaped. A section through this doughnut is a figure of eight. Gain at the side of the antenna occurs at the expense of loss of gain at the ends of the antenna.

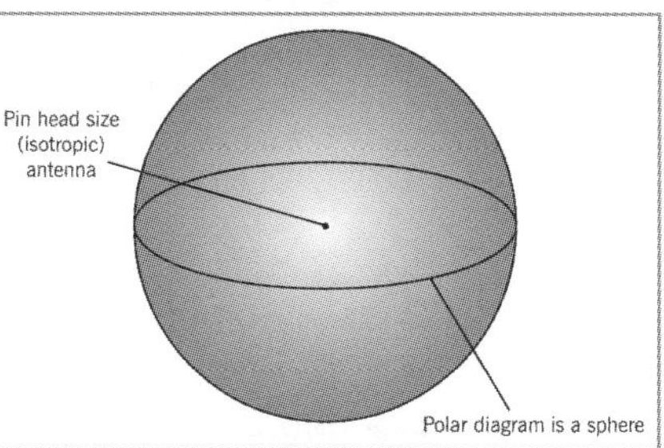


FIGURE 2: The three dimensional radiation pattern of a free-space isotropic antenna is a sphere. Horizontal and vertical sections through this sphere are both circles.

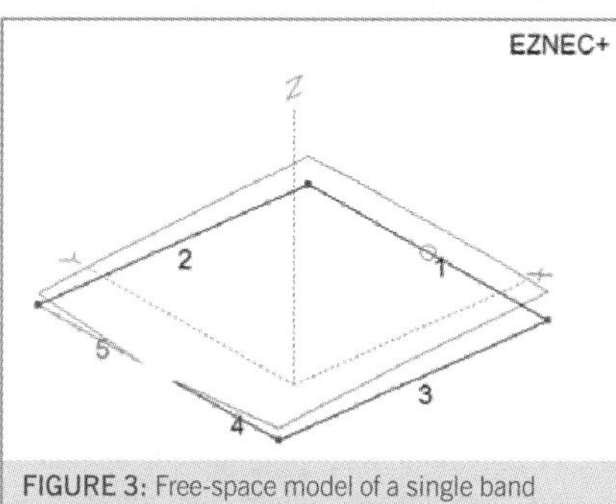


FIGURE 3: Free-space model of a single band CobWeb antenna.

Before responding to G3TPW I would like to try and define what I understand to be the simple basics of antenna performance measuring and modelling.

BASIC MEASUREMENTS & MODELLING. The performance of an antenna can be measured by energising it with a known level of RF power and then performing a number of field strength measurements. These measurements are made at a constant distance in the far field (greater than 2.5 wavelengths) at different angles relative to the antenna under test (AUT). A large number of these measurements can be used to produce a polar diagram or space pattern.

If one antenna system can be made to concentrate more radiation in a certain direction than another antenna, for the same total power supplied, then it is said to exhibit gain over the second antenna in that direction. The gain of an antenna is a combination of directivity and efficiency when compared with a reference antenna.

The simplest practical form of reference antenna is the dipole. Although this antenna may be of any length, the word 'dipole' implies a half-wavelength long resonant antenna, fed via a balanced feeder at the centre. Because of this simplicity the dipole itself has become a reference standard. Gain figures, using the dipole as a reference, are symbolised dBd.

However, the dipole antenna does not radiate equally in all directions because the current along the length of the dipole is not constant and it produces a three-dimensional doughnut shaped radiation pattern as shown in **Figure 1**. By the definition described above the dipole has gain.

For this reason a hypothetical point source antenna, which radiates equally in all directions, has been devised and is known as an isotropic radiator. Because the field strength is the same in all directions it follows that the 3-dimensional polar diagram or space pattern of an *isotropic radiator* is a sphere, as shown in **Figure 2**, and has a reference gain of 1.0. Gain figures relative to this isotropic source are symbolised dBi. As stated earlier our dipole has power gain and this gain is 2.15dbi.

Our isotropic source is a mathematical entity. Even if you could build one, the moment it was introduced into the real world it would be affected by nearby objects and ground and the space pattern would no longer be a sphere. In the world of mathematical modelling, using computer programs such as EZNEC, these nearby objects and ground restrictions do not exist and we can use this isotropic source in what is known as 'free space'. Furthermore we can model our antennas in free space making for a much simpler model.

**THE EFFECT OF GROUND.** The ground under the antenna acts as a reflector. Electromagnetic waves from the antenna radiate in all directions and some of these waves are reflected by ground. If the reflected wave is in phase, or partially in phase, with a direct wave it enhances radiation and increases gain at a particular angle. Other combinations of reflected and direct waves, whose phases tend to cancel, reduce gain at other angles.

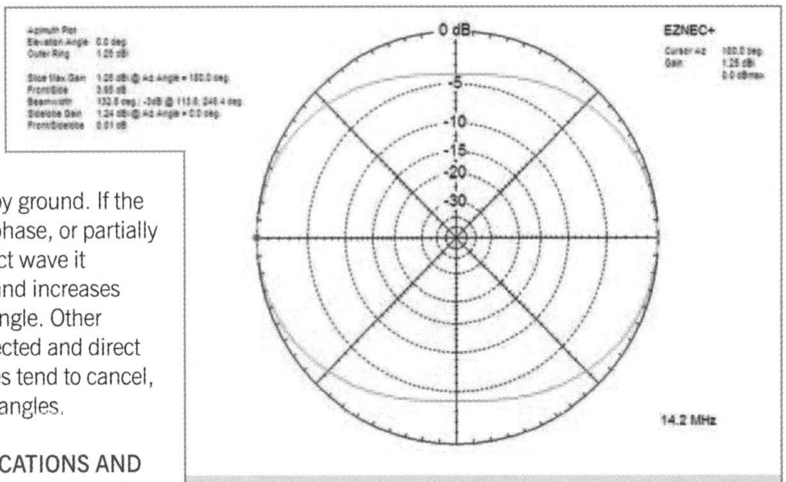

**ANTENNA SPECIFICATIONS AND THE ARRL.** From what I have said, it can be seen that specifying the performance of an antenna can be rather imprecise. The ARRL had problems in the early 1960s, because some antenna manufacturers became engaged in a 'horsepower race' with each other – and they stretched the credibility of their advertising claims to breaking point. The ARRL has a fairly extensive lab, with access to lots of top-notch measuring equipment. Even they, however, would have difficulty verifying the absolute gain of a large multi-element HF Yagi by actually measuring its performance.

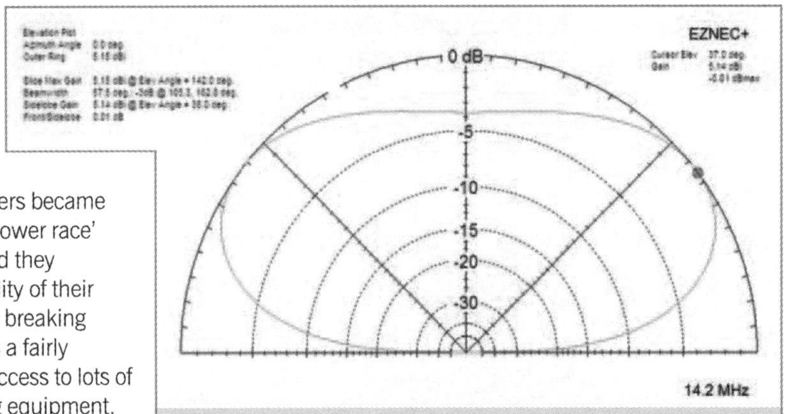

The ARRL web page goes on to say: "Indeed, accurately validating the gain of even a small 2-metre Yagi is not an easy thing to do. Absolute, repeatable measurements of gain and pattern measurements for antennas are very difficult, unless one has access to a large professional antenna range and to very sophisticated (and expensive) measuring equipment. Back in the 1960s, rather than allowing misleading advertisements that couldn't be validated with verified in-field measurements, the League simply amended its Advertising Acceptance Policy to forbid any advertising of specific antenna performance figures, such as forward gain, front-to-back ratio or radiation patterns".

More recently Dean Straw, N6BV, at the ARRL announced **[4]** after more than 35 years, antenna manufacturers may once again advertise performance figures in ARRL publications. One goal of their new advertisement acceptance policy was to set up as few restrictions as possible for the advertiser, while still protecting the interests of their members. They go on to say: "The

**FIGURE 4:** Azimuth plot of a free-space CobWeb antenna showing a gain of 1.25dBi.

**FIGURE 5:** Elevation plot of a CobWeb antenna 7.6m above real earth with a ground conductivity 5mS/m and a dielectric constant of 13. The maximum gain is 5.16dBi at an angle of 37 degrees.

Board requires that at least one fundamental property must be shown if any performance claims are made – the gain in free space at a specified frequency. This must always be shown referenced to a free-space isotropic antenna, meaning that gain must be shown in dBi. This meets the minimum requirements for the new policy and it gives useful information for a potential customer to compare one product with other ones.

"The advertiser may want to show performance over real ground. There's nothing wrong with this approach, provided that performance over ground is advertised in addition to that in free space. Some additional conditions arise for computations done over ground. First, the ground model used must be the 'Sommerfeld/Norton' ground model in NEC-4, with 'typical' ground constants of 5mS/m for ground conductivity and a dielectric constant of 13. These restrictions preclude the use of the simple 'perfect-ground' or 'MININEC-ground' models, which both can inflate performance claims considerably."

**G3LDO MODELLING AND MEASUREMENTS.** The model of the CobWeb I described in [2] is shown in **Figure 3**. It is very simplistic. First of all it is a single band version. Secondly it uses a single wire element instead of a two-wire folded element. It could be argued that this reduces the radiation resistance, thereby increasing losses. This is more than compensated for by using a zero loss conductor in the model. The third simplification is to use a free space model. This meets the minimum ARRL requirements described above and an azimuth plot is shown in **Figure 4**. This model has a free space gain of 1.25dBi, which was quoted in [2].

According to G3TPW I should have used a model that included ground to give ground gain. I use EZNEC5, which has a 'Real Ground' function. The problem with a model that includes ground is you have to specify ground constants and the height of the antenna above this ground (although antenna height is not mentioned in the ARRL document).

The antenna was modelled with a ground conductivity 5mS/m and a dielectric constant of 13 (as specified by the ARRL) and an antenna height of 7.6m (25ft). The elevation diagram of this model, with a gain of 5.2dBi is shown in **Figure 5**. When the antenna in the model was raised to 10.6m (35ft) above seawater the gain increased to 7.26dBi. From this it can be seen that antenna performance is very much affected by its environment and it is for this reason I use a simple free-space model. The exceptions are some vertical or end fed wire antennas where the ground or earth forms an integral part of the antenna.

**REFERENCES**


[1] Antennas, *RadCom* July 2008

[2] Antennas, *RadCom* August 2008

[3] http://www.cebik.com/mm2/register.php

[4] ARRL Advertising Acceptance Policy, Dean Straw, N6BV, *QST* April 1998

# Antennas

Confusion with baluns plus a look at some blue-sky research.

**BALUNS AGAIN.** The most common question I get is about baluns. The main function of a balun is to prevent RF currents flowing on the outside of the coax cable feeding the antenna. In addition, some baluns also provide impedance transformation, normally around 4:1.

Bill Concannon, G4EDM, e-mailed me to say, "I have an unbalanced Trio ATU model AT300 in excellent condition so I purchased a suitable ferrite ring and have tried in vain to convert the unbalanced output of this ATU to balanced output to the antenna. The core I am using came from Howarth Jones who had a business in Wales making baluns and supplied ferrite rings for years. His written description of how to make a 4 to 1 balun and yours are similar. I have followed the instructions but not met with much success. When I transmit RF seems to get into the power supply and destabilises it. The SWR reading seems OK".

This description of the adverse effects of fitting a balun indicates that it is not correctly fitted or that the balun has a serious problem and some tests might be in order. I have, in the past, constructed many baluns and a traditional transformer version, wound on a T-200 core is shown in **Photo 1**. The construction of this balun was shown in detail in **[1]** and is trifilar wound to give ratios of 1:1 or 4:1.

One of the tests that you can apply to a balun is to connect a dummy load to its output and measure the SWR over a range of frequencies. This is most easily done using an instrument such as the MFJ-259 or 269 as shown in Photo 1. An analysis of this balun, using the AIM 4170, is shown in **Figure 1**. It has a load of 119Ω and the ratio is set to 1:1 and you can see that it produces an anticipated SWR of just over 2:1 over a frequency range of 2 to 38MHz.

One of the criticisms of ferrite core design baluns or transformers is that the cores may saturate under high power levels combined with extreme values of antenna system feed impedance. You can make a choke balun with a 16cm (6in) diameter, 6 turn coil of the coax feeder to the antenna. Or you can make a coax transformer balun, designed by PA0SE, which gives an impedance ratio of 4:1 and is illustrated in **Photo 2**.

A plot of this balun, using the AIM 4170, is shown in **Figure 2**. The balun has a load of 199Ω, which is transformed near to 50Ω and an SWR of near unity across the 2 to 38MHz band. A further test that can be used is to note the SWR during transmissions. If the SWR increases during a period of transmitting then there may be problems with the ferrite core of the balun you are using. I haven't experienced this problem myself – I only mention this because it was reported by a reader.

**PHOTO 1:** Traditional transformer balun wound on a T-200 core being tested with an MFJ-269. The balun is trifilar wound to give ratios of 1:1 or 4:1.

**BLUE SKY STUFF.** In this column, I generally concentrate on the practical aspects of antennas. This doesn't mean that I am not interested in the theoretical aspects of the subject. Indeed I have created a section on my website **[2]** (which is in need of some serious updating) on the subject on how various people have described how an antenna radiates.

The problem is that fundamental issues such as the movement of electrons and photon radiation (radio waves) can only be discussed in terms of mental pictures, like the Bohr model of the atom (that is the model that shows the atom as a mini solar system). As noted in **[3]**, "We also use analogies and mathematical concepts, etc., such as 'lines of force'. This is very helpful in enabling people make practical use of things they really don't understand. The fact that nobody knows what electrons are has not prevented them being used in most complicated and ingenious ways. Usually all concerned manage to agree to use the same mental pictures when they discuss these fundamental things or perform the calculations necessary to exploit them to the best advantage.

"Although these concepts are so helpful, and it is difficult to see how we could carry on engineering and other applied sciences without them, they are dangerously liable to mislead us into accepting them as realities. Take 'lines of force' for example. We know by experiment that exceptional things happen in the space around what we are pleased to call 'electrically charged bodies'. We just don't understand why or how these things happen, but it has been found by careful study that they always happen in certain definite ways and with certain numerical relationships. So scientists have defined various quantities such as charge and potential, and have enunciated various laws connecting them, and to help you and me to grasp these they have imagined such things as 'lines of force'. Owing to the care with which these things have been defined, they make up a consistent system, and one can work about with them and design electrical and radio appliances and predict their performance with confidence."

PHOTO 2: PA0SE coaxial 4:1 balun.

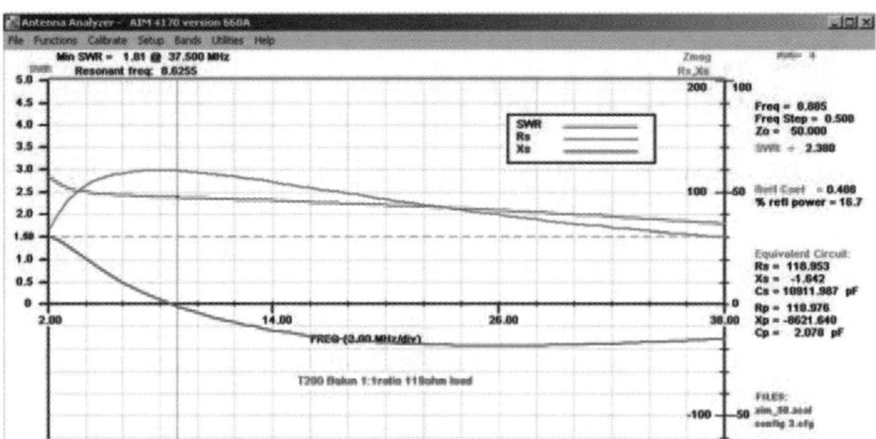


FIGURE 1: Analysis of the home made T-200 transformer balun using the AIM 4170.

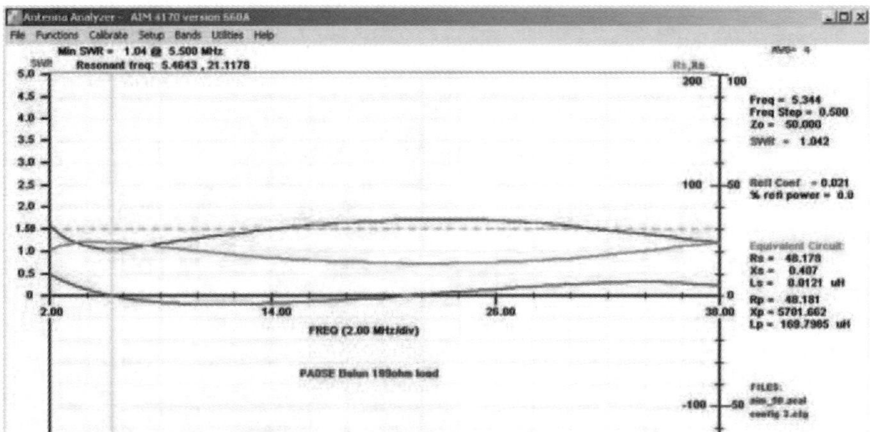


FIGURE 2: A plot of the PA0SE coax transformer balun, using the AIM 4170. The balun has a load of 199Ω, which is transformed near to 50Ω and an SWR of near unity across the 2 to 38MHz band.

Most of our models of electromagnetic radiation are mathematical. One advanced technical book I have in my library [4] commences with a chapter on vector analysis so you have to have to know something of this branch of mathematics before you can even start to understand the rest of the book. Mathematics is a very concise and logical language but if you haven't learned this language then the material could have been written in some esoteric foreign language for all the good it is to you. However, when a mathematical model is built into a user-friendly computer program it can be very accessible and effective. I once attended a lecture where the speaker claimed to have a new antenna design that employed a completely new method of combining the E and H components of an electromagnetic wave to effect radiation and produced an impressive mathematical model to prove it. The fact that the antenna performed rather badly, and not in the way described, indicated that the mathematical model may have been used as a method of obfuscation or self delusion. Nevertheless, the classical model described in [3] has proved adequate for most electromagnetic analysis.

A more complete model of electromagnetic phenomena can be described using quantum electrodynamics (QED). The present view is that the 'waves' are not waves of moving matter or varying fields but are probability waves. Thus the wave-like behaviour of a moving electron is considered to be due to the fact that the chance of it being found in an element of volume depends on the intensity (ie the square of the amplitude) at the point of the electron wave associated with it. Where this is high we are likely to have a high electron density. In the same way, an electromagnetic wave, although undoubtedly connected with electric and magnetic fields, is regarded as consisting of photons (ie bundles of energy) whose probable locations are given by the intensity of the wave.

Unfortunately, this subject is even more esoteric than that described in [4]. There are several books on quantum theory around but are they of any use? The theoretical physicist, Richard P. Feynman, decried popular physics books as achieving "apparent simplicity only by describing something different, something considerably distorted from what they claim to be describing". Instead, he posed himself a challenge of describing QED to the lay audience without "distortion of the truth". He did it by giving a series of four lectures to at the University of Auckland in New Zealand to a lay audience on the subject of QED. Fortunately, video recordings were made of these lectures and you can see them on [5].

Now, while this material is comprehensible to viewers without a knowledge of mathematics it does require some effort to take it all in. Each lecture is around one and a half hours long; six hours altogether, but they are delivered in a particularly Feynman manner, which you should also find entertaining as well as informative. Much of the subject matter is concerned with the interactions of electrons and photons (light and radio waves). An edited edition of these lectures is also available in book form, which I have found a useful supplement to these video lectures [6].

WEBSEARCH

[1] Antennas, *RadCom*, May 2008
[2] http://www.g3ldo.co.uk
[3] *Second Thoughts on Radio Theory*, "Cathode Ray", Wireless World, 1955
[4] *Foundations of Electromagnetic Theory*, John R. Reitz & Fredrick J. Milford, Addison-Wesley Publishing, Inc
[5] The Douglas Robb Memorial Lectures, University of Auckland in New Zealand. Vega Science Trust. http://vega.org.uk/video/subseries/8
[6] *QED, The Strange Theory of Light and Matter*, Richard P. Feynman, Princetown University Press. ISBN 0-691-12575-9.

# Antennas

## Catching up with feedback on baluns, ATU efficiency, the CobWebb and mobile interference

**BALUNS AGAIN.** In Antennas last month, I briefly described a traditional transformer trifilar wound balun on a T-200 core that gives ratios of 1:1 or 4:1. I also discussed how it was tested. Roger Vandenbussche, ON6WR, e-mailed me to ask, "I would like to make a new balun for my ATU on an Amidon T200-2 core. In the photo shown in *Antennas*, May 2008, the three enamelled wires are side by side. I always make baluns with twisted wires. I would like your opinion what is best, twisted or side by side."

I do not have any experience with winding balun transformers with twisted wires but G6XN noted in **[1]** that twisting wires is satisfactory. Just avoid the extremes of too tight a spiral or slack enough for daylight to be visible between the wires. I think the best method is to wrap three straight wires together with PTFE tape and then wind all three onto the former or core; the tape makes the wires lay down flat and parallel.

The simplest 1:1 balun is a just a pair of wires wound onto a ferrite core. The performance of this balun can be improved dramatically by adding a third winding, which provides a necessary current path from end to end of the choke without upsetting the desired voltage and phase relationships. The third (tertiary) winding must have close magnetic coupling with the other two. This is usually achieved by winding all three wires together, in a trifilar winding.

G6XN also noted [1] that it is not necessary to use a toroid; six or seven trifilar turns on a medium wave broadcast type of ferrite rod will work perfectly well – and at far less cost. Such a balun has rather less series inductance than the normal toroidal balun, so it shifts the whole performance band upward in frequency.

This rod-type transformer balun is used in some commercial units. I was testing a commercial W2AU 1:1 transformer balun, shown in **Photo 1**, which was being used in a Comudipole arrangement. The antenna was a 20m horizontal wire fed by 10m of 400Ω ladder line via the balun, which was located in the hedge. I connected the ladder line directly to connecting lugs and the wires; the eyebolts were not used because antenna was not supporting the balun. This turned out to be a mistake. After erecting the antenna, the weather took a turn for the worse with high winds, which caused the ladder line to flap about. This, in turn, caused one of the wires to break off the soldered lug.

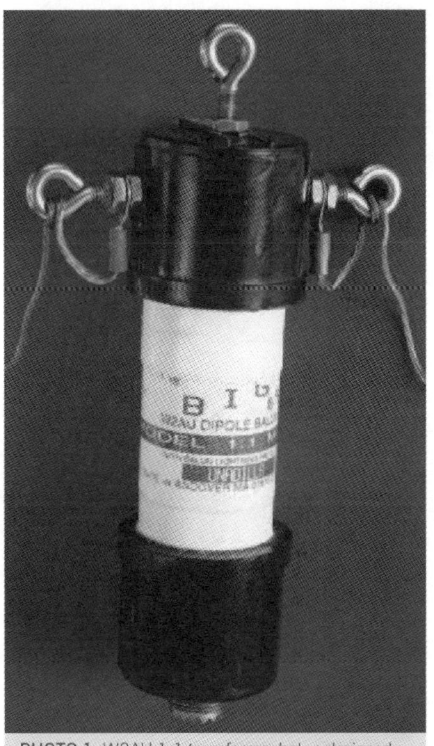


**PHOTO 1:** W2AU 1:1 transformer balun designed for use at the centre connection of a dipole.

**PHOTO 2:** Internal construction of the W2AU 1:1 transformer balun.

This posed a bit of a problem. I couldn't solder a new wire to the connector lug because the top of the case is made of plastic that melts when heated and a note on the side of the unit advised against loosening the eyebolts. In the end, against the advice, I removed the problem eyebolt and connector lug, only to hear the internal nut rattling around inside the unit – it wasn't captive!

There was nothing for it but to try and dismantle the balun. This was done by removing the other eyebolt and then carefully sawing through the white plastic tube and removing the top half as shown in **Photo 2**. As you can see this unit employs a ferrite rod and trifilar wound transformer as described earlier. Suitable brass nuts were soldered to the internal connectors thus making them captive. It was then quite easy to reassemble the unit and fit new external connector lugs as shown in Photo 1.

There is a feature of the W2AU balun that I have not seen elsewhere and that is the EMP spark gap. Although not obvious from Photos 1 and 2, there is a metal strap connected from the top lug along the outside of the balun to the coax connector. As you can see from Photo 2, the internal ends of the three eyebolts are arranged so that they are close enough together to form the spark gap. You might ask why this is necessary; after all the autotransformer arrangement ensures a DC path from the two connector lugs and the coax connector (which would prevent the build up of rain static voltages).

The reason is (I think) the EMP from a nearby lightning strike can induce a high amplitude pulse of very short duration on to the antenna and the balun transformer would present a high impedance to such a pulse. Such a pulse could cause arcing and damage the transformer; a spark gap offers a method of dissipating this energy. Just how wide the gap should be is not known.

The performance of the W2AU balun, terminated with a 119Ω resistor, over a frequency range of 2 to 38MHz is shown in **Figure 1**. The full range of W2AU baluns and isolators (choke baluns) are available, see **[2]**.

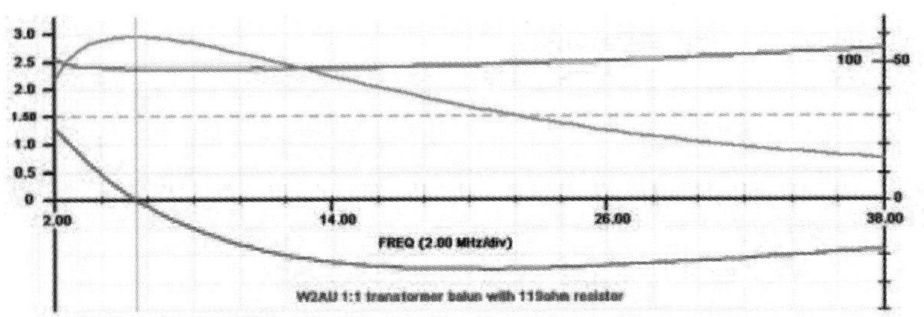


FIGURE 1: Analysis of W2AU 1:1 transformer balun with a 119Ω resistive load, using the AIM 4170. The red graph is SWR (left hand scale) and the green and purple lines represent R and ±j respectively (right hand scale).

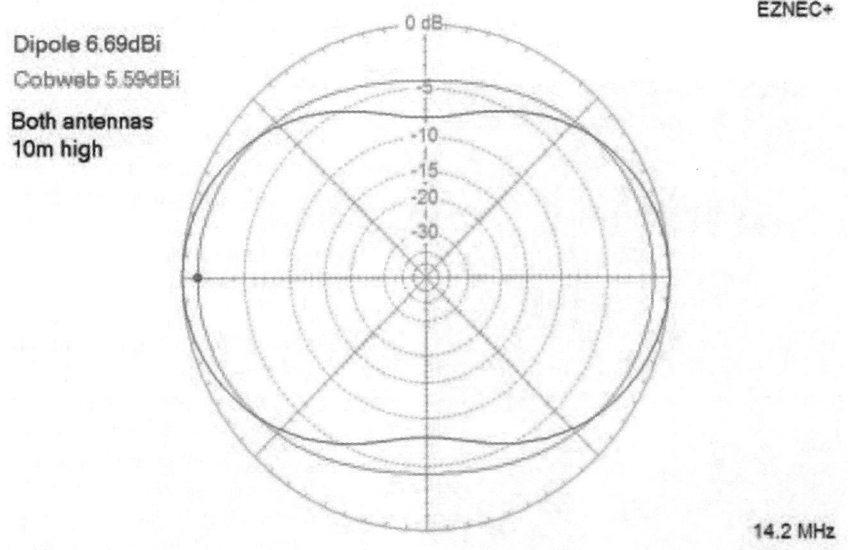


FIGURE 2: Overlay showing a comparison of a dipole and the Cobweb with both antennas 10m high above average ground. These results are made at the angle of maximum ground gain which is about 35° at 14MHz.

**ATU EFFICIENCY.** Ian McGowan, G8OFZ, wrote to me regarding the discussion on ATU efficiency **[3]**. He said: "Having read the above article I believe that there is an error in Table 1 where you tabulate the results of your own tests of 4 different AMUs in matching into a 20m long low doublet on 4 bands between 80m & 15m. In the text you say that you carried out these tests using 20W RF, and Table 1 purports to compare the feeder currents in mA.

"The published figures of average feeder current (between 15.5 and 55mA) suggest unbelievably high best match input impedances for the antenna of 6.6k on 80m, 21k on 40m, 12k on 20m, and 50k on 15m. The likeliest explanation seems to me that the feeder currents quoted in Table 1 have been reduced by a factor of ten. Correcting this (ie 550mA instead of 55mA) would give much more believable impedances of between 66Ω and 500Ω across the 4 bands."

I looked into the figures again and found the comments of G8OFZ to be correct. The cause of the error was my misreading the current scale of the MFJ-845 RF current meter. This instrument has 5 selectable ranges at 30mA, 100mA, 300mA, 1A and 3A. The meter is calibrated from 0 to 100 with divisions 10, 20, 30, etc. Most of the measurements were taken on the 1A range and I had noted them down as I saw them so that 55 should have been 550 as was correctly pointed out. Well spotted, Ian!

I should have followed my own advice in **[4]** regarding collecting data. That is to record exactly what is displayed on the instrument and have an additional column to apply any correction factor (the range in this case). Not all the columns of the data collection table have to be published of course.

**THE COBWEBB ANTENNA AGAIN.** In an e-mail discussion with Steve, G3TXQ regarding the CobWebb antenna, he notes "...the average Ham is not interested in (or conversant with the derivation of) dBi figures – he simply wants to know how much better his new antenna might be than a half-wave dipole in the same place. I feel Steve [G3PTW] has missed promoting the major advantage of the CobWebb after its small size – its omnidirectionality. Let's assume that prospective purchasers of a CobWebb are unlikely to have the space to rotate a half-wave dipole. Overlay the Free Space azimuth plots for the CobWebb and the dipole and, assuming that signals might arrive from any direction, you can honestly make the following claims:

a) Outperforms the dipole over 68% of all azimuth angles.
b) Never more than 1dB below the dipole (at the maximum gain area of the dipole)
c) 17% of the time beats the dipole by at least 10dB".

I made an EZNEC overlay of a dipole and the CobWebb antenna – see **Figure 2**. My model uses average ground rather than Free Space, with both antennas 10m high. These results are made at an elevation angle of maximum ground gain, which is about 35° at 14MHz. This has the effect of filling in the deep nulls found in a Free Space dipole model, so the difference between the two antennas shown in c) is 4dB.

**MOBILE INTERFERENCE.** Some time ago **[5]**, I discussed mobile amateur radio and bemoaned the lack of information from vehicle manufactures regarding the RF immunity of their products. Art Swain, G3KWY, e-mailed me to say: "Just for your interest, I drive a Mercedes A140. The owner's handbook gives the following information for amateur radio operation. The maximum transmission output power to a matched external antenna for each band as follows:

| | |
|---|---|
| Short Wave <50MHz | 100 watts |
| 4m | 20 watts |
| 2m | 50 watts |
| 70cm | 35 watts |
| 23cm | 10 watts |

"Equipment must be type approved, ie with the 'e' symbol.

"Unfortunately there is no value given for 6 metres. Whether this is because my vehicle is 7 years old and in Germany they may not have had 6 metres when then book was printed, I don't know."

It is good to see that some vehicle manufactures are addressing this issue.

**WEBSEARCH**

[1] *HF Antennas for All Locations*, Les Moxon, G6XN
[2] Adur Communications, Tel 01903 879526. www.adurcomms.co.uk/unadilla.htm
[3] Antennas, *RadCom*, September 2008
[4] *The Antenna Experimenter's Guide*, Peter Dodd, G3LDO
[5] Antennas, *RadCom*, May, 2007

# Antennas

## Getting signals in and out of restricted areas.

PHOTO 1: A view from the bedroom window of the QTH and the multiband low visual impact antenna devised by M3RVZ. The feedpoint is through the eves of the roof – the SG-237 is situated at the top of the stairs.

**WHICH RESTRICTED SITE ANTENNA?** I am often asked which is the best commercial antenna they should buy for their particular location. This is a particular problem if you want to operate on 80 or 160m if you only have a very small garden. So it was nice to get an e-mail from Phil Brookshaw, M3RVZ, who sent some details of an interesting experimental antenna. He says, "I live in Belper, Derbyshire, which is a world heritage area. I am located 430ft ASL on the side of the Derwent Valley, 3 parts way up the hill".

He doesn't say what the size of his garden is but as you can see from **Photo 1** it is very small. To get even a 52ft length of wire into this space requires that the antenna be bent into an L shape. A further requirement is that the antenna must have a low visual impact, due to the location, so it cannot be very high. He had considered a vertical antenna but this was excluded because of the restrictions. Various other wire antennas had been previously tried without much success.

M3RVZ matches this antenna to the rig using a SG-237 Smartuner ATU. The SG-273 does have loading coils, in addition to the matching network, that can be switched in when feeding an electrically short antenna (52ft is a short antenna on 80m).

Feeding a single wire with a loading coil inside the ATU is known as base loading and is not the most efficient method of loading a short antenna. However, M3RVZ has added a loading coil at the end of the antenna, which will have improved the antenna efficiency for two reasons. One of these is that the greater current section (and therefore radiation) of the antenna is moved away from the house to an area of greater effective antenna height created by sloping ground. The other reason is that the radiation resistance of the antenna will be raised, reducing antenna losses, particularly ground or earth resistance losses.

The loading coil comprises 105ft of wire wound on a 19 inch length of grey plastic downpipe, weatherproofed and strengthened using fibreglass. The inductive value of this coil is not important because it is not used to determine resonance and the antenna is used with an ATU. The loading coil and antenna is supported by a length of 1½" gas piping fitted inside a short length of scaffold tubing concreted into the ground.

I am impressed with this arrangement because the antenna is designed to make the most of the characteristics and limitations of the QTH although M3RVZ acknowledges help from other radio amateurs. Remember that M3s are limited to 10W RF output so the antenna has to be effective.

**OBTAINING A GOOD RF EARTH.** In an earlier 'Antennas' **[1]** I described the necessity of a good RF earth particularly when feeding an end-fed wire antenna. I also noted the difficulties obtaining a good RF earth if your shack can be if your shack is located in an upper floor room.

With a simple quarter wave end fed antenna the wire element would be connected to the centre pin of the antenna socket of the transceiver in the shack (via the SWR meter), as shown in **Figure 1**. If you had a good RF earth or ground connection it can be connected to the outside connector of the coax socket. A more practical connection point would be the ground connector of the transceiver, which will be at the same RF potential as the outside of the coax socket. If you didn't have a good RF earth then you could use a resonant counterpoise as shown in Figure 1. This arrangement will work only provided that the 'antenna' and the 'counterpoise' are quarter wave resonant (or multiple) at the frequency in use. A multiband antenna could be made up of antenna and counterpoise wires in parallel.

Any conductor carrying a RF current will radiate. A counterpoise is part of the antenna and radiates on transmit so some consideration should be given to where it is placed. Just putting the counterpoise under the shack carpet may not be the best place for it.

For multiband use, instead of multiple wires, a more practical solution is to use a long wire that is quarter of a wavelength long on the lowest frequency in use. This sort of antenna is often referred to as a 'Long Wire' or 'Random wire antenna'. This antenna is connected to the transceiver via an ATU. This device, when correctly tuned, presents a low impedance to the transceiver antenna socket. The multiband counterpoise problem can be solved by connecting quarter-wave radials, one for each band in parallel, to the transceiver and ATU earth connector; then running the free ends preferably outside the shack, away from the transceiver.

Such an arrangement will require some experimenting to find the best position for the radials. They can be bent or even folded but

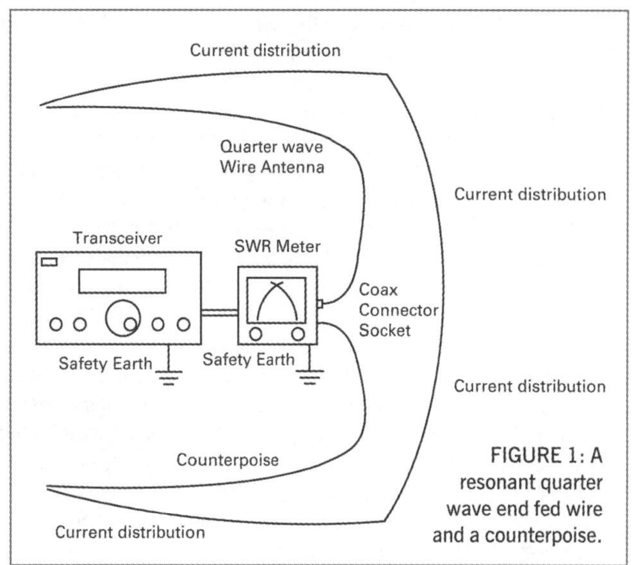


**FIGURE 1: A resonant quarter wave end fed wire and a counterpoise.**

PHOTO 2: The layout of PA1HR's version of GD4EIP's Earth Tuner (from [3])

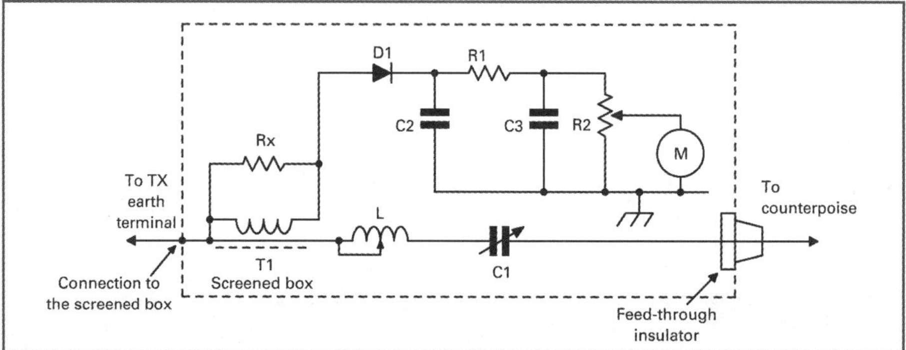


FIGURE 2: SM6AQR's earth lead tuner. T1 =Amidon T-50-43 ferrite toroid; the primary is simply the earth lead through the toroid centre; secondary = 20t small gauge enamelled wire. L = 28iH roller coaster or multi-tapped coil with 10-position switch; see text. C1 = 200pF or more air variable, >1mm spacing, insulated from panel and case. C2, C3 = 10nF ceramic. D1 = AA119; R1 = 1kΩ; R2 = 10kΩ pot, Rx see text. M = 100μA or less.

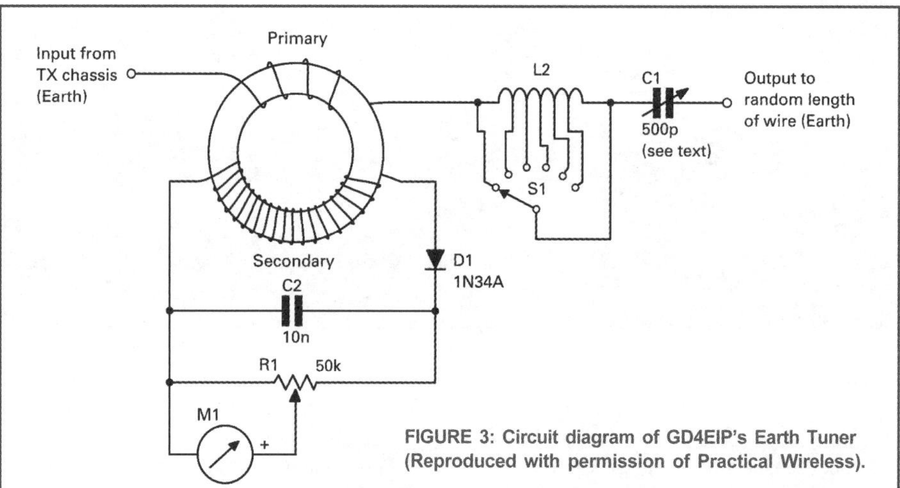


FIGURE 3: Circuit diagram of GD4EIP's Earth Tuner (Reproduced with permission of Practical Wireless).

the length may have to be altered to maintain resonance. The radials are best located outside the house in the horizontal plane to reduce coupling into the electrical wiring. If the radial(s) are used indoors (say round the skirting board) use wire with thick insulation with several additional layers of insulating tape at the ends where the RF voltage can be fairly high when the transmitter is on.

The best way to check resonance of a radial is to connect it to the transceiver earth, make loop in the radial and use a dip meter to check resonance. If such an instrument is unavailable then connect a series RF current meter in the radial and apply a low power transmission. Then adjust the radial length for maximum current.

EARTH LEAD TUNER. Alternatively, one single length radial can be tuned to place a very low RF potential at the transceiver on any band by inserting a LC series tuning circuit between the transmitter and the radial (just like the ATU for the antenna). Such a unit was described by SM6AQR **[2]** and shown in **Figure 2**. It uses a 200 -300pF air spaced tuning capacitor with at least 1mm plate spacing; the capacitor and its shaft must be insulated from the tuner cabinet. The inductor is a 28μH roller coaster. Alternatively, a multi-tapped fixed coil with as many taps as possible could be used.

The tuning indicator consists of a current transformer, rectifier, smoothing filter, sensitivity potentiometer and DC microammeter. The 'primary' of the current transformer is the artificial earth lead itself; it simply passes through the centre of the T1 ferrite toroid, on to which a secondary of 20 turns of thin enamelled wire has been wound. Rx, the resistor across the T1 secondary, should be non-inductive and between 22 and 100Ω; it is selected such that a convenient meter deflection can be set with the sensitivity control R2 on each required frequency and for the RF power used.

I received the following from Colyn Baillie-Searle, GD4EIP, who said, "It was pointed out to me recently that an article you wrote in Antennas, *RadCom* April 2007, included a paragraph and circuit on an 'Earth Lead Tuner'. No reference was made to my 1990 article in **[3]** called 'Earth Tuner'. My original article was offered to *RadCom* in the early 90s but they declined to accept it so I then offered it to *Practical Wireless* and they published it after they had tested my design. I had to send the assembled circuit to them for testing." A circuit of GD4EIP's Earth Tuner is shown in **Figure 3**. PA1HR also constructed this tuner and its layout (from his website [4]) is shown in **Photo 2**.

PHOTO 3: The MFJ Artificial Ground (courtesy of Waters & Stanton [7])

I do like to give credit for the first instance of any design but in this case I simply didn't know about it. I had described SM6AQR's tuner in some of my antenna books written since 2000 **[5] [6]** but until now no one had mentioned an earlier design.

An Earth Lead Tuner is now commercially available **[7]**, the MFJ 931. It is described as an Artificial Ground as shown in **Photo 3** but unfortunately there is no circuit diagram available on MFJ's website. However judging by the controls shown in Photo 3 it is very similar to those already described.

Just as important as setting up the ATU the earth lead or counterpoise tuner should be adjusted on low power. The approximate settings for each band can be recorded and fine tuned on high power. It is important that the appropriate earth tuner band setting is selected as the first action to be taken when changing bands. The reason is that if the tuner was set on 40m and the band changed to 20m then a situation may occur where the presented earth lead impedance could be very high. This would be the same as having no RF earth at all resulting in a high RF voltage on the transceiver case – and all the problems that entails. Using several parallel counterpoises of different lengths would eliminate this potential problem (no pun intended); the lengths of these counterpoises are not critical.

REFERENCES


[1] Antennas *Radcom* April 2007,

[2] Eurotek. Radio Communication, September 1993

[3] Earth Tuner by Colyn Baillie-Searle, GD4EIP. *Practical Wireless* of October 1990

[4] http://remeeus.eu/english/hamradio/artificial_ground.htm

[5] *Backyard Antennas*, Peter Dodd, G3LDO

[6] *The RSGB Communication Handbook,* 9th Edition, Chapter 15.

[7] www.wsplc.com

# Antennas

## Measuring impedance and admittance.

PHOTO 1: General Radio 1602-B UHF Admittance Meter which measures Conductance and Susceptance and is calibrated in millimhos.

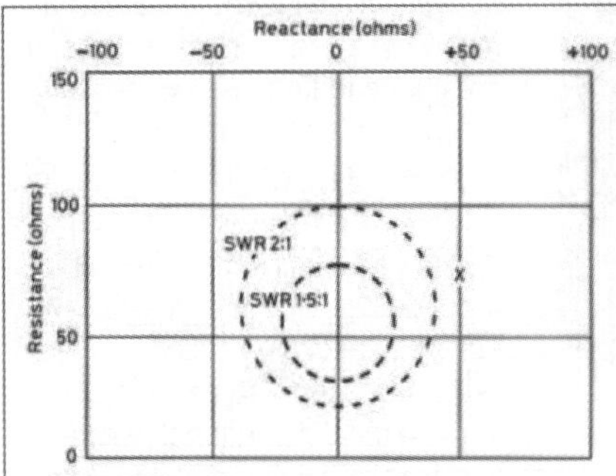

FIGURE 1: Impedance Chart plotted on Cartesian Coordinates. Resistance is given on the vertical axis and reactance on the horizontal axis. X indicates an impedance of 75 +50jX. The circles represent SWRs of 1.5:1 and 2:1 for 50Ω coaxial cable.

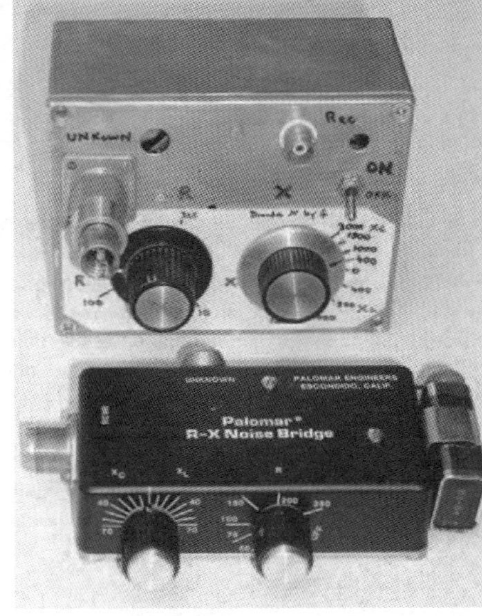
PHOTO 2: Top, home made noise bridge using a reactance scale calibrated in ohms rather than pF. Bottom, Palomar noise bridge with the reactance scale calibrated in pF.

WHAT USE ARE ADMITTANCE MEASUREMENTS? Some of you will know that I am interested in RF test equipment so it was with some pleasure that I accepted a General Radio 1602-B UHF Admittance Meter from Frank James, G0LOF. But the Admittance Meter, shown in **Photo 1**, measures conductance and susceptance and is calibrated in millimhos. Is it of any use for amateur radio antenna work?

UNITS. You are all familiar with 'resistance', which denotes the amount of opposition to current flowing in a circuit. What you may be less familiar with is 'conductance', which is the reciprocal of resistance. Conductance, 1/R, denotes the ease with which electrons may flow. Resistance is the measure of how much a circuit 'resists' current, while conductance is the measure of how much a circuit 'conducts' current. The unit of conductance used to be the mho, which is just 'ohm' spelled backwards. Since 1971 the unit of measurement is Siemens, the symbol for which is G.

Reactive components such as inductors and capacitors oppose current flow with respect to time (and, consequently, frequency), unlike the constant 'friction' of resistors. This time-based opposition to current is called 'reactance' and, like resistance is also measured in the unit of 'ohms'. The reciprocal of reactance is called 'susceptance', which is equal to 1/X. Like conductance, it used to be measured in mhos but is now measured in Siemens - but the symbol is B, to differentiate it from G.

When resistive and reactive components exist together, such as in an antenna, the effects of mixed resistive and reactive components are quantified with the term 'impedance', measured in ohms and symbolised by the letter 'Z'. Likewise, when reactive components conductance (G) and susceptance (B) exist together, such as in an antenna, the effects of mixed resistive and reactive components are quantified with the term 'admittance', which is also measurec in Siemens, and its uses the symbol 'Y'. You might like to think of these terms as follows; while impedance is a measure of how much alternating current is 'impeded' in a circuit, admittance is a measure of how much curren is 'admitted'.

MEASURING IMPEDANCE. Most antennas can be considered as a series tuned circuit comprising resistance, inductance and capacitance (+ or – reactance) so we normally measure impedance. Because impedance comprises both resistance and reactance it is always expressed in two parts, Z = R+jX. An impedance having an resistance of 75Ω and a inductive reactance 50Ω is conventionally written as:

75 +j50

For our consideration, j can simply be regarded as a convention for reactance. The '+j' indicates inductive reactance and a '-j' indicates capacitive reactance. When the frequency of the antenna is resonant the +j and -j parts are equal and opposite so we are left with only the resistive component of impedance.

Impedance can be plotted using a chart with Cartesian coordinates rather like a Mercator projection map, with the latitude and longitude of R and jX respectively plotted to define an impedance 'location'. An example is shown in **Figure 1** of an impedance of 75 +50jX marked with an X. See **Note 1**.

It follows that a number of impedance plots over a range of frequencies will give an antenna impedance signature. Resonance, where the inductive and capacitive reactances are equal and opposite, will exist on the zero reactance vertical line.

The chart shown in Figure 1 can be modified by altering the resistance and reactance lines so that they are sections of an arc, see **Figure 2**. The most noticeable advantage that can be seen is that the SWR circles are concentric. If a calibrated cursor, pivoted at the centre, were to be used with

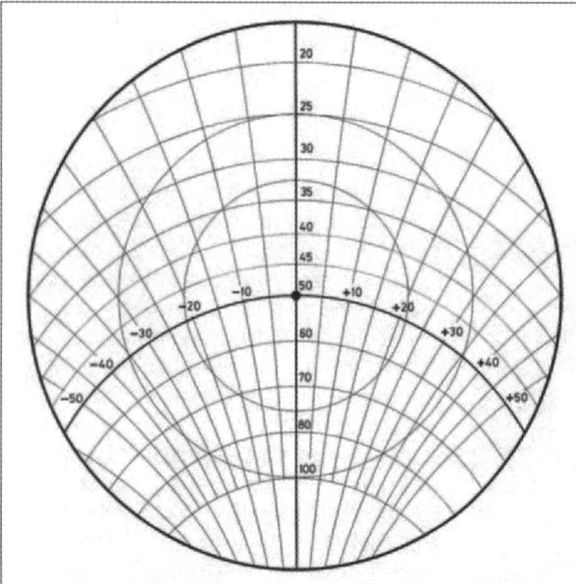


FIGURE 2: Impedance Chart plotted on Smith Chart coordinates. Resistance is given in the vertical axis and reactance in the horizontal axis as in Figure 1 but note that the resistance is low at the top and greater at the bottom. The two circles are 2:1 and 1.5:1 SWR respectively.

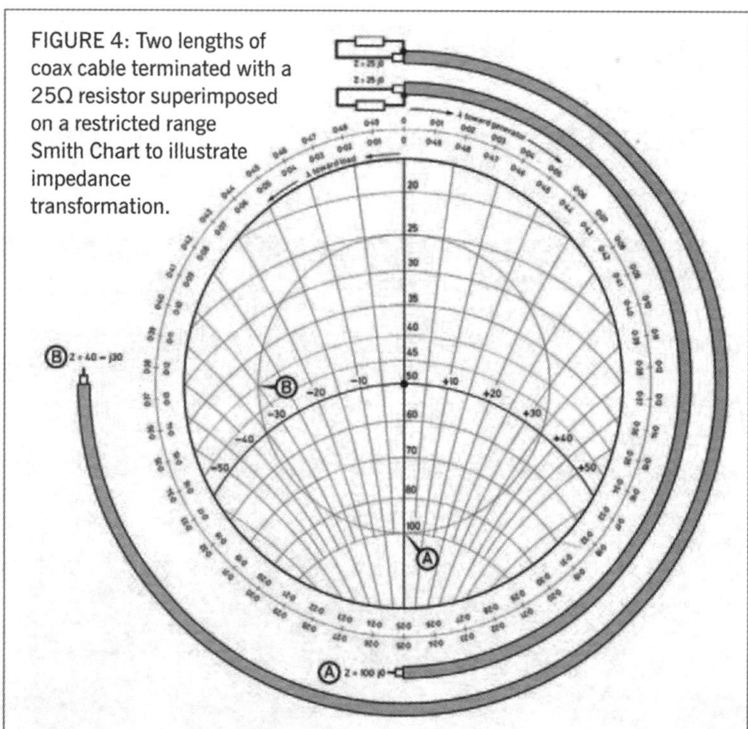

FIGURE 4: Two lengths of coax cable terminated with a 25Ω resistor superimposed on a restricted range Smith Chart to illustrate impedance transformation.

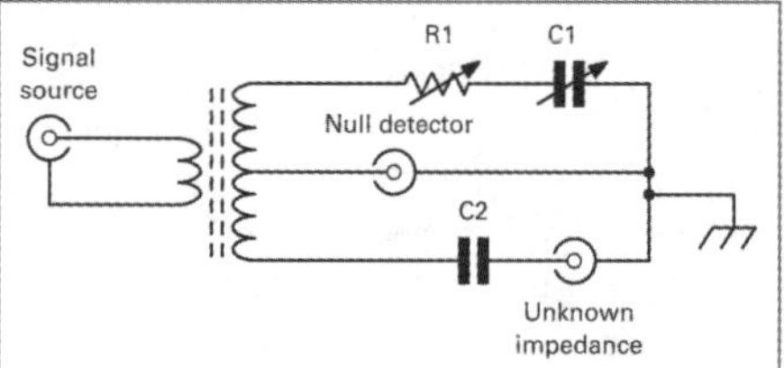


FIGURE 3: Simplified circuit of an RF impedance measuring bridge. The signal source can be a broadband noise source or a signal generator. If a noise source is used a selective receiver is used as a null detector.

PHOTO 3: General Radio 1606 RF impedance bridge. The indicated reactance value is valid for 1MHz and must be divided by frequency to get the true reactance. Inductive or capacitive reactance is established with the use of the switch located between the two dials.

this chart it would be very easy to obtain the SWR of any impedance. On the other hand measurement of SWR can only give any number of impedance values on an appropriate SWR circle. It is for this reason that an impedance measuring device is more suitable for setting up a antenna matching device such as a Gamma match.

The most popular instrument for measuring antenna impedance in amateur radio is the R-X noise bridge, two examples of which are shown in **Photo 2**. The Palomar bridge at the bottom has two controls; the one on the right is resistance (R), calibrated in ohms and the one on the left is calibrated 70-0-70 in picofarads.

Most impedance measurement bridges measure the impedance presented to the UNKNOWN socket by adjusting a calibrated resistance and reactance for a null signal in a detector, see **Figure 3**. The noise bridge uses a broad band RF (noise) source and a selective detector, usually a receiver. When the values of bridge resistance and reactances are equal to the 'unknown' a null in the noise from the receiver indicates that the bridge is balanced.

The capacitor C2 in series with the UNKNOWN is approximately half the value of the variable C1. This allows C1 to be calibrated at zero picofarads in the centre; up to 70pF (XC or -j) to the left and −70pF (XL or +j) to the right. The actual value of C1 at the centre is approximately 70pF and this balances with C2. In practice, C2 is less than 70pF because of other components in the bridge. The actual value can be only found by experimenting.

As shown in **Figure 1** the reactance component j is measured in ohms so the reactance of C1 has to be calculated using the formula $X_C = 1/(2\pi f L C)$ or with a calibration graph similar to that found in **[1]**. The reason for this extra complication is that capacitive reactance is frequency dependent.

If the instrument is to be used for adjusting an antenna matching network such as a gamma match then the actual value of reactance is unimportant. In this case, the instrument controls are set for a resistance value of 50Ω, reactance to centre zero and the matching unit adjusted for minimum noise in the receiver. Incidentally, the self powered FT-817 and the Palomar R-X noise bridge make an excellent combination for task because they can be carried to the feedpoint of an antenna very easily.

The instrument shown at the top of Photo 2 is a noise bridge that I built to a design by G3ZOM. The original design called for the reactance control to be calibrated in pF in the conventional way but, in this case, I calibrated it in ohms. Because this control is frequency dependant it is calibrated at 1MHz and the reading is then divided by frequency to obtain the correct reactance. The venerable General Radio 1606 Impedance Bridge uses this method as shown on **Photo 3** although I have not seen it used in amateur bridges.

The accuracy and the depth of the null depends mostly on the layout of the bridge network and the care taken in balancing out the bridge. Full details of the construction and calibration of the G3ZOM noise bridge can be found in [1].

If you are measuring the feedpoint of an antenna then it follows that the measurements have to be made at the antenna. This is because of the impedance transforming characteristic of transmission line connecting the instrument to the antenna that can affect the readings. This can be illustrated by modifying Figure 2 and adding a transmission line length (in wavelengths) scale as shown in **Figure 4**, which shows a restricted range

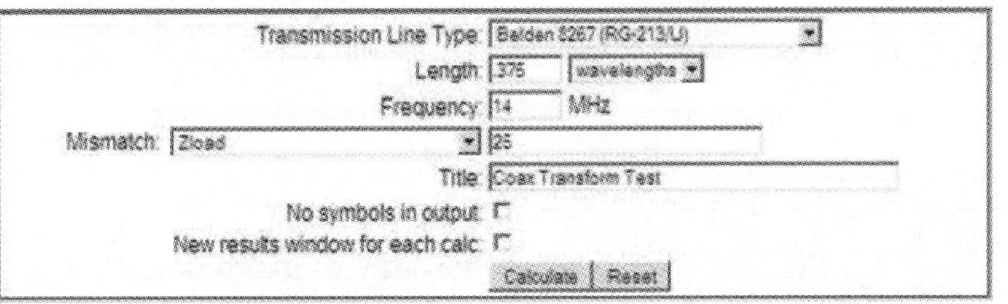


FIGURE 5: Entry to VK1OD's RF Transmission Line Calculator. I have selected RG-213 from the library of coax types, 0.375 wavelengths long with a load of 25Ω. The mismatch (load impedance) must be written as 75+23 or 56-15 for example. Do not use j.

**RF Transmission Line Loss Calculator**

**Coax Transform Test**

| Parameters | | |
|---|---|---|
| Transmission Line | Belden 8267 (RG-213/U) | |
| Code | B8267 | |
| Data source | Belden | |
| Frequency | 14.000 MHz | |
| Length | 0.375 wl | Length of coax |
| Zload | 25.00+j0.00 Ω | Load impedance |
| Yload | 0.040000+j0.000000 S | Equivalent admittance |
| **Results** | | |
| Zo | 50.00-j0.27 Ω | |
| Velocity Factor | 0.660 | |
| Length | 135.00°, 0.375 λ, 5.303 m | |
| Line Loss (matched) | 0.124 dB | |
| Line Loss | 0.136 dB | |
| Efficiency | 96.91 % | |
| Zin | 40.17-j29.42 Ω | Transformed impedance |
| Yin | 0.016204+j0.011867 S | Equivalent admittance |
| VSWR(50)in | 1.97 | |
| Γ, ρ<θ, RL, VSWR (source end) | -2.354e-3-j3.240e-1, 0.324<-90.4°, 9.8 dB, 1.96 | |
| Γ, ρ<θ, RL, VSWR (load end) | -3.334e-1+j2.422e-3, 0.333<179.6°, 9.5 dB, 2.00 | |

FIGURE 6: RF Transmission Line Calculator results page. I have identified the relevant data in red. Admittance is quoted in Siemens (S)

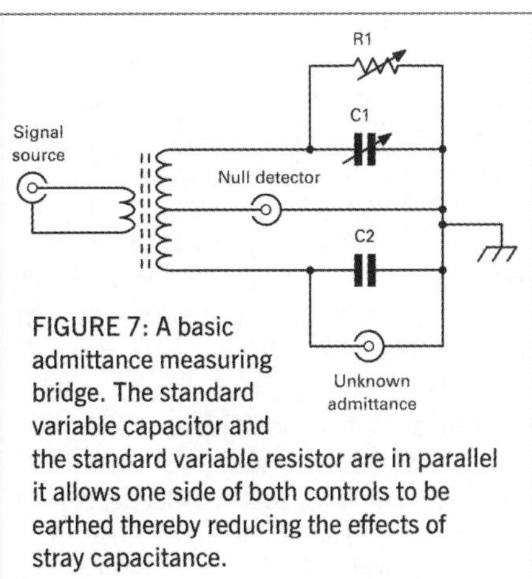


FIGURE 7: A basic admittance measuring bridge. The standard variable capacitor and the standard variable resistor are in parallel it allows one side of both controls to be earthed thereby reducing the effects of stray capacitance.

Smith Chart superimposed on two lengths of coax cable terminated with a 25Ω resistor.

A length of coax 0.25 wavelengths long terminated will transform a 25Ω load to 100 j0 at (A). If the length is increased to 0.375 wavelengths the transformed impedance will be approximately 40 –j30 at (B). A half wave length takes us back to the original load value of 25Ω. **Note 2**.

Multiples of these coax lengths will create repetitions of the impedance transformations. Antenna impedance can be measured via an electrical half wavelength, or multiple, of feeder. **Note 3**. On the other hand if you know the length and velocity factor of you coax you can use a calculator to find what the actual antenna feed impedance is from the measured impedance.

The chart shown in Figure 4 would allow you to make a calculator to determine antenna feed impedance from measured impedance. On my website **[2]** you will find instructions and some charts to make such a calculator and if you have [1] you will find the instructions there also. Full size professional Smith Charts require some skill and experience to use, however just in the same way that computers have eclipsed slide rules the same can be said for the Smith Chart.

The simplest one to use that I have found is called RF Transmission Line Calculator by VK1OD **[3]**. Not only is it simple to use but it is also comprehensive. Entry to the program is shown in **Figure 5**. There is a whole library of coax types (with their characteristics) you can select from and as you can see I have selected RG-213. You can select the coax length in various units of measurement and I have selected 0.375 wavelengths with a load of 25Ω. The purpose of this was to compare it with the Smith Chart results in **Figure 4**. (This page of the software also contains driving instructions, which I have edited out of **Figure 5**.)

When Calculate is selected the page shown in **Figure 6** appears. As you can see the results are close to those shown in Figure 4: 40.17-j29.42 compared with 40 –j30. There is a lot of other data shown particularly in relation to coax losses. You will notice that equivalent admittance is also shown.

**WHY USE ADMITTANCE?** At this point you might ask what is the point of using Admittance when making antenna measurements. As you can see in Figure 3, the variable reference resistor and capacitor in the bridge are in series. The problem with such an arrangement is that of stray capacitance and inductance, which can affect the accuracy particularly if the variable resistor (potentiometer) has a metal case. There are a number of ways in which these strays can be compensated and the General Radio 1606 Impedance Bridge uses a very elaborate system of balancing and screening of the bridge allowing it to make measurements up to 60MHz.

Obtaining greater accuracy with a simple arrangement can be achieved with the use of an admittance bridge, an example of which is shown in **Figure 7**. As you can see, because the standard variable capacitor and the standard variable resistor are in parallel it allows one side of both controls to be earthed, thereby reducing the effect of strays. The dials of such an instrument would be calibrated in conductance and susceptance, in units of mS (millisiemens).

Impedance bridges generally work fine up to 30MHz and, with special care to the construction and calibration, into the lower part of the VHF band. However these measurements at VHF and UHF can only be made using a parallel bridge admittance arrangement using special construction techniques. Next month, I will show how test equipment can be designed to operate in the upper UHF bands.

**REFERENCES**

[1] The Antenna Experimenter's Guide, Second Edition, Peter Dodd, G3LDO.

[2] www.g3ldo.co.uk

[3] www.vk1od.net/tl/tllc.php

**NOTES**

**NOTE 1.** Impedance can also be expressed in polar form, which has been omitted for the sake of simplicity.

**NOTE 2.** In practice the transformed impedances won't be quite as I have stated because of the coax losses, however they are small enough to be ignored for this discussion.

**NOTE 3.** Half wavelengths of feeder are susceptible to common mode or antenna currents, which may result inconsistent measurements. This problem can be fixed by using a current choke.

# Antennas

## Continuing our look at Impedance and Admittance measurements

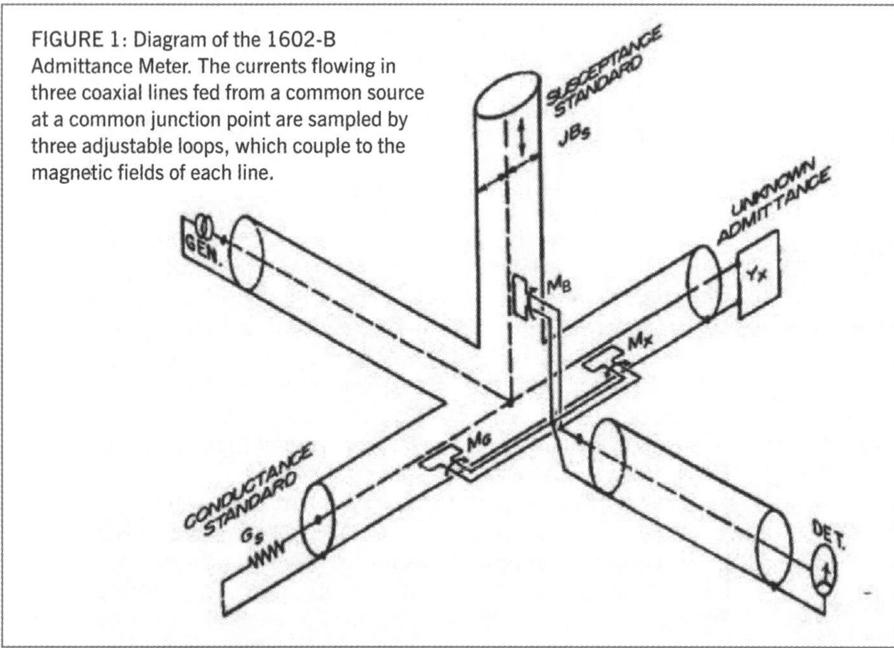


FIGURE 1: Diagram of the 1602-B Admittance Meter. The currents flowing in three coaxial lines fed from a common source at a common junction point are sampled by three adjustable loops, which couple to the magnetic fields of each line.

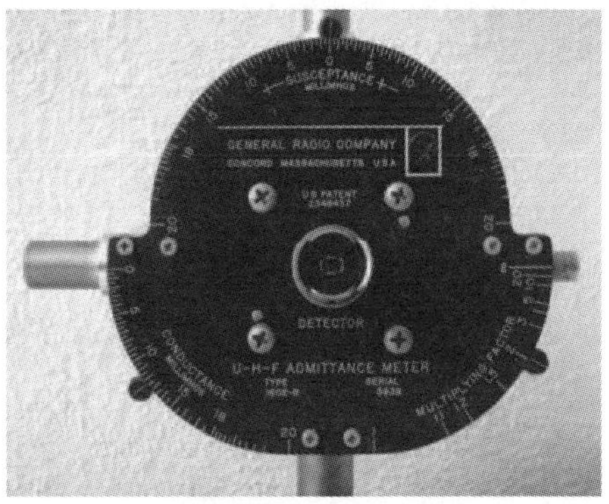

PHOTO 1: Measurement scales of the General Radio 1602-B UHF Admittance Meter.

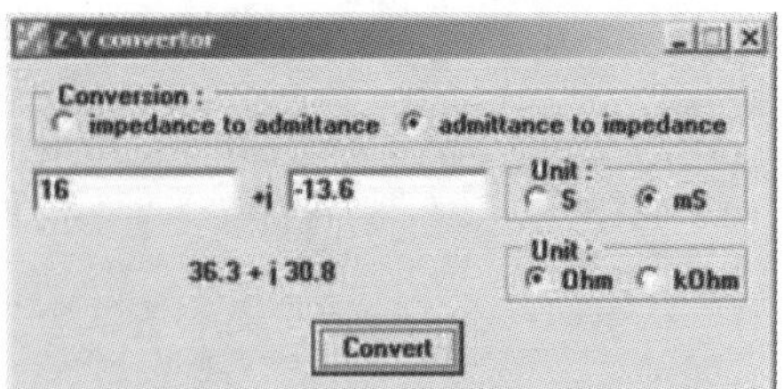


FIGURE 2: Program for converting admittance to impedance or impedance to admittance by Rik Strobbe, ON4YD. Just key in the appropriate values and click CONVERT.

REMINDER. Last month, I described instruments for measuring impedance and briefly described the advantages and a method for measuring the less familiar dual of Impedance – Admittance. What follows should be read in conjunction with [1].

As I mentioned last month, some of you will know that I am interested in RF test equipment so it was with some pleasure that I accepted a General Radio 1602-B UHF Admittance Meter from Frank James, G0LOF. This column is devoted to what I learned about measuring admittance at UHF using this instrument.

Conductance used to be measured in mho (ohm spelled backwards). Since 1971 the unit of measurement is 'siemens', S. In the following discussion, the units millimhos can be read as millisiemens, abbreviated mS. 20mS is equal to 50Ω. An easy method of conversion is described later.

### THE 1602-B UHF ADMITTANCE METER.

The 1602-B UHF Admittance Meter is a simple instrument for the measurement of admittance and impedance over a frequency range of 40 to 1500MHz. As a null instrument, it can be used to measure the conductance and susceptance of an unknown circuit directly.

For admittance measurements using the null method, the magnitude of the conductive component of the unknown admittance is indicated directly on a scale, which is calibrated from 0 to 20 millimhos over a 90° arc [1]. The magnitude of the susceptive component is indicated on another scale, which is calibrated from -20 to 0 to +20 millimhos over a 180° arc. A third scale on the dial indicates the multiplier, from 1 to infinity, which applies to both other scales. **Photo 1** gives a good general view of the instrument. Although the Type 1602-B Admittance Meter makes use of a null indication for measurements, it is not a true bridge. The currents flowing in three coaxial lines fed from a common source at a common junction point are sampled by three adjustable loops, which couple to the magnetic field in each line as shown in **Figure 1**.

The coupling of each of the loops can be varied by rotation of the loop. The first coaxial line is terminated in a conductance standard, which is a pure resistance equal to the characteristic impedance of the line. A further coax line is a susceptance standard, which is a frequency calibrated short-circuited length of coaxial line. The third line is connected to the unknown circuit. The outputs of the three loops are combined by connecting all three loops in parallel. When the loops are properly oriented, the combined output is zero. The device therefore balances in the same manner as a bridge.

At balance, the vector sum of the voltages induced in the three loops is proportional to the mutual inductance and to the current flowing in the corresponding line. Since all three lines are fed from a common source, the input voltage is the same for each line and the current flowing in each line is proportional to the input admittance.

The loops associated with the unknown admittance and the standard conductance can each be rotated through an angle of 90°, but the loop associated with the standard susceptance is arranged to be rotatable through an angle of 180°. This allows the measurement of positive as well as negative values of unknown susceptance with a single susceptance standard.

The orientations of the three loops coupling to the three lines are adjusted by means of the arms attached to the rotatable barrels containing the loops as shown in **Photo 2**. The relative coupling of each loop is indicated by the reading on the calibrated scale on the dial corresponding to the position of the indicator mounted on the end of each arm, as shown in Photo 1.

A unique feature of this instrument, which distinguishes it from bridges and other null devices, is that the susceptance scale, as well as the conductance scale, is independent of frequency. This comes about because the susceptance standard is always adjusted to produce the same magnitude of susceptance at each frequency.

The actual value of admittance is measured at a point inside the junction block directly under the centre of the loop coupling to the unknown connector. The length of coax line from this point to the actual device under test may only be 80 to 100mm (3 to 4 inches) but this can represent a significant portion of a wavelength at UHF. This, in turn, results in an

PHOTO 2: The main block of the 1602-B Admittance Meter split to show the internal arrangement of the coupling loops. The orientations of the three loops coupling to the three lines are adjusted by means of the arms attached to the rotatable barrels. The loop coupling to the lines is made via Faraday screens.

PHOTO 3: Complete set up being used to measure the impedance of a home made dummy load, using a calibrated adjustable constant-impedance line.

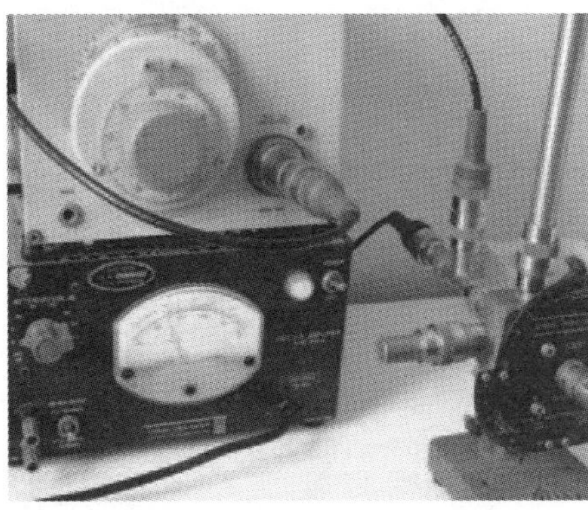

PHOTO 4: The 1602-B UHF Admittance Meter null detector arrangement with the local oscillator source (top left) connected to the top of the T diode mixer (right). The IF unit with the null meter detector is shown bottom left.

PHOTO 5: General Radio Type 874 Coaxial 50Ω, hermaphroditic connectors. They are rotated 90° to each other to allow them to fit.

admittance (or impedance) transformation, which needs to be calculated, see **Figure 4** in [1]. The instrument can be modified to give direct readings by using an adjustable constant-impedance line, which can be set so that it inserts exactly half a wavelength between the device under test and the measurement point inside the instrument. An example of a calibrated adjustable constant-impedance line is shown in **Photo 3**.

Like all impedance or admittance instruments that use the null detection method, the 1602-B UHF Admittance Meter requires a signal source and a null detector. With this instrument, the signal source is a signal generator and is normally connected to the Type 874 Coaxial Connector located at the rear of the junction block of the instrument, while the detector connection is made to the Type 874 Coaxial Connector at the centre of the dial.

These connections can be reversed, as shown in Photo 3, to minimise leakage effects. This is a condition where the null reading is affected when the instrument is touched during measurements and is caused by source signal leakage from the connectors or the connections.

**THE NULL DETECTOR.** The detector, which is a VHF/UHF receiver, requires some comment. It comprises a coax T arrangement, which houses a diode mixer. This mixer is connected to the 1602-B UHF Admittance Meter with an 874 connector. A local oscillator source is connected to the top of the T and the remaining connection is made to the IF unit, which is fitted with an accurate signal strength meter for detecting the null. The complete set-up is shown in **Photo 4**.

This null detector receiver may seem rather cumbersome but it was designed in the days before VHF/UHF solid-state amplifiers and the only UHF/microwave devices in existence were crystal diodes. There were specialised valves (tubes) that could be made to oscillate at UHF and even more specialised microwave oscillators such as klystrons. This meant that receivers could be designed to work as high as 10GHz using IF systems at around 40 to 50MHz where valves could be used to provide the necessary amplification. The 1602-B UHF Admittance Meter uses a four-stage 30MHz valve amplifier.

A modern UHF communications receiver could be used for the null detector provided that it had a very good S-meter. A switched attenuator would also be useful.

**GR CONNECTORS.** Have you ever noticed that whenever you need to interface two coaxial devices, their connections are, more often than not, of the same gender? It is for this very interface challenge that the ubiquitous barrel adapter, with its identical connections at each end, was invented. In phase critical applications, such as antenna stacking, these adaptors can introduce unwanted propagation delays.

The admittance meter uses Type 874 Coaxial Connectors, which have a proper 50Ω characteristic impedance. They also have another interesting feature in that they are hermaphroditic (there is no male and female), so gender-changers are not needed, see **Photo 5**. These connectors operate reliably up to around 4GHz and can be obtained on the surplus market for a lot less than other hermaphrodite connectors such as APC-7.

If the circuit under test is fitted with connectors other than Type 874 Connectors, low-reflection adaptor units can be used to make the connection between the circuit under test and the unknown connector on the admittance meter.

**CONVERSION.** If you make measurements using an instrument that gives the results in millimhos or millisiemens, you would probably like to convert these units to the more familiar impedance units. You can find on my website **[2]** a small program written by Rik Strobbe, ON4YD, which does the job very nicely and is shown in **Figure 2**.

**REFERENCES**

[1] Antennas, RadCom February 2009
[2] www.g3ldo.co.uk

# Antennas

## A big mobile antenna and some mystery boxes

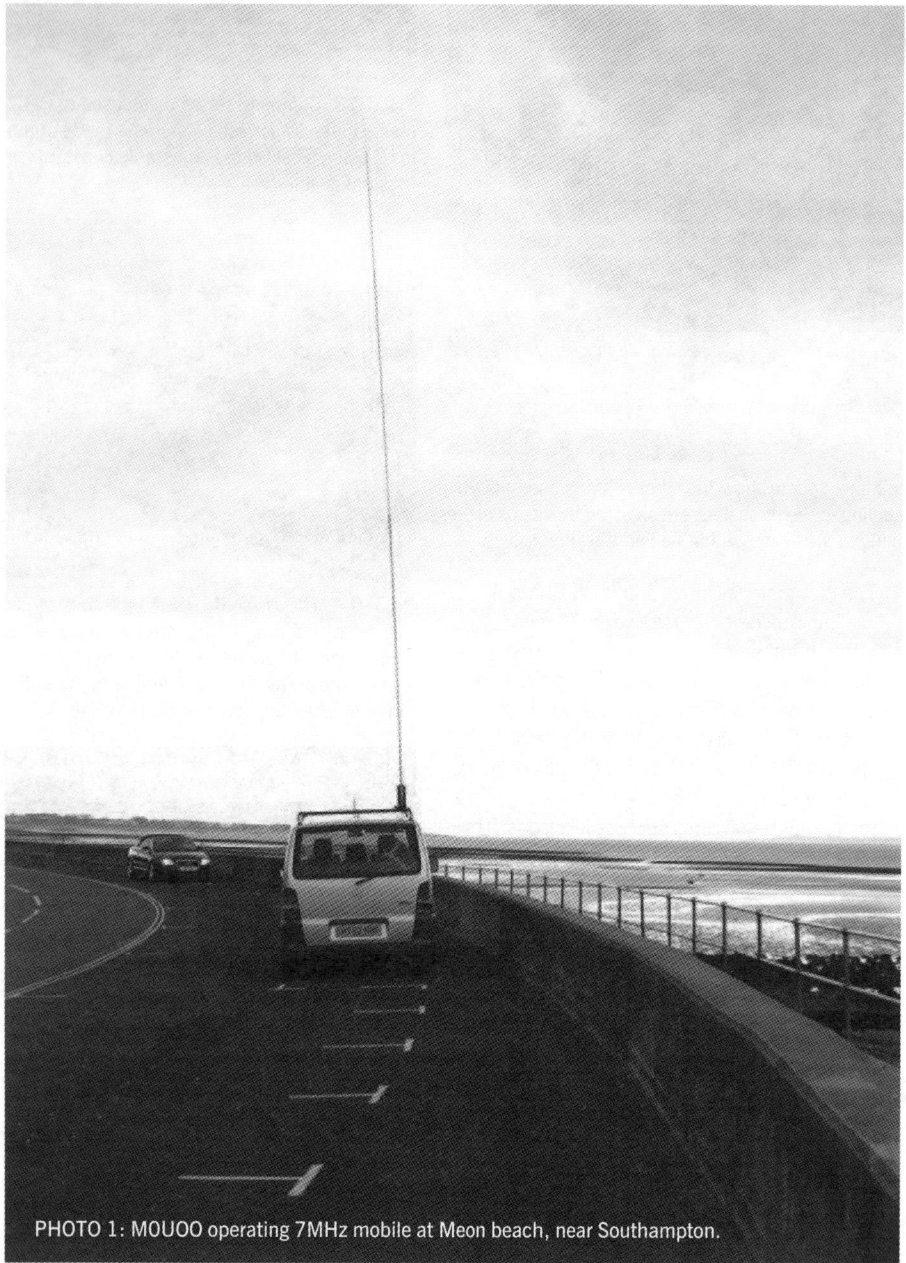
PHOTO 1: MOUOO operating 7MHz mobile at Meon beach, near Southampton.

**TEST YOUR MEMORY.** You may recall that in August 2008 Antennas, I described the HF mobile activities of MOUOO who operates from a very good mobile QTH at Meon beach near Southampton, using his own version of the Cobweb antenna. During the winter months, he has been operating on the 7MHz band with considerable success. In an e-mail late January this year, he goes on to say "...you now how crazy I am about HF mobile, well I have been experimenting with a 1/4 wave vertical for 40m because 20m has been rather dead. I am very pleased with the results; I sit on one frequency and normally get a big pile up. This morning I was only out for about 2 hours and worked six VKs all with 5/9 reports plus lots Europeans." His 7MHz mobile QTH is shown in **Photo 1**.

**SIZE MATTERS.** What MOUOO has done is to make a full size 7MHz vertical. It comprises three 10ft (3m) **[1]** lengths of aluminium tube, each length 1in (25.4mm), 3/4in (19mm) and 1/2in (12.7mm) outside diameter respectively that telescope into one another. The final 3ft (0.9m) or so is made from a 3/16in (45mm) whip.

The lower 1in diameter section of the element is fixed to a hinge arrangement with the coax feed connected as shown in **Photo 2**. The other two lengths are carried on the roof rack when not in use. During the assembly process, these upper sections of the elements are telescoped together while in the folded over position, which can then easily be raised to the vertical and locked in position. The total assembly time is less than five minutes.

**CHALLENGING ANTENNAS.** When I lived and operated from Kenya in the early 1960s, the East African Radio Society used to provide communications for an international car rally known as the East African Safari. These communication links on were on 7MHz AM, mostly from mobile stations located at rally checkpoints, back to the control station in Nairobi. Some of these check points presented a bit of a challenge regarding antennas, particularly as in those days the rigs were not particularly efficient. In my case, the 'mobile rig' was a modified 19 set running about ten watts. An efficient antenna was essential and my solution was a full size 7MHz whip, which was quite a wobbly structure as you can see in **Photo 3**.

**WHEEL CLAMP.** Not for parking in a prohibited area but as an aid to portable/mobile operation. Nothing new in these – they have been around for some time. I am talking about a base for a mast that is held in place with the wheel of a vehicle. The one shown in **Photo 4** has an additional advantage in that the mast and antenna can be assembled in the horizontal position and raised to the vertical using the tilt over arrangement. Once in the upright position the mast is locked. This item is available from **[2]**.

Available from the same source is a sectionalised mast. Each section is 8ft (2.44m) long. One solution to sectionalised masts is to swage the end of each section so that it fits into the adjoining section. The disadvantage of this arrangement is that if the joint comes under any real strain (the sort of thing that can happen when an antenna structure is raised or lowered) then the swaged joint can become distorted and jam.

These mast sections use short lengths of heavy duty tube that fit snugly and fixed into one end of the mast sections, as shown in **Photo 5**. This allows one section to be joined to the other and makes for a much stronger temporary join.

**MYSTERY BOXES.** Dave Dyson, G7DHD sent me a photo of an instrument that he bought at a flea market and would like to know what it is and how you use it. As you can see from **Photo 6**, it describes itself as a RHO meter. The following describes details that are not obvious in Photo 6.

The top connectors are N type and the bottom two are BNC. The switch at the side is labelled 'x1 (battery off)' in the down position and x100 in the up position. The lower BNC connector is labelled 'ALC Output'.

The potentiometer control on the lower right is labelled 'DC Level'. The box measures 50 x 82 x 16mm(less connectors). It may well be that it is part of a test set as there must obviously be some kind of read out meter attached.

So what is Rho? It may be a surprise to some of you to learn that the SWR meter in your shack doesn't actually read SWR. You need to measure the maximum or minimum voltage (or current) of the standing wave at two points on the transmission line to read SWR directly. What your SWR meter is reading is the magnitude of Reflection Coefficient (symbol P). However, Rho is a complex quantity having both magnitude and angle. If measured at various points along a transmission line, the magnitude would remain constant but the angle would vary. If Rho were plotted on the Smith Chart, the result would approximate a circle, just the same as SWR. The relationship between Rho and SWR – and how to make a radially scaled parameters cursor for your Smith Chart calculator – is shown on my website **[3]**.

G7DHD would like to know if anyone has knowledge of how this instrument was used and if there are any operating instructions available.

By chance, I happened to buy a similar instrument some time ago, also from a flea market. My purchase is labelled VHF Bridge Match Meter 410-LRU-1A and is shown in **Photo 7** with the cover removed. It also has three coax connectors and a screened connector for a meter. This instrument came with two dummy load standards, 50Ω plugged into the on the right hand side coax connector and 100Ω to the left.

**INFORMATION PLEASE.** It would be nice to know how this instrument was used and some information on the unusual coax connectors would be welcome. Drop me a line via e-mail to g3ldo@ukonline.co.uk or by post to 37 The Ridings, East Preston, West Sussex BN16 2TW.

**REFERENCES AND NOTES**


[1] Where possible I quote dimensions in metric units. In this case the tubing was only available from the supplier in imperial units.

[2] MOUOO@rjbprojects.co.uk

[3] www.g3ldo.co.uk

PHOTO 2: The base section of MOUOO's full size mobile antenna is 1in diameter aluminium tube. It is fixed to a hinge arrangement and shown folded over.

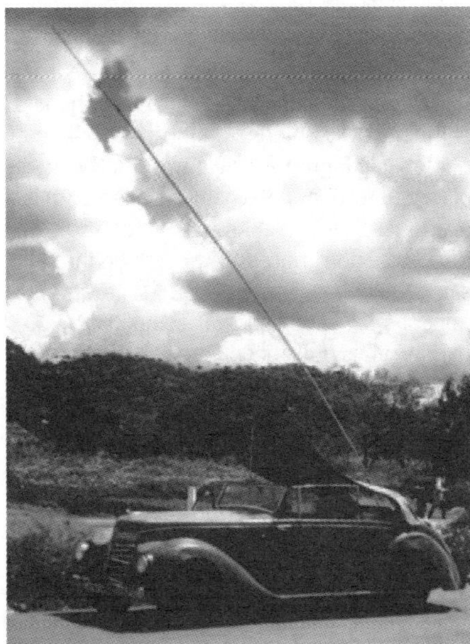

PHOTO 3: VQ4HX/M, Voi in Kenya, circa 1961. Armstrong Siddeley car with full size 7MHz antenna, with the roof raised to provide shade and ventilation.

PHOTO 4: Antenna mast wheel clamp with mast in vertical position.

PHOTO 5: The three section mast uses short lengths of heavy duty tube which fit snugly shown here with the antenna mast wheel clamp.

PHOTO 6: The RHO-Bridge. Connectors 1, 2 and Input are N type and the bottom two BNC.

PHOTO 7: VHF Bridge Match Meter 410-LRU-1A. The 100Ω dummy load removed to show the unusual coax connector.

# Antennas

## Compact antennas for portable use.

PHOTO 1: The M0UOO Cobweb antenna fixed to a portable fold over mast.

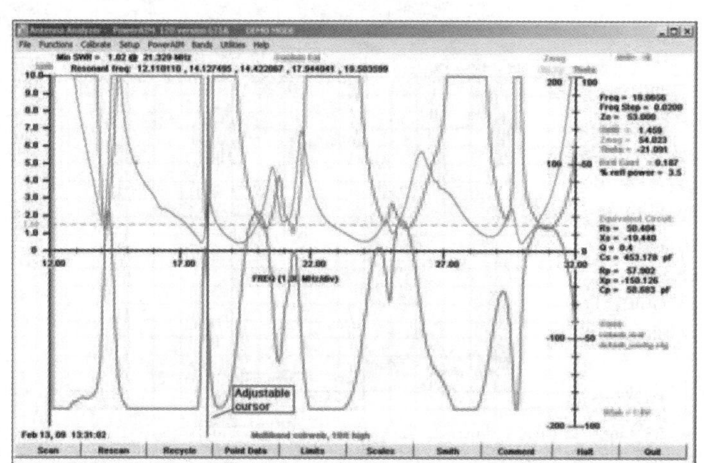


FIGURE 1: Analysis of the M0UOO Cobweb antenna using an AIM-417 with a frequency sweep from 12 to 32MHz.

**RECENT HISTORY.** You may recall that in August 2008 and April 2009 'Antennas' I described the HF mobile activities of Richard Bone, M0UOO who operates from a very good mobile QTH at Meon beach, near Southampton. At the time, he was using his own version of the Cobweb antenna. M0UOO let me borrow his Cobweb antenna for analysis. This antenna was fixed to a portable fold over mast as shown in **Photo 1** and the analysis was performed using an AIM-417 analyser. The advantage of this instrument is that it reports the actual impedance at the antenna feed point, although the feed cable has to have been calibrated before this can be done – a relatively simple procedure.

The result of a frequency sweep from 12 to 32MHz is shown in **Figure 1**. SWR is plotted in red and impedance is shown in polar coordinates with Zmag in green and angle Theta in purple. The more familiar Cartesian equivalent coordinates (R±jx) are displayed under the heading *Equivalent Circuit* on the right hand side of the display (as *Rs* and *Xs*) when the movable cursor is moved to the frequency under examination.

As you can see the 14 and 18MHz resonances are reasonable but the higher frequencies display some double resonances; this may be due to element interaction. I had a similar problem with a multiband quad. Originally, I advocated just connecting the loops in parallel and feeding from a common feed point, a solution that appeared to work with multiband parallel dipoles. More recently, I found connecting them via a length of twin feeder as shown in **Photo 2** produced a more satisfactory result.

An expanded analysis of the performance of the M0UOO antenna on the 14MHz band is shown in **Figure 2**. The cursor has been placed at resonance, where theta (and Xs) is nearly zero. Note that lowest SWR and resonance don't necessarily occur on the same frequency. I have added 2:1 lower and upper limits, which show that the SWR bandwidth is quite good for a compact antenna.

The M0UOO antenna has a further interesting feature in that it can be folded rather like an umbrella for transportation. As can be seen in **Photo 3**, the element supporting arms are hinged and, when folded open, the arms are held in place with clips. The tube holding the feeder and element distribution box is plugged into the centre hub after the antenna is assembled.

**MODELLING THE COBWEB.** In October 2008 'Antennas', I described modelling a single band Cobweb. I used a single conductor element with no resistive losses, making the assumption that this would only affect the feed impedance and not the field distribution and gain. In this model, the feed impedance of a single element Cobweb varied from 12 to 10Ω between 5.5 and 12m (18 and 40ft) in height.

I have since revised this model, using folded elements as shown in **Figure 3**, with the calculated SWR shown in **Figure 4**. The assumptions described previously turned out to be correct but I don't propose to quote the distribution pattern or gain; for some reason they appear controversial.

What I did was to make a single band folded dipole, configured into a square like a Cobweb element, which is shown in **Photo 4**. The purpose of this was to verify (or otherwise) the model described previously. I didn't cut the antenna for any specific frequency – I just made sure that the element, constructed from 1.5mm speaker flex, was fed in the centre. In the event, the resonance occurred at 11.46MHz.

SWR and impedance analysis of the Portaloop and the single element Cobweb element is shown in **Figure 5**. A cursor has been placed over resonance and the measured parameters displayed on the left. As you can see the rounded impedance is R52 +j0.6 and the SWR 1.2:1.

**THE PORTALOOP.** The M0UOO antenna is well engineered but weighs in at 9kg and I

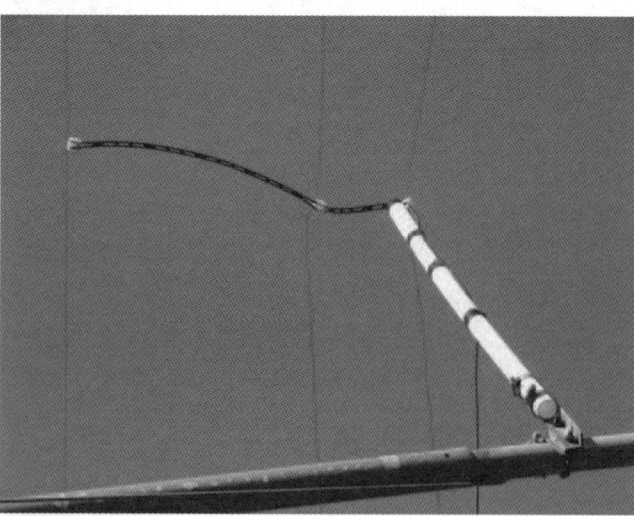

PHOTO 2: Solution to feeding a multiband the quad antenna, which may be used in the Cobweb antenna to solve the multi resonances on the higher frequency bands.

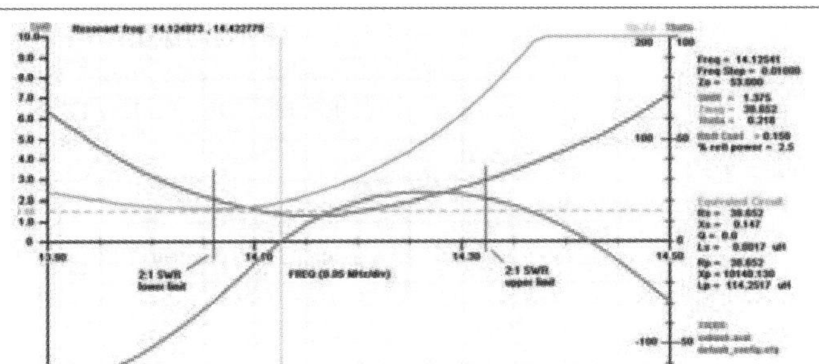


FIGURE 2: An expanded analysis of the performance of the M0UOO antenna on the 14MHz band. The cursor has been placed at resonance. I have added 2:1 SWR lower and upper limits which show the bandwidth to be 260kHz, quite good for a compact antenna.

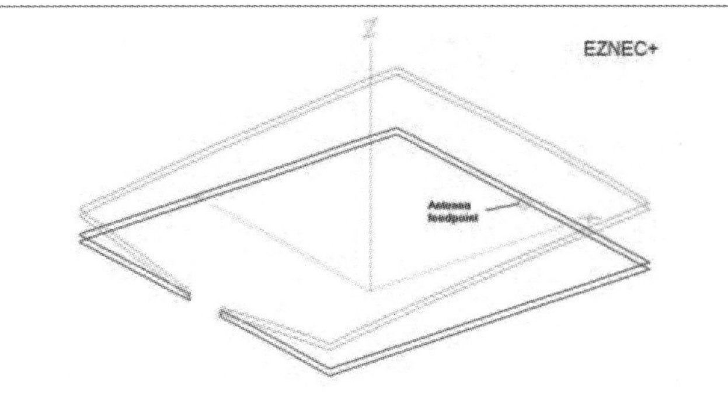


FIGURE 3: Free space model of a folded dipole configured into a square as used in the Cobweb showing the current distribution.

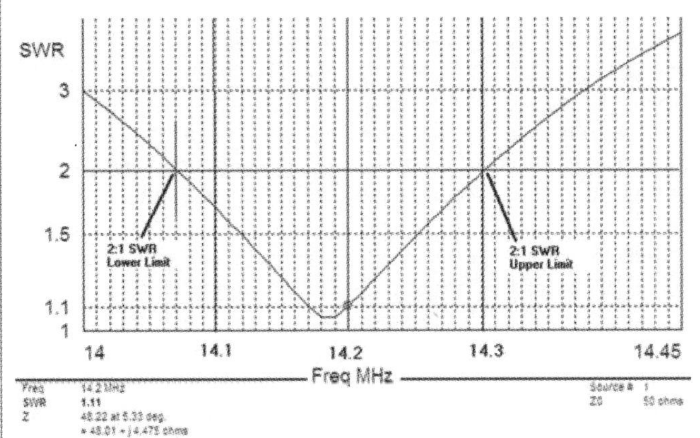


FIGURE 4: Calculated SWR of the antenna shown in Figure 3. The calculated 2:1 SWR bandwidth of 230kHz is close to the measured 260kHz bandwidth of the real antenna shown in Figure 2.

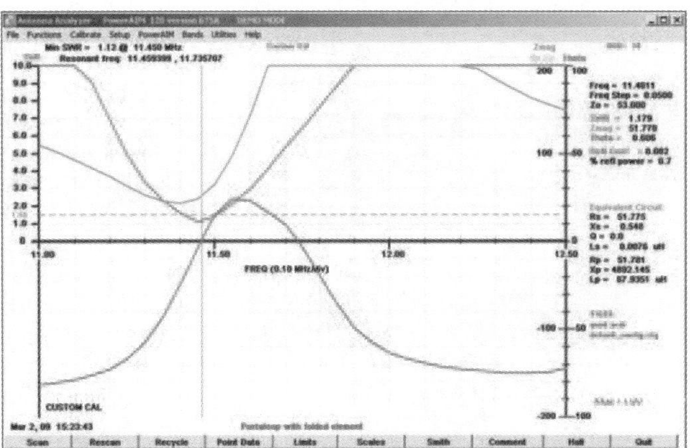


FIGURE 5: Analysis of the Portaloop and the single element Cobweb element. A cursor has been placed over resonance and the measured parameters displayed on the left. As you can see the rounded impedance is R52 +j0.6 and the SWR 1.2:1.

PHOTO 3: Detail of the M0UOO antenna showing the method of folding for transportation.

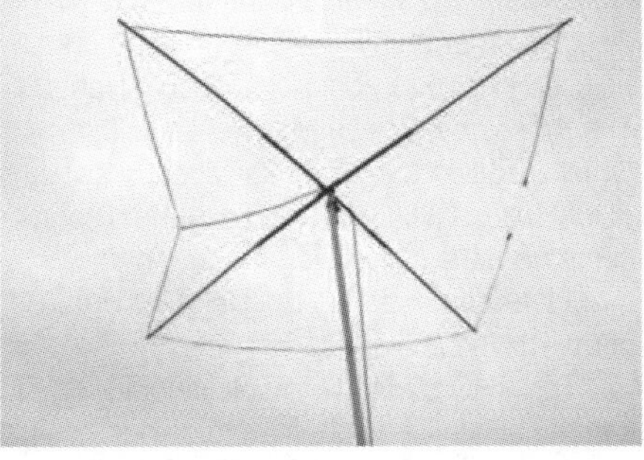

PHOTO 4: A single band folded dipole, configured into a square like a Cobweb element. The element is constructed from 1.5mm speaker flex and fed in the centre.

PHOTO 5: The Portaloop antenna. This arrangement allows the element support to double as a feeder support. The open ends of the element are located in the opposite corner.

have difficulty (being a G3!) of raising the antenna to a height much greater than 6m in a portable environment. On the other hand, my single band arrangement is less than half this weight and is much easier to erect at a greater height.

The arrangement shown in **Photo 4** really requires a support for the feeder so I tried a different configuration with the feed point located in the corner which, for want of a better name, I have called it the Portaloop. This arrangement allows one element support to double as a feeder support. The open ends of the element are located in the opposite corner as shown in **Photo 5**. The only difference in characteristics between the Cobweb single element and the Portaloop is a shift of 45° to its minor directivity. The impedance and SWR are unaffected and resonance, in this case 11.46MHz, is also unaffected.

However, the antennas I have just described cover only one band – but wait a minute, don't we make multiband antennas out of a single wire by feeding them via an ATU? I tried out this idea by feeding the antenna via an ATU using 300Ω twin feeder. As I have already mentioned, the antenna was resonant on 11.46MHz, however it loaded up on all bands between 7 and 52MHz with the ATU. I also tried using a coax feed (mini-8) and the performance was very similar.

According to the model, this antenna will also work on VHF (with an appropriate ATU) and on 144MHz (only) it appears to work as a resonant rhombic with a free-space gain of over 10dBi.

This antenna can also be used as a vertical for the lower frequency bands using the feeder and the antenna at a top capacity loaded vertical resonated against a vehicle or a counterpoise using an ATU. The standard Cobweb can also be used this way provided the feeder is routed clear of the supporting mast.

# Antennas

## Continuing our look at vintage test equipment.

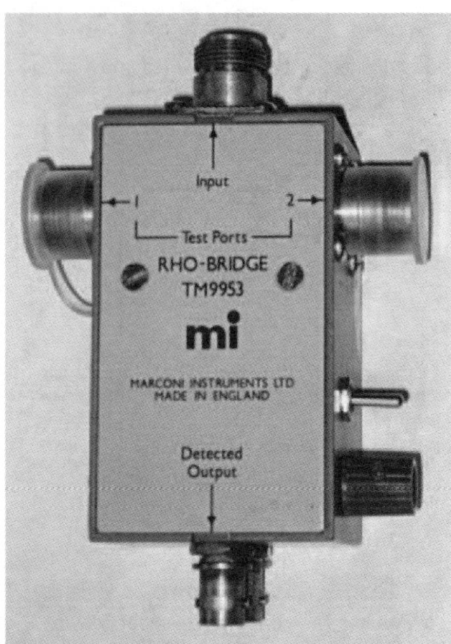


PHOTO 1: The Marconi Instruments TM9953 RHO bridge.

MORE ON TEST GEAR. As many of you are aware, I have a keen interest in test equipment for use with antennas and transmission lines. In this column over the last few years I have described various items of test equipment, mostly home made. More recently, I came across some older commercial items of test gear and have discussed them when I have found out how they work. The GR1602 Admittance Bridge was one of these. In the April edition of Antennas I described a request from G7DHD to identify the Marconi TM9953RHO bridge shown in **Photo 1**.

While I was aware of measurement bridges generally, I had not come across an instrument that measured RHO, hence the question. I hazarded a guess that it might have measured SWR because of the mathematical relationship between RHO and SWR. This relationship is shown in **Figure 1**, which is a radially scaled parameters overlay for a Smith chart.

I received a considerable amount of correspondence on this subject, which not only explained how the instrument worked and how it was used but also included lots of fascinating historical detail.

RHO BRIDGES AND A BIT OF HISTORY. An example of this is in this letter from Alan Notschild, G3RSF. He says, "Having used a RHO bridge for many years, I can tell you something about them and the particular use that we had for them at Coline Ltd.

"We used the Marconi Instruments (MI) RHO Bridge as an automated SWR test set for production line testing of our dummy loads. Prior to the RHO bridge becoming available, we used to use a General Radio 900 series slotted line powered by a GR disc seal triode oscillator for 500MHz to 1GHz and we also had a GR 1-4GHz Klystron oscillator. SWR was read off from a Hewlett Packard meter. The Klystron oscillators were modulated with a 1kHz sine wave and the HP meter had a demodulator and 1kHz narrow filter. Signal levels were fairly small. This equipment was very expensive and was slow to use and hence unsuitable for large volume production line testing of our dummy loads.

"The MI RHO Bridge is rather like an RF version of a Wheatstone bridge. Power is fed into the Input connector and a reference load, usually a precision 50Ω termination, would be put on port 1. The unknown would then be connected to port 2. The output in our case was fed to a Marconi Instruments XY display, although a DC millivoltmeter could be used for fixed frequency measurements. The RF source was an MI swept oscillator, which had two plug-in units covering about 500kHz to 1GHz. The X drive to the display came from the sweep generator and the Y input was connected to the Detected output of the RHO bridge.

"The RHO bridge/XY display would, of course, only give a certain voltage out dependant on the SWR and it was necessary to calibrate the bridge before use, for example 1cm in height could be set to represent a SWR of 1.05:1 and so on. In order to do this, a precision mismatch would be applied to port 2 and the amplitude of the XY display adjusted to give the desired amplitude.

"Marker pips were available from the generator to be superimposed on the X drive signal to give horizontal calibration of frequency. The output levels from the sweep oscillator were very small, typically 5mW. Therefore, a lot of gain was required in order to make a readable display. That is where the 'bat switch' and DC level pot comes into use. When set to 'bat off', the output was taken directly from the diode detectors; with the switch ON, the detector output was amplified by an op amp and the DC level control was used to offset the standing DC voltage of the op amp if required. The XY display then showed an instant graph of the SWR over the entire swept frequency range. Once set up, a semi skilled test operator could then rapidly test a batch of terminations or mismatches."

THE TM9953 OPERATING INSTRUCTIONS. Pat McAlister, G3YFK very kindly sent me a copy of an operating manual for the TM9953 RHO Bridge from an original that he found in a scrap dump! He notes that there is a matching logamp unit called the TM9954. I have included an edited method of use and a circuit description from the information supplied in this document.

These instructions describe the TM 9953, which is basically a Wheatstone bridge with two arms built in and the other two constituted by the loads connected to the two test ports. When the loads connected to the two test ports are both 50Ω the characteristic impedance of the bridge at the input socket is 50Ω. Normally the instrument will be used with a 50Ω generator and a graph is provided in the instructions to show the error with deviation of a load from 50Ω. This error does not occur if the ALC output is used to control the sweep generator output voltage, because in this case the input voltage across the bridge is held constant.

The voltage across the bridge is sensed by a symmetrical diode detector and the output of the detector fed either directly to the Detected output socket or via a x100 amplifier. Thus if the two loads connected to the test ports are identical the voltage across the detector is zero. As the difference between the two loads increases the detector output voltage increases.

For a test load SWR below about 1.2:1 the x1 amplification (ie direct) mode may not give sufficient discrimination, but switching to x100 amplification enables measurement to be made of SWR as low as 1.01:1. However, for SWR of 1.4:1 or greater with 0.5V input the amplifier will saturate and x1 amplification must then be used. A test set-up is shown in **Figure 2**.

You may wonder why we should be looking at such low SWRs. We are, after all, told that for normal amateur radio purposes,

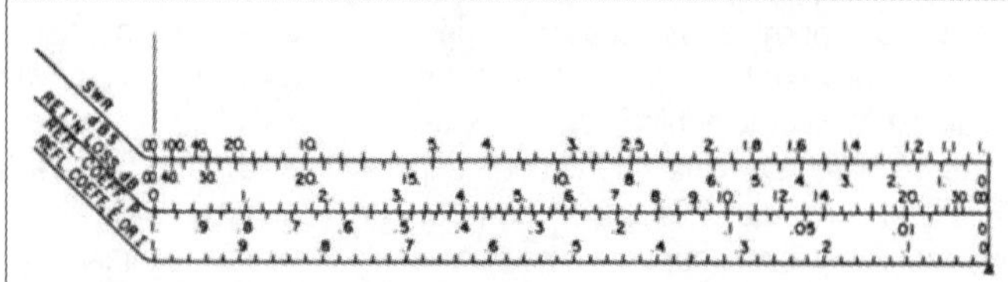


FIGURE 1: A radially scaled overlay for a Smith chart showing the relationship between Reflection Coefficient and SWR.

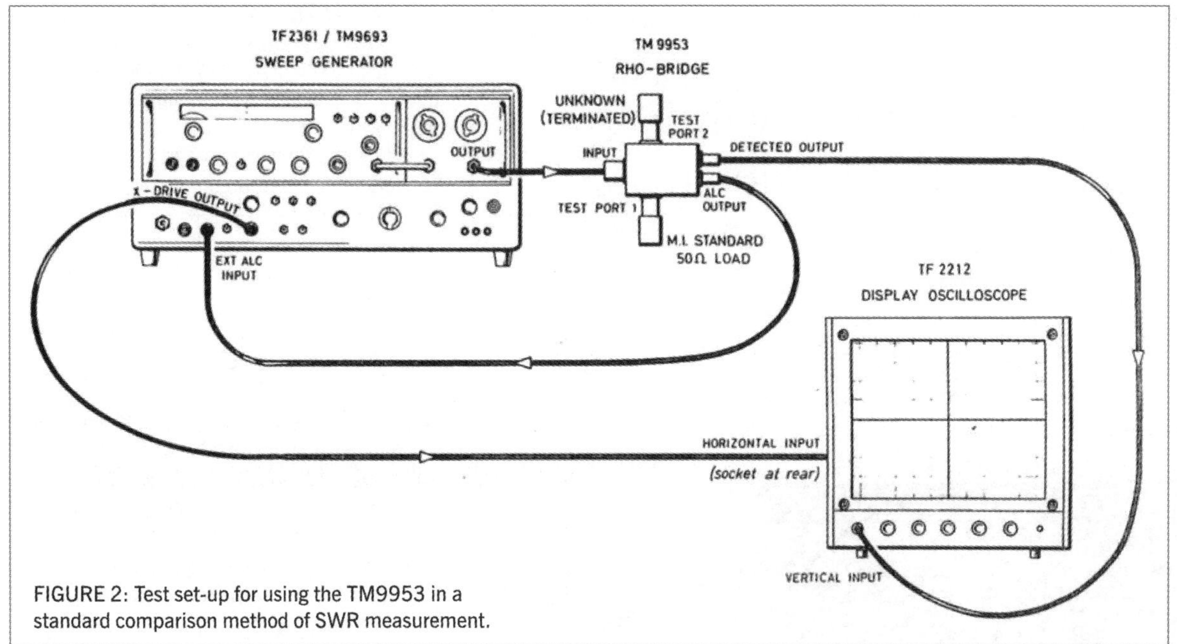


FIGURE 2: Test set-up for using the TM9953 in a standard comparison method of SWR measurement.

aiming for very low SWRs is a bit pointless. However, antennas for TV are different. Any significant reflected wave due to mismatch will cause 'ghosting', a faint displaced image superimposed on the main image.

RHO-BRIDGE TM 9953 CIRCUIT DESCRIPTION. The accuracy of SWR measurement is determined by the residual SWR of the built-in arms (resistors R1 and R3 of the bridge) and the accuracy of the standard loads connected to the test ports (sockets SKT2 and SKT4), see **Figure 3**.

In order that the detector across the bridge should not destroy the bridge symmetry, it also is symmetrical. To each side are connected 10kΩ resistors R4 and R5 followed by 500pF feed-through capacitors C5 and C6. At all but relatively low frequencies (4 or 5MHz) C5 and C6 are effectively a short to earth and thus make the bridge perfectly symmetrical. At lower frequencies, when the reactance of C5 and C6 is no longer low, the impedance following C5 (ie either the x100 amplifier or the load on the DETECTED OUTPUT socket SKT5) is seen by the bridge, so the 100kΩ in the earth path (R6) approximately compensates for this.

The x100 amplifier utilises an opamp (IC1). The gain is set by the ratio of resistors R10 and R8, (1MΩ/10kΩ). Potentiometer R11 is the front panel DC LEVEL control and adjusts the DC offset of the amplifier so that the DC levels of x1 and x100 modes can be equalised on the display.

The facility for ALC levelling of input voltage to the bridge is provided by the circuit consisting of diode D1, feed-through capacitors C1 and C2 and resistor R2. Its operation is standard and it provides negative polarity output via BNC socket SKT3.

THE RHO-TECTOR. Neil Sandford, VK2EH and Gordon Lean, G3WJG, provided me information on another instrument called a Rho-Tector VSWR Detector, made by Telonic. This is essentially the same sort of instrument as the TM9953 but is much smaller and does not contain an amplifier. There are several models, some of which will function up to 4GHz.

G3WGJ notes, "To actually use it with any meaning, you also need the accompanying set of calibrated mismatches, corresponding to various SWRs - 1:1.1, 1:1.2 and 1:1.5 (corresponding to 5% 10% and 25% reflection coefficient) and you also needed a powerful sweep signal generator capable of volts of output as the units weren't very sensitive. Also, if you were testing on a site that had active transmitters, crosstalk could upset the measurements so a 30W wideband amp was sometimes necessary on the sweep generator to get the necessary accuracy.

"The antennas were designed using the GR bridge (shown in a recent *RadCom*) and when assembled on the mast and checked on the Rho-Tector. If it didn't pass this test the whole lot had to be taken down and readjusted (usually at night!). When you watch your digital television tonight the chances are that it will be coming to you via from some these antennas as they were made to a very good wideband specification."

ACKNOWLEDGMENTS. I am grateful to the following readers who also supplied information on these SWR/RHO Bridges: Bryan Harber, G8DKK, Trevor Clarke, G3UYD, Peter Martinez, G3PLX, Julian Hardstone, Ray Hills, G3HRH, Roy Powers, G8CKN, Peter Brooker, G3WXC, Alan Strong, G3WXI and Ken May, G4APB.

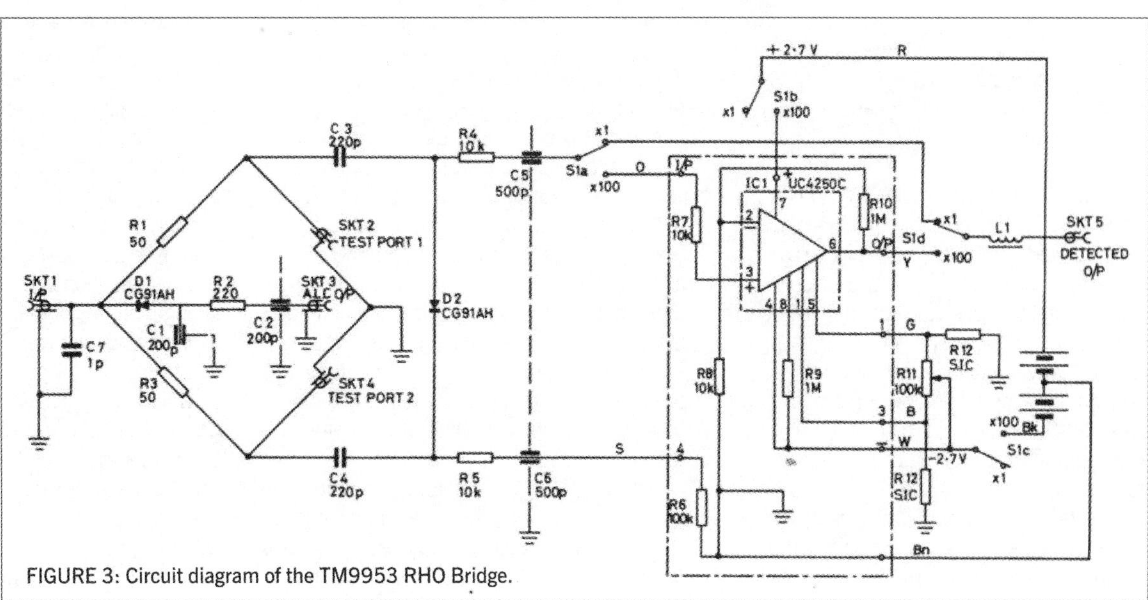


FIGURE 3: Circuit diagram of the TM9953 RHO Bridge.

# Antennas

## Using a receiver to accurately measure field strength, plus the low-down on antenna gain figures.

**PHOTO 1: Signal strength reading set up using a receiver and attenuator.**

RECAP. In the April 2004 Antennas I described the use of the field strength meter (FSM) and cited the following uses to which such an instrument could be put; namely:

- Make comparative measurements of various antennas to assess relative gain
- Plot a polar diagram to record antenna directivity
- Tune a transmitter antenna for maximum efficiency or gain
- Locate the source and measure the level of radio interference.

THE COMMUNICATIONS RECEIVER AS A FSM. While it is possible to make or buy a FSM, every radio shack already has one in the form of a receiver or transceiver. On the face of it the receiver section of a modern transceiver should make good field strength meter. Many are small, portable and convenient to use. The downside is the receiver's sensitivity is too great, because it requires the RF gain be turned to maximum for the S-meter to function correctly. The fix is a variable attenuator, necessary for adjusting the signal strengths so that they fall in a useful region of the S-meter range.

A conventional S-meter is preferred for measuring a change in signal strength. However, most transceivers and receivers have S-meters that consist of a bargraph indicator. Many of these only read signal strength in steps of 1 S-point (theoretically 6dB), which is the case of the IC-706 shown in **Photo 1**. However, a more accurate estimate of field strength can be achieved if a receiver with a bargraph S-meter is used in conjunction with a good RF attenuator. The trick is to use interpolation.

The procedure is to adjust the signal level with the attenuator so that the S-meter reads S9. The attenuator is then adjusted so that the S-meter just reads S9+10dB and the attenuation figure noted. The attenuator is then adjusted so that the S-meter just reads S8 and the attenuation figure noted. If the first reading was 28dB and the second 34dB then the mean would be 31dB, which would be a good reference point for an S-meter reading of S9.

This could be your reference point for any subsequent comparative measurement where the attenuator is adjusted for a reading of S9, again using the procedure described. The difference in signal level is read off the attenuator settings, which gives a far more accurate record of signal variation that using the S-meter to indicate the differences. Note that the RF attenuator with the rotary switches shown in Photo 1 is more convenient to use than the small press switch selector attenuators normally available.

**IMPORTANT.** If you use an attenuator with a transceiver, disconnect the microphone to prevent the attenuator being burned out by an accidental transmission.

ANTENNA GAIN FIGURES. I have received more than one response to say that the antenna performance figures quoted in a recent antenna review I wrote on the YP-3 were meaningless – and with good reason.

Antenna performance is determined by comparing it with some reference antenna. Mathematical models of antennas use a hypothetical point source antenna, which radiates equally in all directions, known as an isotropic radiator. (Isotropic means having the same physical properties in all directions).

The field strength or radiation pattern of an antenna is one of its most important characteristics and its complete description requires field intensity measurements in all directions. It follows that the field strength diagram of our isotropic antenna is a sphere, as shown in **Figure 1(a)**. Antenna mathematical models using this isotopic source as a reference are defined using the symbol dBi. Remember that this isotropic antenna is a mathematical entity – it is *not* possible to construct a *truly* isotropic antenna.

In practice, a full three-dimensional description is not used very often and a section through the three-dimensional space pattern will provide enough information. A useful analogy is the contour line of equal height on a map of a hill, which shows the general shape of the hill. A section through the spherical isotropic radiation pattern is a circle.

If we now consider a vertical half-wave dipole shown in **Figure 1(b)** it can be seen that the three dimensional polar diagram is doughnut shaped. A section through this doughnut is a figure of eight (on its side). It can be seen that the radiation pattern of this dipole is not uniform and that field strength in some directions has been increased at the expense of the field strength in other directions. This increase in field strength at area of maximum radiation is defined as power gain. The power gain of the dipole is generally considered to be 2.15dBi.

Mathematical models of antennas can be constructed using antenna modelling software such as EZNEC or MIMA and, in general, give very good indications of antenna performance, provided the methods of calculation are clearly specified. So far we have only considered antennas in free space.

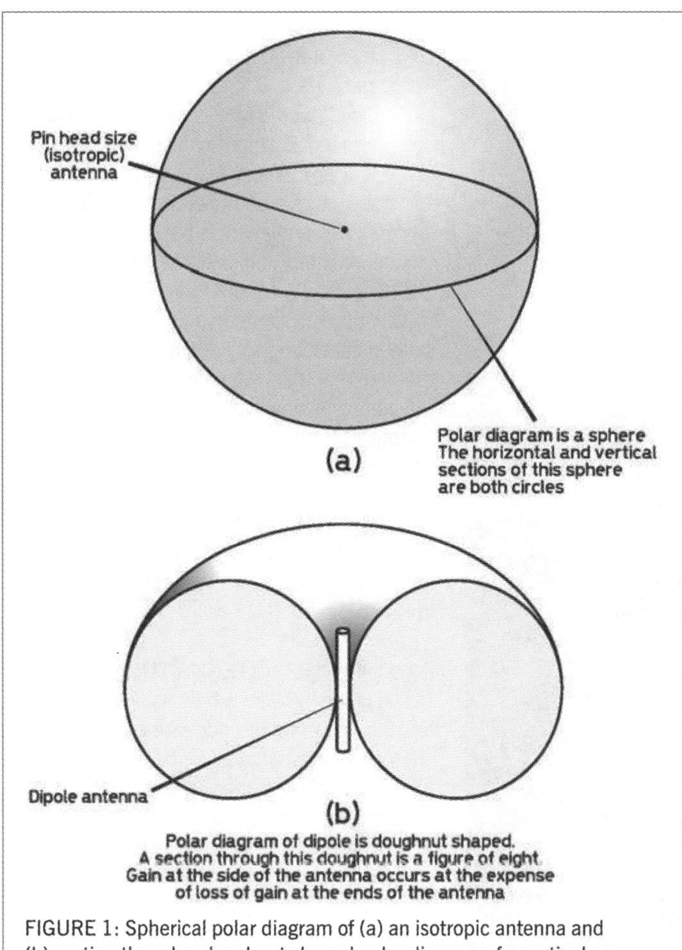


FIGURE 1: Spherical polar diagram of (a) an isotropic antenna and (b) section though a doughnut shaped polar diagram of a vertical free-space dipole.

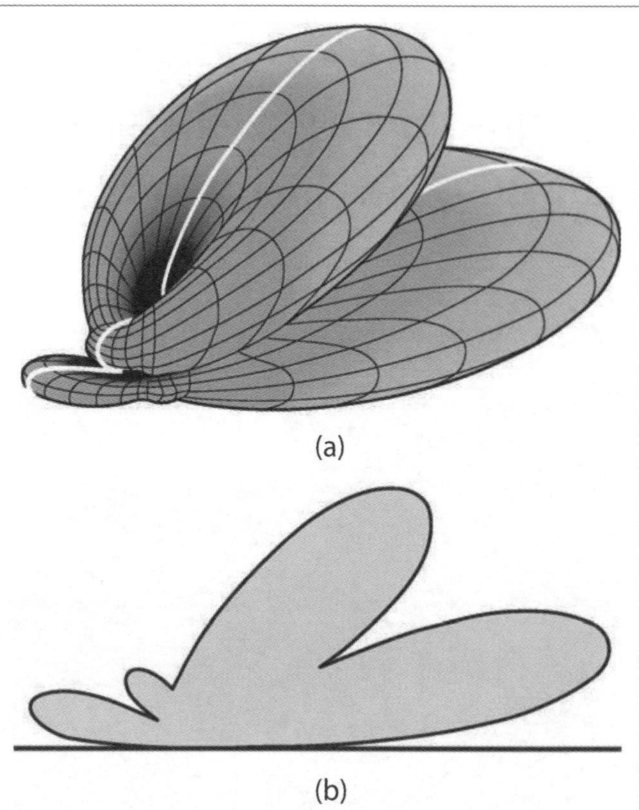


FIGURE 3: (a) Three-dimensional polar diagram of a three-element beam, one wavelength high. The white line shows where the vertical section is calculated. (b) Vertical diagram obtained from this section.

FIGURE 2: Diagram illustrating the effect of ground reflection on directly radiated waves.

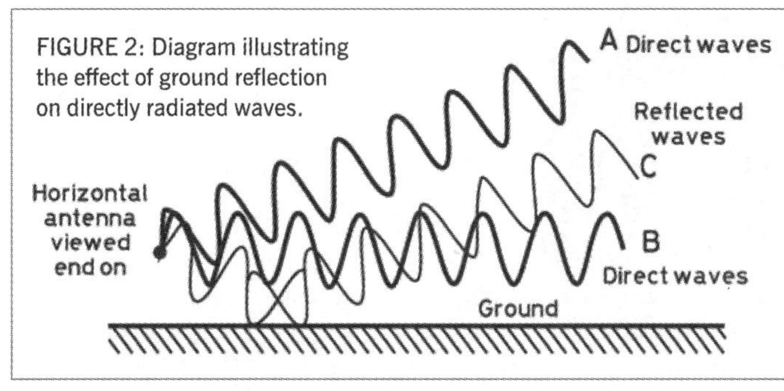


Problems sometimes arise because the effect of the antenna in the real world has not been considered, or considered incorrectly.

GROUND GAIN. The ground under the antenna acts as a reflector. Electromagnetic waves from the antenna radiate in all directions and some of these waves are reflected by ground. If the reflected wave is in phase – or partially in phase – with a direct wave, it enhances radiation and increases gain at a particular angle. Other combinations of reflected and direct waves, whose phases tend to cancel, reduce gain at other angles.

This is illustrated in **Figure 2**, which shows that waves A and C enhance gain while B and C tend to cancel and reduce the gain. This is the cause of the familiar elevation antenna field strength diagrams. An example of a three-element beam is shown in **Figure 3**.

The gain of the antenna in this diagram is calculated over average ground with the main lobe 13.5dBi at an angle of 14 degrees above the horizontal. The same antenna gave a free space gain of 8.4dBi. The difference between these two gain figures is known as ground gain. In the real world, almost all antennas are affected by the ground and therefore have ground gain.

REAL WORLD ANTENNAS. So what can the gain figures of commercial antennas tell us? Before the days of mathematical modelling the most practical method of measuring the gain of an antenna was to use an antenna testing range and compare the antenna under test (AUT) with a reference antenna such as a dipole. Because ground gain affects the both the reference antenna and the AUT it was important that the reference antenna, AUT and the signal level detection antenna were at the same height for the comparison measurements. Under these circumstances an optimised three-element Yagi gave a gain of around 8dB compared with a dipole, so was quoted in dBd.

These days a fairly accurate estimate of the performance of most antennas can be done using a computerised mathematical model. In this case we can use a free space model of the antenna compared with the isotopic reference. Here we are dealing with mathematical entities that give proven computed antenna performance, which avoids the complications of specifying ground characteristics or antenna height above ground.

An antenna manufacturer has no idea where or how the antenna will be located once it is sold. Specifying ground gain relative to isotropic will give a nice high gain figure but, as our readers noted, it is meaningless.

I have to say that the reputable beam antenna manufacturers such as Hi-gain and Cushcraft give sensible gain figures for their antennas. It is one or two of the smaller manufacturers of antennas who sometimes push the credibility of their gain figures past sensible limits. A specification in one of my catalogues quotes a Windom with "Gain, low angle 5-10dB". 5-10dB above what (and under what conditions) we are left to guess.

It is my contention that with antennas it is a case of location, location, location – it is more important *where* it is than *what* it is. When my namesake VQ3PBD moved to Malawi (7Q7PBD) he installed a multiband trap dipole some 80ft (24m) up in some nearby tall trees. He said it was the best DX antenna he had ever used.

# Antennas

## A fix for the UHF switch on the MFJ-269, plus baluns and ATUs

**PHOTO 1: A modification to protect the MFJ-269 UHF switch from being pressed accidentally.**

**THE ACTIVE SWR METER.** Probably one of the most popular antenna parameter measuring instruments to become available in the last twenty years or so is the SWR analyser. An SWR analyser, or impedance measuring bridge, requires a source signal and detector as well as the measurement bridge. Gerd Janzen, DF6SJ described an 'Active Standing Wave Ratio Meter'; a battery powered, comprehensive antenna measuring instrument all in one box. Gerd devoted a book **[1]** to whole range of RF measurements to which one of these instruments can be used and this formed the basis for a range of commercially produced instruments.

Included in some of the goodies I brought back from Dayton in 1994 was such an instrument described above, the MFJ-249 SWR analyser. This was the earlier version of MFJ-259/269, which is very popular these days. The MFJ-249 had only one meter so only read SWR, unlike the later models, which had an additional meter to read the magnitude of impedance.

I later bought a kit from **[2]** which comprised a new front panel, an additional meter and components, which enabled me to an upgrade my instrument to a MFJ 259. This SWR analyser provided me with good service until about three years ago when the frequency band selector switch failed.

**MFJ-269 UHF SWITCH FIX.** Just over two years ago I upgraded to an MFJ-269. Unfortunately, the calibration wasn't all that good but it gave useful results during antenna experiments. I had been making some measurements on a 70cm transmission line and tuner when the instrument just died. I suspect I may have overlooked the warnings in the instruction book about having the UHF selector switch activated **before** the instrument was switched on. Fortunately I was able to get the MFJ-269 repaired and calibrated at **[2]** and my most-used bit of test kit is back in service.

I consider this oddity of the UHF selector switch a design flaw. It is not easy to see if UHF is selected until the instrument is switched on. I have made a simple modification that ensures that the UHF section cannot be selected by accident and requires that the switch can only be pressed using a screwdriver. The modification is simply an 8mm length of metal tube having an internal diameter of 8mm. This is Super Glued to the front panel so that it covers the switch as shown in **Photo 1**. The source of tubing to make this modification can be the end of a 75Ω coax connector, also shown in Photo 1.

**BALUNS WITH ANTENNA TUNERS.** Most ATU designs provide a balanced output for feeding open-wire or ladder-line transmission lines by placing a balun in the output circuit of an unbalanced tuner. Most of the baluns used are transformer-type, 4:1 voltage baluns wound around ferrite cores, usually toroids.

This practice has been roundly condemned by many authorities with W2DU **[3]** giving the reasons as follows: "unfortunately, the output circuit is not necessarily the ideal place for the balun... And further, the voltage balun is vastly inferior to the current balun in obtaining balanced currents in the feed line... the ideal arrangement for an antenna tuner is to place the balun at the input of the tuner, and for the balun to be a choke-type current balun such as the W2DU balun.

"Let's first examine some of the problems encountered when you use a ferrite core, transformer-type voltage balun in the output circuit of the tuner. When a transformer balun has a ferrite core, the core is subjected to the total magnetic flux developed by the load current, and the resulting high magnetic flux density can cause the core to saturate. When the core saturates, the RF waveform in the output becomes distorted, creating undesirable harmonic signals. A transformerless choke balun made with coiled-up coax, or a short coax with external ferrite beads, has no core to saturate. And, in addition, the external beads are not subjected to the magnetic flux developed by the load current. The beads are subjected only to the flux developed by the very small current flowing through the high impedance that the beads create on the outside surface of the outer conductor. Hence, no harmonics are generated with the ferrite bead current balun.

"Another problem encountered with the ferrite-core transformer-type voltage balun is the distributed capacitance between its windings, which causes current unbalance between the two output ports that feed the balanced feed line. The input impedance of a balanced feed line can range in value from low to very high, and generally has a reactance component. The higher the line-input impedance and the higher the operating frequency, the greater is the effect of the distributed capacitance in contributing to output current unbalance. On the other hand, output current unbalance is negligible with the ferrite-bead current balun.

"Another undesirable feature of the 4:1 ferrite-core balun placed at the output of the tuner is that it can easily be permanently damaged. This can happen from overloading the balun when you operate with high power into a line having a high SWR that results in a high input impedance containing a large amount of reactance.

"A still further undesirable feature of the 4:1 ferrite-core balun is its contribution to power loss. Typical losses with this type of balun range from around 0.5dB at 2MHz to 2dB at 30MHz. In contrast, the loss in the W2DU balun is minimal, only from 0.1 to 0.2dB across the band, because the only loss involved is in the attenuation suffered in a 10.5 inch length of coaxial line."

W2DU cited other eminent authorities including John Belrose, VE2CV who endorsed these views.

**CONVENTIONAL ATU/BALUNS IN PRACTICE.** I did a bit of amateur radio operating as CN2PD while on vacation in Marrakech in 2003. The rig was an IC-706 Mk 1 and the antenna a simple 20m length of wire fixed to the roof of the hotel, fed in the centre with 300Ω ladder-line feeder.

An essential item was a small ATU with provision for feeding a balanced antenna. I tried to make one that would handle 100W but found obtaining the right sized components rather difficult. I finished up buying an MFJ-901B, which was claimed to handle 100W and weighed only 600g.

I noticed that the balun on the output of this ATU was very small, see **Photo 2**, and in view of the dire warnings regarding this design was concerned that it would overheat with a 100W from the IC-706. Because of this I used the ATU without its cover so that I could check that none of the components were cooking. The QTH proved to be a particularly a good one and CW pile-ups on all bands 7 to 21MHz were the order of the day (and night). After a couple of hours of such operating the balun was just perceptibly warmer than the other components and the chassis.

The antenna and ATU performed very well and it wasn't just due to the CN2 call. When I first switched the rig on I did a test call and, from force of habit, keyed TESTING DE G3LDO and was immediately answered by a W4... followed by an embarrassing silence!

**PHOTO 2: The tiny transformer balun at the output of the MFJ-901B ATU, which was able to handle 100W without stress.**

**SUPPORTING PORTABLE ANTENNAS.** The business of getting an antenna up high enough to be of any use is a subject that is frequently discussed in amateur radio literature. Usually, the problem is one of visual impact and planning restrictions. On the other hand the requirements of HF portable operation or the holiday DXpedition requires something considerably more compact and lightweight.

G3CWI **[4]** recommends a telescopic roach pole for this purpose. By chance I purchased one of these poles from a stall at one of my XYLs equestrian venues about 10 years ago and for a while it remained in the garage as a solution looking for a problem. In the event it was used for the antenna in the aforementioned trip to Marrakech. Like G3CWI, I discarded the top section of the pole because it was too thin to support any sort of antenna; also, when the pole was expanded, the joints of each section were secured with insulating tape.

The pole was configured to support a 20m length of 18SWG insulated wire as an inverted V. It was supported and fed in the centre, with 300Ω slotted line feeder taped to the pole, while the ends of the antenna were fixed to convenient support points found on the roof of the hotel. The whole antenna structure had a very low visual profile yet at the same time was efficient and effective when used with the MFJ-901B ATU.

A telescopic roach pole is convenient transporting an HF antenna by air because when telescoped it is only 1.2m (4ft) long. At the baggage check-in I was asked what it was. While trying to decide whether to call it a fishing pole or a walking stick the XYL chipped in to say that it was an aerial. That in turn resulted in a lot of questions such as "does it have any metal bits?".

I managed to rescue the situation by saying that it was a walking stick and backing this up by pointing to the rubber bung at the end, which gave it a walking/hiking stick appearance. It was consequently allowed as hand luggage and continued its merry way through X-ray scrutiny without further incident.

Note that some airlines may have different rules regarding what can be carried as hand luggage.

**FINALLY.** This discussion on ATUs and baluns was prompted by an item on the website of Roy Lewallen, W7EL. His item on this subject of baluns commences:

"I am here to eat some words. For a long time I've promoted the idea of putting a 1:1 current balun at the input of a tuner to improve current balance. This doesn't work. In fact neither the current balance in the input conductors nor the voltage across the balun are any different when the balun is put at the input or the output of the tuner". You can read the detailed analysis at **[5]**.

REFERENCES


[1] RF Measurements with an Active Standing Wave Ratio Meter, Gerd Janzen, DF6SJ. DARC Verlag GmbH, Baunatal. ISBN 3-88692-023.

[2] MFJ 259B and 269, available Waters & Stanton. Tel. 01702 20683/204956, www.wsplc.com.

[3] Reflections, Transmission Lines and Antennas. M. Walter Maxwell, W2DU.

[4] 'Fishing for DX' 'Portable' column, Richard Newstead, G3CWI. RadCom July 2009

[5] www.eznec.com/miscpage.htm. Download files IBALBRF.TXT and IBALUN.TXT.

# Antennas

## Chasing the mobile Holy Grail

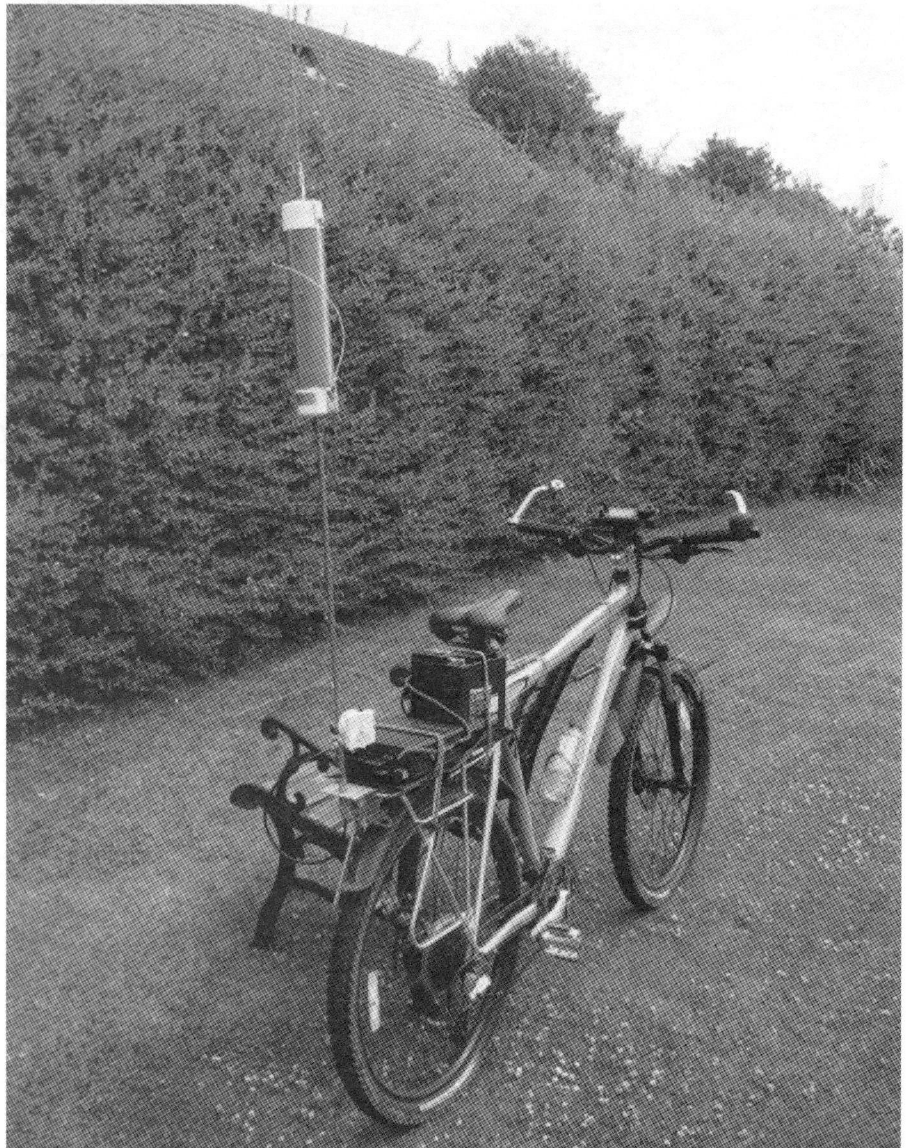

**PHOTO 1: The G3LDO bike mobile with the IC-707 Mk2, which provided 10W of RF for the tests. The antenna shown is a cut-down version of the Texas BugCatcher antenna, which was used as a reference. The RF current meter can be seen at the base of the antenna.**

LIGHTWEIGHT HF MOBILE ANTENNAS. One of the holy grails is to find a small HF antenna that will perform as well as a large one. Because of the restricted size of modern dwellings many of us have to address this problem. But perhaps the greatest challenge to the mobile operator is that not only does the antenna have to be small but it has to be fairly rugged. For pedestrian or bike mobile a further limitation is that the antenna has to be lightweight.

LIGHTWEIGHT MOBILE ANTENNAS. My particular interest is bicycle HF mobile. For this I have favoured the helically wound antenna that found much favour with CBers in the past. My recently acquired mountain bike used as a mobile base is shown in **Photo 1** using a cut down version of the Texas BugCatcher antenna. Although this is a well-regarded antenna it is rather cumbersome for bike mobile. Is there lighter, and probably safer, antenna that could be used?

Over the years I have collected a few mobile antennas and the ones chosen for the tests are shown in **Photo 2**. These include a cut down Texas BugCatcher as a reference standard; two helically wound commercial mobile antennas of unknown pedigree, a modified CB FireStik and an MP-1 portable manual 'screwdriver' antenna.

The tests were performed on 18MHz because this is my favourite mobile operating band – and two of the test antennas were already pre-tuned to this frequency. The parameters measured were antenna current (at the base of the antenna), field strength and SWR bandwidth.

TEST EQUIPMENT. The current meter I used was designed to measure RF current in the presence of strong electrical fields. It was built to measure RF current distribution over the whole length of the antenna so it contains as little metal in the construction as possible, eg by using a plastic-bodied meter. For constructional details, see **[1]**. In this case I was only concerned with the current at the base of the antenna where the current is maximum and the electrical field is minimum so the more common clip-on RF current meter would probably have worked just as well in this application.

Field strength measurements were made using a Bruel & Kjaer heterodyne voltmeter type 2006.

It was important that each antenna was equally well matched to the feedline and that the power level was the same for each antenna. This was monitored using a power/SWR meter although an MFJ-269 was used to assist in the initial tuning of the antennas.

TESTS. Each antenna was tested with 10W of RF at 18.12MHz and the results are shown in **Table 1**. These results are purely comparative because both the current meter and the heterodyne voltmeter were uncalibrated. Furthermore, it took some practice obtaining the meter readings without affecting the results. The results in Table 1 were obtained using three sets of measurements and taking the average.

ANTENNA DESCRIPTIONS & ANALYSIS. It came as no surprise the Texas BugCatcher gave the best results with the large high-Q coil presenting the lowest losses, even though the stinger **[2]** was only half the recommended length. The 2:1 SWR bandwidth was small compared with the other antennas.

The mobile helical is a commercially produced antenna using what is known as continuous loading. It is constructed by winding a helical coil along much of the total length of an insulating support, with a coarse pitch being used for the lower high current area and close wound at the top (higher) end. Finally, the antenna is resonated using stinger. Mobile antenna 2 has a facility for plugging in stingers of different lengths for different bands and locking them in place.

The modified CB FireStik antenna is one that I have used for many years. This CB antenna was originally resonant on 27MHz and was designed to work with a long close-

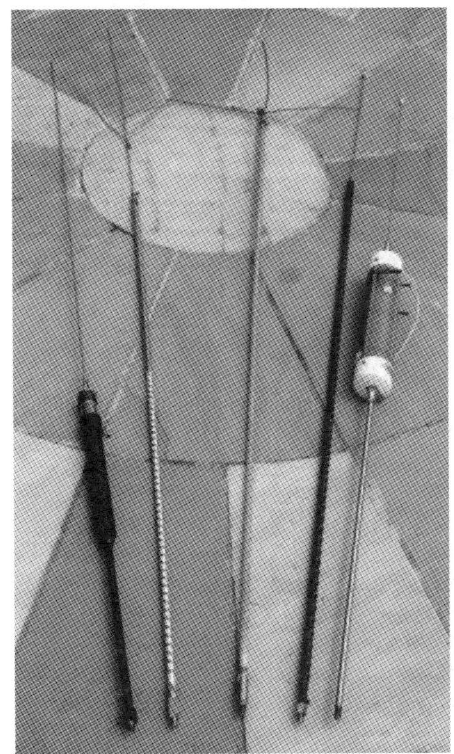

PHOTO 2: (r-l) a cut down Texas BugCatcher; helically wound commercial mobile of unknown pedigree; a modified CB FireStik, another unknown commercial helical; and an MP-1 portable manual 'screwdriver' antenna.

wound coil at the end, rather than a stinger.

It was easy to modify this antenna to operate on 28MHz by simply removing some of the turns. A stinger was required to enable this antenna to resonate on the lower bands. One was constructed from 14SWG hard-drawn copper antenna wire and fixed using small jubilee clips to the top of the insulated rod that supports the helix, as shown in **Photo 3**. Different stinger lengths enabled the antenna to be resonated at 24 and 21MHz but for the lower bands the stinger was becoming impractically long.

The problem was fixed by adding additional wires as shown in Photo 3, effectively making a capacity hat. This had the additional advantage of making the stinger/hat capacitance variable by aligning the additional wires along the stinger for minimum capacitance or bending them into the horizontal position for maximum capacitance. This, in turn, gave the antenna wider resonance range, which can be useful.

Mobile antenna 4 also used the variable pitch helix wound arrangement. The only difference was that the windings comprised three wires in parallel, wound flat against the insulated rod support, which gave the effect of being wound with copper tape.

I am not sure of the origin of this antenna; it is a multiband arrangement as already described but only had one stainless steel stinger that resonated the antenna on 21.2MHz. I made a variable capacity hat of copper wire, which was fixed to the stinger by soldering it to a connector removed from a screw connector block as shown in **Photo 4**. The capacity hat can be moved to any part of the stinger to vary the capacitance and locked into position with the screws shown in Photo 4. The remarkable characteristic of this antenna is the wide 2:1 SWR bandwidth which, if Table 1 is anything to go by, is achieved without loss of performance compared with antennas of a similar design.

PHOTO 3: The top portion of the CB FireStik antenna, showing the method of fixing 14SWG copper wire top loading.

TABLE 1: Relative antenna performance. Current and field strength figures are relative and uncalibrated.

| No. | Antenna | Antenna current | Field strength | 1:2 SWR bandwidth |
|---|---|---|---|---|
| 1 | Texas BugCatcher | 82 | 90 | 180kHz |
| 2 | Mobile helical | 50 | 65 | 240kHz |
| 3 | FireStik | 55 | 75 | 360kHz |
| 4 | Mobile tri-helical | 56 | 70 | 450kHz |
| 5 | MP-1 | 52 | 55 | - |

Finally, included in the test was a MP-1, which is a lightweight manual 'screwdriver' antenna, designed for pedestrian portable operation. It was included in the test because I was curious as to how well it performed in comparison to the other antennas.

**BICYCLE COMPUTER MODEL.** While it is easy to work short skip EU stations from a bike mobile, working DX was a little more difficult than operating from the main station – as you might expect. A computer model was made of the Photo 1 bicycle installation. I felt that this was an interesting exercise to see if it would give some idea of the performance of the bike mobile set up.

The model is shown in Figure 1. I had to take some liberties with the shape of the modelled bicycle with what were considered to be non-critical dimensions. Square wheels would make for a very impractical bumpy ride but should not make much difference to its electrical characteristics. A further concession to the model is that the wheels are offset so that they are not in contact with the frame. The reason for this is that contacts with the 'wires' of the model are only allowed at 'wire' ends.

PHOTO 4: Method of adding 14SWG copper wire top loading to an existing stainless steel stinger.

A more critical dimension is the antenna itself. A centre-loaded antenna based on the Texas BugCatcher was used because the structure of a variable pitch continuously loaded FireStik was an impractically complex item to model.

The green line shows the current distribution throughout the antenna and the bike and the blue line is a section of the elevation plot. It predicts a gain of -2.3dBi over average ground when using a centre-loaded antenna. From Table 1 it can be seen that the gain will be down by about 30% in terms of antenna current and field strength less when using a continuously loaded FireStik.

I have used this method of assessing the performance of an antenna using a mixture of computer modelling and measurement with LF antennas.

**FINALLY.** Clearly the BugCatcher type of antenna, or any antenna with a large, high Q coil has the edge regarding performance. However, the tests show that a lighter and more practical continuously loaded antenna will give a reasonable performance provided it has a good top loading arrangement.


REFERENCES

[1] Building a low capacitance, voltage immune RF current meter, W8JI: www.w8ji.com/building_a_current_meter.htm

[2] An American term to describe the whip section above a loading coil on a short centre fed antenna or on a continuous loaded antenna.


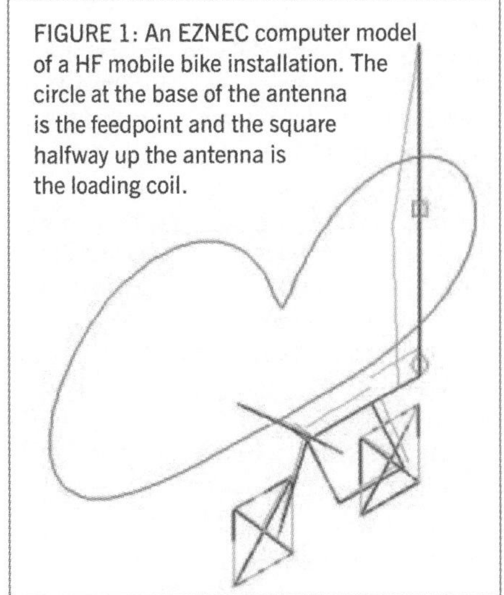

FIGURE 1: An EZNEC computer model of a HF mobile bike installation. The circle at the base of the antenna is the feedpoint and the square halfway up the antenna is the loading coil.

# Antennas

## One good turn...

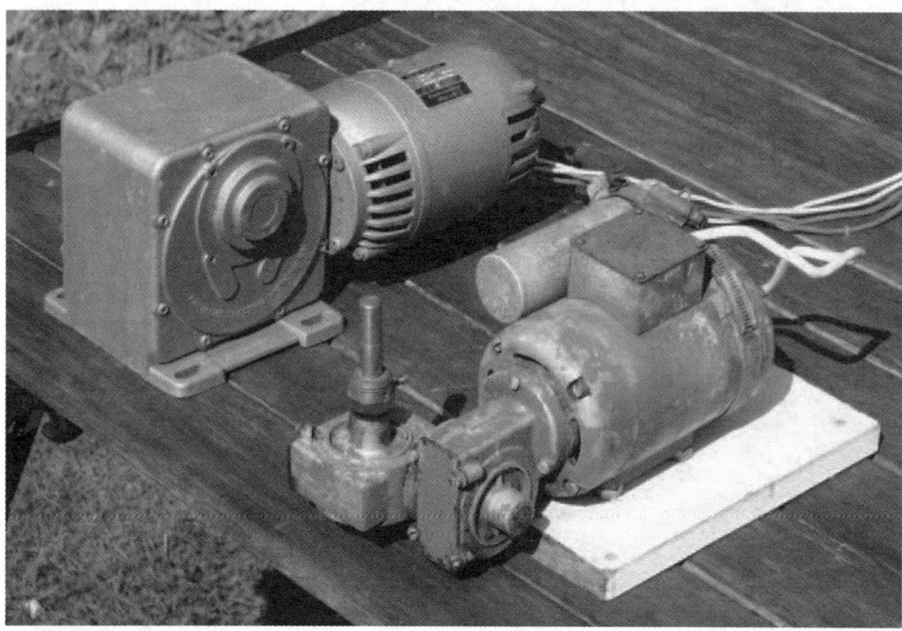

PHOTO 1: Motor and gearbox by Pavalux (left) and Hillman (right).

**STANDARD PRACTICE.** The rotary beam has become the standard antenna for VHF/UHF and the upper HF bands. This antenna has the ability to change the direction of maximum gain to enhance the transmitted and received signals towards the station of interest while at the same time providing a reduction in interference from unwanted signals. The downside of using beam antennas is that some method of rotation is required.

**ROTATOR SYSTEMS.** The usual way of overcoming this problem is to buy one of the many electrically driven rotators on offer. Making the correct decision as to how much capacity the rotator must have is important to ensure trouble-free operation.

Almost any rotator will turn any antenna with appropriate gearing. It will just take longer for the smaller rotators overcome the antenna inertia and get up to speed. With braking there are other considerations. A lightweight rotator may lack braking or holding capability. High winds may turn the rotator motor via the gear train in a reverse fashion, resulting in damage to the gears.

Higher power rotators suitable for rotating a full size 14MHz monobander Yagi usually include a braking arrangement, whereby the antenna is held in place when power is not applied to the rotator. Generally speaking, the brake prevents gear damage on windy days. Rotators in this category include the HyGain Ham-series and the T2X Tail Twister.

Vine Antennas [1] has a criteria list of what constitutes a good antenna rotator, which is determined by the gear drive mechanism. The rotators just mentioned above come in the 'pretty good' category. An improvement on the brake type mechanism is the worm drive motor through a gear train. By its very nature a worm-gear drive is self locking.

Most rotators are capable of accepting mast sizes of different diameters, and suitable precautions must be taken to shim an undersized mast to ensure dead-centre rotation. It is very desirable to mount the rotator inside and as far below the top of the tower as possible. The mast absorbs the torsion developed by the antenna during high winds, as well as during starting and stopping.

**ARMSTRONG ANTENNA ROTATORS.** In the early days, many owners of beam antennas, including myself, turned the mast and antenna by hand – the well-known 'Armstrong' method. The disadvantage of turning the antenna by hand is the inconvenience of having to go outside in all weathers to operate it, although it will keep you fit. Because the antenna is operated from ground level the whole mast must be rotated, but this is not a problem for arrangements that use a guyed pole supported by rotating bearings at the guying points. A method of locking the antenna into place is required to prevent the antenna windmilling in heavy weather.

Some ingenious mechanical arrangements for rotating antenna have been devised in the past. Probably, the most fascinating rotation system that I know of was that used by Henning Overgaard, VQ4DT (Kenya, 1960).

The mast supporting Henning's multiband beam was a wooden pole about the thickness of a telephone pole and some 40ft in length. Fixed to this pole were stand-off metal bearing supports, which held in place a long 45ft section of thin steel pipe. The beam was fixed at the top of this pipe and a motor bike wheel (less tyre) was fixed to the bottom. A rope was wound around the tyre groove of the bike wheel; one end went through a hole in the wall of the shack and the other end over a pulley to a sack of sand. The rope at the shack end had a series of knots along its length, which could pass through keyhole shaped hole.

The beam was rotated anticlockwise by just pulling on the rope, which turned the bike wheel at the base of the mast and hence the beam, while at the same time lifting the bag of sand. The appropriate knot, calibrated in general azimuth directions, could be jammed in the narrow part of the hole, thereby locking the antenna in the required direction. Clockwise rotation was achieved by unhitching the knot from the slot, allowing the weight of the bag of sand turn the antenna, while the rope was run out to the next appropriate knot.

It was a beautifully simple system that gave both remote rotation and beam heading data.

**HOME MADE ELECTRIC ROTATORS.** While small rotators for rotating small VHF/UHF beams are moderately priced, the larger models suitable for turning a HF beam may cost as much as your transceiver. Is it possible to make a rotator?

I think that I have mentioned before my visits to local junk yards for materials or

PHOTO 2: The motor and gearbox made by Pavalux Electric Motors, which has a final rotation speed of 360° in 90 seconds.

PHOTO 3: An example of a fold-over mast rotated by a home-made rotator, which is housed in the large box at the base of the mast. The rotator is uncoupled from the mast when the antenna is lowered.

inspiration for making antennas and antenna fittings. Junk yards located near industrial estates often have quite a range of electric motors and gear boxes from decommissioned processing plants that may have possibilities as rotator drive mechanisms. The following are some of my acquisitions.

The motor and gearbox to the left of **Photo 1** is made by Pavalux Electric Motors. It has a gearbox output speed of 8RPM and a torque of 300lb/in. The motor is a 30VDC compound shunt wound motor with coloured leads identifying the field and armature. The gearbox is a worm drive in an oil bath. The DC compound shunt wound motor has a particular advantage when it comes to arranging a supply that will allow the motor to be rotated in either direction. All that is required are two wires to connect this supply directly to the rotor. The field winding is supplied via a bridge rectifier. AC connections of the rectifier are connected to the supply and the DC connections to the field winding. All that is required to change the direction of the rotator is a reversal of the polarity of the DC supply, which can be achieved via a single-pole centre-off three way switch. The output speed of 8RPM is rather fast for a rotator so a further reduction gear would be required.

PHOTO 4: Example of a large prop pitch motor refurbished by K7NV. As you can see it has been modified to take the rotatable section of a mast. The motor was used to rotate an 80m beam! Four different motor sizes are commonly found. (Photo: K7NV).

The other motor and gearbox is by Hillman Electric Motors. It uses a 230V two-phase AC motor, which has two windings joined to a common lead. One winding is fed directly from 230VAC, and the other one via a capacitor, which introduces a phase shift. The phase difference between the alternating voltages on the two windings causes the motor spindle rotate.

If the phase difference is reversed by inserting the capacitor in series with the other winding, the motor turns the opposite way. This is done very easily using a double-pole, centre off, two-way switch, a basic arrangement found in almost every rotator. The gearbox is a double worm drive and the complete assembly produces a final rotational speed of 4RPM. It has been used for rotating VHF antennas on my garden antenna test range for many years.

The motor and gearbox made by Pavalux Electric Motors, shown in **Photo 2**, is rather special. There were two of these motors and gear boxes in one weatherproof casing for moving something rather big and heavy in azimuth and elevation. I suspect it was used for a video camera in the days when these items were very big and heavy. The motor is a 250V two-phase AC motor with a worm-drive output, which drives a set of brass gear wheels for the final rotation speed of 360 degrees in 90 seconds, just about right for an antenna rotator. The unit also has adjustable limit switches.

You will have noticed that two of these motor/gearbox arrangements so far described are for mains operation. Most rotators sold these days are low voltage, nominally 28VAC, for safety reasons. If you are going to use 230VAC motor units then extra precautions are necessary. When I use the Hillman rotor on my antenna test range I connect it via the same earth leakage trip that I use for the electric hedge trimmer. Needless to say, I have ensured the controller is well earthed. Furthermore, this arrangement is only used in dry weather.

Any sort of antenna rotating mechanism using one of these scrap motor gearboxes is an impractical arrangement for the top of a tower. Some amateurs have used a long pole from the top to the base of the tower with conventional rotators because this pole to acts as a torsion shock absorber. In our case the ground level installation is the most practical for our ungainly home-made rotator.

An example of such an installation is shown in **Photo 3**, taken in Whangaparaoa, New Zealand in 1991. The fold-over mast supports a three band quad. When the antenna is raised, the lower part of the mast docks into a large home-made rotator.

A description of antenna rotators would not be complete without the mention of the prop pitch motor. The prop pitch motor is usually 28V DC and drives a planetary wheel gearbox used to change the pitch of the blades of an aircraft propeller. These units were very popular and were adapted for use by radio amateurs in the early days as antenna rotators. They are very powerful and made to aeronautical engineering standards. They come in three sizes, with the smaller ones being more practical for standard smaller tower sections. However, there are mechanical problems of modification, which can only be addressed if engineering facilities and skills are available.

K7NV provides a service in the rebuilding and refurbishment of prop pitch motors. He has a very interesting website **[2]** which shows many photos of these units being disassembled and rebuilt. An example of one of these is shown in **Photo 4**.

**FINALLY.** I usually have a beam antenna mounted on the chimney of my house; either a HF minibeam of some sort or a VHF beam. Some years ago I was looking for a suitable rotator for this purpose. When visiting my mother, who lived in Ambergate in Derbyshire, we went out for a drive and I found myself on the way towards Lowe Electronics, who were located in nearby Matlock. My mother asked why we were going to this place and I said that I was looking for a rotator. We walked around the store and sniffed at the various items of expensive kit – including rotators. I decided it was all a bit too expensive and as we walked out she said, in a loud voice so that everyone could hear, "Did you find that rotavator you was looking for, dear?"

**REFERENCES**

[1] www.vinecom.co.uk
[2] http://k7nv.com/notebook/ppinfo/index_m.htm

# Antennas

## Measuring and plotting antenna radiation patterns

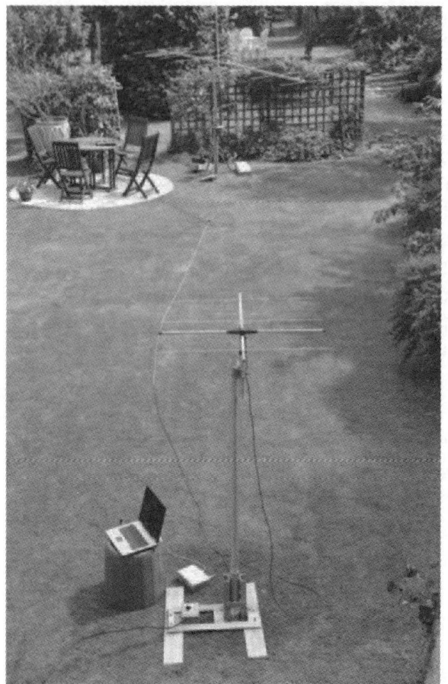

**PHOTO 1: My improved VHF test range. The distance between the test antenna (nearest camera) and the AUT has been set up for the photo. In practice the test antenna was twice the height and nearly twice the distance from the AUT.**

TESTING ANTENNAS. I was recently asked to review two VHF antennas whose performance was documented using computer-modelled free-space radiation patterns; I was curious to know how the real world antennas compared with these models. So, this month, I will describe how you can assess antenna performance by plotting its radiation pattern. From this you can obtain some idea of its gain and directivity. You might question why such measurements are necessary. After all, antenna computer modelling programs are very good – so why make measurements on a real antenna? The answer is that however good the mathematical model may be, the proof of the pudding is in the real-world measurements on a real antenna made by real human beings, with all their failings and inaccuracies.

I have been testing antennas this way for many years and already had an arrangement for testing small VHF antennas This 'antenna test range' was subsequently modified to accommodate higher performance VHF antennas. This new arrangement is shown in **Photo 1**.

MAKING A SIMPLE VHF TEST RANGE. You can make a test range for VHF antennas in an average size garden. The equipment for a simple test setup is shown in **Figure 1**.

The antenna under test (AUT) is energised using a QRP transmitter or transceiver. You could use a signal generator if it has a high level output of a few tens of milliwatts. The test antenna is connected to a simple receiver, which comprises a diode detector and digital voltmeter (DVM).

A manual rotator can be constructed using a wooden board with a long bolt through the centre and held in place with a nut. A metal tube whose internal diameter is a snug (but not tight) fit over the bolt is used to support the AUT. By adding to the board a scale calibrated in degrees and putting a pointer on the AUT support tube, we can create a manual rotator with a directional indicator.

On 144MHz, the distance between the test antenna and the AUT need only around 5 – 6m (20ft) so such a test range could be accommodated in a moderately size garden. If you don't have a garden then the simple equipment described (and using a handheld to excite the AUT) can be used in a remote site such as a park because no additional power is required.

MEASUREMENTS. Start by feeding an RF signal to the AUT, having first checked that the frequency is clear (not usually a problem on VHF).

Adjust the AUT matching (if any) for the lowest SWR. Rotate the AUT and note if the SWR varies. If it does, check for the presence of any electromagnetic obstacles such as metal garden furniture or wire fences. Move the obstacle or the AUT to minimise the variation in SWR.

Beam the AUT at the test antenna and note the reading on the DVM. Rotate the AUT for the lowest reading on the DVM. This reading should be slightly more than 0.5V to remain in the linear portion of the diode characteristic of the diode detector.

Commence taking DVM readings at a beam heading of say 270°. You will have to move away from the AUT when taking the readings because your presence close to the antennas will affect them. Taking readings every 10° will detect the depth of the nulls in the radiation pattern but making 36 separate reading can be quite tedious. A measurement every 20° (18 readings) will give an adequate representation of the performance of your antenna. Your data can then be plotted on a polar graph. You can buy polar graph paper but I made mine up using a compass and a ruler and photocopying the original.

If you then replace the beam with a reference dipole and take another set of measurements you will have some indication of the gain of your beam referenced to a dipole.

These measurements give useful data but gathering the data manually and plotting it by hand on a polar graph is very laborious and time consuming. The system really needs automating...

AUTOMATING THE TEST RANGE. A method of data acquisition, data digitising, data recording plus a method of displaying the results of a plot is required, definitely a job for a computer. Digital data can be processed in a manner that bypasses the error-prone method of recording the data manually. In a

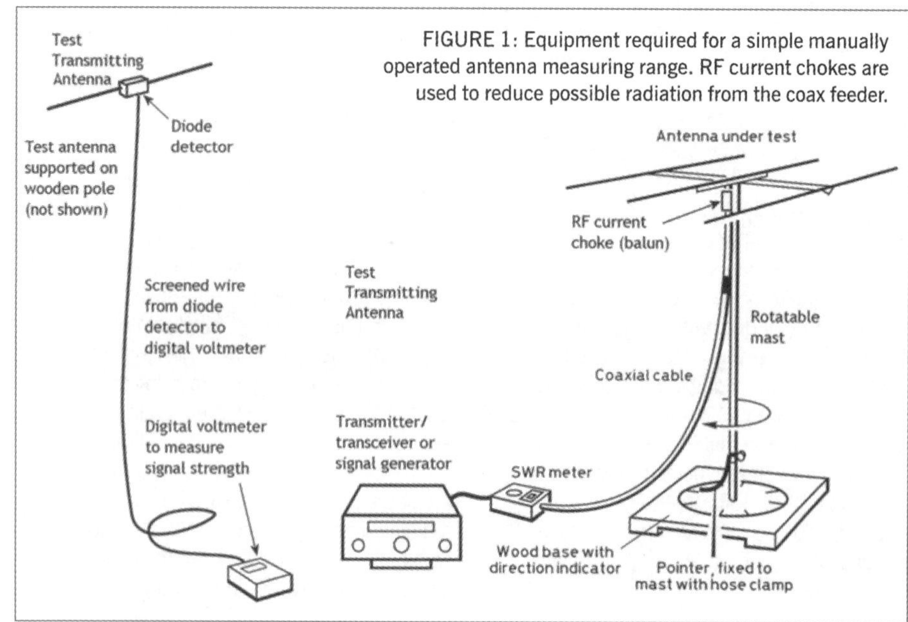


**FIGURE 1: Equipment required for a simple manually operated antenna measuring range. RF current chokes are used to reduce possible radiation from the coax feeder.**

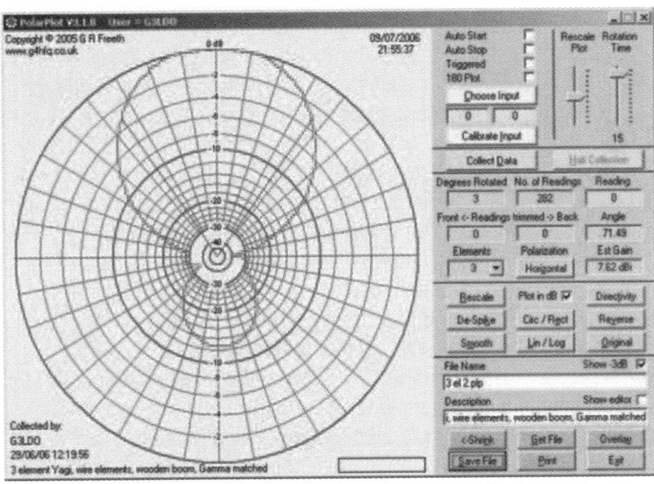

FIGURE 2: Polar diagram of a three element VHF Yagi plotted using the ARRL tapered dB Log scale. The setting boxes to the right illustrate the range of processing available with Polar Plot.

FIGURE 3: Receiver/sound card and RF micro power linearity compared using 10dB stepped signal. The receiver/soundcard is shown in red and the power meter in green.

properly designed data acquisition system, the only inaccuracies will be in the actual analogue circuit, due to either non-linearity or noise. Once the data is digitised, there should be no change in accuracy due to subsequent processing such as conversion from linear to log scales displays etc.

To enable the output from the field strength meter to be input to the computer we need an analogue to digital converter. Fortunately every computer theses days has one – it is called a sound card. We also need:

- A remotely controlled rotator whose rotation speed is accurately known.
- A receiver with good frequency stability and linearity.
- Appropriate software to allow the computer to record and display the results.

The main difficulty with using a receiver and sound card is linearity and dynamic range. Furthermore, a soundcard operated on the level of an audio signal to the receiver must be set to SSB or CW to produce a beat note from the receiver, hence the need for stability. To obtain maximum linearity it must be possible to turn the receiver's AGC off. There are not many of these around. KL7AJ **[1]** uses a homebrew direct conversion receiver with no AGC. He claims that the output from the balanced modulator of this receiver is extremely linear and proportional to the received voltage at the antenna terminals.

This automated range requires the only the same amount of space as the simple one described earlier. However, it is not suitable for setting up away from the home QTH because of the requirements of the rotator – most of them run from the mains supply.

In previous Antennas column I have described a very good antenna program by GR Freeth, G4HFQ, called PolarPlot, which measures and displays the radiation pattern of an antenna. **[2, 3]**. This program is free and is used with a sound card and a receiver. The radiation pattern of a gamma matched three-element beam using this program is shown in **Figure 2**.

As already mentioned, the main limiting factor is the receiver linearity. However, PolarPlot can use the signal strength acquired by an external micropower meter. This arrangement enables better resolution to be obtained for nulls below -30dB. Suitable meters are based on the Analog Devices AD8307 logarithmic amplifier IC, which will work up to 500MHz. I use a 'Polar Watt' power meter designed by M0DFT specifically for use with Polar Plot. Unfortunately this was not produced as a kit; however there are other possibilities.

In June 2007, G4HFQ added the ability of PolarPlot to read power levels using LP-100-VCP and FTB Meter. This wattmeter is designed by Larry Phipps, N8LP, to be used as an in-line instrument in the same manner as a conventional SWR/power meter. Full details can be found in **[4, 5]**. OZ2CPU also made a digital power meter based on the Analog Devices AD8307. At one time OZ2CPU used to supply kits but this not done any more. However Dinesh Gajjar, VU2FD still does some AD8307-based kits using the OZ2CPU PIC program. It's called the PM3 kit, but it now appears to have been superseded by the PM3A **[6]**.

**Figure 3** shows some linearity calibration tests I made using a receiver /soundcard (red trace) and compared them with a test using an RF micropower circuit using the Analog Devices AD8307 (green trace). The signal source was a signal generator and the output was plotted on PolarPlot in 10dB steps. Most of the non-linearity on the red plot was due to the receiver. KL7AJ's homebrew direct conversion receiver with no AGC would have probably given greater linearity.

**HINTS AND TRICKS.** KL7AJ suggests that the distance between the antennas should be 10 times the AUT's longest dimension. This will assure that the antenna appears essentially as a point source of radiation, which eliminates parallax error and makes the centre of the AUT easier to define.

All antennas I have ever plotted show some degree of asymmetry and exhibit spurious minor lobes. These are often at odds with the neat, symmetrical antenna radiation patterns produced by antenna modelling programs. I hope to address how these differences can occur in the next Antennas.

To ascertain whether measured spurious lobes are a characteristic of the antenna or reflections within your antenna range, G4HFQ advises making a further plot with the antenna upside down and plotting in the same direction. If the new plot is a mirror image of the first then the sidelobes are a characteristic of the antenna; if it remains the same then it is caused by objects within the antenna range.

The most important characteristic of a radiation pattern is its directional properties and the magnitude of the main lobe compared with the minor ones. Minor lobes better than 20dB below the major lobe maximum indicates good directivity, though in this month's In Practice, Ian White expands on this simple statement. The elevation angle of measurement does not seem too critical. The two measurements shown in **Figure 4** were made at angles of 0° and 10° and then superimposed; they agree quite closely.

REFERENCES


[1] 'Data Acquisition of the Antenna Experimenter', Eric P. Nicholas, KL7AJ. *The ARRL Compendium*,

[2] Antennas, *RadCom* Nov 2002, Antennas, *RadCom* Oct 2005, *RadCom* Sept 2006, Oct 2006

[3] Antenna Workshop, *Practical Wireless* June 2006

[4] www.g4hfq.co.uk

[5] www.telepostinc.com/

[6] www.foxdelta.com/products/swr/pm3/pm3.pdf.


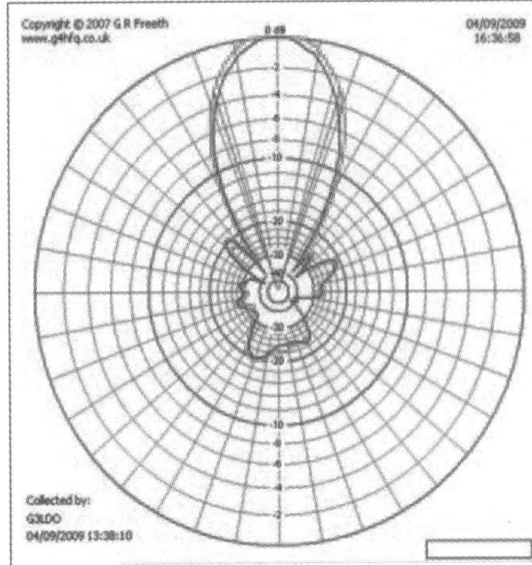

FIGURE 4: Measurements of a 9 element 2m Yagi made at zero (red) and 10° (green) elevation, showing very little change in antenna pattern characteristics.

# Antennas

## Continuing our look at interpreting computer modelling in the real world.

PHOTO 1. A W2DU HF Inline Isolator made by Unadilla, comprising over 50 ferrite rings on a 260mm length of RG-303 or similar.

COMPUTER ANTENNA MODELS. Antenna simulation or modelling programs have made a big impact on the design of antennas in the amateur radio world. Modelling is a technique for assessing the performance of one object or system by evaluating the performance of a substitute called a model. Models can be physical objects like reduced size scale model (eg a VHF model to evaluate a large HF antenna). The simple antenna range described in last month's column was originally designed for this purpose.

Models can also be purely mathematical and an antenna simulation program such as *EZNEC* produces computer mathematical models of real antennas. When used skilfully and sensibly within their limitations, they do a remarkable job of evaluating an antenna.

It is important to remember that when you are using such a program it is analysing a *model* of an antenna and not a real antenna. Some physical objects like wire and metallic tube are easily modelled with high accuracy, while metal plate structures such as vehicles or the effect of ground can only be approximated.

Ground has a profound effect on the performance of an antenna and is one of the most difficult to model. For this reason modelling programs offer methods of modelling ground in different ways, depending on the requirements of the model. The easiest is Free Space – that is, no ground at all. It is useful when comparing antennas when the eventual operating environment isn't known, or for comparing the pattern of a model antenna with the published free space patterns of other antennas.

COMPARING ANTENNAS. Many antenna manufacturers produce a free space computer model of their products, which goes a long way to documenting an antenna's performance, but it doesn't tell the whole story. The range of intensities measured in plotting these diagrams can exceed 50dB, so the scaling of the polar graphs used to represent the antenna radiation pattern is of some consequence.

What follows are radiation patterns of the same multi-element Yagi beam antenna but using polar graphs with different scales. These graphs where produced by measurement (rather than modelling) using Polar Plot as described last month; nevertheless, two of these scales are used in computer modelling programs.

The first example is a Linear Plot, which is shown in **Figure 1**. You would get this type of plot if you used a diode field strength meter on a simple antenna range. It can only show features of the field strength from maximum signal strength down about -15 to -20dB or so, which gives a very optimistic picture of directivity and suppresses the minor lobes. The linear scale has the advantage of being very sensitive to changes in level in the region of maximum signal strength and is useful for making gain comparisons between different antennas. The linear plot was used in all early radio and antenna books to illustrate antenna radiation patterns but has been superseded in modern antenna literature.

If your main interest is a low noise antenna, as described by Ian White in [1], then you will be more interested in the proportions of the minor lobes of the antenna. The polar diagram plotted on a logarithmic (linear dB) grid is of the same antenna is shown in **Figure 2**. The display shows the radiation pattern over a range of 50dB and emphasises these minor lobes to enable them to be examined in more detail.

The ARRL devised a polar diagram having a log periodic grid. Instead of the graduations varying linearly with the log of the field intensity they vary periodically. The constant of this periodicity is 0.89, for 2dB intervals. This represents a compromise between the extremes of linear and linear dB grids so far described. It possesses good sensitivity to small changes in maximum signal while at the same time is able to display the minor lobes. A field strength polar diagram of our VHF beam antenna using this scale is shown in **Figure 3**.

REAL WORLD VERSUS COMPUTERS. The examples of polar plotting scales shown in Figures 1, 2 and 3 show a plot of a 9-element VHF Yagi. You may have noticed that although the main lobe is nice and symmetrical, the minor lobes are asymmetrical and ragged. This is in contrast to the nice symmetrical diagrams produced by a computer-modelling program shown in **Figures 4 and 5**. Why should this be?

Ian White [1] described a possible cause as being the unwanted RF currents flowing on the outside of the coaxial feedline along the metal boom. If these currents are large enough they can cause distortion of the Yagi's radiation pattern. He explains the cause of these unwanted currents and a method of reducing them in this month's In Practice.

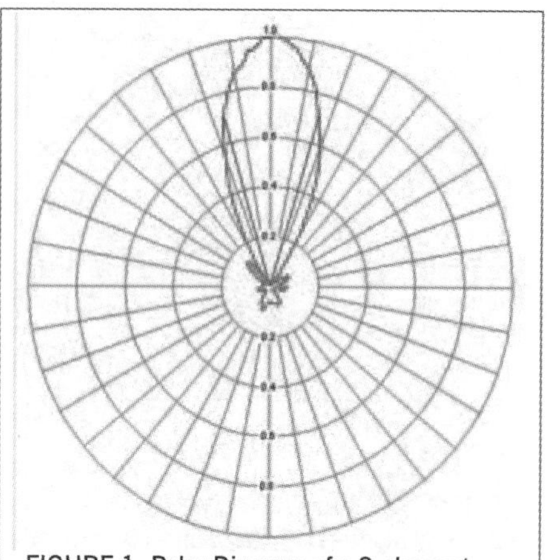

FIGURE 1: Polar Diagram of a 9-element VHF Yagi using a linear scale.

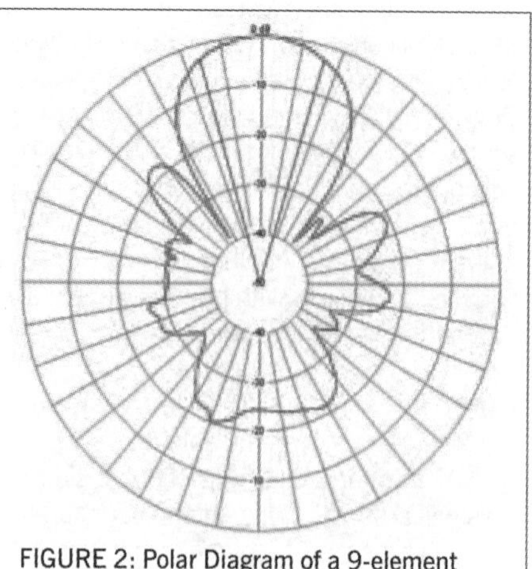

FIGURE 2: Polar Diagram of a 9-element VHF Yagi using a linear log plot

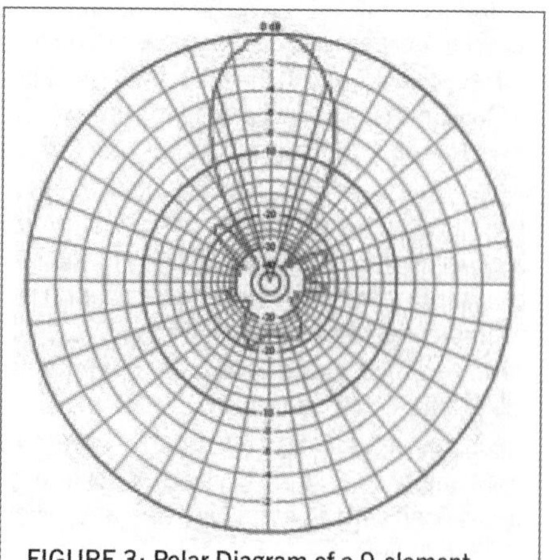

FIGURE 3: Polar Diagram of a 9-element VHF Yagi using a log periodic plot.

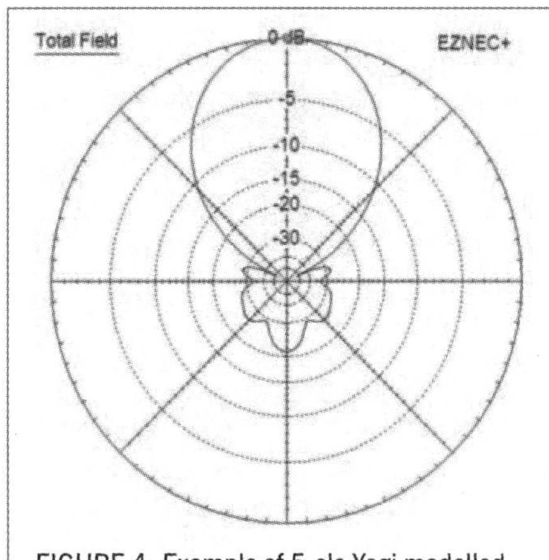


FIGURE 4: Example of 5-ele Yagi modelled using a log periodic plot.

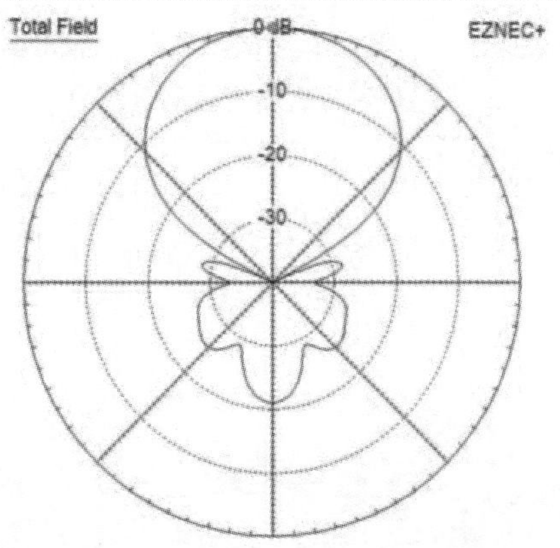


FIGURE 5: Example of 5-ele Yagi modelled using a linear log plot. Note that centre of this plot cuts off at –40dB.

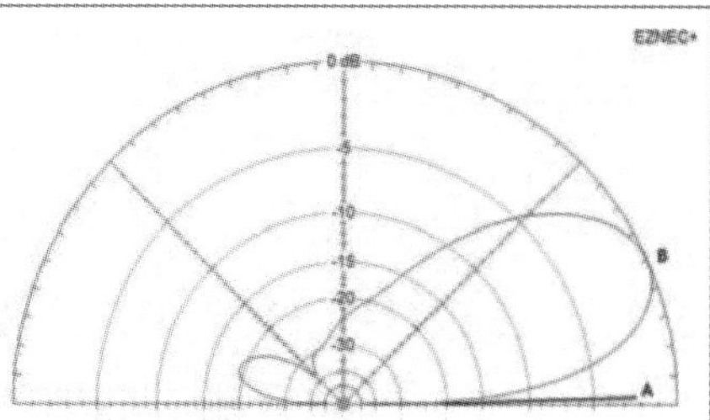


FIGURE 6: An elevation plot of a three-element beam 0.5 wavelengths high. The program indicates zero signal at A and maximum signal at B.

Other examples are shown below.

It is important when comparing the radiation patterns of antennas to be aware of the type of scale used. Generally it is safe to say that the ARRL Log Periodic Plot is now the most common in amateur radio literature although you do see others here and there.

SOME LIMITS OF A COMPUTER MODEL. A very common method by which radio amateurs check the performance of their beam antennas is to ask a local radio amateur to produce a transmitted signal and then for you to rotate the beam and note the signal strength on the S-meter at various beam headings. These readings can be used to plot a polar diagram if you wish; or you can use Polar Plot as described in November 'Antennas'. The other method is for you to transmit a steady signal and for the local station to record the readings as you announce the beam headings.

Some years ago I wrote an article in *SPRAT* (the G QRP club magazine) on compact beam antenna I had designed called the Double-D. I described the 'testing with a local' method used to produce a polar diagram of this antenna and included it in the article. A reader then wrote to me and complained that my description of antenna tests with a local amateur was meaningless because there is no signal at zero degrees elevation and he had a computer program to prove it. Both you and I know very well that you get a strong signal from a local station, so what did he mean by that?

When you check your horizontal beam antenna with a nearby radio amateur, his and your antennas are approximately the same height. This means that the signal path elevation angle is approximately zero degrees. If you were to ask your computer analysis program to produce an azimuth plot of a horizontal beam antenna at zero degrees elevation it will report back that there is no signal at that angle and refuse to make a calculation.

This is illustrated in **Figure 6** and is because the computer model only predicts far-field reflected waves. The far field is determined by the electrical field of the antenna calculated at large distance from the antenna. It is the far field radiation in (predominantly) the HF region that is involved in skip propagation, the refraction of sky waves through the ionosphere layers.

These far field calculations do not account for radiation at elevation angles ranging from zero to negative angles relative to the horizon. Downward radiation from an antenna at a very high location would be most relevant to direct space wave or point-to-point communications. These phenomena fall into the realm of ground-wave analysis rather than far-field analysis.

However, RF is radiated from an antenna in all directions in a manner determined by the geometry of the antenna. Those waves closer to the antenna less affected by ground reflection can be considered as Ground Waves. These in turn can be considered to have two components, as shown in *Figure 7*, which contribute to the strong signals we get from local radio stations. The first component is direct space waves. If two antennas are within line of sight of each other, their signal path at HF and above is normally dominated by these direct space waves. The second category of ground wave is the surface wave. These are propagated along the surface of the earth caused by interaction of the wave and the imperfect conductivity of the earth. This causes the wavefront to be tilted forward, giving the elevation pattern of the antenna a downward component. I must emphasise that an HF or VHF surface wave does not travel far (unlike at MF and LF) and does not contribute to the reflected sky wave signal.

Ground wave analysis is available only in the more advanced computer programs such as *EZNEC Pro* or *EZNEC/4*.

CURRENT CHOKES AND BALUNS. Earlier I made reference to current chokes that can be used to reduce or eliminate RF currents on the outside of coax transmission line. The way that this is done is to introduce impedance to the outside of the outer braiding of the coax to oppose these currents. One method that is gaining popularity is simply to place ferrite rings on the along a portion of the coax feeder. The method is attributed to Walter Maxwell, W2DU **[2]**, although I have an earlier reference to the technique by Doug DeMaw **[3]**.

I received an e-mail from G4ZQC, asking if I knew of a UK source of Amidon FB-77-1042 ferrite rings or sleeves to fit over RG213 coax. I replied that I was unaware of any such source but that I had obtained a device described as a'W2DU HF Inline Isolator', which may suit his purpose. This item is made by Unadilla, shown in **Photo 1** and was obtained from Adur Communications **[4]**.

I was curious as to what ferrites were used in my W2DU HF Inline Isolator so I cut a hole in the side and had a look. The coax in the isolator was certainly not RG213 because the outside diameter of the ferrites was only 9mm, see **Photo 2**. However, W2DU did all his experimental work using RG-303 and claims that it can handle the full USA legal power limit so perhaps Amidon FB-77-1042 ferrite rings on RG213 coax is unnecessary.

PHOTO 2: Internal structure of a Unadilla W2DU HF Inline Isolator.

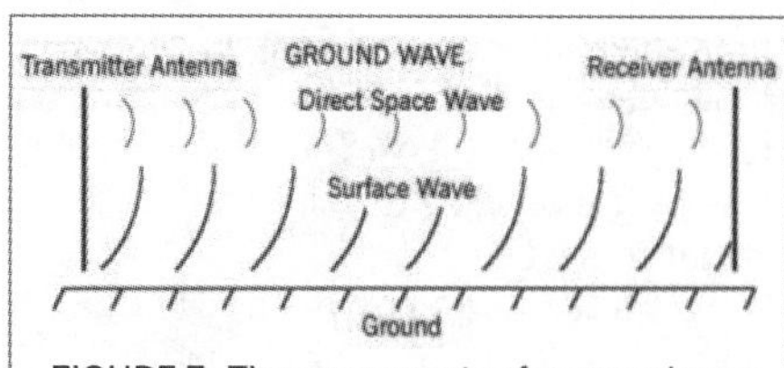


FIGURE 7: The components of a ground wave; the surface wave and the direct space wave.


REFERENCES

[1] In Practice, Ian White, GM3SEK, *RadCom* November, 2009

[2] *Reflections, Transmission Lines and Antennas*, Walter Maxwell, W2DU (ARRL publication)

[3] *Ferromagnetic-core Design* and *Application Handbook*, MF "Doug" DeMaw

[4] www.adurcomms.com

# Antennas

## Getting a quart antenna into a pint pot garden

**PHOTO 1: The elevated radial system being tested with a Hustler 6BTV antenna.**

SMALL SPACE, BIG PROBLEM. The most frequently asked questions I receive in my e-mail, or raised at when I give talks on antennas, is the subject of making or selecting a suitable HF antenna for a restricted QTH. The situation is worse for the lower HF bands where the efficiency of the antenna falls dramatically if you try to make it too small. A half wave dipole for 3.6MHz is 130ft (40m) long and most modern QTHs do not have anything like that sort of space.

A BACKYARD ANTENNA. What I am about to propose, as a possible solution to antennas in QTHs with very little space, is based on an antenna I made many years ago for an amateur friend. He wanted an antenna for the 80m band but lived in a small two-up two-down house with nothing more than a back yard that was about 18ft (5.5m) square. Furthermore, it was paved, with no provision for an earth connection. The only redeeming feature was concrete washing line pole in the far corner of the yard.

I made a scaffold pole extension to the clothes post for a mast. The chimney was pressed into service as an additional support. The objective was to get as much wire into the restricted space as possible, with the area of greatest current as high as possible. The length of the wire element was not measured, just made to fit the space. It resulted in an open loop structure as shown in **Figure 1**. To my recollection the whole structure was about 16ft (4.9m) square. The antenna was fed in the centre and matched to the rig using an ATU in the shack.

Surprisingly, we were able to work stations around the UK on 80m SSB using a QRP rig. Theoretically, the performance of this antenna is very poor. According to EZNEC, the feed point has a feed resistance of about 3Ω and a reactance greater than –j1000, which should have put it outside the impedance matching range of any normal ATU. No doubt matching efficiency was also poor and the feedline loss was high.

I recently used an EZNEC model in an attempt to improve the performance of this antenna. I started with the introduction of a couple of loading coils. A value of 70μH brought the structure into near resonance with a feed impedance of R13 +j20, which is a lot more manageable as far as matching is concerned. A 70μH coil can be made by winding 75 turns of 18SWG wire on a 1.6in (40mm) diameter section of plastic waste pipe. This value is not critical because the antenna is tuned with an ATU.

The model predicted a gain of –6dBi; probably due to the current in the lower section of the open loop cancelling the radiation from the upper section. (To put this into perspective, a good quality 80m mobile antenna has a gain of around –10 to –12dBi.) The gain can be improved by routing the end sections away from each other.

The model also predicts that the antenna will work on other bands but, for some bands, such as 7MHz, the coil may have to be shorted out using jumper wires. The required accessibility of these coils is the reason why they are placed fairly close to the ends of the elements, which are close to the ground.

This antenna does not have to be a true square or even orientated in the vertical position. It can be made so that the square is sloping or lopsided. The most important consideration is to make it as large as your small QTH will allow. The chances are that if you can make it larger than shown in Figure 1, the antenna will work without loading coils on 80m. The antenna is fed with 300Ω balanced line feeder because it has a lower loss than coax with high values of SWR. The ribbon feeder is connected straight to a short length of RG213 via a 1:1 balun.

The shack end of the coax feeder is connected to the coax connector on the ATU. Do not take the twin feeder straight to the balanced feeder connections of the ATU because this routes the connections via a 4:1 transformer found in most ATUs. This will worsen the impedance matching ratio. Because the antenna is electrically small, the feeder will be in close proximity to the radiating elements. This will probably cause common mode currents on the feeder and a 1:1 current choke will be useful in minimising these.

VERTICAL ANTENNAS. For small spaces, vertical antennas appear to be an attractive option. They can generate low takeoff angles of radiation, which means long skip distances. However, there can be problems with installing verticals. The instructions with some commercial verticals allege that you can use them without radials. With the exception of the vertical dipole, a dipole on its end, a vertical antenna is only half an antenna, the radial and the ground is the other half.

ELEVATED RADIALS. You can use resonant elevated radials with a feed point at least 5ft (1.5m) above the ground. With this you need at least two tuned radials per band, and they must not touch the ground. For a small number of radials, the higher you can get the feed point (and radials) the better.

Walter Blanchard, G3JKV tested a Hustler 6BTV on behalf of the Dorking Amateur Radio Club using this approach. The instructions stated that Hustler antennas will work with just a simple earth rod but will perform better with radials. To test this out, G3JKV mounted the antenna it on a tilt-over swivel so it could be lowered for easily for adjustment. The swivel point was about 5ft above ground. The aluminium ground pole was 2in diameter and sunk 5ft (1.5m) into the ground, giving a 10ft (3m) total length. It would not work properly using just the ground pole for earth, which may have been the result of a poor sandy earth. It would not resonate anywhere near the ham bands and where it did resonate the SWR was very high.

Various radials were tried. All the radials were attached at approximately the swivel point. The antenna worked well provided 3 or 4 radials were used, but fewer radials resulted in a reduced performance. Radials spaced out equally around 360° (about every 20°) gave the best results.

After many experimental antenna and radial adjustments a SWR 1.2:1 or less on every band was achieved. However, to get this sort of performance, a cat's cradle of radial wires and sticks was required. With three radials per band, nearly 500ft (150m) of wire was used, all up on sticks at head height around the garden – and that made the garden unusable. Hustler recommends 14SWG or larger gauge copper wire. G3JKV priced the radial wire material on the web at over £200, which is nearly as much as the aerial.

G3JKV goes on to say that this vertical definitely picked up more local noise than his 40ft (12m) high horizontal dipoles. WSPR **[1]** worked and heard a lot more DX using the wire dipoles than this vertical. Averaging over a large number of different stations and bands using WSPR showed the dipoles had something like a 10dB advantage.

If you haven't got 40ft (12m) high dipoles then a vertical may still be the way to go. It has a low visual impact and has a low angle of radiation provided that they are in the clear of other metal objects and as far away as possible from house electrical wiring.

If you can settle for a single band antenna, the radial problem is nowhere near as acute. My first DX in the late 1950s was working all around South America on 15m using a vertical with four sloping radials. The base was around 12ft high and, as I recall, it was a very simple antenna to construct.

**GROUND RADIALS.** Most lower HF band DXers use vertical antennas, usually in some sort of multiple antenna gain configuration such as a four square. These antennas are normally ground mounted, that is to say the feed point is just above the ground, with lots of radials on (or slightly under) the soil.

For a ground-mounted vertical mounted over average soil, you will need at least 16 radials, 30ft (9m) long for frequencies 3.5MHz and above. That is 480ft (144m) of wire. More and longer is better, especially for 40/80m operation. John Stanley, K4ERO, notes **[2]** that if you have the luxury of laying down 120 radials, 33m (108ft) long, the same antenna will have 3dB extra gain compared with the 16 radial model described previously. The downside is that it will take around 13,000ft (4000m) of wire – yes, two and a half miles! Small diameter wire can be used for these radials because there are so many of them to share the return currents. They are also in parallel with the ground currents in the earth.

FIGURE 1: Suggested layout of a compact 80m plus other bands antenna. The RF voltages at the ends of the antenna are high during transmit so they should be high enough to avoid accidental contact. The loading coils can be provided with jumper wires if the antenna is used on the higher frequency bands.

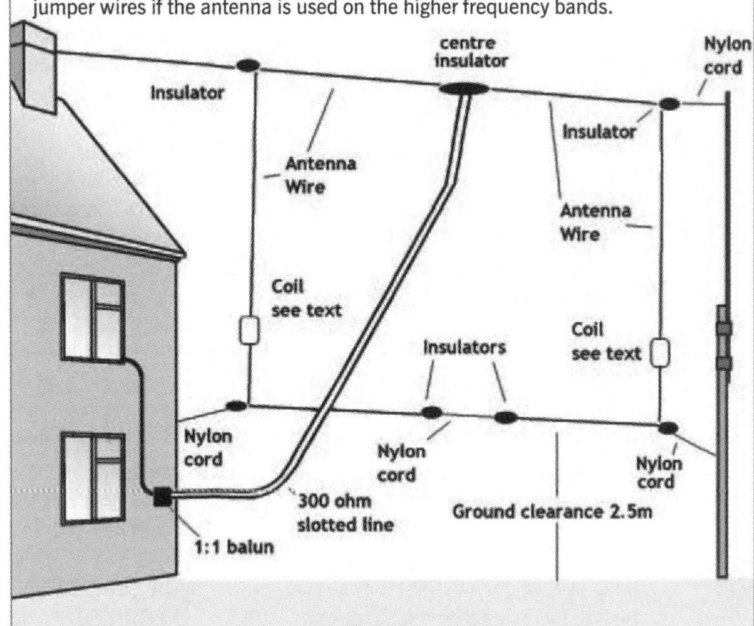


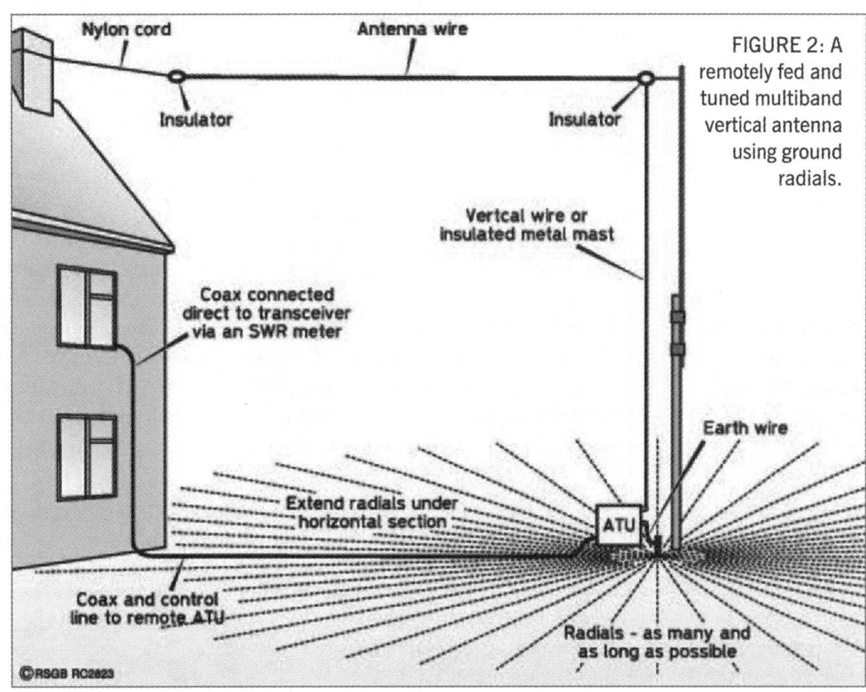


FIGURE 2: A remotely fed and tuned multiband vertical antenna using ground radials.

Ground radials need not be resonant. This is a misconception based on elevated or ground plane type elements. They are different from the elevated ground plane radials in this regard since ground radials supplement ground currents and do not try to replace them entirely. Elevated ground plane radials, especially if few in number, need to be bit longer than 1/4 wave at the operating frequency.

What you absolutely have to avoid with ground radials is to put the feed point a short distance in the air, then run radials down and along the ground.

Ground radials do not actually need to be much longer than the antenna is tall. A shortened antenna with loading coils will have a more compact near field where the majority of the antenna field is. The ground needs only reach out as far as the near field extends. Field intensity drops off with the square of the distance from the base of the antenna.

Keen lower HF band DXers invest a lot of time and effort in building a good ground radial system, particularly with a multi element vertical where a radial system is required for each vertical element.

A practical remotely tuned multiband antenna used with an automatic ATU is shown in **Figure 2**. If we assume the vertical and horizontal sections of the antenna are each 25ft (7.6m), this will make a near quarter wave antenna on 80m and a half wave on 40m. If you want the antenna for 40m and above the total length of the antenna can be shortened and the lengths of the radials can be halved.

REFERENCES

[1] I hope to describe a method of testing antennas using WSPR in next month's Antennas.

[2] 'Optimum Ground systems for Vertical Antennas', John Stanley, K4ERO, *QST* December 1976

# Antennas

## More on baluns

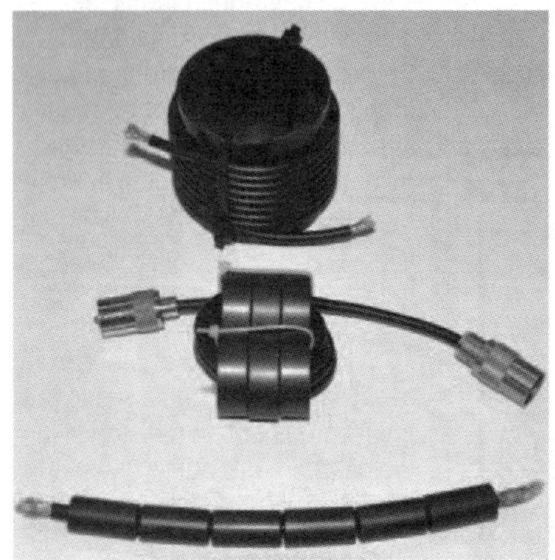

PHOTO 1: Balun types. Top: 8 turns of RG58 on a section of 70mm plastic pipe. Middle: 8 turns of RG58 through 6 ferrite rings. Bottom: 6 ferrite beads threaded on a length of Mini8 coax.

**CURRENT CHOKES AND BALUNS.** I have previously made reference to current chokes that can be used to reduce or eliminate RF common mode currents (currents on the outside of coax transmission line). The way that this is done is to introduce impedance on the outside of the outer braiding of the coax to oppose these currents while at the same time leaving the inner side of the braid unaffected. The subject was discussed in detail by Ian White, GM3SEK **[1]** so I don't propose to repeat it here. What I will do is discuss some of the practical aspects of constructing a current choke and my attempts at measuring balun performance.

Before I start I will clear up some points of terminology. A balun (balanced to unbalanced network) is a device that allows you to connect an unbalanced transmission line (coax) to an unbalanced line (twin line feeder or a balanced antenna such as a dipole). It has been common practice to use a 4:1 transformer in this application. This is probably because coax has an impedance of 50Ω and twin line feeder is normally 300 or 450Ω, although these impedances are unlikely to be encountered in a multiband antenna system. As GM3SEK pointed out, a transformer does little to reduce common-mode currents. A current choke is much more effective in this application.

**TYPES OF CURRENT CHOKE.** What is required is a high impedance on the outside of the coax braiding that does not affect the normal transmission line characteristics. This impedance should be high over the whole desired frequency range. The only practical component that can be used for the job is an RF choke. As you are aware, the characteristics of an RF choke in normal RF circuits is large inductance with a very small self-capacitance. Because this capacitance is low, the off-resonant reactance is high, giving the component a broadband characteristic.

**COILED COAX.** The simplest method of introducing inductance on the outside of the coax is simply to make part of the coax feedline into a coil, with just a few turns of coax in a loop of diameter 150 to 300mm (6in to 12in). The coils of coax make up the inductance of the choke so not any old roll of coax will do. See **Table 1** for the number of turns required for various antenna applications. At higher frequencies the coil choke should be wound on a former, as shown at the top of **Photo 1**.

I made some measurements of various baluns using the AIM-4170. Using this method, the characteristics of the coil balun were measured. The results are shown in **Figure 1**. This and most of the following measurements using the AIM-4170 show the magnitude of impedance only; for clarity, I have turned off the other parameters. In some cases a second scan was done, with the balun placed or connected differently. These results are overlaid. The measurements in Figure 1 show an initial scan (in red) where the balun is placed on a table covered with an earthed conductive anti-static mat. The second scan (blue) shows the balun placed 6in clear of the table on a cardboard box, which indicates that care is needed when performing these measurements. The colours for these parameters have been modified in the AIM-4170 configuration file for improved print reproduction. Note that characteristics are not measured above 2000Ω; this scale was chosen as being the most appropriate for balun characteristic measurements.

**COAX WOUND ON FERRITE.** The characteristics of a balun can be improved considerably by using ferrite material. The coax feeder can be wound round a large ferrite ring as described and illustrated by GM3SEK **[1]** or wound through a small number of ferrite rings as shown in the middle of Photo 1. The advantage of this illustrated arrangement is that a larger diameter coax such as RG-213 can be used to make a QRO balun. The characteristics of this balun are shown in **Figure 2**. The inductance of this arrangement is rather large for HF general coverage but is excellent for the lower frequency LF bands.

**FERRITE BEADS ON COAX.** Yet another alternative, popularised by W2DU, is to feed the coax feeder through ferrite tubes or beads to form a sleeve. An experimental arrangement, using FairRite 43540001 (or equivalent, obtainable from JAB **[2]**) is shown at the bottom of Photo 1. This ferrite material fits nicely on Mini8 coax cable. For this type of balun to be effective the ferrite beads should be a reasonably snug fit on to the coax.

This arrangement was tested and the results are shown in **Figure 3**. A balun with reasonable characteristics is achievable with just four beads (shown in red). An improved performance, shown in blue, is achieved with six beads. This implies that eight or ten beads are required for a balun to cover the HF bands. I wasn't able to test this assumption because I had run out of ferrite beads!

I tested a commercial version of the W2DU coax current choke of the type I have just described. I cut a hole in it to see how it was constructed and found it comprised around 30 ferrite beads, each 10mm OD and 7mm long. I was unable to see clearly the size of coax that the beads were threaded on but it looked like RG58. The characteristics of this balun are shown in **Figure 4**. I have included an additional Theta (angle of impedance) graph to show that this type of balun also has resonance (just the same as a coil of coax), in this case just over 7MHz.

**BALUN CHARACTERISTICS AND FERRITES.** An important characteristic of a balun is that it should have a reasonable impedance to prevent common mode currents in the frequency range for which it was designed. The coil of coax balun at the top of Photo 1 appears to have an impedance greater than 1000Ω (Figure 1) in the range 17 to 40MHz and has a peak at 28MHz greater than 13kΩ.

The balun made with coax and ferrite rings in the middle of Photo 1 appears to have an impedance greater than 1000Ω Figure 2 in the range 1 to 15MHz and has a peak at 3.5MHz greater than 57kΩ.

On the other hand, the W2DU balun has a much flatter response of impedance relative to frequency as shown in Figures 3 and 4. It should be noted that baluns so far described

TABLE 1: Coiled-coax feeding chokes for HF. Wind the indicated length of coaxial cable into a flat coil and tape it together. Source: W7EL, ARRL Antenna Handbook.

| Frequency | feet RG213/UR67 cable | turns RG213/UR67 cable | feet RG58/UR76 cable | turns RG58/UR76 cable |
|---|---|---|---|---|
| *Single band (very effective)* | | | | |
| 3.5MHz | 22 | 8 | 20 | 6-8 |
| 7MHz | 22 | 10 | 15 | 6 |
| 10MHz | 12 | 10 | 10 | 7 |
| 14MHz | 10 | 4 | 8 | 8 |
| 21MHz | 8 | 6-8 | 6 | 8 |
| 28MHz | 6 | 6-8 | 4 | 6-8 |
| *Multi band (good compromise)* | | | | |
| 3.5-30MHz | 10 | 7 | 10 | 7 |
| 3.5-10MHz | 18 | 9-10 | 18 | 9-10 |
| 14-30MHz | 8 | 6-7 | 8 | 6-7 |

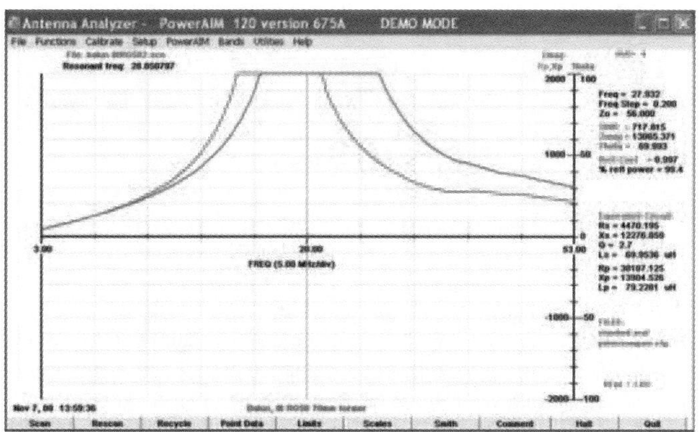


FIGURE 1: Characteristics of the top balun in Photo 1.

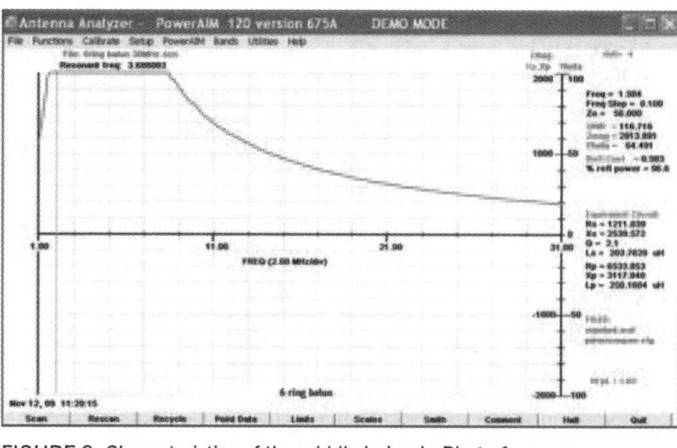


FIGURE 2: Characteristics of the middle balun in Photo 1.

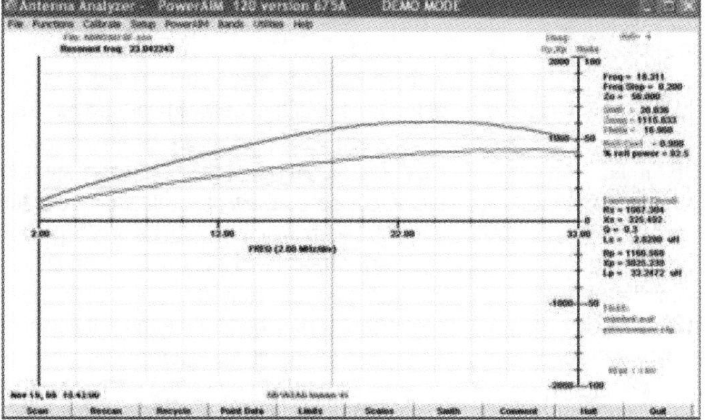


FIGURE 3: Characteristics of a home made W2DU type balun with four ferrite beads (red) and six beads (blue).

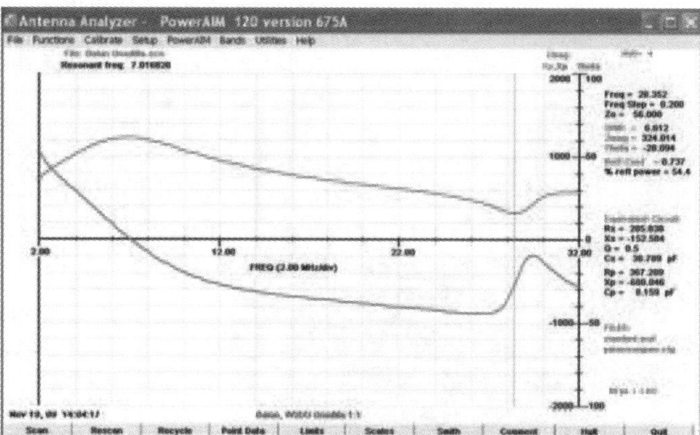


FIGURE 4: Characteristics of a commercial W2DU coax current choke with magnitude of impedance (red) and Theta (purple).

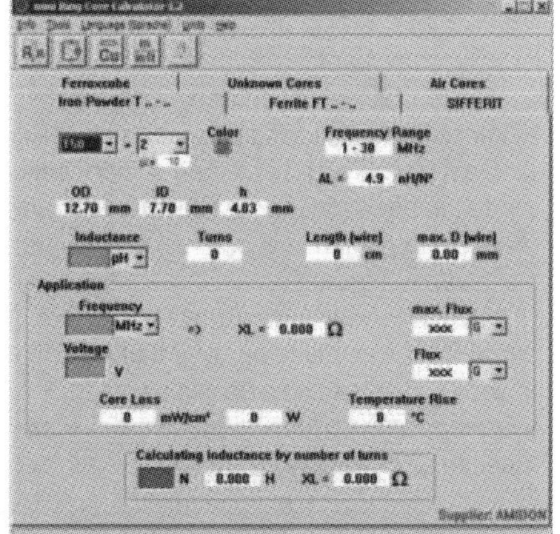


FIGURE 5: Main window of *Mini Ring Calculator.*

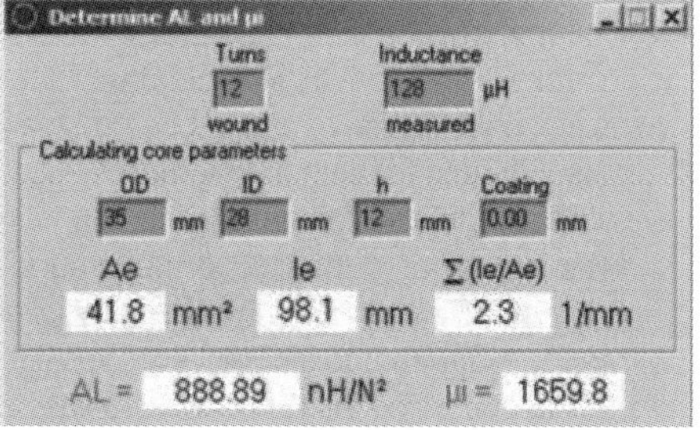


FIGURE 6: Sub window of *Mini Ring Calculator* (see text).

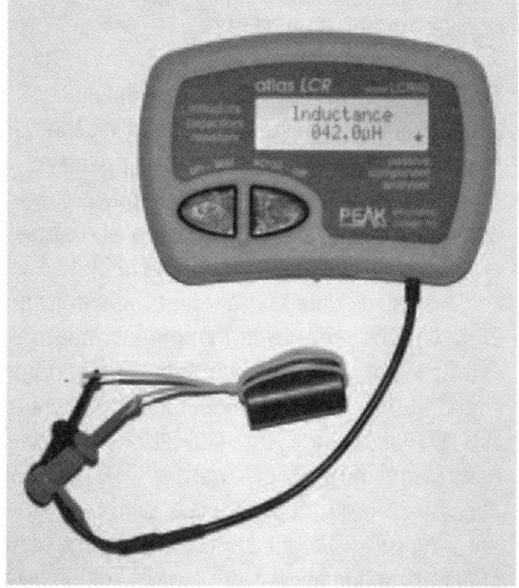


PHOTO 2: Measuring the inductance of a coil wound on ferrite.

do not represent any sort of 'design'. All I have done is made up baluns with odd lengths of coax and items of ferrite, mostly from the junk box, just to examine the characteristics of these constructions.

The classification and characteristics of ferrite material with various manufacturers using different units can be confusing. What follows is a method for determining if the ferrite rings you have in your junk box are suitable for making a current choke balun.

Wind 10 turns of wire around your mystery ferrite ring or bead and measure the inductance as shown in **Photo 2**. I use an Atlas LCR40 for this job, one of the best and most-used instruments in my shack apart from the multimeter.

Use *Mini Ring Calculator* by DL5SWB, a program that can be downloaded for free [3]. I am indebted to DJ4RAJ for bringing this to my attention. The main page of *Mini Ring Calculator* is shown in **Figure 5**, which shows many measurement options outside the scope of this discussion. The help file in particularly informative.

Click on the $R_L?\mu_i$ button in the top left hand corner and the program will display the part we are really interested in, see **Figure 6**. Enter the measured inductance and the dimensions of the ferrite into the appropriate boxes and it will come up with the permeability value $\mu_i$ of your ferrite ring. This core should have a permeability of at least 1500 if it is to be any use as a current choke.

FINALLY. The impedance presented to common mode currents should be well above 500Ω. If you are running a QRO transmitter, low choke impedances can allow enough current to flow that the ferrites will overheat. Theoretically, these baluns should have no loss to differential mode currents (normal coax RF current). This is supported by the fact that no measurable power loss could be detected with the baluns described above when I made this test. Next month, I will describe some practical designs for current balun chokes.

REFERENCES

[1] In Practice, Ian White, GM3SEK, *RadCom* November, 2009
[2] JAB Electronic Components www.jabdog.com.
[3] www.dl5swb.de

# Antennas

## More on the Hustler 6BTV, and did *RadCom* "Goof"?

PHOTO 1: The Hustler 6BTV installation of Duncan Tribute, G1OEQ.

**THE HUSTLER 6BTV.** Early this year I described G3JKV's experiences with the Hustler 6BTV vertical antenna using raised radials **[1]**. He compared the performance of the 6BTV with a 40ft high dipole antenna on long haul paths such as VK and ZL.

This raises two issues regarding antennas. First, it is more important where an antenna is than what it is. The second is a question of expectations. For example, Duncan Tribute, G1OEQ, also has a Hustler 6BTV, which he uses from a pint-pot size garden in Truro. He claims remarkable success with this antenna now for over a year, without the use of any radials. He goes on to say "The picture (**Photo 1**) tells the story of my installation, which is located between the house and an external garden wall and surrounded by overhead power lines and telephone wires. The mount of the antenna was prepared in accordance with the manufacturer's instructions using a 4ft length of 1½in aluminium mast, driven into the ground to leave 18in exposed to which the 6BTV is attached".

G1OEQ runs 100 watts to the 6BTV using an Icom 706 MKIIG. At the time of writing his longest distance QSOs have been into Ontario and Milwaukee on 20 metres and Malta on 40 metres. He also gets good reports across Europe on 80 metres, plus one contact in Newfoundland. All these contacts were using SSB. Duncan is content with these results because he was previously operating from a location in Surrey on VHF and UHF so an occasional transatlantic QSO is very satisfying.

It is interesting to read the experience of others with the Hustler 6BTV. Check out the eham.net **[2]** website, who publish reviews on all manner of equipment including the 6BTV. In general, the reviews on this antenna are positive, particularly if a radial system is used.

**RADCOM ARTICLE BOOB?** In November 2009 I reviewed two antennas from Vine Antennas, one for 6 metres and the other 2 metres, plus their baluns. In response to this the designer of these antennas, Justin Johnson, G0KSC, placed an item on his website **[3]** under the heading RadCom Article Boob. In this, he said, "Whilst he (G3LDO) reported the best patterns he had seen, the real world polar plots showed pattern distortion yet he failed to mention the reasons why. Furthermore, I am surprised he did not contact me and question this problem at which time I could have given him the answers he should have reported.

"The patterns for both a 4 element 6m version and a 9 element 2m version showed a small amount of distortion around the base of the antenna and particularly within the rearward lobes. This is the result of the antenna being fed WITHOUT a true 1:1 balun. This fact can be proven by switching the coax from side to side (reversing connections) which will swap the distortion from one side of the antenna to the other.

"Within the article Peter experiments with both the Vine supplied Choke balun (coiled coax) and a toroid variant of the same. However, while these are called baluns, they do nothing to rectify the mismatch between an unbalanced feedline (coax) and a balanced antenna (the Yagi). The Choke balun merely helps prevent the resulting common mode currents from travelling back down the coax, radiating and de-tuning the Yagi. This said, one or the other baluns being used in the article (perhaps both) where not effective in this task as the antennas bandwidth moved when switching between the two clearly indicating the coax WAS becoming apart of the antenna and as a result, de-tuning the array.

"By not using a true 1:1 balun at the feed point, pattern distortion will be seen. The resulting pattern is typical of that found within Yagis fed with a gamma match which is an unbalanced matching arrangement. A true 1:1 balun connects to the unbalanced coax with an unbalanced feedpoint one side and provides a balanced output at the antenna side of the balun which in turn, keeps the radiation pattern symmetrical. I have several examples of these upon my 'creating a balun page', my favourite being the Grounded Pawsey Stub.

"Be sure not to make the same mistake with your next Yagi and ensure a true 1:1 balun is used at the feedpoint for best results!"

**REVIEWING ANTENNAS.** As I understand it, the purpose of a review of any item of equipment is to comment on various aspects of construction and performance of it *as supplied* and check out how it compares with the literature and specification provided by the manufacturer. The literature in this case comprises radiation diagrams using computer free-space models and SWR plots, all of which can be found on the G0KSC website [3]. A stated key feature of these antennas is 'Low Noise', a characteristic recently described by Ian White, GM3SEK **[4]**. In essence, this means small rear-facing lobes.

The G0KSC model of the 144MHz 9 element Yagi produces a very symmetrical plot in azimuth and (because it is a free space model) in elevation. The model also indicated that this antenna had very small minor lobes, as shown in **Figure 1**.

The field strength measurement method of the 144MHz 9 element Yagi was described in **[5]** and the results indicated a nice symmetrical main lobe although there were small irregularities in the minor lobes as

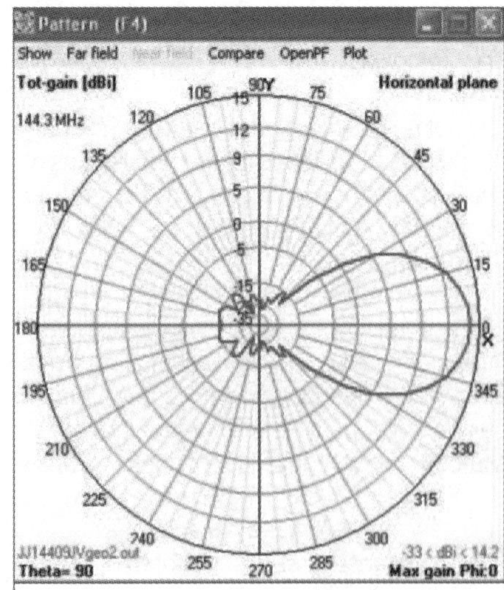


FIGURE 1: The G0KSC free space model of the 144MHz 9 element Yagi using NEC4.

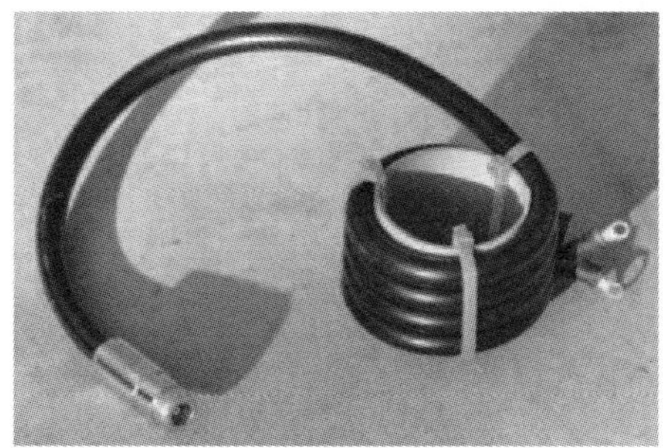

**PHOTO 2: Coiled coax choke balun as supplied by Vine antennas.**

shown in **Figure 2**. In the review I said it was a good antenna.

The supplied baluns for both the 6m and 2m antennas were nicely constructed and one of them is shown in **Photo 2**. Both these baluns were the same size. At the time I knew less about baluns than I do now although I didn't think a single size balun would cover the 6m and 2m bands. Later, a test showed this balun had a parallel resonance at 61MHz and a series resonance at 127MHz. At 51.15MHz the impedance was R560 +j950Ω.

I tried various baluns and feed arrangements but the result shown **Figure 2** was the best that could be obtained. I did try swapping over the connections from balun to the driven element but this did not cause any measurable minor lobe pattern changes. It is for this reason that I didn't say what caused these asymmetrical minor lobes – I just didn't know.

THE PAWSEY STUB. G0KSC believes that I was using the wrong sort of balun and that a 'true 1:1 balun' should be used for best results, preferably a Grounded Pawsey Stub as shown in **Photo 3** (from the G0KSC site, [3]).

Although I was unable to find a description of a 'true 1:1 balun' in any of my antenna literature the Pawsey Stub was another matter. It was apparently invented by Australian radio astronomer Dr J L Pawsey (1908-1962) **[6]**. However, it also appears in **[7]** (1945) without a device name, just the description 'Balanced output from concentric feeder – second method'. The same device is also described in **[8]** (1955) as a Balanced Bazooka. It has appeared in many antenna books to the present day and they all agree on the construction as shown in Figure 3.

This device uses the characteristics of a twin line quarter wave stub constructed by adding a quarter wave section of coax as shown in **Figure 3**. This added section is shorted to the outer braid of the feedline a quarter of a wavelength from the antenna feedpoint. This transforms to a very high impedance on the outer braiding of both sections of coax and is very effective in preventing common mode currents on the outside of the feeder without affecting the impedance of the main feeder. For this stub to work the same precautions are required as

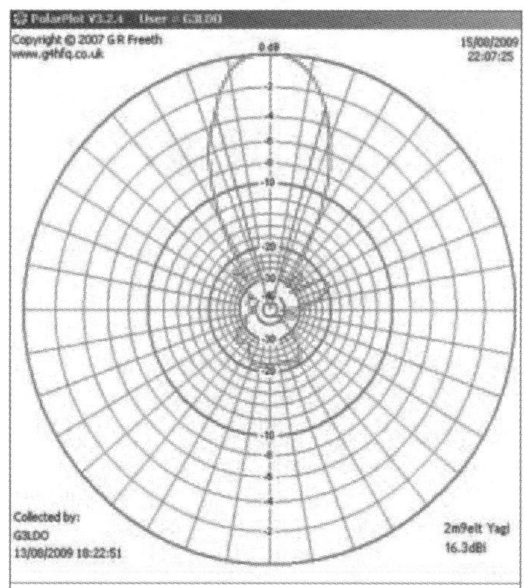


**FIGURE 2: Test range measurements on a Vine/G0KSC 144MHz 9 element Yagi.**

for any twin line feeder – to be mounted clear of any metal structure and certainly not rolled up into a coil. It is clear that by comparing Figure 3 and Photo 3, the device in Photo 3 is not a Pawsey Stub.

CHOKE VERSUS TRANSFORMER BALUNS. There has been some debate regarding the effectiveness of transformer (voltage) baluns and that choke (current) baluns are way to go. An interesting exchange on the subject appeared on the web page RadioBanter **[9]** and I quote the input of Roy Lewellen, W7EL, to the discussion.

"The difference between a 1:1 current balun and a 1:1 voltage balun is that the latter has a third (tertiary) winding. I'll assume for a moment that the baluns are perfect, ie, have an infinite common mode impedance.

"If the load is balanced, that is, if the two load terminals have equal impedances to the 'cold' side of the balun input, the third winding of the voltage balun carries no current, and there will be no current on the outside of the coax. Because the third winding has no current, it can be removed with no effect, so the voltage balun acts exactly like a current balun when the load is balanced. However, if the load isn't perfectly balanced relative to the input terminal of the balun, a current balun will still prevent current from flowing on the outside of the coax. The voltage balun, however, will force the voltages at the two output terminals to be equal and opposite relative to the cold side of the balun input. This will cause unequal currents from the two terminals. The difference flows along the outside of the coax.

"In summary, the best a voltage balun can do in preventing current flow on the outside of coax is to be as good as a current balun, and this happens only if the load is balanced.

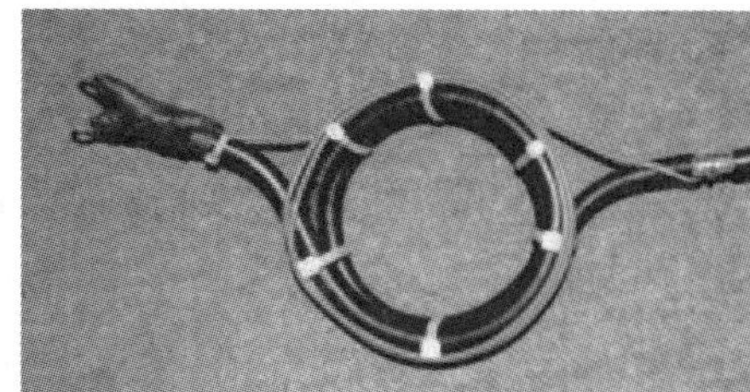

**PHOTO 3: The G0KSC-recommended balun, described as a Grounded Pawsey Stub, from [3].**

In all other cases, using a voltage balun will cause current to flow on the outside of the coax while a current balun will prevent this flow. For more information, see the article posted at **[10]**."

From this it would appear the device in Photo 3 is a 1:1 transformer.

FINALLY. The G0KSC model of the 144MHz 9 element Yagi produced a very symmetrical plot (Figure 1). It is a free-space model where the antenna mounting and general environment is not considered. Although environment can be modelled, it is not a realistic option for an antenna designer/manufacturer because an antenna's eventual location is unknown. The feed point in the model is assumed to be perfect with a balanced feed with no feeder common mode currents to disturb the radiation pattern. For these reasons the radiation pattern symmetry of a real antenna is unlikely be as good as predicted by a model.

From W7EL's analysis above, the best option is to use a current balun and that the driven element be adjusted for balance. This should be achievable with the G0KSC antenna because each side of the driven element loop can be adjusted in size, while monitoring with two clip-on RF current meters for balance and a SWR meter for matching.


REFERENCES

[1] Antennas, *RadCom* January 2010
[2] www.eham.net/reviews/detail/248
[3] www.g0ksc.co.uk
[4] In Practice, Ian White, GM3SEK, *RadCom* November, 2009
[5] Antennas, *RadCom* November 2009.
[6] *Amateur Radio Astronomy*, John Fielding, ZS5JF
[7] *R.A.F Signal Manual* AP1093 (1945)
[8] *Beam Antenna Handbook*, Bill Orr, W6SAI (1955)
[9] www.radiobanter.com/showthread.php?t=69938
[10] www.eznec.com/Amateur/Articles/Baluns.pdf.


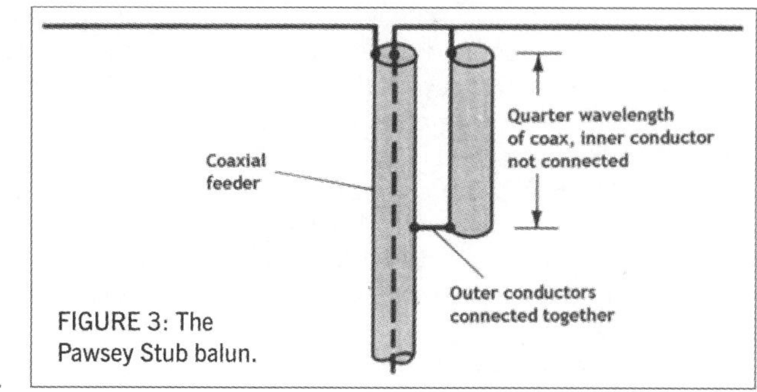


FIGURE 3: The Pawsey Stub balun.

# Antennas

## More on the Vector Impedance Analyser

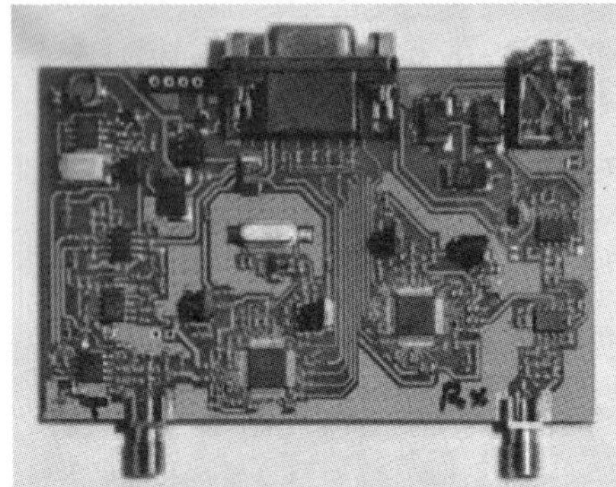
The DG8SAQ VNWA board.

**THE AIM 4170.** As many of you are aware the subject of antenna parameter measurements and test equipment is my main interest and this is reflected in the subjects discussed in Antennas. One of the most useful items of test kit that I have had is the AIM 4170, which has been used for the analysis of antennas and baluns in Antennas columns since late 2008. It is very intuitive to use with only occasional recourse to the instruction book being necessary.

It measures the impedance at the RF connector and normally presents these measurements in terms $Z_{mag}$/Theta (θ). It can simultaneously display SWR as shown in **Figure 1**. The more familiar R ±j and reflection coefficient are displayed on the right hand side. This instrument is called vector impedance analyser or in some cases a vector network analyser (VNA).

These instruments have been around for some time now (the first I heard of them was in G3VA's Technical Topics in September 2004). The construction and use of N2PK VNA was described by G(M)3SEK **[1]** and is a home brew project. The lack of availability of some of the required components outside the USA meant that only a small group of dedicated constructors originally built them.

Additionally there is the miniVNA from Mini Radio Solutions. This instrument is based on a design by IW3HEV, details of which can be found at **[2]**.

**THE DG8SAQ VNA.** More recently I was loaned a similar instrument designed by DG8SAQ by Graham Rumsey, M0GCR, who asked if I would like to experiment with this item and perhaps describe it in the Antennas column. The DG8SAQ instrument is rather a different instrument from the AIM 4170. It appears more technical and has a frequency range of 1kHz to 1.3GHz. In common with the N2PK VNA it uses two RF connectors instead of the one as used on the AIM 4170. While I had no difficulty setting up and calibrating this unit, the terminology in the help file was, to me, unfamiliar. Which RF connector should be used was unclear; and just what did S11, S12, S21 and S22, shown in **Figure 2**, mean?

**VNA TERMINOLOGY.** To answer this question we have to look at some basic terminology. The measurement of incident, reflected, and transmitted waves on a transmission lines is a subject which you are probably already familiar. It is the measurement of these parameters that allow us to measure SWR, see **[3]**.

An analogy using optical wavelengths is given in Agilent AN 1287-1 application note **[4]**. When a light beam (incident waves) meets a clear lens, some of the light is reflected (reflected waves) from the lens surface, but most of it continues through the lens (transmitted waves) as shown in **Figure 3a**. This analogy applies to RF fed into a transmission line, some of which is reflected back down the transmission line toward the source due to impedance mismatch. Most of this RF is successfully transmitted to the terminating device, usually the antenna.

Network analyser terminology generally compares measurements of the incident waves with reflected waves. With the amplitude and phase information in these waves, it is possible to quantify the reflection and transmission characteristics of a transmission line or electronic device, normally referred to as the device under test (DUT). The reflection and transmission characteristics can be expressed as vector (magnitude and phase) or scalar (magnitude only) quantities. For example, impedance is a vector reflection measurement while return loss is a scalar measurement of reflection (**Figure 3b**).

Ratioed measurements allow us to make reflection and transmission measurements that are independent of both absolute power and variations in source power versus frequency. Ratioed reflection is often shown as reflected over incident and ratioed transmission as transmitted over incident, relating to the measurement channels in the instrument.

The transmission coefficient is defined as the transmitted voltage divided by the incident voltage (**Figure 3c**). If the absolute value of the transmitted voltage is less than the absolute value of the incident voltage, the DUT is said to have attenuation or insertion loss. This would apply if the DUT was a long length of transmission line. If the absolute value of the transmitted voltage is greater than the absolute value of the incident voltage, a DUT is said to have gain. This would apply if the DUT was an amplifier.

**S-PARAMETERS.** In answer to the question posed earlier, S11, S12, S21 and S22 are known as S- (for 'scattering') parameters. S-parameters are widely used for UHF and microwaves because they can be applied to a device embedded in a circuit or a test fixture. The advantage of using S-parameters is that the DUT can be as simple or as complicated as you like – it is treated as a 'black box' with input and output connections or 'ports'. A two-port device can be resistor network (attenuator), amplifier or a length of transmission line, which has both an input at Port 1 and an output at Port 2 (sharing a common ground) as shown in **Figure 4**.

With the input port is labelled '1' and its

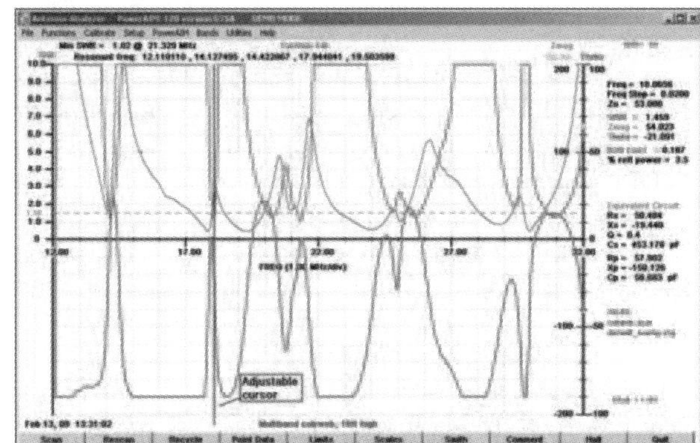

**FIGURE 1: AIM 4170 analysis of a multiband cobweb antenna built by M0UOO.**

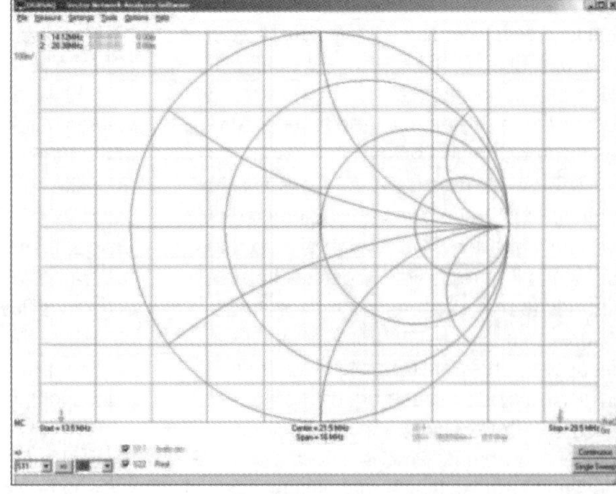
**FIGURE 2: The DG8SAQ VNA main page. Most of the displays in the instruction manual show the Cartesian scale and SWR and superimposed.**

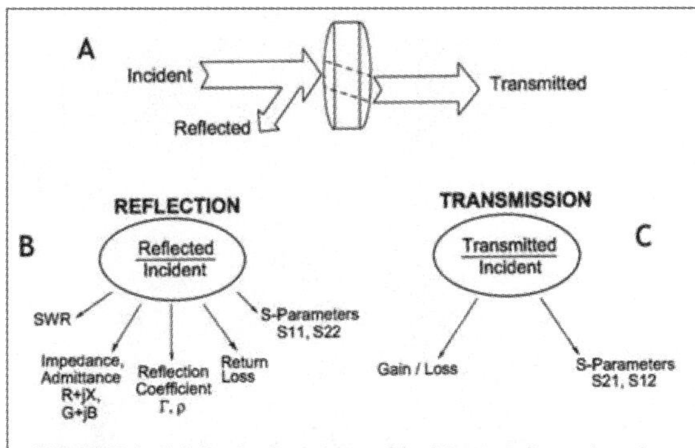


FIGURE 3: (a) Optical analogy of incident, reflected and transmitted waves. (b) Characteristics of reflected waves. (c) Characteristics of transmitted waves.

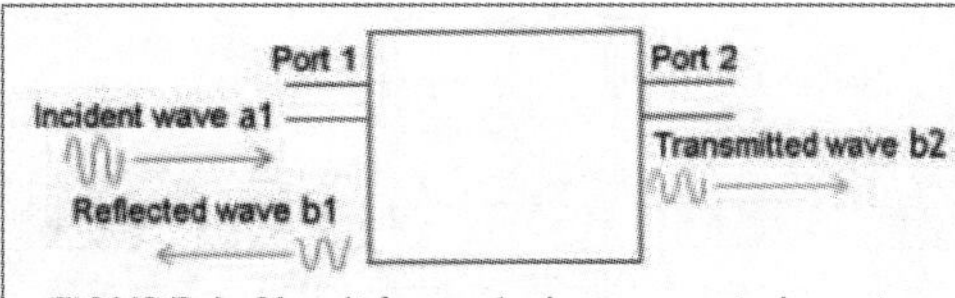


FIGURE 4: Circuit for analysis represented as a two port 'black box' with the incident, reflected and transmitted parameters.

$$\begin{pmatrix} b_1 \\ b_2 \end{pmatrix} = \begin{pmatrix} S_{11} & S_{12} \\ S_{21} & S_{22} \end{pmatrix} \times \begin{pmatrix} a_1 \\ a_2 \end{pmatrix}$$

FIGURE 5: Matrix algebraic representation of 2-port S-Parameters.

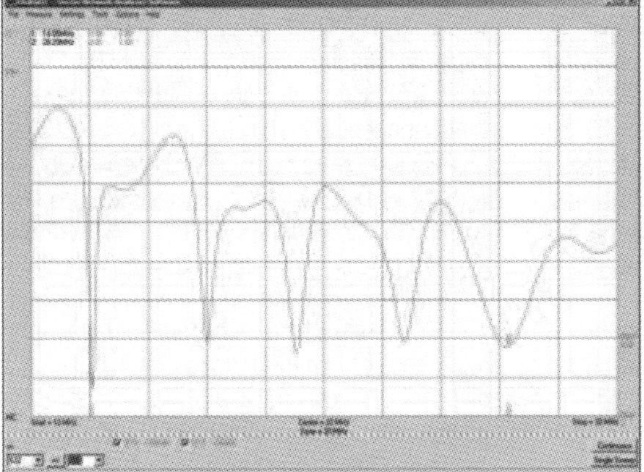

FIGURE 6: SWR plot of a HF multiband dipole.

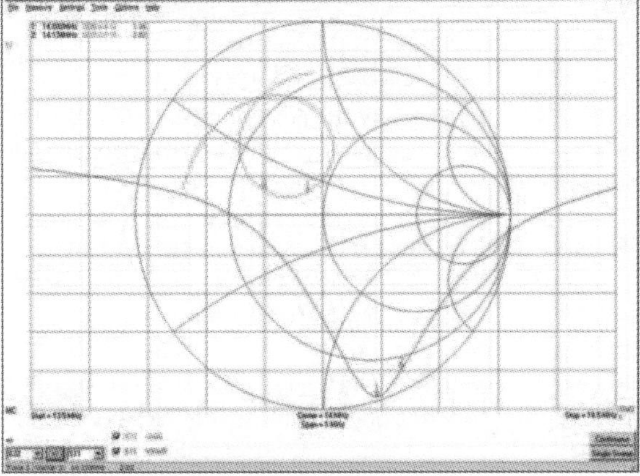

FIGURE 7: The Impedance characteristics (Smith chart) display superimposed on a SWR characteristics display of the 14MHz section of the multiband dipole.

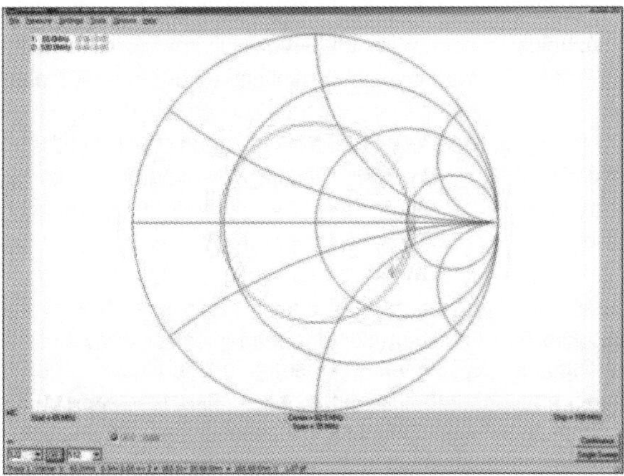

FIGURE 8: The results of a test obtained by measuring a 200Ω resistor over a two-metre length of 50Ω cable.

See Note [9]

output port '2', as shown in Figure 4, the gain of this device is found by dividing the output voltage from port 2, by the signal applied in to port 1, The corresponding S-parameter is S21. Since two distinct subscripts are involved, this is pronounced 'S sub two, one' and not 'S sub twenty-one'.

If the impedance of any port of our DUT is imperfectly matched to the previously specified system characteristic impedance, reflections will result when a signal is applied to that port. The amplitudes of these reflections, which can be determined independently with a directional coupler, defines the remaining two S-parameters, S11 (for the voltage reflected out of port 1, divided by that applied to port 1), and S22 (similarly defined for port 2).

A simple impedance meter is said to be a 'one-port device'; it only has one pair of terminals (one of which is ground) called Port 1. S11 is simply the reflection coefficient or return loss looking into Port 1. In other words, S11 is 'the signal coming out of Port 1, relative to the signal going into Port 1'.

S-Parameter scattering actually refers to scattering matrices, a tool of matrix algebra from which S-parameters were derived, see **Figure 5**. You don't really have to utilise scattering matrices, or even understand matrix algebra at all, to apply S-parameters successfully. Once you know how to use S-parameters, devices can be chained together and the effects calculated of their interacting port impedances. There are many modelling programs that allow this to be done.

This brief and simplistic description of S-parameters has been included to illustrate the range and versatility of the VNA. For most of our antenna measurements there are simpler ways of using such a device as I will now describe.

## REFLECTION MEASUREMENTS.

Most of the measurements we perform on antenna systems and components are Reflection measurements. An example of such measurement, or should I say a series of measurements to plot an antenna characteristic, were done using the AIM-4170, see Figure 1. Provision is made to calibrate any length of feeder so that the AIM-4170 measures the impedance at the point where it is connected to the antenna. This instrument is a one-port device as described above.

The DG8SAQ instrument uses two RF connectors instead of the one as used on the AIM 4170. The connector on the right, see **Photo 1**, is the transmitter and the one on the left the receiver. If I wanted to plot the characteristics of a filter then I would connect the input of the filter to the transmitter and the output to the receiver. The instrument can then compare the incident wave and the transmit wave as described above.

If we are only interested in reflected parameters then the DUT is connected to the transmitter connector and the instrument the compares incident waves with reflected waves. I used the DG8SAQ to measure the SWR characteristics of a multiband dipole as shown in **Figure 6**. The DG8SAQ does not appear to allocate scales to the graphs but instead allows one to analyse the curves with the use of markers controlled by the computer mouse.

The characteristics of the 14MHz section of the same multiband dipole shown in are shown in **Figure 7**. In this case the SWR plot is shown on the Cartesian scale and the impedance signature is shown on the superimposed Smith Chart.

The DG8SAQ VNA Smith chart plot shown in **Figure 8** is the result of a frequency sweep test (65 to 100MHz) of a 200Ω resistor at the end of a two metre length of 50Ω coax cable. The near circular plot around the prime centre of the chart is a good indication of the accuracy of the instrument, a method proposed by W N Carron **[5]**.

The tendency of the plot to spiral towards the centre as the frequency is increased is caused by coax cable loss not by any inaccuracy of the instrument. Impedance at any point on the graph can be read out by moving a cursor to the appropriate point and reading the measured impedance in the top left-hand corner.

### REFERENCES

[1] In Practice, *RadCom* October 2004
[2] www.miniradiosolutions.com/
[3] In Practice, *RadCom* January 2010
[4] Enter Agilent AN 1287-1 into Google
[5] The Hybrid Junction Admittance Bridge', W N Carron, *Antenna Compendium Vol 3* ARRL 1992.

# Antennas

## More on the Grid Dip Oscillator (GDO)

PHOTO 1: Q-Max GDO-1A uses a 12AT7 double triode, one half used as an oscillator and the other half as a half-wave rectifier.

**GRID DIP OSCILLATOR.** A very useful item of test equipment when working with antennas and tuned circuits is the Grid Dip Oscillator, generally known as a GDO. For newcomers who may not know of this device, it is used for measuring the resonance of tuned circuits and antenna elements without actually connecting the instrument to the circuit under test.

When a tuneable oscillator is placed close to a nearby resonant circuit, some of the oscillator power is absorbed when the oscillator is tuned to the same frequency. Some indication of oscillator energy loss is can be used to indicate this condition. The original instruments used a valve with a microammeter connected between the grid and earth, as shown in **Figure 1**. This measured grid current, which is proportional to the peak-to-peak level of the oscillator waveform. In practice a dip in the grid current level is observed as the oscillator is tuned past the resonant frequency of circuit under test, hence the title of this instrument: Grid Dip Oscillator (GDO).

The circuit shown in Figure 1 is from the *ARRL Radio Handbook*, 1947 **[1]**. This instrument is designed as a portable workshop item of equipment for measuring the resonance of tuned circuits. It uses a probe made from a short length of twin transmission line and a loop L2 to access tuned circuits within transmitters or receivers. This GDO was built into an enclosure 150mm (6in) square so was quite different from the shape of GDOs to which we are now accustomed.

It was also used for determining the values of capacitors and inductors using the arrangements shown in Figure 1a and b. The link-coupled probe L2 is used to measure the resonances of tuned circuits in confined spaces. It can also be used to measure the resonant frequency of a tuned circuit where the inductance is a ferrite ring by coupling L2 around the ring. There was no mention in [1] of using this GDO to measure transmission line or antenna element resonances.

An example of a later GDO is shown in **Photo 1**. It is an old Q-Max GDO-1A that operates very well right up into the VHF band. It comprises a 12AT7 double triode, one half used as an oscillator and the other half as a half-wave rectifier for the 330V HT supply.

**A FET GDO.** These days most of these instruments use solid state devices, usually a FET. In this case we are interested in the variations in gate current so we can still call it a GDO (Gate Dip Oscillator). The subject of GDOs was prompted by a question from Paul Badley, MOPIB, who was building a published version a GDO **[2]**. He wanted to know where he could obtain a dual-ganged 365pF variable capacitor shown in this circuit and the diameter of the coils. The circuit I described in [2] was based on two very similar designs published in *QST*, Technical Correspondence **[3] [4]**. The circuit of my variation of these two designs is shown in **Figure 2**.

This circuit does not measure FET gate current directly; instead it measures the total source current, which is affected by the voltage at the gate of the FET. However, the variation of current through resonance is only a small part of the total source current. The dip is enhanced by offsetting the meter reading using a potentiometer in a bleeder network. This is set so that the meter reads about 75% FSD when the instrument is not coupled to the resonant circuit under test.

I built one version of the FET GDO into a defunct Japanese nuvistor LDM-810 GDO by using the chassis, case, calibrated tuning mechanism and coils. The value of the twin-ganged capacitor turned out to be 120pF as shown in **Photo 2**.

At a later date, G3ZOM used this circuit as a basis for a GDO kit and he specified a two-ganged 365pF polyvaricon variable capacitor together with the speaker DIN plugs as coil formers, shown in the circuit that appears in [2].

A GDO should possess good sensitivity, which can be checked by squeezing the coil of the GDO between the thumb and forefinger and noting the meter deflection; this should dip to at least 50% of the maximum reading. The GDO should also be capable of measuring resonance of a high-Q tuned circuit at a distance of 6 to 7cm (2-3in). I use a parallel tuned circuit, comprising a 5mH inductor with a 100pF capacitance, as a 7MHz standard. The circuit shown in Figure 2 possesses this sensitivity in the HF and lower VHF bands but is unsuitable for VHF without modification to some component values.

A good indication of the resonance dip is important. Some commercial GDOs have small meters, which are a problem for optically challenged old-timers like me. A large meter makes using this instrument much easier. The G3WPO FET dip meter **[5]** uses an audio indication of dip, which is very nice – rather like using a metal detector.

**A QUESTION OF VALUES.** In answer to MOPIB's question regarding the value of the variable tuning capacitor, various capacitance values have advantages and disadvantages. If a large value of capacitance is used then fewer coils are required to cover a given frequency range. The down side is that the resonance dip will be more difficult to locate because of the large oscillator frequency shift for a give amount of capacitor rotation. If a smaller capacitance is used it gives the frequency dial a bandspread effect and the dip is easier to locate, however more coils will be required to cover a given frequency range. The Q-max GDO uses quite a small dual ganged 40pF capacitor and the frequency coverage 1.5 to 300MHz requires 8 coils. It does make for a readable frequency dial as shown on **Photo 3**.

Building many items of electronic equipment can be likened to following a cooking recipe. You can use the 'Delia Smith method' where you follow the recipe exactly using the exact

PHOTO 2: A FET GDO using the chassis, case, calibrated tuning mechanism and coils of a defunct LDM-810 nuvistor GDO.

PHOTO 3 : Frequency dial of the Q-Max GDO.

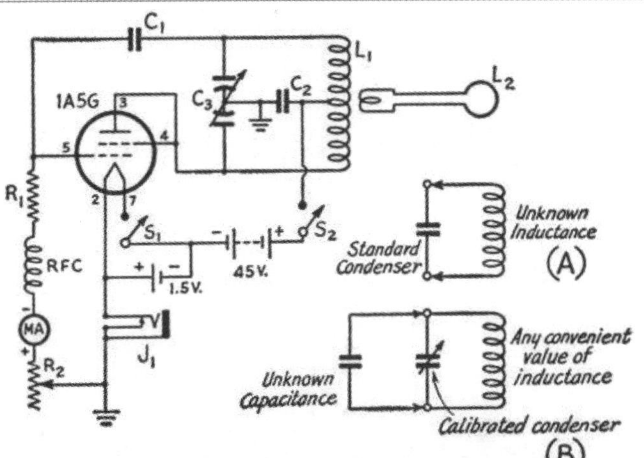

FIGURE 1: Grid dip oscillator for 3 to 60MHz using a battery valve type 1A5G. Reproduced from the *ARRL Radio Handbook*, 1947.

values of specified components. Or you can use the more interesting 'Jamie Oliver approach' where you throw in components whose values or types you know from experience will do the trick. In this way the design can be built around the components from the junk box.

The most important part of a dip oscillator is the tuning capacitor, slow motion drive and if possible a read-out dial that can be calibrated in frequency. Sometimes a whole assembly can be obtained from an old transistor radio. Choose a coil plug and socket arrangement that is practical. The circuit shown in Figure 2 uses 2-pin coils, which allows the use of crystal holders or 2-pin plugs and sockets for the coil.

**JUNK BOX GDO.** A junk box GDO, using the circuit shown in Figure 2, is shown in **Photo 4**. It uses a two-ganged 60pF variable capacitor for tuning and a crystal holder for the plug in coils. The coil socket should be located as close to the tuning capacitor as possible so that the coil leads can be kept short. The rest of the circuit can be wired around these main components.

The arrangement shown in Photo 4 was designed for a specific application, measuring the resonant frequency of antenna elements. There are two main departures from the traditional GDO design.

The first is the coil. Coupling a small diameter GDO coil to wire or tubular antenna elements is almost impossible because the coupling is very loose. G6XN suggested using a coat hanger shaped coil where flat section of the coil can be arranged in close proximity to the antenna element. While this is fine for VHF this arrangement is very cumbersome at HF frequencies because of physical size of the coil. A more practical solution is to wind the coil on a rectangular section using several turns to make up the required inductance. This former can be a short wooden board, say, 4 inches wide and half an inch thick.

The coil shown in Photo 4 uses 7 turns of 16SWG (or similar) plastic covered wire, which tunes from 8 to 18MHz, covering the 14MHz band (the band of interest at the time). The other departure from the traditional GDO is the use of a frequency counter instead of a calibrated frequency dial. A frequency counter is a worthwhile investment and has many other uses in home construction projects. If you are using a GDO without a connection for a frequency counter the frequency can be sampled using single turn loop round the GDO coil. The coupling of this pick-up coil to the coil winding can be adjusted with respect to the main winding until just enough energy is available to operate the frequency counter.

The coil former board also provides a platform for the GDO, frequency counter and even a note pad. The flat sided coil couples into any antenna element, with the board providing a stable point to rest the measuring kit against the element while measurements are being made. The coupling between the GDO coil and the wire antenna element is maintained by placing the wire antenna element in the grove formed by plastic wire fixing clips. This is a useful feature if you are balanced on top of a step-ladder trying to measure the resonance of a parasitic quad element.

REFERENCES

[1] *The Radio Amateur's Handbook, 1947 Edition*, ARRL.
[2] *The Antenna experimenter's Guide, Second Edition*, Peter Dodd, G3LDO.
[3] 'Technical Correspondence', *QST* June 1972, Peter Lumb, G3IRM.
[4] 'Technical Correspondence', *QST*, November 1971, W1CER.
[5] 'The G3WPO FET Dip Oscillator Mk2', by A L Bailey, G3WPO *RadCom* April 1987.

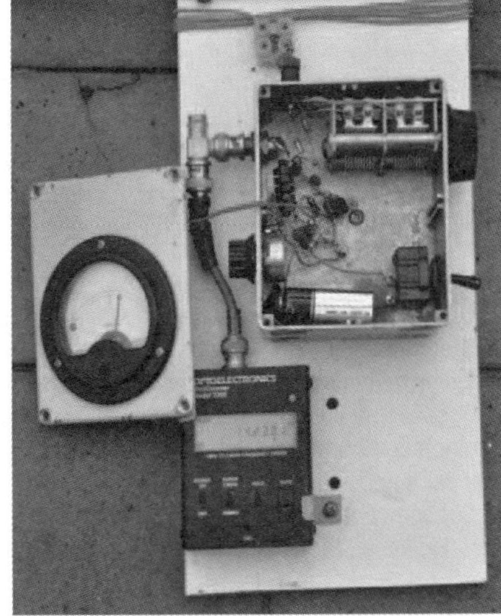
PHOTO 4: The antenna element resonance measuring kit. Note the method of maintaining a constant coupling to the antenna element (red wire) and the GDO coil.

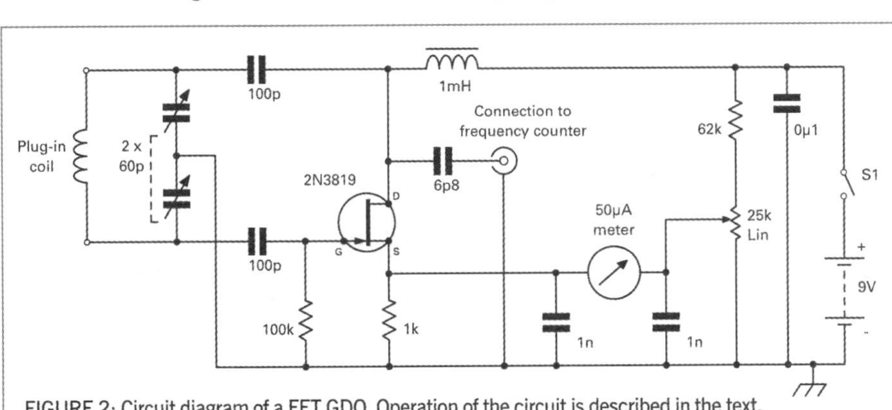

FIGURE 2: Circuit diagram of a FET GDO. Operation of the circuit is described in the text.

# Antennas

## Is this the ultimate indoor antenna?

PHOTO 1: The large barn that houses W1GN's HF beam antenna.

**THE ULTIMATE INDOOR ANTENNA.** I often join the midday Mid Sussex Amateur Radio Club net on 21MHz. The net is run by Ken, G3WYN and many of the club members join in. I am some distance away down on the coast but I can just make it on ground wave.

David, W1GN (ex G3HWU) located in New Hampshire has, when conditions are favourable, been joining the net for some years now and is considered an honorary member. He puts in quite a good signal and, as it turned out, has a very interesting antenna arrangement. It seemed to me the ultimate indoor antenna.

W1GN uses a full size three-element single band Hy-Gain LJ-153BA Yagi, located in a barn. This is no ordinary barn, being some 75ft long (22.8m) and 45ft (13.7m) wide, as shown in **Photo 1**. The roof ridge is at 48ft (14.6m) above the concrete base. The covering consists of strips of galvanized metal with assumed poor electrical bonding. All walls, flooring, roof trusses and sheathing are made of wood.

The horizontal plane of the Yagi is 27ft (8.2m) above the concrete basement and is suspended by ropes at the barn's north end, across the 45ft width, with the director 2ft (0.6m) away from the wall as shown in **Photo 2**. The boom is about 21ft (6.4m) beneath the apex of the roof. The suspension ropes are attached to a short wooden boom, which is mounted on the metal boom, one at each end. There is no contact between the ropes and antenna elements.

However, the adjacent soil grade level with respect to the concrete base varies from 2ft (0.6m) to 6ft (1.8m). This reflects the natural, gently west to east sloping topography of this property. New Hampshire sits on granite and is known as the Granite State for good reason. Elevation is approximately 800ft ASL.

W1GN puts a good signal into Europe with this arrangement, which is quite surprising. My experiences of some roof antennas in some QTHs I have operated from are very varied. The slate roof of one QTH acted as a complete screen to RF – perhaps there was a lead content in the slate.

I wondered about the effect of a metal roof so I made a computer model, as shown in **Figure 1**. This model is very much simplified. The enclosure has for example a flat roof. I found constructing a sloping roof with an apex a bit beyond me! Even so, this simplified roof comprised a mesh of 170 wires with 700 segments. This method of modelling a sheet of metal is now well known and practised. In this model, the roof is 42ft (12.8m) high with the beam antenna 25ft (7.6m) high, about 17ft (5.2m) below the roof.

The result can be seen in the elevation diagram shown in **Figure 2**, which shows only a small 1dB loss in gain caused by the roof, provided the wall is transparent to RF, and the suppression of a high angle lobe. The probable reason the metal roof does not affect the elevation polar diagram that much is that this field strength pattern is formed by interaction with the earth at an area well clear of the building.

**SKELETON SLOT ANTENNA.** John Farrer, G3XHZ, e-mailed me about a HF skeleton slot he was considering building as per G3VCG 's website **[1]**. I checked out this website and found the antenna G3VCG had constructed based on a computer model was the same as one I described in *The ARRL Antenna Compendium, Vol. 6*. As my antenna was also based on a computer model, it is not surprising that the dimensions were the same.

The skeleton slot is very easy to construct and is a simple design with no traps or critical adjustments. This antenna has a turning radius of only 1.5m (5ft) although it is 14m (47ft) tall. However, its construction means that it has a much lower visual impact than a conventional multi-band beam. The antenna is bi-directional and has a calculated gain, over average ground, of 8dBi on 14MHz and 11dBi on 28MHz.

As far as I am aware, the skeleton slot antenna was proposed by Bill Sykes, G2HCG. This element was originally designed to be resonant on one frequency and formed the driven element for two stacked 144MHz 5-element beams **[2]**. An HF non-resonant version was built and documented by Bill Capstick, G3JYP **[3]**. His antenna was also the same size, achieved without the benefit of computer modelling.

My version of the HF skeleton slot uses wire for the vertical elements, resulting in a more simplified and rugged construction. I was at first concerned that this method of construction would not work because [3] gave minimum tube diameters for the elements. However, computer modelling with *EZNEC2* reassured me that this method of construction would be suitable for this particular application so I went ahead.

The antenna essentially comprises three aluminium tube elements fixed to the mast at 4.6m (15ft) intervals, with the lowest element only 4.6m from the ground. The mast is an integral part of the antenna, as a boom is to a Yagi. The general construction is shown in **Figure 3**.

The centre element is fed in the centre with balanced feeder and the upper and lower elements are fed at the ends by copper wire

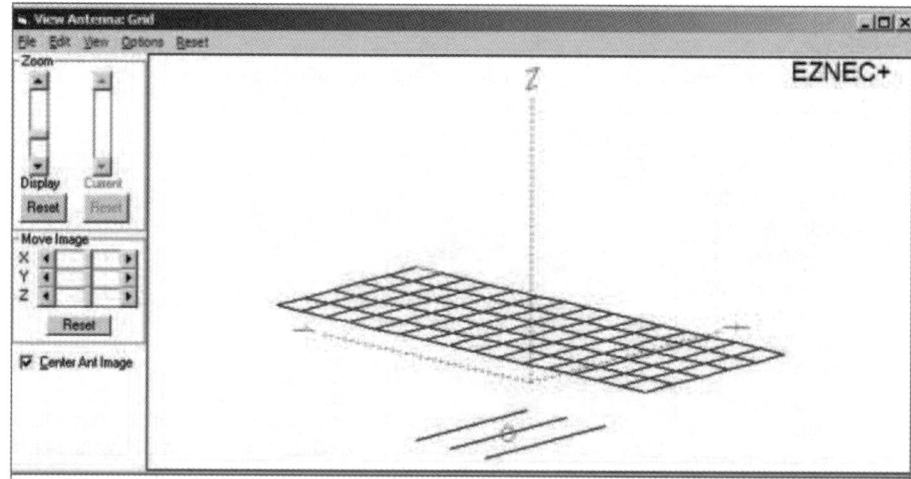


FIGURE 1: Computer model of 21MHz three-element beam located under a sheet metal roof.

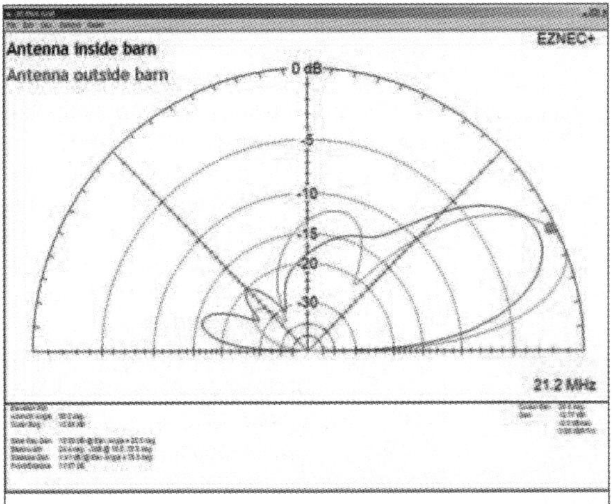


FIGURE 2: Comparison elevation diagram of a normally mounted three-element beam compared with one located in a building with a metal roof.

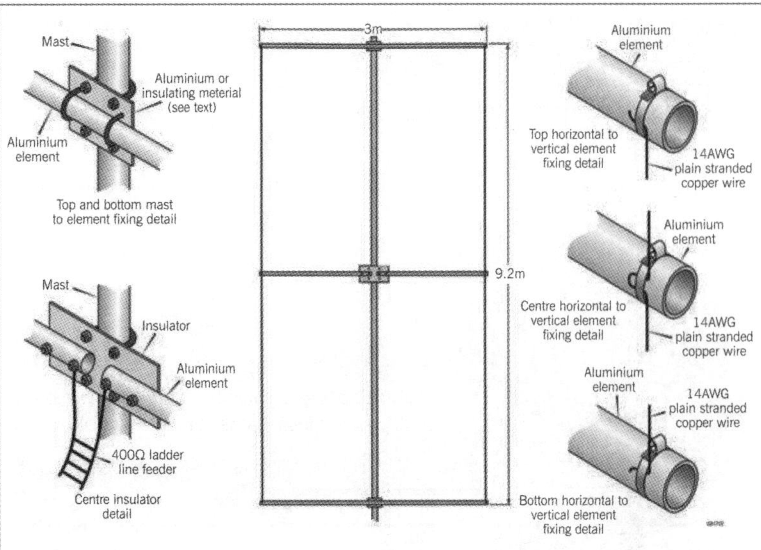


FIGURE 3: The G3LDO multiband skeleton slot antenna for 14 to 28MHz. The elements are fixed to the mast and the whole mast is rotated.

from the driven dipole. The aluminium tubing and copper wire are fixed using hose clips. These dissimilar metal connections should not present corrosion problems provided they are well coated with grease to keep moisture out.

The centres of the upper and lower elements can be fixed directly to a metal mast using an aluminium plate and U-bolts as shown in Figure 3. The dimension of this antenna regarding aluminium tube/wire diameters and length are not critical.

The antenna requires a balanced feed such as 450Ω slotted line, although the feeder impedance is not critical. The feeder should be fixed on standoff insulators about 6in (150mm) from the mast until clear of the lower element to prevent it blowing about in the wind and affecting the impedance. An ATU with a balanced output is required when using this arrangement. I tried various ATUs located at the bottom of the mast because it was inconvenient to bring a balanced feeder all the way from the antenna to the shack. Another way of feeding the antenna is to use a good quality coax from the ATU to the antenna feedpoint with a current choke (balun) at the feedpoint. The feeder from the ATU to the antenna feedpoint should be as short as practicable to reduce the SWR losses.

The dimensions shown in Figure 3 seem near optimum for the five higher HF frequency bands, see the elevation diagrams in **Figure 4**. While the DX performance of this antenna is good up to 30MHz it deteriorates at frequencies higher than this. The azimuth diagram is very similar to a dipole, with deep side nulls that can be used to minimise QRM from some locations.

When this antenna was first used in 1995, the sunspots were reasonably high and the conditions on the upper HF bands were good. On the 21, 24 and 28MHz bands the antenna performed very well, particularly when conditions were marginal. On 21MHz, DX stations consistently gave 2 S-points better than received when using a linear. Early morning contacts with the Pacific had noticeable echoes, possibly due to the bi-directional nature of the antenna.

G3XHZ asked if the dimensions of this antenna could be increased so that it would give a reasonable performance on 7MHz even at the expense of the higher frequencies. The existing dimensions will allow this antenna to work on 7 and 10MHz but the performance is not too good. I consulted *EZNEC* again and found that increasing the dimensions by a factor of 1.5 resulted in reasonable performance on 7MHz and that the upper cut off frequency occurred just above 21MHz.

The only downside to this antenna is that it really has to be mounted on a rotatable self-supporting mast. However, some guying can be accommodated because the antenna can obtain full coverage with a rotation limit of 90°.

**NEIGHBOUR WARS.** Those of us who live in suburban houses with a garden often don't realise the difficulties some radio amateurs have with difficult QTH-related antenna problems.

One such gentleman wrote to me recently. He is a keen HF operator who lives on the third floor of a multi-storey block. There is no balcony. He has been experimenting with various antennas and one of these was a top fed quarter wave vertical. It consisted simply of a quarter wavelength of wire hanging from the window, fed against radials (presumably routed around the floor of the apartment). This arrangement worked reasonably well until he moved to a lower frequency band, necessitating a longer piece of wire.

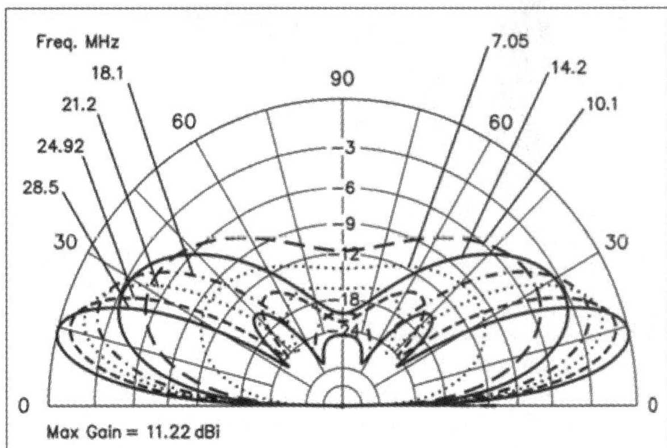


FIGURE 4: Elevation diagrams for the HF skeleton slot using the dimensions shown in Figure 3.

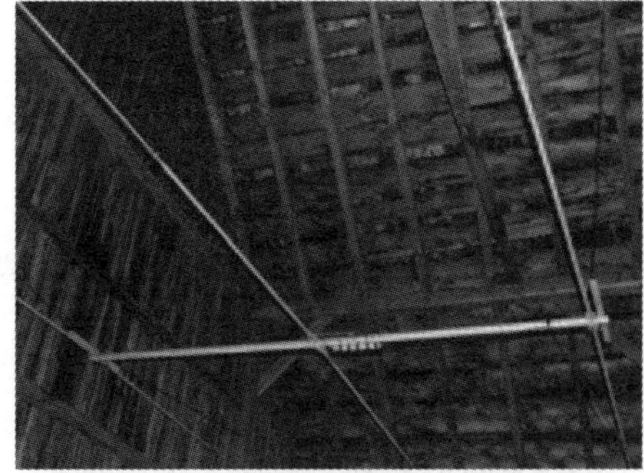

PHOTO 2: W1GN's full sized three-element single band Hygain LJ-153BA indoor Yagi.

The end of the wire now ended against a neighbour's window on a lower floor. This neighbour reacted by grabbing the wire and giving it a good tug, which resulted in some of the amateur's radio equipment being pulled off the operating table and on to the floor.

He is now considering a more compact loaded antenna system.

**REFERENCES**

[1] www.drwilks.freeuk.com/
[2] *Skeleton Slot Aerials*, B. Sykes, RSGB Bulletin (forerunner of *RadCom*), January 1953
[3] *The HF Skeleton Slot Antenna*, Bill Capstick, G3JYP, *RadCom* June 1996.
[4] *The ARRL Antenna Compendium, Vol. 6*

# Antennas

## Lightning and another look at small loops

PHOTO 1: A tree destroyed by lightning.

**LIGHTNING.** I started writing this column in a hotel in Singapore. At the time a severe electrical storm reminded me of a subject I had been considering for some time and that was how best to protect your antenna and rig from lightning.

I must confess to having a bit of a phobia regarding lightning – and for good reason. In the early 1960s, when I lived in Sierra Leone, my antenna mast was struck by lightning. The incident occurred in the early hours of the morning before daylight and I experienced a blinding blue flash with the sharp sound like a pistol shot being fired close to my ear.

All the security lights went out so I found a torch and shuffled out to the pantry, where all the electrical switches and fuses boxes were located, to reset the over-current trip. I found that all the electrical items had disappeared – with just the electrical wires sticking out of the wall where the fuse boxes and switches had been. The floor of the pantry was covered with bits of broken Bakelite and annealed copper. Furthermore, the glass envelopes of the bulbs in the security lights had all burst.

The antenna mast comprised a tapered steel 60ft steel tube supporting an all-metal 20m quad antenna. The coax feeder from the antenna to the transceiver in the outside shack had also been earthed and the equipment suffered no damage. I was intrigued to know why so much damage had been done to the mains electrical components of the house. I think the reason was that the mains supply was routed to the house on overhead wires, fairly close to the antenna.

I also had a 7MHz dipole strung between trees some distance from the house. The 50Ω RG8 feeder to this antenna had been damaged, with holes punched in the braid where it touched the ground.

**REAL HIGH POWER.** The power of a lightning strike is quite phenomenal. An example of damage done to a tree is illustrated in **Photo 1**. In this case, the damage was probably caused by the sap flashing off to steam and blowing the tree apart. This is a very good reason for not standing under a tree in a thunderstorm!

Although all this seems a bit scary, one has to keep the risk in perspective. G3MYA **[1]** has calculated that the chances of a direct strike on a single property works out at once every 500 years. This calculation is for average properties with perhaps a single TV antenna. Radio amateurs tend to put up larger metallic structures in their quest for better DX radio communications, which may change the odds a bit. If you have a metal tower near the centre of your property that is a few metres taller than anything else around, it should provide protection from a direct strike to your shack and house.

G3MYA recommends a short thick copper rod with a sharp point at the top be fixed to the top of the mast; it should have a good electrical connection to the mast. The base of the mast should be connected to an earth rod of 0.5in galvanised steel or, better still, a hardened copper rod or 'T' sectioned earth rod. This earth rod should be 4ft long for normal ground. I personally rely on the RF ground system, which is made up of buried lengths of old coax cable and thick electrical wire.

There is a further issue with lightning and that is EMP (electro magnetic pulse). It used to be a real problem in the days of overhead telephone wires. Telephone exchanges were fitted with protection panels comprising resistors and fuses to protect the exchange from voltages induced into the telephone wires due to nearby lightning strikes. These same voltages can be induced into your antenna system and damage the front end of your receiver. Coax spark protection devices are often recommended but I feel the best method is to disconnect the coax to the back of the transceiver if an electrical storm is imminent or if you will be away for a while.

**SMALL TRANSMITTING LOOPS.** Earlier this year Mike Underhill, G3LHZ, gave a lecture to the Worthing and District Amateur Radio Club on the subject of small transmitting loop antennas. He brought along a commercial transmitting loop that had been modified using a shunt coupling arrangement instead of the loop coupling supplied with the antenna.

G3LHZ connected this antenna to an IC-706 and fired up the transmitter. It must have radiated reasonably well – the next moment an irate building maintenance man put his head around the door and wanted to know who had set off the b#@&* fire alarm.

Most early descriptions of transmitting loops repeated the claim that the performance at the higher end of the HF bands could approach that of a halfwave dipole provided the loop was well constructed. In 1991, G4XVF **[2]** wrote a two part article in *RadCom* giving well reasoned doubt as to the efficiency of small transmitting loops. His study was based on calculating the Q from the measured bandwidth of a small loop whose inductance could be calculated. He concluded that the radiation efficiency was below 10%, compared with a dipole efficiency of near 100%.

However, there have been difficulties in relating these theoretical calculations with on-the-air results by radio amateurs using home made and commercial loops. In 1994, Peter Hart, G3SXJ, reviewed four models of loops from three manufactures **[3]** and was surprised at how effective these small loops could be. He noted that these loops were roughly equivalent in performance to a dipole or a multiband vertical provided they were mounted vertically and clear of electromagnetic obstructions.

G3LHZ's lecture to the Worthing club was based on material he presented to the IEE **[4]** and was centred on the commercial AMA3 loop antenna. These loops were manufactured by Advanced Antennas and Ancillaries, no longer trading. The AMA3 antenna is a German design intended for use over the range 14 to 29MHz. It is constructed from 32mm aluminium tubing and the loop diameter is 0.9m.

The loop antenna demonstrated by G3LHZ and shown in **Photo 2** has an interesting feed variation compared to the normal loop coupling. In Photo 2 the original small loop feed is disconnected and is now grounded at the feed point. The horizontal pattern has typical loop nulls, which implies there is no dominant feeder radiation. If there was, these nulls would disappear and the horizontal pattern would become omnidirectional. It is not! However, the nulls are actually displaced in a downward direction in practice. This ties up with the observation that the loop always radiates best towards the capacitor.

G3LHZ describes his work with the feed method as follows. "There are various ways of putting the twist in this 'twisted gamma' match. With 2.5mm single core PVC covered mains wire, I use either a left hand or a right hand screw winding. There is no discernable difference. There can be two different lengths of gamma wire that allow a perfect 1:1 50Ω match. With these I use a movable crocodile clip termination to fine match to 50Ω. Q and efficiency measurements show no discernable difference between the short and long twisted gamma matches. I prefer the longer gamma wire length choice. It allows the loop to be matched with an ATU for operation above its highest tuning frequency; for example for the AMA3 operation on 6m and 4m is possible. The pattern is then omnidirectional.

"The twisted gamma match shown in the AMA3 pictures has a double twist. One half is left-handed and the other half is right-handed. A coaxial cable outer conductor is used as the gamma wire. Coarse matching is achieved by altering the position of the jubilee clip. Fine matching is achieved by rotating the cable under the cable tie. (Note that any shift in tuning as the match is changed can always be cancelled by normal retuning of the loop.) Once again there is no discernable change in loop Q or loop efficiency.

"In summary, the twisted gamma matches are easier than the small loop feed to adjust to exact 1:1 SWR. In fact, the loop feed as shown does not achieve exact 1:1 SWR at all. It has to be distorted in shaped and or rotated out of the plane of the main loop. The best way of adjusting the loop feed is to make it slightly oversized and then slide the loop so that only part of it overlaps the main loop. The rest of it remains outside the main loop.

**PHOTO 2: G3LHZ's AMA3 transmitting loop antenna with the 'twisted gamma' match. The original coupling loop shown is disconnected.**

In terms of loop Q, bandwidth and efficiency there is no discernable difference between the various feed methods."

**LOCATION.** I have made the point before, that it is perhaps more important as to where an antenna is than what it is. VK5KLT, in his paper An Overview of the Underestimated Magnetic Loop HF Antenna [4] has some interesting findings and comments regarding the best location for a transmitting loop antenna. He notes, "In comparison to a vertically mounted/oriented loop, the bottom of the loop does not need to be more than a loop diameter above ground, making it very easy to site in a restricted space location. There is no significant improvement in performance when a small loop is raised to great heights; all that matters is the loop is substantially clear of objects in the desired direction of radiation! Mounting on an elevated roof ground-plane yields excellent results.

"Failure to pay very careful attention to construction details in relation to eliminating all sources of losses and making bad siting choices such as close proximity to ferrous materials are the two main reasons why small magnetic loop antennas sometimes fail to live up to their performance potential. When the loop is mounted over a perfectly conducting ground plane reflector or copper radial wire mat an electrical image is created that effectively doubles the loop area. This in turn beneficially increases the loop's radiation resistance by the substantial factor of four times.

"Conversely if the loop is placed over average ground (a reasonable reflector) the radiation resistance increases but a reflected loss resistance is also introduced due to transformer effect coupling near-field energy into the lossy ground. Similarly when ferrous/iron material is too close, the magnetic near-field of the loop will induce, by transformer action, a voltage across the RF resistance of the material, causing a current flow and associated $I^2R$ power loss. This situation might for example arise when the loop is mounted on an apartment balcony with nearby iron railing or concrete rebar etc; the deleterious influence can be minimised by simply orienting the loop to sit at right angles to the offending iron or steel material. Another loss-contributing component is due to current flowing in the soil via capacitance between the loop and the soil surface. This capacitive coupling effect is again minimised by keeping the loop at least half a loop diameter above the ground."

**REFERENCES**


[1] Alan Martingale, G3MYA. Lightning, The nature of the beast and how to survive its fiery fingers. *RadCom* January 1984. Also included in The HF Collection by G4LQI.

[2] Loop Antennas- Facts not Fiction, Tony Henk, G4XVF, *Radio Communication* September/October, 1991.

[3] Loop Antennas for the HF Bands, *Radio Communication* July 1994, Peter Hart, G3SJX.

[4] www.qsl.net/vk5bar - go to 'Papers' and select 'Small (loop) antennas'.

# Antennas

## The Windom off-centre fed dipole

PHOTO 1: MOCVO HW-40HP off-centre-fed dipole antenna.

**THE DIPOLE.** The centre-fed dipole is the most fundamental of all antennas. It is the most popular antenna used by amateurs worldwide, largely because it is very simple to construct and is an effective performer. A centre-fed dipole can be any electrical length as long as it is configured in a symmetrical fashion with two equal length sides. However, in its simplest form, it is made half a wavelength long at the operating frequency because such an arrangement is easiest to feed. The current and voltage distribution on a half wave antenna is shown in **Figure 1**, with high current and low voltage in the centre. Impedance is a ratio of current and voltage, which indicates a low impedance at the centre; a suitable point to feed the antenna using low impedance 50Ω feeder.

At the ends of the antenna, the voltages are high and the current low so the impedances at these points are high. Note that the current and voltage ratios either side of the centre feed point are mirror images of each other and such an antenna is said to be balanced. Ideally, the dipole antenna should be fed with twin wire feeder where the RF power in each conductor of the transmission line is equal, thereby cancelling radiation or interference pickup on the line.

In previous Antennas, I have discussed the pros and cons of a balanced feed and balanced antennas **[1]**, noting that it is probable that the strictly balanced feeder arrangements were derived from commercial practice. These commercial installations used multiple transmitters and antennas. Furthermore, the antennas were located some distance from the transmitters and any unbalance on the feeders resulted in radiation loss and cross-talk to nearby feeders.

**OFF-CENTRE-FED ANTENNAS.** The half wave dipole is just fine for a single band but if used on higher frequencies the feed impedances can vary dramatically. However, if the feed point is moved part of the way from the centre of the dipole the feed impedance can be increased to any impedance; a 300Ω point is shown in Figure 1. It also has some implications for multibanding the dipole. The current distribution diagram shown in **Figure 2** is based on one by DJ2KY. It shows the current on a half-wave length of wire on 80m superimposed on the current distribution on other higher bands. It can be seen that the current amplitudes on some of the bands coincide at sixth of a wavelength from the end, described by DJ2KY as a 'Windom point' **[2]**.

The current distributions shown in Figure 2 are idealistic, showing the current distributions in free space. In practice, these currents can have slightly different amplitudes and phases due to the proximity of the ground. Furthermore, amplitudes of the current variations along the antenna element may not be constant on the higher frequencies when the antenna is fed off centre. Nevertheless, the impedances found at the sixth of a wavelength point are fairly close together on some bands.

Most off-centre-fed dipole (OCFD) antennas appear to be fed with coaxial cable (**Figure 3**). The currents on the centre core of coax cable ($I_1$) and the inside of the shield ($I_2$) are equal and opposite. The two conductors are closely coupled along their entire length, so the equal and antiphase current relationship is strongly enforced. This $I_1/I_2$ relationship is completely independent of the coax environment. The cable can be taped to a tower or buried, yet the equal and opposite nature of $I_1$ and $I_2$ inside the cable remain the same.

Enter the 'skin effect' **[3]**, which causes HF currents to flow only (very) close to the surfaces of conductors. This causes the inner and outer surfaces of the coaxial shield behave as two entirely independent conductors. When a coaxial feed is used, the unbalanced nature of an OCFD antenna causes a difference between the currents flowing either side of the feed point. This difference current is shown in Figure 3 as $I_3$, and is equal to ($I_1$-$I_2$). Current $I_3$ has to flow somewhere. It cannot flow down the inside of the cable because $I_1$ and $I_2$ must be equal, so instead it flows down the outside of the outer sheath. As a result, the feed line becomes part of the radiating antenna **[4]**.

**A COMMERCIAL OCFD.** There are many commercial OCFD antennas on the market and the MOCVO HW-40HP antenna, shown in **Photo 1**, is one of them **[5]**. The centre consists of a plastic balun box with a SO239 input socket and screws with wing nuts for connection to the dipole elements. Strain relief and a support point are provided by three metal key rings attached through holes in the flange at the top of the box. The insulators at the other ends of the elements are of a very decent, heavy duty type. The antenna is supplied fully assembled as shown in Photo 1. Overall, it is 21.28m (66ft) long and described as an off centre fed dipole designed to operate on the 40m (7MHz), 20m (14MHz), 15m (21MHz) and 10m (28MHz) bands. The documentation with this antenna goes on to say, "Having a feed point 1/3 of the way along instead of halfway gives an impedance of between 300 and 400Ω... a 4:1 current balun is added at the feed point to alter the impedance to something closer to the required 50Ω. This then allows the antenna to be fed using standard 50Ω coaxial cable such as RG8 or RG213".

The balun was tested and found to have a transformer action of 4:1 as claimed. It was not possible to determine if the balun was a current (as claimed) or voltage transformer because the unit was sealed. The antenna

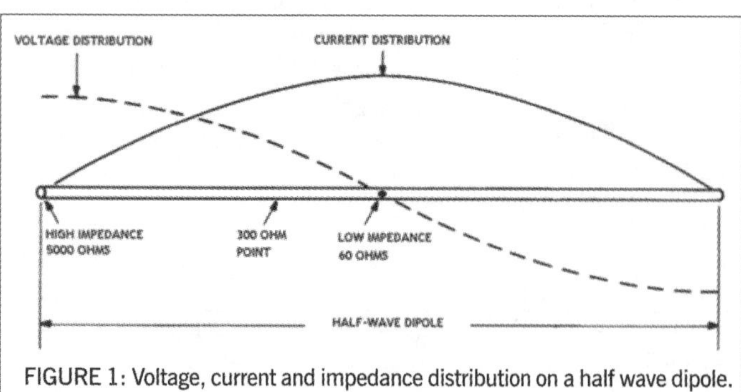


FIGURE 1: Voltage, current and impedance distribution on a half wave dipole.

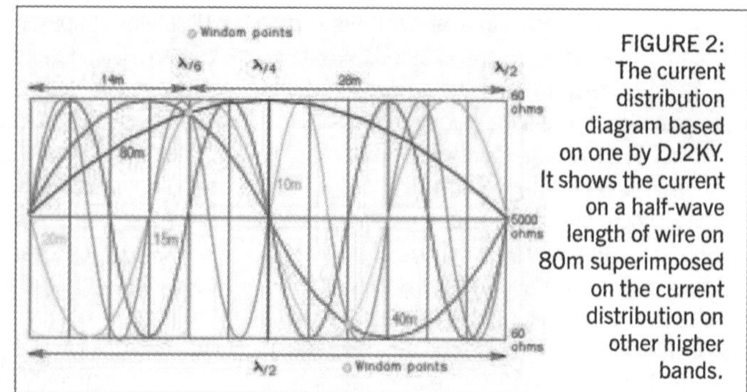


FIGURE 2: The current distribution diagram based on one by DJ2KY. It shows the current on a half-wave length of wire on 80m superimposed on the current distribution on other higher bands.

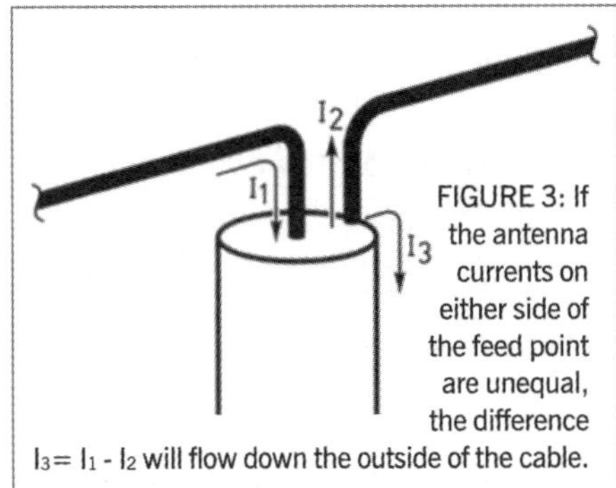


FIGURE 3: If the antenna currents on either side of the feed point are unequal, the difference $I_3 = I_1 - I_2$ will flow down the outside of the cable.

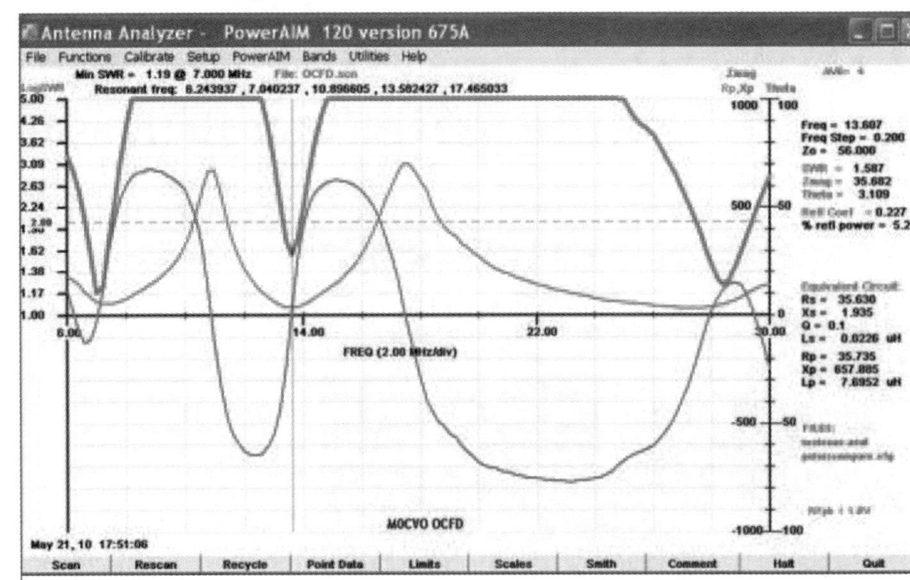


FIGURE 4: Impedance and SWR measurements of the M0CVO HW-40HP antenna, measured using the AIM 4170.

was fixed 10m high at one end and 7m high at the other, with the long element at the high end. (I had previously used this location for a 7MHz dipole during 501kHz/7MHz cross-band tests with VO1NA).

The results of impedance and SWR measurements, measured using the AIM 4170 via a 9m calibrated length of RG58, are shown in **Figure 4**. SWR is indicated with the thick red graph. Impedances Zmag and Theta are represented by the thin red and purple lines respectively. I noticed that the SWR on 7MHz varied when I touched the coax PL259 connector, indicating the presence of $I_3$ currents on the outer braid of the coax. Lowest SWR readings were obtained when the coax was laid on the ground. The antenna was then connected via a 25m length of coax to the shack and an MFJ-854 RF current meter was used to measure $I_3$ currents. With 100W of 7.02MHz RF fed to the antenna, the RF current $I_3$ at the bottom of the vertical section of coax to the antenna was 500mA. I measured 300mA at the shack end of the coax. These currents were less on the higher frequency bands. In spite of these currents on the outside of the coax no adverse affects such as RF in the shack, TV or audio equipment interference were experienced.

In general, the antenna performed reasonably well. Eastern USA and EU contacts were made on 7MHz without any difficulty. The antenna could be fed without an ATU on the 7, 14 and 28MHz bands (as you might expect from looking at Figure 4), in spite of the resonances being rather low in frequency. The antenna certainly would not load directly on 21MHz as claimed but this band and all the others could be loaded easily using an ATU.

Bearing in mind the asymmetrical nature of the feed, currents on the outside of the coax are inevitable. Some method of controlling them is necessary. Some OCFD builders go to a lot of trouble to eliminate common mode currents from the feed line. The arrangement shown in **Figure 5 [6]** is a multiband OCFD, which uses a 4:1 transformer plus two additional current chokes on the coax. Additionally the coax braid is connected to earth. All these precautions minimise radiation from the feeder on transmit, particularly important if one is using high power. It also reduces interference pick up on receive. I managed to reduce the current on the M0CVO antenna to 120mA in the shack by using a single W2DU current choke.

Overall, I was reasonably impressed with this antenna, although I wonder whether the metal rings would eventually wear through the flange of the plastic balun box.

**THE CAROLINA WINDOM.** Other antenna designs use the feeder radiation to advantage, a method described by G2HCG as 'Controlled Feeder Radiation' **[7]**. With this method, a current choke is placed some distance from the feed point so that the length of the radiating section of the feeder is preset. A commercial application of this is used with an OCFD known as the Carolina Windom. This antenna is also fed approximately 1/3 from the end using 50Ω coax and the feeder is encouraged to radiate due to the asymmetrical feed point. The physical length over which the feeder radiates is limited to 3m (10ft) by a 'line isolator', presumably a coax outer braid current choke. Radio Works who manufacture this antenna **[8]** have coined a title for the radiating section of feeder and called it VERT (Vertically Enhanced Radiation Technique). Several versions of the Carolina Windom are marketed by Radio Works.

It occurred to me that the M0CVO HW-40HP antenna could be converted to a Carolina Windom simply by adding a current choke 3m (10ft) down from the balun at the antenna feed point. While this reduced the common mode currents considerably, it had an adverse effect on the SWR – to such a degree that the ATU was necessary for all the bands. I don't know why this should be; suffice it to say there is more to the OCFD than meets the eye.

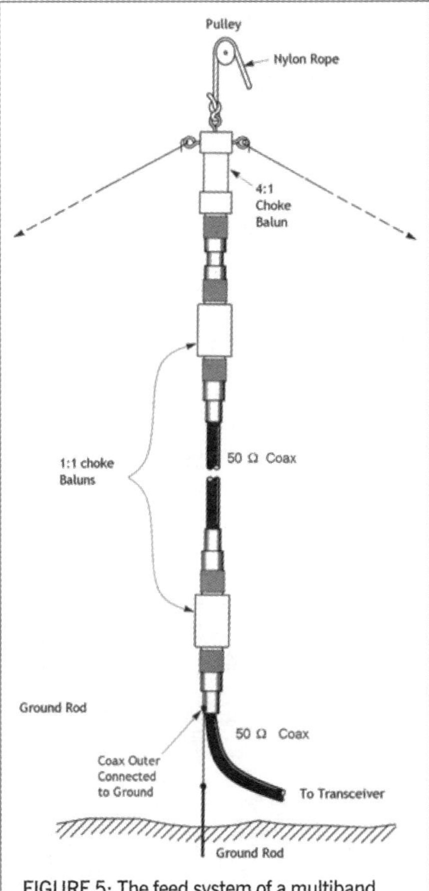


FIGURE 5: The feed system of a multiband OCFD, showing a method for eliminating antenna ($I_3$) currents.


REFERENCES AND NOTES

[1] 'Antennas', *RadCom* January 2006 & March 2006.

[2] The original Windom antenna, popular in the 1940s, comprised a wire element fed by a single wire 'feeder' approximately 1/3 from the end. Such a configuration had to be fed against ground similar to an inverted L antenna.

[3] http://en.wikipedia.org/wiki/Skin_effect

[4] The equal and opposite currents $I_1$ and $I_2$ are often referred to as differential mode currents. $I_3$ currents are often referred to as common mode currents; in some literature they are also referred to as antenna currents presumably because they cause radiation.

[5] m0cvoantennas.co.uk

[6] From How to Design Off-Center-Fed Multiband Antennas Using That Invisible Transformer In The Sky, Frank Witt, AI1H, *The ARRL Antenna Compendium, Volume 3*.

[7] Controlled Feeder Radiation, B Sykes, G2HCG, *Radio Communication* May 1990.

[8] www.radioworks.com

# Antennas

## G3LDO's experiences with a small transmitting loop antenna

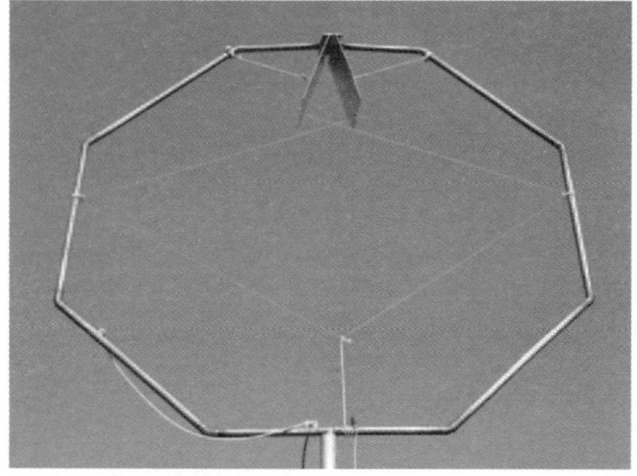

PHOTO 1: The G3LDO loop antenna with mechanical capacitor tuning.

SMALL TRANSMITTING LOOPS. I have talked about loop antenna several times but all this has been the work of other people. I had never actually built a small transmitting loop so I felt that it was high time this omission was rectified. This column is devoted to my experiences with this antenna.

The limiting factor in homebrewing a small transmitting loop is the tuning capacitor. You need a good quality two-ganged or butterfly transmitting capacitor or a fairly rugged vacuum capacitor. It also has to be well engineered into the loop. Because the bandwidth of the antenna is so small, a method varying the capacitor also has to be built into the system.

For the purposes of just trying out the transmitting loop I used a capacitor arrangement using hinged plates, as described by Martin Ehrenfried, G8JNJ [1]. I will describe its construction later.

COMPUTER MODELS. My first step was to make a computer model of the loop using EZNEC 5. I had heard that EZNEC did not model a transmitting loop accurately but this suggestion may have been propagated by someone whose theories on the loop did not match the modelled data. Part of this loop-building project was to investigate the suitability of a computer model.

The free-space model of a 1.5m diameter hexagonal loop made from 22mm diameter copper tube is shown in **Figure 1**. The model was brought into resonance with a 24pF capacitance load, giving a 2:1 SWR bandwidth 24kHz as shown in **Figure 2**. The model predicted a maximum gain of 1.34dBi (including 22mm copper losses) compared with 2.2dBi for a loss-less free-space dipole. This loop model predicts that my loop will be around 80% efficient compared with a dipole.

If you are considering constructing a small transmitting loop antenna, there are a few interactive computer programs on the Internet. The 66Pacific.com magnetic loop antenna calculator **[2]** shown in **Figure 3** is based on *ARRL Antenna Handbook* material and is the one used to calculate the parameters of the loop I intended to build.

LOOP CONSTRUCTION. The loop is made from 22mm copper tubing in an octagonal configuration as shown in **Photo 1**. The loop described by G8JNJ also used 22mm copper tubing but in a square loop and for this he used four 90° elbow soldered couplings to form the square.

Almost all of the material used to construct this loop was obtained from a local DIY shop except the eight 45° couplings that were not available locally and had to be sourced from a plumbers outlet. A Tee coupler was used at the base of the loop to provide a short stub mast for fixing the loop to an antenna support.

Most designs seem to use a 1m diameter loop for the bands 20 to 10 metres. In view of the state of the sunspots at the time of writing, I used a larger loop of 1.5m diameter loop to hopefully cover 7 to 22MHz.

CAPACITOR CONSTRUCTION. The capacitor is made from two aluminium plates fixed on hinges at the ends of the copper loop. I used 6 x 12in plates because that is what I happened to have to hand. A drawstring and bungee cord arrangement is used to adjust the angle of the capacitor plates relative to each other, which in turn adjusts the value of the capacitance. The ends of the loop were flattened, which made a convenient point onto which to solder the brass hinges.

All descriptions of small transmitting loop construction emphasise the importance of overcoming the RF resistance of the capacitance to loop connection. This arrangement is no exception – the hinge, although made of brass, would probably present a relatively high RF resistance, which is circumvented using coax cable braid as shown in **Photo 2**. Copper pads are used to make the connections to the aluminium capacitor plates.

The capacitor plates held in the open position with ¼ in (6mm) bungee cord. Capacitor variation is achieved using strimmer line and nylon cord to pull the capacitor plates together against tension created by the bungee cord, which is best seen in Photo 1. The bungee tension is found by trial and error. The strimmer cord is connected to the ends of the aluminium capacitance plates in a cross-diagonal manner using 22mm plastic tube clips as shown in Photo 1. The strimmer cord runs through small holes drilled in these plastic clips.

I calculated the maximum capacitance with the plates 4mm apart as 100pF, which

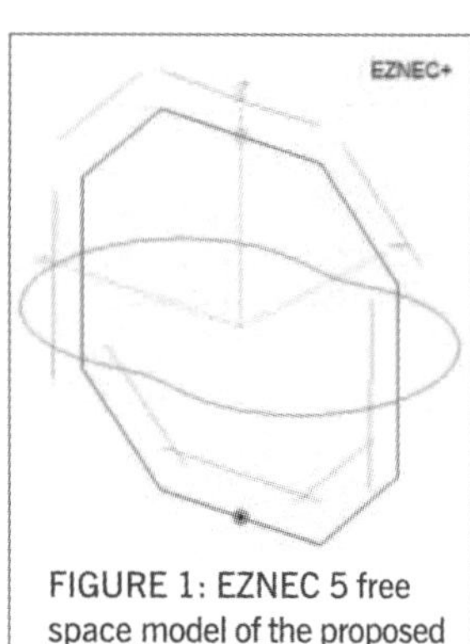


FIGURE 1: EZNEC 5 free space model of the proposed loop antenna.

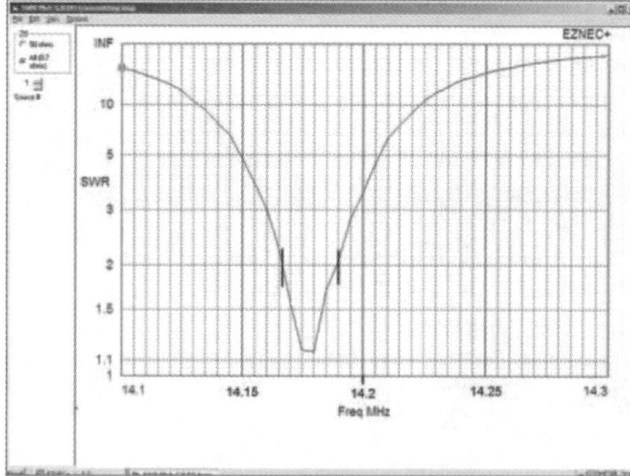


FIGURE 2: SWR curve the loop predicted by EZNEC.

PHOTO 2: Detail of the capacitor hinge.

PHOTO 3: Construction of the variable capacitor with an additional parallel fixed lower frequency capacitor made from a short length of RG213 (see text).

**Length of Conductor (antenna "circumference")**
4.712 meters

**Diameter of Conductor**
(For efficiency, should be > 3/8" or 1 cm)
2.2 centimeters

**Frequency**
14 megahertz

**Transmitter Power (optional)**
100 Watts

**Units of Measurement**
English (feet and inches)
Metric (meters and centimeters)

**Calculate**

**To use the calculator:**
**1.** Choose the units of measurement, English or metric.

**2.** Enter the length of the antenna conductor, which is the distance around the loop. The length should be between 0.1 and 0.25 wavelength at the desired operating frequency.

**3.** Enter the diameter of the conductor.
**Note:** Small transmitting loops have very low radiation resistance and very high circulating current, so the diameter of the conductor must be large to assure reasonable efficiency—around 1" or 2.5 cm for the HF bands. #12 wire (for example) will *not* work.

**4.** Enter the frequency of operation.

**5.** Enter the transmitter power. This is optional, but it must be entered if you want to calculate the voltage at the capacitor and the circulating current.

**6.** Press **Calculate**.

**RESULTS:**
Antenna efficiency: 86% (-0.6 dB below 100%)
Antenna bandwidth: 41.3 kHz
Tuning Capacitance: 34 pF

Capacitor voltage: 3,350 volts RMS
Resonant circulating current: 10.1 A
Radiation resistance: 0.422 ohms
Loss Resistance: 0.067 ohms
Inductance: 3.77 microhenrys
Inductive Reactance: 331 ohms
Quality Factor (Q): 339
Distributed capacity: 13 pF

Antenna "circumference": 4.712 meters

Side length: 0.589 meters

Antenna diameter: 1.4 meters

**Comments:**
The specified conductor length of 4.712 meters is OK.

**Conductor length should be between 2.60 and 5.20 meters at the specified frequency of 14 MHz.**

For highest efficiency, the conductor length for a small transmitting loop antenna should be greater than 1/8 wavelength (greater than about 2.60 meters at the specified frequency of 14 MHz).

To avoid self-resonance, the conductor length for a small transmitting loop antenna should be less than 1/4 wavelength (less than about 5.20 meters at the specified frequency of 14 MHz).

**Input Values:**
Length of conductor: 4.712 meters
Diameter of conductor: 2.2 centimeters
Frequency: 14 MHz
Transmitter power: 100 watts

**Source:**
The ARRL Antenna Book: The Ultimate Reference for Amateur Radio Antennas, Transmission Lines And Propagation

**References:**
The ARRL Handbook for Radio Communications

**Related Pages:**
Design your own tuning capacitor for use with this antenna with the
Capacitance Calculator (Capacitor Design)

FIGURE 3: Calculations of the proposed loop antenna.

theoretically should tune my loop down to 10MHz. An insulator block is required to fix the distance between the two hinges. I used a block of dark coloured Perspex 10mm thick of unknown pedigree.

The complete capacitor is shown in **Photo 3**. A coax fixed capacitor stub shown in the photo was used during the experiments with this capacitor arrangement – I will describe the reason for this later.

Almost all loop capacitor methods use a motor/gear box arrangement to vary the capacitor and tune the loop. I used a simpler arrangement where the lower part of nylon cord section is wrapped around the lower part of the loop and secured with a plastic clip when the tuning point is found. This method of tuning was fine for testing the viability of the loop and was adopted because a suitable motor/gearbox was not available.

FEED METHOD AND TUNING. I chose the simple shunt feed (some call it a Gamma match) as shown in Photo 1. I made a guess as to where to connect the shunt feed clip to the loop, connected the MFJ 259 analyser (set to 14.2MHz) to the feed point and pulled the cord of the tuning mechanism. The MFJ 259 registered an SWR dip of 1.5:1 on the first attempt. A small position adjustment of the shunt feed clip to the loop reduced the SWR to a much lower value.

I also tried the G3LHZ 'twisted gamma' match described in my July Antennas column, using the centre conductor and insulation of a section of 75Ω coax (1mm conductor with 2.3mm thick insulation). The SWR and impedance matching results shown in Figure 3 showed no discernable difference between the short and long twisted gamma matches. G8JNJ is of the opinion that these gamma matches are a sort of loop rather than a shunt feed.

OPERATIONAL TESTS. Tuning was quite straightforward, particularly with an active SWR meter such as the MFJ 259/269 type of instrument. Otherwise you can tune for maximum noise and signals on receive and fine tune on low power transmit with an SWR meter. The tuning arrangement performed reasonably well with just a bit of friction where the strimmer cord goes through the plastic pipe clip holes.

The tuning range was not as great as the model suggested; the practical range covered only the 10, 14 and 18MHz bands. The reason is that the minimum capacitance of the hinged plate capacitor is greater than expected, although it was not possible to measure this capacitance with it connected to the loop. Adjustment of the capacitance at the lowest frequency range proved to be rather critical with this tuning arrangement. You can appreciate why when you consider that the difference in capacitance with plate spacings from 4 to 8mm results in a capacitance change of 50pF.

The solution is to add a fixed capacitor in parallel with the variable one when using the antenna on the lower frequencies. This has the effect of 'bandspreading' the tuning. I tried a short length of RG-213 coax as shown in Photo 3 and this worked quite well up to 100W; however, it flashed over at 200W. A better arrangement would be a fixed capacitance made from two aluminium plates fixed to the brass bolts and nuts seen in Photo 3. The minimum capacitance could be reduced by cutting off the two top (hinge) corners of each of the variable plates.

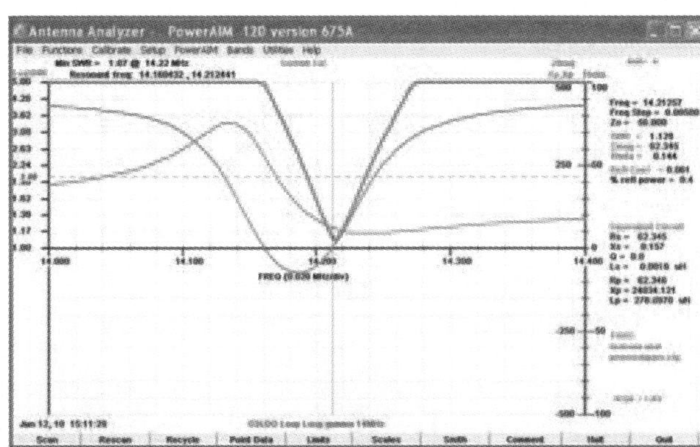

FIGURE 4: Measurements of SWR, Z magnitude and Theta of the finished loop. Compare the SWR with that predicted in Figure 2.

This loop was tested only on the 14 and 18MHz bands. My initial impressions were that it performed as well as a very good mobile antenna. The loop was mounted 2m above the ground well away from the house via a feeder comprising 43m of RG213 and 10m of RG58. The comparison antenna was an 11m high multiband rotary dipole on top of the house, fed via 15m of RG213.

There was very little difference between the two antennas on short skip contacts. Sometimes the loop gave the best results, other times the dipole did best. DX signals were a different matter, with the dipole 2 to 3 S-points ahead of the loop. On the other hand, the loop was often better on receive because it was so quiet.

REFERENCES

[1] http://g8jnj.webs.com
[2] www.66pacific.com/calculators/small_tx_loop_calc.aspx

# Antennas

## More on HF magnetic loops and impedance measurements

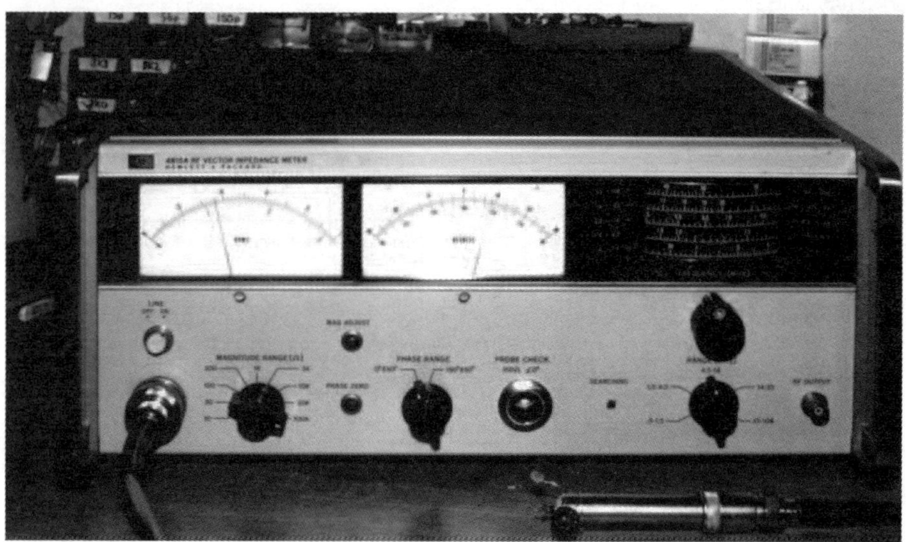

PHOTO 1: HP4085 vector impedance meter. The meter on the left indicates Zmag in ohms while the right hand meter indicates Theta in degrees.

**RF CONDUCTORS.** In the September Antennas I described a loop antenna tuned by a capacitor that consisted of two aluminium plates fixed on hinges at the ends of the copper loop. One of the issues with this design was how to reduce the RF resistance across the capacitor hinges. The mechanical arrangement of these hinges, although made of brass, would probably present a relatively high RF resistance, which I said could be circumvented using coax cable braid.

The advantage of braid in this application is its flexibility. Some people question the effectiveness of braid at radio frequencies. The argument is that each strand of the braid weaves in and out and back and forth across the braid. Currents must either follow that inductive weaving path, or jump from strand to strand where strands touch. There are, of course, many individual strands in parallel, so overall inductance should be low. Tinned copper braid is probably best because oxidation between various strands of bare untinned copper braid may degrade performance.

Having said that, most coaxial cables for RF applications have a braided outer conductor to give them flexibility. The better grades use tinned braid. Very high performance low-loss coaxial cables use a solid outer conductor.

Copper strip is the best type of RF conductor because has the greatest surface area for a given amount of copper. Due to the skin effect, RF currents tend to flow along the outside surface of a conductor. Copper strap has a large, smooth surface area to take full advantage of this effect.

The disadvantage of copper strap is that it is not flexible and is unsuitable for bonding straps across the hinges of our loop capacitor. G8JNJ **[1]** tried thin sheet brass (obtained from a model shop) to make the bonding straps on the capacitors of his loop antenna. While brass does not have the conductivity of copper, he does report that it seemed to improve the Q slightly compared to using copper braid, although no actual figures are supplied. Another type of material that might be suitable for this purpose is phosphor bronze strip (used in door draught excluders).

**MAKING COPPER STRIP.** If you have difficulty in finding a source of copper strip for parts of a loop made from copper tubing (other than the capacitor hinge bonding strip mentioned above) you can make it from readily available 22mm or 15mm copper pipe. A short length of heavy duty strip suitable for fixing the SO239 socket to the loop can be made by flattening a short length of 22mm copper pipe in a vice. Smaller and thinner copper straps for making the shunt match connection to the loop can be made from flattened 15mm copper pipe. The edges of the flattened pipe are then filed down until it breaks into two thin strips.

**OTHER COMMENTS ON THE LOOP.** One of the oddities of the model shown in **Figure 1** is that the nulls in the sides of the azimuth plot are not very deep compared with a free space dipole. Measuring the nulls of the real loop using a selective level meter resulted in nulls of −20dB on one side and −11dB on the other; the cause of this asymmetry at the time of writing is unknown. The coax feed to the loop should be routed vertically down from the loop to the ground to get the best SWR and to minimise common mode currents on the coax. A current choke would also be of some help in this regard.

G8JNJ suggests making the capacitor plates teardrop shaped. This would give a smaller minimum capacitance and make the angular movement of the plates relative to frequency more linear.

**RF MEASURING INSTRUMENTS.** Many of you are aware my main interest is RF measuring instruments and their uses. For many years, the most popular and practical instrument for measuring the most useful of parameters, impedance, was the R±jX noise bridge.

There are times when measurements accuracies greater that provided by the standard noise bridge are required, particularly when the results have to be committed to print. I had used the 3-meter instrument **[2]** to good effect for many years but what was really needed was some sort of standard. Over a period of time, I acquired two old commercial instruments capable of making precision measurements.

The first was a General Radio 1606 Impedance Bridge, which I bought in 1985. This instrument comprises a precision bridge with variable calibrated components. As with all bridges of this type the bridge is energised using a signal generator. The bridge measures

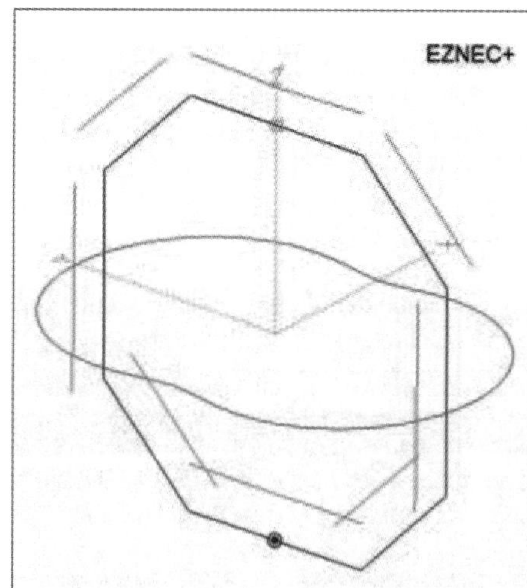


FIGURE 1: *EZNEC* 5 free space model of the G3LDO magnetic loop antenna showing current distribution (red) and azimuth radiation diagram (blue).

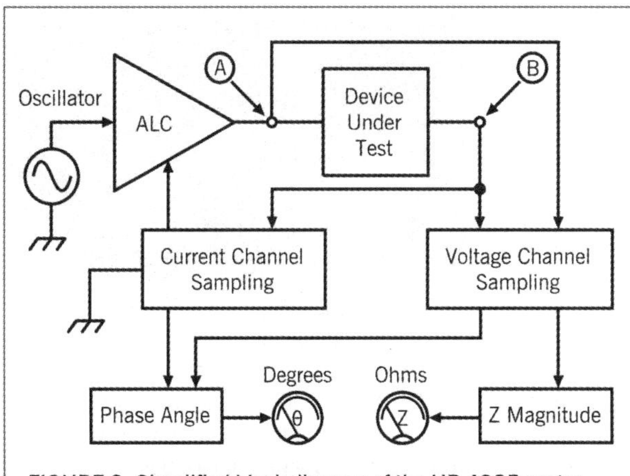


**FIGURE 2: Simplified block diagram of the HP 4085 vector impedance meter. The device under test is connected to terminals A and B.**

**FIGURE 3: An AIM 4170 display showing a Smith chart superimposed on swept frequency graph, the result of measuring a 200Ω resistor over a three metre length of RG58.**

the impedance presented to the UNKNOWN socket by adjusting calibrated components for a dip (or null) in a detector, usually a communications receiver with an S-meter. The impedance (R±jX) is measured on the dials of the bridge-calibrated components at the point of maximum dip.

While the GR 1660 gave good results, its weight of 10.5kg (23lb) together with an appropriate signal generator and communications receiver represented a lot of equipment for making an impedance measurement.

Later, I obtained a HP4085 vector impedance meter at a radio rally. At 17.6kg (39lbs), this instrument is heavier than the GR 1660 but has the advantage of being self-contained with its own signal generator supplying test signals from 0.5 to108MHz. This instrument doesn't have calibrated bridge components and a null detector. Instead, it measures impedance directly by comparing the ratio of voltage and current injected into the circuit or antenna under test. An automatic level control circuit (ALC) holds the current constant so that the impedance magnitude is directly proportional to voltage. Phase angle is measured by detecting the phase relation between the voltage and current waveforms. Impedance is read out directly on two meters, one showing impedance magnitude and the other phase as shown in **Photo 1** and **Figure 2**.

It measures the impedance using a probe and presents these measurements in terms Zmag/Theta. In the days when this instrument was state of the art (circa mid 60s), HP provided a slide rule calculator to convert these polar coordinates into the more familiar R±jX format.

**VECTOR IMPEDANCE ANALYSERS.** These instruments have been around for some time now (the first I heard of them was in the September 2004 Technical Topics). Vector impedance analysers are now commercially available. There is the miniVNA from Mini Radio Solutions and the AIM 4170, designed by Bob Clunn, W5BIG, which was reviewed in *RadCom* **[3]**.

I bought an AIM 4170 early in 2007 after being inspired by it during a visit to Dayton. It has been used for the analysis of antennas and baluns in Antennas columns since August 2007. It is very intuitive to use with only occasional recourse to the instruction book being necessary.

A length of feeder acts as an impedance transformer, the ratio of which varies with frequency. This means that the impedance you measure at the end of the feeder will generally not be the feed impedance of the antenna if you are using one of the instruments described earlier. There is an exception and that is when the feeder is an electrical half wavelength long. In this case the transmission line theoretically acts as a 1:1 transformer but note the measurement described below.

One of the features of the AIM 4170 is its ability to calibrate the feeder between the instrument and the device under test, which circumvents the problem described above.

The AIM 4170 performs a number of parameter measurements over a given swept frequency range; the most well known being SWR and impedance. This latter parameter is given in Zmag/Theta and/or the more familiar R±jX. It will also plot Reflection Coefficient and Return Loss; it'll even do all these parameters at the same time if so desired. Mind you, if you try to display them simultaneously the display gets a bit messy so in practice I generally stick with just SWR and impedance.

The AIM 4170 also has Smith chart display. This is a useful feature for checking the accuracy of this type of instrument. The display shown in **Figure 3** is Smith chart superimposed on a swept frequency graph, being the result of measuring a 200Ω resistor (one that came with the calibration pack) over a three metre length of RG58.

The green circle is a SWR 2:1 marker. It can be seen that the actual plot (shown in red) is a smooth circle showing a tendency to spiral towards the centre as the frequency is increased; an effect caused by coax cable loss. Any errors with measurements will cause irregularities in the smoothness of this plot.

In the background plot of Figure 3, you can see a green marker placed over the point where Theta is zero. This is the half wavelength point away from the 200Ω load. The data to the left of the display shows the Zmag and Rs both 175.8Ω. At a full wavelength, it was 158Ω. I had not appreciated how much the cable attenuation would affect the divergence from the 1:1 transforming ratio but it is obvious when you think about it.

I have only just scratched the surface of what this instrument can do. If you wish to know more then I recommend you attend the RSGB 2010 Convention on Sunday 10 October **[4]** where Ian Wade, G3NRW, is giving two presentations on the AIM 4170 antenna analyser. The first will cover the basics of antenna measurement, and the second will illustrate the use of the 4170 as a design tool.

Live demonstrations of the AIM 4170 will be the main feature of the presentations, and will include tuning a 4m ground plane, trap tuning, designing a 160/80m trap dipole, measuring quartz crystal parameters, using the Smith chart, quarter-wave stub tuning and measuring the impedance at the antenna feedpoint. The final demonstration will show how to control the analyser remotely via a Wi-Fi link, allowing you to tune your antenna while standing in the garden (or on the roof or at the top of the tower). The presentations will be based on the material at G3NRW's website **[5]**.

REFERENCES

[1] http://g8jnj.webs.com
[2] *The Antenna Experimenter's Guide*, Second Edition, Peter Dodd, G3LDO.
[3] *RadCom* July, 2007
[4] RSGB Convention: www.rsgb.org.uk/rsgbconvention
[5] http://homepage.ntlworld.com/wadei/aim4170.htm

# Antennas

## More on G3LDO's small loop testing methods

**PHOTO 1: ZL1VL's 400 sq ft (37m²) of galvanised chicken wire counterpoise system, which gave a definite all round improvement to the performance of the Hustler 6BTV.**

ANTENNA COMPARISON TESTING AND *WSPR*. In the January Antennas I described the experimental work of Walter Blanchard, G3JKV, who was testing a Hustler 6BTV on behalf of the Dorking Amateur Radio Club. Most of this work involved trying different radials and ground systems and conducting comparative performance tests.

This description brought a surprising amount of e-mail and an example was published in March Antennas; the experiences of Duncan Tribute, G1OEQ and his Hustler 6BTV, which he uses from a restricted site in Truro.

LETTER FROM NEW ZEALAND. Additionally Vince Lear, ZL1VL (ex G3TKN), sent me details of experimental work comparing a ground mount Hustler 6BTV vertical against full sized inverted V's for 20, 30 and 40m at apex heights of 29ft (9m). He goes on to say "I live in a typical suburban environment in Auckland and the aerial is not out in the clear, so my results are probably fairly typical of what the average ham can expect living in these sort of surroundings. The low height of 29ft is also probably typical for most hams with restricted space.

"When rapid switching of different antennas takes place (especially when one is a vertical and the other a horizontal) there will always be times when one antenna may have an advantage over the other depending on time of day, propagation conditions and of course distance. Sometimes the advantage can swing back and forth by the minute. The results below are a broad summary to give an overall idea of what I found was happening most of the time.

"20m: I found the inverted V dipole to be consistently better on just about every station; sometimes 2 S-units and sometimes more. On one short path QSO to G the Hustler got a 4/2 while the inverted V was 5/6 although the inverted V had a greater signal to noise ratio. GM3PPE in Kelso who also runs a Hustler did similar tests a while back and found his 20m inverted V at 30ft (9.1m) to be around 10dB better on average in the broadside direction compared to his Hustler at all ranges. His Hustler was mounted clear of obstructions.

"30m: There were times when the inverted V was slightly better (especially up to JA) but overall the two antennas seemed about equal on Europe and Stateside.

"40m: The Hustler was the clear winner at DX as obviously an inverted V at 29ft (9m) is just too low. In the late afternoon on the long path to Europe there were some weak EUs that could be copied on the vertical that were virtually inaudible on the inverted V.

"80m: I have not compared the Hustler with any other antenna at this QTH, but it has proved itself on DX at distances up to 5000 miles (JA) running just 100W.

"I feel if one is living in a suburban environment, ground mounted verticals are to be avoided on 14MHz and higher frequencies. However, they can work well on frequencies below 10MHz given a good ground. My original ground system comprised some 20 radials around 20ft (6m) long. This radial system was replaced with 400 sq ft (37m²) of galvanised chicken wire mesh, see **Photo 1**. At that point, I felt there was a definite all round improvement in the performance of the Hustler 6BTV. There was a reduction in the base impedance of the vertical showing lower earth losses with the wire mesh.

"Finally, I thought I would experiment with a 20m ground plane (spaced well away from the Hustler) using 2 quarter wave radials and with its base elevated 13ft (4m). The elevated GP was noticeably better than the Hustler by 1 and sometimes 2 S-units but I still felt the 20m inverted V at 29ft (9m) was better than the GP. I had taken the 20m inverted V down, so I was not able to do direct comparisons between the GP and the inverted V."

ANTENNA PERFORMANCE COMPARISONS. Some of you may be aware that a method I used to make comparison tests on antennas has been the subject of discussion, so in this column I will explain antenna testing in general and my QTH in particular.

The general layout of one half of my back garden is shown in **Photo 2**. The loop antenna in the foreground is being compared with the multiband rotary dipole on the roof.

The loop was mounted 2m above the ground well away from the house via a feeder comprising 43m of RG213 and 10m of RG58. The comparison antenna was an 11m high multiband rotary dipole on top of the house fed via 15m of RG213. This gave the dipole an obvious advantage but, in spite of this, the loop did very well on short skip contacts. Sometimes the loop gave the best results, other times the dipole did best although DX signals on the dipole were 2 to 3 S-points ahead of the loop.

As reported in September, VK5KLT **[1]** had some interesting findings and comments regarding the best location for a transmitting

TABLE 1: Part of the edited G3LDO transmission data from the *WSPR* web

| Time | Frequency | SNR | Call | Locator | km | miles |
|---|---|---|---|---|---|---|
| QUAD | | | | | | |
| 14:52 | 14.097161 | -15 | NB3N | FM19ki | 5875 | 3651 |
| 14:48 | 14.097149 | -9 | W3GXT | FM19ol | 5844 | 3631 |
| 14:48 | 14.097199 | -14 | WOOGH | DM43ci | 8502 | 5283 |
| 14:48 | 14.097163 | -5 | NB3N | FM19ki | 5875 | 3651 |
| 14:40 | 14.097148 | -15 | W3GXT | FM19ol | 5844 | 3631 |
| 14:40 | 14.097200 | -11 | WOOGH | DM43ci | 8502 | 5283 |
| DIPOLE | | | | | | |
| 14:32 | 14.097161 | -18 | NB3N | FM19ki | 5875 | 3651 |
| 14:32 | 14.097156 | -19 | WA8KNE | EM90gg | 6846 | 4254 |
| 14:26 | 14.097153 | -18 | KF1Z | FN33na | 5282 | 3282 |
| 14:26 | 14.097128 | -21 | WA3DNM | FM29fw | 5728 | 3559 |
| 14:26 | 14.097156 | -20 | WA8KNE | EM90gg | 6846 | 4254 |
| 14:18 | 14.097197 | -23 | WOOGH | DM43ci | 8502 | 5283 |

loop antenna and that the bottom of the loop does not need to be more than a loop diameter above ground. He also noted that there is no significant improvement in performance when a small loop is raised to great heights; all that matters is the loop is substantially clear of objects in the desired direction of radiation and that mounting on an elevated roof ground-plane yields excellent results.

The important point is that "the loop should be substantially clear of objects in the desired direction of radiation". As you can see from **Photo 2** this isn't the case. I hope to repeat the comparison with the loop mounted on the flat roof of the house extension and fed with a short length of RG213.

*WSPR*. There is another interesting way that you can use to check the comparative DX performance of antennas. G3JKV mentioned the use of *WSPR* in the January Antennas. For those of you who have never heard of this before, *WSPR* (Weak Signal Propagation Reporter) **[2]** is a free software application that can enable your station to send and receive signals from similarly equipped stations worldwide.

The *WSPR* transmission contains the transmitter's callsign, locator and power (in dBm). Once set up, operation of *WSPR* is completely automated. The software logs every transmission you make, as well as all the decoded signals received.

Because participating stations usually upload signals that they receive in real time to a web server, you can find out within seconds of the end of each transmission exactly where and how strongly it was received. It is these reports that are of interest. My *WSPR* signals are shown in **Figure 1**. The station reporting the signals, together with location and distance from my QTH, are shown in each row. The most important information, the received signals, are reported as SNR (signal to noise ratio), rather than a specific signal level. Remember that these signals are very weak, often way below what is audible in the CW mode.

| Date | Call | Frequency | SNR | Drift | Grid | Power dBm | Power W | Reported by | Reported loc | Distance km | Distance mi |
|---|---|---|---|---|---|---|---|---|---|---|---|
| 2010-09-02 13:58 | G3LDO | 14.097160 | -19 | -3 | IO90st | +37 | 5.012 | NB3N | FM19ki | 5875 | 3651 |
| 2010-09-02 13:58 | G3LDO | 14.097158 | -21 | -3 | IO90st | +37 | 5.012 | DF2LV | JO44rs | 798 | 496 |
| 2010-09-02 13:52 | G3LDO | 14.097155 | -21 | -4 | IO90st | +37 | 5.012 | WA8KNE | EM90gg | 6846 | 4254 |
| 2010-09-02 13:52 | G3LDO | 14.097152 | -13 | -3 | IO90st | +37 | 5.012 | 4X1RF | KM72ls | 3504 | 2177 |
| 2010-09-02 13:52 | G3LDO | 14.097164 | -26 | -3 | IO90st | +37 | 5.012 | W0BLD | EM37jc | 7081 | 4400 |
| 2010-09-02 13:52 | G3LDO | 14.097164 | -14 | -3 | IO90st | +37 | 5.012 | IZ6QZB | JN62qi | 1411 | 877 |
| 2010-09-02 13:52 | G3LDO | 14.097197 | -21 | -3 | IO90st | +37 | 5.012 | W0OGH | DM43ci | 8502 | 5283 |
| 2010-09-02 13:52 | G3LDO | 14.097146 | -22 | -3 | IO90st | +37 | 5.012 | W3GXT | FM19ol | 5844 | 3631 |
| 2010-09-02 13:52 | G3LDO | 14.097150 | -15 | -3 | IO90st | +37 | 5.012 | M0ORE | IO90er | 83 | 52 |
| 2010-09-02 13:52 | G3LDO | 14.097181 | -16 | -3 | IO90st | +37 | 5.012 | N6QW | CM88ob | 7725 | 4800 |
| 2010-09-02 13:52 | G3LDO | 14.097164 | +4 | -4 | IO90st | +37 | 5.012 | S51CN | JN65tm | 1196 | 743 |
| 2010-09-02 13:52 | G3LDO | 14.097126 | -21 | -3 | IO90st | +37 | 5.012 | WA3DNM | FM29fw | 5728 | 3559 |
| 2010-09-02 13:46 | G3LDO | 14.097156 | -2 | -3 | IO90st | +37 | 5.012 | DF2LV | JO44rs | 798 | 496 |
| 2010-09-02 13:46 | G3LDO | 14.097150 | -16 | -3 | IO90st | +37 | 5.012 | M0ORE | IO90er | 83 | 52 |
| 2010-09-02 13:46 | G3LDO | 14.097156 | -12 | -3 | IO90st | +37 | 5.012 | WA8KNE | EM90gg | 6846 | 4254 |
| 2010-09-02 13:46 | G3LDO | 14.097164 | -18 | -3 | IO90st | +37 | 5.012 | W0BLD | EM37jc | 7081 | 4400 |
| 2010-09-02 13:46 | G3LDO | 14.097180 | -21 | -3 | IO90st | +37 | 5.012 | N6QW | CM88ob | 7725 | 4800 |

FIGURE 1: Screen dump of G3LDO signal reports by *WSPR*.

PHOTO 2: The antenna arrangement at the QTH of G3LDO.

**ANTENNA TESTS USING *WSPR*.** I decided to use *WSPR* to compare the multiband trapped dipole on the roof with my multiband quad (located behind the camera that took Photo 1). These antennas have been in use for some time so I had a fair idea of their relative performances and the tests were more to assess how well *WSPR* performed as an antenna performance-measuring tool. *WSPR* can collect a considerable about of data in a short space of time so some method of selecting and processing the data is necessary.

G8JNJ has used this method, which he describes as follows: "What I do is transmit on one band with one antenna on a specific frequency, then swap antenna and frequency on the same band. I then download all the stations that have spotted me over a few hours from the *WSPR* website database.

"I then dump them into an *Excel* spreadsheet and sort by frequency and distance. That way I can separate out the transmissions that were on each antenna and plot different graphs against the reporting stations, which will be at the same distance for individual spots (for directional antennas you can also sort by bearing if required)."

I felt that the G8JNJ method required modification for my tests. First of all, I rotated both antennas so that their maximum gain patterns were headed northwest. With *WSPR* running, I connected each antenna in turn to the radio for a period of 15 minutes over a total period of one and a half hours. Not having the know how to download the *WSPR* data into *Excel* I downloaded the data as an image file (partly shown in Figure 1) and scanned it into a *Word* file using a character recognition application. Once the data was in *Word* I deleted all data except transatlantic reports and unwanted column data.

The data was then sorted into time slots that coincided with the time the appropriate antenna was used. An example is shown in **Table 1**. The most important data is the SNR; the smaller the SNR negative number the stronger the signal (-10 is better than -15). Table 1 only shows part of the picture. Altogether there were 59 signal reports, 33 for the dipole and 26 for the quad. The average signal reports for the dipole were –22.33 while the reports for the quad gave –15.38. This gave the quad a gain of just under 7dB over the dipole.

There are feeder losses to consider. The quad was fed via 53m of RG213 while the dipole was fed with only 15m of RG213. With an SWR of 1.3:1 the feeder losses of the quad and dipole were 1.4dB and 0.4dB respectively. This gives the quad an 8dB advantage over the dipole using this antenna testing method, about what you might expect.


REFERENCES

[1] www.qsl.net/vk5bar; go to 'Papers' and select 'Small (loop) antennas'.

[2] *WSPR*, written by Joe Taylor, K1JT. Obtainable at www.physics.princeton.edu/pulsar/K1JT

# Antennas

## The GM3RVL 'Joiners Delight' loop antenna

PHOTO 1: The overall construction of the 'Joiners Delight' antenna. The element is made from a 3m length of 22mm copper tube bent into an approximate circle of approximately 950mm O/D.

**REDUCING LOOP LOSSES.** The description of my magnetic transmitting loop in September's Antennas resulted in some feedback. The most interesting of these was a description of a loop antenna designed and built by Harry Brash, GM3RVL. He has been fascinated by small transmitting and receiving loops for a long time and followed the controversy about them in *RadCom* and elsewhere. His view is that losses are the limiting factor and the trick is to make the loop as loss free as possible – and that has to include the immediate surrounding electrical environment.

As part of the investigation into loop losses, GM3RVL made some tests with loops constructed using standard plumbing angle joints, soldered and mechanical. As a rather primitive test, he passed significant DC currents across joints and was surprised at the poor electrical connections at DC. He assumed losses would be worse at RF but had no suitable test equipment to make the appropriate measurements (more about this later). He goes on to say, "The other obvious issue regarding loop Q was the connection to the tuning capacitor. I was surprised how some constructors put great effort into making a high performance loop and then used quite crude connections to a standard variable capacitor. I felt that the arrangement I finally chose was as close to the ideal as possible, apart from making the whole thing from silver. It would have been good to use copper capacitor plates and spot welding in place of soldering but soldering was my only option at that time."

**CONSTRUCTION.** The overall construction of the antenna is shown in **Photo 1**. The element is made from a 3m length of 22mm copper tube bent into an approximate circle of approximately 950mm O/D. The ends are flattened and soldered to two 8in square 1/16in thick brass plates, which form the capacitor. The rest of the structure is made of wood, apart from some Perspex insulators to mount the plates to the two long strips of hardwood.

The mechanical tuning arrangement is shown in **Photo 2**. There is a hinge at each point marked with an arrow. The offset arrangement of the hinges results in the two capacitor plates being moved closer together as point A is raised, and vice versa. Tuning is therefore accomplished by moving point A up and down using the hardwood dowel D. Rough adjustment (band change) is accomplished by releasing the clamp C and setting to marked positions of the dowel. Fine adjustment is by moving lever F.

The mechanism as illustrated in Photo 2 is set so that the capacitor plates are spread apart for the higher frequency bands. With the dowel raised, as shown in **Photo 3**, the capacitor plates are moved so that they are close together for the 30 and 40m bands. On the 40m, the plate spacing is only a few millimetres and GM3RVL reports that the tuning was very 'touchy', although he made some contacts. When the loop is mounted outside, any movement due to wind affects the tuning due to the small capacitor plate separation.

**OTHER CONSTRUCTION ISSUES.** To overcome the perceived losses due to joints in the loop element, GM3RVL made his loop out of a single section of 22mm copper tube as shown in the photos. He used a bending spring with a wire extension so that the spring could be placed anywhere along the 3m length of the tube. This worked well, provided the bending was done gradually. He avoided the temptation to bend too much at a time, which could cause the spring to jam in the tube. Be warned, bending the tube is hard work!

The first version of this loop used aluminium plates for the capacitor. These were tinned using so-called aluminium solder (possibly the Radiospares version). The solder appeared to tin the aluminium well enough but difficulty was experienced soldering this arrangement to the ends of the copper loop. The aluminium capacitor plates were replaced by brass plates at a later stage and fixed to the loop ends using conventional solder, which gave joints that looked more 'convincing'. No change in performance has been noted.

**MATCHING.** Various methods of matching the feeder to the loop were tried. GM3RVL notes, "The biggest SWR improvements occurred when I moved from loop coupling to a gamma match. It wasn't so much that the loop wouldn't match; it was that the gamma match was easier to tune. It didn't require so much critical adjustment. Additionally it was less sensitive to band changes."

GM3RVL has since reverted to loop coupling because he was unsure of the gamma match efficiency and he wanted to avoid coupling the feeder directly to the loop. He goes on to say, "I'd be interested in your comment on current loop coupling practice. The Faraday screened loop in Figure 15.55 on page 15.28 of the *RSGB Handbook* (later editions) is wrong, in my opinion. I have seen this arrangement described in several places. As I understand it, the broken braid on both sides at the top of the coupling loop should be unconnected and only joined to the other braid and the centre conductor at the bottom feed point.

PHOTO 2: The mechanical tuning arrangement of the 'Joiners Delight' antenna.

Otherwise it is not a Faraday screen.

"I made a Faraday screened coupling loop (1/5 diameter of main loop) using RG213. Without adjustment, it tunes up on 20m (SWR ≈ 1.3:1), 15m (SWR ≈ 1.1:1) and 10m (SWR ≈ 1.1:1). The loop will tune up to 29.5MHz and down to 40m provided there is no wind. The very close spacing of the capacitor plates on that band makes the tuning quite critical, hence the wind 'interference'. The loop has not been tested on 30m at the time of writing."

**Photo 4** shows the coupling coil and the fine-tuning lever in more detail. The adjustment at the end of the tuning lever is about 25mm to cover the 20m band, 35mm to cover the 15m band and about 100mm to cover the 10m band up to 29.5MHz. The tuning range on 40m is just a few mm. The tuning movement can of course be changed by altering the mechanics.

As I am responsible for the above-mentioned Faraday coupling loop appearing in the *RSGB Handbook* I feel that an explanation is in order. This coupling loop was included in a magnetic loop design 'Abstimmbare Magnetische Antennan (AMA)' by DL5CZ. Variations of this antenna have been manufactured by FunkTechnik Beese since 1983. Additionally, this type of coupling loop was included in the design by Roberto Craighero, I1ARZ so I had no hesitation of including it – although I must confess I was a little unsure of its Faraday status. Furthermore, I became aware of some disquiet about it so I included the proviso in **[1]**, **[2]** and **[3]**, "The coax inner and braid at the apex of the (coupling) loop (in the illustration) is shown to be joined, which would make it a Faraday half loop. The inner to braid connection should be removed but the gap in the braid should remain."

PHOTO 3: The mechanical tuning arrangement set so that capacitor plates are close together for the 30 and 40m bands.

**TESTS.** If you use copper pipe joints to make the loop as described in September's Antennas then some method of measuring the resistance of the joint is beneficial. GM3RVL fed 5A DC through the pipe from a current limited power supply and measured the voltage (in mV) across the joint with a digital multimeter. He then calculated the resistance using Ohm's law. He also made a measuring bridge designed for low resistance measurements. One side of the bridge is capacitive, powered by a signal generator, and uses a receiver as a detector. So far it is working correctly with test resistors down to about 0.1Ω but he thinks it needs to go down almost two orders of magnitude to test the pipe joints. Overcoming the mechanical layout for testing the pipes is a challenge, particularly the construction of reliable connections at the ends of the test pieces.

PHOTO 4: The Faraday coupling coil and the fine-tuning lever in more detail.

I used the high current DC method of measuring resistance of my loop by incorporating the pipe section under test in the circuit of high current 10A charger and a lead acid battery (not having a current limited power supply). This worked to a degree but was limited by the 0.1mV resolution of my digital multimeter. Most of the joints caused a voltage drop of 0.1mV although one joint was 0.2mV. This suspect joint was resoldered and further tested to give 0.1mV. The voltage drop of the whole copper loop including the variable capacitor hinges was 18.1mV at 10A, ie a total resistance of 1.81mΩ.

**FINALLY.** I often receive e-mail (and occasionally letters) requesting advice on certain problems regarding antennas, most of which is to do with fitting HF antennas within the confines of postage stamp locations. I am more than happy to continue doing this and the e-mail system provides a quick and easy way of communication when dealing with these queries. My main difficulty is sometimes trying to envisage the general situation from a plain description. It is much easier for me if a drawing or photograph (or both) of the antenna and layout is provided, bearing in mind the saying that a picture is worth a thousand words.

**FINALLY FINALLY.** I wish you all a happy Christmas and a pleasant ham radio New Year.

REFERENCES

[1] *RSGB Radio Communications Handbook*, later editions
[2] *Backyard Antennas* P85
[3] *Building Successful HF Antennas*, P108

# Antennas

## Modelling, measuring and more on loops

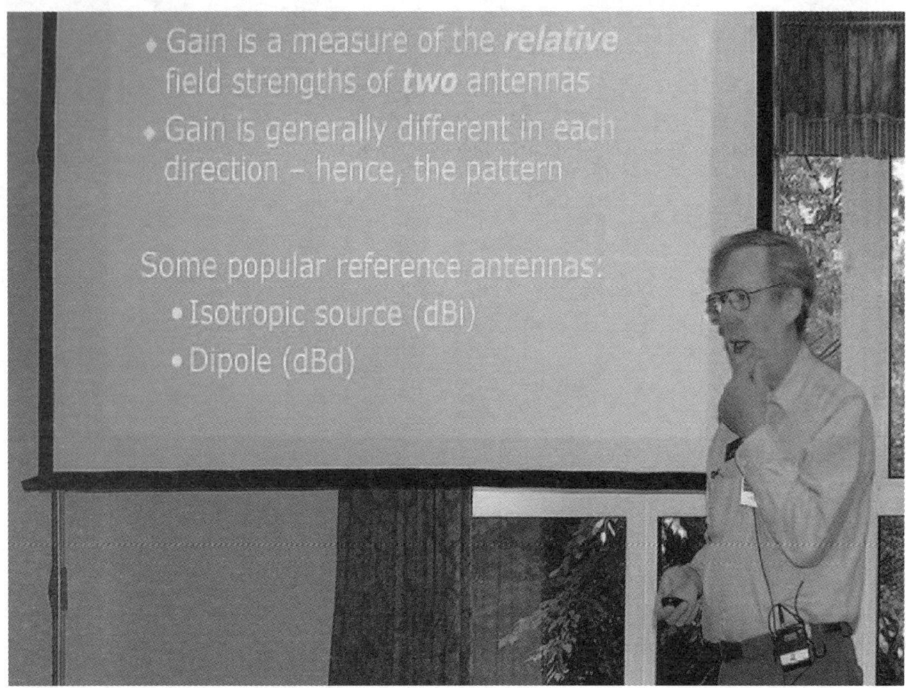


**PHOTO 1: Roy Lewallen, W7EL giving an antenna lecture at the RSGB Convention.**

COMPUTER MODELLING PROGRAMS. Antenna performance modelling using a PC and appropriate software is used extensively these days although my first encounter with an antenna modelling program was not very auspicious. Early in 1989, I received a letter from a reader in the USA regarding an article I had written on in the G QRP club *Sprat* magazine. This article described an antenna I had devised called the Double-D and included performance measurements. The writer said that my VHF model polar diagrams were suspect because I did not give details of test methods and my full-sized HF model ground-wave tests with a local radio amateur 'irrelevant' because they were not taken at the elevation angle of maximum radiation.

He then gave figures that had been obtained from a computer program called *MININEC 3* that gave the 'correct' results and showed that the reflector of my antenna design was in fact working as a director.

Meanwhile my antenna on the roof, totally unaware of *MININEC 3*, continued to operate with the parasitic element working as a reflector. It turned out that these early programs were inaccurate when modelling bent elements, a characteristic of the Double-D antenna. I hasten to say modern programs are accurate in this respect.

A year later, a derivative of *MININEC 3* became available called *MN*, which I used and described in *The Antenna Experimenter's Guide*. Later a new program by Roy Lewallen, W7EL called *ELNEC* became available. Again, it was essentially based on the original *NEC* program but was much more user friendly. W7EL's program has been constantly upgraded and improved and is now *EZNEC5*.

So it was with great pleasure that I finally met Roy at the RSGB Convention on 9 October to talk about antennas in general and modelling in particular. I also attended his lecture 'Blowing away the smoke and mirrors of antenna operation', see **Photo 1**, which was both entertaining and informative. It exposed the sort of stuff you sometimes see in antenna sales literature. W7EL noted that for antenna performance to mean anything it has to be compared with a known reference and that phrases like "exceptional performance" or "compared with any other whip you have used – you will be amazed" are meaningless.

DIP OSCILLATORS. A dip oscillator is an instrument for measuring the resonant frequency of a tuned circuit or an antenna element, or even a length of transmission line. The main advantage of this instrument is that a direct connection between it and the tuned circuit being measured is unnecessary, the coupling being either inductive or capacitive.

The dip oscillator is simply a calibrated tuneable oscillator. Energy from this oscillator is absorbed by a resonant circuit under test when it and the oscillator are tuned to the same frequency. A meter is used to give an indication of oscillator energy loss. In practice, this results in a dip in the meter reading as the frequency is swept past the test resonant circuit, hence the name of the instrument.

I was also pleased to meet Richard Brett-Knowles, G3AAT, at the RSGB Convention. He was demonstrating the principle of the dip oscillator.

The demonstration setup is shown in **Photo 2** and comprises a FET oscillator powered from an old PC power supply. The milliammeter with the wooden surround is used to measure the current through the gate resistor of the FET, which indicates the RMS level of oscillator waveform. The Marconi valve voltmeter measures the voltage across the circuit being investigated, comprising a coil plus a tuning capacitor that can be attached using crocodile clips. The arrangement is used to show the difference in coupling required to induce the same voltage across the test circuit with or without the capacitor when resonant.

The small item wound on a yellow former near the edge of the table is a 7MHz aerial trap; it is bifilar wound using PTFE covered wire. The inter-turn capacity of this device resonates with the inductance.

COMMERCIAL DIP METERS. I do like radio club junk sales. Not only is there a chance to get you hands on some bargain goodies but also the whole evening can be very entertaining, particularly when you have a good auctioneer. Then there is the fun of smuggling your acquired treasure into the house before the station manager sees it!

Most of the collection of dip meters I possess have been acquired this way. The one I bought at the last Worthing and District Amateur Radio Club junk is shown in **Photo 3** and is the Trio DM-800, which covers 700kHz to 250MHz in seven bands. It has many good engineering features. For a start it is built into a case made of 2mm thick aluminium and is constructed so that it comes apart in two sections. The coils are colour coded to match the scales on the dials and the unused ones are stowed away in plug-in box that fits into the bottom of the instrument. Furthermore, you don't have to take the instrument apart to change the battery; access to the battery compartment is achieved by just removing the coil case.

So how did it perform? Well, rather badly, I'm afraid. With the DM-800 coupled to a test tuned circuit set to resonate at 7MHz as shown in Photo 3, the meter dipped about

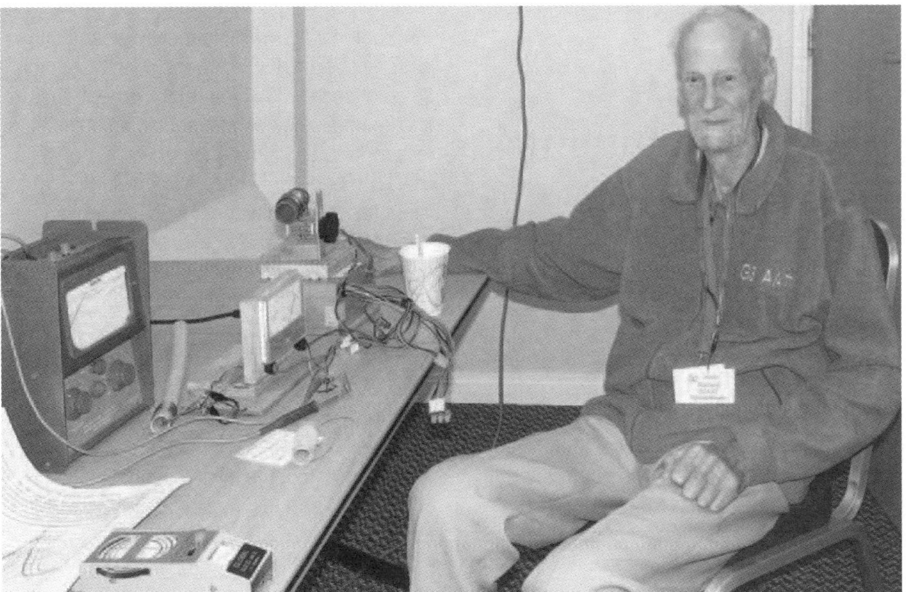

PHOTO 2: Richard Brett-Knowles, G3AAT, at the RSGB Convention, discussing the principle of the dip oscillator.

1mm as it was swept through resonance, very easy to miss. Closer coupling only made the miniscule dip characteristic asymmetrical.

MORE ON DIP OSCILLATORS. I received an e-mail from Clive Young, M0BGA, on this subject. He says, "Some time ago you kindly helped me trace details of my old Cirkit dipper. I happened to mention the topic at the local radio club and was persuaded to give a talk and demonstration. I would value your opinion on my proposed answer to question I'm sure someone will raise, namely: if the impedance of a parallel tuned circuit is high at resonance why does the circuit absorb power from the dip oscillator?

"My answer is on the following lines: The impedance of the parallel circuit is judged to be high from the point of view of an external generator (or signal) as this is the condition for minimum line current into the parallel L/C combination. When the coil of the dip oscillators is coupled to the coil of the parallel circuit we have, in effect, an RF transformer. In this case, the coil of the parallel circuit acts like a secondary winding and this is now in series with the C as far as EMF generated in the coil is concerned. Series resonance results in maximum current at resonance and this absorbs maximum energy from the dip oscillator."

M0BGA went on to say that a transistor dippers makes a useful and interesting projects for Intermediate Licence exam students. A simple circuit for such a project can be found in May 2010 Antennas.

I replied that it was interesting to note that there are no articles I know of that address this little conundrum for tuned circuits. There is a chapter in *Second Thoughts on Radio Theory* called Conventions and Viewpoints which starts with a simple circuit of two resistors in a loop and poses the question, "are R1 and R2 in series or parallel?" The author then goes on to discuss the matter at some length.

LOOPS. The subject of small transmitting loops continues to generate interest. Bob, G3IXZ, e-mailed me to say, "I was interested by your recent comments on loop antennas, following on from the piece by G3LHZ in July *RadCom* in your column. I am not an *EZNEC* user unfortunately so my own observations are really empirical but I have always been puzzled by the apparent indifference of the loop performance to height above ground level (AGL).

"One would expect a small magnetic loop with a diameter of a metre or two to almost look like an isotropic source on the HF bands and for the performance to be poor unless it was well elevated.

"The idea that a height of at least 0.75 of a wavelength AGL is desirable for the transmitted wavefront to benefit from ground reflection is a hard one to dispel. Certainly if (as I often hear) the loop receive performance is only about 2dB down on a dipole, they ought to be a great temptation for would be DXers in poor locations lacking the space for a decent piece of wire.

"I suppose the narrow bandwidth remote tuning problems mitigate against them in many cases, however having just acquired a very good wide spaced twin gang capacitor, which should enable a reasonable swing in split stator mode, I am going to have another go at a loop for 80m - possibly 40/30 as well. If your work led to any observations of your own on height AGL I would value your comment."

I am in the process of making lots of measurement compared with a dipole but at the time of writing they have not been completed. In the meantime, to answer G3XIZ's question I will quote part of VK5KLT's paper *An Overview of the Underestimated Magnetic Loop HF Antenna*:

"When a dipole antenna is placed horizontally above ground, its electrical 'image' in the ground is of the opposite phase. As a consequence, if the height above ground of a horizontal dipole is reduced to less than ¼ wavelength, fairly high system losses develop due to a rapid decrease in radiation resistance concurrent with a rapid rise in loss resistance resulting from dissipation of power within a less than perfect ground. This represents a classic double-whammy scenario and deleterious performance for dipoles deployed at insufficient height above ground.

"By way of contrast, the oscillatory RF currents associated with the image of a small vertical oriented loop antenna above ground are 'in-phase' with those of the loop. Therefore, the effect of ground on the performance of a vertically oriented loop is relatively small. In fact, because the magnetic component of an electromagnetic wave is maximum at the boundary between the ground and the space above, loop performance is usually best when the loop is located near the ground at a distance outside of the loop's close-in induction field (just a loop diameter or two).

"There is no significant improvement in performance when a small loop is raised to great heights; all that matters is the loop is substantially clear of objects in the desired direction of radiation. Mounting the loop on an elevated roof ground plane yields good results."

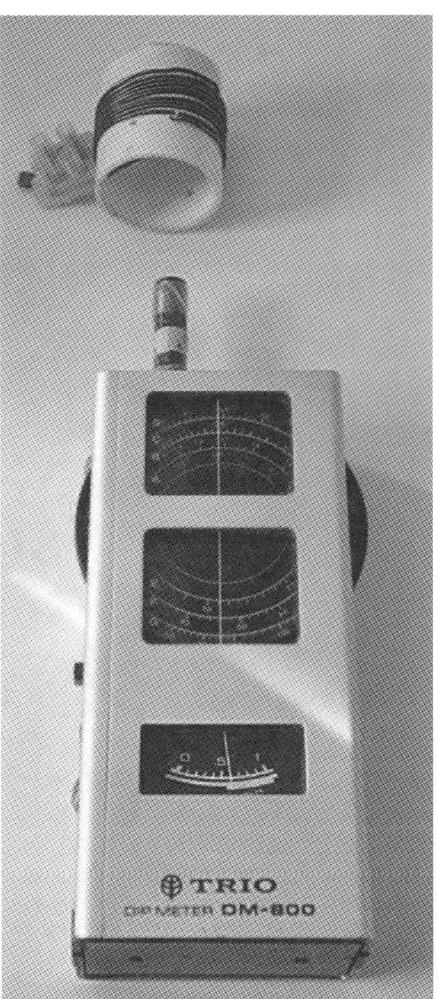


PHOTO 3: Testing the Trio DM-800 dip meter.

# Antennas

## An alternative mode in HF mobile antennas

**PHOTO 1: A Texas Bugcatcher antenna mounted on the tow bar on the rear a vehicle. It uses a single large inductance with tapping points and a wander lead to short out the unused sections of the coil.**

SIMPLE MOBILE. The vertical whip antenna is the most popular antenna for mobile use. The easiest way to feed such an antenna is to make it a quarter wavelength long at the frequency in use, which allows it to be fed directly with 50Ω coax at the low impedance base. The resonant quarter wavelength is a function of frequency and is 1.48m (58.5in) on 50MHz, 2.5m (8ft 2in) on 28.4MHz and progressively shorter on the higher VHF bands. Quarter wave antennas on the 28MHz bands and higher are quite practical, but on the lower HF bands it is a different matter. Even on 21MHz, a quarter wavelength is 3.45m (11ft 2in) and on 14MHz is 4.99m (16ft 4in). It follows that a practical mobile antenna for the HF bands must be shorter than a quarter wave.

For a given antenna length, as the frequency of operation is lowered the feed point exhibits a decreasing resistance in series with an increasing capacitive reactance. In order to feed power to such an antenna it must be brought to resonance so that the feed point is resistive. This is achieved by adding some inductance and is known as inductive loading.

Each band requires a different value of inductance. This can be achieved using separate single band antennas with built in inductance or separate plug-in coils for each band. The most common method used now is by using one long coil and shorting out the unwanted inductance of the lower frequency bands not in use. The antenna on the rear of the vehicle shown in **Photo 1** is the commercial Texas Bugcatcher **[1]**. It uses a single large inductance with tapping points and a wander lead to short out the unused sections of the coil.

THE OUTBACKER. Another interesting method of the shorting out the unwanted inductance is used in the design of the Outbacker. These antennas come in several versions and the one I acquired recently is the Outbacker Outreach, which covers all bands from 160m to 10m. It is not possible to see how the inductors are formed but it is obvious they are wound continuously along the length of the antenna, in some ways rather like the Firestik CB antenna.

The Outbacker is made up of three sections: a lower section with the 160, 80 and 30m inductors; a centre section with the higher frequency HF band inductors and finally a whip (the 'stinger'). The centre section is shown in some detail in **Photo 2** because it is the basis of a discussion in this column. The inductances and physical lengths of the band inductances are also shown.

The inductors are selected using a wander lead terminated with 4mm diameter banana plugs, which fit very snugly into the 4mm inductor selector sockets. As you might expect, the higher frequency bands require progressively less inductance to resonate the antenna and the 15m band only requires 1.4μH plus the inductance of the wander lead, which is wrapped around the lower section of the antenna in a loose anticlockwise spiral (as recommended in the instructions).

However, you might have noticed that the 10m coil selection point is at the bottom of Photo 2. This indicates there is a total of 50μH of inductance in the antenna when 10m is selected. The 12m tapping point is located at the top end of the lower section (not shown in Photo 2) and includes an extra 14μH on top of the 50μH already mentioned.

The instruction book makes no mention of this oddity but the sales material **[2]** says "... 10, 12 and 15m are 5/8 wave". I think that only the 10 and 12m bands use the '5/8 wave' effect.

I had never seen any reference to 5/8 wave HF antennas. On VHF, a 5/8 wave antenna is quite common and comprises a full halfwave whip antenna matched to the feeder with a tapped inductance.

I constructed a computer model based on the data measured in Photo 2. The *EZNEC5* software allows effects of 'loads' (inductance, capacitance and resistance) to be modelled. Inductances are shown as small square icons in **Figure 1**.

The current distribution on the antenna shows a top section with a halfwave current distribution and a lower section with a near quarter wave current distribution. Note that there is current flow in the modelled vehicle body that shows that the vehicle also radiates during transmit and is part of the antenna system.

I made a further model using a full sized quarter wave antenna for comparison. The comparison elevation polar diagrams are shown **Figure 2**. I had to make a guess as to the resistive losses in the loading inductors so the diagrams in Figure 2 should not be taken as definitive. What is interesting is how similar they are. Note also that the total installation becomes quite directive when the vehicle is near to quarter of a wavelength long and the antenna is mounted at the end of the vehicle; with the lobe of maximum gain at the opposite end of the vehicle to where the antenna is mounted. This phenomenon has also been measured and documented in **[3]**. If the antenna is mounted in the centre of the vehicle then the system is omnidirectional.

It occurred to me that when the 10m or

**FIGURE 1: Computer model of an Outbacker Outreach antenna on 10m (28MHz) mounted on an estate car. The model is depicted with black lines and the current magnitude in magenta.**

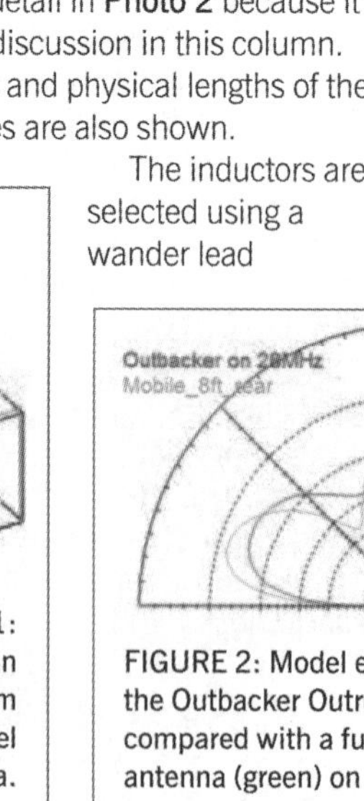

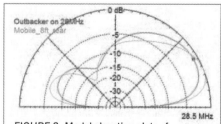

**FIGURE 2: Model elevation plots of the Outbacker Outreach antenna (black) compared with a full size quarter wave antenna (green) on 28MHz.**

12m taps are selected, with 60µH or more inductance above the tapping points, the antenna should also exhibit lower resonances. A frequency sweep of the antenna set at 12m showed that this was the case and a resonance occurred at 5.5MHz, as shown in **Figure 3**.

The impedance at the 12m resonance point was measured at over 100Ω, which resulted in an SWR of more than 2:1 – I initially though this might be due to the position on the vehicle where the antenna was mounted. On the other hand the conventional mode on 20m, see **Figure 4**, exhibited good matching characteristics.

**THE TEXAS BUGCATCHER.** This antenna has a good performance reputation, particularly on the lower HF bands. The reason for this is that it is a large antenna with a large coil wound on high quality, low-loss former. Some idea of its size can be seen in Photo 1. Its only drawback is that the SWR bandwidth is very small and the business of setting the wander lead taps can be tricky. Of course, the screwdriver type antennas overcome this problem but the construction of such an antenna is beyond the resources of my garden shed workshop.

It occurred to me that solutions suggested in an early edition of the ARRL *Radio Amateur's Handbook* (**Figure 5**) might make the adjustment less critical. **Figure 5A** is a simple sliding contact that shorts out the unused turns. (I am not sure how **Figure 5B** works: I would be interested in hearing from anyone who knows of this arrangement. There was no description in the text that came with these illustrations).

I modified the Bugcatcher coil to work much the same as Figure 5A. A movable contact arrangement was constructed as shown in **Photo 3**. It comprises a short length of 22mm copper tube drilled to fit the lower element of the Bugcatcher; the other end is drilled to take the 8mm copper tubing contact holder. The contact itself is made from a small piece of phosphor bronze draft excluder.

Regrettably, this arrangement was not an unqualified success because sometimes the sliding contact alighted on one turn and other times shorted out two turns. The result was an uneven inductance change with the slider position. Nevertheless, it allowed me to investigate other modes with the Bugcatcher antenna. One of the results shown in **Figure 6**.

WEBSEARCH

[1] GLA Systems, who manufactured the Texas Bugcatcher antennas, ceased production late 2009. An archived description of the Bugcatcher is at http://tinyurl.com/RC1102-bug

[2] www.adurcomms.co.uk/outbacker.htm

[3] Computer Modelling of the HF Mobile Antenna, Peter Dodd, G3LDO, *The ARRL Antenna Compendium, Vol 7*.

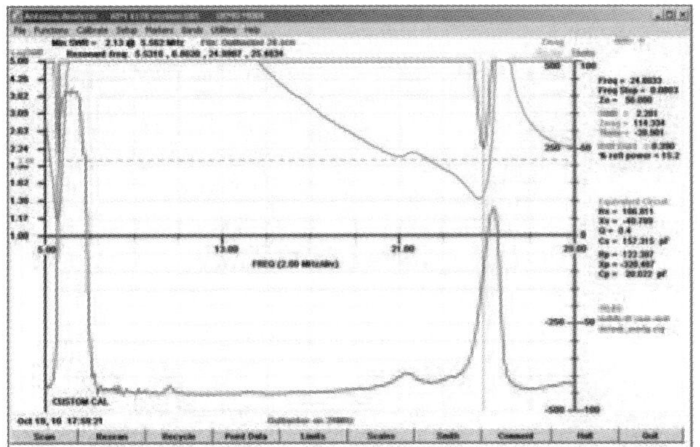

FIGURE 3: Frequency sweep of the Outbacker Outreach antenna on 12m using the AIM 4170. Note the lower resonance at 5.5MHz.

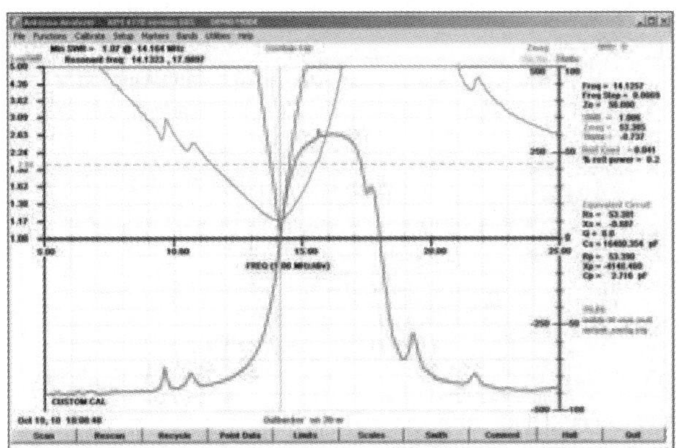

FIGURE 4: Frequency sweep of the Outbacker Outreach antenna on 20m using the AIM 4170. The off-resonance blips are due to strong out of band station interference.

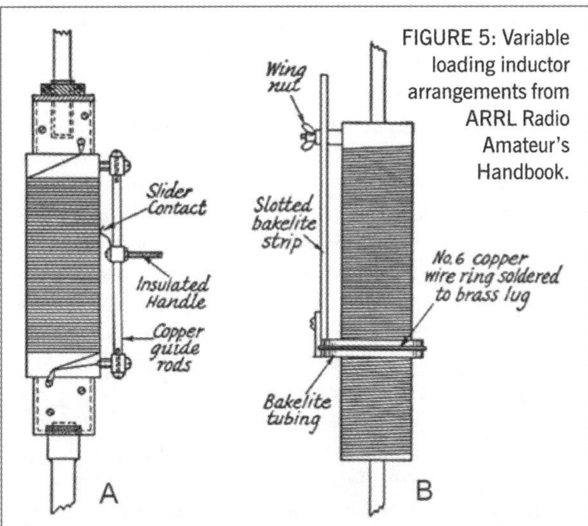


FIGURE 5: Variable loading inductor arrangements from ARRL Radio Amateur's Handbook.

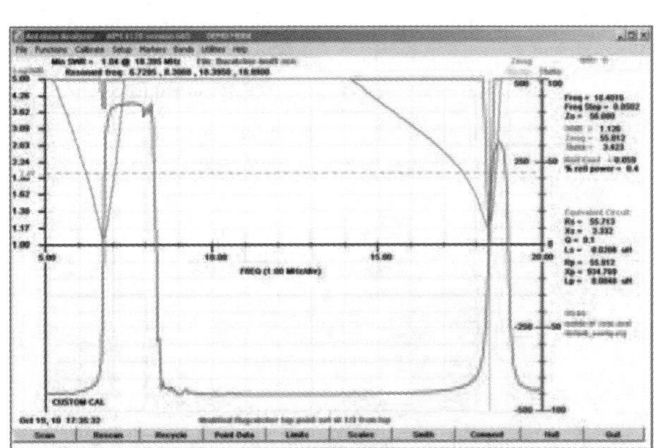

FIGURE 6: Frequency sweep of the Bugcatcher antenna on 17m using the AIM 4170. Note the lower resonance at 6.7MHz.

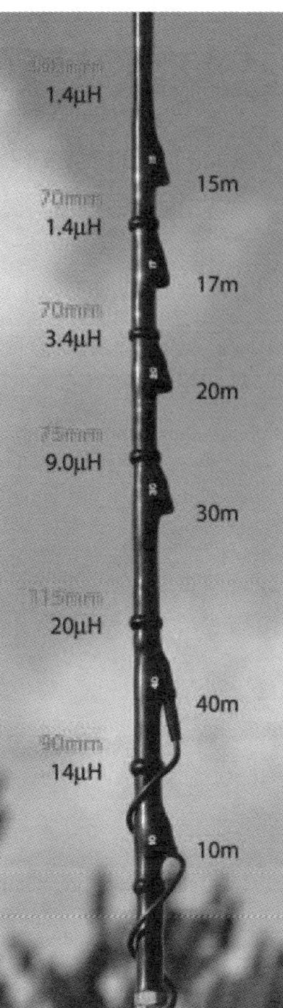


PHOTO 2: The centre section of an Outbacker Outreach antenna, with measured inductances for the bands 10, 15, 17 20 and 40m. The wander lead is shown with the 40m band selected.

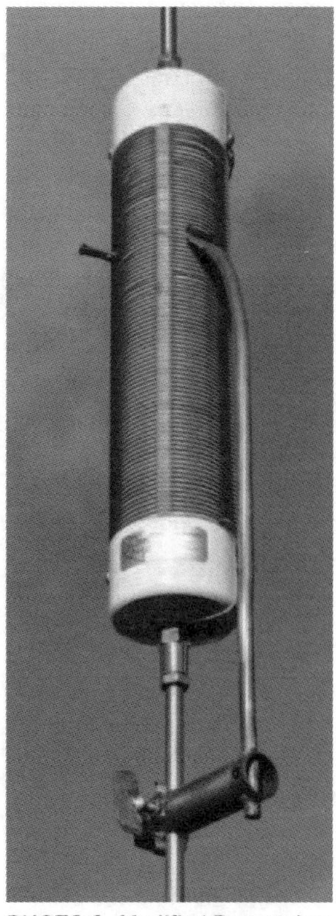

PHOTO 3: Modified Bugcatcher coil with sliding contact.

# Antennas

## Multiband dipole antennas

**PHOTO 1: A practical installation of a multiband dipole constructed from drop feed telephone wire and plastic high pressure water pipe as spacing insulators. The spacing between each of the elements should be about 6cm (just over 2in).**

**MAKING IT BETTER.** I often receive e-mails from readers who have an existing antenna arrangement that is not performing as well as it should, asking if I can advise on a way of effecting an improvement. Recently I received an e-mail from Chris, M0PSK, who was quite happy with the performance of his antenna but wondered why it was so good. He says, "Maybe you could comment on the following questions? I live in a second floor apartment (about 200m from the Mersey estuary) with parallel attic dipoles for 15, 17 and 20m, running NW-SE. The wires are a couple of inches apart and horizontal, maybe a foot below the roof ridge at 38 feet. And there is a common coax feed to a room below the attic.

"The question that intrigues me is this: what is the radiation pattern? Initially, I assumed that it would be the same as those for the individual dipoles. However, I've had around 3,000 QSOs over the last 6 years with this setup, and am surprised at the number of good contacts in the NW-SE directions, as well as the SW-NE directions. My understanding is that computer modelling may not necessarily provide an answer, as the coded algorithms start to break down when the wires get too close. Is it possible that I do have extra lobes in the NW-SE directions?

"There is a secondary question on which I would appreciate advice. It would be physically possible to add further parallel dipoles for 10, 12 and 30m. However, I do not want to degrade the good performance of the existing dipoles. Are any of these extra choices likely to do that?"

**DIPOLE POLAR DIAGRAMS.** We know that the azimuth polar diagram of a dipole is a figure of 8 with the nulls at the ends of the elements. Some people are surprised when they appear to work stations off the ends of the dipole when some antenna theory books imply that this should not be feasible. The answer can be seen in **Figure 1**. The blue pattern is for the theoretical dipole in free space and shows nulls at the ends of the dipole, over 30dB down on the maximum of 2.2dB relative to isotropic. When the dipole is erected about a wavelength high then the gain increases to 6 or 7dB relative to isotropic (due to ground gain but depending on the quality of the ground) and the nulls fill in to just over -10dB relative to maximum.

But this isn't the end of the story. Any radiation from the feeder or re-radiation from nearby electromagnetic obstructions will further fill in the nulls so that it is impossible to predict how the antenna will perform. So there should be no difficulty in working stations off the ends of the multiband dipole. I maintain that is more important where an antenna is than what it is. It would appear that M0PSK's antenna is in a favourable location, some 38ft above ground.

**PHOTO 2: The original two-element beam hybrid quad by TGM Communications.**

**MULTIBAND DIPOLES.** I modelled M0PSK's multiband dipole. The radiation pattern for all dipoles in the multiband structure were very similar. It was not possible to predict any adverse effect on the existing structure when a lower frequency element is added because the environmental effects cannot be modelled. The only solution would be to add the additional element and check the performance of the existing system. I feel sure that added elements will not be harmful.

The method of connecting multiple dipoles is to connect them in parallel as shown in **Figure 2**. I used to think that connecting them at single points and just fanning out the separate elements would do the trick but my attempt at that sort of structure was not successful. The elements are best spaced apart in a parallel manner with insulated spacers and brought to the feedpoint over, say, the last 25cm (10in).

A practical installation is shown in **Photo 1** using drop feed telephone wire for the elements and plastic high-pressure water pipe as spacing insulators. The spacing between each of the elements should be about 6cm (just over 2in) so the arrangement used by M0PSK seems about right.

I started to model this multiband arrangement using EZNEC by creating a basic dipole (I will call this the main dipole) and testing its performance, with and without ground, to obtain the images in Figure 1. I then added an extra band element and made a further check before connecting it to the main dipole and found

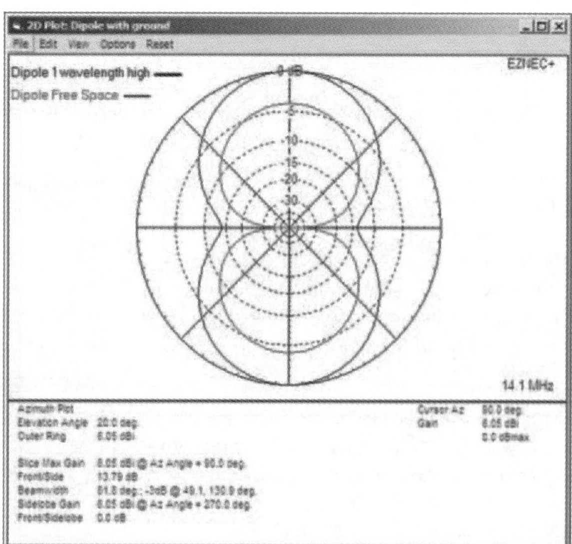


**FIGURE 1: Comparison polar diagrams a dipole antenna in free space (blue trace) and the same antenna mounted 10m above ground (black trace), modelled at 20° elevation.**

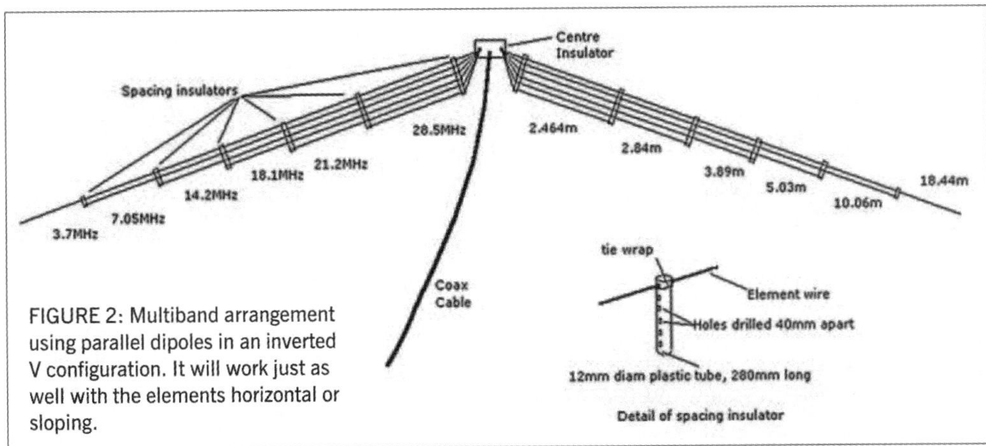


FIGURE 2: Multiband arrangement using parallel dipoles in an inverted V configuration. It will work just as well with the elements horizontal or sloping.

that the antenna exhibited a dual band characteristic. I then added a further band element, again without connecting it to the main dipole. The antenna then had a tri-band characteristic.

In reality this is nothing new and can be found in *The ARRL Antenna Handbook* as the Coupled-Resonator Antenna. I will write about this interesting multiband arrangement in a later Antennas but, in the meantime, I would like to know if anyone out there uses or has used one.

**ROTATABLE DIPOLE.** While on the subject of dipoles, Steve DeVille, G6TJC, e-mailed me to say "In the November 2010 *RadCom* on page 34, there is a picture of your house showing a rotatable dipole of the roof. May I ask what it is and, assuming you are using it, would it be recommended? I would like to use one as it seems very low profile and neighbour friendly.

This multiband dipole was originally a commercial two-element beam by TGM Communications, called (I think) the MQ-5. It is shown in **Photo 2**. I had this antenna for review. While the SWR characteristics were satisfactory, I found that the F/B directivity was non-existent on the lower frequency bands but reasonable on 10m. Nevertheless, I felt that this arrangement had potential so I bought the antenna after completing the review.

I was not convinced the quad structure was any better than a straight element so I rebuilt the antenna as shown in **Photo 3**. The rebuild included extending the elements and boom and modifying the element end resonators. The object of all this was to hopefully make the directivity adjustment less critical.

In the event the improvement in F/B directivity was not a good as I had hoped but the SWR bandwidth was increased. Furthermore, the antenna performed reasonably well so it stayed up on the chimney for many years, until I did some maintenance work on it in the summer of 2010.

Getting a two-element beam off the roof proved to be problematic for this 78 year old G3 so I reduced it to a dipole by dispensing with the reflector and boom. I removed the silicone compound that covered the element end resonators and inspected the trap inductors, which proved to be in remarkable good shape considering my QTH is only about 400m from the beach. New silicone compound was applied to the resonators and the antenna reinstalled.

The simple dipole antenna was much easier to fix in place, see **Photo 4**. It and performs much the same as it did before removing the reflector. An SWR plot is shown in **Figure 3**. The SWR bandwidth is very narrow at 14MHz and has been tuned to the CW section of the band. It will operate up as the SSB end when used with the internal ATU of my FT-990.

The null at the end of the elements is about 12dB down on the main lobe, which is what you might expect for a dipole in the clear. The only downside it that it picks up electrical noise from the house. I use this multiband dipole as standard for testing other antennas (as described in recent Antennas when comparing it with the multiband quad and the magnetic loop).

In reply to G6TJC's question – would I recommend it? The answer is yes, however at this time I regret I am unable to give constructional details of the resonators. The method I used to modify them was to couple the element to a GDO and adjust the coil turns until the element dipped at the right frequency. I will probably convert the unused reflector into a multi-band dipole when I get the inclination and time and make a note of how it was done.

The only similar dipole I know of is the MFJ-1775, which covers 40 to 10m but not the WARC bands. It also claims to cover the 6 and 2m bands.

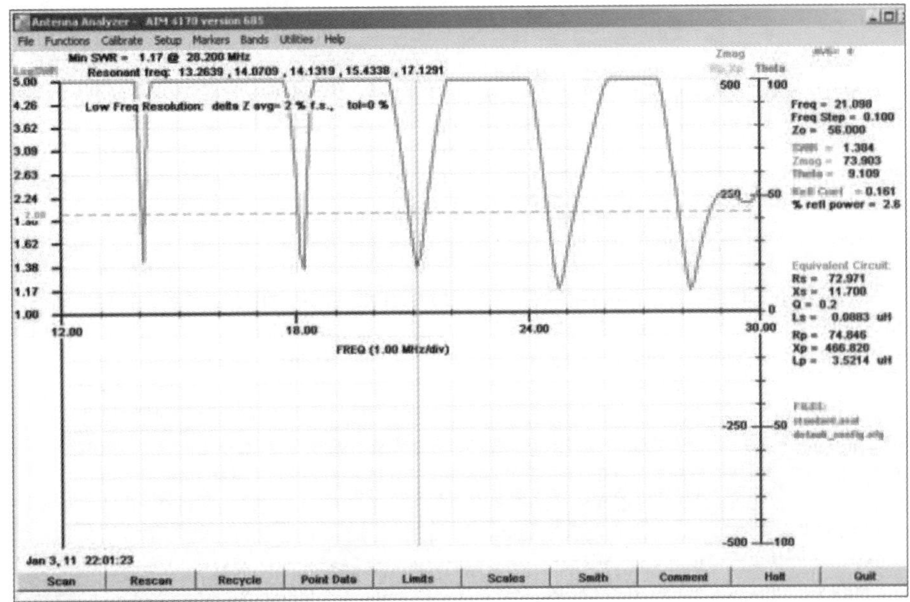


FIGURE 3: SWR plot of my multiband dipole measured using the AIM 4170. The impedance plots have been switched off for clarity.

PHOTO 3: The antenna in Photo 2 rebuilt by extending the elements and boom and modifying the element end resonators.

PHOTO 4: The antenna in Photo 3 converted into a multiband dipole by removing the reflector and the boom.

# Antennas

## Shorted turn inductance tuning and another look at loop antenna Faraday coupling loops

PHOTO 1: The experimental setup to measure the effects of a shorted turn, brass slug and ferrite rod on the inductance of a coil.

SHORTED TURN TUNING. Ted, G3IVH contacted me regarding a question I posed regarding how the tuning arrangement in Figure 4B of February Antennas (repeated here as **Figure 1B**) worked. This tuning method employs a shorted turn that can be positioned anywhere along the length of the coil. But how effective is it?

He constructed a coil 4½in (11.4cm) long and 1¾in (4.4cm) diameter on a ceramic former. The former had grooves for the winding, accepting 81 turns. It was thought to have been part of a roller coaster. The coil inductance measured 99.9μH. The shorted loop was moved along the coil in steps of ½in and the measured results are shown in **Table 1**.

I repeated the measurements using a coil 8.3cm long x 5.5cm diameter, which measured 135.7μH. The shorted turn comprised a loop of 14SWG wire with two layers of insulation to maintain a constant distance from the inductance wires as it was moved. The experimental setup is shown in **Photo 1**.

The coil former of my inductor was longer than the coil itself and I noticed that the shorted turn had some effect on the inductance when placed on the coil former around 3cm from the end of the coil (shown as –3cm in **Table 2**). As the shorted turn is moved closer to the inductance the μH value decreases but the greatest rate of change occurs when the shorted turn is moved over the first 3cm of the inductance. Note that there is very little inductance rate of change as the shorted turn is moved over the centre of the inductance. Table 2 shows the tuning range of the shorted turn method is over 30μH.

I tried adjusting the inductance by moving a brass slug in and out of the coil. The brass slug was made up of several lengths of brass rod fixed together with tape as shown in Photo 1, although it didn't fill up all the space within the diameter of the coil. The brass slug tuning method resulted in a tuning range of only 7μH. The effect of a ferrite rod of unknown pedigree, also shown in Photo 1, was also measured. This resulted in the much more dramatic tuning range of over 200μH.

For many years I have been experimenting with LF, first with 73kHz, then 136kHz and finally 501kHz. An e-mail LF reflector was created to exchange information and it is fortunate that within that group is a body of expertise that I occasionally draw on. I put the question of shorted turn tuning to the reflector and received the following comments:

Markus, DF6NM, found that the method worked very well. He goes on to say: "The nice thing is that you don't need the flexible connections for the rotating part (like a variometer) whereas the downsides may be less tuning range (and only 'up' in frequency because the loop decreases the inductance). There may also be a slight increase in losses. The wire loop can be replaced by a metal plate, but (at least for LF), a shorted multiturn coil made from RF litz wire would minimize induced losses".

DF6NM has also been experimenting at VLF (9kHz) and has tried rotating a ferrite plate, sandwiched between two copper sheets. In an orientation parallel to the magnetic field, the ferrite enhances inductance, whereas in the orthogonal position the eddy currents decrease it. The tuning arrangement finally ended up without the copper as sufficient tuning range was obtained with the ferrite alone. He notes: "The 90° turning range (compared to 180° for a traditional variometer) feels a bit unusual, but allows the use of a very simple mechanical arrangement comprising a string attached to one side of the plate".

John, W1TAG, tells me that it used to be common MW broadcast practice to use 'eddy current disks' comprising aluminium rings. In some cases, the ring was put inside the coil, with the ability to rotate it in and out of the plane of the turns. A simpler setup was to have it at one end, mounted on a threaded rod, allowing it to be moved along the axis of the coil. He goes on to say "I'm sure there were consequences for 'Q', but I don't recall any heating issues".

The coil in Figure 1B was suggested as a method of tuning a mobile antenna although I had never heard of anyone using it. So I was interested to receive the following from G4GVW. "Many years ago, when I did 160m mobile, I used an arrangement where the mobile antenna had a loading coil, which used a copper disc approximately 150% of the coil diameter.

TABLE 1: The effect of a shorted turn on a 99.9μH coil measured by G3IVH.

| Position (cm) | Inductance (μH) |
|---|---|
| 0 | 99.9 |
| 1.3 | 97.4 |
| 2.5 | 96.9 |
| 3.8 | 96.9 |
| 5.7 | 96.5 |
| 7.6 | 96.9 |
| 8.9 | 97.9 |
| 10.2 | 97.4 |
| 11.4 | 99.9 |

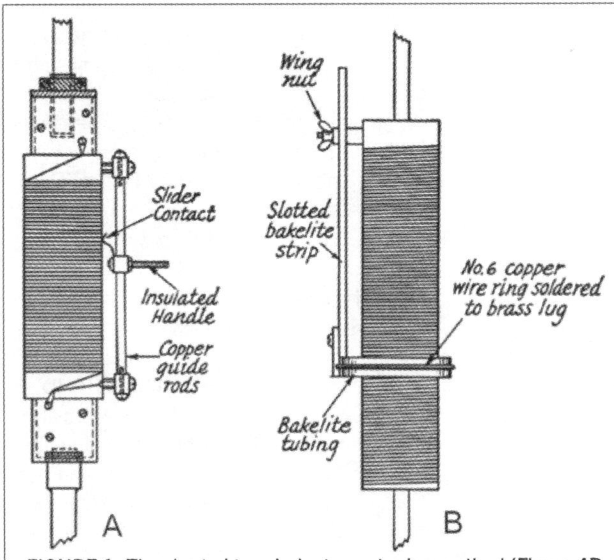


FIGURE 1: The shorted turn inductance tuning method (Figure 4B of February Antennas) repeated here as the subject for discussion in the text.

This was fixed to a centre boss that could be adjusted and locked along the whip with a screw at a point close to the coil. I used to puzzle over the difference between capacitive or 'shorted-turn' effects but in the end just accepted that it worked for whatever reasons. From memory I think the coil was about 5in diameter".

LOOPS LOSSES. Dave Penny, G3PEN e-mailed on the subject of small transmitting loop losses. He notes: "Regarding your recent article in *RadCom* on loop aerials (December 2010), I may be able to add something to the comments about the resistance of joints. I'm not sure where I read this, but I know that the skin resistance of solder is considerably higher than it is for pure copper and, at HF, the skin depth is very small. Consequently, if you make a joint in a copper pipe as is often done for water pipe usage, with a nice flow of solder beyond the actual copper join, the RF loss is increased – though by how much I haven't a clue because the RF has to flow through (over?) the solder surface.

"It is therefore considered important to clean off the surplus solder that is on the copper pipe, so that the only solder is that between the two pieces being joined, leaving polished copper right up to each side (edge) of the joining piece (if using plumber's sleeves) or to the single edge that shows if using a swaged joint (considered slightly better in fact, if made very tight). This gives an absolute minimum of solder surface across which the RF has to flow. Within the joint, I am not sure what is actually happening, as in theory all the RF current ought to be on the outside only – which perhaps makes the DC current tests for joint integrity somewhat dubious as regards a low loss at RF.

"I have been a little bit bothered by the various articles written over the past year or so in various publications, without this point being made, although it is only now that I have found time and energy to comment! Also, referring back to polishing the copper, again because skin resistance is so important, a very clean smooth surface for the entire loop, polished and then protected by a good-quality varnish, may be very worthwhile in the longer term."

The soldered joint problem could possibly be overcome using compression joints. These are a bit more expensive than soldered joint fittings. Furthermore they only seem to come in 90° angles and not 45°. This means that you could only make a square loop rather than a hexagonal using these items. An additional advantage of compression fittings is that a loop constructed using these can be dismantled for transportation or for moving through a hatch into a loft space. A square loop can be designed so that it can be fed at one corner with the capacitor at the other corner and orientated so that it fits into the apex of the roof inside a loft.

LOOP COUPLING. Alan Strong, G3WXI, noted my remarks regarding Faraday loop coupling in small transmitting loop antennas and says: "I read your comments with interest. I too was puzzled by the arrangement suggested by Robert, I1ARZ when I first read his February 1998 and subsequent articles. I wondered if the object may be to create a more balanced feed but in the absence of any definitive reference source I had to let the matter rest.

"A few days ago I dug out an unused AEA Isoloop still in its packaging, with a view to using it in my current experiments with WSPR, so the arrival on Friday of *RadCom* containing your piece was most timely. I had a problem with the Isoloop (which proved to be a faulty RF connector) and in the course of finding the fault I looked carefully at the coupling arrangement. That also does not appear to have any connection at the gap in the screen of the coax coupling loop. Furthermore I recently revisited a piece 'A Compact HF Antenna for Portable or Base Operation' by G3KPV (*RadCom*, September 1983) and that also does not show a connection in the gap". See **Figure 2**.

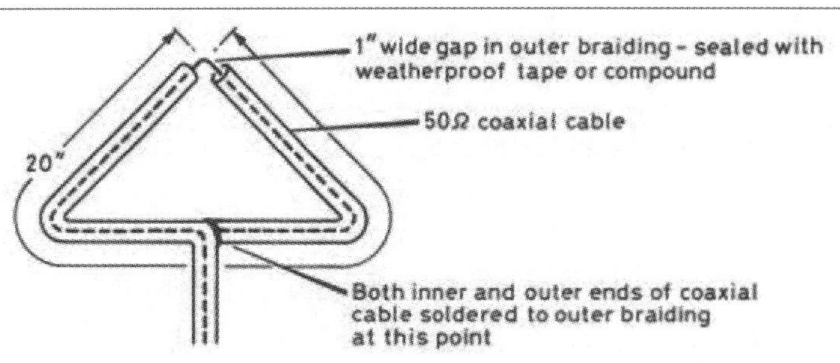


FIGURE 2: A transmitting loop antenna coupling loop from by G3KPV (*RadCom*, September 1983).

COMMUNICATION. I feel that I have to explain the changing e-mail addresses that have recently appeared in this column and apologise for any problems that you might have had trying to contact me. I was with UKONLINE for many years, in fact since the days of dial-up. In late November 2010 I received notification that the service had been bought out and the new owner was closing down the UKONLINE mail server. My e-mail address would cease to function. The new owner offered me generous terms to sign up with them and I was told that the transfer would be quick and painless. Because I wanted a simple and speedy solution to get the e-mail address into the Antennas column heading (bear in mind this column is written up to two months before it appears in print) I phoned straight away and asked to transfer. I put the promised new e-mail address in the January column. But by early January I hadn't heard anything from them so I started making enquiries. To cut a long story short, I changed service provider again and my e-mail address is now g3ldo@o2.co.uk. I haven't done anything about my web pages as yet. I was surprised to see that my website is still active but it is woefully out of date. Furthermore, I am now unable to update it so I am unsure what to do next. If you are interested just type G3LDO into Google and see if it is still active.

TABLE 2: The effect of a shorted turn on a 135.7μH coil measured by G3LDO. Position 0 is the end of the coil. The negative position number represents distance from the end of the coil.

| Position (cm) | Inductance (μH) |
|---|---|
| -3 | 135.0 |
| -2 | 134.2 |
| -1 | 131.4 |
| 0 | 126.0 |
| 1 | 125.0 |
| 2 | 113.6 |
| 3 | 104.3 |
| 4 | 103.2 |
| 5 | 103.5 |

# Antennas

## Loop antennas again

PHOTO 1: The G0UVR 11.70m diameter loop for 40 and 80m, almost perfectly camouflaged against the woody background.

BETTER THAN EXPECTED. Small transmitting loop antennas (sometimes referred to as magnetic loops) have been discussed in considerable detail, to such an extent that I felt reluctant to air this subject further. Additionally, some of this very detailed literature has been at the centre of controversy regarding the efficiency and effectiveness of these antennas. As a result I had avoided getting involved with them, that is until last year when I constructed one using a novel tuning capacitor design by G8JNJ and found that the antenna performed better than been I had been led to believe.

LOOP DESIGN PROGRAM. Ger Akse, G0UVR (PA0AXE), e-mailed me to say, "When we came to live at our present address in 1994, it became clear that I had to erect my aerials in a small wooded area, full with mature high trees. As the many branches and the canopies of these trees make it practically impossible to put up a dipole for the lower bands at a reasonable height, I decided with some reluctance to try a magnetic loop. Our move from using tank-gas to natural gas in 1996 had left me with a nice supply of 22mm diameter copper pipe.

"Before I decided to build a loop, I read whatever I could find about this type of antenna. I collected the formulae ruling the properties of magnetic loops and wrote a program in Turbo Pascal (under MS-DOS) to analyse the properties of magnetic loops".

The formulae used by the program are shown in **Figure 1**. **Figure 2** shows of the properties of the loop made by Harry Brash, GM3RVL, described in December 2010 Antennas. Assuming that the formulae are right and that the joints of the loop to the capacitor plates are loss-free, the efficiency figures should be reasonably reliable. Figure 2 shows that the efficiency on 30m drops to 36%, requiring tuning capacitor of 100pF. The bandwidth narrows to 8kHz.

GM3RVL suggested that his loop would cover 40m but on that band the efficiency drops to a mere 14%, the values for the tuning capacitor have to be increased to 203-216pF and the bandwidth narrows to 5kHz. I personally think that 30m is the lowest band that can used with his loop design."

G0UVR goes on to say: "In your article the importance of keeping the loss resistance as low as possible is stressed and rightfully so. However, getting the radiation resistance of the loop as high as possible is likely equally important. To do so the area of the loop needs to be increased. As bending a 3m length of 22mm diameter copper tubing into a circle was already described as hard work, increasing that length will make bending almost impossible. A circle, for a given circumference, has the greatest area (and thus the greatest radiation resistance) and can be constructed using 7/8in diameter hard-line coax.

"If that is not available there is the alternative of abandoning the circle and going instead for an octagonal or a square shape, using straight sections of 22mm tubing soldered together with angle joints. For an octagon seven angle joints of 45° are required; for a square we need only four right angle (90°) joints. From this point of view the square is to be preferred, however the octagon has a bigger area than the square. As I do not know how much RF losses the joints cause, it is impossible to say which shape would be better."

LOOP DESIGN FOR THE LOWER BANDS. G0UVR wanted a loop for 40 and 80m and chose the optimum size for 40m, being about 11.70m diameter. The loop is shown in **Photo 1**. This arrangement is upside down (compared with most loop designs) to allow access to the tuning capacitor for maintenance purposes.

The loop was constructed from six 1.50m and two 1.35m lengths of 22mm tube, arranged to leave enough space for the box containing the tuning capacitors. Two 500pF wide spaced capacitors in series (each good for 7.5kV) are used to tune the loop. The method of connecting the capacitors to the loop is best described by referring to **Photo 2**. Two flat pieces of tubing are bolted thoroughly on the stators of the two capacitors. They protrude through the Plexiglas top of the tuning box and their top-ends are again thoroughly bolted to the two bottom tubes of the loop.

The properties of this loop, calculated by the program, are shown in **Figure 3**. As the formula for loss-resistance does not take into account the losses in tube-joints, the losses in connecting the tube-ends to the capacitors and the losses in the capacitors, the efficiency figures may be slightly inflated.

COUPLING ARRANGEMENT. The coupling loop is a half Faraday loop, with the coax inner and braid at the apex connected. The loop is not made of standard coaxial cable such as RG213 and is described by G0UVR as follows:

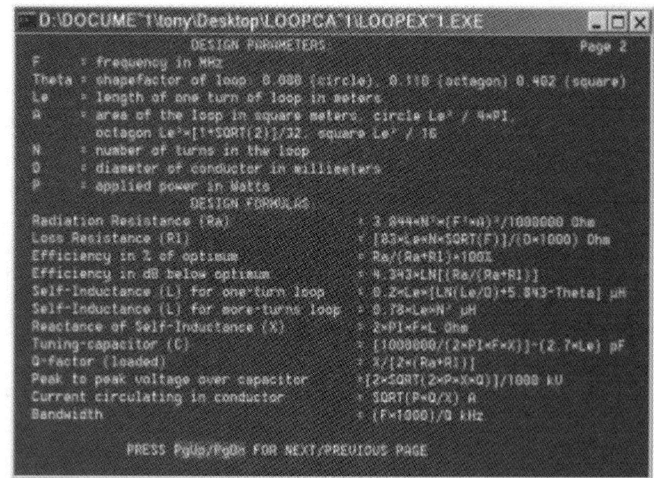



FIGURE 1: The formulae on which G0UVR's loop calculation program is based.

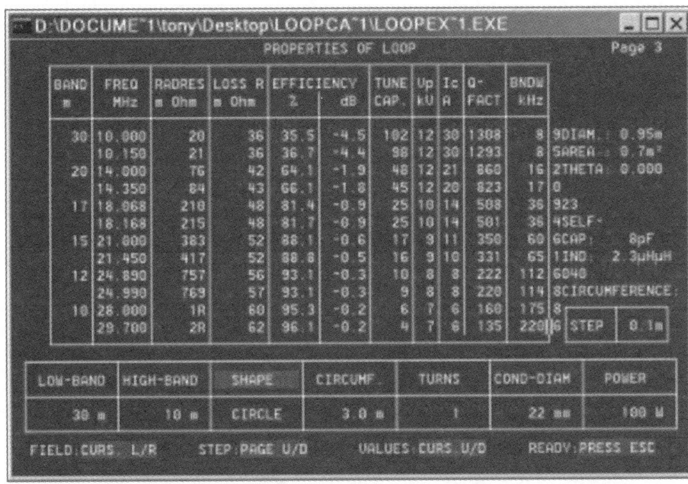
D:\DOCUME~1\tony\Desktop\LOOPCA~1\LOOPEX~1.EXE

PROPERTIES OF LOOP — Page 3

| BAND m | FREQ MHz | RADRES m Ohm | LOSS R m Ohm | EFFICIENCY % | EFFICIENCY dB | TUNE CAP. | Up kV | Ic A | Q-FACT | BNDW kHz |
|---|---|---|---|---|---|---|---|---|---|---|
| 30 | 10.000 | 20 | 36 | 35.5 | -4.5 | 102 | 12 | 30 | 1308 | 8 |
| | 10.150 | 21 | 36 | 36.7 | -4.4 | 98 | 12 | 30 | 1293 | 8 |
| 20 | 14.000 | 76 | 42 | 64.1 | -1.9 | 48 | 12 | 21 | 860 | 16 |
| | 14.350 | 84 | 43 | 66.1 | -1.8 | 45 | 12 | 20 | 823 | 17 |
| 17 | 18.068 | 210 | 48 | 81.4 | -0.9 | 25 | 10 | 14 | 508 | 36 |
| | 18.168 | 215 | 48 | 81.7 | -0.9 | 25 | 10 | 14 | 501 | 36 |
| 15 | 21.000 | 383 | 52 | 88.1 | -0.6 | 17 | 9 | 11 | 350 | 60 |
| | 21.450 | 417 | 52 | 88.8 | -0.5 | 16 | 9 | 10 | 331 | 65 |
| 12 | 24.890 | 757 | 56 | 93.1 | -0.3 | 10 | 8 | 8 | 222 | 112 |
| | 24.990 | 769 | 57 | 93.1 | -0.3 | 9 | 8 | 8 | 220 | 114 |
| 10 | 28.000 | 1R | 60 | 95.3 | -0.2 | 6 | 7 | 6 | 160 | 175 |
| | 29.700 | 2R | 62 | 96.1 | -0.2 | 4 | 7 | 6 | 135 | 220 |

DIAM.: 0.95m
AREA: 0.7m²
THETA: 0.000
SELF-CAP: 8pF
IND: 2.3µH
CIRCUMFERENCE:
STEP 0.1m

| LOW-BAND | HIGH-BAND | SHAPE | CIRCUMF. | TURNS | COND-DIAM | POWER |
|---|---|---|---|---|---|---|
| 30 m | 10 m | CIRCLE | 3.0 m | 1 | 22 mm | 100 W |

FIELD:CURS. L/R STEP:PAGE U/D VALUES:CURS.U/D READY:PRESS ESC

FIGURE 2: Characteristics of the GM3RVL loop on the bands 10 to 30m.

D:\DOCUME~1\tony\Desktop\LOOPCA~1\LOOPEX~1.EXE

PROPERTIES OF LOOP — Page 3

| BAND m | FREQ MHz | RADRES m Ohm | LOSS R m Ohm | EFFICIENCY % | EFFICIENCY dB | TUNE CAP. | Up kV | Ic A | Q-FACT | BNDW kHz |
|---|---|---|---|---|---|---|---|---|---|---|
| 80 | 3.500 | 68 | 83 | 45.3 | -3.4 | 138 | 4 | 6 | 888 | 4 |
| | 3.800 | 95 | 86 | 52.5 | -2.8 | 112 | 4 | 5 | 804 | 5 |
| 60 | 5.000 | 285 | 99 | 74.3 | -1.3 | 51 | 4 | 4 | 499 | 10 |
| | 5.500 | 417 | 104 | 80.1 | -1.0 | 37 | 4 | 3 | 405 | 14 |
| 40 | 7.000 | 1R | 117 | 90.4 | -0.4 | 11 | 3 | 2 | 221 | 32 |
| | 7.200 | 1R | 118 | 91.2 | -0.4 | 8 | 3 | 2 | 205 | 35 |

DIAM.: 3.72m
AREA: 10.9m²
THETA: 0.000
SELF-CAP: 32pF
IND: 12.2µH
CIRCUMFERENCE:
STEP 0.1m

| LOW-BAND | HIGH-BAND | SHAPE | CIRCUMF. | TURNS | COND-DIAM | POWER |
|---|---|---|---|---|---|---|
| 80 m | 40 m | CIRCLE | 11.7 m | 1 | 22 mm | 10 W |

FIELD:CURS. L/R STEP:PAGE U/D VALUES:CURS.U/D READY:PRESS ESC

FIGURE 3: Characteristics of his G0UVR's enlarged loop (see Photo 1) on the 40, 60 and 80m bands.

"The inner conductor is made from 5 or 6mm diameter brass or copper tubing. This is then covered with heat-shrink. The outer conductor is made from the braid of coax, which is then for weatherproofing covered with vinyl tape. In January 1997 I read an article in *PW* written by Des Heath, G3ABS, under the title 'Postage Stamp Loops'. He claimed that a coupling loop made this way provided better coupling than could be achieved using standard coax. Whether that is true or not, I do not know, but I made my coupling loop (which is 2.40m long) that way. For aesthetic reasons I shaped it the same as the main loop (ie octagonal) and clamped it on two sides to the main loop using PVC pipe clamps.

"Although the term 'small' may not strictly be applicable for a loop of this size, it is still very small in terms of wavelength. The bottom of the loop sits about 1m above the ground as shown in Photo 1 and the plane of the loop is in the East-West direction.

"As shown in Photo 2, the capacitors are driven by a small 1.5-3V electric motor via a multi-ratio gearbox (available from Maplin), set for 1 to 2 rpm.

"The loop worked from scratch and its performance exceeded my expectations. The antenna puts out a good signal all over Europe and, with good luck, I managed a QSO on 80m with Canada (Prince Edward Islands) and even with New Zealand on 40m. It has been in use since 1997 and so far the tuning motor has only been replaced once."

PHOTO 2: Detail of the tuning capacitance mechanism.

COMPARISONS. I made a model of the GM3RVL loop using *EZNEC*. This program uses a totally different method of calculating antenna performance to the method so far described, so a comparison seemed to be in order.

The gain of the GM3RVL loop on the 10m and 30m bands using the G0UVR's program (Figure 2) is -0.2dB and -4.4dB respectively, while the tuning capacitors required are 6pF and 98pF respectively. The same antenna, analysed using *EZNEC* on the same bands, resulted in a gain of 0.5dBi and –2.01dBi respectively, while the tuning capacitors required are 8pF and 88pF respectively. The gain reference for the G0UVR program is dB down from a 100% efficient antenna, while the *EZNEC* reference is an isotropic source.

In addition I used the loop calculation program from 66pacific calculators [1], described in September 2010 Antennas, to model this same loop on 30m. It predicts a gain -4.6dB below 100%. It also makes comments regarding the loop length relative to frequency, in particular that the conductor length for a small transmitting loop antenna should be greater than 1/8 wavelength.

The efficiency of a loop antenna falls dramatically as the loop size is reduced (or the operating frequency of a given loop is reduced). For example, the efficiency of the GM3RVL loop drops to a mere 14% when tuned down to 40m using a 210pF tuning capacitor.

CONTROVERSY. There is nothing more likely to put one off an antenna type than the label 'controversial'. It implies unproven performance. As I mentioned at the beginning of this column, these transmitting loop antennas have been discussed in considerable detail by eminent antenna experts, often with differing views regarding the antenna's efficacy, hence the controversy. [2] [3] and [4] represent a small sample of this discussion. However, note the variation in antenna efficiencies over the frequency range 10 to 28MHz shown in Figure 2.

If you have a restricted QTH and conventional antennas are a problem then the loop antenna could well be the one for you. Provided that you make the loop the appropriate size for the frequency bands of interest, keep the losses low using appropriate construction practices and don't position it close to electromagnetic obstacles then you could be pleasantly surprised by its performance.

Finally I leave the last word to G0UVR. "Encouraged by the success of the 80/40m loop I decided to make another two magnetic loops to take with me on camping holidays on the continent. The larger of the two has the maximum size for 20m and works on 40m also when I parallel the two tuning capacitors with a fixed capacitor made of double-sided PCB. In the late nineties I tried this loop when on holiday near Florence. It appeared to work fine on 20 and 40 and I even managed to work Japan on these two bands on 20m with good reports, albeit on 40 with some difficulty. The smaller one that I made a few years later has the maximum size for 10m and thus works down to 17m but not fully tested as yet because of the poor propagation on these bands."


REFERENCES

[1] www.66pacific.com/calculators.

[2] *Loop Antennas* – Facts not Fiction, Tony Henk, G4XVF, *Radio Communication* September/October, 1991.

[3] *Electrically-small transmitting loops*, Dr Jack Belrose, VE2CV, *RadCom* June/July 2004.

[4] *New truths about small tuned loops in a real environment*, Professor Mike Underhill, G3LHZ, *RadCom* August/Sept 2004.

# Antennas

## The Coupled-Resonator multiband antenna

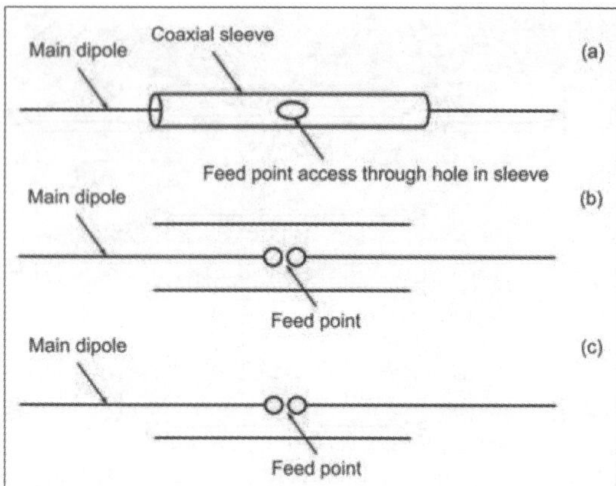


**FIGURE 1: Evolution of the Coupled-Resonator antenna. (a) Coaxial sleeve dipole. (b) Open Sleeve dipole, where two outer conductors make an 'open sleeve'. (c) Coupled-Resonator dipole, where the dual band effect is achieved with a single conductor. (illustration after *The ARRL Antenna Book*, 21st Edition).**

**RECAP.** In the March Antennas I described building a computer model of a multiband antenna using EZNEC. I created a basic dipole (I will call this the main dipole) and tested its performance, with and without ground. I then added an extra band element and made a further check before connecting it to the main dipole and found that the antenna exhibited a dual band characteristic. I then added a further band element, again without connecting it to the main dipole and the antenna had a tri-band characteristic. At the time I promised to write about this interesting multiband arrangement – so here goes.

**HISTORY.** A little research shows that this antenna multiband principle has been around since the late 1940s. A comprehensive description of a multiband antenna using close coupled elements by Gary Breed, K9AY, appears in **[1]** and **[2]**. In its original form it was apparently known as the coaxial sleeve antenna, which covered two frequency bands. This was achieved by surrounding a dipole or monopole with a cylindrical tube resonant at the higher of the desired frequencies as shown in **Figure 1(a)**. In the 1950s, one antenna manufacturer apparently marketed a two-band antenna based on this design.

However, experimenters soon determined that two conductors at the second frequency, placed on either side of the main dipole or monopole, would make a skeleton representation of a cylinder (**Figure 1(b)**). This was called the open-sleeve antenna. The Hy-Gain Explorer tribander uses this method in its driven element to obtain resonance in the 10 metre band. Later, a few antenna developers found that these extra conductors did not need to be added in pairs and that a single conductor at each frequency could add the extra resonance (**Figure 1(c)**). This is the method used by Force 12 in some of their multiband antennas. I seem to recall seeing a BBC Band 1/ITV television antenna using this technique.

**EXPERIMENTAL SETUP.** I decided to examine this technique using the AIM4170 and made a simple dipole arrangement using old TV/VHF radio antenna hardware as shown in **Photo 1**. A coupling arrangement using a PL259 was necessary to allow calibration of the coax feed to the dipole, so that the feed impedance at the antenna could be examined. Next, an additional element was added to the boom using an arrangement that would allow the alternative elements to be tested and the spacing between the dipole and this additional element to be adjusted. The general test arrangement is shown in **Photo 2**.

The element lengths were not specially selected and it was only by chance that the lengths fitted to the dipole caused it to resonate at just over 51MHz. The lengths of various parasitic elements selected for the tests were judged to fall between 60 and 100MHz. To this end the AIM4170 was programmed to scan between 40 and 100MHz and the coax feed calibrated for this range of frequencies.

The first measurement used a 20mm diameter parasitic element spaced 80mm (centre to centre) from the dipole and the result is shown in **Figure 2**. The blue marker has been placed over the parasitic element resonance. The frequency, 72.38MHz and the impedance, around 70Ω, are shown on the right hand side of the display. The driven element also has an impedance of around 70Ω so that the minimum SWR for both elements is no better than 1.4:1. Note that the impedance graphs are set to Zmag (green) and Theta (purple). The more familiar impedance equivalent R $\pm$ j is displayed on the right hand side.

The spacing between the parasitic element and the dipole was adjusted to 60mm. This resulted in an impedance of 57Ω at 73MHz with very little change at 51MHz, as shown in **Figure 3**. Clearly this arrangement would make a simple 50/70MHz dual band antenna with a dipole matched to 50Ω and a parasitic element of the appropriate length. It should be possible to make the antenna also cover 144MHz with an additional parasitic element although this was not tried at the time.

It is obvious from these experiments that there are three variables that affect the performance of the parasitic element: the conductor diameter, the conductor length and the position relative to the driven element. While this is no problem with the construction of a VHF antenna such as the one shown in Photo 2, K9AY has proposed it as solution for a multiband wire antenna for the HF bands. Such an arrangement does have the difficulty of maintaining the critical spacing required between the driven element and the parasitic elements, as K9AY admits. Nevertheless, such antennas have found favour with some amateurs.

**FEEDBACK.** Andy Malbon, G8MIA, emailed me to say, "I have read your article on multiband dipole antennas in *RadCom*. You ask if anyone has tried using the Coupled-Resonator Antenna described in *The ARRL Antenna Book*. I have been using one for over a year and find it a very competent antenna as it is resonant on all the design bands.

"I use an Excel spreadsheet to calculate the wire spacing and wire length. For the higher bands (12m and 10m) I use smaller diameter wire so they sit between the resonators for 17m and 15m but this means the bandwidth is narrower on these bands. Length of the resonators is critical and much time was spent getting the lengths right! The main problem is keeping the wires at the correct distance apart so lightweight spacers are used every 0.5m and the wires are kept taut."

However, not everyone found this arrangement successful. I monitored a QRZ Forum on the internet on the subject of the Coupled Resonator antenna. EA3GC built a K9AY Coupled Resonator Dipole for 28-21-14MHz (as described on page 7-22 of *The ARRL Antenna Book*). It consisted of three dipoles made of enamelled copper wire 1.5mm diameter. The 14MHz dipole was fed at its centre with RG58 coax and the 21 and 28MHz dipoles were coupled to the 14MHz by just placing them parallel to it using plastic spreaders, at a distance of 28 and 35mm respectively. The 14MHz dipole was fed via a common mode RF choke

**PHOTO 1: Construction of a two-band Coupled-Resonator antenna allowing easy adjustment of the element spacing.**

**PHOTO 2: Test arrangement showing the antenna under test, the AIM4170 and the laptop computer.**

consisting of some turns of the coax line.

EA3GC noted that the antenna performed fairly well but the SWR results were poor as shown below.

On 28MHz the SWR bandwidth was very narrow band (but a figure not given)
On 21MHz the SWR was 3.1 at 21.0MHz and 1.25 at 21.45MHz
On 14MHz the SWR was 3, being fairly flat from 14.0 to 14.35MHz

This was the best that could be achieved after a lot of pruning. EA3GC asked if anyone could help.

Jerry, K4SAV answered, saying "The 10m dipole is too far away from the 20m dipole to obtain a 50Ω impedance on 10m with that size wire. The 15m dipole placed 28mm below the 20m dipole should give an OK match on 15m, but a spacing of 40mm would be better. The 10m dipole needs to be about 15mm above the 20m dipole to give a good match. These numbers don't agree with the tables in the article because there is a lot of interaction between the three elements.

"With the size wire you are using, this antenna will have a very narrow bandwidth, especially on 10m where it will probably be no more than 400kHz for less than 2:1 SWR. If you build this out of 1in (25mm) diameter tubing, the bandwidth (SWR < 2.0) on 10m will go to about 650kHz and the spacings will go to about 18cm and 14cm for 15 and 10m".

K9AY makes the statement that this antenna is easily simulated with EZNEC as I did when investigating multiband antennas a few months ago but I was only checking to see if the antenna would work in principle and not overly concerned with the actual impedance presented on each band. It is a very difficult antenna to model correctly and, as K9AY admits, you need to use lots of segments, carefully aligned. You also need to test the model for errors.

AE6TY has come up with an interesting arrangement that uses only one extra element to provide a reasonable match for most of the HF bands. He goes on to say, "I read with interest your article in the March 2011 *RadCom* on multi-band antennas. You indicated in your article that you would be interested in hearing from folks who use a Coupled-Resonator antenna. I use a two element version. The larger of the two is a 69ft (21m) Off Centre Fed dipole fed at the 1/3rd point. The second element is 49ft

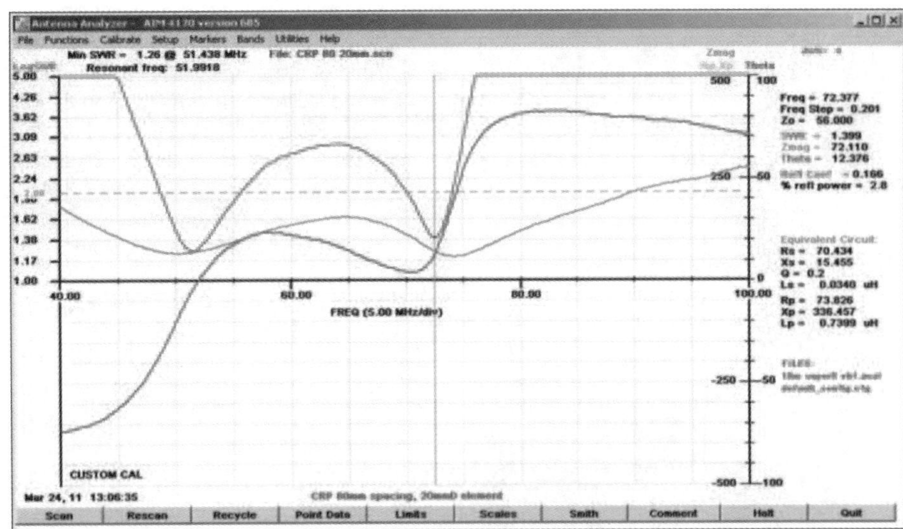


FIGURE 2: A measurement of the Coupled-Resonator antenna shown in Photo 2 using the AIM4170 and an element spacing of 80mm. The blue marker has been placed over the parasitic element resonance and the parameters measured at this point are displayed on the right.

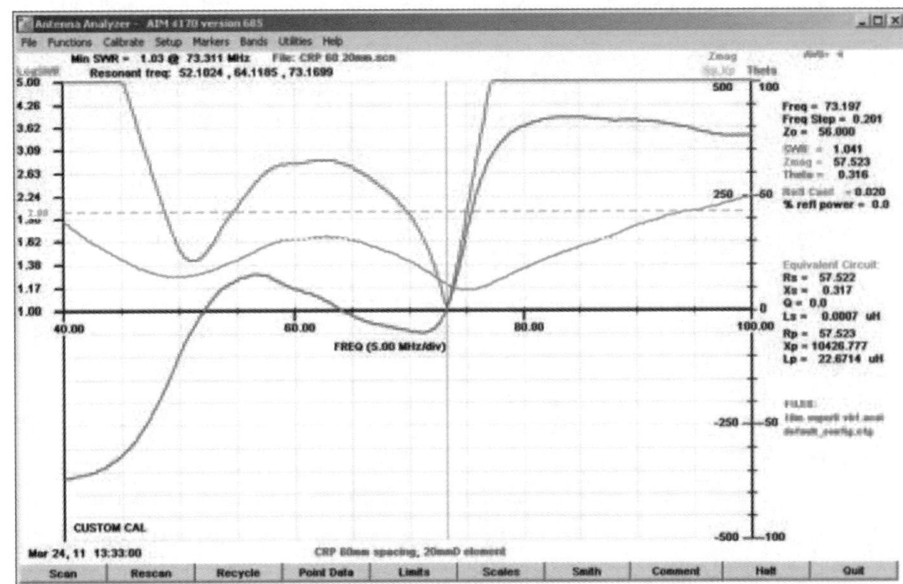


FIGURE 3: A second measurement with the element spacing reduced to 60mm.

(14.9m) long and is also Off Centre. The longer element gets me 7, 14 and 28MHz. The shorter one gives me 10 and 20MHz (roughly!) and the antenna is fed via a 4:1 current balun at the feed point as shown in **Figure 4**. These lengths get me close and a built in antenna tuner gets me the rest of the way. I have found that, over time, getting more than a few elements resonating at a chosen frequency and at the correct impedance is difficult.

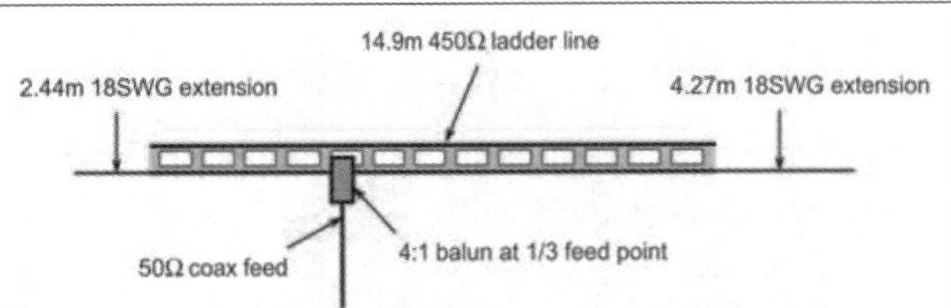


**FIGURE 4: Details of AE6TY's Off-Centre Fed Coupled-Resonator antenna constructed using 14.9m of ladder-line with wire extensions (not to scale).**

"This is why I use Off-Centre Fed Dipoles; they give me the even harmonics and cut the number of elements significantly. I get 5 workable bands with just two elements. The ladder line ensures that the two elements are spaced correctly."

**FINALLY.** My view is that you can circumvent all these impedance problems of a wire Coupled-Resonator HF antenna by just connecting all the elements to the feeder as shown in Figure 2 of March 2011 Antennas. However, the Coupled-Resonator principle does seem an excellent way of adding an additional VHF band to an existing VHF antenna without disturbing the characteristics of the original antenna.

REFERENCES

[1] The Coupled-Resonator Principle: A Flexible Method for Multiband Antennas. Gary Breed, K9AY, *The ARRL Antenna Compendium, Vol 5.*
[2] *ARRL Antenna Book, 21st Edition.*

# Antennas

## Shorted turn tuning

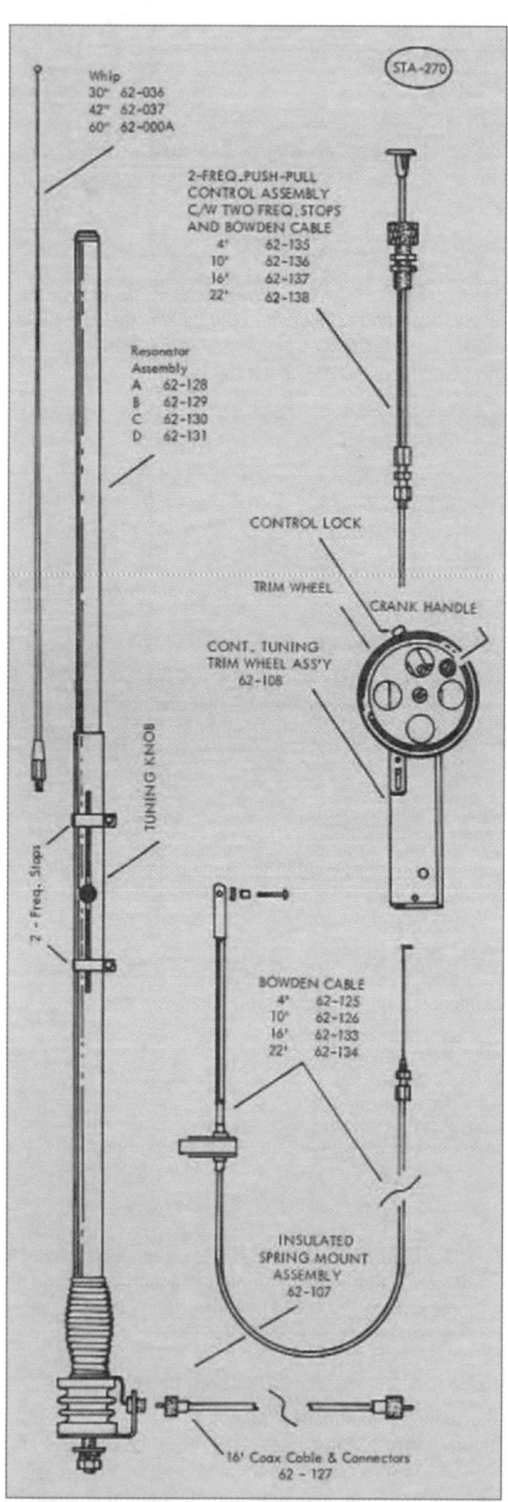


FIGURE 1: A diagram of the Spilsbury antenna and its remote tuning method using a Bowden cable (taken from Spilsbury Communications brochure).

**RECAP.** In the February edition of Antennas I described a method of tuning a loaded mobile whip antenna from an *ARRL Handbook* using the 'shorted turn technique' that I had never seen before or since (at the time of writing). Martin Feeney, K1OYB, e-mailed to say "Your recent articles on Shorted Turn tuning inspired me to do some research into the matter. There are several versions of slug and other 'non-contact' tuned antennas in old *QST* articles including W2ABS, August, 1950; W1BDV, August, 1951; W1IKU, February, 1952 and W0DQW, October, 1953.

"The W2ABS version reports a 3.9 to 4.0MHz tuning range with a 10kHz bandwidth. W1IKU appears to be the originator of the 'Figure 4B' version discussed in the February 2011 column. He reports a 100kHz tuning range at 4.0MHz with most change in the centre of the coil. Also W1HDQ and W1QDF describe a shorted turn tuning system for a 50MHz amplifier in the November 1970 *QST*."

**THE SPILSBURY COMMUNICATIONS ANTENNA.** Martin Ehrenfried, G8JNJ, e-mailed to say "I saw your notes regarding shorted turn antenna tuning and thought you may be interested in an antenna I bought at the Newbury rally two years ago. It's a commercial HF mobile antenna made by a Canadian company Spilsbury Communications (no longer trading). I think it was intended for use on logging trucks. It consists of a loading coil and short whip antenna. The coil is tuned by sliding a copper/ferrite core stack in and out of the winding. My antenna tunes from 3.5 to 13.9MHz with the standard whip." See **Photo 1** and **Photo 2**.

A diagram of this antenna from the brochure is shown in **Figure 1**. Note that this antenna can be also be tuned remotely using a Bowden cable.

G8JNJ included a copy of a patent **[1]** and a sales brochure. From this latter document it appears that Spilsbury Communications produced four different antennas that covered 1.6 to 6.5MHz, 2.0 to 8MHz, 2.3 to 9.1MHz and 3.5 to 13.4MHz. They were designed specifically for commercial concerns such as logging companies, who needed HF communications in hilly areas outside the range of VHF systems.

**HOW THE SHORTED TUNE TUNING WORKS.** The patent is very detailed and includes a description of how the shorted turn method works, which is as follows: "The inductor ring operates in accordance with Lenz's Law, which shows that the current induced in the inductor ring has 180° phase difference to the current in the coil. The flux in the inductor ring opposes the flux in the main coil and reduces the total inductance of the coil. This has the effect of increasing the resonant frequency of the antenna. In order to attain the maximum effect it is necessary that the outer diameter of the inductor ring closely approximates the inner diameter of the coil. In other words, the space between the inductor ring and the coil must be kept to a minimum consistent with providing the required insulation between the two."

Spilsbury Communications had obviously done a lot of research into the most effective construction of the inductor ring and found copper tube to be the most effective but it had to be the right shape. "...if the inductor ring length extends over a considerable part of the total length of the coil a capacitively coupled circuit is presented across the axial length of this portion of the coil and across the high RF voltage existing therein. This results in an unwanted and wasteful current being set up through the length of the inductor ring, which lowers the voltage across the coil and reduces its effectiveness. In order to minimise this loss it is necessary to divide the inductor ring into a number of sections. The number of divisions used is limited only by the added complexity and cost of the design. In practice, it has been found that an acceptable compromise is to reduce the length of the individual inductor ring section to a figure not exceeding its diameter.

"In order to further reduce the loss current set up through the inductor rings it is desirable to reduce the wall thickness of the rings as much as possible to reduce the electrical capacity between rings. The point beyond which the thickness cannot be effectively reduced is reached when the current carrying capacity of the ring becomes insufficient and/or the mechanical strength of the ring is insufficient. As an example a wall thickness of 0.001in has been found to be satisfactory in this antenna".

In practice the conductor rings are in the form of a cup to allow them to be fixed to central rod together with spacing insulators to maintain the distance between them and to prevent them touching.

PHOTO 1: The Spilsbury Communications antenna.

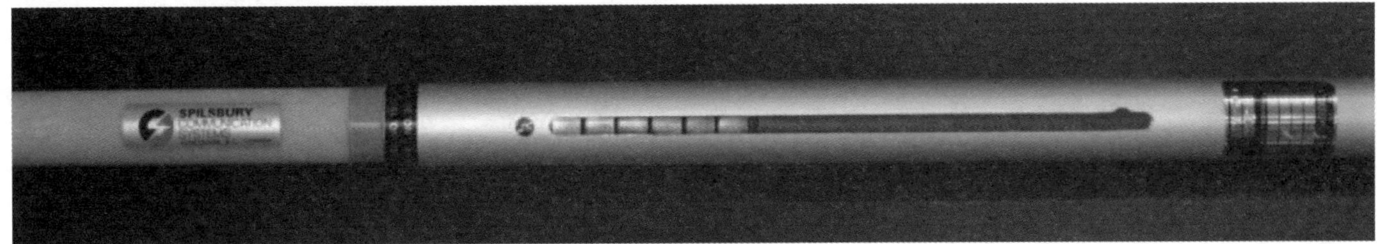

PHOTO 2: Closer view of the tuning arrangement used in the Spilsbury Communications antenna.

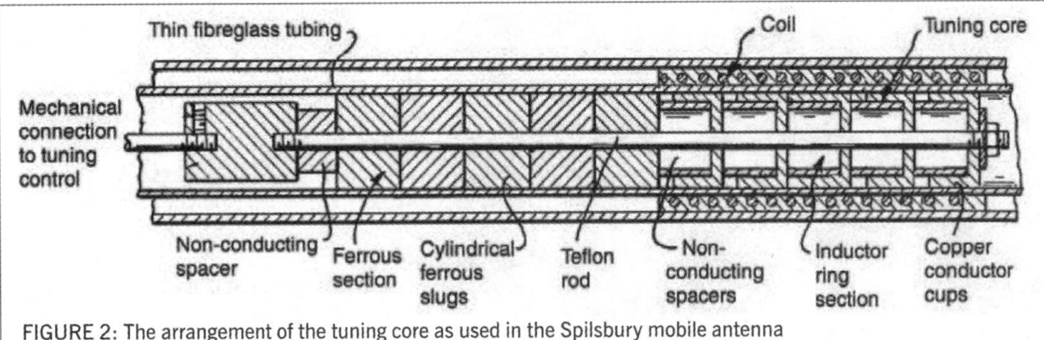


FIGURE 2: The arrangement of the tuning core as used in the Spilsbury mobile antenna showing the copper cups section of the core inside the coil resulting in minimum inductance.

CONSTRUCTION OF THE SPILSBURY ANTENNA. The antenna comprises a metal tube, a coil section and a top whip section as used in a conventional mobile antenna. However, the diameter of coil is small but is relatively long to allow it to be used with a tuning core.

The tuning core is arranged so that it can move into and through the coil. In addition to the conductor rings described above this core also has a section made of short cylindrical ferrous slugs, which are held together under tension on the same conducting rod as the conductor rings.

The lengths of the ferrous and ring sections and are positioned relative to each other so that at the extreme lengths of travel one section is completely within the coil, the other section is completely outside it, although most of the tuning range of both sections will be in the coil at the same time. The arrangement is shown in **Figure 2**.

The loading coil is space wound on a thin-wall fibreglass tubing and embedded in an epoxy resin. The size and spacing of the turns of wire of the coil are determined to provide the correct inductance for the frequency range desired and also with regard to the amount of RF power for which the antenna is designed. The patent gives an example of an antenna designed to cover 2-8MHz and with a maximum power rating of 120W peak power, which used 196 turns of wire wound on a 22mm round coil form and evenly spaced over a total length of 7in (175mm).

The patent is described in detail in [1] and the method of tuning proposed was an electro-mechanical method as used in most 'screwdriver' antennas. However, the production model described in the brochure uses a local tuning method at the antenna, which simply moves the core up and down with a knob as shown in Figure 1. Provision for remote tuning using a Bowden cable was also available.

It is probable that the customers who purchased these antennas would have been allocated a single frequency in the lower HF bands. A continuously tuneable antenna was not necessarily required for this service but the ability to conveniently set the antenna to a given resonant frequency was obviously a good selling point. Provision was made for two separate frequency settings by the simple expedient of using two hose clamps to restrict the movement of frequency selector knob as shown in Figure 1.

THE LABGEAR PORTABLE ANTENNA. Peter Chadwick, G3RZP, informs me that in the 1960s, Labgear had a line of commercial HF SSB equipment. They used loaded whip antennas with ferrite slugs, which were moved mechanically to achieve tuning. For pack sets, this was less than ideal because keeping water and dirt out was difficult. G3RZP goes on to say, "For the Compak 8 transceiver, Ian Leybourne, (whose callsign I can't remember but he was a G3S) came up with a different approach in 1969. He put the loading coil in the antenna, with some ferrite, to make a sealed, robust antenna. Ian's approach to tuning was to use a plastic sleeve with embedded rings of metal, such that it could slide it over the loading coil to increase the frequency".

The tuning could have been done using a metal tube but this results in capacity across the coil, which has an adverse effect on Q; metal rings circumvent this problem. G3RZP adds, "Anyway, the system was very good in the pre-production trials: I don't know if it was used in production, as I left Labgear at the end of 1969, but I'm pretty sure that it was patented. So, as usual, there's nothing that new in radio! Biggest problem with shorted turns is the same as the variometer – as the inductance reduces, so does the Q, since there is the same amount of wire in the inductor and thus the same resistance".

It could be that Ian Leybourne thought of the multiple ring shorted turn tuner first because the Spilsbury Communications US patent was not registered until June 1972. On the other hand I do not have access to the early *QST* articles mentioned at the beginning of this column.

SHORTED TURN TUNING FOR LF. For the LF fraternity the shorted turn may be a solution to fine tuning the inductance of the loading coil at 136kHz and 501kHz. A variometer can be relatively difficult structure to construct. Indeed Kevin, ZL4MD, has used the shorted turn approach on LF. He says, "I use a large ex-NDB loading coil that can be tapped on any single turn. For fine-tuning there is a single rotary shorted turn. To minimise losses the cross-section of the shorted turn is large [about 40mm x 10mm] and the whole thing is constructed using silver-plated brass.

"Although I have never bothered to measure the inductance variation it works well for transmitting on 180 and 500kHz. I intend to try it on 136kHz over our coming southern hemisphere winter".

LOOP CORRECTION. The sharp-eyed amongst you spotted an error in the May 2011 Antennas in the description of low band version of the magnetic loop. Walter, DF2NC noted "You probably meant circumference instead of diameter in the third line of paragraph LOOP DESIGN FOR THE LOWER BANDS".

Ken, M0DKC, also noted the error. The figure of 11.7m is quoted as CIRCUMF in G0UVR's loop calculation program in Figure 3 of the article.

REFERENCES

[1] US Patent 3,671,972
www.freepatentsonline.com/3671972.pdf

# Antennas

## A magnetic loop automatic ATU

**PHOTO 1: The complete BRATS project magnetic loop auto tuner control unit.**

**MANUALLY TUNING A LOOP.** In spite of the controversy regarding the efficiency and effectiveness of small magnetic loop antennas in the past, I constantly receive e-mails to the effect that this type of antenna has solved an HF antenna problem.

The high Q of the magnetic loop means that its usable SWR bandwidth is only a few kHz wide; retuning is necessary whenever the frequency is varied. Some amateurs consider this need for retuning to be a disadvantage of the magnetic loop and that adjusting the tuning can be tricky. However, this sharp tuning is a consequence of the magnetic loop's high Q, the factor that makes it so efficient for its small size.

**BRATS RADIO CLUB PROJECT.** It was with interest that I read an e-mail from Geoff Wooster, G3YVF, in which he described his involvement (with two other members of BRATS Radio Club [1]) in designing an auto tuner for magnetic loops, thus circumventing the tuning problem described above. The automatic ATU uses a stepper motor, a homebrew design laser cut variable capacitor together with a kit of parts. Many members of the club have built magnetic loops plus the auto ATU to complete the project. The tuner is designed to work with a magnetic loop constructed to operate in part(s) of the range of 1.5 to 30MHz; the tuner should be able to operate from RF powers as low as one or two watts up to around a hundred.

Charles, G4VSZ, and John, G8JAD started the club project for BRATS in 2008 and were joined later by Geoff, G3YVF. John, G8JAD, wrote the PIC software. The team made their own PCBs and even the strip line VSWR sensors in house, building the complete automatic ATU for only a few score of pounds. The finished project in its box is shown in **Photo 1**. Obtaining suitable variable capacitors for magnetic loops can be a challenge but the BRATS team solved the problem by designing and building their own tuning capacitors from scratch. An example is shown in **Photo 2**.

A reduction drive is required because the tuning of the loop is critical. Direct drive from the motor to the capacitor is not a problem if the capacitor has a small value, say 50pF, but a reduction drive is needed if the capacitor is larger, otherwise the increments will be too big. An insulated shaft from the motor/reduction drive to the tuning capacitor is essential.

**OPERATING THE ATU.** As shown in Photo 1, the control unit has simple controls: a power switch, auto/manual tuning selection and, on the left side, pushbuttons for fast/slow up/down control of the stepper motor. In addition there is a row of LEDs to indicate the 'dead band' setting. This dead band is the SWR range over which no tuning occurs. It prevents activation-deactivation cycles (hunting) of the automatic system. The reason for having a variable dead band is to allow the ATU to match to the minimum SWR achievable on the loop to which the ATU is connected.

The width of the SWR bandwidth is indicated by the number of LEDs lit from the left, ie four LEDs would indicate an SWR dead band of 1.9:1. The default setting is 1.4:1 (two LEDs illuminated).

By pressing two of the manual buttons at once the SWR display can be scrolled and left at the desired auto tune SWR setting. Pressing one of the buttons again stores this in the PIC for use on the Auto setting.

You might question why it's important to have an 'infinity' dead band setting. G3YVF tells me that the LED display had to end somewhere and it got called 'infinity' because it is off scale! The LED display is really only intended to give the operator some confidence. It also allows one to set up the ATU to any new loop. This is done by adjusting the loop capacitor manually on the SLOW setting to observe the lowest SWR figure that can be obtained; this figure is then used when setting up the ATU in automatic mode.

It has been found that if you QSY only a small amount, the tuner will tune so fast on seeing RF from the transmitter that you can miss the fact it has re-tuned. If it needs to do a full sweep to find a new setting, this can take 8 or more seconds, depending on where the tuning capacitor was to begin with. There are no stops on the loop tuning capacitor so it can rotate round and round. The stepper motor runs from the 12V DC fed to the tuner; this is just enough to rotate the capacitor.

Loops fed with a balun appeared to perform best with the tuner, with the flying leads from the balun being connected equidistant from the mid point of the loop. The actual connection points were found by testing whilst watching the SWR to locate the two 'sweet spots' on the loop.

Interestingly, the tuner will sense and tune with ease with powers from 100W to below 1W. Also note how the strip line PCB sensor is screened from the main PCB (**Photo 3**). There is only one known issue: if your transmitter has spurious outputs, ie on more than one frequency, it will confuse the tuner. This would not normally be a problem with a loop antenna due to its very high Q (almost single-frequency operation), which naturally rejects off-tune signals.

**CONSTRUCTION.** There is no kit of parts available, but a comprehensive set of building instructions in PDF format can be found at [1]. These contain building instructions, PCB layout of the main board and the sensor, capacitor construction and schematic. I found these very well written. The instructions do include a caveat that this is an experimental project and you must be prepared for setbacks, but I am told they are not aware of any up to now.

The BRATS PCBs are designed the other way up compared with the conventional method of having the tracks on one side and the components on the other. This method allows the constructor to see the track and solder components directly to it. It's less critical regarding component type and appears to be a very good method of making PCBs for homebrew projects. As you can see from **Photo 3** the layout is neat and practical.

The PIC firmware is also available from [2]. Be aware that the intellectual rights of this firmware belong to John, G8JAD. While this has been made freely available to *RadCom* readers it is not for commercial use.

**OTHER ISSUES.** The performance of the system will depend on the construction and location of the antenna. G3YVF uses a 50ft circumference loop made from 22mm copper water pipe and compression fittings. Situated

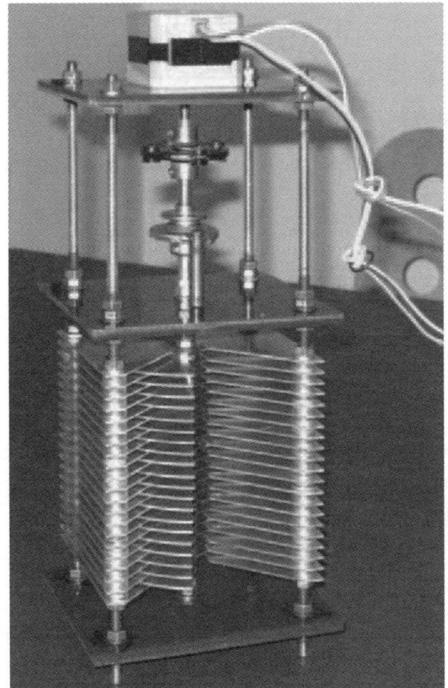

**PHOTO 2: The complete capacitor tuning unit with the stepper motor and the slow motion drive designed by the BRATS team. Note the ball reduction drive and the insulated shaft between the reduction drive and the capacitor.**

in the loft, it tunes both 80 and 40m with the 150pF variable capacitor shown in Photo 2.

When used on 80m, the auto tuner will retune to any new frequency in a split second. He adds that he can often hear 80m stations on the loop that cannot be heard on his sloping 66ft vertical (and he lives on an island with a sea earth at the bottom of the sloping vertical).

Note that you cannot retro fit this auto ATU to a loop controlled by an AC/DC motor without changing the capacitor drive to use a stepper motor. Note also that the tuning capacitor designed for the project has 360 degrees of rotation and has no mechanical stops.

It seemed to me that there could be further uses for this auto ATU. For example, with my mobile setup I have a screwdriver antenna,

**PHOTO 3: The general construction of the BRATS automatic loop tuner. Note the method of soldering the components to the track side of the PCB.**

which works OK but is very critical to tune. It occurs to me that this ATU could be beneficial because trying to make critical adjustments to radio equipment while driving a vehicle could be hazardous. I put this to G3YVF, and he replied "Oh yes, we have a couple of members who are looking at all sorts of things. It does not matter one jot to the electronics if the capacitor drive stalls. The stepper will only draw current according to Ohm's Law and its resistance is high. This will never cause either a motor failure or driver transistor failure.

"You can use it for an L match ATU. Use a switch so the variable capacitor can be put on input or output. It rotates in one direction only and will find a match.

"When mobile with a screwdriver antenna, use the manual buttons to run it to one end – a stall does no damage. Now switch to auto. Your screwdriver will be tuned as soon as you squirt some RF into the ATU.

"This hasn't yet been tried, but you could build a T match ATU where both variables and roller coaster are on one shaft. Manually set it one end of travel. Now go to auto and transmit. It looks interesting, as every revolution brings the T match closer to a match. Think about it. A T match ATU where roller coaster and variables rotate all at once. This one is good but might require a stronger stepper or higher supply voltage as more power will be needed.

"I am sure there is spare I/O on the PIC. We were going to make it remember the frequency and where it went to match the loop, for a quicker auto tune. RF on the board caused a bit of trouble and so we dropped this. Some one out there might like to tinker with the program and make it go in reverse for a second before it goes forward to try and match. This would enable a QSY feature. We never fully mastered it because it tended to go unstable on us.

"At 12V operation the stepper has just enough power to do what we asked of it. Fit for purpose. If your variable capacitor does not turn freely then a bigger motor might be needed. BFY51s will switch a lot more current than we asked from them for the stepper motor we used." You may well need a bit more 'oomph' if you were driving a vacuum capacitor to tune the loop.

**REFERENCES**

[1] www.brats-qth.org
(you need to be a member to access the project files)
[2] gw.woo@btinternet.com
[3] g3ldo@o2.co.uk

# Antennas

## Downsizing, the G4LQI multiband antenna and a planning saga

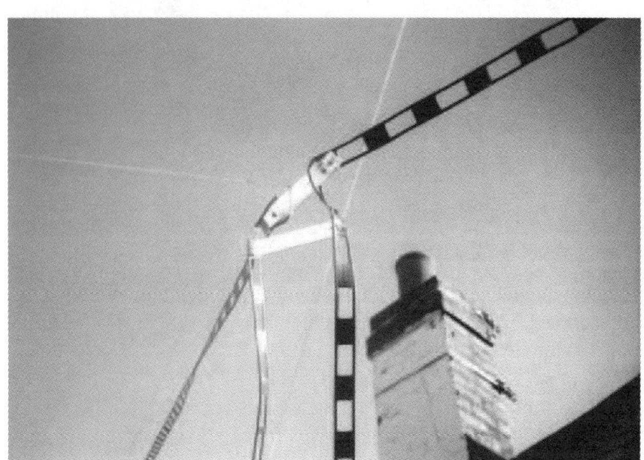

PHOTO 1: The arrangement of the feeders used in the G4LQI quad-plane antenna.

**GETTING SMALLER.** With advancing years, many of us are faced with the prospect of having to downsize. My garden is over 200ft long and 40ft wide (61m x 12m), has a large hedge running the full length of it plus trees and lawns. This poses maintenance tasks that are within my capabilities now – but will I be able to handle it 5 years hence? If I moved, I would miss my multiband quad and all the space for making and testing antennas.

The XYL is talking about a bungalow with a modest garden, which doesn't appeal to me at all. Erwin David, G3LQI e-mailed me with a possible solution. He says, "With old age creeping up, we had to move from our beachfront house to a 3rd (top) floor flat, albeit one with a wrap-around balcony. Gone is my 500W linear; I would not dare to use one in an apartment building and anyway I could not lift it any more.

"I am pleasantly surprised by what quarter-wave whips on the balcony railing counterpoise will do from 14MHz up. On 7MHz I just have a 10m wire, 7m from that railing up at a slant to the top of a flagpole and 3m down in another direction. With my 100W I can work all I can hear. Bottom-loaded with 23 turns on a 3in red Amidon toroid, that wire can be made to resonate on 3.7MHz. I have even been able to check into the Trans Canada PowWow Club (3.75MHz SSB at 0500Z, the control station in Central Ontario using a four-square) when conditions are halfway decent."

**THE G4LQI QUAD-PLANE MULTIBAND HF ANTENNA** Also contained in G4LQI's e-mail was a description of an antenna he had used at his previous QTH, which you might find useful. It is described as a quad-plane multiband HF antenna with a bonus. The upper half of the antenna is a quad loop. The lower half comprises horizontal radials or counterpoises, which makes an excellent space and height saving antenna. It is essentially a vertically polarised DX antenna but with additional characteristics. This antenna arrangement has the following advantages:

- Shack-tuneable 3.5 to 30MHz with vertically polarised broadside radiation on all bands
- No outdoor pruning, tuning or weatherproofing
- Two shack-selectable horizontally polarised 'bonus' modes of operation, created by judicial arrangement of feeders.

The physical dimensions and layout are shown in **Figure 1**. The antenna was constructed using 1.5mm PVC-covered stranded copper wire. The feeders are of 450Ω slotted twin lead, chosen because of the greater strength of its Copperweld wire, although 300Ω slotted twin lead would serve the same purpose. Where two twin leads run parallel with each other they can be spaced anywhere from 2 to 15cm using spreaders, as shown in **Photo 1**. Enough spreaders should be used to roughly maintain the chosen spacing in rough weather. The feeders should also be kept away from energy-absorbing walls by several times the chosen spreader length.

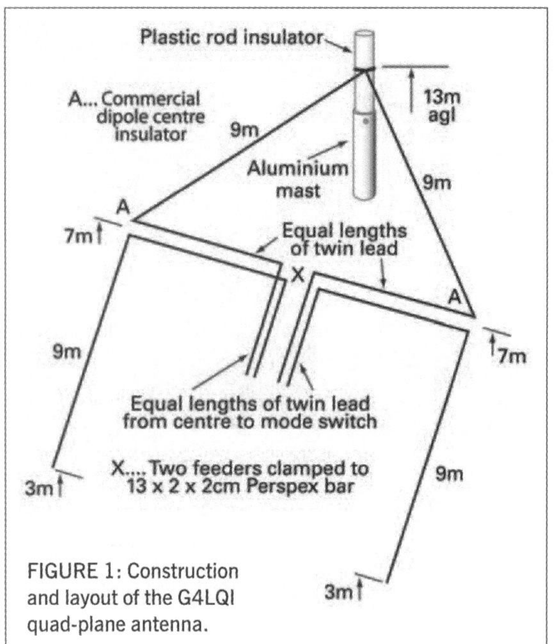


FIGURE 1: Construction and layout of the G4LQI quad-plane antenna.

**MODES OF OPERATION.** The various modes of operation of this antenna are shown in **Figure 2**. Mode 'A' is the basic 'quad-plane', which is vertically polarised and good for East/West DX on bands 7-28MHz. It's also good for ground wave 28 & 29MHz. The 9m leg length was chosen to have a vertical component of approximately 5/8 wavelength on 29MHz. This size fitted the available space and promised efficient quad operation on all bands from 7 to 29MHz. It can be tuned to 3.5MHz, but inadequate leg length and wire size means that it is not an efficient radiator on this band.

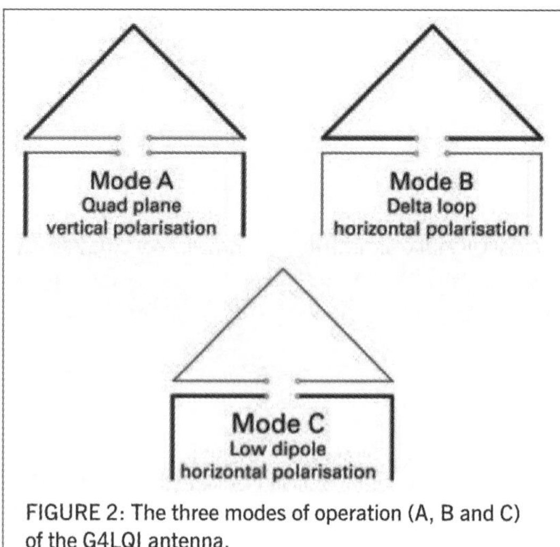


FIGURE 2: The three modes of operation (A, B and C) of the G4LQI antenna.

In mode 'B' the antenna is a horizontally polarised delta loop consisting of the two upper quad-plane legs and one side of each feeder. G4LQI found this mode useful for European contacts on 14 & 21MHz and occasionally for DX reception in heavy local QRN.

In mode 'C' the

antenna is a low horizontal U-shaped dipole consisting of the 'other' side of each feeder, end-loaded by the lower legs of the quad-plane. This results in a 30m long centre-fed wire which is effective for short skip on 3.5 & 7MHz.

The feeders entered the shack through two 38mm PVC conduits inserted through the brickwork. Each conduit was capped on both ends. A slot to fit the twin lead was cut into each cap. After installation of the feeders all outside openings were sealed with bathtub sealer.

The mode switch was located just inside the feeder entrance. G4LQI used a receiver-sized ceramic switch, which withstood 400W PEP without problems. A four pole-switch with at least three positions is required.

This antenna used a balance feed, so an ATU designed for balanced feeders was required. G4LQI used a KW E-Zee match, which provided a good match on all bands. He cautioned against using an unbalanced tuner with a ferrite or powdered iron core balun on the grounds that these types of baluns are generally not suitable for the high impedance levels encountered in this system on some bands. He recommends an air-wound type.

I had heard of this concern before so when I went on holiday (see below) with an IC-706 and a simple centre fed antenna I wondered how the diminutive MJF-901B ATU would cope, because it had a very small toroid ring transformer balun. After several hours operation on several bands I checked out the balun and it was just slightly warm. I wondered if it was doing anything, so I bypassed it – and got an RF 'bite' from the ATU chassis for my efforts.

So how did the quad-plane antenna work out? G4LQI says it's "very hard to compare the new system with something that one had to tear down to make room for the new. I previously had a full-size G5RV on the same masts, which I also used as a top-loaded vertical for DX on 3.5MHz, a VK2ABQ beam for 14, 21 & 28MHz, 8m high. I missed neither for my DX working, most of which was towards the West. Short-skip around Europe and local working were well provided for."

**HEIGHT MATTERS.** Some years ago I operated from a 5th (top) floor apartment in Eindhoven. I was using a single band (14MHz) homebrew transceiver running about 80W and I used a simple dipole stuck out over the balcony using a bamboo stick. It worked exceptionally well.

More recently I operated from Marrakech from a hotel room. It wasn't a tall building; it had just three floors. The shack was located on the top floor and there was a flat roof above. I installed a 20m long wire supported in the centre with a telescopic fishing pole I had brought with me for the purpose. I fed the wire in the centre with 400Ω ladder line. The rig was an IC-706 and the antenna was fed using an MJF-901B ATU. Again, this worked very well.

My view is that it is much more important *where* an antenna is than *what* it is. If you are planning to downsize, a location with a bit of height might be the answer, but do check out the restrictions on putting up antennas.

**PLANNING RESTRICTIONS.** While on the subject of planning restrictions, many years ago I was forced into applying for planning permission on my antenna mast after a complaint from a distant neighbour. This planning application was refused because of the activities of this neighbour, who orchestrated opposition. I did eventually obtain planning permission on appeal, although it had a couple of restrictions. One of these was that the mast must be folded down during the hours of daylight. I objected on the grounds that this meant it had to be raised and lowered in the dark, which posed a safety issue. The council changed the wording so that the mast could only be raised during hours of darkness plus one hour after sunrise and one before sunset! I went along with it, knowing that such a restriction is nearly impossible to police.

I live on a private estate. Most of the neighbours are elderly/retired and I get on very well with most of them. Over the years, all those who made lots of noise about my antenna, including the original complainant, have died. Since then I have had no problems, although I am not sure whether it is a case of indifference or fear that the Curse of the Multi-band Quad will strike again.

The fold-over mast is counterweighted so that it can be folded over or raised in about 30 seconds using a rope – no winch is required. The multiband quad currently fitted to this mast, shown in **Photo 2**, can be used when the mast is folded over, in which case it is vertically polarised (although it can only beam north or south). The most noticeable characteristic if the antenna in the vertical polarised mode is that it is that the noise level is higher and the signals from the numerous short skip stations are weaker.

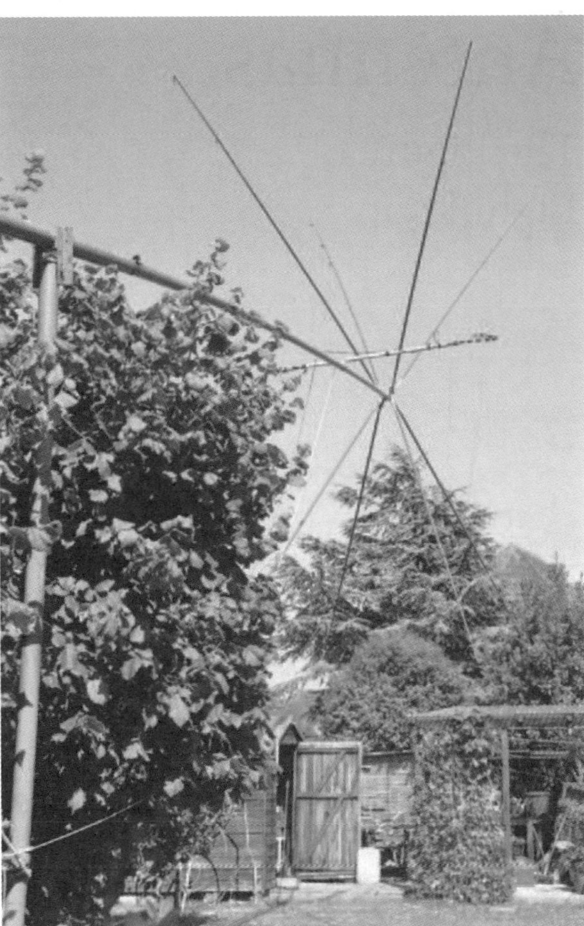

PHOTO 2: The G3LDO multiband quad on the folded over mast.

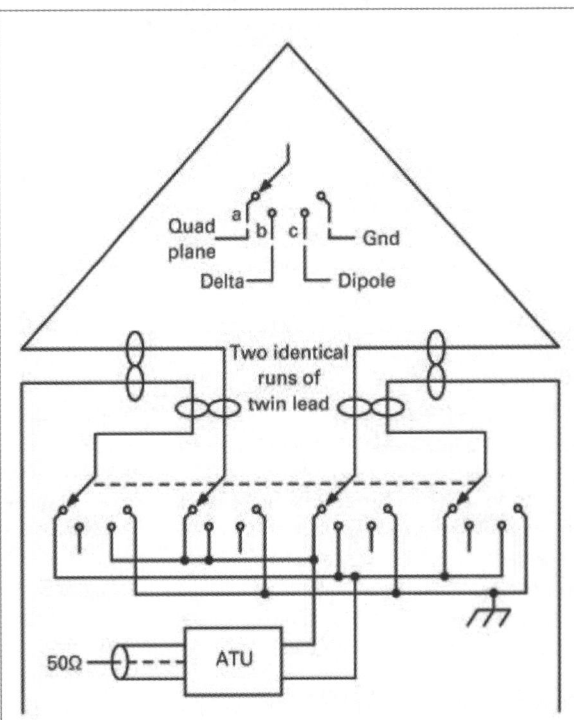


FIGURE 3: The mode selection switch used in the G4LQI quad-plane antenna. The 'earth' position is optional.

# Antennas

## The Figure of Eight Loop

PHOTO 1: GM0SDV's figure of eight loop HF antenna.

**NOVEL LOOP.** This month I will be describing a rather unusual antenna that was built by Victor Borisov, GM0SDV. The antenna, shown in **Photo 1**, comprises a figure of eight loop constructed from 22mm copper tube. Each loop is one metre in diameter and the total size of the antenna is 100 x 200 x 19cm. It covers a frequency range of 13.5 to 31MHz and therefore includes all bands from 14 to 28MHz. It is tuned with a capacitor in a manner similar to a conventional magnetic loop. The capacitor is controlled using a conventional motor control box as shown in **Photo 2**. Initial tests showed that this antenna's characteristics are very similar to a conventional loop. Some other issues were raised while trying to obtain comparative data and some of these will be discussed.

**EUROTEK.** This figure of eight loop design is not new. Last month I described an antenna designed and built by Erwin David, G4LQI. What I omitted to mention was that Erwin used to write the Eurotek column for *RadCom*, using his linguistic skills to translate work from Dutch, German and French radio magazines. One of these items was an article by Fritz H V Geerligs, PA0FRI, published in the Dutch magazine *Electron* in January 1997. This gave details of a figure of eight loop antenna, which was described as a 'Meight' (magnetic 8) antenna. A VHF version of this antenna is shown in **Figure 1**. The objective of the design was to improve the SWR bandwidth and efficiency compared to a single loop antenna.

**PA9OK.** At a later date Otto Kühn, PA9OK [1] worked on the PA0FRI eight-shaped magnetic loop. Many experimental designs were tested to gain experience for building a double loop for HF.

PA0OK went on to say "The reason for using a double loop is that two magnetic fields enhance each other, and because the two loops are in parallel, the impedance at the tuning point will be lower and the bandwidth greater compared to a single loop. The narrow bandwidth of a single loop, just a few kHz, makes tuning difficult. A loop's perimeter, in this case the sum of both perimeters, determines the antenna's inductance. This should be borne in mind when calculating the size of the coupling loop. The two loops, exactly equal in size and calculated for a certain frequency, are tuned to the frequency band by a capacitor. The loops are 180° out of phase relative to one another. The experiments with the small eight-shaped VHF loop have shown that its practical behaviour is in reasonable agreement with theory".

**LOOP MODEL.** I wasn't all that sure about all of the above statement so I constructed a computer model of this antenna (**Figure 2**) to see what EZNEC had to say about this strange configuration. The purpose of the model was to see how the azimuth field strength pattern and the SWR curve compared with the real world. There were two considerations: first of all, it was free space model. Secondly, the model does not use a transmission line matching arrangement.

The free space model is the simplest method of determining the relative gains of antennas. The gain of a free space dipole is 2.14dBi but, with resistive losses, it is probably just over 2dBi. By comparison, a model of the GM0SDV antenna on 18MHz resulted in a free space gain of 1.08dBi, ie a loss of 0.92dB relative to a dipole, see **Figure 3**.

The transmission line matching is, for simplicity, overcome by using a transmission line impedance that matches the antenna. In this case the model exhibits an impedance at resonance of just over 1Ω so, in the simulation, I used a transmission line with an impedance of 1Ω. You won't find any of this material in the real world but it is fine for making a model and it allowed me to plot an SWR curve, as shown in **Figure 4**, without having to worry about a suitable matching arrangement. EZNEC calculates the impedances around resonance, which are then converted into SWR readings.

**CONSTRUCTION.** The antenna arrived as a kit of parts, as shown in **Photo 3**. It is comprises pre-formed semicircular sections of 22mm copper tubing. This arrangement means that the tube connections are made simply by using straight compression couplings. The preformed half loops mean that the antenna can be dismantled easily for installing into a restricted opening loft space or for transporting by car to a portable site.

The capacitor is specially designed and constructed by GM0SDV and is housed in the grey cylindrical plastic container shown in Photo 1. It comprises a butterfly arrangement as shown in **Photo 4** and has a capacity range of 16 to 126pF with a fixed-to-variable plate spacing of 3mm. Because a butterfly arrangement is used the total fixed-to-fixed plate spacing is 6mm. The butterfly capacitor arrangement overcomes the problem of rotating connection resistance that would occur if a conventional tuning capacitor were used. The capacitor is driven by a DC motor through a reduction gear. The capacitor tuning speed from minimum to maximum is 17 seconds on the control box HIGH setting and 40 seconds on the LOW setting.

The loop is matched to the transmission line using the small loop that can be seen in Photo 1.

**OPERATION.** Initial checks showed that the matching arrangement was good over most of the frequency range, being less than 1.05:1 on most bands and rising to 1.5:1 on the 10m band. Interestingly, the SWR curve at 14MHz (**Figure 5**) has a similar V shaped characteristic to the computed one shown in Figure 4, although the SWR bandwidths are different.

Tuning is quite straightforward. The loop is tuned for maximum receiver noise using

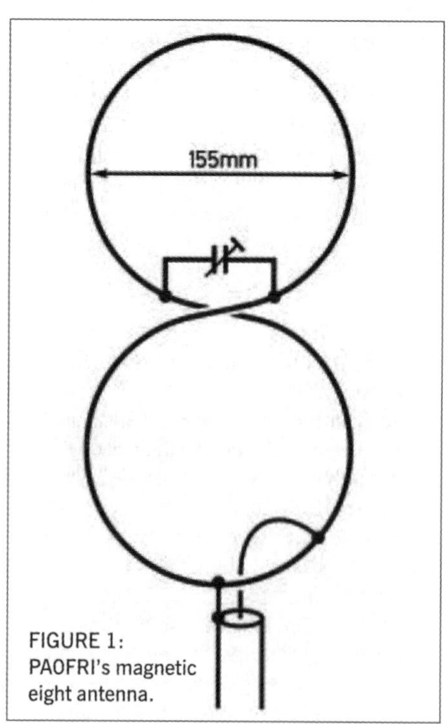


FIGURE 1: PA0FRI's magnetic eight antenna.

PHOTO 2: Control box for the GM0SDV antenna.

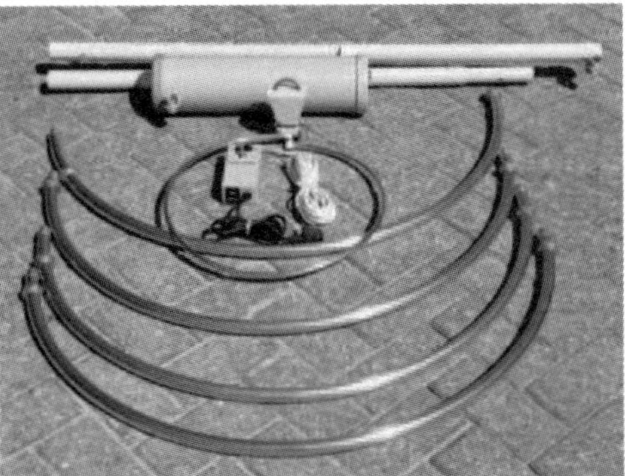

PHOTO 3: The kit of parts for the GM0SDV antenna.

PHOTO 4: The loop tuning capacitor.

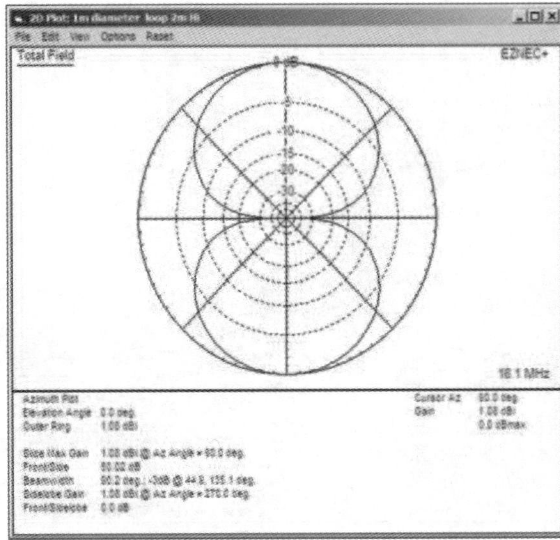


FIGURE 3: Free space azimuth field strength diagram of the GM0SDV antenna.

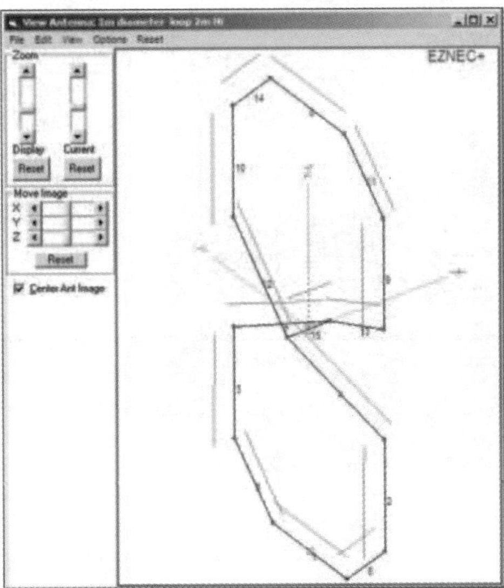


FIGURE 2: EZNEC free space model of the GM0SDV antenna. All the wires used to make up the model are straight so the model is constructed as a hexagon.

TUNING switch with the SPEED switch set to HIGH, then tuned for lowest SWR using the LOW speed setting.

I tested the antenna running 200W from an FT-990 with no obvious problems. GM0SDV tells me that he tested loop with 400W for 20 minutes without any arcing or SWR drift.

**COMPARATIVE TESTS.** The initial tests were done with the feedpoint of the loop around 1.5m high. I used this antenna to make QSOs around Europe. I found no difficulty in tuning the loop when QSYing to different frequencies and bands. The loop exhibited 14dB nulls on 14MHz in field strength tests. Improved SWR figures, see **Figure 5**, resulted when the loop was placed on the flat roof of the house extension (about 3m high).

These tests coincided with very poor DX conditions (late July and early August). Additionally the weather took a turn for the worse, with some very heavy rain. The SWR on all bands increased to greater than 1.5:1 so, at the time of writing, the antenna has been dismantled for inspection. The surfaces of the copper elements of this antenna have tarnished very quickly in the sea air around here so I need to see if this is a factor.

GM0SDV claims that he obtains a 1 to 2 S-point improvement on receive and transmit (particularly on DX) using the figure of eight loop compared with a conventional loop. I have not been able to verify this because of the difficulties described above but I hope to have more information for the next month's Antennas. His figure of eight antenna is to be distributed by KMK UK Ltd **[2]**.

I note that PA9OK found that a VHF figure of eight antenna was 3dB better than a conventional VHF loop.

**ENGINEERING.** Constructing antennas for HF normally requires fairly modest engineering facilities. Most of us get by with just a screwdriver, hacksaw, a set of spanners, an electric drill plus a selection of bits and a vice. When I was writing the RSGB Mobile Handbook I really wanted to test out a mobile 'screwdriver' antenna but had neither the money to buy one or the engineering facilities to make one.

While visiting a local rally I came across GM0SDV's antenna stall and bought a screwdriver antenna that he had constructed – for around a third of the price of what was currently available. GM0SDV's hobby is apparently building antennas that require some engineering skill and selling them to finance further experimental work. The quality of the workmanship can be seen in the motorised capacitor shown in Photo 4. He also has facilities for forming thick copper tubing into semicircles, see Photo 3.

I have suggested that he provides an engineering service for building antenna and linear amplifier components.

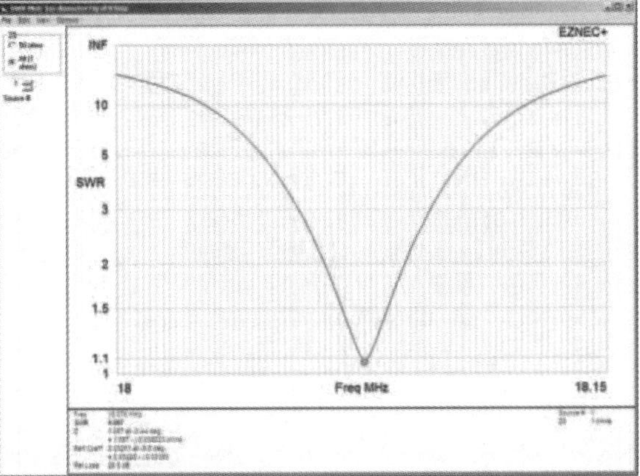


FIGURE 4: The modelled SWR curve of the GM0SDV antenna.

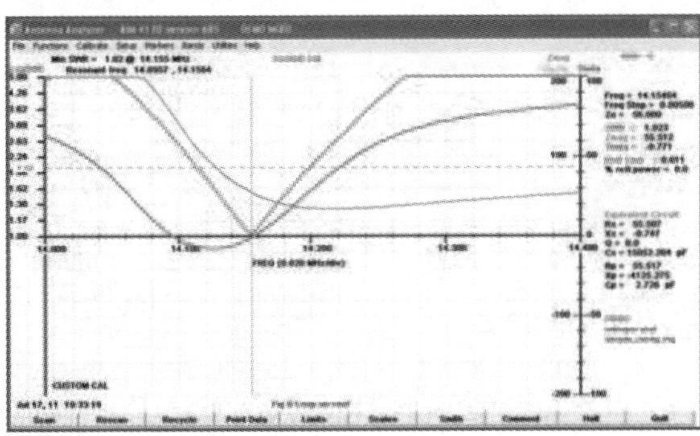

FIGURE 5: Measured impedance and SWR characteristic of the GM0SDV antenna on 14MHz.

For further discussion he can be contacted via **[3]**.

WEBSEARCH

[1] PA9OK's website
– http://pa9ok.nl/pages/magnetic-loop-for-hf.php
[2] KMK UK Ltd – www.mixw.co.uk
[3] gm0sdv@gmail.com

# Antennas

## Tools for ascertaining antenna performance

PHOTO 1: Location of the two antennas tested using *WSPR*.

**RECAP.** Last month I looked at a figure of eight loop antenna constructed from 22mm copper tube, built by Victor Borisov, GM0SDV. I obtained impedance and SWR characteristics of this antenna, however comparative tests were held over because of very poor DX conditions that existed at the time (late July and early August). Conditions improved later so further progress was possible.

The whole exercise obliged me to re examine some of my test methods and I will describe two easily available tools used in this project.

*WSPR. Weak Signal Propagation Reporter* [1] is a free software application that can enable your station to send and receive signals from similarly-equipped stations worldwide. Participating stations usually upload signals that they receive in real time to a web server [2], so you can find out within seconds exactly where and how strongly each transmission was received. It is these reports that are of interest. The station reporting the signals, together with location and distance from my QTH, are shown in each row. The most important information, the received signals, is reported as signal to noise ratio (SNR), rather than a specific signal level. Remember that these signals are very weak; often way below what is audible in the CW mode. In an earlier edition of Antennas I advocated the use of *WSPR* as a method of testing antennas [3] by comparing the performance of multiband dipole on the roof with a multiband quad.

On this occasion the *WSPR* method was used to compare the performance of the GM0SDV loop (positioned on the roof of the house extension) against a multiband antenna on the chimney of the house, as shown in **Photo 1**. Each antenna was connected to the radio in turn. First impressions gave the dipole the advantage on mainly short skip EU stations.

The *WSPR* tests coincided with an improvement in transatlantic DX conditions; a DX path is a more critical test for an antenna than a short skip path. This test resulted in 69 separate SNR reports of my 2W transmitted signal measured over a period of nearly one and a half hours. This data was imported from [3] as a text file, edited to remove most much of the data regarded as not applicable for this test then imported into *Excel*, shown in **Figure 1**. The most important data is the SNR figure (in blue); smaller SNR negative numbers mean stronger signals. *Excel* is ideal for calculating the average SNR.

The average data from the dipole and the loop were -16.74 and -17.0dB SNR respectively, meaning that the performances of the two antennas were very similar. This surprised me, considering the locations of the antennas (Photo 1).

A perceived weakness of this method is that a superior antenna in the test can radiate a signal that can be measured by a distant station that is not measurable by a signal from the comparison inferior antenna. This measured signal would probably have a marginally high SNR level. In a statistical list would tend to increase the overall SNR (reduce the perceived performance) of the superior antenna. The fix is to use data only from stations that report signals from both antennas.

**A COMPUTER MODEL OF A LOOP.** I previously described [1] building a computer model to examine the characteristics of the GM0SDV figure of eight loop antenna using *EZNEC 5*. What follows is a brief description of how this was done, although a conventional small loop antenna is the subject of this model. Originally I was dissuaded from using computer modelling for examining small loops following a comment by W7EL **[4]** because *NEC-2* (the computing engine of *EZNEC*) is unable to accurately model small loop antennas. However later versions of the program are better able to handle small loops

| | A | B | C | D | E | F | G | H | I |
|---|---|---|---|---|---|---|---|---|---|
| 1 | | DIPOLE | | | | | LOOP | | |
| 2 | Time | Freq | S/N | Call | | Time | Freq | S/N | Call |
| 3 | 21:42 | 14.09703 | -6 | VE4KE | | 21:06 | 14.09703 | -15 | VE4KE |
| 4 | 21:42 | 14.097047 | -17 | K0GUN | | 21:06 | 14.09703 | -14 | K9AN |
| 5 | 21:42 | 14.097029 | -12 | K9AN | | 21:06 | 14.09704 | -16 | W3GXT |
| 6 | 21:36 | 14.097034 | -24 | W2GNN | | 21:06 | 14.09704 | -21 | K5DNL |
| 7 | 21:36 | 14.097032 | -11 | VE4KE | | 21:06 | 14.09704 | -27 | W2GNN |
| 8 | 21:28 | 14.097033 | -18 | VE4KE | | 21:06 | 14.097 | -19 | WA3DNM |
| 9 | 21:12 | 14.097044 | -26 | K5DNL | | 21:02 | 14.09703 | -26 | KE7A |
| 10 | 21:28 | 14.09703 | -12 | K9AN | | 21:02 | 14.09705 | -21 | K0GUN |
| 11 | 21:24 | 14.097026 | -21 | W5CGC | | 21:02 | 14.09703 | -12 | K9AN |
| 12 | 21:24 | 14.097033 | -25 | W3GXT | | 21:02 | 14.09703 | -20 | W5CGC |
| 13 | 21:24 | 14.09703 | -15 | K9AN | | 21:02 | 14.09704 | -18 | K5DNL |
| 14 | 21:24 | 14.097031 | -4 | VE4KE | | 21:02 | 14.09703 | -10 | VE4KE |
| 15 | 21:24 | 14.097049 | -20 | K0GUN | | 21:02 | 14.097 | -16 | WA3DNM |
| 16 | 21:20 | 14.09703 | -16 | K9AN | | 21:02 | 14.09703 | -11 | W3GXT |
| 17 | 21:20 | 14.097049 | -19 | K0GUN | | 21:02 | 14.09703 | -21 | W2GNN |
| 18 | 21:20 | 14.09703 | -11 | VE4KE | | 21:00 | 14.09705 | -22 | K0GUN |
| 19 | 21:20 | 14.097036 | -23 | W2GNN | | 21:00 | 14.09704 | -20 | K5DNL |
| 20 | 21:12 | 14.097051 | -18 | K0GUN | | 21:00 | 14.09703 | -16 | W5CGC |
| 21 | 21:12 | 14.097031 | -12 | K9AN | | 21:00 | 14.09703 | -15 | K9AN |
| 22 | 21:12 | 14.097033 | -9 | VE4KE | | 21:00 | 14.09703 | -27 | WA5VRO |
| 23 | 21:12 | 14.097036 | -17 | W3GXT | | 21:00 | 14.09703 | -10 | VE4KE |
| 24 | 20:30 | 14.09703 | -9 | VE4KE | | 20:56 | 14.09705 | -26 | N5WY |
| 25 | 20:30 | 14.097033 | -23 | W3GXT | | 20:56 | 14.09703 | -13 | W5CGC |
| 26 | 20:30 | 14.097033 | -27 | K1JT | | 20:56 | 14.09704 | -16 | K5DNL |
| 27 | 20:30 | 14.097047 | -19 | K0GUN | | 20:56 | 14.09703 | -13 | K9AN |
| 28 | 20:30 | 14.09703 | -21 | K9AN | | 20:56 | 14.09703 | -16 | W3GXT |
| 29 | 20:26 | 14.097029 | -11 | K9AN | | 20:48 | 14.09704 | -20 | K5DNL |
| 30 | 20:26 | 14.097027 | -29 | W5CGC | | 20:48 | 14.09703 | -7 | VE4KE |
| 31 | 20:26 | 14.097032 | -13 | VE4KE | | 20:48 | 14.09703 | -11 | K9AN |
| 32 | 20:26 | 14.097047 | -21 | K0GUN | | 20:48 | 14.09703 | -26 | W3GXT |
| 33 | 20:24 | 14.097029 | -10 | K9AN | | 20:46 | 14.09703 | -15 | K9AN |
| 34 | | | | | | 20:46 | 14.09703 | -7 | VE4KE |
| 35 | Total | -519 | Average | -16.74194 | | 20:46 | 14.09703 | -26 | W3GXT |
| 36 | | | | | | 20:40 | 14.09703 | -11 | K9AN |
| 37 | | | | | | 20:40 | 14.09703 | -20 | W5CGC |
| 38 | | | | | | 20:40 | 14.09703 | -7 | VE4KE |
| 39 | | | | | | 20:34 | 14.09703 | -22 | W3GXT |
| 40 | | | | | | 20:34 | 14.09703 | -13 | K9AN |
| 41 | | | | | | | | | |
| 42 | | | | | | Total | -646 | Average | -17 |

FIGURE 1: *Excel* computation of average SNR, using 69 separate DX signals-to-noise reports of my transmission, measured by other stations over a period of nearly one and a half hours.

than previous ones and the following is a method of building such a model.

**BUILDING AND USING THE MODEL.** All actions are controlled from a Control Panel window, seen at the top left of **Figure 2**. All antenna models are built using straight line wires and a wires window is opened by clicking on Wires, top right in Figure 2. Each wire end is fixed with X, Y and Z spatial coordinates (ie two coordinate sets per wire). As the model is built, progress can be seen in the View Antennas window, bottom right in Figure 2, by clicking View Ant on the Control Panel.

Building a wire in free space to simulate a dipole is quite simple but arranging 8 wires to form loop requires some practice. However, W7EL has provided a facility for building a loop, which is accessed by clicking Create/Loop in the Wires window. All you have to do is select the size of the loop and the number of wires. The model shown in Figure 2 is the result of selecting eight wires to make a hexagon structure.

A capacitor is required to tune the loop. This is inserted into the model by selecting Loads at the Control Panel, which creates a Loads window, bottom left of Figure 2. The load has been placed on wire 5 (top wire), 50% along its length. The load is then defined as a capacitor and assigned a value of 47.5pF. This load is shown as a small red square in Figure 2.

The feedpoint is selected by clicking Sources and selecting the wire (and position on the wire) to which it is to be connected. In this case it is connected to the centre of the bottom wire 1; this feedpoint is shown as a small red circle on the View Antenna box in Figure 2.

The transmission line matching is, for simplicity, overcome by using a transmission line impedance that matches the antenna, rather than the other way around. In this case the model exhibits an impedance at resonance of just over 0.1349Ω, so a transmission line with an impedance of 0.14Ω was used; this is entered at the Control Panel via AR SWR Z0.

The model is run by clicking FF Plot. This produces an azimuth, elevation or 3D field strength plot window (not shown in Figure 2) depending on the Plot Type selected at the Control Panel. The gain of the model is shown relative to a pre-selected dBi level. A pre-selected (blue) azimuth plot is shown superimposed on the View Antenna image in Figure 2.

Relative antenna current is also shown in the View Antenna window as magenta lines near the wires carrying the current. The current magnitude is represented as the space between the current line and the antenna element – in the case of this loop, the relatively constant space indicates that the current around the loop is also relatively constant.

Those of you who have experimented

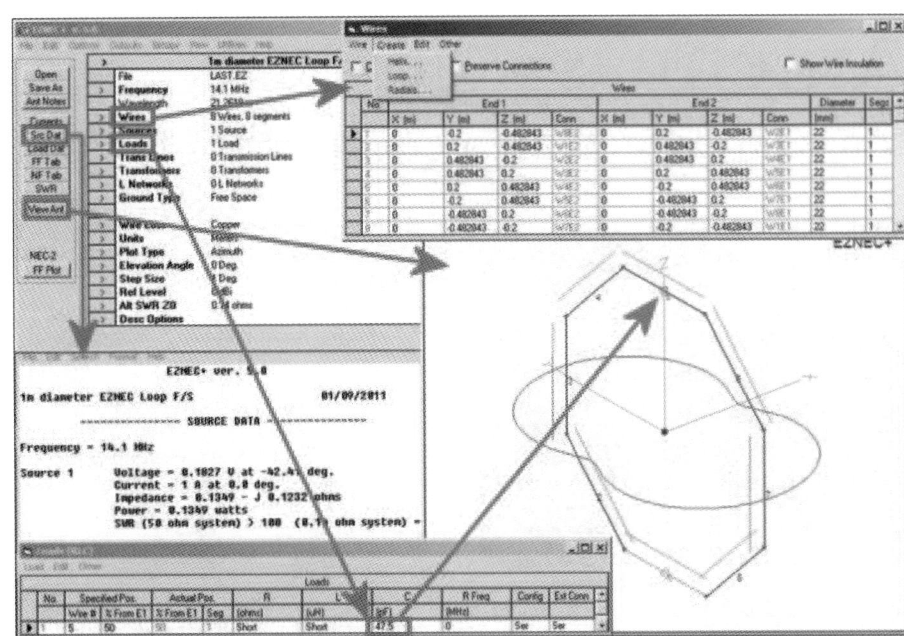

FIGURE 2: Screen display showing Control Panel, View Antenna, Wires, Source Data and Load windows while modelling a small loop antenna using *EZNEC* 5.

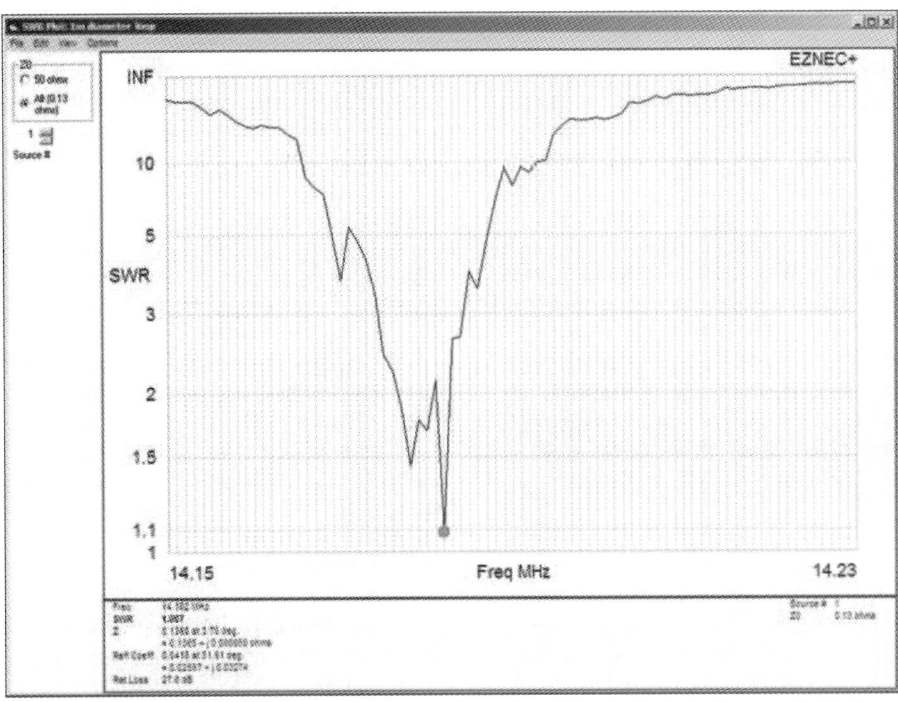


FIGURE 3: SWR plot of a small hexagon loop using 7 segments per wire. It shows inaccuracies in the impedance calculations from which this SWR plot was derived. Using 1 segment per wire produced much improved impedance calculations.

with this type of loop antenna might question the absence of the high voltage (which would be shown as low current in the model) known to exist across the tuning capacitor on a real loop. The reason is that in the model the capacitor is simply a mathematical entity with no physical dimensions. If the capacitor is constructed using two wire grids instead of a load, the high voltage will be represented as near zero currents on the extreme edges of the capacitor's surface.

A frequency sweep of the resonant section of the loop can also be performed. This calculates feed impedances over the frequency sweep range, which can be presented as an SWR curve by selecting SWR at the Control Panel. An SWR plot of a small hexagon loop using 7 segments per wire is shown in **Figure 3**, which shows inaccuracies in the impedance calculations from which this SWR plot was derived. When the model was modified to one segment per wire the impedance calculations were much improved. An example was illustrated in Figure 4 of last month's Antennas.

**WEBSEARCH**


[1] *WSPR*, written by Joe Taylor, K1JT. Obtainable at www.physics.princeton.edu/pulsar/K1JT

[2] http://wsprnet.org/olddb

[3] Antennas, *RadCom* November 2010

[4] *EZNEC 4* (which can model loops) comes free with *The ARRL Antenna Handbook* from the 21st Edition onwards. Available from RSGB Bookshop.

# Antennas

## Impedance measurement and the feedline problem

**PHOTO 1: General Radio 1606 RF impedance bridge. The indicated reactance value is valid for 1MHz and must be divided by actual frequency to get the true reactance. Inductive or capacitive reactance is established with the use of the switch located between the two dials.**

IMPEDANCE. An impedance matching arrangement is often necessary to match the feedpoint impedance of an antenna to its transmission line. Matching adjustment is mostly done with an SWR meter, which indirectly measures the degree of match or mismatch. A more direct method is to measure the actual impedance causing the mismatch, which gives a more informative picture of what is required of the matching arrangement. Impedance comprises both resistance and reactance, so it is always expressed in two parts, Z = R±jX. An impedance having a resistance of 75Ω and an inductive reactance of 50Ω is conventionally written as:

75 +j50

For our consideration, 'j' can simply be regarded as a convention for reactance; '+j' and '-j' indicating inductive and capacitive reactance respectively. When the frequency of the antenna is resonant, the +j and -j parts are equal and opposite so we are left with only the resistive component of impedance.

Impedance can be plotted using a chart with Cartesian coordinates (rather like a Mercator projection map), with the latitude and longitude of R and jX respectively plotted to define an impedance 'location' **[1]**. **Figure 1** shows an example; the impedance 75 +50jX is marked with a red X.

It follows that a number of impedance plots over a range of frequencies will result in a number of impedance points that can be plotted on the impedance graph to give an antenna impedance signature. Resonance, where the inductive and capacitive reactances are equal and opposite, exist on the zero reactance vertical line.

An instrument is required to measure the impedance so that it can be plotted on the impedance chart. The venerable General Radio 1606 Impedance Bridge shown in **Photo 1** was the instrument we all wished for in the early days. It has two calibrated scales: the one on the right is used to measure resistance while the scale on the left is calibrated in reactance. This instrument measures the impedance presented at the terminals just above the reactance scale.

THE SMITH CHART. A different type of impedance chart is shown in **Figure 2**, which shows the reactance and impedance lines as sections of an arc. The advantage of this Smith Chart arrangement is that the SWR circles are concentric **[2]**. If a calibrated cursor, pivoted at the centre, were to be used with this chart it would be very easy to obtain the SWR of any impedance on the chart.

If the impedance measurement of the antenna or matching network is made via a length coax it will be different from that presented at the measuring device because of the impedance transforming characteristic of transmission line. This transforming effect is illustrated in Figure 2, which uses a wavelength scale on the perimeter. Additionally, two lengths of coax cable terminated with a 25Ω resistor are shown against the chart. A length of coax 0.25 wavelengths long terminated will transform the 25Ω load to 100 j0 (at point A). If the length is increased to 0.375 wavelengths the transformed impedance will be approximately 40 –j30 (point B). A half wave length takes us back to the original load value of 25Ω, illustrating the one-to-one transform.

MEASURING ANTENNA R +JX VIA COAX. It follows that antenna impedance can be measured via an electrical half wavelength (or multiple) of feeder. **[3]**. From the above it is obvious that this one-to-one transform is only valid at one particular wavelength or frequency but in practice it is useable over a single HF band.

On the other hand if the length and velocity factor of the coax is known, the antenna feed impedance can be determined from the measured impedance by using appropriate formula. This computation is not simple and, in 1939, P H Smith published the design of his famous chart **[4]** to ease these calculations. The simplified version, shown in Figure 2, gives some idea of how the calculation is accomplished. Full size professional Smith Charts require some skill and experience to use, however just in the same way that computers have eclipsed slide rules, the same can be said for the Smith Chart. There are many programs available for performing these transmission line calculations. One of these is TLW, which comes free with the *ARRL Antenna Handbook*.

AIM 4170 CUSTOM CALIBRATION. Instruments are now available that have built in transmission line calculators and the AIM 4170, designed by Bob Clunn, W5BIG, is one of them. This feature requires that the feeder between the instrument and the antenna be calibrated so that it presents a one-to-one transform over the calibrated frequency range. You can appreciate this is a huge improvement of on the methods so far described.

Each length of coax line used for measuring

TABLE 1: Excerpt from example calibration data for the AIM 4170.

| Index | Real | ±j | Frequency (MHz) |
|---|---|---|---|
| 0 | 55.1579 | -49.7761 | 5.600000 |
| 1 | 54.4949 | -42.1281 | 5.800000 |
| 2 | 53.9956 | -35.2165 | 6 |
| 3 | 53.6601 | -29.0413 | 6.200000 |
| 4 | 53.4882 | -23.6027 | 6.400000 |
| 5 | 53.3115 | -18.4841 | 6.600000 |
| 6 | 53.1811 | -13.7135 | 6.800000 |
| 7 | 53.1344 | -9.1917 | 7 |
| 8 | 53.1322 | -4.8476 | 7.200000 |
| 9 | 53.1648 | -0.5855 | 7.400000 |
| 10 | 53.2016 | 3.6467 | 7.600000 |
| 11 | 53.3369 | 7.8935 | 7.800000 |
| 12 | 53.5593 | 12.3199 | 8 |
| 13 | 53.7244 | 16.6331 | 8.200000 |
| 14 | 54.0005 | 21.3498 | 8.400000 |
| 15 | 54.3822 | 26.3818 | 8.600000 |
| 16 | 54.8341 | 31.7333 | 8.800000 |

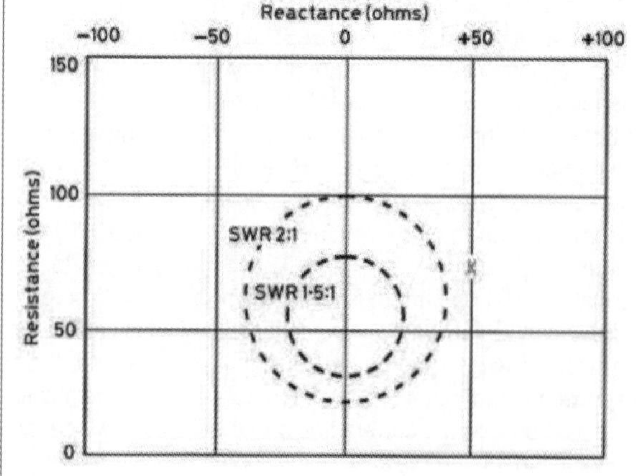


FIGURE 1: Impedance chart using Cartesian coordinates. Resistance is given on the vertical axis and reactance on the horizontal axis. X indicates an impedance of 75 +50jX. The circles represent SWRs of 1.5:1 and 2:1 for 50Ω coaxial cable.

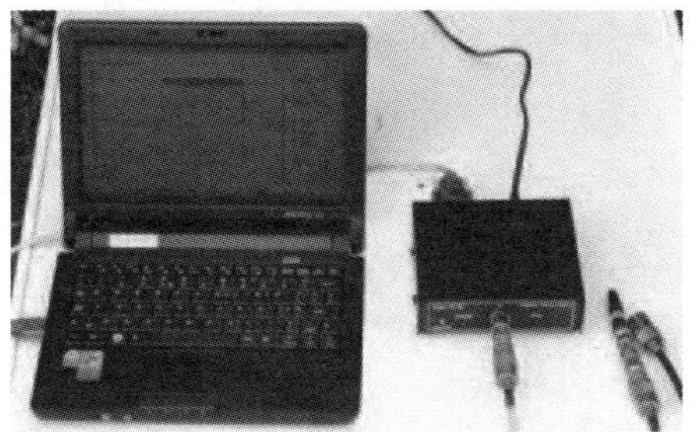

PHOTO 2: Calibrating lengths of coax using the AIM 4170. Each length of cable is colour coded and identified in the calibration file name.

the characteristics of an antenna has to be calibrated. For example I have several lengths of feeder that require calibration. There is the feeder to the quad, two feeders on my mobile installation (HF and VHF) and three additional separate feeders used for testing any HF and VHF antenna that might come my way.

The frequency range of the calibration is specified by the user entering the custom calibration START and STOP frequencies. Within this frequency range a number of frequency points labelled STEP are specified. These are the frequencies where the calibration calculation is actually made and are known as 'delta frequency' in the AIM 4170 literature. After each of these limits is entered, there are prompts to attach the short, open and resistor calibration loads. After calibration, a scan is done automatically (without plotting the data) to see if the custom calibration data is likely to be accurate enough for a particular measurement.

I have separate calibration files for each coax cable length mentioned above. Sometimes I need to check the limits of the data to ensure that it is applicable for the job in hand. The calibration file can be viewed using a text editor such as *Notebook*. An example of a part of a calibration file can be seen in **Table 1**.

In general, transmission lines and antennas with narrow bandwidth will need more calibration points. The idea is to have calibration data with a smooth transition between the points. Although the gaps between the cal points are interpolated, this interpolation will not be smooth if these gaps are too wide. When the external circuit has rapid changes in phase (such as a filter), the custom delta frequency has to be small enough to include data during the phase transitions.

The AIM 4170 also has a Smith Chart display. This is a useful feature for checking the accuracy of this type of instrument. The display shown in **Figure 3** is Smith Chart superimposed on a swept frequency graph that is the result of measuring a 100Ω resistor at the end of a length of RG58 over the frequency range 30 to 47MHz.

The green circle is a SWR 2:1 marker. It can be seen that the actual plot (shown in red) is a smooth circle indicating the data is good; any measurement errors will cause irregularities in the smoothness of this plot. The start and stop SWR values don't meet exactly because of coax cable loss.

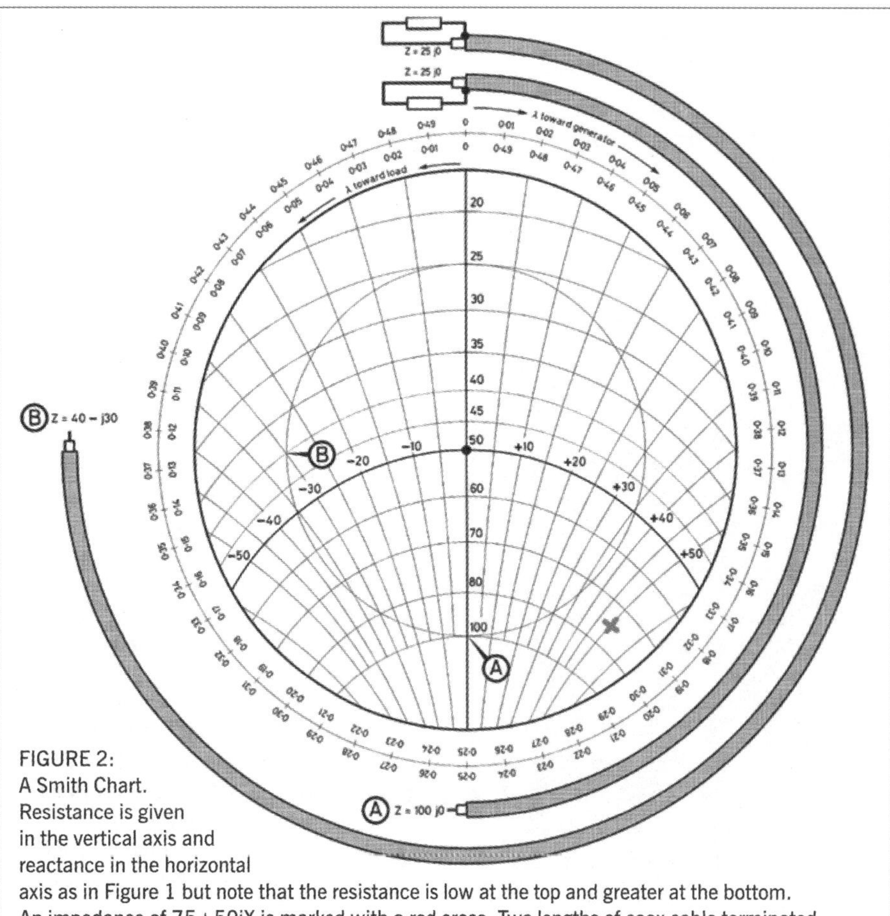


FIGURE 2: A Smith Chart. Resistance is given in the vertical axis and reactance in the horizontal axis as in Figure 1 but note that the resistance is low at the top and greater at the bottom. An impedance of 75+50jX is marked with a red cross. Two lengths of coax cable terminated with a 25Ω resistor superimposed on the chart to illustrate impedance transformation.

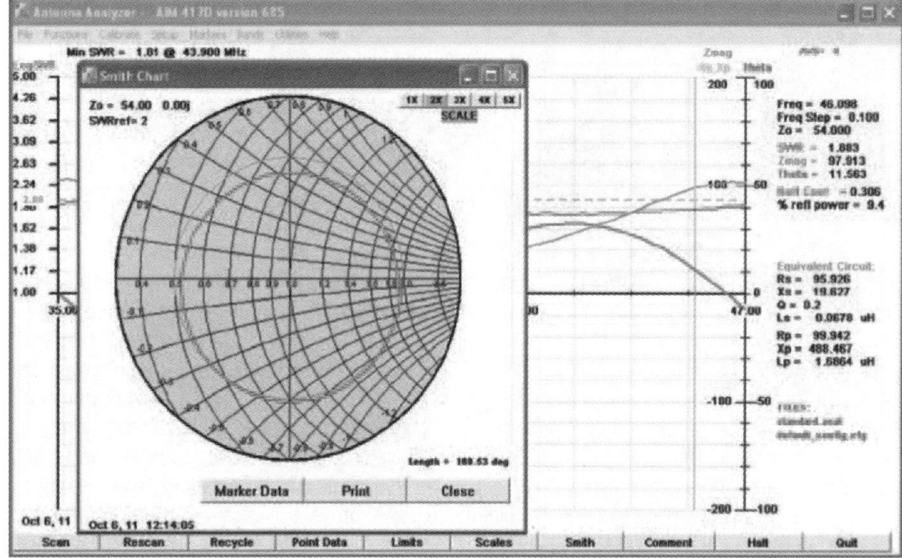


FIGURE 3: A Smith Chart superimposed on swept frequency graph being the result of measuring a 100Ω resistor over a length of RG58 over a frequency range 30 to 47MHz.

The Smith Chart shown in Figure 3 uses a normalised scale, where 50Ω is represented by 1, 25Ω by 0.5 and 100Ω by 2 etc. Additionally it uses the more modern convention where the resistance (real) scale is in the horizontal plane, with the low impedance (or short) to the left.

**FINALLY.** I would like to extend to you all best wishes for Christmas and good antenna experimenting in 2012.

NOTES AND REFERENCES

[1] Impedance can also be expressed in polar form, which has been omitted in this discussion.

[2] Note that the resistive scale is upside down compared with Figure 1. This is a convention with the Smith Chart.

[3] In practice the transformed impedances won't be quite as I have stated because of the coax losses, however they are small enough to be ignored for this discussion.

[4] Transmission line calculator, P. H. Smith, *Electronics*, January 1939

# Antennas

## The G0CBM pedestrian mobile antenna

PHOTO 1: The complete G0CBM antenna and backpack installation.

**A TALE OF TWO PARTS.** The function of the counterpoise on a vertical antenna is often overlooked or ignored. It is important to realise that the counterpoise carries RF current and is much a part of the antenna as the vertical section. A discussion of the role of the counterpoise can be found at **[1]** and **[2]**.

In the case of a mobile antenna, the metal structure of the vehicle provides a reasonable counterpoise. However, with a HF pedestrian mobile station, providing a counterpoise is much more of a problem.

**THE G0CBM ANTENNA.** Charles Wilkie, G0CBM, a keen HF mobile and pedestrian mobile operator, has come up with an interesting antenna. This design provides a suitable counterpoise and overcomes the difficulty of feeding such an arrangement.

The design is basically a centre-loaded half-wave antenna for 14 and 18MHz (although this frequency range can be extended, as will be described later). The physical size of an antenna can be considerably reduced by using a loading coil and end capacitances, which is done in this case. Traditionally, small antennas are loaded using a solenoid shaped coil, as was done in G0CBM's earlier designs **[3]**. To get the best Q and low loss from a solenoid coil the spacing between each winding of the coil should be at least the diameter of the wire. Feeding such a half-wave antenna with the loading coil at the centre can be a problem.

G0CBM's latest design uses disc shaped loading coil, which he describes as a basket weave coil, although a more accurate description is a 'spider' coil **[4]**. This type of coil construction is favoured by people who make crystal sets; construction details of the coil used with this antenna are given later.

The antenna is fed via a link coupling coil. This again is similar to crystal set technology, where coupling is varied by altering the distance between the coupling coil and the loading coil. A further advantage is that it is easier to suppress common-mode currents on the coax feeder, which can cause RF on the case of the radio and 'hot microphone' problems.

The antenna support comprises a 2.4m telescopic fishing rod with a capacitance hat of six 0.3m spokes fixed to the top. The vertical wire element is simply a length of insulated wire loosely wound around the fishing rod from the inner part of the loading coil to the capacitance hat.

The disc shaped loading coil is fixed one metre from the bottom antenna support, with the adjustable coupling coil located just below.

Four 0.6m long radials are fixed 0.9m from the lower end of the antenna support; this lower end acting as a 'mounting pole'. The complete antenna weighs only 950g. The general construction of the antenna is shown in **Photo 1**.

**CONSTRUCTION.** The antenna support is constructed from a fibreglass telescopic fishing rod with the top two or three sections removed to ensure that it stays rigid enough to withstand the whipping motion caused by walking. The fishing rod needs to be of good quality with tight fitting sections.

The six capacitance hat spokes at the top of the antenna are made from 1.6mm stainless 'tungsten inert gas' (TIG) welding wire pressed into a brass hub, which is then screwed onto a brass bush at the top of the fishing rod.

The inner sections of the four radials are each made from to 0.3m copper plated steel tube (salvaged sections from a military manpack whip), fitted to the brass centre boss. The ends of the radials are made from 0.3m of 1.6mm stainless TIG welding wire. G0CBM has the necessary facilities for turning the capacitance and radial bosses and the loading coil sliding bush, although he has used salvaged CB antenna parts in the past. TIG welding wire was used for the capacitor hat and the outer part of the radials because it can be easily reformed if it is bent after snagging on bushes or trees.

The loading coil former is made from a 90mm diameter disc of 6mm polycarbonate, although thick PCB (without copper) could also be used. Nine radial slots are cut into the polycarbonate using a 5mm cutting disc and angle grinder. The odd number of slots in the disc allows the wire to lay alternatively from one side to the other on each successive turn, creating a space between each winding of the coil. This effectively gives an approximate adjacent wire spacing of the diameter of the wire, which reduces the self capacitance of the coil and improves the Q. The coil comprises 12 turns of 2mm enamelled copper wire wound into the slots (**Photo 2**).

A spade connector is soldered to the inner end of the coil to connect the wire from the capacitor hat. Tapping points are soldered onto the last turn of wire at every segment to connect the flying lead from the radials.

The coupling coil is made from a 75mm disc of PCB. Three spiral turns are etched on to the copper laminate and the coax feeder soldered to the ends of the coil as shown in **Photo 3**. The copper laminate coil is flow soldered to reduce tarnishing and probably

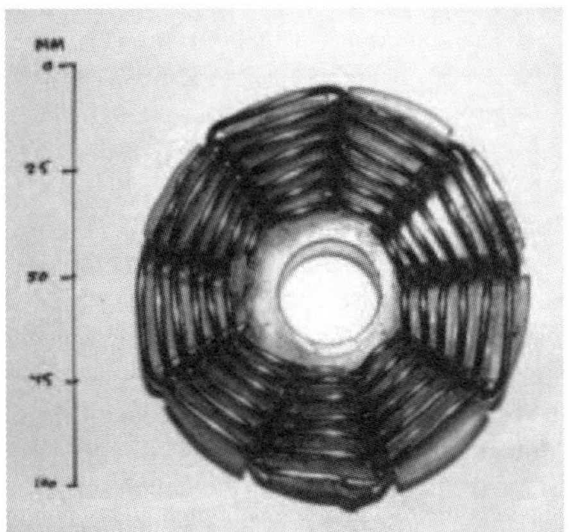

PHOTO 2: The centre loading coil.

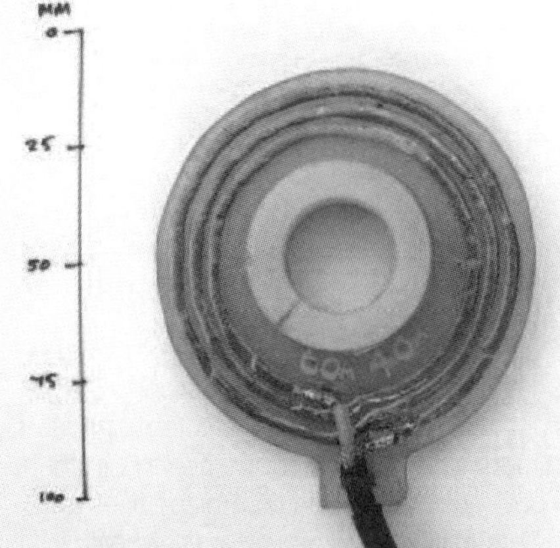

PHOTO 3: The coupling coil.

PHOTO 4: Details of the positioning and connections of the loading coil, coupling coil and radials.

improve efficiency. The coupling coil is fixed on a sliding bush just below the loading coil and connected to the transceiver via a short length of 50Ω coax. Ferrite sleeves are threaded on to the coax near to the coil to reduce common-mode currents. A flying lead is used to connect radials to the any one of the tapping points on the outer part of the loading coil, as shown in **Photo 4**.

The various components that make up the antenna are shown **Photo 5**. The TIG wire extensions of the radials are folded back along the steel tubing sections.

**OPERATION.** An antenna analyser such as the MFJ 269 or a noise bridge is connected to the short coax lead on the coupling coil. The required resonant point is set by connecting the flying lead from the radials to the appropriate tapping point on the loading coil, indicated by a minimum SWR or the nearest you can get to 50Ω impedance. (If you have a GDO then this can be used to set up resonance without any connection to the coupling coil).

Adjustment for the lowest SWR is achieved by sliding the coupling coil closer to or further from the loading coil. The resonant frequency will change slightly as the coupling coil coupling is adjusted, so final adjustment to the loading coil taps might be necessary.

It is important that a very low SWR is obtained at the frequency of interest. This ensures maximum efficiency and the widest low SWR bandwidth. The position of the taps and the coupling coil can be marked as shown in Photo 4 for rapid reset when the frequency is changed.

**OTHER BANDS.** The antenna works well on 17m by adding more taps to the 3rd turn from the outside of the loading coil and clipping the radial flying lead to any one of these. The coupling coil is adjusted for minimum SWR in the same manner as for 20m.

Further taps can be added for 15 and 10m but a significant proportion of the loading coil will be left open, which may result is a lower efficiency. The solution may be to make an additional loading coil with fewer turns plus a coupling coil with just two turns for these higher frequencies.

Some mobile antennas such as the Texas BugCatcher short out the unused turns with the flying lead rather than leaving them open. When I asked G0CBM if he had considered this approach he replied that experimental work done with G0UOO indicated 'free' or 'bridged out' turns reduce efficiency.

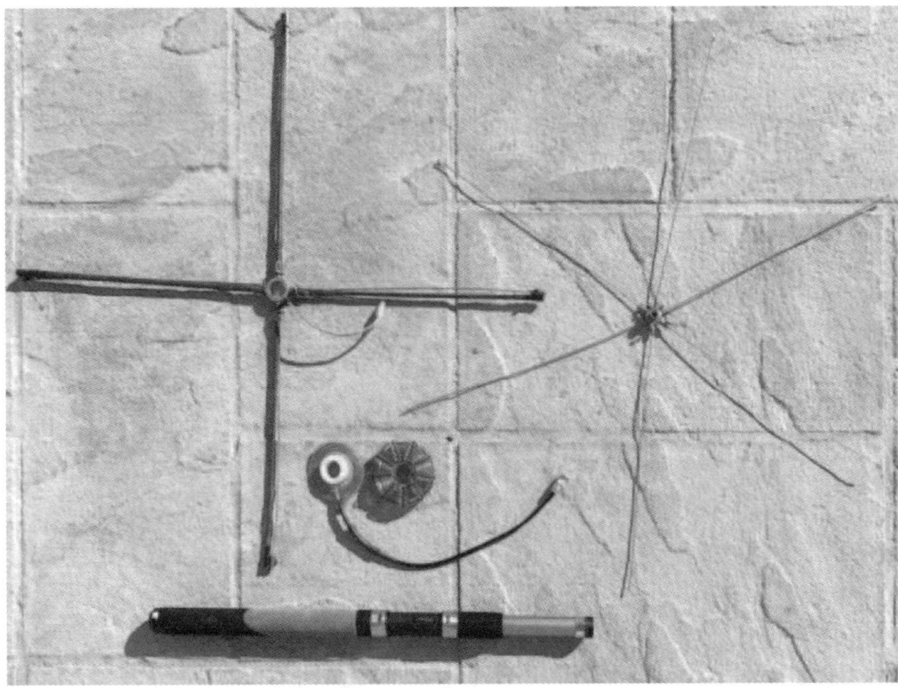

PHOTO 5: The antenna components.

**PERFORMANCE.** I am not particularly keen on anecdotal descriptions of antenna performance but in this case G0CBM is using QRP power with a very small antenna. To work any DX at all with such a pedestrian mobile installation means that the antenna is certainly no dummy load.

He goes on to say, "The performance on the 17 and 20m bands is very good and the majority of stations called have replied. With just 5 watts from an FT-817, I had a QSO with an American serviceman YI9GYS, in Tikrit, Iraq, from the beach at Skegness. While on holiday in the Algarve, Portugal, again using 5 watts, I had a QSO with Ron, VK3IO, in Melbourne."

G0CBM has been a keen /pedestrian mobile operator for many years and makes the following comments about it. "Although /pedestrian mobile may seem a disadvantage at first because of the small antenna and 5 watts, full advantage can be made of the effects of sea and summits to aid propagation. The suffix /pedestrian mobile always gives at least a 10dB advantage over the competition as well".

**REFERENCES**

[1] Antennas, *RadCom* April 2007

[2] *Building Successful HF Antennas*, Peter Dodd, G3LDO

[3] *The Amateur Radio Mobile Handbook*, Peter Dodd, G3LDO

[4] http://makearadio.com/coils/spider.php

# Antennas

## RF engineering of a different kind

PHOTO 1: The 602-B UHF Admittance Meter arrangement.

**OFF BEAM.** This month is a bit of a departure from the normal Antennas column. It is a brief description of the largest scientific laboratory on the planet, how radio frequency engineering plays an essential part in its function and radio amateurs involvement in the project.

In February and March 2009 I described a method for measuring the less familiar dual of Impedance – Admittance. A General Radio 1602-B UHF Admittance Meter was used to illustrate an early method of measuring this parameter at UHF. This instrument, see **Photo 1**, was given to me by Frank James, G0LOF, together with lots of other interesting goodies such as a calibrated adjustable constant-impedance line, a VHF/UHF signal generator, a couple of boxes of coaxial plugs and adapters and a king sized Smith chart some 400mm in diameter.

To my mind anyone who has this sort of equipment in their garage must have had an interesting life. I learned that G0LOF had worked at Manchester University and CERN (the European organisation for nuclear research). That work involved the design, construction and testing of RF amplifiers, transmission lines and matching systems used in particle accelerators. These are used by physicists to explore new territory in matter, energy, space and time.

**PARTICLE ACCELERATORS.** These are devices that use electrostatic or electromagnetic fields to propel charged particles to high velocities and to contain them in well-defined beams. Beams of high-energy particles are used for both fundamental and applied research in the sciences. For the most basic inquiries into the dynamics and structure of matter, space, and time, physicists seek the simplest kinds of interactions at the highest possible energies. These typically entail particle energies of many gigaelectronvolts (GeV).

Particles can only be propelled in a hard vacuum. All particle beam control and switching is achieved using powerful electromagnets. To reduce the energy requirements of both beam acceleration and control, devices are cooled to a very low temperature where the copper conductivity is excellent due to superconductivity – more on this later. All of this imposes some exacting engineering standards.

An example of a low energy electrostatic particle accelerator is the cathode ray tube (CRT) used in an oscilloscope or in some older televisions. Electrons emitted from a heated cathode are accelerated and focussed with positive charged arrangement of metal tubes and disks. A final boost to the electron beam velocity is supplied by a positively charged metallised coating sprayed on the inside of the tube near to the screen.

Historically, many of the first particle accelerators used the simple technology of a single static high voltage to accelerate charged particles similar to that described above. Very high electrostatic voltages were obtained using a Cockcroft-Walton voltage multiplier, an extension of the well-known voltage doubler circuit, where an AC supply is rectified and the DC voltage stepped up by cascading diodes and capacitors in series. An example Cockcroft-Walton voltage multiplier is shown in **Photo 2**.

The particle of choice for high energy particle physics is not the electron as described earlier but the proton, which has a mass nearly 2000 times greater than the electron. A popular particle source is hydrogen gas (whose atoms comprises one proton and one electron), which are ionised in a small high voltage chamber and the protons ejected into the particle accelerator.

There is a limit to the energy that can be imparted to a particle beam using the electrostatic method, due to the engineering problems of handling very high voltages. A more elegant solution is to use RF energy. An example of how this is achieved is by using a linear array of tubes (called drift tubes) to which a high energy RF field is applied, see **Figure 1**.

As the particles approach the first tube from the particle source they are accelerated towards it by an opposite polarity charge applied to the tube on the first half-cycle of the RF excitation. As they pass through the centre of the tube, the polarity is switched by the next half-cycle of RF excitation so that the particles are now accelerated by it towards the next tube where the process is repeated. Obviously the size of the tubes and the frequency and power of the RF have to be carefully considered. Only particles that are in the right place at the right time are accelerated so the output from the accelerator comprise 'bunches' of particles.

These devices are called linear accelerators or 'Linacs' and are mostly used in particle physics for the creation of low or medium power particle beams for injecting into more powerful accelerators. See [1] and [2] for more information.

**CAVITY RESONATORS.** These devices are very high Q parallel tuned circuits and are often used as high Q filters and high power diplexers in VHF/UHF applications. A cavity resonator is simply a metal box having a resonant frequency that depends on its size. This is similar to a two-conductor transmission line with closed ends that will resonate at wavelengths at particular multiples of the line length. However, cavity resonators have additional resonances in more than two dimensions, which are referred to as 'modes'.

Most of the particle accelerators used in particle physics use cavity resonators rather than drift tubes described earlier. Furthermore, most accelerators are circular rather than linear, which allows the same cavity resonators to be used repeatedly to impart additional energy to the particle beam. High velocity particles like to travel in straight lines and so very strong electromagnets are used to bend the beamlines into the desired circular path. High-speed particles can be held in a ring

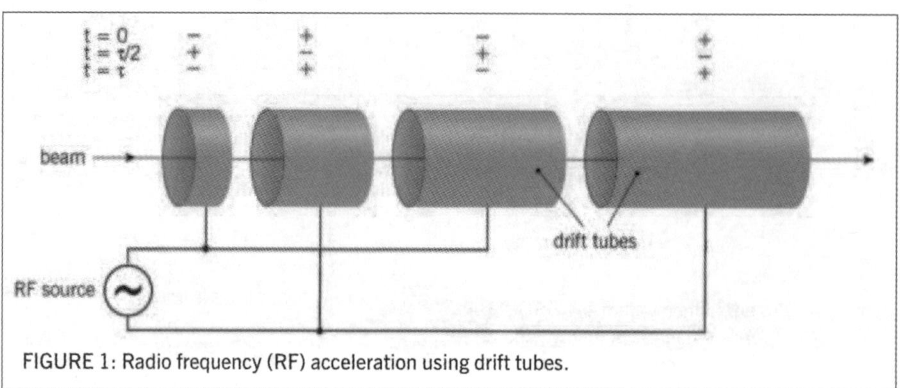


FIGURE 1: Radio frequency (RF) acceleration using drift tubes.

PHOTO 2: A Cockcroft-Walton voltage multiplier, no longer used and put out to grass in the garden of Microcosm, the CERN particle physics museum.

PHOTO 3: The LEIR accelerator/storage ring. Two of the eight cavity resonators in the accelerator ring are shown on the right-hand side.

PHOTO 4: Johannas Broere, PA0NOS (left) who took over from Frank James, G3LOF (right) on his retirement.

until required for a specific experimént or transferred to a higher energy ring. For this reason they are called accelerator/storage rings.

Cavity resonators for particle accelerators are normally semi-cylindrical and mounted horizontally with holes in the centre of the end surfaces to allow a clear passage for the particles. The standing wave within the cavity sets up an alternating field, which energises particles travelling through the holes in the end surfaces of the cavities, thereby increasing their velocity and energy. Sometimes the cavities are made of low-temperature superconductors; these can have incredibly high values of Q **[3]**.

**RF ENGINEERING.** The accelerator excitation source is essentially a radio transmitter with an oscillator, multiplication driver stages and a power amplifier as in a normal transmitter. Early RF sources used thermionic valves of varying sizes, with power ratings from watts to megawatts, but these devices have since been replaced by solid-state technology.

With systems using VHF or UHF frequencies the cavity is coupled to the RF source using coaxial cable; this cable is usually terminated with a small loop projecting into the wall of the cavity. When the system is operational energy is transferred from the cavity to particles and this causes a loading effect. The degree of loading is monitored and corrected with an electronic control system using directional couplers and other sensing systems.

**A VISIT TO CERN.** At the end of October 2011 Frank organised a group visit to CERN near Geneva. It is the home of the Large Hadron Collider (LHC), which is installed in a 27km circular tunnel buried 50-150m below ground. It produces head-on collisions between particles of the same kind, either protons or lead ions. CERN's accelerator complex is a succession of particle accelerators used to boost the speed of the particle beam before injecting it into the next one in the sequence, see **Figure 2**.

Protons are created as described earlier and given their inirial acceleration in a linear accelerator, in this case LINAC 2. From there they are injected into the PS Booster, then to the Proton Synchrotron (PS). The particles are then directed to the Super Proton Synchrotron (SPS) before finally reaching the Large Hadron Collider (LHC). Protons will circulate in the LHC for 20 minutes before finally reaching their maximum energy. When two of these beams are collided they have twice this beam energy. CERN also uses lead ions in some collision experiments which are generated in LINAC3 and further accelerated in the Low Energy Ion Ring (LEIR) before being injected into same accelerator complex used for protons. Lead ions can have a much higher final collision energy because of their greater mass.

The facilities for visitors to CERN are most impressive. I was surprised that some operational sections of the above ground sections complex were open to visitors. An example of one of these is the LEIR accelerator shown in **Photo 3**. It is the smallest accelerator/storage ring in the CERN complex, having a circumference of 178m. The complexity of the engineering can be seen in the photo. Two of the cavity resonators in the accelerator ring are shown on the right-hand side. The orange blocks in the foreground are powerful electromagnets for holding the particle beam within the accelerator ring. These magnets are encased in blocks of material to suppress radiation caused by beam bending by the magnets.

There is a considerable amount of information on the internet on CERN and other particle accelerator facilities. Just key in 'CERN' or 'particle accelerator' into Google and see what you get. It is also interesting to note that the world wide web (WWW) was created at Cern [4].

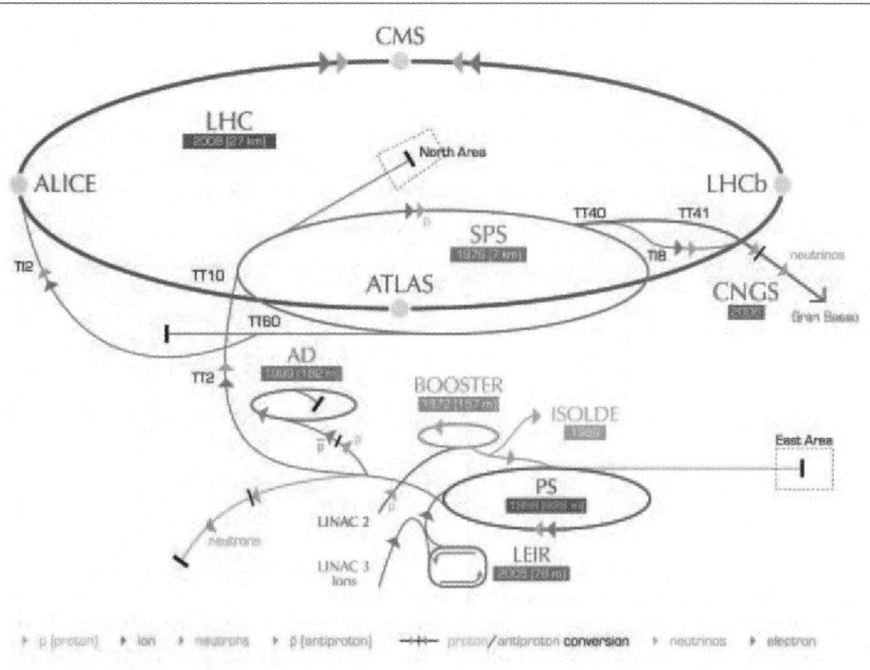


FIGURE 2: Diagram of the CERN accelerator complex. The numbers associated with the accelerator identification refer to year of commissioning and circumference, eg LHC 2009 [27]. Reproduced by kind permission of CERN.

**WEBSEARCH**

[1] http://en.wikipedian.org/wiki/Australian_Synchrotron
[2] http://en.wikipedia.org/wiki/Superconducting_Radio_Frequency
[3] http://en.wikipedia.org/wiki/Superconducting_RF
[4] http://en.wikipedia.org/wiki/Www

# Antennas

## Compact beam antennas without loading or traps

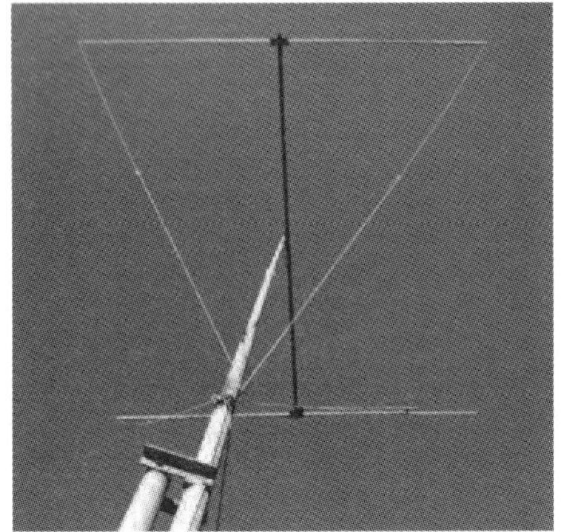

PHOTO 1: A Double-D Antenna with the end sections of the elements secured to the mast via insulators. The boom and horizontal sections of the elements are constructed from aluminium tubing.

UPPER BANDS COME TO LIFE. As the sunspot cycle increases, there is a corresponding increase in activity in the upper HF bands, particularly 28MHz. Not only do the propagation paths have a much lower attenuation than the lower frequency bands (DX signals are much stronger), there is the added advantage that antennas are smaller for these bands. If you can build a beam antenna, so much the better. A rotatable beam with gain and directivity improves the strength of your transmission and results in an improved signal to noise ratio on receive. However, the 'wingspan' of a 2-ele Yagi is over 33ft at 14MHz and 16ft on 28MHz. In this column I will describe again more compact designs for a beam antenna.

The span of a dipole can be bent to allow it to be fitted into a postage size plot. Can the same be done with a two-element Yagi? And how does it affect its performance?

W1QP/W8CPC TWO-ELEMENT ANTENNA. As with any antenna design there is very little that is new. Burton Simson, W8CPC, constructed a two-element beam antenna with bent elements for 14MHz (first suggested by John Reinartz, W1QP), which was described in October 1937 [1]. The antenna used the typical construction techniques of the day, with elements supported using insulators on wooden square frame and the ends of the driven element and the reflector folded towards each other. This configuration, shown in **Figure 1**, allowed the 'wingspan' to be halved. The elements were constructed from ¼in (6.35mm) copper tubing with brass tuning rods that fitted snugly into the ends of the elements for tuning. The tuning rods were simply adjusted for maximum current in the reflector, which coincided with maximum antenna front-to-back directivity.

THE VK2ABQ ANTENNA. The W1QP antenna design faded into obscurity for many years until a similar design appeared in 1973. This configuration, by VK2ABQ [2] and reported in [3], used elements made from wire, with the tips of the parasitic and driven elements supporting each other in the horizontal plane via insulators. Furthermore, three separate antennas for the 14, 21 and 28MHz band could be nested as shown in **Figure 2**, making it a lightweight multiband antenna.

The insulators were constructed so that the tips of the elements were only 6mm (¼in) apart. According to the VK2ABQ original description, this capacitively coupled the reflector and driven element although the gap between the tips of the elements were described as 'not critical'.

THE MOXON RECTANGLE. Les Moxon, G6XN, did a lot of experimental work with the two-element Yagi with bent elements [4], particularly regarding optimising the element spacing. He changed the original structure design from a square to a rectangle, thereby reducing the centre section spacing of the elements from 0.25λ to 0.17λ. This resulted in improved gain and directivity. Later, C B Cebik, W4RNL [5], further reduced the element spacing further to 0.14λ, obtaining yet more gain and improved directivity in a design he called the Moxon Rectangle. The downside of this higher performance is that it is difficult to make a multiband structure using this design. The three structures are shown superimposed in **Figure 3**.

The remarkable characteristic of this close-spaced arrangement is its very high front-to-back ratio. It also has a feed impedance is close to 50Ω. The dimensions for the Moxon rectangle can be found at [5]. According to computer modelling, free space gain and front-to-back ratio are consistent for all the models, averaging 5.8dBi and greater than 30dB in free space, respectively.

EXPERIMENTS WITH OTHER CONFIGURATIONS. In the mid 1980s I was looking for a small, compact beam for 21 and 28MHz in anticipation of the then-forthcoming sunspot cycle 23 and considered the VK2ABQ antenna described above. At the time, the only information I had was via Pat Hawker, G3VA [3]. G3VA had some issues with this design, although not all were specified.

In view of this I felt that I should get some idea of the performance of this antenna before building it, but this was before the days of antenna modelling computer software for radio amateurs. What I had been using for some years at the time was VHF modelling, described in [6]. This method uses a small VHF model of the HF antenna, which allows measurements and modifications to be easily performed.

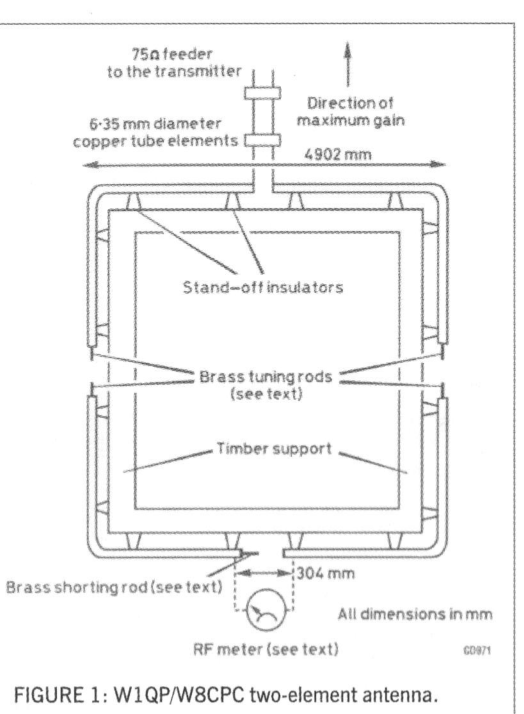


FIGURE 1: W1QP/W8CPC two-element antenna.

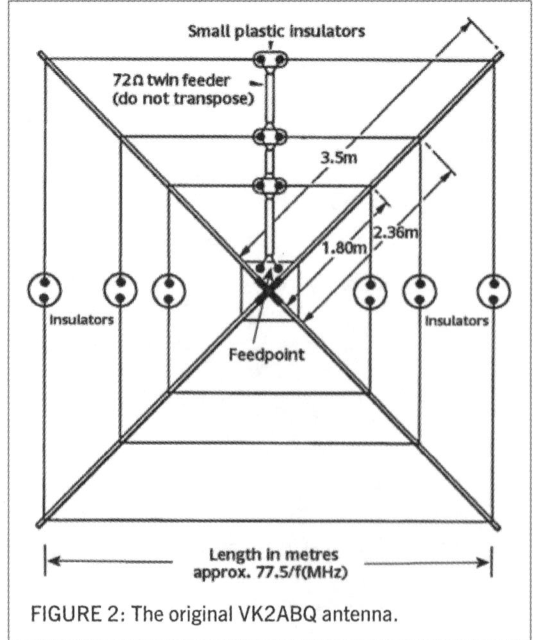


FIGURE 2: The original VK2ABQ antenna.

PHOTO 2: A 21MHz version of the Double-D antenna using a 144MHz J-pole antenna to support the ends of the 21MHz elements.

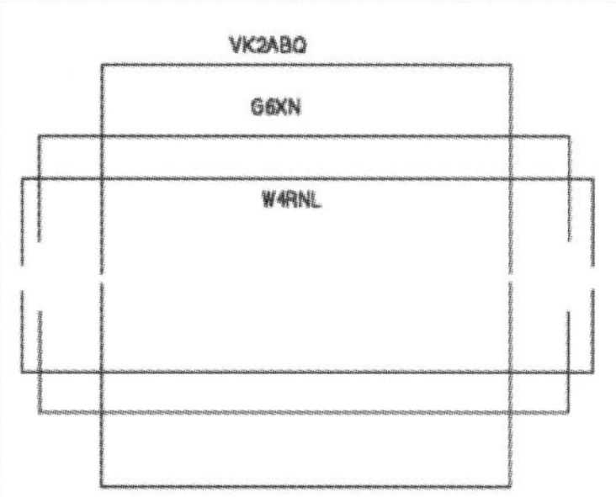


FIGURE 3: The G6XN and the W4RNL antenna structures compared with the original VK2ABQ design.

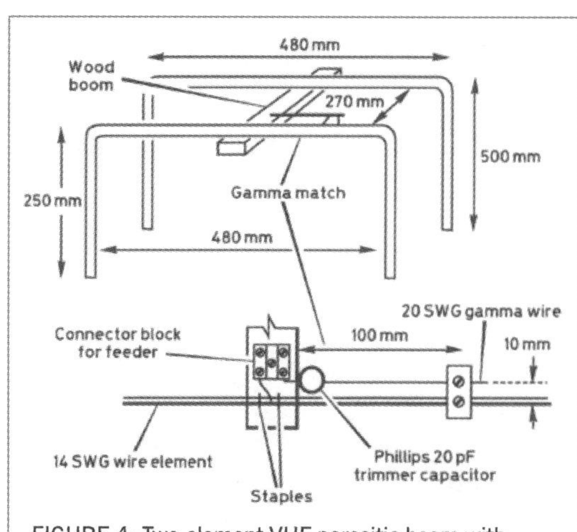


FIGURE 4: Two-element VHF parasitic beam with bent elements.

A two-element VHF antenna was constructed using hard drawn copper wire as elements fixed to a wooden boom using staples. This flexible arrangement allowed the elements to be bent into any shape. Initially, the ends of the elements were folded back to each other in the VK2ABQ configuration but early measurements were rather disappointing.

THE G3LDO DD ANTENNA. I tried various element tip spacings and wire lengths on the VK2ABQ model and succeeded in obtaining some directivity, but the gain was very little more than that of a dipole. However, if the elements were bent in a manner shown in **Figure 4** the performance improved considerably.

While the antenna shown in Figure 4 performed well, it was hardly a practical design for HF. The problem was what to do with the element ends. This was solved by making the end sections from wire and folding them back towards the mast, as shown in **Photo 1**. This resulted in very little change in gain and directivity compared with the arrangement in Figure 4.

A preferred arrangement is to have lightweight extension above the main antenna structure and have the end sections of the elements bent upwards as shown in **Figure 5**. This arrangement is more convenient for fixing a rotator and the additional vertical support can be a VHF antenna as shown in **Photo 2**. This shape proved to be a simple and stable mechanical arrangement and an all-metal 21MHz model survived the hurricane that hit the south coast of England in October 1987.

A compact antenna for the lower frequency bands is shown in **Figure 6**, together with approximate data. It is difficult to firm up these data – the shorter you make the horizontal lengths, the longer you have to make the vertical sections.

The Double-D antenna can be made from wire using the type element support shown in Figure 2.

A number of these antennas, for different bands, can be nested on the same support. Information regarding the development of this antenna can be found at [7] and [8].

PERFORMANCE. On 14MHz the compact Double-D antenna exhibited reasonable directivity and a lot of DX was worked, but my signal was rather outclassed by those using 3 or more element beams at more than one wavelength in height.

The antenna shown in Photo 1 was designed for 10MHz and had a 'wingspan' of just 4.7m (15ft 6in). Between May 1998 and April 1999, using a Drake C-line, a KW600 linear and this antenna, this station turned out to be a relatively 'big gun' on 10MHz in those days. It netted over 50 VKs, 26 ZLs, over 20 JAs plus lots of real DX and USA stations.

MODELLING. Discrepancies have been noted between computer and VHF modelling. I hope to investigate this further at a later date. The difficulty I had modelling the VK2ABQ antenna at VHF is possibly due to capacitive end coupling. With VHF modelling the wavelengths, capacitances and inductances in the VHF scale model are reduced in proportion to the linear dimensions while gains and impedances are unchanged. However, the insulator represents a fixed capacitor whose reactance is frequency dependant. If we assume a value of around 0.2pF for the wires held in the insulator by knots, ¼in apart, the coupling reactance is 38kΩ at 21MHz and 5.5kΩ at 145MHz. On the other hand, *EZNEC* predicted good gain and directivity for this antenna.

REFERENCES

[1] Concentrated Directional Antennas for Transmission and Reception, John Reinartz, W1QP and Burton Simson, W8CPC, *QST*, October 1937

[2] VK2ABQ Antenna, Fred Caton, VK2ABQ, *Electronics Australia*, October 1973

[3] Technical Topics, *Radio Communication*, January 1974

[4] *HF Antennas for all Locations*, 2nd Ed, Les Moxon, G6XN, RSGB

[5] L B Cebik, W4RNL (SK), www.cebik.com

[6] *The Antenna Experimenter's Guide*, 2nd Edn, Peter Dodd, G3LDO, RSGB

[7] Wire Beam Antennas and the Evolution of the Double-D, *QST*, October 1984, also *Radio Communication*, June/July 1980, Peter Dodd, G3LDO

[8] Further Evolution of the Double-D, *Radio Communication*, April 1990, Peter Dodd, G3LDO

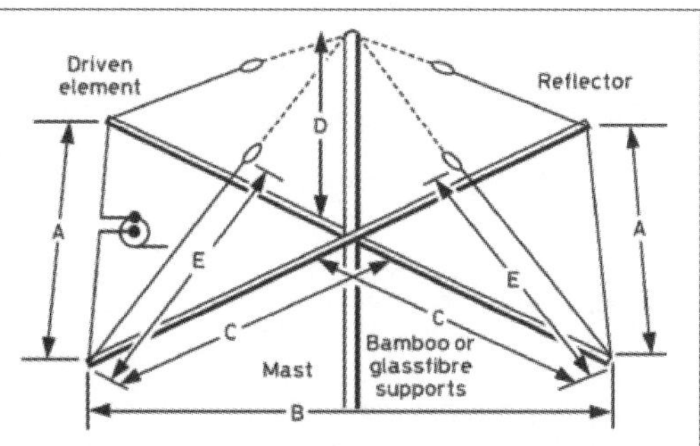


FIGURE 5: Basic Double-D approximate length data (in m; f in MHz): A=79/f, B=50/f, C=56/f, D=16/f, E=31.5/f.

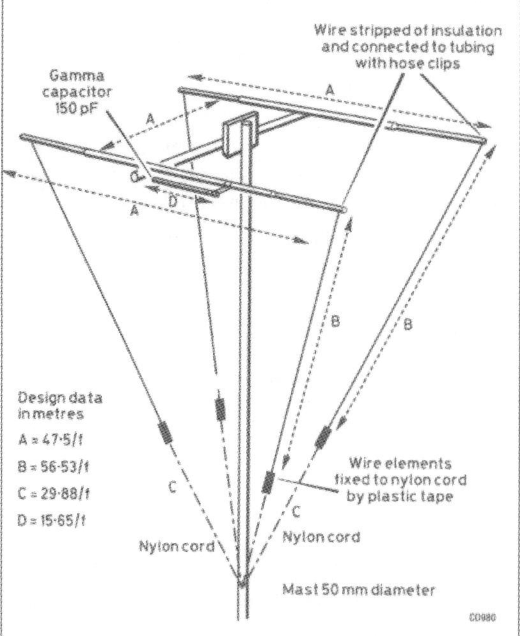


FIGURE 6: Compact Double-D approximate length data (in m; f in MHz): A=47.5/f, B=56.5/f, C=30/f, D=15.65/f.

# Antennas

## Antennas small and big

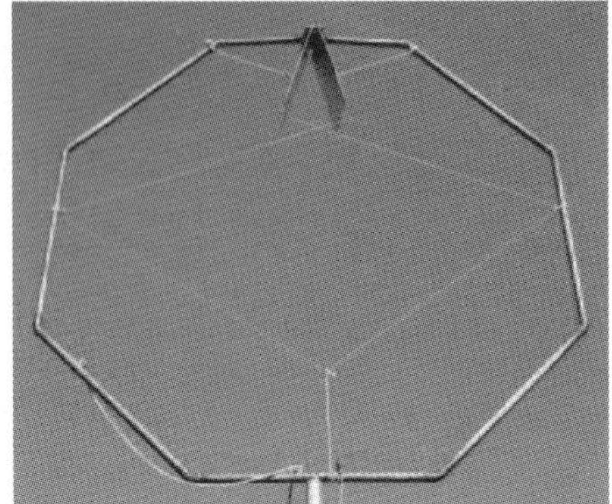

PHOTO 1: A loop antenna.

**LOOP MISUNDERSTANDING.** I recently received an e-mail from someone who had designed a small loop antenna. The author advocated using resistance wire for the loop itself, reasoning that the higher resistance would give wider a SWR bandwidth and greater radiation efficiency. He also suggested feeding the antenna near the capacitor, where the 'resistance' was higher than at the traditional feedpoint, again improving antenna efficiency.

I have the impression that the loop designer had considered the feedpoint impedance (when suitably matched to the feeder) to be an indication of the efficiency of his antenna.

**RADIATION RESISTANCE.** The diagram in **Figure 1** shows how power is dissipated in an antenna at resonance, where the inductive and capacitive reactances are equal and opposite. The antenna comprises resistance losses caused by the material with which the antenna elements are constructed. These elements are made from a high conductance material such as copper or aluminium, so this resistance is usually low. The other component is a virtual resistor, which dissipates the same power as radiated by the antenna. This resistor is Radiation Resistance, whose value is related to antenna size; generally, the smaller the antenna, the lower the radiation resistance.

Because antenna current varies along its length, some think that the radiation resistance also varies along its length. The assumption is sometimes made that radiation resistance changes in a favourable proportion to loss resistance as feed impedance increases. All that happens is that the feedpoint is placed in series with a smaller portion of NET current causing the radiation.

Probably the IRE definition of radiation resistance is the most useful: radiation resistance is obtained by dividing total radiated power in all directions by the square of NET current causing the radiation.

There are a few interactive computer programs for designing loop antennas on the internet. The one shown in **Figure 2** is based on *ARRL Antenna Handbook* material and is included here to illustrate the relationship between radiation resistance and radiation loss. These are calculations for my 1.4m diameter loop antenna (described in the September 2010 Antennas), shown in **Photo 1**.

Radiation resistance is measured at 0.442Ω, loss resistance at 0.067Ω, resulting in an antenna efficiency of 87%. Reducing the antenna element diameter from 22mm to 3mm and then 1mm results in loss resistances of 6.55Ω and 14.6Ω (with efficiencies if 18% and 7%) respectively. However, in all cases, the radiation resistance stays the same. You can access this program at **[1]** and try it out for yourself.

**CURRENT IN A SMALL LOOP.** The current level of a small loop is often described in literature as being constant throughout the loop. If that is the case why is there a high voltage across the tuning capacitor? I know this to be true because fairly high voltage fixed padding capacitor made from a short length of Ecoflex 15 on my loop flashed over during power tests.

Out of interest I modelled my 1.4m hexagonal loop using *EZNEC5*. The current distribution in **Figure 3** appears fairly constant, with the loading/tuning capacitor specified as 24pF to tune the antenna into the 14MHz band. You will notice that the currents are high, even adjacent to the load capacitor. So where are the high voltages known to exist at the capacitor? It is probable that high current (hence low voltage) is presented in the model because the capacitor load is a mathematical entity with no physical dimensions.

I made a further model, see **Figure 4**, using two close-spaced parallel elements instead of the supplied 'load' function that comes with *EZNEC5*. In this case you can see a steep current gradient over the physical dimensions of the capacitor. I have modelled loops using other capacitor structures and they all exhibit high current where the capacitors are connected to the loop elements and low current/high voltage extremities.

Interestingly, the currents in the elements of both models are very similar, with 1A at the feedpoint and around 0.75A at the connection to the capacitor, so the current around the loop does vary a small amount. Furthermore, the current variation throughout the loop is greater with larger loops.

**THE RHOMBIC ANTENNA.** In complete contrast the antenna described above I would like to mention the rhombic. One of the strongest DX signals I ever heard came from ZL2BE in the early 1960s. He was using one of these antennas and it is one that I have has some success with – as I will explain later.

The rhombic consists of four wires in the form of a diamond lying in the horizontal plane above earth and fed at the left hand apex with open wire feeders. The general arrangement is shown in **Figure 5**.

Each wire in the antenna produces main hollow cones of radiation plus a number of side lobe cones. The patterns shown in **Figure 6** are for wires around 3 wavelengths long.

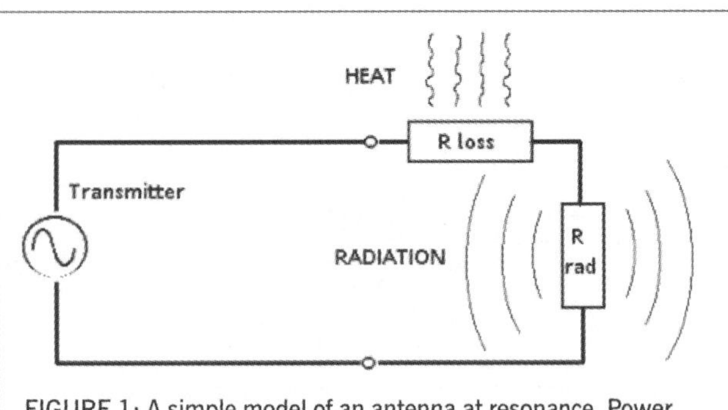


FIGURE 1: A simple model of an antenna at resonance. Power in R loss is dissipated as heat; power dissipated in R rad results in electromagnetic (RF) radiation. If both resistors were equal then the antenna would be 50% efficient.

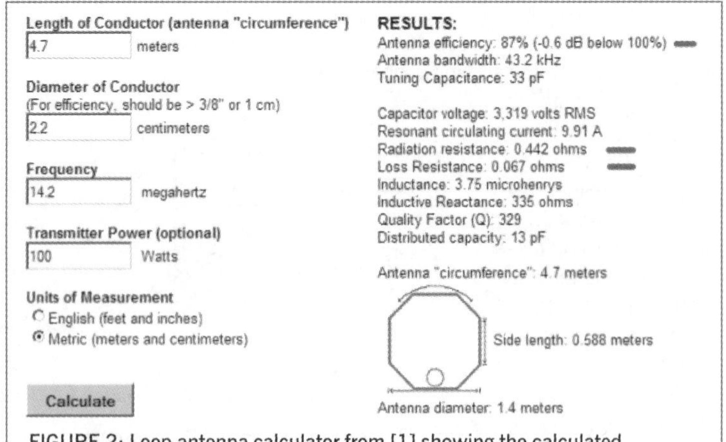


FIGURE 2: Loop antenna calculator from [1] showing the calculated characteristics of my 1.5m diameter magnetic loop antenna.

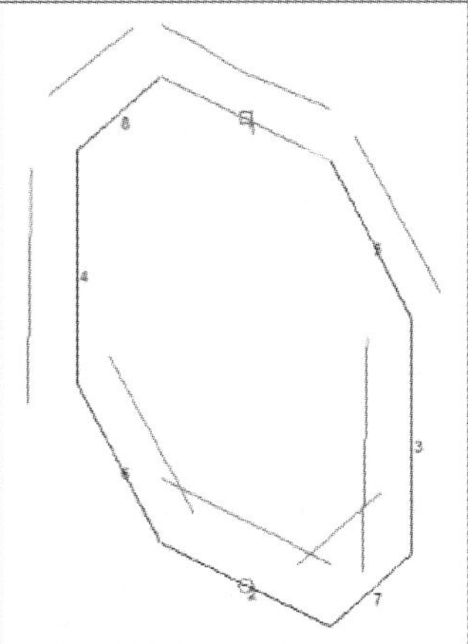

FIGURE 3: *EZNEC5* model of my 1.5m diameter magnetic loop using a capacitive load (the small square on wire 1). The antenna current is indicated by red lines whose distance from the antenna element indicated current amplitude.

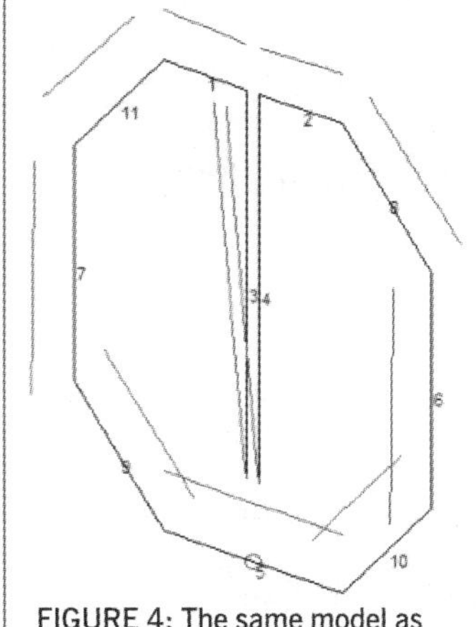

FIGURE 4: The same model as Figure 3 but using a physical capacitor made from two parallel conductors. Note the zero current (and high voltage) at the ends of the capacitor elements.

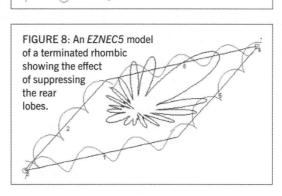

FIGURE 5: Isometric view of a rhombic antenna. When a terminating resistor is connected, the antenna supports travelling waves rather than standing waves.

The longer the wire length the closer the main cones align to the axis of the wire. The ideal arrangement is where the main lobes combine in phase along the antenna axis.

The performance of the rhombic is based on three factors: the leg length l, tilt angle ø and height h although, in practice, the design of rhombic antennas is quite flexible. It will work over a 2:1 frequency range or even more, provided the legs are at least two wavelengths at the lowest frequency. For such wide-band use the angle is chosen to suit the element length at the mid-range frequency. Generally the beamwidth and wave angle increase at the lower frequency and decrease at the upper frequency, even though the apex angle is not quite optimum over the whole range.

The *ARRL Antenna Handbook* has a compromise design that will work over a frequency range of 14 to 28MHz with a leg length of 210ft, a total length of 184ft and a tilt angle of 64°.

I appreciate that this antenna is not for everyone, but there are certain situations where one might be useful. When I was stationed in Kenya I was fortunate to live in a bungalow with a fairly large garden; the total plot size was around 30m by 68m. Two of the far corners of the plot aligned with EU and the USA I so decided to try a rhombic. I bought four 30ft (9.15m) wooden poles and a large reel of electrical copper earthing wire. I constructed an antenna very similar to that shown in Figure 5.

The size of the plot restricted the length of the antenna (distance between the apex poles) to 65m and the width (spacing of the two side poles) to 28m. It turned out to be a superb antenna on the 21 and 28MHz bands (this was before the days of the WARC bands) and not a lot of good on 14MHz. A model of this antenna is shown in **Figure 7**. The antenna was fed using home made 600Ω open wire feeder and a balanced feeder ATU.

Before I constructed this antenna I hadn't appreciated the amount of static such an arrangement would collect, especially in the tropics. The fix was a large RF choke from the antenna feeders to ground to get rid of rain static. My lightning protection method was to disconnect the feeders from the ATU and lower them to the ground outside using a length of cord when there was an impending thunderstorm.

The rhombic is often the antenna of choice for many military and civil communications systems. The RAF had a communications organisation with an antenna farm using many rhombics at Christmas Island when I was there in 1957. They would have been very useful for the T32C DXpedition if they had still been there!

Rhombics in commercial use are usually terminated with a resistor at the apex opposite to the feedpoint, as shown in Figure 5. This resistor changes the antenna from a standing wave to a travelling wave antenna, effectively suppressing radiation from the rear, as shown in **Figure 8**. The terminating resistance also absorbs noise and interference coming from the rear direction as well as transmitter power, which would otherwise be radiated backwards. This results in an improved signal to noise ratio by up to 3dB without affecting signals transmitted in the wanted direction.

My ideal antenna would be a rhombic, orientated on the long path to VK/ZL and the Pacific, with possibly an arrangement for transposing the feedpoint and the terminating resistor. The main advantage of the rhombic is that it is a simple, non-critical design with a low visual impact; the downside is that it takes a lot of room.

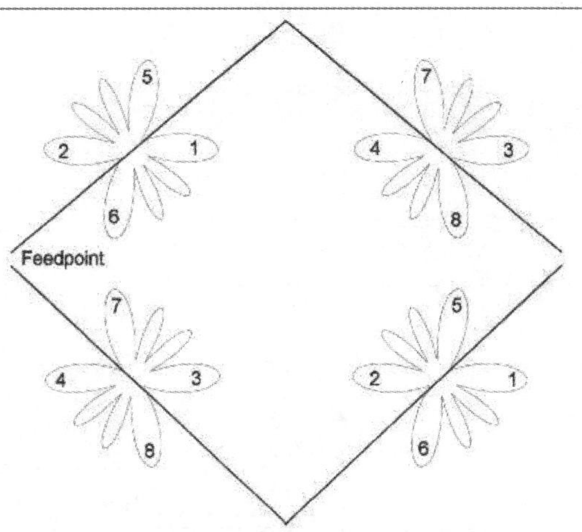


FIGURE 6: Lobes 1 and 3 phase combine to give the antenna forward gain; lobes 2 and 4 produce rear gain. All other lobes are out of phase and are partially suppressed. If a terminating resistor is connected, the antenna becomes a travelling wave antenna and the rear lobes are suppressed.

FIGURE 7: An *EZNEC5* model of the VQ4HX rhombic antenna showing bi-directional gain characteristics. The model predicts a gain of 11.25dBi on 21MHz and 16dBi on 28MHz.

FIGURE 8: An *EZNEC5* model of a terminated rhombic showing the effect of suppressing the rear lobes.

**WEBSEARCH**

[1] http://www.66pacific.com/calculators

# Antennas

## The slot antenna and an interesting application

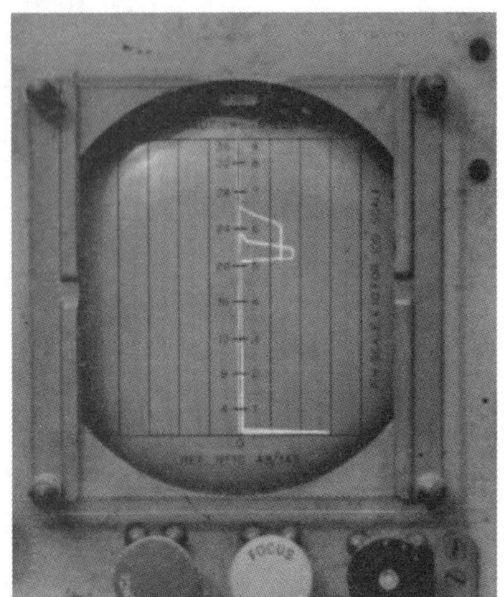

PHOTO 1: Rebecca Mk II indicator. The simulated display shows what would have been seen in an aircraft two degrees off the centre line of the runway in the dot sector and 5 nautical miles from the end of the runway.

THE SLOT ANTENNA. This antenna consists of a radiator formed by cutting a narrow slot in a large metal surface as shown in **Figure 1(a)**. The slot length L is a half wavelength at the desired frequency and the width w is a small fraction of a wavelength. The antenna is frequently compared with a dipole constructed from two metal strips that would fit into the slot cut out of the metal sheet as shown in **Figure 1(b)** and in such a comparison the dipole is often described as complementary to the slot.

There are several important differences between these two antennas. In the case of the dipole in Figure 1(b) the current flows along the vertical the axis, producing horizontal concentric rings of magnetic flux, which in turn produce a vertical electric field. Thus the dipole shown is said to be vertically polarised. Furthermore, the standing wave current on the dipole is high in the centre and very low at the extremities.

In 1948 a description of how the current and voltage distribution of a slot was measured, comparing it with theoretical predictions **[1]**. Measurements were made of electric and magnetic vectors of the RF fields near a radiating slot operated at 1000MHz. The slot was rectangular and 14 x 1cm in size, ie it was nearly half wave resonance. It was cut in the centre of a thin circular metal sheet, nine wavelengths in diameter. The sheet was supported horizontally and the slot was energised from the underside via a balanced transmission line connected to the centre of the opposite edges.

A series of holes were drilled in the sheet in a rectangular lattice in one quadrant of the area next to the slot. Relative measurements of the distributions of amplitudes of the electric vector on the upper surface of the upper side of the sheet were made by inserting a short vertical probe aerial through the small holes in the sheet.

The magnetic vector, parallel with the metal sheet, was measured using a balanced loop of wire small enough to pass through the holes in the sheet. Its component of amplitude in various directions was found by orientation of the loop. All the measurements were compiled into a graph, which indicated that the contours of electric field were highest across the centre of the slot.

The standing wave voltages and currents in the slot are opposite to those on a dipole, see **Figure 2**, with the currents very high at the slot ends and low in the centre. The current around the slot creates an electric field across the narrow dimensions of the slot and the polarisation is aligned with this electric field.

From Figure 2 you can see that the impedance of the slot is high in the centre and very low at the ends (impedance being a ratio of current and voltage). This antenna can be fed with coax by selecting a point along the slot where the impedance is the same as the characteristic impedance of the coax feeder.

Textbook descriptions of slot antennas often portray the slot in an infinite plane. Such an arrangement is clearly impractical and in reality a sheet somewhat larger than the slot is nearly as good as an infinite plane. A practical solution is to bend the sheet into a cylinder whose axis is the same as the long dimension of the slot. The result is a slotted cylinder antenna. If the diameter of the slot is less than 1/8 wavelengths the azimuth pattern is nearly omni directional with horizontal polarisation.

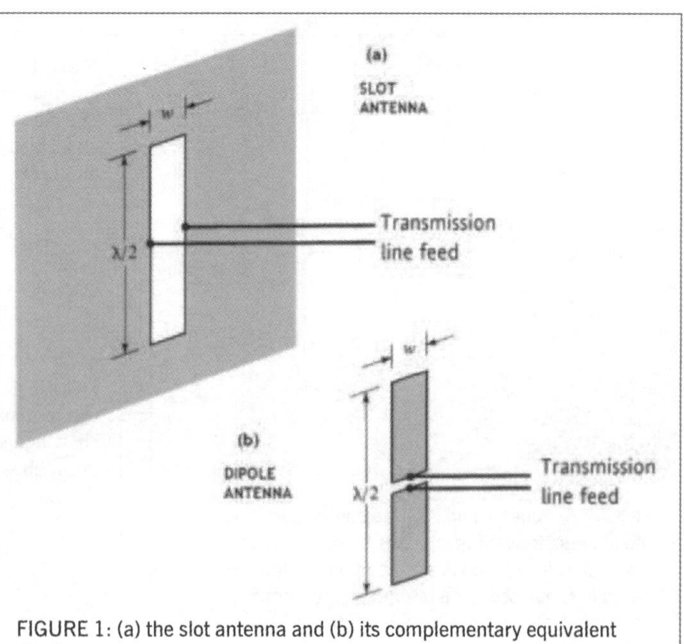



FIGURE 1: (a) the slot antenna and (b) its complementary equivalent dipole.

By stacking several slots on a long cylinder the gain can be increased by narrowing the vertical radiation pattern. This is an ideal arrangement for VHF/UHF radio/TV broadcasting and repeaters.

As I understand it, the slot antenna was invented in 1938 by Alan Blumlien, specifically for VHF TV broadcasting. A further development was the Alford Slot antenna, designed in 1946 by Andrew Alford. A slot antenna for beacon and repeater use has been developed by G3JVL. There are numerous references regarding this antenna on the internet. *[By coincidence, this month's ATV column looks at the 'skeleton slot' antenna – Ed]*

BEAM APPROACH BEACON SYSTEM. Many years ago the RAF used a radar landing aid called the Beam Approach Beacon System (BABS). It was one of my jobs as a Radio Mechanic to maintain such a system – and it used a slot antenna.

The function of the BABS equipment was to allow an aircraft to approach the runway of an airfield from the correct direction for landing, particularly at night or in bad visibility. It comprised a transponder situated at the far end of the runway. When interrogated by radio pulses from radar equipment in the aircraft, the transponder transmitted two overlapping mirror image polar diagrams either side of the runway in turn, as shown in **Figure 3**. The transmission from the transponder operated on predetermined spot frequencies between

214 and 234MHz. It comprised wide pulses from the left antenna and narrow ones from the right, described as dashes and dots respectively.

The earlier version of BABS suffered from some deficiencies. The transponder used two separate Yagi antennas with narrow band characteristics and large side lobes. It is difficult to design a Yagi free from side lobes – and this was in the days long before computer antenna modelling. These lobes provided false equi-signal paths, the first of which were some 40-50° off the line of the runway. This could be a potential danger for less experienced crews.

In addition, each antenna was fed with separate lengths of coax cable and these had to be matched to the antennas very carefully. Mismatches inevitably occur in any antenna system in practice and it is almost impossible to ensure that both transmitting arrays radiate exactly equally. Furthermore, the characteristics of the cable changed slightly due to weathering, with the result that the signals arriving at the two antennas were not equal. This caused the equi-signal zone to swing to one side of the runway by an amount depending on this difference and this was a dangerous feature of these early systems. Other inaccuracies arose owing to cross-polarisation effects caused by metal frameworks and wires in the vicinity of its transmitting antenna, which re-radiated horizontally polarised signals and distorted the carefully designed polar diagrams.

The fix was to use cavity backed slot antennas and these were a feature of BABS Mk II, introduced in 1944. The resonant cavity was described briefly in the February 2012 Antennas. Cavity resonators are very high Q parallel tuned circuits and are often used as high Q filters and high power diplexers in VHF/UHF applications. A cavity resonator is simply a metal box

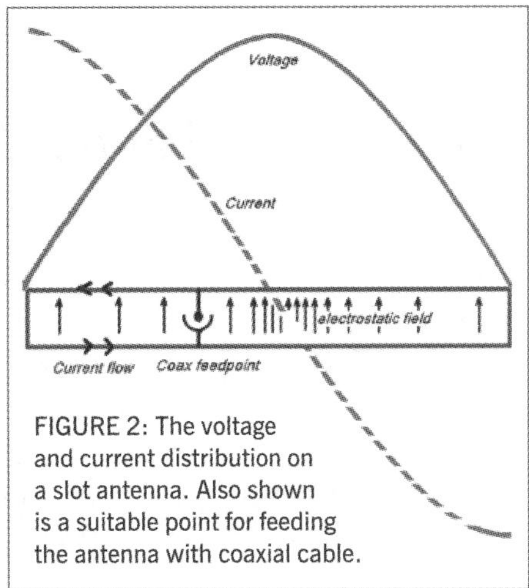


FIGURE 2: The voltage and current distribution on a slot antenna. Also shown is a suitable point for feeding the antenna with coaxial cable.

having a resonant frequency related to its size. This is similar to a two-conductor transmission line with closed ends that will resonate at wavelengths at particular multiples of the line length. A half-wave slot cut in this cavity will radiate when RF power is fed to it and is an alternative method of feeding a slot, compared with the transmission line feed method described earlier.

The cavity resonator used in the BABS antenna consisted of a large rectangular box with two half-wave slots cut opposite to one another in the corners. The cavity was energised with a quarter wave vertical probe.

At the centre point of each of the slots, relay-operated shorting contacts prevented radiation when closed and allowed radiation when open. During operation the relays were closed alternately so that each slot transmitted in turn, synchronised with the appropriate pulse width from the transmitter. The cavity resonator was placed in front of a corner reflector, see **Figure 4**, to tailor the polar diagrams to the required mirror-image overlapping beams and to minimise spurious side lobes.

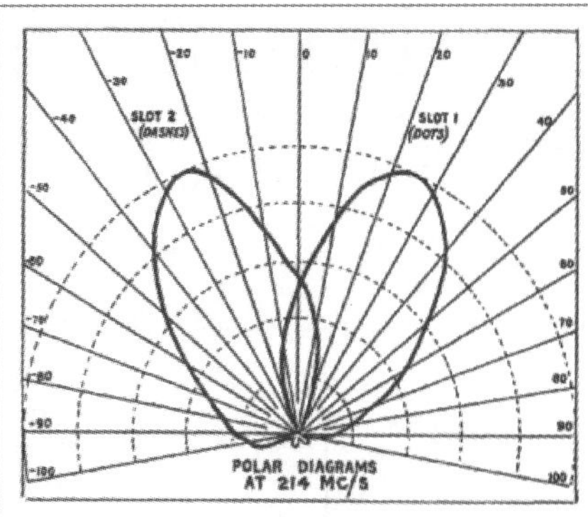


FIGURE 3: The transmitter slot antenna polar diagrams from AP 1093JD, Vol 1, Chap 6.

A further advantage of this arrangement was that any mismatches or attenuation occurring in the feeder system between the transmitter and the antenna were exactly similar for both transmitting slots because they were fed by a single probe. The only factor that could cause a difference between the signals radiated from the two slots would be lack of symmetry in the system. Provided that the two slots were identical, in identical positions relative to the corner reflector and to other conductors, the radiation pattern must have been the same for each.

Cross-polarisation effects were cut down to a minimum by reducing the number of metal supports and cross members as far as possible, by designing the corner reflector to give as much electrical shielding as possible and by making the whole arrangement perfectly symmetrical so that what cross polarisation there was would have the same effect for both antennas.

The same slots were used both for transmission and for reception and the system was almost entirely free from side lobes, so that there are no false equi-signal lines within 150° of the correct heading. The slot antennas were switched so that each antenna transmitted for 1/15th of a second in turn.

The interrogating equipment in the aircraft was Mk II Rebecca and an example of the display received from the BABS beacon is shown in **Photo 1**. When the aircraft was correctly aligned with the runway both wide and narrow pulses had the same amplitude. If, how ever, the aircraft is to one side or the other runway, one of the pulses appears larger than the other, as shown in Photo 1. The accuracy was said to have been between 0.5° and 0.75° in azimuth.

My overwhelming recollection of maintenance on this equipment is of humping the very heavy Marconi signal generator type 53, the wavemeter Type W-1649 and the RF power meter from the signals vehicle to the BABS installation.

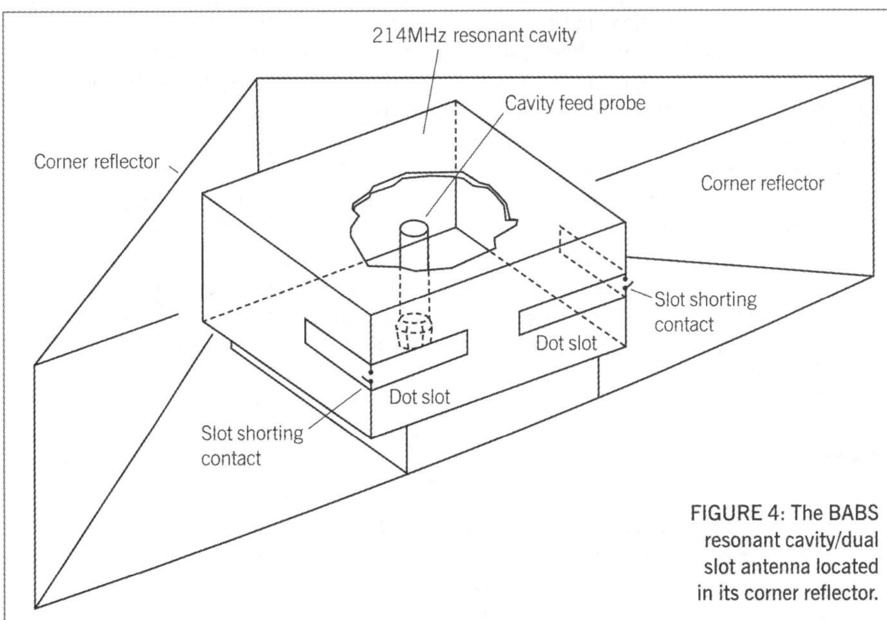


FIGURE 4: The BABS resonant cavity/dual slot antenna located in its corner reflector.

**REFERENCES**

[1] 'Field Distribution near a Centre-Fed Half-Wave Radiating Slot' by PJ Putman MA, B Russell MA, BSc and W Walkinshaw MA, *Journal of the IEE*, July 1948

# Antennas

## The Non Antenna, the loop revisited and *EZNEC*

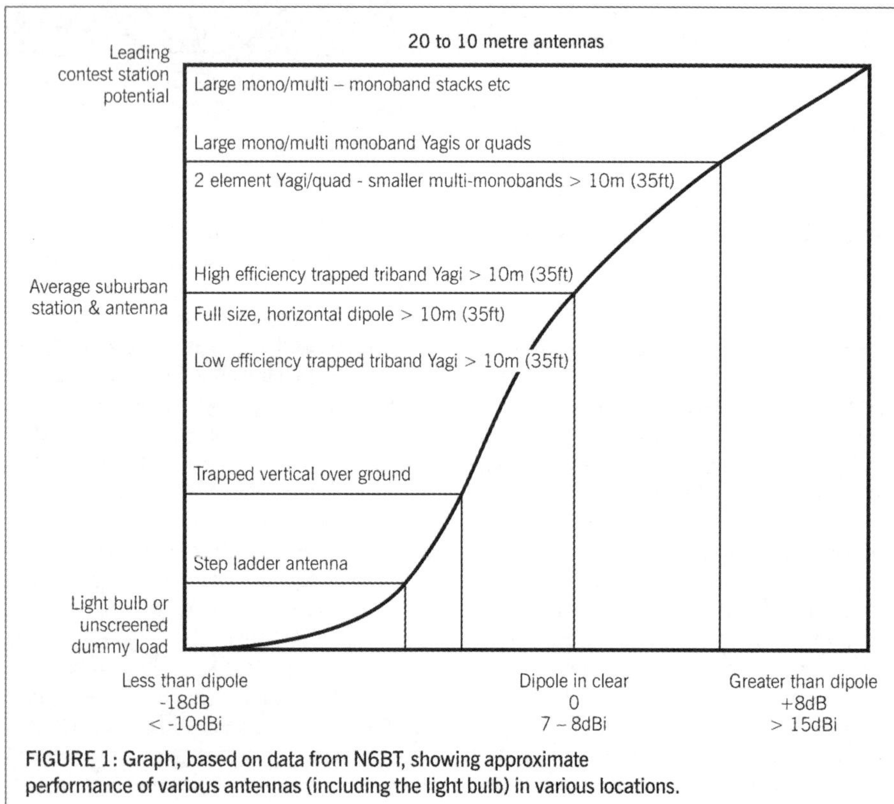


**FIGURE 1: Graph, based on data from N6BT, showing approximate performance of various antennas (including the light bulb) in various locations.**

**THE NON ANTENNA.** I have a rather convoluted antenna feed system because of the need to test and compare various antennas. The main operating takes place from the bedroom shack at the house. I also have a vintage radio project comprising a refurbished HRO receiver and a rebuilt Harvey Radio Laboratories transmitter (circa 1939) located in a shed at the bottom of the garden. This rig is normally used with an end fed wire antenna and is matched to the rig with a manual MFJ-989c ATU. A separate automatic ATU (DGC SC-230) is used when this wire antenna is connected to the rig in the bedroom shack. Changing over from local to remote use entails changing the feed and antenna connections to the appropriate ATU.

Recently I changed over the ATUs to connect the long wire via the automatic SC-230 on 7MHz. I noticed that the ATU was struggling to find the right matching spot but it eventually settled. I then worked a couple of EU stations but I had the feeling that the band wasn't as lively as it should have been.

On inspection of the antenna connections in the shed I found that, while I had changed the coax feed over, I had neglected to change the antenna over – I had been in QSO without an antenna having been connected at all! It seemed hard to credit. It is fortunate that I was using relatively low power or I might have done the ATU a mischief. The antenna has a reasonable ground system and is fed via a long feedline so it must have been a combination of these two that allowed the system to work as an inefficient antenna. There is no current choke on this feeder.

It makes one wonder about the operation of some electrically small commercial antennas where operational descriptions include strong indicators of feedline common-mode current. If instructions warn against feedline chokes or give advice regarding the length and positioning of feedlines then there is a good chance the feedline is contributing to the antenna performance through common mode currents (or antenna currents as we used to call them).

It is surprising what will work as an antenna. Those of you with long memories may recall the Strange Antenna Challenge hosted by Erik Weaver, N0EW, described in Antennas, June 2006. The idea of the challenge was simple: construct an antenna from something not normally used as an antenna such as metal folding chairs, shopping trolleys, chicken wire, fences, ladders and trucks.

Inspired by this, I 'constructed' an antenna from two step ladders, placed them on a garden table and fed them as two elements of a dipole using a two metre (6ft) length of 400Ω ladder line feeder. Using a SEM Z-match and an IC-706 on CW, QSOs were no more difficult than working with QRP (less than 5 watts) into a 'normal' multiband dipole antenna. In just over an hour I made 5 QSOs around Europe and, on average, my reports were about 2 S-points down on the ones I gave out.

Thomas Schiller, N6BT, writing in *QST*, claimed 'Everything Works' and demonstrated the point by having QSOs using an antenna comprising of nothing more than a light bulb fixed on top of a short pole. He also produced a graph, see **Figure 1**, showing what you might expect from various antennas (including the light bulb) in various locations. One thing that you will notice is that the dipole performs quite well provided it is high and in the clear. I have added my step ladder antenna to Figure 1.

**HIGH VOLTAGE ON SMALL LOOP ANTENNAS.** Almost all textbooks on antennas show the standing wave current on a half wave dipole as shown in **Figure 2**, with high current and low voltage at the centre (low impedance) and low current and high voltage (high impedance) at the ends. This is shown in the *EZNEC* dipole model, see **Figure 3**, which shows the current distribution over the length of the antenna structure. RF currents in an antenna structure are responsible for overall antenna performance. High voltage and high impedance is implied by low current.

In the April Antennas I noted

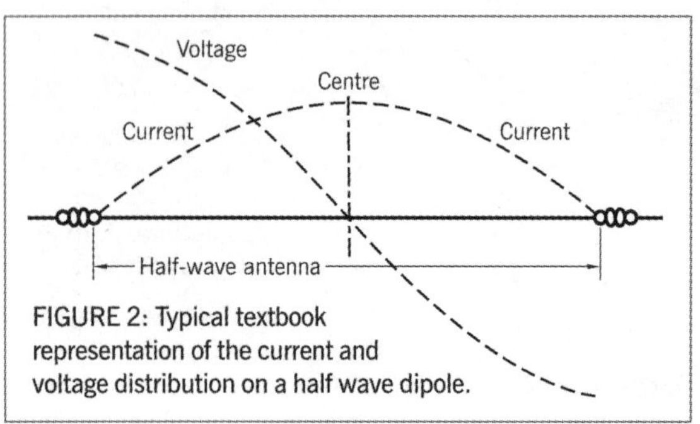


**FIGURE 2: Typical textbook representation of the current and voltage distribution on a half wave dipole.**

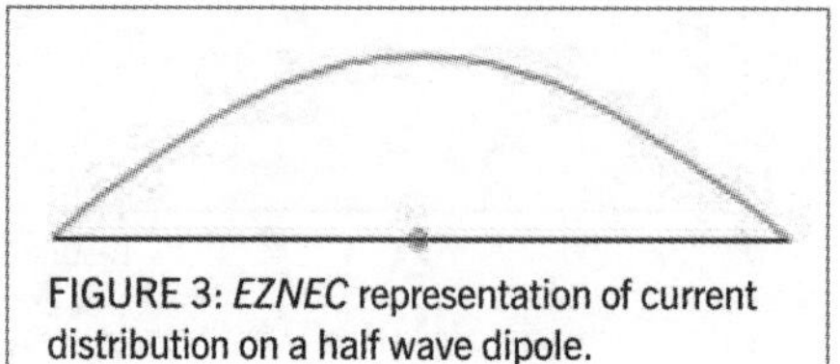

**FIGURE 3: *EZNEC* representation of current distribution on a half wave dipole.**

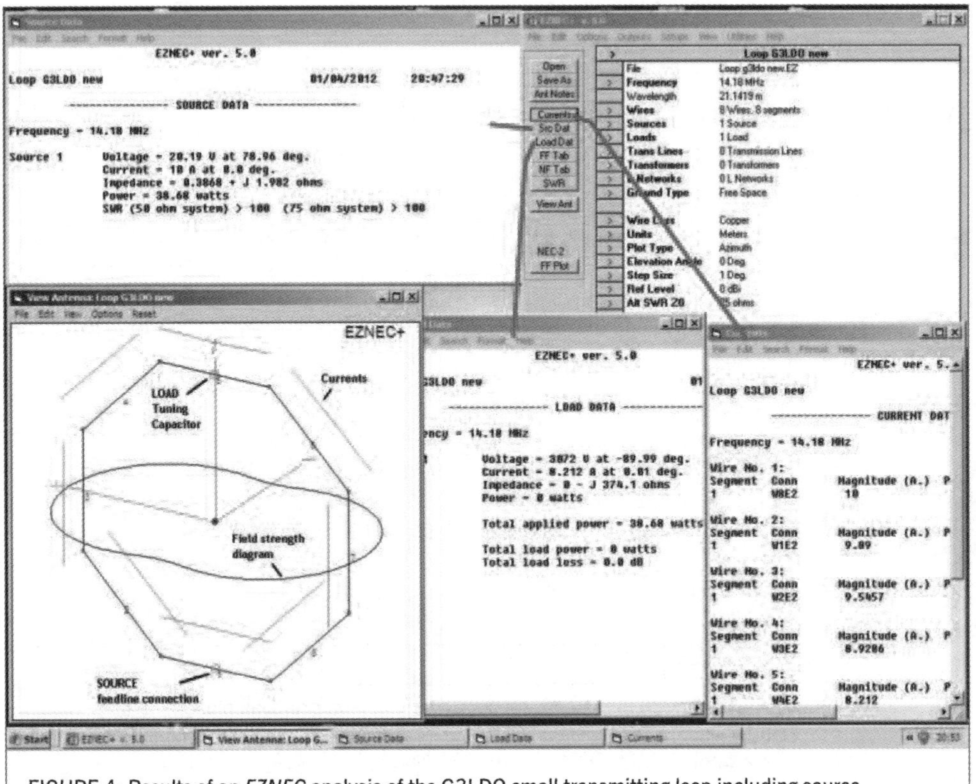


FIGURE 4: Results of an *EZNEC* analysis of the G3LDO small transmitting loop including source, load and current sub menus.

that the current in a small transmitting loop is high and fairly constant throughout the structure, yet it is well known that very high voltages exist across the tuning capacitor. Peter Martinez, G3PLX, explained, "If I read your column correctly, you are puzzled by an apparent contradiction between (a) the statement that the current round a small loop is fairly constant and (b) the presence of high voltages across the capacitor. You seemed to be trying to find ways to make one of these conditions vanish in order to resolve the contradiction.

"The answer lies in Ohm's law. Not the V = I x R version but V = I x (2 x pi x F x L). That is, the voltage is the product of the current and the reactance of the loop inductance. From your Figure 2 the loop reactance is 335Ω and the circulating current is 10A. The product of these two is 3.3kV. This will be the voltage across the capacitor.

"Since the loop is small, this analysis is sufficient. I think you may have been trying to think of the loop in the same terms as much larger antennas with standing wave patterns, which always have currents OR voltages but not both!"

This is echoed by Brian Austin, G0GSF: "You talked of high current being associated with low voltage but that's only true when there is a significant standing wave of current (and hence voltage) present along the conductor – as it the case with antennas that are a significant fraction of a wavelength, such as a half wave dipole for example. As you said yourself, the small loop's current is essentially constant in amplitude, hence the voltage across the capacitor is simply given by Ohm's law".

G0GSF also takes issue with the data produced by the loop design program (www.66pacific.com/calculators) and notes, "I must admit to being somewhat puzzled by the numbers given in the simulation you show. Assuming the current is correct (9.91A), then for a total antenna resistance of Rrad + Rloss = 0.442 + 0.067 = 0.509Ω, the input power to the loop is $(9.91)^2$ x 0.509 = 50W whereas the transmitter power is given as 100W. That would require a loop current of around 14A. Similarly, the loop's Q is given as 329, but since X = 335Ω then with total resistance of 0.509Ω the Q = 335/0.509 = 657, which is twice as large as that given."

A design program like this is only as good as the formula on which it is based. There is something seductive about computer programs that produce results down to three decimal places but if the program base is incorrect all you finish up with is precise inaccuracy. I must confess to not having checked this data produced by this program. In the bottom RH cornerthis web page is "Source: the *ARRL Antenna Handbook*" and I had relied on the veracity of that document. Having said that, I did use the program to design the loop antenna shown in Photo 1 of April Antennas where I was only concerned with how large to make the structure and the approximate value and voltage rating of the tuning capacitor.

## *EZNEC* AND LOOP CONSTRUCTION.

I have used Roy Llewellen's *EZNEC* program for analysing antennas for many years and these have included small transmitting loops. The antenna structure is modelled as a series of straight wires as shown in **Figure 4**. The ends of these wires are defined using XYZ coordinates as shown in the wire table, **Figure 5**.

You can appreciate that it is difficult to position the wire ends with the correct coordinates so that they meet up in such a manner that they all connect together as a loop. In the past if I wanted to build a new model of a loop I simply modified an old one I had previously and laboriously constructed. I had got into the habit of doing this over the years and had overlooked a feature in later *EZNEC* upgrades that builds a loop automatically once certain parameters have been entered. This feature is accessed via Create (wires table, Figure 5), which results in a loop construction window seen in **Figure 6**. The loop design illustrated in Figure 4 was the result of data entered into Figure 6.

Although outside this discussion it is worth noting that an even more complex structure, the helix antenna, can be constructed automatically using *EZNEC* via the Create function.

Wires
Wire Create Edit Other
Coord Entry Mode Preserve Connections Show Wire Insulation

| No. | End 1 | | | | End 2 | | | | Diameter | Segs |
|---|---|---|---|---|---|---|---|---|---|---|
| | X (m) | Y (m) | Z (m) | Conn | X (m) | Y (m) | Z (m) | Conn | (mm) | |
| 1 | 0 | -0.273125 | -0.659382 | W8E2 | 0 | 0.273125 | -0.659382 | W2E1 | 22 | 1 |
| 2 | 0 | 0.273125 | -0.659382 | W1E2 | 0 | 0.659382 | -0.273125 | W3E1 | 22 | 1 |
| 3 | 0 | 0.659382 | -0.273125 | W2E2 | 0 | 0.659382 | 0.273125 | W4E1 | 22 | 1 |
| 4 | 0 | 0.659382 | 0.273125 | W3E2 | 0 | 0.273125 | 0.659382 | W5E1 | 22 | 1 |
| 5 | 0 | 0.273125 | 0.659382 | W4E2 | 0 | -0.273125 | 0.659382 | W6E1 | 22 | 1 |
| 6 | 0 | -0.273125 | 0.659382 | W5E2 | 0 | -0.659382 | 0.273125 | W7E1 | 22 | 1 |
| 7 | 0 | -0.659382 | 0.273125 | W6E2 | 0 | -0.659382 | -0.273125 | W8E1 | 22 | 1 |
| 8 | 0 | -0.659382 | -0.273125 | W7E2 | 0 | -0.273125 | -0.659382 | W1E1 | 22 | 1 |

FIGURE 5: *EZNEC* wires submenu. Access to the loop creation facility is by clicking Create in the top left hand corner.

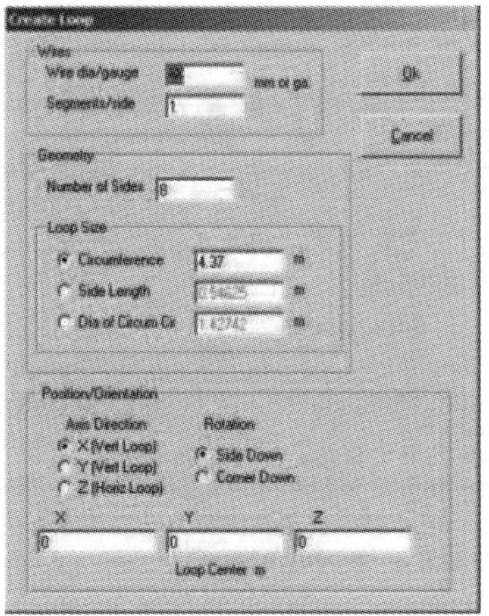


FIGURE 6: *EZNEC* 'loop create' submenu.

# Antennas

## The homebrew Yagi and common mode problems

PHOTO 1: The G8PJC 145MHz three-element Yagi located in the loft. The elements are not hard drawn copper so need to be supported on wood battens.

HOMEBREW 145MHz YAGI. Before the days of computer modeling of antennas I used to model HF antennas using VHF antennas. Of course a model VHF antenna can be used for normal VHF activity and, if weather protection isn't an issue, the construction can be very simple with the antenna being made from wire and wood. An example is that of a three-element Yagi using 2mm hard-drawn copper for the elements. These are fixed to a wooden boom with wire netting staples, as shown in **Figure 1**. The antenna dimensions are:

145MHz: D=940mm, A=990mm, R=1072mm, S1=250mm, S2=313mm

430MHz: D=310mm, A=322mm, R=352mm, S1=103mm, S2=103mm.

The total length of the VHF antenna gamma match is 150mm and the spacing is approximately 26mm. This spacing is not critical.

THE G8PJC ANTENNA. John McDonald, G8PJC, needed a 145MHz directional antenna so that he could communicate with Bracknell Radio Amateur Club members. He built the antenna shown in Figure 1 and fixed it in his loft as shown in **Photo 1**. He says, "My version of the VHF Yagi is made from 2.5mm$^2$ mains wire supported on a wood battens with the driven element fed via a gamma match. Connection to the coax feeder is via a terminal block and a PL259 socket.

"The problem with the antenna is a high level of common mode signal on the coax cable as detected by changes in SWR when the down lead is moved or the cable touched. All the testing is carried out with a MFJ-259 analyser. I would like to know what to expect from this antenna and how should it be tuned."

I don't recall having common mode problems with the VHF Yagi feeder when I originally built my antenna. At the time (1989) I didn't have instruments such as the MFJ259. I just used an old valve transmitter and a SWR meter.

I needed to investigate these problems but my original Yagi had long gone, so I felt there was no alternative but to build a new one. I didn't have any 14SWG (2mm) hard drawn copper wire. The only material available was 16SWG (1.6mm), which seemed is a bit thin for the elements of a 145MHz antenna. However, I did have some 10SWG (3.2mm) enamelled wire among my antenna material so I used that. The new antenna is shown in **Photo 2**.

You may notice small extensions to the length of the driven element – I had originally cut this element too short. The rule for measuring and cutting (forgive the pun) antenna elements is the same as for carpentry or joinery – measure twice and cut once.

The antenna was placed on top of a plastic garden table as shown in Photo 2 but when I came to adjust the gamma matching adjustments I found it impossible to get a low SWR on the MFJ-269. Repositioning the antenna so that it was about quarter of a wavelength above the surface of the table on a wooden box made a huge difference. It was now possible to obtain a feeder to antenna match as shown in **Photo 3** and **Figure 2**.

DETUNING EFFECTS. There was something strange about this table. Plastic is used throughout its construction, including the legs. The detuning effect caused by the table was worse than when the antenna was placed

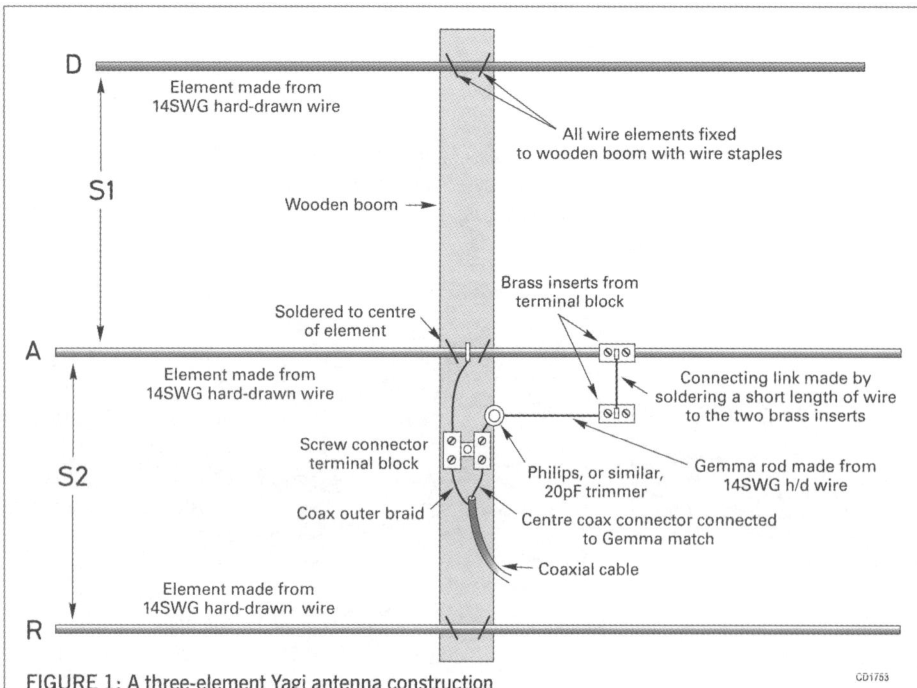

FIGURE 1: A three-element Yagi antenna construction using copper wire elements fixed to a wooden boom.

PHOTO 2: The latest edition of my 145MHz three-element Yagi with the elements made from 10SWG (3.2mm) enamelled wire.

PHOTO 3: Setup for adjusting the antenna gamma match using the MFJ-269.

on the grass below the table. Environment can play a part in the performance of a high Q antenna such as a Yagi. When such an antennas is located in a loft location its position relative to any electromagnetic obstructions such as electrical wiring has to be considered.

My advice would be to make all measurements in an open space with the antenna three quarters of a wavelength high. When you install it in the loft space, note if there are any changes from the 'open space' measurement settings.

While in the open space testing phase it is a good idea to check the directivity, which can be done using the S-meter of a transceiver tuned to a local repeater. By holding the antenna by the boom at the reflector end, vertically polarised, you should be able to locate the position of the repeater. Then repeat with the antenna in the opposite direction. There should be a difference of at least 4 S-points in the two readings if the antenna is working properly.

**CURRENT CHOKES.** Let's return to the common mode problem reported by G8PJC. As you know, one method of making a current choke to minimise common mode effects is just to just roll the feeder into a coil near to the antenna feed point. During an exchange of e-mails I received the following:

"As you can see from the attached photo (Photo 1) I am now using just three turns of coax as a current choke balun . I was able to achieve a SWR of 1.1:1 measured at the transceiver end of 6m of RG58 C/U but slight common mode effects are still observed when the coax is moved about at the transceiver end. To achieve a low SWR I noted that the choke needed to be at 90° to the plane of the antenna and the coax down lead must not be a vertical drop. Also I noted that making the coax coil a bit more symmetrical improved the SWR."

I made a similar current choke balun to the one described by G8PJC, although my model might have been slightly smaller, having a diameter of around 100mm. The measured resonant frequency was 94MHz, where its impedance was well over 1000Ω, see **Figure 3**. At 145MHz the impedance was down to just over 300Ω and, as you might expect, was rather reactive.

**PHOTO 4: A 145MHz current mode choke made simply by winding just over two turns of RG8 Super on a short length of 35mm plastic waste pipe.**

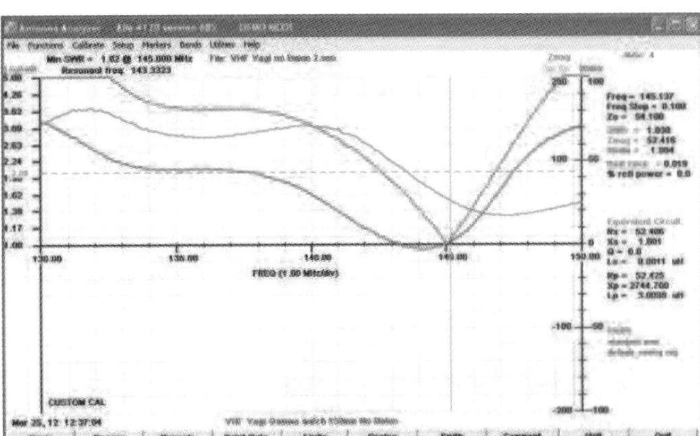

**FIGURE 2: The frequency/matching characteristics of the three-element Yagi measured using the AIM 4170. SWR is shown by the light red trace while the green and purple traces indicate impedance (polar form).**

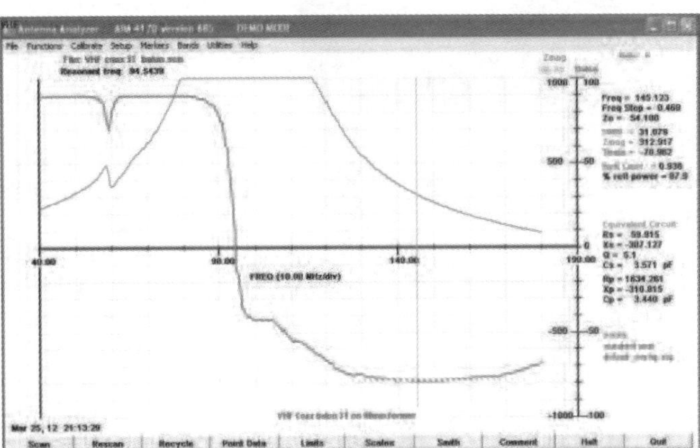

**FIGURE 3: Frequency characteristics of 3 turns of RG8 Super wound into a 100mm diameter coil. The resonant frequency is near to 94MHz.**

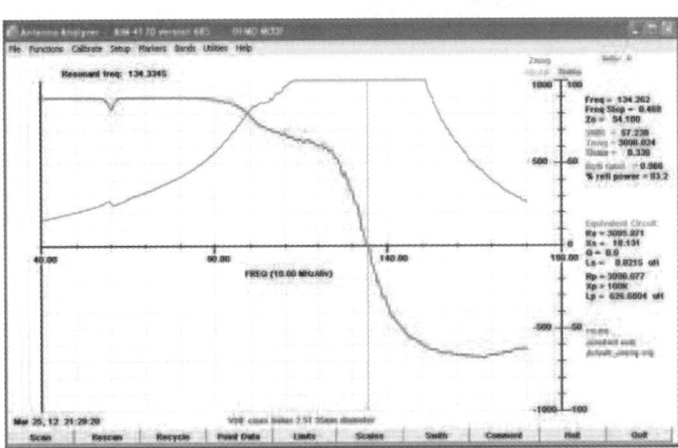

**FIGURE 4: Frequency characteristics of the current choke shown in Photo 4. Although not quite on resonance at 145MHz, its impedance is well over 1000Ω.**

The resonant frequency of this type of choke arrangement is fairly sharp and not just any coil of coax will do. I tried various coils of coax during my attempt to make an effective VHF coax choke. I found that just over two turns of RG8 Super wound on a short length of 35mm plastic waste pipe, illustrated in **Photo 4**, gave a suitable characteristic. Although not quite on resonance, its impedance at 145MHz is well over 1000Ω. The characteristics of this choke can be seen in **Figure 4**.

**GAMMA MATCH.** As you can see from Figure 1 and Photo 3 I use a gamma match to transform the feeder impedance to the driven element impedance. G8PJC is of the opinion that the gamma match creates a significant contribution to common mode currents on the feeder. I know the gamma match is not popular with everyone; the rather asymmetrical layout of the matching system gives the impression of an asymmetrical current distribution on the driven element. The opposite side of the element to the feed point is a counterpoise and the currents should be equal – provided that some of the current on the counterpoise side is not travelling down the outside braid of the coax as common mode current.

The obvious disadvantage of the gamma match in most VHF and HF permanent Yagi antenna structures is the small adjustable capacitor, usually housed in a nearby plastic box where it is difficult (if not impossible) to protect it from the ingress of water.

A more practical approach is to adjust the gamma rod to the correct length and the capacitor to the right value for the correct match. The variable capacitor can then be replaced with a good quality fixed one. This gives a much more weatherproof arrangement without having to build a special weatherproof box for the capacitor. You might have to make up the fixed capacitor with several in parallel to get the desired value.

# Antennas

## RigExpert AA-1000 antenna analyser

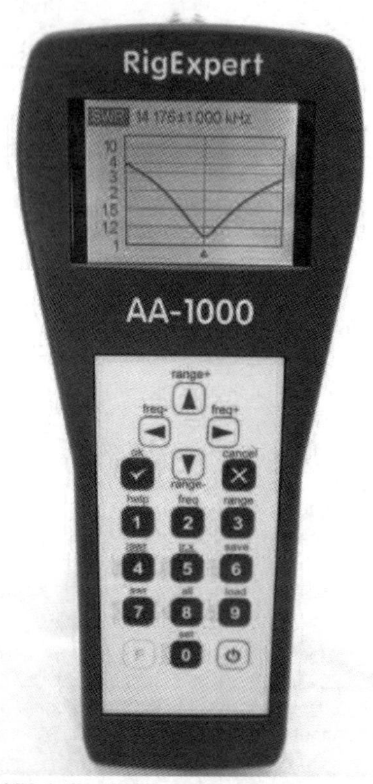


**PHOTO 1: The RigExpert AA-1000 Antenna Analyser showing an SWR display.**

INTRODUCTION. In a change from my normal column style, I've reviewed a piece of equipment this month. The RigExpert AA-1000 Antenna Analyser is a portable instrument made in Ukraine. It can be used to perform antenna and transmission line measurements over a wide range of frequencies from 0.1 to 1000MHz. It is housed in a blue plastic case of 23 x 10 x 5.5cm (9 x 4 x 2in) with a water resistant control panel at the front. The AA-1000 is shown in **Photo 1**.

The device under test is connected via an N connector on the top of the instrument. An adapter to SO239 is also provided. At the bottom of the case is a socket for a USB connection to a PC. A case is included; it has a neck strap and a clear plastic front so that the instrument can be used while still in the case.

OPERATION. The simplest measurement is SWR on a single frequency. The frequency is set using the FREQ key and numeric keypad and the SWR is displayed digitally and on a graphical bar meter. The left and right arrow buttons can be used to change the frequency and home in on the lowest SWR point.

This instrument has the ability to display the SWR for up to five different frequencies at a time, which is a useful feature for tuning multiband antennas. The SWR measurement range is 1 to 100 in the numerical mode and 1 to 10 in graph mode.

The AA-1000 will show various parameters of a load on a single screen, as shown in **Photo 2**.

The most useful information is obtained when parameters are measured using a frequency sweep. In this way the SWR characteristics of an antenna can be plotted on a graph as shown in **Figure 1**.

An alternative graph option lets you plot R (impedance) and X (reactance). The AA-1000 can display both positive and negative values of R and X. This option can be used to measure capacitance and inductance, to tune traps and coaxial stubs, measure the characteristic impedance of coaxial cable.

The results of up to 100 plots can be saved to the device's internal memory to be recalled and displayed later.

The AA-1000 can also be used as a signal generator for test purposes. The output signal has a level of about +10dBm into a 50Ω load.

POWER. The RigExpert AA-1000 is powered powered by three 1.5V AA 2300mAh Ni-MH batteries that give a maximum of 3 hours of continuous measurement or two days in stand-by mode. A charger is included, which charges the batteries fairly quickly (although no time test was performed). The charger is designed to take from one to four batteries, although only three are used in this instrument. Red LEDs on the charger indicate that the batteries are being charged, changing to green to indicate when the batteries are fully charged. A nice feature is clip-on battery cover, see **Photo 3**. You don't have to take the instrument apart to fit the batteries.

COMPUTER CONTROL. The USB socket allows the AA-1000 to be connected to a PC. Applications for Microsoft Windows are contained on the CD that accompanies the unit. Linux and Mac applications are available from the manufacturer via the internet.

The *AntScope* software allows you to carry out measurements controlling the AA-1000 from the computer rather than the keypad. The main benefits are a much increased resolution; also, graphs can readily be captured to the Windows clipboard from where they can be pasted into a graphics application and saved in any convenient format. The computer generated charts also allow you to see all the measurements at any point just by running the mouse over the graph.

ACCURACY. There are a couple of methods that can be used for checking impedance measuring accuracy. One is to measure the value a precision dummy load. I have a couple of General Radio precision 50Ω loads fitted to Type 874 coaxial connectors. These connectors are hermaphroditic (there is no male and female), so gender-changers are not needed, however they do need to be adapted to N connectors. Type 874 connectors reportedly maintain a 50Ω characteristic up to around 4GHz so I had some confidence in their value at 900MHz. I also had other dummy loads, which you can see in **Photo 4**. Test results using these loads are shown in **Table 1**.

The above method is fine for a single impedance measurement, but what about

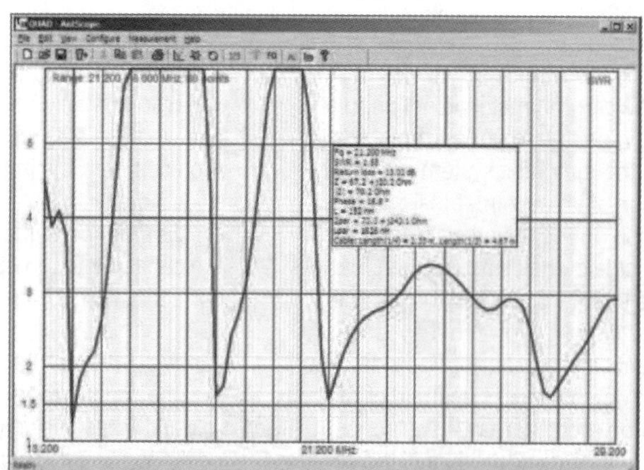

**FIGURE 1: The SWR characteristics of my multiband quad (14, 18 and 21MHz) plotted using the AA-1000 but shown on the screen of a connected computer.**

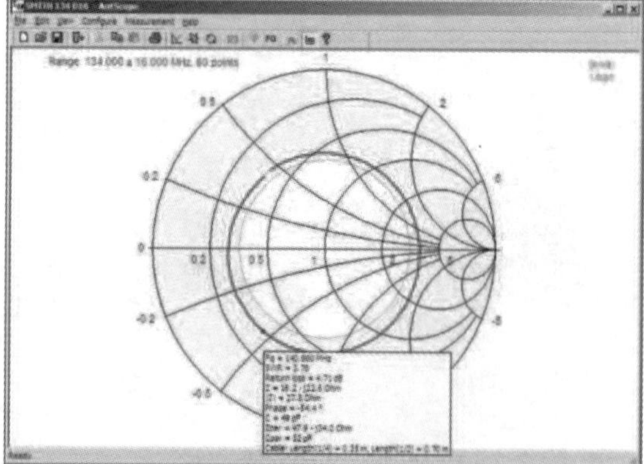

**FIGURE 2: AA-1000 Smith chart impedance plots of a 204Ω load measured via a 3m length of 5D-2V 50Ω coax over a frequency range of 118 to 150MHz. Note the data presented at the variable marker.**

PHOTO 2: The AA-1000 display showing measurements of SWR, RL (return loss), |Z| (Impedance magnitude), R and X (R ±jX).

TABLE 1: Measurements of four different loads at 21, 200, 400 and 900MHz.

| Load | Measured R ±jΩ at frequency | | | |
|---|---|---|---|---|
| | 21MHz | 200MHz | 400MHz | 900MHz |
| Homebrew 204Ω | 194 -j47 | 95.4 -j77 | 41.6 -j37 | 26.7 +j21 |
| General Radio GE 1602 50Ω | 50.4 j0 | 50.2 j0 | 49.0 -j.02 | 48.3 +j1.9 |
| General Radio 874 WM 50Ω | 50.0 j0 | 49.0 -j0.1 | 48.0 +j2.0 | 51.0 +j1.4 |
| RS 50Ω | 52.0 -j1.2 | 48.0 -j0.6 | 45.0 -j3.0 | 51.0 +j1.4 |

other impedance values? A method of checking the accuracy of an impedance measuring instrument over a range of impedance values was described in the December 2011 Antennas using the AIM 4170 (which I now use as a standard comparison). A range of impedances can be provided by using various electrical lengths of coax terminated with fixed load of around 200Ω. A more convenient method of changing the coax electrical lengths is to plot impedances over a range of different frequencies.

When these measurements are plotted on a Smith chart they should follow the SWR circle of the chart. Any deviation from this circle indicates a measurement inaccuracy. The RigExpert AA-1000 has a facility for automatically plotting a range of impedance measurements over a range of different frequencies and an example of such a plot shown in **Figure 2**.

There are no deviations from the measurements circle indicated the instrument is measuring impedance accurately. This circle is not quite concentric with the 3:1 SWR marker – this is thought to be caused by the difference between the actual coax impedance and the assumed impedance value built into the software.

The Smith chart shown in Figure 2 uses a normalised scale where 50Ω is represented by 1, 25Ω by 0.5 and 100Ω by 2 etc. Additionally, it uses the more modern convention where the resistance (real) scale is in the horizontal plane, with the low impedance (or short) to the left.

**CALIBRATION.** A feature of better-designed modern antenna analysers is calibration. The RigExpert AA-1000 comes in this category. Calibration enables the feeder between the instrument and the antenna to be calibrated so that it presents a one-to-one transform over the calibrated frequency range. Calibration is achieved using three different calibration standards, namely 'open', 'short' and a 'load', usually 50Ω. These standards should be of high quality, particularly when preparing calibration cables at UHF. Calibration standards are not provided with the AA-1000.

**TDR (TIME DOMAIN REFLECTOMETER).** The RigExpert AA-1000 has a feature called Time Domain Reflectometry. This can be used for locating impedance discontinuities or faults in transmission lines.

Traditional TDR instruments function by sending a short electrical pulse (impulse response) or a step function (step response) pulse over the transmission line and analysing the reflected waveform. The time delay, amplitude and shape of the reflected pulse indicate the position and nature of a discontinuity or fault.

According to the user manual, the AA-1000 uses a different technique for measuring TDR. "First, R and X (the real and the imaginary part of the impedance) are measured over the whole frequency range (up to 1000 MHz). An IFFT (Inverse Fast Fourier Transform) is then applied to the data. From this the impulse response and step responses are calculated".

An example of the TDR display can be seen in **Figure 3**. The horizontal axis is calibrated in physical distance to the discontinuity while the vertical axis is calibrated in reflection coefficient, (0 for matched impedance load, -1 for a short load and +1 for an open load).

**BOTTOM LINE.** I found the AA-1000 accurate over its wide frequency range and an easy and convenient instrument to use. All measurements and storage of data can be performed without a computer being connected. I employed it to resolve to some outstanding transmission line and standards issues; so much so that the XYL asked when I was going to stop playing with my new toy.

My main question is to wonder what market is the AA-1000 aimed at? In the UK there is no amateur frequency allocation between 440MHz and 1000MHz, so although it is a nice instrument for amateur radio, over half of its spectrum coverage is inappropriate. However, it probably has a commercial use for the wide range of users in that part of the UHF spectrum.

The AA-1000 is priced at £1050 from KMK UK Limited, www.mixw.co.uk.

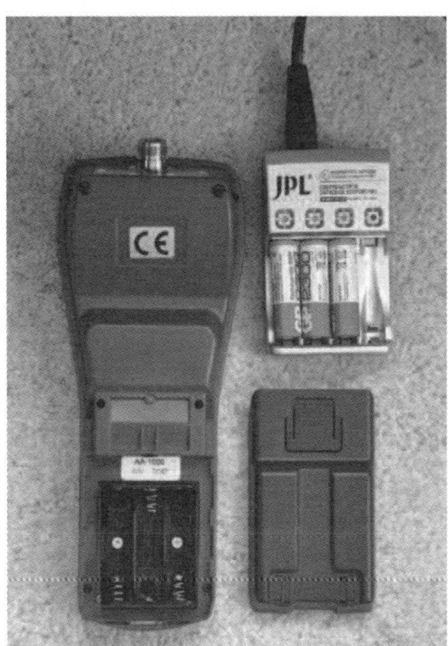


PHOTO 3: Rear of the AA-1000 showing the battery compartment and the battery charger.

PHOTO 4: Dummy loads used for the measurements in Table 1. From left to right, General Radio GE 1602 50Ω, General Radio 874 WM 50Ω, Homebrew 204Ω and RS 50Ω.

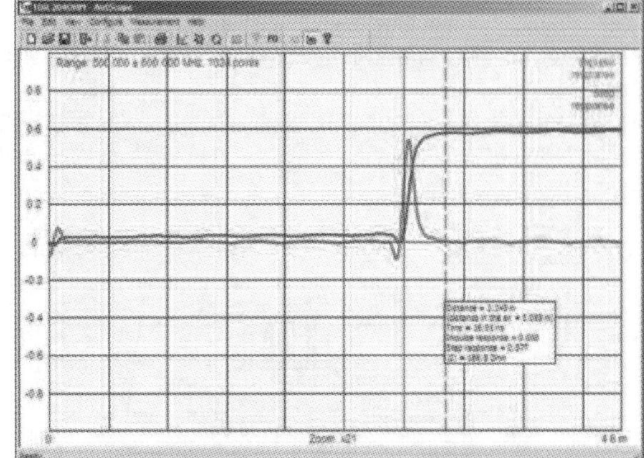

FIGURE 3: AA-1000 TDR display of a 204Ω load measured via a 3m length of 5D-2V 50Ω coax.

# Antennas

## The Controlled Feeder Radiation Dipole and the G3ENI/G3ZUN 5MHz NVIS variation

**PHOTO 1: A vertical Controlled Feeder Radiation dipole for 14MHz, constructed by taping multi strand insulated copper wire and RG58 coax to a fibreglass support. The coax coil current choke can be seen in the foreground.**

THE G3ENI/G3ZUN REQUIREMENT. There are many locations where an end-fed antenna can be more convenient than a centre or off-centre fed system. However, feeding an end-fed wire against an earth system can lead to high RF voltages or currents in the shack.

John Pegler, G3ENI and Dan Sharpe, G3ZUN required a portable antenna for their 5MHz NVIS experiments. A search through literature indicated that 'controlled feeder radiation' would prevent the RF in the shack problem while at the same time allowing the convenience of an end-fed structure. G2HCG described methods of feeding antennas using this technique in **[1]**.

**Figure 1** shows the version selected by G3ENI and G3ZUN

The authors noted, "This flexible design enabled the antenna to be placed in a variety of ways. For example, lying on the ground, hung from an upstairs window, on top of a hedge or the far end up a tree. At G3ENI it was sited on a hedge for the majority of its length at an average height of 3 metres. At G3ZUN the feeder dropped down from an upstairs window and then ran along a hedge at similar height to G3ENI's, rising to about 4 metres at the far end up a tree. The standing wave ratio was found to be well below the 2:1 figure for all 5MHz frequencies.

"The join between the wire and coaxial centre was by means of an eye-bolt to cope with the strain. It was protected from the weather with self-amalgamating tape".

The type of 50Ω coax used on this antenna was not specified but if the antenna is to be portable or light weight then RG-58 or Super 8 would be the most practical. The material used in the top quarter wave section was also unspecified but as it may need to be laid across hedges or trees then a flexible, insulated conductor is called for.

HOW DOES IT WORK? If we consider the simple dipole fed with coax, the coax is connected to the wire elements as shown in **Figure 2**. The two opposing currents, I1 and I2, in the coax feeder are equal but because of the physical differences between the two conductors of the coax feeder it is unlikely that I1 and I2 will be the same in the two conductors of the dipole. The difference between I1 and I2 flows down the outside of the coax as I3 and is known as common mode current.

This current causes the coax to be part of the radiation and reception characteristic of the antenna instead of sticking to its design role as transmission line. This uncontrolled characteristic can cause TVI/BCI on transmit and an increase in noise on receive. It also can cause directional pattern distortion if it occurs on the feeder of a beam antenna. Generally, common mode currents are regarded as undesirable and literature abounds with solutions to minimising them.

However, common mode currents can be put to use – the secret is control. Consider the antenna shown in **Figure 3**. It is a vertical quarter wave antenna with no radials. In this case all the current on the inside of the coax braid will flow down the outside of the braid because it has nowhere else to go. If a high impedance choke is placed a quarter wavelength down from the feed point, the coax outer braid will function as the counterpoise to the vertical element.

This then is the Controlled Feeder Radiation antenna. Its main advantage is mechanical simplicity and there is no requirement for a separate antenna tuner. The antenna can be easily stored and unwound from a cord reel without a tangle of cable and wire so it is fine for portable use. The downside is that it is a single band antenna and that special attention needs to be paid to the design of the choke.

THE G3LDO VERSION. By chance the arrival of the material on the Controlled Feeder Radiation antenna from G3ENI/G3ZUN coincided with a particular requirement of my own. I give a demonstration of an operational vintage (circa 1939) radio station **[2, 3]** at the local East Preston Carnival and I needed a 14MHz antenna. The space available for this antenna measured 1m x 4m and so a vertical was the only option. Last year a vertical

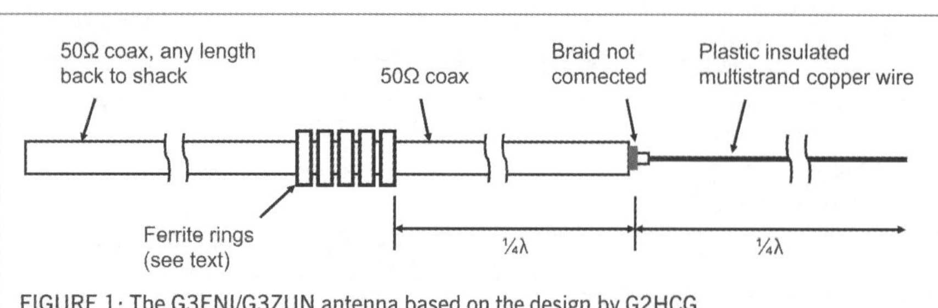


**FIGURE 1: The G3ENI/G3ZUN antenna based on the design by G2HCG.**

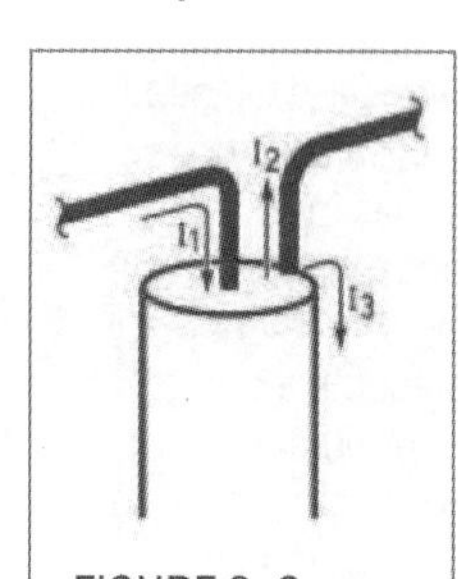


**FIGURE 2: Coax cable connected to a dipole antenna showing the I1, I2 and I3 currents.**

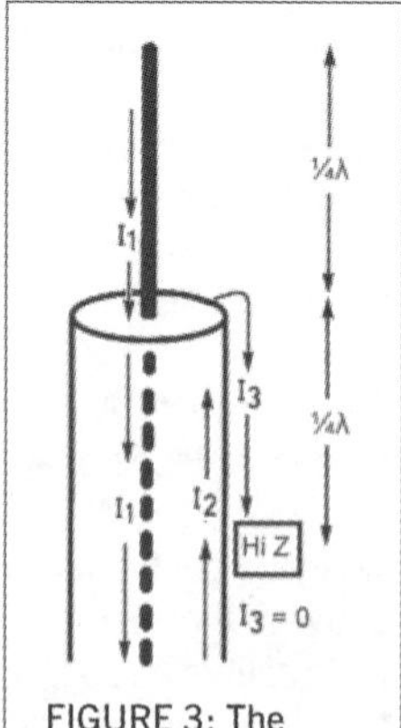


**FIGURE 3: The Controlled Feeder Radiation dipole. It can be deployed vertically as shown or horizontally, such as from an upstairs bedroom window.**

**PHOTO 2: A coax current choke constructed from of 9 turns of RG super 8 coax wound on a 4.25in (110mm) plastic pipe.**

wire was fed against a suspect earth using an ATU but was not very successful.

In the meantime I had also read an article by W2OZH [4] (described in Technical Topics [5]). His antenna for 80m uses a coaxial choke balun comprising 13 turns of cable coil on a cord reel (13 turns, 6 inch diameter) as shown. **Figure 4** shows the construction, schematically, for a frequency of about 3.95MHz (in the American 3.5MHz band). Other frequencies can be simply computed from the equation for simple dipole antennas.

I constructed my version of the antenna by taping 16.5ft of 16SWG multi strand insulated copper wire to a fibreglass support. The bottom end of this wire was connected to the centre conductor of a 17ft length of RG57. Initially, a Ferromagnetics ferrite balun (as shown in Figure 1) was used, but this proved to be unsatisfactory. I then considered a coax coil current choke proposed by W2OZH and this worked very well, with transatlantic QSOs achieved in the middle of the day in poor conditions. The final arrangement of the complete antenna is shown in **Photo 1**.

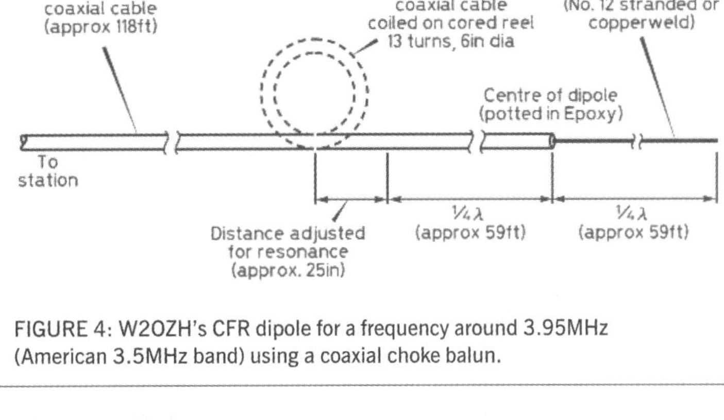


**FIGURE 4: W2OZH's CFR dipole for a frequency around 3.95MHz (American 3.5MHz band) using a coaxial choke balun.**

COAX CURRENT CHOKE. I made some measurements of the resonances and impedances of various coils of coax wound on a 4.25in (11mm) plastic pipe. I finished up with of 9 turns of RG super 8, as shown in **Photo 2**. The choke exhibited a very high impedance of over 12kΩ at resonance when measured using the AIM-4170, as shown in **Figure 5**.

You can appreciate that the resonant frequency of this choke arrangement is very much dependent on the value of any parallel capacitance. The AIM-4170 appears to have a loading capacitance of 10pF. The resonance characteristics shown in Figure 5 occurred with 15pF of capacitance; 10pF from the AIM-4170 and an extra 5pF from a homemade twisted wire arrangement.

This begged the question: what would the resonance of the choke be when inserted into an antenna system with an indeterminate choke loading capacitance? One method tried was by measuring the choke resonance using a dip oscillator. The resonant frequency of the choke (with 15pF) while not connected to the antenna was the same as that measured with the AIM-4170.

When the choke was connected to the antenna shown in Photo 1 it was not possible see a resonance dip. It seems that the antenna loads the choke and it is probable that in practice its impedance is less than the 12kΩ shown in Figure 5. Nevertheless the SWR characteristic of the antenna as a whole was very good, as shown in **Figure 6**.

You often see choke baluns wound without a plastic coil former by scramble winding the coax into a coil and taping it together. This could result in the first and last turns touching each other and cause the distributed capacitance of the choke to be increased. Additionally, the RF-lossy vinyl jacket of the coax may be subjected to a high RF voltage. A single layer winding on a former ensures the RF voltage gradient across the coil is even – and it is easier to predict the resonance.

FERRITE RING CHOKE. A ferrite ring choke is advocated by G3ENI and G3ZUN, see Figure 1. They note, "The cylindrical or clip-on ferrite rings should have a reasonably high $\mu$ and could be Type 43 or 77 material. A length of about 10cm was used".

I tried a W2AU type choke but this didn't work, probably because its impedance is only around 500 – 600Ω. I know that ferrite current choke will work provided it has a high enough impedance. I will return to this subject in a later column.

REFERENCES

[1] 'Controlled Feeder Radiation', G2HCG, *RadCom*, May 1990
[2] G3LDO QRZ.com for photo of vintage rig.
[3] www.g3ldo.co.uk
[4] 'Resonant Feed-Line Dipoles' (*QST*, August 1991, pp24-27)
[5] TT *RadCom*, June 1997 (also *Technical Topics 1995-1999*)

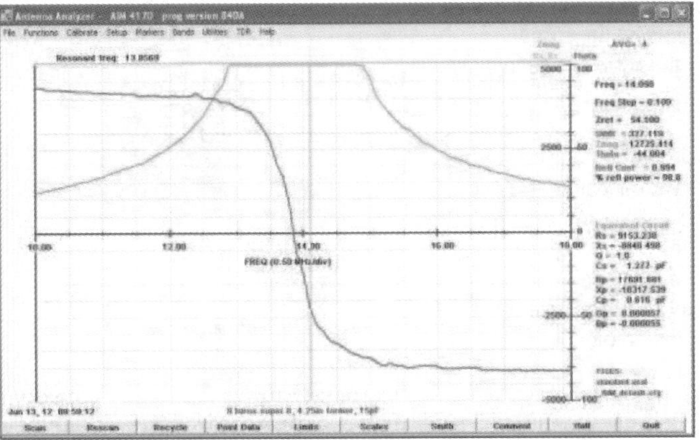

**FIGURE 5: The impedance characteristics of the coax choke shown in Photo 2, measured using the AIM-4170.**

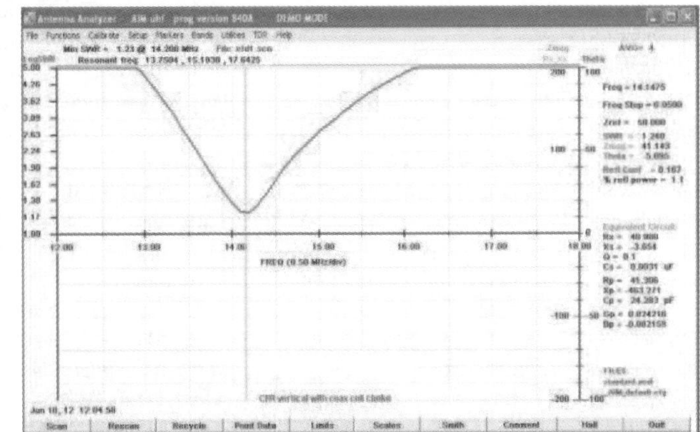

**FIGURE 6: SWR characteristics of the CFR vertical dipole shown in Photo 1. The impedance graphs have been switched off: they wouldn't mean much because the connecting cable was not calibrated.**

# Antennas

## More on the CFR dipole and coax chokes

**PHOTO 1: A vertical Controlled Feeder Radiation dipole for 14MHz. A fluorescent lighting tube has been fixed close to the antenna end of the choke, indicating a high impedance – enough to strike the tube using only 20W of power.**

CONTINUED... This month is a further discussion the Controlled Feeder Radiation (CFR) dipole I described last month, with particular emphasis on the coax choke. I used the same antenna constructed with 16.5ft of 16SWG multi strand insulated copper wire fixed to a fibreglass support and the lower end made from 17ft length of RG57. The complete antenna is shown in **Photo 1**.

The antenna described last month was fed via a current choke constructed from 9 turns of RG super 8 coax wound on a 4.25in (110mm) plastic pipe. This choke had a resonant frequency of around 18MHz in isolation. However, I was concerned as to what this resonance would be when the choke was inserted into an antenna system with an unknown loading capacitance. In the event the SWR at 14.15MHz was 1.24:1, with a 1.5:1 SWR bandwidth better than 500kHz. Experimental evidence was that the capacitive loading on the antenna on the choke was around 15pF.

This seemed to be a remarkable bit if serendipity; there was no way of knowing that the antenna would place the correct capacitance across the choke and tune it for optimum performance. It occurred to me that it might be an idea to use less inductance and place a physical capacitance of known value across the choke. This would reduce the detuning effect when the choke was installed into an antenna system.

EARLIER REFERENCES. Whenever I think of a good idea it seems that someone has thought of it before. The CFR dipole using a tuneable current choke is no exception. A search through Technical Topics **[1]** revealed that this exact design had been published by A F Stahler, AA6AX, in the June 1978 *73 Magazine* **[2]**, although he had a different name for it – describing it as the 'T2LT (Tuned Transmission Line Trap).

The arrangements used by AA6AX were shown in TT [1] and are reproduced here in **Figures 1** and **2**. The coax choke arrangement works because of the ability of the coaxial cable to simultaneously carry separate currents on the inside and the outside of the braiding. The currents on the centre conductor and the inside of the braiding are equal and opposite – in other words working as a conventional feeder, unaffected by the manner in which the coax is coiled or folded.

The current on the outside of the braiding forms the counterpoise to the top section of the antenna and for this to work a high impedance must be inserted into this braiding, ¼ wavelength down from the feedpoint. In a normal vertical dipole this high impedance would be provided using an insulator. With our dual function feedline, this is provided using a parallel tuned circuit. Note the high impedance demonstrated by the fluorescing tube in Photo 1.

This antenna feeding arrangement has apparently been described even earlier. AA6AX, then W6AGX, published a description of an antenna in 1976 **[3]** using the same feed arrangement (although I have not been able to confirm the details).

EXPERIMENTAL MEASUREMENTS. The antenna shown in Figure 1 is very similar to the one shown in Photo 1. The coil is formed by the outer braiding of the coax feeder and the capacitor having a value required to resonate the coil at the operating frequency. AA6AX was of the opinion that a high C tuned circuit (few turns and a large capacitance) was preferable to a high L tuned circuit because it has a Q, which resulted in an improved performance.

The tuned circuit is provided, in this case, with 7 turns of RG super 8 wound on a section of 4¼ inch (110mm) plastic tube. It is tuned with a 15pF wide spaced variable capacitor, as shown in **Photo 2**. The frequency response of this arrangement, measured using the AIM-4170, is shown in **Figure 3**. When the capacitor was set at 11pF, the frequency response neatly covered the 14MHz band with a 2000Ω bandwidth of 70kHz. The AIM-4170 has a loading of around 9pF so the total capacitance was 20pF. The characteristics of the choke in Photo 2 are:

7 turns + 17pF*, impedance at resonance 21.8k, 2000Ω bandwidth = 566kHz

7 turns + 20pF*, impedance at resonance

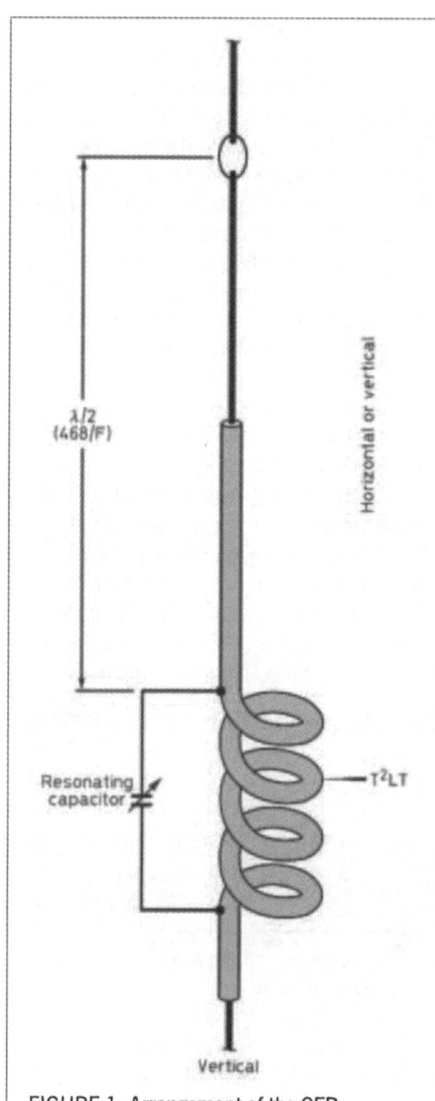


**FIGURE 1: Arrangement of the CFR dipole, where it is called the T2LT (Tuned Transmission Line Trap) antenna.**

PHOTO 2: A coax current choke constructed from of 7 turns of RG super 8 coax wound on a 4.25in (110mm) plastic pipe.

23.9k, 2000Ω bandwidth = 70kHz
7 turns + 24pF*, impedance at resonance
33.9k, 2000Ω bandwidth = 54kHz

Compare this with the original choke with no attached capacitance:

9 turns + 9pF*. impedance at resonance
33.5k, 2000Ω bandwidth = 1.79MHz

* includes capacitance of antenna.

**PRACTICAL CONSIDERATIONS.** My antenna differed from that shown in Figure 1 in that that the lower coax section of the dipole is dressed away from the vertical by about 45 degrees. This resulted in an improved match, as indicated by a lower SWR.

The choke is tuned simply by varying the choke capacitor. This capacitor should be connected so that the fixed vane section is connected to the antenna end of the choke – this reduces the hand capacitance effect. All you have to do is to tune for minimum SWR – the effect of tuning on SWR can be seen in **Figure 4**.

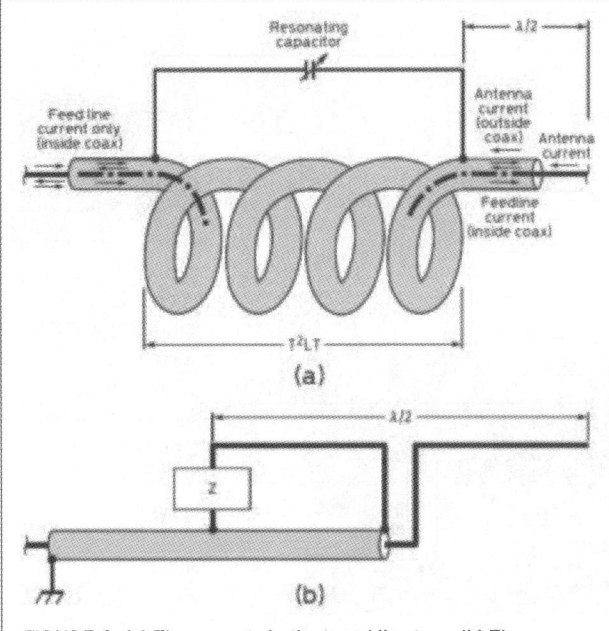


FIGURE 2: (a) The currents in the tuned line trap. (b) The coax line shows the coax braid inner and centre conductor currents equal while the leg of the dipole terminated in Z represents the outer coax braid.

You have to be aware that the RF voltage at the antenna end of the tuneable choke is high. This can be seen by the effect on the fluorescent tube in Photo 1 with only 20 watts of RF. This is a demanding application for a RF current choke or trap.

In e-mail correspondence with Steve Hunt, G3TXQ, he notes: "For the most demanding applications I reckon that there is no real alternative to measuring the CM current in-situ and adjusting the choke until the current is a minimum. I have a current probe with an 80dB dynamic range that helps that process. Some time ago I tried to measure the feedpoint impedance of a dipole operating well away from its resonant frequency; I only got sensible results when I included an air-cored choke and adjusted it for minimum CM current at the measurement frequency".

I did try a small uncalibrated μA RF current meter in the coax connector between the lower end of the choke and the SWR meter/radio (bottom right of Photo 1). This did show a small amount of common mode current and was only slightly affected when tuning the choke capacitor. It may have been the case that the meter was not sensitive enough that I didn't find it to be a good indication of the correct tuning. This length of feeder is not at all critical.

**FINALLY.** AA6AX pointed out that the use of such a high-Q resonant trap rather than an RF choke (as in the W8NX and the earlier designs of end-fed dipoles of this general type) provides superior performance since it copes with the considerable difference between the end impedance of half-wave dipoles fed against real rather than ideal earth.

In practice, AA6AX used his system as an end-fed 14MHz vertical dipole for QRP operation (2W HW-7 transceiver) and from the photographs appears to have used a fairly conventional variable capacitor. For QRO operation a wide spaced capacitor would be required to avoid RF arcing. As a vertical dipole this antenna does not depend on radials or an earth mat, making it a good choice for portable operation.

REFERENCES

[1] TT, *RadCom*, June 1997 (also *Technical Topics* 1995-1999)

[2] New dipole feeder - tuned feeders, yet! A F Stahler, AA6AX, *73 Magazine*, June 1978

[3] Catch Standing Waves, A F Stahler, W6AGX, *73 Magazine*, May 1973

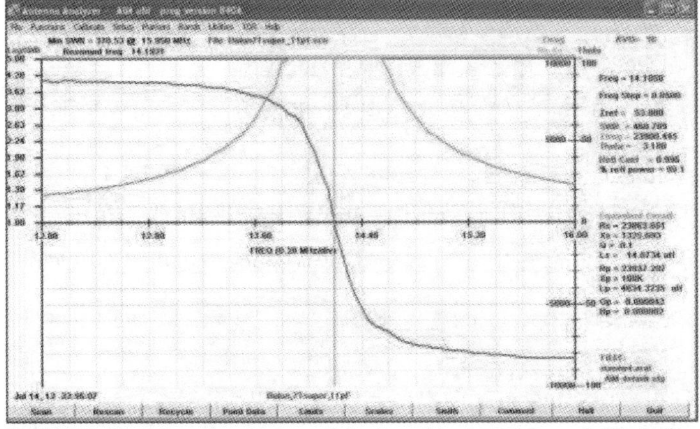

FIGURE 3: The frequency response of the tuneable choke (shown in Photo 2) tuned with 11pF; measured using an AIM-4170. Note the change of impedance with frequency.

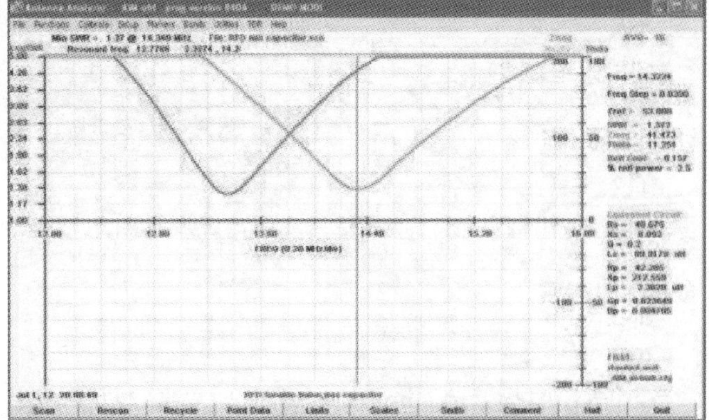

FIGURE 4: SWR characteristics of the CFR vertical dipole shown in Photo 1. The lower frequency SWR is with the capacitor set at 15pF; the higher frequency SWR occurs with 10pF (not quite tuned for optimum 14MHz operation).

# Antennas

## Can the *ACE-HF* propagation software be used to check antenna performance?

PHOTO 1: Trampoline antenna by Chris Jacobs, M0KTT.

STRANGE ANTENNA. Chris Jacobs, M0KTT sent me details of the 'non antenna' he has been using. He says, "I read your Antennas article in June with great interest, so I thought I'd try something different. I used a trampoline, see **Photo 1**. It is 3m in diameter and the eight vertical posts are 2.4m high. The shield from the coax feed is connected to the main station antenna ground system and the centre is connected to the base of one leg of the trampoline.

"While running 50W and using this 'antenna' I've contacted many G stations around England on 40m and Top Band on our local nets here in Havant. I also get the occasional EU contact. Signal reports appear to be 2dB or so less compared with my 128ft inverted L".

I consider the trampoline to be a real antenna and not a 'non-antenna'. It is more of a contender for the Strange Antenna Challenge hosted by Erik Weaver, N0EW [1]. The performance reports of M0KTT's antenna are restricted to the lower HF bands. It might have some interesting properties on the higher bands.

While I commend the experimental use of various metal objects around the garden being given temporary status as an antenna I should point out that these experiments should be carried out under strict supervision. As shown in last month's Antennas, even relatively low RF power can generate an RF voltage strong enough to strike a florescent tube. While unlikely to be fatal if accidentally touched when the transmitter is switched on, an unpleasant RF burn could be caused.

ANTENNA PERFORMANCE PREDICTION & *ACE-HF*. An article by NW7US in the Propagation column of *CQ* magazine [2] described the relative performances of SSB and CW. He used *ACE-HF* [3] propagation forecasting software to compare the relative effectiveness of these two modes. The images in this article prompted me to buy a copy of *ACE-HF* because I felt that this might be a useful tool for visualising the real world performance of various antennas.

The radio wave prediction model that this software is based is a mathematical formulation extracted from empirical data. In the case of HF radio it considers radio wave propagation over a given path as a function of transmitter power, antenna type and gain, frequency, distance, ionospheric conditions, mode and receiver noise environment. One example of this type of software is *VOACAP*, which was designed by the engineers and programmers of the Voice of America for predicting the coverage of their large broadcasting stations.

*ACE-HF* uses *VOACAP* to compute its predictions but has many interface options, which make the program more specific for amateur use and much more user friendly. The ACE aspect is 'Animated Communications Effectiveness', a coverage display technique originally developed for the US Navy submarine communications.

*ACE-HF* is normally set up to show various quality charts for point-to-point paths. I have set up a circuit between G3LDO and Ottawa in Canada and the program produces charts showing the predicted best times and frequencies, see **Figure 1**, given the restrictions of our stations and the prevailing ionospheric conditions.

*VOACAP* was originally designed to predict the reliability of a circuit path. In this regard just producing signal strength levels at the receiver site does not tell the whole story. A more useful figure is signal to noise ratio (SNR). A monthly median SNR expressed in dB is the primary measure of circuit quality. This figure is dependent on the receiver noise environment and the modulation mode/bandwidth. The default values of required SNR for a given mode and man-made noise that can be selected using an *ACE-HF* sub-menu as shown in **Figure 2**. However, having said that, the received signal level in the path analysis pop-up menu (at the bottom of Figure 1) can be switched to measure SNR, dBμV, S units/elevation angle, among others.

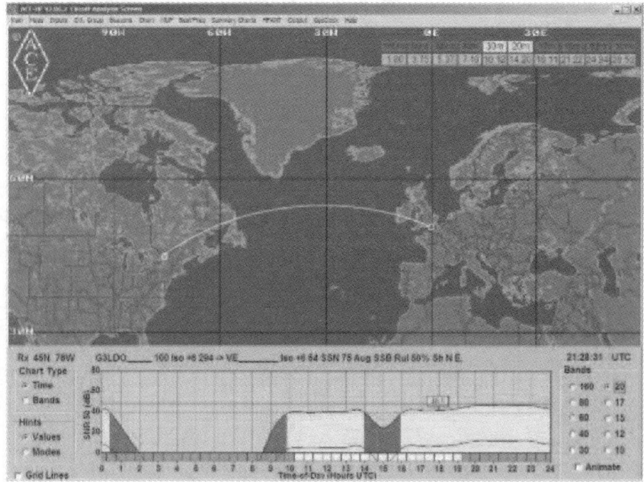

FIGURE 1: The path between G3LDO and Ottawa in Canada shown on the main *ACE-HF* screen. The submenu predicts the best times and frequencies given the restrictions of the stations and the prevailing ionospheric conditions.

Service Type

| Type | Required SNR dB-Hz | Required SNR dB-BW | BW Hz | Standard Defaults |
|---|---|---|---|---|
| SSB | 48 | 13 | 3000 | x |
| AM | 51 | 13 | 6000 | x |
| IB (AM) | 67 | 29 | 6000 | x |
| RTTY | 55 | 25 | 1000 | x |
| Mil Std 188 | 55 | 20 | 3000 | x |
| AMTOR | 37 | 11 | 370 | x |
| CLOVER | 54 | 21 | 2000 | x |
| PACTOR I | 39 | 12 | 450 | x |
| PACTOR II | 39 | 12 | 450 | x |
| PACTOR III | 44 | 11 | 2200 | x |
| PSK31 | 23 | 8 | 31 | x |
| CW | 27 | 0 | 500 | x |
| Custom | 24 | 0 | 250 | x |

Standard Defaults x

DX/Contest Defaults

Man-made Noise at Receiver (for 1 Hertz bandwidth at 3 MHz)

| Type | dBW-Hz | Default |
|---|---|---|
| Remote | 164 | x |
| Rural | 155 | x |
| City | 145 | x |
| Industrial | 140 | x |
| All Types | | x |

Include Sporadic-E ? No / Yes

Absorption Model: NORMAL / IONCAP

FIGURE 2: The default values of required SNR for a given mode and man-made noise that can be selected using *ACE-HF*.

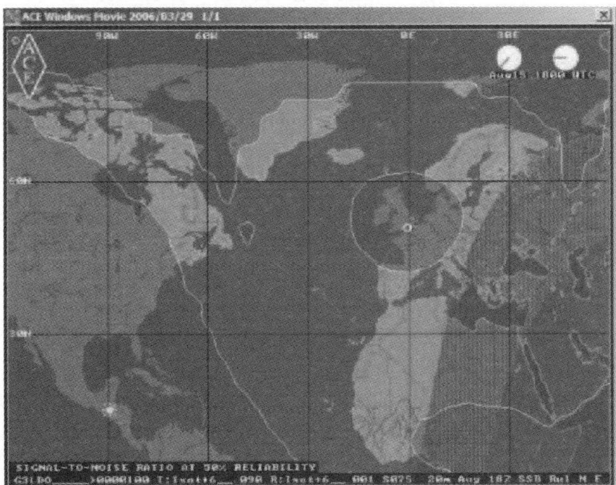

FIGURE 3: Predicted coverage of a 14MHz 100W SSB station with a reasonable antenna (see text).

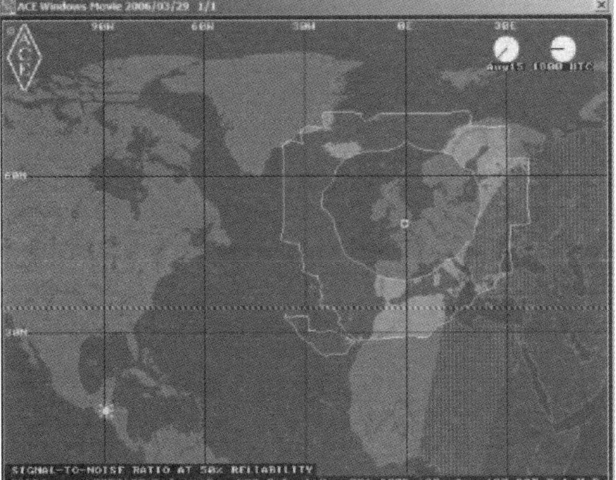

FIGURE 5: Predicted coverage of a 14MHz 100W SSB station with modest antenna (see text).

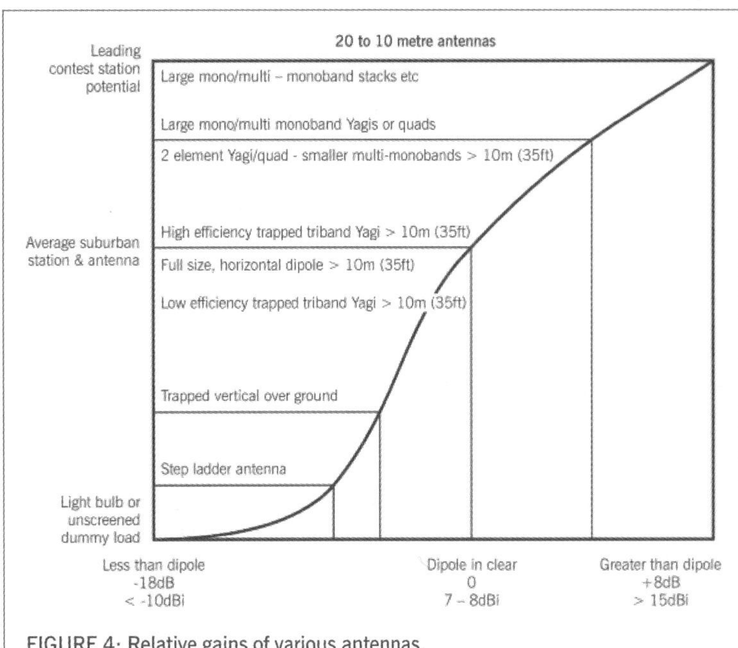


FIGURE 4: Relative gains of various antennas, based on a diagram by Thomas Schiller, N6BT.

**PREDICTIONS.** The *ACE-HF* program is designed to predict the reliability of a circuit path over a 30-day month, taking into account the many parameters described earlier. One of the parameters used by *ACE-HF* not mentioned so far is reliability (time available) and this is entered as a percentage, with a default value of 50%. This value indicates that SNR level will be as predicted or better during 15 days of a 30 day month.

Reliability is particularly important parameter for military and commercial organisations that need greater reliability than amateurs. They usually use 90% reliability, which gives a predicted usable SNR over 27 days of a 30 day month. This is achieved at a reduced coverage unless compensated by greater antenna gain or transmitter power.

**AREA COVERAGE MAPS.** It is the area coverage maps facility described by NW7US that is of the main interest to me. An example is shown in **Figure 3**, which shows the coverage of a 14MHz 100W SSB station with a reasonable quality antenna, say a 12m (40ft) high half-wave dipole. Other input data included is a SSN (Smoothed Sunspot Number) of 75, date/time August 1800hrs UTC. I also assumed any stations area to be located in a quiet rural noise environment.

The blue/green parts in Figure 3 indicate areas of the world where the band is open; the brown parts indicate areas out of range. You will notice that the band is open to parts of Europe, Scandinavia, Russia, the USA and Canada. It is also open to North and West Africa together with the Near East (although you might be forgiven for not believing it due to the low activity from these areas). The area around the UK and near Europe is also out of range; this is due to the well-known skip zone.

So how might a 'strange antenna' such as the one shown in Photo 1 perform under the same conditions? By comparing antennas in graph produced by N6BT (**Figure 4**) and assuming that the trampoline antenna and my step ladder antenna have a similar performance, I have guessed the M0KTT antenna to be 6dB down on a dipole in the clear on 14MHz.

I ran the program again with the same inputs as described above but with this reduced performance antenna. This resulted in the coverage shown in **Figure 5**. In comparing these two coverage areas you will see that for short skip contacts into Europe there isn't a great deal of difference. When it comes to DX it is a different matter…

**ANTENNAS.** As you are probably aware the gain and angle of maximum radiation are all important, especially on long DX paths. Creating the area coverage maps of Figure 3 and 5, showing openings in all directions, required an antenna that radiates equally in all directions in both azimuth and elevation. No such antenna exists in the real world. However, the *ACE-HF* antenna library has an isotropic theoretical point source antenna with adjustable gain settings for both the transmit and receive stations. The default setting is +6dB, which equates to the gain of many amateur stations. The 'dipole in the clear' in Figure 1 is the probably the nearest practical antenna, although this antenna has some directivity. An antenna gain setting of +6dB was used to produce the Figure 3 area coverage map and a setting of 0dB was used for Figure 5.

**FINALLY.** The question was asked in the heading; can *ACE-HF* be used to check antenna performance? Yes, I do believe it can, although I need to do more research. The *ACF-HF* help tutorials comprise 61 pages of close-typed text with no illustrations. When it comes to propagation prediction, the antenna is an important part of the equation. The *ACE-HF* antenna library has a 1650 real antenna models to choose from. Furthermore, you can import your own models from *NEC* or *EZNEC*. There is a wealth of information on HF propagation models and software comparisons by LX4SKY at **[4]**.

WEBSEARCH


[1] www.strangeantennachallenge.com, also Antennas column, *RadCom* April 2006 and June 2012

[2] Propagation, Thomas Hood, NW7US, *CQ Amateur Radio* July 2012

[3] www.mygeoclock.com/acehf

[4] www.astrosurf.com/luxorion/menu-qsl.htm – various articles under 'Propagation' by LX4SKY

# Antennas

## SWR, reflection coefficient & return loss

**SWR.** The standing wave ratio (SWR) meter is an instrument found in almost every ham shack. It is used to measure how well an antenna is matched to the feedline but it may surprise some that this meter does not actually measure SWR. Perhaps it might be useful, for the benefit of newcomers, to describe just what SWR is and what the instrument actually does measure.

When RF power from a transmitter is fed to an antenna via a length of transmission line, all this power is absorbed by the load (antenna) and radiated – provided the load impedance is the same as the transmission line impedance. When a wave travelling along a transmission line from the transmitter to the antenna (the incident wave) encounters impedance that is not the same as the impedance of the line then some of the wave is reflected (the reflected wave). Whenever two same-frequency sinusoidal waves travel in opposite directions along the same transmission line, a static interference pattern (a standing wave) is formed along the line, as illustrated in **Figure** 1.

Standing wave ratio (SWR) is defined as the ratio of the voltage or current maximum to the voltage or current minimum along a transmission line. Note that these maximum/minimum measurement points are a quarter of a wavelength apart on the transmission line. Also note that the incident and reflected waves, together with static SWR pattern, are equal and opposite on the transmission line conductors (see **Figure 2**), so radiation from the transmission line is suppressed.

**EARLY PRACTICAL SWR MEASUREMENTS.** Long before their use in amateur radio, commercial station engineers used the SWR meter to adjust antennas to match the transmission line. These antennas were mostly located some distance from the transmitters and fed by 600Ω twin-wire feeder. The business of adjusting any antenna matching arrangement could be managed much more conveniently if a method of measuring the transmission line/antenna matching was available close to the antenna.

One such method is illustrated in **Figure 3**. A single-loop coil is arranged so that it couples with the magnetic field of one of the transmission line conductors. The induced EMF causes current to flow in an RF meter, whose reading is proportional SWR current (I). The trolley is moved along the line using the towing cord to a position where the current maximum and the level recorded. The loop is then drawn along the line to a current minimum and the level noted. The ISWR is then obtained from:

$$ISWR = I_{max} / I_{min}$$

**MEASURING SWR ON COAX.** The instrument shown in **Figure 4** is a coax line SWR meter for VHF/UHF. In this method an air-spaced coaxial line is constructed with a narrow slot in the outer conductor so that standing waves may be detected. The slot is at least a half wavelength long so that at least one maximum and one minimum can be observed. The slot has a negligible effect on the characteristic of the line because current flow is axial so the voltage distribution is not disturbed.

A voltage probe is used to pick up a voltage (V) that is proportional to that between the centre conductor and the inner surface of the outer conductor. The measurement procedure is similar to that carried out on twin line feeder as described previously. Note that in this case the instrument is sensitive to the voltage component of SWR and the method of measurement is the same as for current, ie:

$$VSWR = V_{max} / V_{min}$$

**THE DIRECTIONAL COUPLER.** It can be seen that two measurements at two different positions on the transmission line are required. However, SWR meters in use these days are located in one position in the line. They use a device called the directional coupler, also known as a reflectometer, which measures the characteristics of the incident and reflected waves and not resultant standing wave. It works because the currents and voltages of the incident wave (see Figure 3) are in phase while the currents and voltages of the reflected wave are 180° out of phase.

A simplified diagram of a directional coupler is shown in **Figure 5**. It comprises a small length of coaxial cable with a small loop of wire inserted running parallel with the centre conductor, with one end terminated in a resistance, R. **Figure 6** shows the equivalent electrical circuit. C is the capacitance between the loop and the centre conductor, M the mutual inductance between the two and E is the voltage between the outer and the inner conductors. I is the current in the centre conductor.

The loop and the centre conductor can be considered as a transformer, with the induced current in the loop converted to a voltage across R. This voltage is summed with E to produce a vector e. These currents and voltages are the components of the incident wave. The directional coupler has two loops, each with its own measurement meter or a meter that can be switched between them (or one loop whose direction

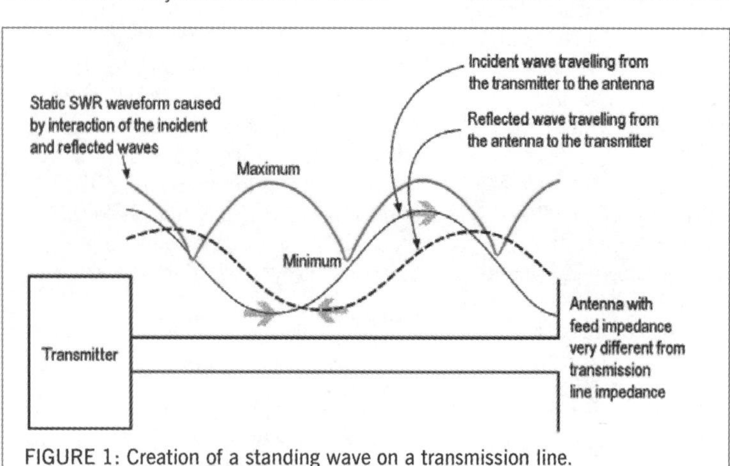


FIGURE 1: Creation of a standing wave on a transmission line.

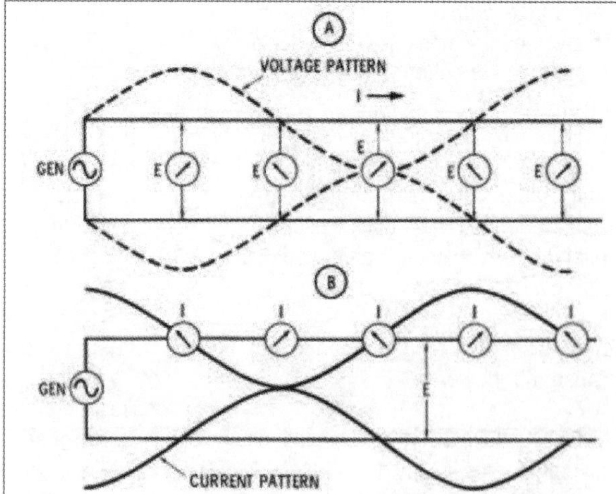


Figure 2: A two wire open-circuit line showing total reflection showing (A) voltage standing wave pattern and (B) a current standing wave pattern. (From *Radio Handbook 21st edition*, William I Orr, W6SAI).

can be switched). When the second loop is switched in, the current vector is 180° out of phase from the first reading (while the voltage phase is the same as the first measurement). These currents and voltages are the components of the reflected wave and their ratios are determined by the load at the antenna connection of the directional coupler. The method is described in greater detail in [1].

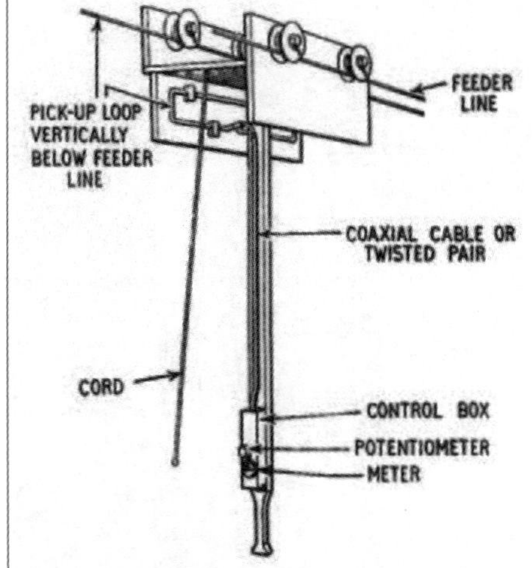


**Figure 3: A current standing wave indicator for open-wire line. The instrument could be transferred to the other feeder conductor for checking the feeder balance. (From *The Services Textbook of Radio, Volume* 5).**

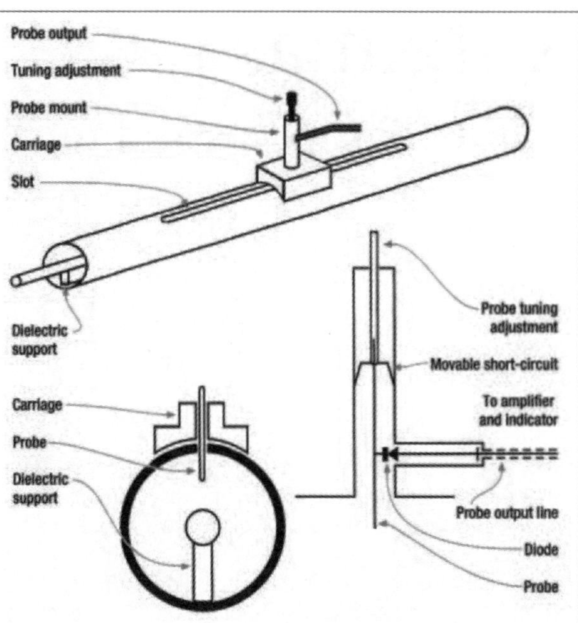


**Figure 4: Details of a slotted line type of standing wave detector for coaxial line.**

UNITS AND TERMS. What the SWR meter actually measures is the magnitude of reflection coefficient (rho) as compared to a given reference, usually 50Ω. The scale is marked in SWR units; this is possible because reflection coefficient magnitude and SWR are mathematically related. The reason why SWR is used is, I guess, is that everyone is used to it, the term being handed down from earlier methods as already described.

The term VSWR (rather than ISWR) is also firmly entrenched, even though current and voltage in the directional coupler have been used to create the measurement. My view is that SWR is more appropriate.

N6TZ, commenting on the term VSWR in [2], says "You will notice that I have steadfastly avoided the use of the expression 'voltage'. I do so to differentiate between parameters and units of measure. The parameter EMF (or electrical potential) is measured in the unit volts. If you step on a scale you are measuring the parameter mass (or weight) in the unit kilograms (or pounds). You are not measuring 'kilogramage' or 'poundage'; neither is the term 'voltage' grammatically correct for electrical potential, although it is widely used".

The relationship between SWR and reflection coefficient is shown in **Figure 7**. Such a scale can be used as a cursor on a Smith chart with the SWR 1:1 point pivoted in the centre of the chart and the infinity point on the outer edge. Such an arrangement enables SWR to be determined from any impedance measurement for example. Such a scale, when used on a Smith chart, is called a Radial Scaled Parameter. There are many of them.

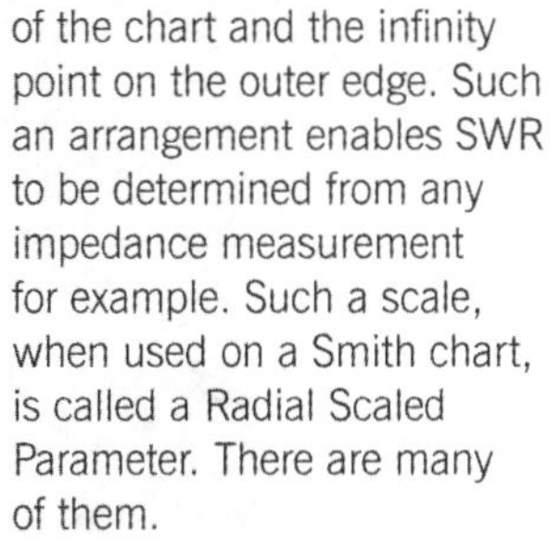

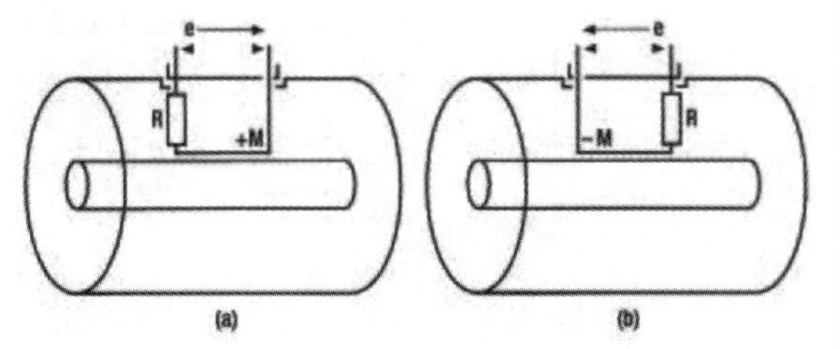


**Figure 5: The directional coupler sensing circuit. At (A) the mutual coupling is positive, at (B), negative.**

RETURN LOSS. One scale that is commonly used in literature these days is return loss (RL); this has been added to Figure 7 to show its relationship with SWR. The reason given for its use is that it gives a better resolution of small values of reflected wave compared with SWR. Return loss is defined as the measure in dB of the ratio of power in the incident wave to that in the reflected wave and has a positive value.

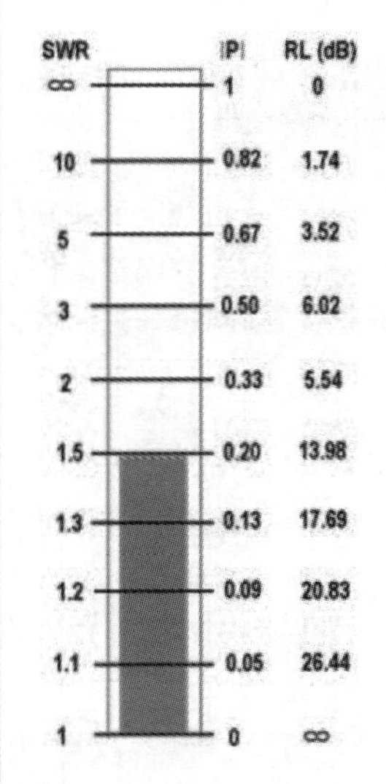


**Figure 7: Various units of transmission line reflection compared. |P| is magnitude of reflection coefficient described as (rho) in the text**

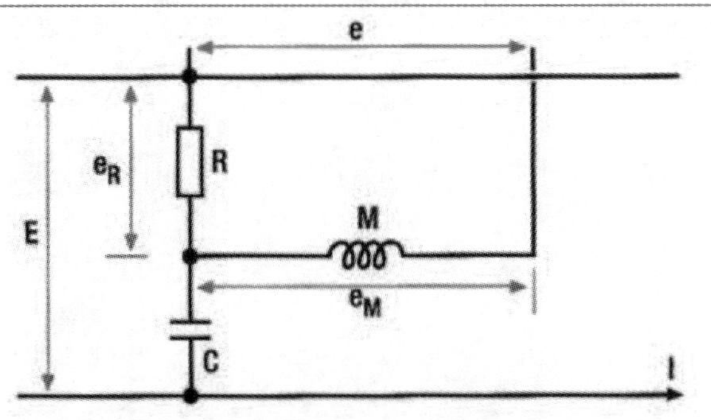


**Figure 6: The basic directional coupler sensing circuit. C and R are the voltage dividing network. M is the mutual inductance between loop and centre conductor, E the voltage between the outer and centre conductor and I is the current in the line.**

$$RL = 20*\log_{10} |(Z_1 + Z_2)/(Z_1 - Z_2)|$$

where $Z_1$ and $Z_2$ are the two impedances.

For example, if a load has a return loss of 10dB then 1/10 of the incident power is reflected. The higher the return loss, the less power is actually lost. To my mind this makes the term return loss rather counter intuitive. I may not be alone. The Editor-in-Chief of the IEEE noted [3] that the occasional incorrect use of the term return loss has grown into a flood of misuse and that 30% of antenna papers submitted have used return loss incorrectly.

FINALLY. I wish you all a happy Christmas and a pleasant antenna experimenting New Year.

REFERENCES

[1] Reflectometers and directional power meters, M M Bibby, G3NJY, *RadCom* June 1968, also in *HF Antenna Collection*.

[2] *The ARRL UHF/Microwave Experimenter's Manual P5.38*, Dr H Paul Shuch, N6TZ

[3] Definition and Misuse of Return Loss, Trevor S Bird, Editor-in-Chief, Engineering, *IEEE Transactions on Antennas and Propagation Vol 51 No 2, April 2009*

# Antennas

## VHF CFR dipoles and more on common mode chokes

**CONTROLLED FEEDER RADIATION DIPOLE FOR 145MHz.** There appears to be a lot of interest in the CFR dipole, judging from e-mail I have received. John McDonald, G8PJC, constructed a CFR dipole for 145MHz. His design uses just the antenna coax feeder – no other materials are used. It is constructed using an appropriate length of feeder. Two metres from the end of the feeder a choke is made by winding three turns of the feeder on a 40mm pipe. The coax coil is then removed from the pipe and taped so that it forms the same shape and the number of turns it had when on the former. At not less than 1 metre from one end of the coax a quarter wave length of outer sheath and braid is removed. The exposed inner conductor and the inner insulation form the top section of the dipole.

The construction is shown in **Photo 1**. G8PJC goes on to say, "Initially the dipole upper and lower sections were 495 + 495mm long, which gave a minimum SWR of 1.1 at 137MHz. A longer section of 480 + 480mm resulted in a SWR of 1.0 at 140MHz. A final length of 460mm (lower section) + 450mm gave the best results with an SWR of 1.2, which was flat over the frequency range 142.50 to 146.50MHz.

"The antenna is supported on a spider pole, which is a 12m (40ft) long light weight fibreglass mast made from telescopic sections. Photo 1 shows the arrangement with the pole collapsed with just one section extended. Measurements/adjustments to dipole length were carried out with four sections extended. It was interesting to note that SWR varied from 1.4 to 1.1 with height. I found that the choke needed to be at least one wavelength above ground."

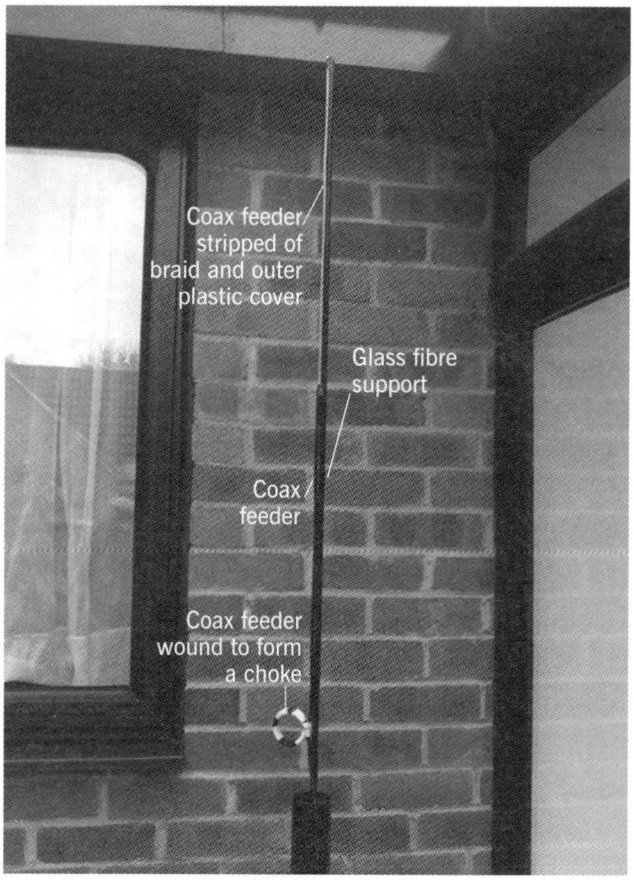

**MEASURING CHOKE IMPEDANCE.** I received a couple of e-mails asking how I connected the choke to the AIM4170 to make the impedance measurement. The method is shown in **Photo 2**. Each end of the choke coax braiding is connected to the inner and outer of the AIM4170 coax-measuring socket. The photo shows 3¾ turns of RG Super 8 around 90mm in diameter. This resonates at 33.5MHz with the capacitive load of the AIM4170.

The accuracy of such a measurement is discussed later but I was mainly concerned with the choke characteristic as shown in **Figure 1**. The first thing you will notice is that the impedance is very high and that this high impedance occurs over a narrow frequency range. Furthermore there is a rapid change in reactance versus frequency represented by the red theta plot.

PHOTO 1: G8PJC's 145MHz CFR dipole.

**CHOKE MEASUREMENTS, ACCURACY.** So how accurate are these impedance measurements shown in Figure 1? I expressed some misgivings in an earlier Antennas, noting that the smallest amount of capacitive loading on a parallel tuned circuit can have a significant effect on its resonant frequency.

Steve Hunt, G3TXQ agrees and notes: "I enjoyed reading your July column in *RadCom*, as always. I had just one observation on your choke measurements. I have recently been re-measuring some choke impedances using a 2-port analyser

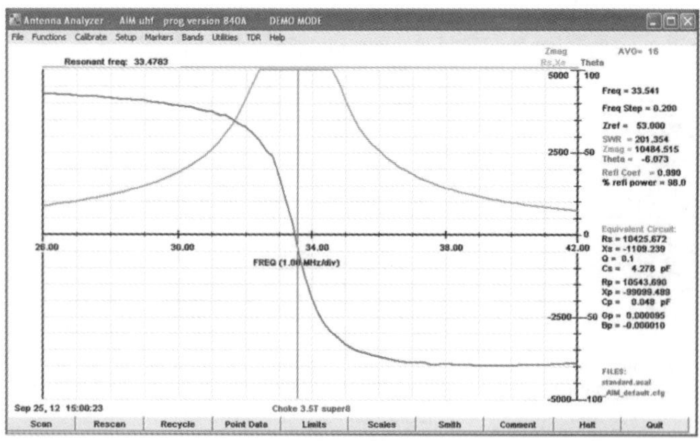


FIGURE 1: Impedance measurement of 3¾ turns of RG Super 8 some 90mm in diameter. Note the high impedance over a narrow frequency range (green) and the rapid change in reactance (red).

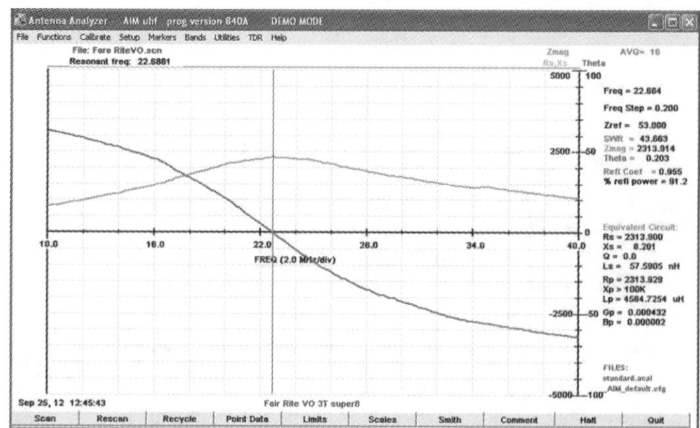


FIGURE 2: Impedance measurement of 3 turns of RG Super 8 wound on a Fair-Rite 0431173551. Note the medium impedance over a wide frequency range (green) and slower change in reactance (red).

and comparing the results with what I got previously on my AIM4170. It's evident that, despite doing a very thorough calibration of the AIM, it still introduces some unwanted stray capacitive effects.

"On one set of measurements – 12 turns on a FT240-61 core – I estimated the AIM strays as close to 1pF. That doesn't sound a lot but it shifted the apparent resonant frequency to 19.3MHz from an actual 24.5MHz; on VHF air-cored chokes the results could be very misleading. I no longer trust any of my AIM4170 measurements made on high-Q chokes and use the 2-port VNA in preference. The test jig I use there has measured strays of 0.22pF; still not perfect, but a significant improvement. I still am happy to use the AIM4170 on low-Q chokes – Type 43 or Type 31 material, for example".

However, G3TXQ goes on to say, "For the most demanding applications I reckon that there is no real alternative to measuring the common mode current in-situ and adjusting the choke until the current is a minimum. I have a current probe with an 80dB dynamic range that helps that process. Some time ago I tried to measure the feedpoint impedance of a dipole operating well away from its resonant frequency; I only got sensible results when I included an air-cored choke and adjusted it for minimum common mode (CM) current at the measurement frequency. Trying to tune the choke on the AIM4170 before installation just didn't work.

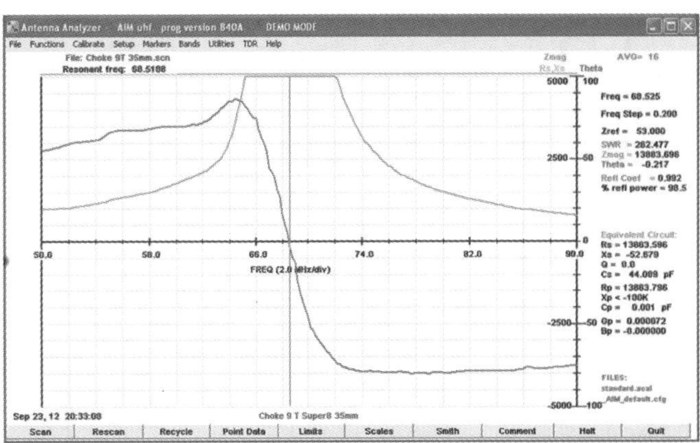


**FIGURE 3: Impedance measurement of 9 turns of RG Super 8 wound on a 35mm plastic former (plastic waste pipe).**

"But, other than for very demanding applications it probably doesn't matter. If the antenna is a reasonable 50Ω match and reasonably well balanced, the impedance looking into one dipole leg at the feedpoint will be around 25Ω; a modest choke impedance of only 250Ω would then guarantee CM current 20dB below the dipole current, provided of course that the 250Ω was resistive rather than reactive".

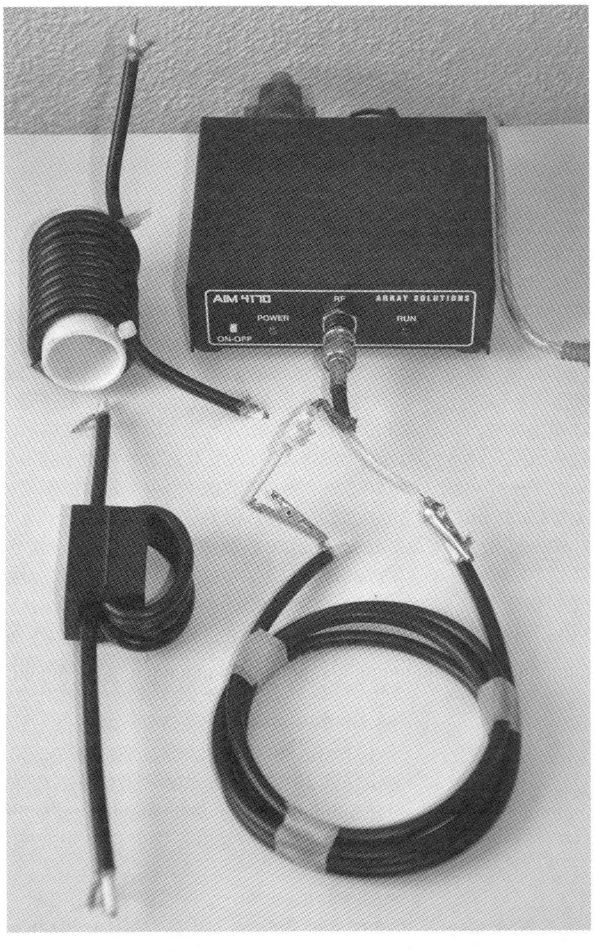

**PHOTO 2: Showing the method of connecting a coax choke to the AIM4170 for impedance measurement. The choke under test comprises 3¾ turns of RG Super 8 about 90mm in diameter; the characteristics of this choke are shown in Figure 1. Also shown is the ferrite choke and the 9 turn air spaced choke described in the text, whose characteristics are shown in Figure 2 and 3 respectively.**

G3TXQ has performed and recorded measurements on a whole range of common mode chokes and these are presented in a colour chart, which can be seen on his website **[1]**.

I did try tuning the choke of my 14MHz CFR dipole for minimum CM current on the feeder. This test was not successful. My MFJ-854 RF current meter developed a fault and I didn't have another one to hand with sufficient dynamic range to complete the test. I have been asked to provide a simple method of tuning the choke of a CFR dipole so this is one of my forthcoming projects.

Chris Bryant, G3WIE, e-mailed me to say, "I read your articles in *RadCom* on CFR with interest; it's nice to see some real measurements to complement the usual 'this worked for me' recipes for chokes made from coils of coax. As part of a larger project, I'm researching simple-to-get-going antennas for 4m – the CFR has great attraction.

"Some time ago I came across a useful lump of ferrite, the Fair-Rite 0431173551. According to the data sheet, three turns round one of these provides 1200Ω impedance at 6m and possibly 1k at 4m. I've been using them on my 4m antennas for a while but I've never been able to measure one in real life. As you are clearly able to measure this sort of thing with your an AIM machine, I wonder if you'd like to try one out for repeatability? I can easily stick one in the post."

G3WIE was as good as his word, sent me the Fair-Rite device and generously suggested I keep it. I wound three turns of RG Super 8 on to it as shown in **Photo 2**. The results of the test are shown in **Figure 2**. It is resonant at 22.6MHz, with an impedance at resonance of over 2300Ω. It has a much wider impedance/frequency range and would make a fine general purpose upper HF band CM choke. It has the advantage of being 'snap-on', which means that it can be clipped on to an existing feeder. Although having said that, the ferrite is not large enough to take three turns of RG-213 but is OK for RG Super 8 or RG-58.

I have made what I think is a suitable choke for G3WIE's 4m CFR dipole. It is constructed from 9 turns of RG Super 8 or RG-58 on a 35mm plastic former (plastic waste pipe) as shown in Photo 2 and has a very high impedance around 70MHz, as shown in **Figure 3**.

**WHAT'S IN A NAME?** The device I have been discussing is, in most literature, called a 'balun'; being short for 'balanced to unbalanced [transformer]'. The balun is used to connect a balanced device (for example a centre fed dipole antenna) to an unbalanced device (for example, coax feed line). However, there are many times when the same device is used to connect 'unbalanced to unbalanced' and thus should not really be called a balun. For this reason I have chosen to use the term 'choke' in order to refer to the primary purpose of the device, the suppression of common mode currents on the transmission line.

**WEBSEARCH**

[1] www.karinya.net/g3txq/chokes

# Antennas

## The time domain reflectometer

**SWR.** The standing wave radio (SWR) meter is used to measure how well an antenna is matched to the feedline, as described in **[1]**. It can be found in every ham shack, often permanently connected into the feedline so that the condition of the antenna can be constantly monitored.

There are times when the SWR reading can be misleading. If the coax becomes lossy due to weather and corrosion then the reflected wave will be attenuated, resulting in a reduced standing wave ratio. In this case the low SWR reading may lead you to believe the antenna system is performing well when in fact there may be considerable feeder line losses or poor coax connections.

One of the best tools for examining the condition of coax transmission line is the time domain reflectometer (TDR). In its simplest form, a short electrical pulse is sent over the coax line and any impedance discontinuity causes a pulse to be reflected. By knowing the delay between two pulses, the speed of light and the cable velocity factor, the distance-to-fault is determined. This is known as the Impulse Response method and is illustrated in **Figure 1A**.

The original TDRs used analogue pulse generators and oscilloscopes, as shown in **Figure 2**. Articles on the subject have been regularly published in American amateur radio literature over the years and an example can be seen in **[2]**; another was published in *RadCom* in 1998 **[3]**. This was the only practical way to implement TDR before low cost powerful computers became available.

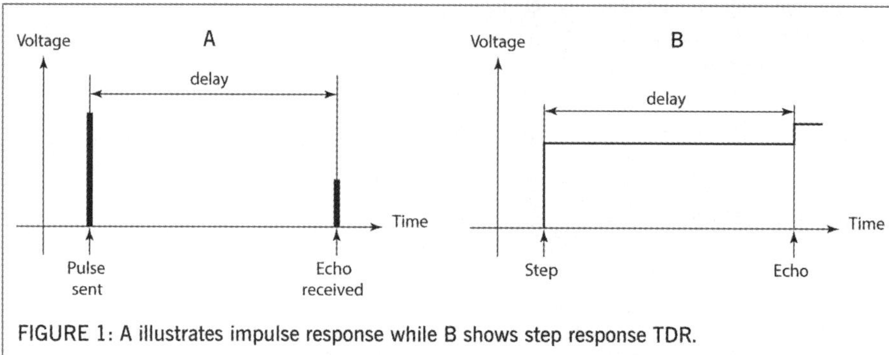


**FIGURE 1: A illustrates impulse response while B shows step response TDR.**

**TDR ON THE AIM 4170.** The AIM 4170 uses a 'step' function, see **Figure 1B**, rather than the pulse method described earlier. **Figure 3** shows the basic components of a step function TDR. A pulse generator provides a test pulse with a rise time that is short compared to the proposed time measurements. The trailing edge of the pulse is much wider than any time to be measured and is not used.

The amplitude of the pulse is not critical, since the measurements involve ratios. In this example a pulse amplitude of 10V is used, whose leading edge steps to 10V at point A at time T = 0. The voltage at point A is always the same regardless of the connected load. The test coax and load is connected to the pulse generator via a series resistor, typically 50Ω. In this example, the coax has a characteristic impedance Zo of 50Ω ohms, is 100 feet long and it has a velocity factor of 0.66.

The waveform is monitored at point B and at T = 0 the Zo appears as 50Ω. The 50Ω resistor in series with the generator output and the Zo of the transmission line form a voltage divider of 50Ω and 50Ω, resulting in 5V at B when T = 0.

As the leading edge of the pulse (incident pulse) travels down the line the Zo at B measures 50Ω until this pulse edge meets an impedance discontinuity. The pulse edge is then reflected back (reflected pulse) along the coax where it is added or subtracted with the 5V value at B depending on the impedance value of the discontinuity. In an extreme case, shown in Figure 3 where the end of the coax is terminated in an open circuit, a 5V reflected pulse is added to the incident pulse. This 10V pulse arrives back at B and is measured using an oscilloscope or a computer voltage probe. The 50Ω resistor in the generator is the same as the Zo of the test line, so there is no reflection at the generator and the final value seen at point B is 10V.

The incident pulse and reflected pulses travel along the coax at the speed of light times the velocity factor of the coax. In our example of a 100ft of coax with a velocity factor of 0.66 it would take 300ns for the wave to travel down the line and back.

In the case illustrated in Figure 3 the incident pulse and reflected pulses are added. The ratio of these pulses is called the reflection coefficient and in this case is +1. If the coax was terminated in a short circuit the reflected pulse would be inverted, producing a –5V pulse, resulting in a 5 - 5 = 0V step at B after 300ns. In this case the reflection coefficient is –1.

In summary, the reflection coefficient is always in the range of +1 to –1. It can't be greater than one because the reflected wave cannot be greater than the incident wave.

An example our 100ft of coax now terminated with a 100Ω resistor is shown in **Figure 4**, which does not match the coax characteristic impedance of 50Ω. The generator output pulse is now 10V, fed through voltage divider of 50Ω and 100Ω, so the final value at point B has to be 6.66V.

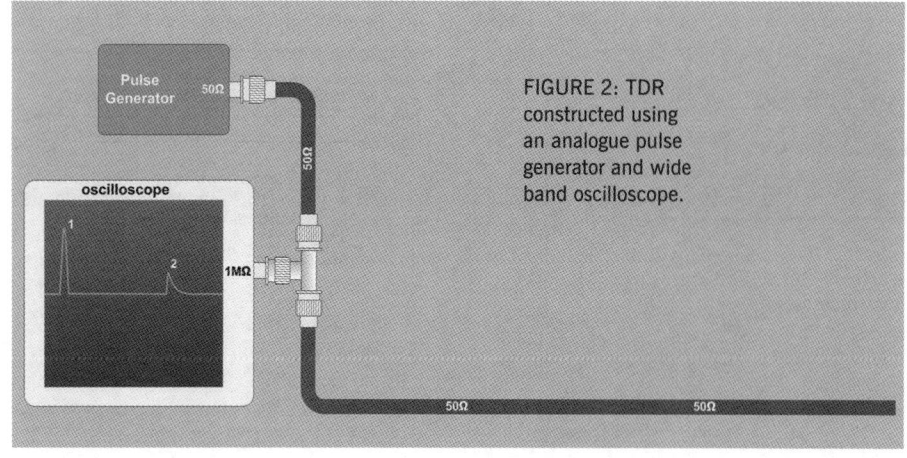


FIGURE 2: TDR constructed using an analogue pulse generator and wide band oscilloscope.

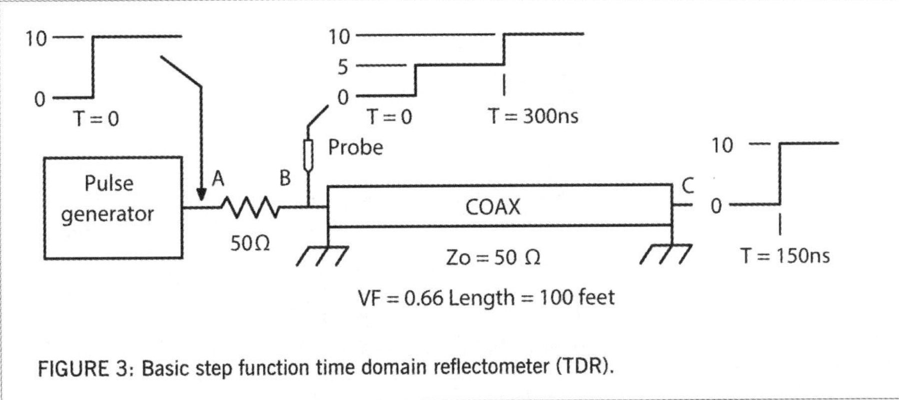


FIGURE 3: Basic step function time domain reflectometer (TDR).

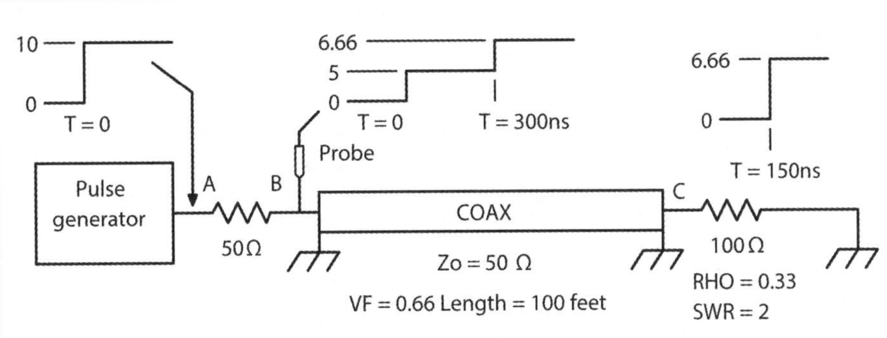


FIGURE 4: Example of a TDR being used to measure a 100ft length of 50Ω transmission line terminated with 100Ω.

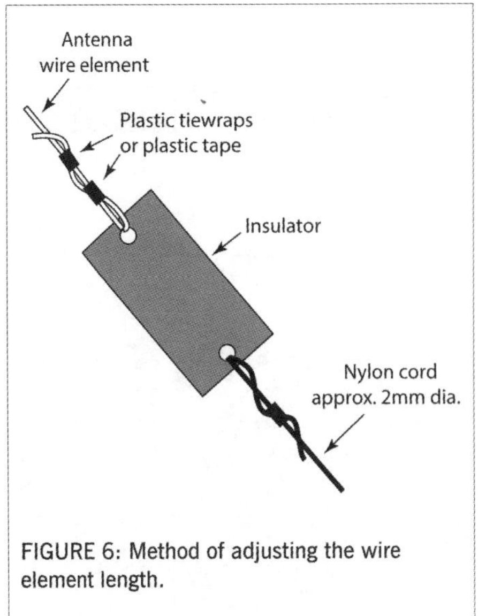


FIGURE 6: Method of adjusting the wire element length.

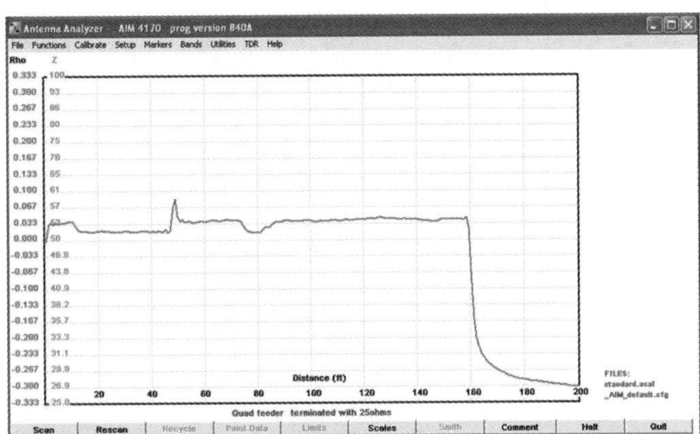

FIGURE 5: An AIM 4710 TDR plot of my less than perfect antenna feedline.

**TDR MEASUREMENT EXAMPLE.** The trace shown in **Figure 5** is a TDR analysis, using the AIM 4170, of the coax line running from my shack to the base of the antenna mast and terminated with 25Ω. The small plateau on the left represents 10ft of Super 8 running from the rig to a coax selector switch. The second section of the trace represents a 40ft length of 7mm OD solid dielectric 50Ω coax of unknown pedigree. The rest of the rest of the coax is 40ft length of 10mm OD solid dielectric 50Ω coax also of unknown pedigree. The 'cliff' on the right is caused by the 25Ω termination.

The impedance 'bump' at 50ft, where the two lengths of coax are joined, is caused by the temporary coax joint I made using an electrical two-pole block – well it was supposed to be temporary but got forgotten about. The cause of the dip at the 75ft mark is unknown.

One thing is for sure; this length of feeder is to be replaced as soon as there is a spell of good weather.

This description of time domain reflectometry is based on the AIM4170 manual, from which Figures 2 and 3 were also drawn. This material is used with the kind permission of Array Solutions, www.arraysolutions.com.

**FOLDED BACK ELEMENTS.** Peter, G8CKB, has experimented with wire antennas and has made up several for use at exhibition and JOTA stations.

He goes on to say, "I started off trimming the ends to achieve resonance, and a reasonable match but I found the elements quickly become shortened too much.

"Then some years ago I was advised that there was no need to cut the ends off of a dipole for use at different sites or at different heights, one could instead fold the excess of wire back and lay it parallel with the wanted length; ensuring that the 'folded back' part was securely taped to the working part."

Adjusting the length of a wire element can sometimes be a problem, particularly with a narrow bandwidth (compact) wire antenna. It is easy to overshoot during the pruning process.

While making adjustments to the compact Double-D antenna (a compact beam with bent elements), where the length of the parasitic capacitor was very critical I used the method of cutting the wire length longer than was considered necessary and folding the excess back along the element and fixing it in place either with tie-wraps or insulation tape. The method is shown in **Figure 5**. When an element is folded back on itself the electrical length ends at the fold.

**PARALLEL VERTICALS.** Tony, G7JAV wrote to say, "I have just brought a FT-8900R quad band radio. I have a quad band vertical for mobile use. I ideally would like a quad band dipole for home use. Is such an antenna a viable item?"

The answer is yes, but a suitable counterpoise is required. With a mobile installation, the vehicle forms a wide band counterpoise. You could use a resonant counterpoise but you would need one for each band. In my experience I find that an 8m (or so) length of scaffolding pole acts as a mast and a wide band counterpoise for VHF/UHF.

**REFERENCES**

[1] Antennas, December 2012

[2] A Practical Time-Domain Reflectometer, *The ARRL Antenna Handbook 21st Edition*

[3] A Time Domain Reflectometer, Eurotek, *RadCom* January 1998

NOTE Figure 3 and Figure 4 are from the AIM operating instructions while some of this text is an edited version from these instructions.

# Antennas

## Mobile antenna mounts

PHOTO 1: A metal plate fixed to a roof rack, which makes a reasonable base for a HF antenna mount. Note the earth braiding strap connected to a point by the tailgate hinge.

**WHERE SHOULD IT GO?** One of the main problems regarding operating mobile, particularly with a new vehicle, is where to fix the antenna. *EZNEC* models of mobile installations indicate that the optimum location for a mobile antenna is in the centre of the roof of the vehicle, as shown in **Figure 1**.

The model including ground and loading coil losses predicts a maximum gain of -3dBi and a radiation resistance at 14MHz of 20Ω [1]. For this arrangement to be effective the antenna base must be fixed into the metal skin of the roof, which means drilling a hole. A new or fairly new vehicle represents a large investment for most of us; the last thing we want to do is compromise its resale value by making holes in it.

One method of mounting an HF antenna on the roof of a vehicle is to mount it on the roof rack. An example of such an arrangement is shown in **Photo 1**. Here the antenna mount is fixed to a metal plate, which is in turn clamped to the roof rack. Such an installation still requires the antenna base to be earthed to the vehicle body.

**THE MAGNETIC MOUNT.** If you haven't got a roof rack then one solution is to use a magmount, which is an antenna base fitted to a magnet. This allows the antenna to be fixed to a horizontal flat surface of ferrous metal vehicle body. They have the advantage of simplicity and require no special fixing arrangements, enabling them to be used with a vehicle on a temporary basis if necessary. For VHF antennas the base comprises a single magnet with a SO-239 socket.

For larger HF antennas the surface area contact between the vehicle body and a single magnetic base is insufficient to hold the antenna when travelling at any speed. You could use a much larger diameter magnetic base but this is rather impractical. The solution is to use three or four magnets held together in a frame. This arrangement spreads the load over a much wider area than a single magmount and can be used to support larger HF mobile antennas.

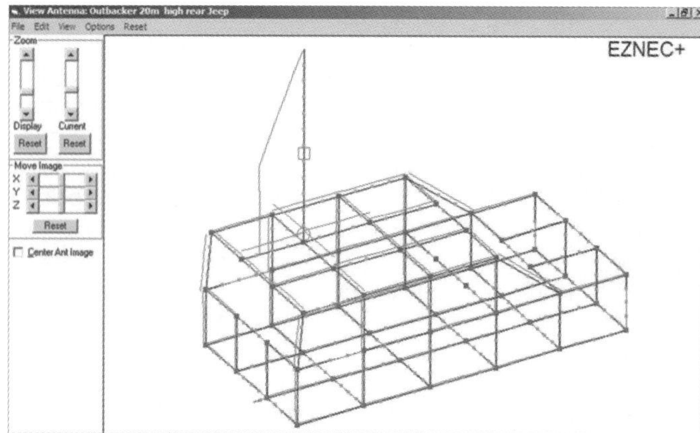


FIGURE 1: *EZNEC* model of a vehicle with a loaded HF antenna fixed to the roof. The small square in the vertical antenna represents the loading coil and the circle, the feedpoint. The red lines indicate the current distribution.

The most common multiple-magnet magmounts use three magnets. An example of one of these is the WMM-340 series made by Watson and shown in **Photo 2**, which can support average size HF mobile antenna (this model has now been supersedec by the W300T). It can also support a large antenna if operating from a stationary vehicle. These antenna mounts come with either SO-239 or 3/8in antenna fixing – the 3/8in stud mounting is usually recommended for HF antennas.

I used to be of the opinion that the capacitive reactance between a magmount and the body of the vehicle represented a serious loss. The tests shown in **Figure 2** and **Figure 3** indicates this not to be the case. The capacitance is in series with the vehicle body (counterpoise) and just shifts the resonant frequency, which can be compensated for by altering the antenna length. A coax current choke in the feeder was necessary to get meaningful measurements. Thc G3WIE choke (using the Fair rite 0431173551, described last January) worked very well.

Just how much extra loss is incurred using a magmout has not been possible to calculate but the Figure 2 and 3 measurements give a clue. In both cases the measured impedance at resonance is 62Ω [2].

**MAGMOUNT DISADVANTAGES.** Attaching and removing these more powerful magmounts requires care. First, ensure that the surface of the magmount magnets and the vehicle body are free of dust and grit before placement to avoid any scratches to the vehicle paintwork. The trick to attaching such a magmount is to use a lever to lower the mount in a controlled way when fitting it to the vehicle body, as shown in **Photo 2**. The magmount is removed by tilting it up and gently rolling it off in one smooth motion.

The coax feeder is routed either through the door seal (if you are using thin coax) or through a partly opened window (if you are using thicker coax). If you do route the cable through the window it is important that this is so arranged that opening a car door will not result in the magmount being dragged across the vehicle body work, damaging the connection to the magmount or the vehicle paintwork.

In general, magmounts are not suitable for permanent installations. Security could be an issue.

**ALTERNATIVE TO THE MAGMOUNT.** Phil Godbold, G4UDU, is a keen mobile/portable operator and likes to get on the HF bands radio whenever possible when he is away from home.

PHOTO 2: A triple magnet mount, comprising three 127mm diameter magnets held together in a frame. These magnets are very powerful and the magmount is being lowered with the aid of two screwdrivers.

PHOTO 3: The G4UDU suction cup antenna mount. The copper braid earth strap was essential.

He often operates from a mobile home, which has an aluminium outer shell. Now this does present a minor problem, in that magmounts tend to be rather ineffective, so an alternative solution was required that didn't require drilling holes to install the antenna mounting.

Writing in *Ragchew*, the newsletter of the Worthing and District Amateur Radio Club, G4UDU said, "I thought about those handles used for carrying sheets of glass or large tiles. These devices have rubber suction cups operated using levers to get a very secure vacuum grip".

These double suction cups are very modestly priced; mine came from a local hardware store for a mere £8.99.

"An antenna 3/8in antenna fixing mount, designed to clamp around a luggage rack, was fixed to the handle of the suction cup tool. The addition of feeder cable and a short section of copper braid terminated with a croc clip completed the project. The clip attaches to a thicker braid connected to the aluminium vehicle body, which acts as a counterpoise." The complete antenna mount is shown in **Photo 3**.

Details of some of these suction tools, gleaned from the internet, are given in **[3]**.

**EARTH CONNECTION.** Some of the antenna mounts described require that the antenna base be earthed to the vehicle metal body. The favourite material for this job is braided wire, which should be flat and wide. RF flows at the surface rather than through the wire and flat braid has more surface area for any given current carrying capacity. Thus it provides less resistance to RF than an equivalent round wire. Flat braid is also much more flexible and less likely to fail due to repeated flexing.

The braiding from RG8 or RG213 is suitable for relatively short lengths. Just take care when you strip off the outer jacket that you don't cut through the shield itself.

Connections to the vehicle body might be difficult to find. The method I used was to scrape away the paint just under the tailgate hinge. The antenna ground strap is then fixed to the vehicle with a self-tapping screw and a washer, protected against corrosion with a thin film of grease.

This may not be the best way. The reason is that bodies and frames of modern vehicles are dipped in a zinc compound. This zinc compound oxidises in the presence the oxygen in air and seals any scratches in its surface. So a better way may be to use self-tapping screws with star washers. When properly installed, they bite through the various finish layers and into the base metal below. Once exposed, the zinc compound seals the connection and the zinc oxide does its job of preventing rust.


REFERENCES

[1] The radiation resistance was calculated by setting all resistances such as antenna material and load resistances to zero and by using a perfect earth.

[2] The measurements were performed using a calibrated length of feeder so the impedance measurements in Figures 2 and 3 are the values measured at the feedpoint.

[3] **Draper 71172 Twin suction-cup Lifter.** Manufactured from tough plastic with rubber suction cups of 118mm diameter. Maximum lift 40kg; safe working load 20kg. Typically £10-£12. **Draper Triple-suction cup.** Natural rubber suction cups. Max load 60kg, safe working load 30kg. Around £23.49. **B & Q Double suction lifter**, around £9.98. As used with the G4UDU antenna in Photo 3.


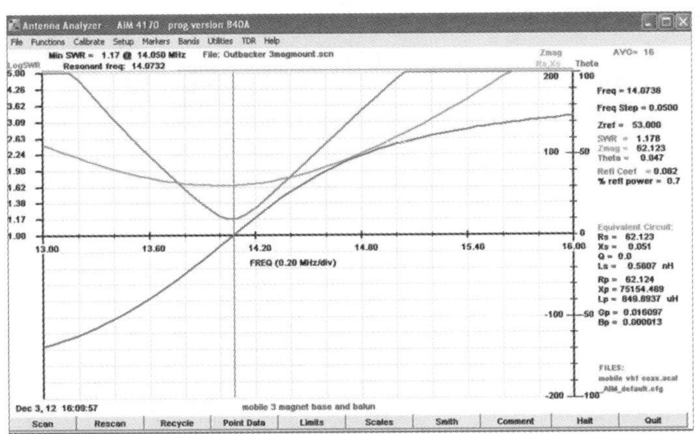


FIGURE 2: Impedance and SWR measurements using the AIM 4170 of an Outbacker antenna mounted on a three-magnet magmount and using an earthing strap.

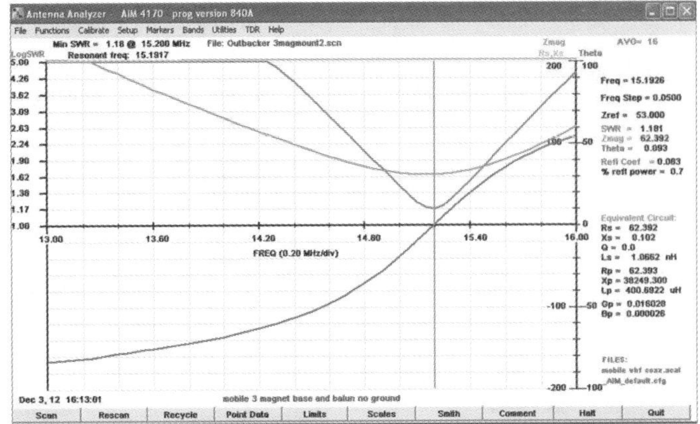


FIGURE 3: Same measurement as for Figure 2 but with the earth strap removed. Note that the feed impedance is relatively unchanged but note the increase in resonant frequency.

# Antennas

## Multiband wire antennas and the G4UDU portable antenna

**TRADITIONAL MULTIBAND DOUBLET.** The antenna, shown in **Figure 1**, is a simply a length of wire fed in the centre using ribbon or open line feeder to create a multi-band system. Open line feeder has a much lower loss than coax in such an application. This sort of arrangement must be fed via an ATU with a balanced line output, usually achieved using a transformer balun at the output of the tuner.

There are further considerations. When the antenna impedance is much lower than the feedline impedance, an odd quarter wavelength feedline converts the low antenna impedance to a very high impedance at the tuner. A similar problem occurs if the antenna has an extremely high impedance and the transmission line is a multiple of a half wavelength. The half wavelength line repeats the very high antenna impedance at the tuner. Incorrect feedline and antenna lengths can make an otherwise good antenna system very difficult or impossible to tune.

Most ATUs used today are L-C networks, with the most common configuration being the C-L-C network. The efficiency of L-C networks is dependent on the value of impedance transformation and phase shift. Any power not transferred to the antenna due to inefficiency is dissipated in the ATU, which can cause component arcing and heating. These problems can be avoided by ensuring that the impedance presented to the output of the ATU is not too wild. Operating instructions for ATUs often advise lengths of antenna and feeder to be avoided.

A further issue with twin line is routing it into the shack. Twin wire feeder should not be bundled with other feeders or allowed near metal objects such as metal window frames.

**PHOTO 1: The G4UDU portable antenna.**

**THE COMUDIPOLE.** This problem of routing an open-wire feeder into the shack can be overcome by using coax on a short section of the transmission line. In this case the transformer balun in the ATU is bypassed and a new balun inserted in the feedline where the coax and twin feeder is clear of obstructions, as shown in **Figure 2**. This solution (particularly relevant for apartment dwellers) was first described by PAOSE **[1]** and later by PA2ABV as the Comudipole (coaxial cable fed multiband dipole). The antenna length and twin feeder length restrictions for the conventional multiband antenna also apply to the Comudipole.

**OFF CENTRE FED DIPOLE.** The OCFD is a multiband antenna, usually half a wavelength long on the lowest frequency.

As already mentioned, the impedance of a half wavelength of wire is low in the centre (high current) and high at the ends (near zero current). Generally, the impedance at the centre is around 60Ω and rises to 5000Ω at the ends. At twice the frequency the wire is a full wavelength long and the impedance is very high. Making a multiband antenna like that may not be that easy and you have to abide by lengths of wire element and feeder as described in the traditional multiband antenna mentioned earlier. A solution is to feed the wire element one sixth of a wavelength (at the lowest frequency) from the end, as shown in **Figure 3**. This avoids wild extremes of feed impedance on some bands. A possible downside is that the twin feeder is unbalanced, which means it radiates and receives RF. The possibility of RF common mode currents on the feeder coming into the shack is prevented by a suitable RF choke on the coax section of the feedline.

**G4UDU MULTIBAND VERTICAL PORTABLE ANTENNA.** In last month's Antennas I mentioned that Phil Godbold, G4UDU, is a keen mobile / portable operator and has devised a vertical multiband portable antenna to cover his favourite bands, 7 and 18MHz. It will also work on other bands. This antenna, shown in **Figure 4**, is similar to the two just described except that it is smaller, with an overall element length of just 10.65m.

The antenna is orientated as a vertical with the top of the vertical (element A) fixed to a convenient tree or to a fibreglass fishing pole, with the twin feeder feedpoint around 1.5m above the ground. Element B, the counterpoise, is allowed to lie along the ground, running in the opposite direction to the placement of the feeder. The antenna is shown with the elements oriented horizontally for clarity.

G4UDU loaned me his antenna and I set it up as shown in **Photo 1**, with the feedpoint around 4 metres high; this orientation was dictated by the space available at the front of the house. I measured the impedance at the ferrite feeder decoupling box from 6 to 30MHz and the results are shown in **Figure 5**. With the exception of 14.2MHz, the impedances are not all that 'wild'

End insulator
Centre insulator
End insulator
Nylon cord
Antenna wire element
Antenna wire element
Nylon cord
Spacers
Open wire feeder
Transceiver
SWR meter
ATU

**FIGURE 1: Conventional twin line fed multiband antenna. An ATU with a balanced line output is required to feed this antenna.**

**TABLE 1: Measured impedances at the ferrite feeder decoupling box of the G4UDU antenna (converted to the more familiar rectangular coordinates).**

| | Feedpoint 4m high | | Feedpoint 0.5m high | |
|---|---|---|---|---|
| Freq MHz | Z | j | Z | j |
| 7.05 | 105 | -203 | 28 | -39 |
| 10.1 | 15 | +154 | 47 | +320 |
| 14.2 | 636 | -60 | 216 | -340 |
| 18.15 | 47 | -30 | 51 | +38 |
| 21.2 | 180 | +439 | 220 | +293 |
| 24.9 | 262 | -744 | 262 | -609 |
| 28.3 | 60 | -337 | 49 | -138 |

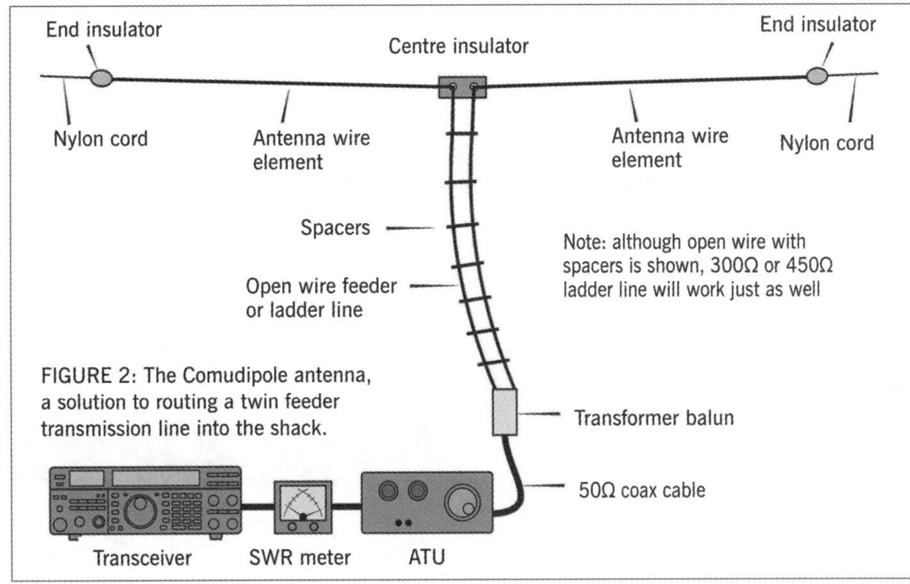


FIGURE 2: The Comudipole antenna, a solution to routing a twin feeder transmission line into the shack.

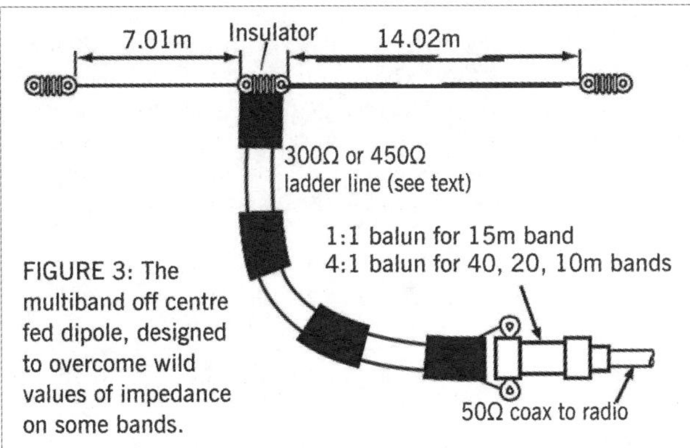


FIGURE 3: The multiband off centre fed dipole, designed to overcome wild values of impedance on some bands.

within the amateur bands. Even at 14MHz the impedance becomes more reasonable when the antenna is orientated as designed, see the inset to Figure 4. The impedance values measured on the amateur radio bands is shown in **Table 1**.

With the antenna set up as shown in Photo 1 it loaded quite well using the diminutive MFJ-901B ATU. There was no problem in transmitting but the noise level on receive was so high (S8.6 on 7MHz and S6.2 on 18MHz) that contacts were possible only with very strong stations. This noise level seems to come from the telephone drop wire at this QTH, which is why I locate my permanent HF antennas away from the house.

I tried a couple of high impedance current chokes at each end of the coax section of the feeder; this reduced the noise to S6.5 on 7MHz and S4 on 18MHz, which allowed me to test the antenna with DX stations. If you have a receive noise problem at your QTH then common mode chokes may be the answer.

The impedance of the common mode (CM) ferrite tube located in the ferrite feeder decoupling box that comes with the antenna is around 200Ω. This is rather low but seems to be enough to reduce CM currents where the antenna is used in a portable location and where noise isn't an issue.

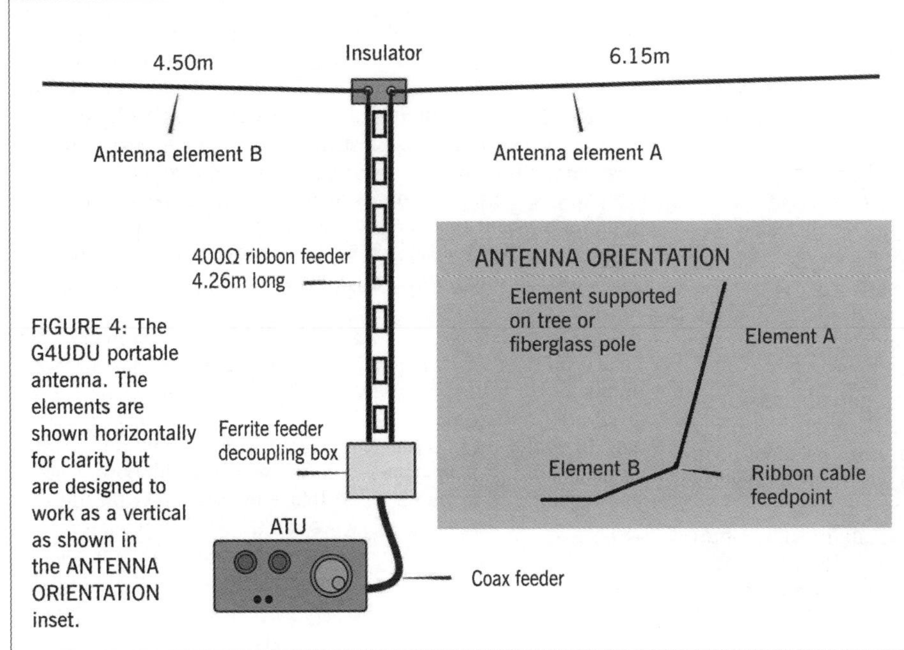


FIGURE 4: The G4UDU portable antenna. The elements are shown horizontally for clarity but are designed to work as a vertical as shown in the ANTENNA ORIENTATION inset.

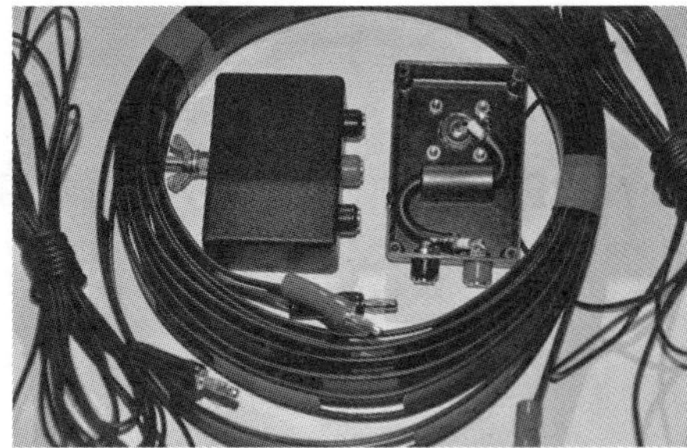

PHOTO 2: The G4UDU portable antenna kit with the cover of the ferrite feeder box removed to show the simple RF current choke.

Both transmitting and receiving reports were around 1 to 2 S-points down on short skip and DX contacts compared with my 80ft (24m) end fed on 7MHz and the 30ft (10m) high multiband dipole on the roof on 18MHz; although in some cases the signal reports were the same. Vertical antennas can be adversely affected by surroundings and they perform best when placed clear of electromagnetic obstacles. When choosing a portable site, selecting a reasonable antenna location can often be easier than from the home QTH.

G4UDU sells his antenna as a kit **[2]**. All the components of the antenna are fitted with gold plated 4mm plugs and sockets to allow the antenna components to be quickly connected and disconnected when on site. It will operate in wet weather but as a kit it is a portable antenna and is not designed for use in a permanent installation. The antenna kit, with the cover of the ferrite feeder box removed to show the simple RF current choke, is shown in **Photo 2**.

If you have a restricted QTH and room only for a vertical, a permanent version of this antenna can be constructed from the dimensions given in Figure 4. You can see a possible deployment of this antenna on the cover of **[3]**.

WEBSEARCH

[1] PA0SE Commudipole, *Electron* (December 1992) and also described in *TT* May 1994
[2] Antenna kit available from Adur Communications for £25, contact sales@adurcomms.co.uk
[3] *Building Successful HF Antennas*, G3LDO, RSGB Bookshop

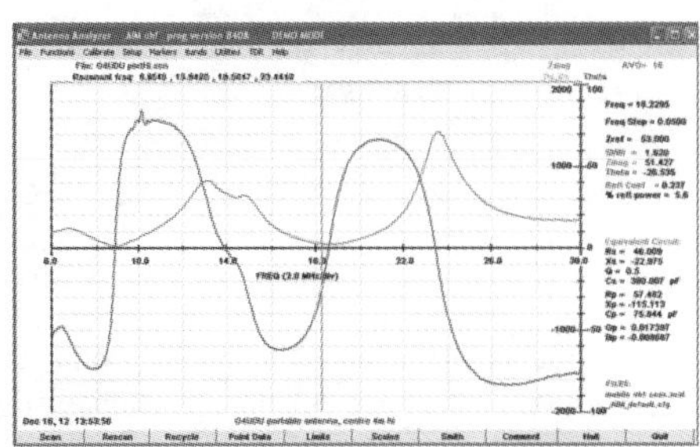

FIGURE 5: Impedance variations from 6 to 30MHz measured at the SO239 socket of the ferrite feeder-decoupling box. The blip on the purple theta trace at 10MHz is caused by a strong RTTY signal at the low end of the band.

# Antennas

## Another portable multiband antenna idea plus using the MFJ analyser as a GDO

FOLDED BACK ELEMENTS. In the February Antennas I included part of an e-mail from G8CKB. He had been experimenting with wire antennas and had made up several for use at exhibition and JOTA stations. He went on to say, "I started off trimming the ends to achieve resonance and a reasonable match, but I found the elements quickly become shortened too much.

"Some years ago I was advised that there was no need to cut the ends off of a dipole for use at different sites or at different heights; one could instead fold the excess of wire back and lay it parallel with the wanted length, ensuring that the 'folded back' part was securely taped to the working part."

I noted that adjusting the length of a wire element can sometimes be a problem, particularly with a narrow bandwidth (compact) wire antenna. It is easy to overshoot during the pruning process. While making adjustments to the compact Double-D antenna (a compact beam with bent elements), where the length of the parasitic capacitor was very critical, I used the method of cutting the wire longer than was considered necessary and folding the excess back along the element, fixing it in place either with tie wraps or insulation tape.

While recently browsing through an old copy of *QST* [1] I came across an item in the 'Hints & Kinks' page with the intriguing heading, 'A Push-Button Memory Antenna Tuner For $2!' by Terry Schieler, WOFM. He said, "When I travel, I like to take along a simple, lightweight dipole. It usually serves my needs for average operation within a limited timeframe. Without fail, however, I always seem to hear more activity on a band *not* covered by that particular antenna. With (literally) all the 'ups and downs' involved, changing bands or fine-tuning a dipole antenna can be a real pain, particularly in a vacation situation."

The solution to speeding the tedious task of dipole tuning and retuning came to WOFM using the same folding back of the wire elements as described by G8CKB. If the element resonance can be fine tuned to an exact frequency, could it also be used to change bands? The device WOFM chose to hold the wire elements to a specific frequency is called a 'cord stop', a device often used to adjust the length of a drawstring on sports clothing.

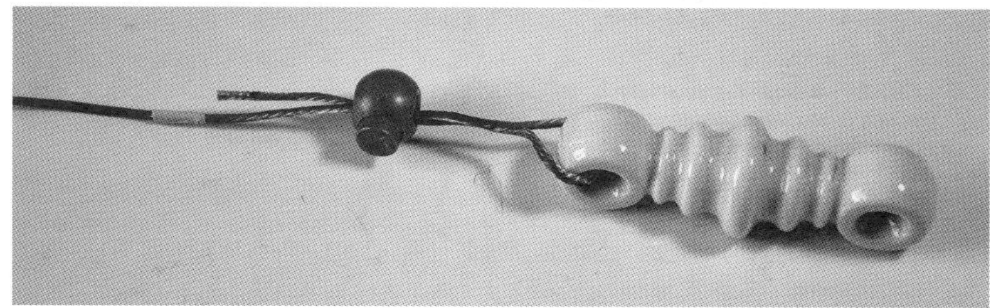

PHOTO 1: A drawstring clamp used to fix the folded back section of wire around the insulator.

It is made of metal or plastic and, typically, shaped like a little barrel (see **Photo 1**). It has a single hole through the side to accommodate the drawstring and an internal spring to hold it snugly closed. The two ends of the barrel are squeezed together to release pressure on the drawstring for repositioning, then released so that the spring pressure locks it down on the drawstring again.

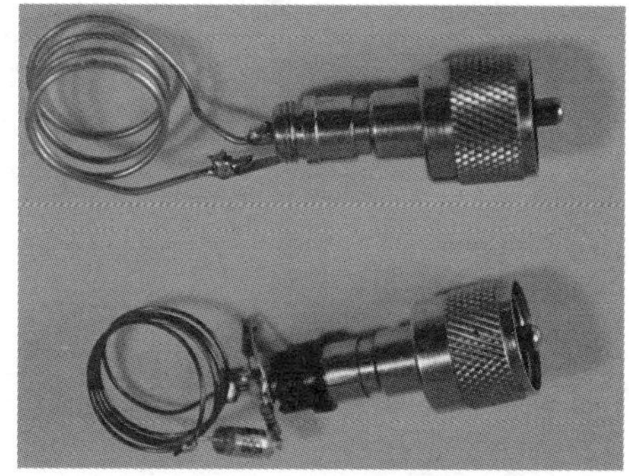

PHOTO 2: Experimental coupling loops for converting an MFJ antenna analyser to a GDO.

WOFM made a pocket size, multiband travel dipole using these cord stoppers and Flex-Weave bare antenna wire because the cord stoppers grip the Flex-Weave well and the wire is very travel-friendly. This arrangement is suitable for centre-supported dipoles or inverted Vs, where there is minimal pull at the ends of the antenna. There is a limit to the range of frequency bands that can be covered because the folding arrangement only allows the highest band to be twice the frequency of the lowest one.

WOFM's instructions for constructing and antenna for 17, 15 and 12m are as follows. "Calculate the length of the element for the *lowest* frequency on which you want to operate. Cut two lengths of Flex-Weave 8-10in longer than your calculated element length and slip two or three stoppers onto each leg (see **Figure 1**). Pass the tip of the wire through the end insulator and fold it back along itself. Next, slide one stopper down the antenna element wire, (encompassing the excess wire as well), and right up against the end insulator. Wrap the wire once, *lightly* around itself and place another stopper at the tip of the excess wire, clamping it to the element wire.

"Fine-tune the length for minimum SWR on the lowest operating band of interest (longest element length) by releasing the stopper and slightly changing the element length as needed. Then, reposition the stoppers with one flush against the end insulator and another one at the tip of the folded-back wire, clamping the tip of the excess wire against the element wire...

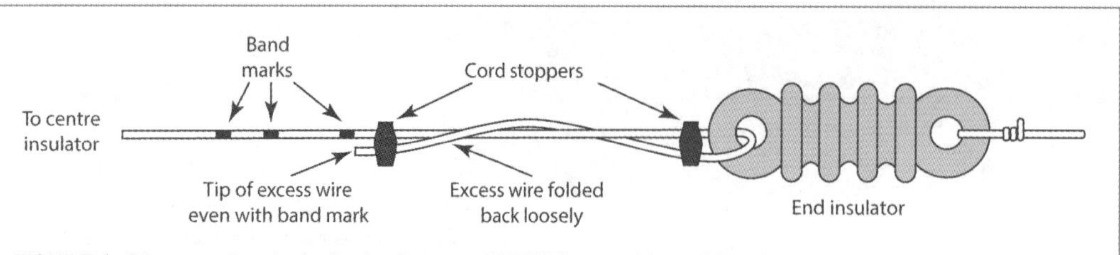


FIGURE 1: Diagram of a single dipole element of WOFM's portable multiband antenna showing the cord stoppers and band markers (not to scale).

"Mark the point where the tip of the folded-back wire ends up on the element leg with tape or a permanent marker. This is the 'memory' position for your lowest frequency band. Then, adjust (shorten) the antenna for the next *highest* frequency of interest, and again mark the spot where the folded-back wire tip ends up on the element. For example, the outer-most mark on each leg could indicate resonance on, say, 17m, the next mark toward the feed point might indicate 15m and the mark closest to the feed point could indicate 12m. You might include CW and SSB frequencies within the same band.

"The marks on the wire, combined with the stoppers, now provide for fast, easy 'memory tuning'. When you want to readjust the antenna's resonant frequency, simply position the innermost stopper just outside the desired band mark. Press the button to release the stopper and pull the antenna wire through the stopper to align the tip with the desired band mark. Then, simply reposition and release the outer stopper at the insulator."

Note that you can use plastic insulated wire as a cheaper alternative to Flex-Weave, which will work just as well.

**USING A MFJ ANTENNA ANALYSER AS A GDO.** John McDonald, G8PJC, required a grid dip oscillator (GDO) for his investigations into the controlled feeder radiation (CFR) dipole and the current choke. In an e-mail he recalled that sometime in the past the MFJ-249 had been pressed into service as a GDO.

By chance, out of the large pile of American ham radio magazines in the corner of my garage with yellow stickers pointing to articles that might be useful one day, was *QST* for November 1993 **[3]**. The article, by AF6F, describes a plug-in coupling coil, which fits into a PL-529 socket enabling it to be connected to the MFJ-249, as shown in **Figure 2** and **Figure 3**.

I recall trying to use the MFJ instrument as a GDO some years ago but found it rather insensitive; it had to be coupled very close to the tuned circuit under test to obtain any sort of measurement.

I decided to try using the MFJ instrument again as a GDO to see if the components added to the coupling coil (Figure 3) might improve sensitivity. Furthermore, the design of the MFJ antenna analysers had moved on and I now have the MFJ-259 and MFJ-269. My coupling coils where soldered to phono sockets and connected to the MFJ-259/269 using phono to SO-329 adaptors, see **Photo 2**. The reason for using this arrangement was that it is easier to make experimental loops to phono jacks than to PL-259 plugs.

The MFJ-259 was tried as a GDO to measure the PA tank circuit resonance of a vintage transmitter as shown in **Photo 3**. While it measured the resonance without difficulty, the MFJ loop had to be coupled very close to the tank circuit to get any dip at all.

According to AF6F, the resistors and capacitor shown in Figure 3 causes the SWR meter reading to be a constant 3.6 when not coupled to a tuned circuit (the SWR reading on my setup was 3.5). You can use a coupling coil on its own but the SWR reading is FSD. The effect of resistors and capacitor is to slightly improve the sensitivity because meter needle is varying in a more readable portion of the scale.

G8PJC e-mailed a photo of his MFJ analyser coupling loop being used to measure the current choke resonance. This arrangement is sheer simplicity, just a piece of wire connected to the MFJ analyser SO-329 socket, which works because very close coupling is possible – as shown in **Photo 4**.

**REFERENCES**

[1] A Push-Button Memory Antenna Tuner For $2! Terry Schieler, WOFM, Hints & Kinks, *QST*, April 2003

[2] An Accurate Dip Meter Using the MFJ-249 SWR Analyser, David M Barton, AF6S, *QST*, November 1993

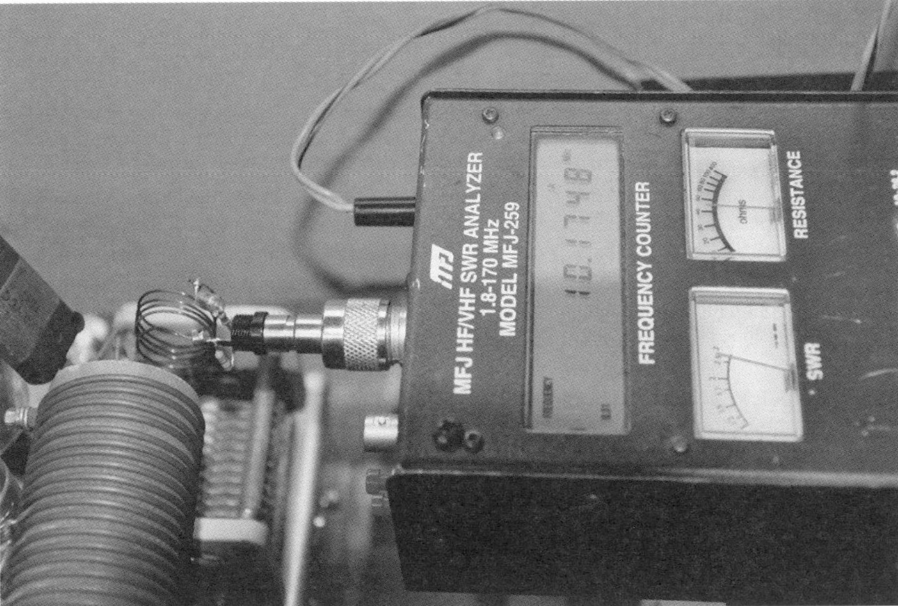


**PHOTO 3:** MFJ-259 being used as a GDO to measure the resonance of a vintage transmitter PA tank circuit. Resonance is indicated by a dip in the SWR meter reading.

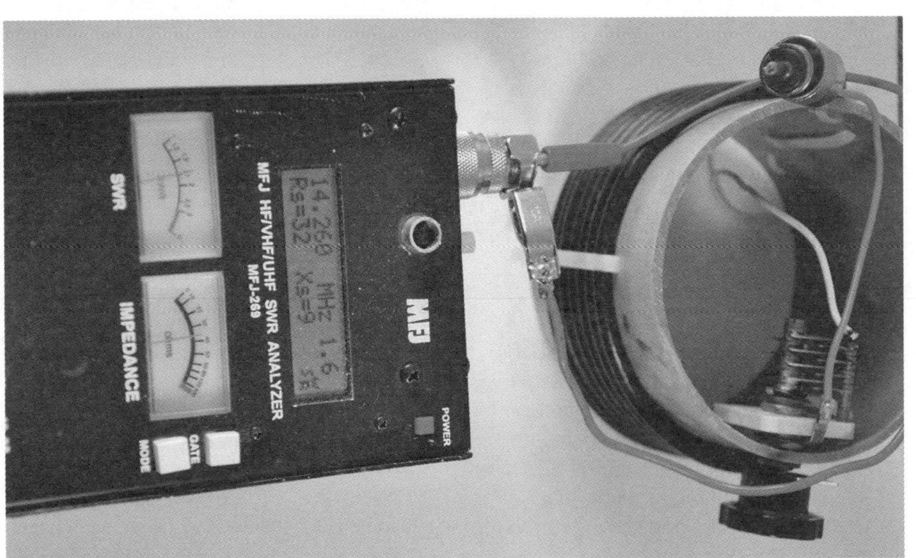


**PHOTO 4:** G8PJC method of using an MFJ analyser and a wire coupling loop use to measure current choke resonance.

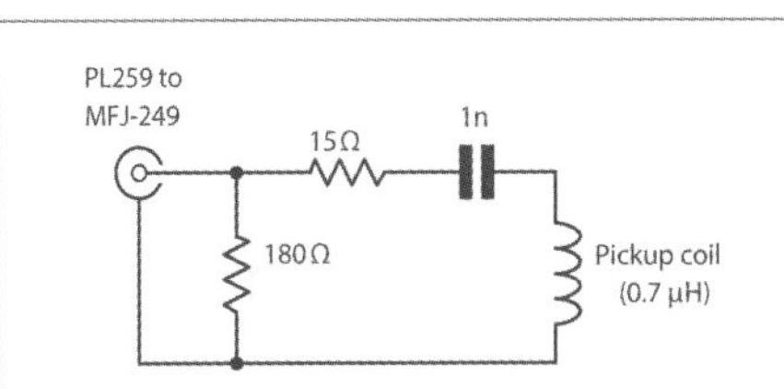


**FIGURE 2:** Circuit of AF6F's plug-in coupling coil enabling the MFJ-249 to be used as a GDO.

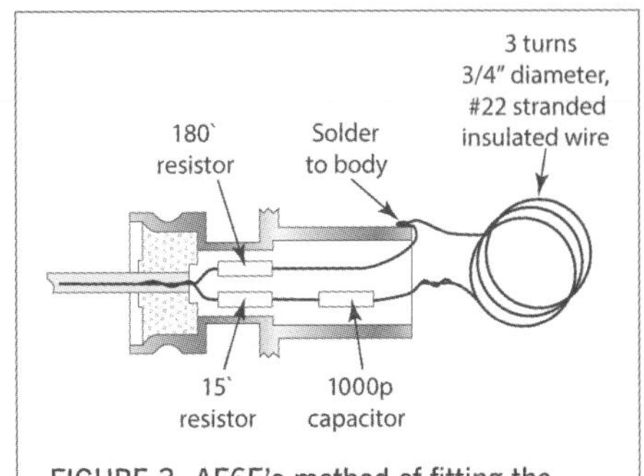


**FIGURE 3:** AF6F's method of fitting the coupling coil into a PL-259 plug.

# Antennas

## Fixing HF mobile antennas to a vehicle

**PHOTO 1: An antenna mount fixed through the roof of a Jeep Cherokee.**

MOBILE OPERATING. It is summer time and time to get out and about and do some mobile operating. A few months ago I bought an old 1999 Jeep Cherokee Sport. We needed a vehicle that would pull the XYL's horsebox and provide me with a mobile shack. The diesel powered Jeep proved to be electrically quiet and, being an old vehicle, I had no qualms about drilling a hole in the roof for an antenna mount.

The antenna mount is shown in **Photo 1**. A spring has been added to the antenna mount to prevent damage to the antenna, the antenna mounting or the vehicle roof in the event of the inevitable collision with an overhanging tree branch.

I realise that most of you would not relish the thought of drilling a hole in the roof of your pride and joy just to install an antenna mount. This month, I'll look other possible solutions for mounting a mobile antenna to a vehicle.

MAG MOUNT. One solution might be to use a magmount but the type of magmount and the type of antenna used with it requires careful consideration.

Nick Plumb, G0PBV cautions. "Your most recent reflections on magmounts reminded me of the particular loss of an almost brand new Watson antenna for 6m-2m-70cm, which came to an untimely demise while I was trying to operate (with my wife driving) travelling along the A27 travelling west from Shoreham, having just passed under the high bridge to Truleigh Hill. A gust of wind unbalanced the magmount, which clattered briefly on the side of the car before becoming detached from the coax and falling into the road. We managed to carefully retrieve it in the following 10-15 minutes by which time successive vehicles had caused a fair amount of damage.

"The questions I have on this topic are: Has anyone done any studies with a variety of mobile antennas and magmounts to work out the maximum wind speed tolerated by any particular combination or in a more indirect way what moment about the magmount is required to begin to detach it from the roof surface? Should manufacturers produce a chart for each of their mobile antennas advising or recommending a certain size of magmount?"

There is no easy answer to this question. Magmount sales literature avoids the problem simply by not mentioning it. When magmounts are sometimes demonstrated they are stuck to a thick chunk of metal. Since the amount of sticking force is reliant on the thickness and composition of the material it is stuck to, the actual force may be may not be as great when located on the top of your vehicle. On the other hand a three-magnet type magmount appear to hold very tight and requires some leverage to remove it, see **Photo 2** but I still wouldn't trust it with a HF mobile antenna while travelling at any speed.

**PHOTO 2: A three-magnet antenna mount being removed from the roof of a vehicle using a spanner as a lever.**

My view is that magmounts should not be used as a permanent solution to mounting a mobile antenna. Security is not the only issue. Magmounts can collect road debris such as metallic brake dust that gets between the magnet and the vehicle roof. You can, of course, regularly clean the surface(s) of the magnet(s) and the vehicle surface but these minute sized particles and are difficult to remove.

THE W0IVJ MOBILE ANTENNA MOUNT. Tom Thompson, W0IVJ tried an alternative approach to the mobile antenna ground plane problem and by using a separate ground plane some 46in x 55in (1.17m x 1.4m) with the antenna mount fitted to the centre. The ground plane is fixed to the top of the vehicle using a roof rack as shown in **Photo 3**. This rack is removable and not grounded to the car body.

A computer model of this arrangement indicated that an antenna mounted this way would perform in a similar manner to one mounted directly on the roof.

W0IVJ then made measurements to check the modelling results. He says, "I used a tuned loop and a Boonton Model 92B RF millivoltmeter as a field strength meter, see **Photo 4**. This receiving antenna was mounted at a height of about 10 metres and a distance of about 75 metres from the car in order to intercept the radiation lobe at its predicted maximum. The loop was oriented for vertical polarisation. The transmitting power was 100 watts.

"Measurements were taken with the car oriented in four different directions. F, P D and R, which refer to the front, passenger side, driver side and rear respectively pointing toward the receiving antenna."

Tests were performed first with the ground plane connected to the vehicle at the four corners (grounded configuration). A second set of tests were performed with the ground plane isolated from the vehicle. The test results are shown below.

40 metres

| | Grounded | Not Grounded |
|---|---|---|
| F | -9 dBm | -8.5 dBm |
| P | -9.3 dBm | -9.9 dBm |
| D | -9 dBm | -9.5 dBm |
| R | -9 dBm | -9.8 dBm |

20 metres

| | Grounded | Not Grounded |
|---|---|---|
| F | -1.6 dBm | -1.4 dBm |
| P | -1.6 dBm | -1.6 dBm |
| D | -1.6 dBm | -1.8 dBm |
| R | -2.3 dBm | -2.4 dBm |

The resonant frequency of the antenna system differed when the ground plane was isolated or grounded to the vehicle

PHOTO 3: The W0IVJ mobile antenna with separate ground plane

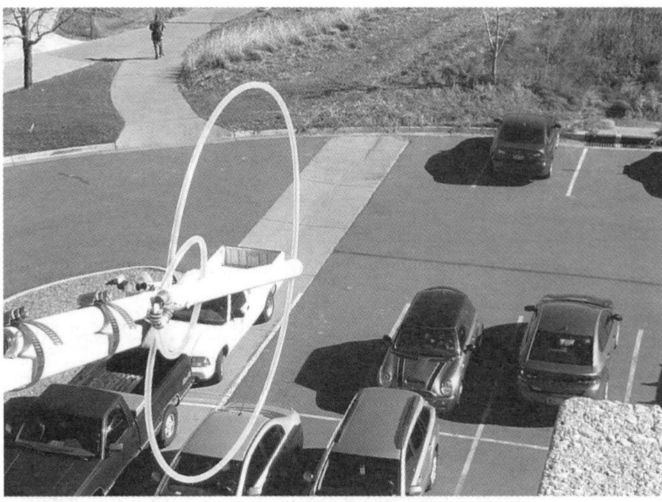

PHOTO 4: Tuned loop used with the field strength meter for mobile antenna testing

and separate resonating coils were used to maintain resonance in each configuration. The computer model indicated less than a dB difference between the grounded and isolated configurations. According to W0IVJ these tests appear to support modelled predictions.

**ANOTHER ANTENNA MOUNT SOLUTION.** It would appear some vehicles have roof rack fixing arrangements that make it easy to install an antenna mount. Barry Keal, G4HDU found this out when he bought an adapted wheelchair accessible VW Caddy. He says "...I wanted to continue mobile operation with my FT-8900 but didn't want to drill holes in the vehicle. I also wanted to add the provision for HF mobile operation with my FT-897D and therefore required two antenna fixings.

"...I found that there were four threaded holes with screws in the roof for mounting roof bars and roof racks. Removing one of the screws revealed that secure fixing could be made using these mounting holes. (It would be interesting to know what other vehicles have this roof rack fixing arrangement.)

"I checked the internet for a suitable antenna mount and matching SO239 cable assembly. The mounting bracket I finished up required modification because the plates had ridges for mounting on roof bars. The fix was to straighten out one plate using a blowtorch and hammer. An extra hole to clear an M8 threaded machined screw was drilled in to the plate and a small piece of plastic cut out to go between the bracket and vehicle roof to protect the paintwork. The SO239 mount was mounted on the bracket along with a short length of braided wire to connect to ground under the mounting screw washers.

"The original screws provided by VW were not very long and made from a rather soft metal. I tracked down some hex socket set screws of the correct length and made from stainless steel from the Internet. The antenna mount is shown in **Photo 5** and now supports an ATAS 120A to go with the FT-897D".

PHOTO 5: G4HDU Mobile antenna mount on the roof of a VW Caddy.

**SUCTION CUP ANTENNA MOUNT.** You may recall a suction cup antenna mount used by G4UDU and briefly described in March 2013 Antennas. A search of the internet revealed a whole range of these suction pad lifters and so I invested in a four-suction pad from Silverline, according to the instructions, capable of lifting a load of 120kg!

This turned out to be not a good idea for fixing an antenna mount to a vehicle. The reason being that these devices are used for lifting heavy sheets of glass and they work well providing that the surface is smooth and flat. If the surface is not flat then one or more of the suction cups is not in full contact with the surface and nearly all vehicles have curved surfaces. (This problem is not as bad when using a two-suction pad).

The idea was quietly forgotten until I received a request from John Glennon, G4ZQK on a method of fixing an 8m fibreglass pole to a motor home for portable use. Now I don't have a motor home, but the XYL does have a horsebox with flat sides. The Silverline suction pad has a hollow handle, which takes a 22mm copper pipe, which in turn allowed a telescopic roach pole to be fixed very firmly to the side of the horse box as shown in **Photo 6**.

PHOTO 6: A five-metre roach pole fixed to the side of a horsebox using a four-cup suction pad and a length of 22mm copper tube.

# Antennas

## Tuning the CFR antenna and measuring a ¼ wavelength of coax

HISTORY. In a previous edition of Antennas [1] I described an antenna constructed by John Pegler, G3ENI and Dan Sharpe, G3ZUN for portable operation on 5MHz NVIS experiments. Their design was based on the CFR (Controlled Feeder Radiation), advocated by G2HCG [2]; an explanation of how the CFR dipole works is described in [1].

My research into this antenna arrangement indicated that it has been around for some time although each reincarnation is given a new name, which makes tracking its history interesting. For example, the earliest account of this antenna I can find was christened the COBRA [3], described by W6SAI in his Wire Antennas book of 1972 [4] and illustrated in **Figure 1**.

As already mentioned in earlier editions of Antennas (including February and May 2005), I have also found the same antenna described as an End-Fed Resonant Feed-Line Dipole by W2OZH [5], a T2LT [6] (Tuned Transmission Line Trap) by AA6AX [7] and, most recently, the HAK antenna by G8HAK [8]. I have settled on calling this antenna the Controlled Feeder Radiation (CFR) dipole because it partially describes how it functions and it also has a neat acronym.

HOW TO TUNE THE CFR. Some readers have built the CFR dipole antenna and I received a couple of enquiries asking how to tell when the antenna is tuned for optimum performance. This subject also came up during an exchange of e-mails with G3TXQ.

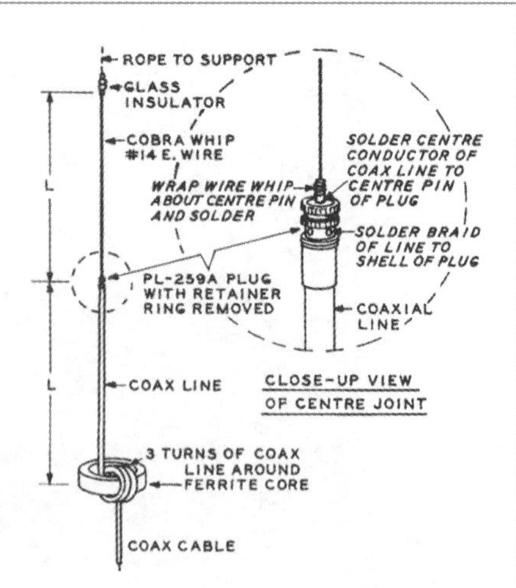


**FIGURE 1: The Cobra antenna. Dimension L in feet is approximately 234/f, or 72.42/f for L in metres. The original specified ferrite core was a #CF-123 of Q-1 material, 2.4in in diameter and 0.5in thick.**

He advocated using a current meter to measure the common mode current in the coax where resonance could be indicated by minimum current, a logical assumption.

My existing CFR antenna for 14MHz is made simply by taping 16.6ft (5.1m) of 16SWG multi strand insulated copper wire to a fibreglass support. The bottom end of this wire is then connected to the centre conductor of a similar length of RG57. The antenna was configured as an inverted L as shown in **Photo 1** rather than a completely vertical arrangement as illustrated in Figure 1. This inverted L arrangement resulted in a lower SWR, probably because the feed impedance was nearer 50Ω compared with 72Ω for straight vertical dipole. The inverted L arrangement also lent itself to the experimental layout shown in **Photo 2**.

**PHOTO 1: An inverted L CFR dipole setup. The feedpoint is located in the top right hand corner where the coax is fixed to the vertical section.**

My original attempt to determine optimum performance by measuring coax common mode (CM) current, as described by G3TXQ, was inconclusive. After reading an article on a low capacitance, voltage immune RF current meter by W8JI [9] I decided to build one and try the CFR current measurements again. I measured the SWR over a range of frequencies using the AIM4170 (checked with a Daiwa CN-601 SWR meter); the results are shown in **Figure 2**.

I then measured the current on the coax feeder to the radio. Using a transmitted power of 10W the measurements were plotted relative to SWR, see Figure 2. Although current did vary over the frequency range I didn't get the expected minimum within this range. I also measured the RF level at the antenna, which remained fairly constant over the frequency range.

As a result of these measurements I will continue to use SWR as an indication of the correct tuning when using this antenna. I use the choke tuned with a 22pF wide spaced parallel capacitor. Varying the capacitor does not change the SWR shape shown in Figure 2 – it just moves it left or right along the frequency axis.

ELECTRICAL LENGTH OF COAX. Ron Bennett, G4DIY, e-mailed me to say, "I am constructing an antenna project and there is the requirement for me to use an electrical quarter wave of RG213. I know that I have to multiply the physical half wave length of coax by its velocity factor to get the electrical length, 0.66 in the case of RG213". In a further discussion he asked if there was a way to actually measure this velocity factor.

There are several ways. My favourite for many years was to use a grid dip oscillator (GDO) but these instruments have fallen out of favour and fashion in recent times. However, if you are into any sort of antenna experimental work you may have an antenna analyser such as the MFJ-259 or MFJ-269. An instrument that has a method of measuring impedance, such as shown in **Photo 3**, is suitable for measuring coax electrical length.

I decided to measure the electrical quarter wavelength of a length of coax, the characteristics of which were unknown to me. This coax has a grey plastic outer jacket and is labelled SD-2V DAIYU DENSON; it is 2.82m (111in) long and terminated at each end with a PL-259 plug.

The diagram in **Figure 3** illustrates the impedance (Z) transform effect of a quarter wavelength of 50Ω coax terminated with a 25Ω resistor, resulting in a measured impedance of 100Ω at the opposite end. If the cable is not terminated – just left open circuit, then it is terminated with a

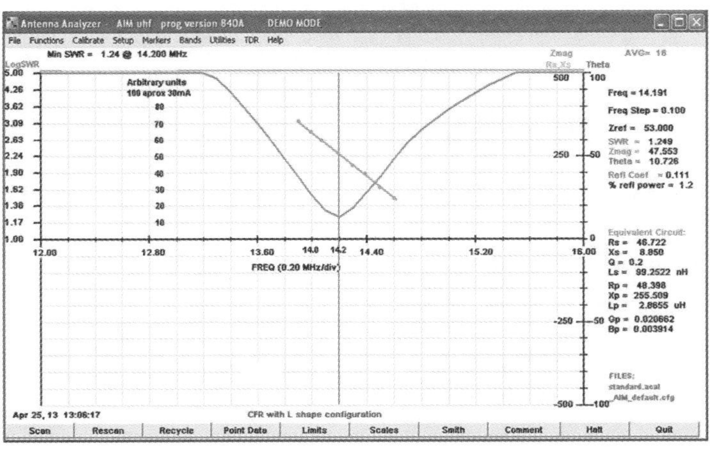


FIGURE 2: SWR plot of the inverted L configuration CFR antenna. The green trace shows the hand plotted current variations.

PHOTO 2: Test set up to compare the current variations relative to SWR on a CFR antenna.

theoretically infinite impedance. This should reflect a zero impedance to the measuring instrument.

I attempted the measurement of the 2.82m length of SD-2V using the old MFJ-259 by starting at the lowest frequency and increasing this frequency until the Z meter made a sharp dip towards zero at 16.49MHz, see Photo 3. A second zero reading occurred at 49.76MHz. The first reading represents the frequency at which the coax length is an electrical quarter of a wavelength long, the second three quarters of a wavelength. The frequency of the electrical half wavelength can be determined by subtracting the lowest from the highest frequency, ie 9.76 – 16.49 = 33.27MHz.

On the other hand you could just multiply the lowest frequency by 2, which gives 32.98MHz for a half wavelength.

**ACCURACY.** You will notice that the two methods of measuring a half wavelength value described above result in slightly different values. This probably is a result of instrument measurement inaccuracies. The problem arises when trying to determine the lowest value of Z. On the MFJ-259 the frequency can be swept over 400kHz (at 16MHz) with no perceptual variation around zero. Accuracy can be improved by sweeping the frequency either side of zero until the Z reading is, say, 10Ω. The average of these two measurements is then 17.99 + 14.99 = 16.49MHz.

The reason for making two frequency measurements is that the rate of impedance value change with frequency is greater away from zero. In this case the frequency sweep was reduced to 8kHz before a perceptual variation of the reading at 10Ω occurred.

These measurements give the electrical length of the coax, which is determined by the velocity factor of the coax. According to the literature on the web the velocity factor can be obtained as follows:

Velocity factor Vf = Physical length (ft) x frequency/246

My 9.25ft length of SD-2V = 9.25 x 16.49/246 = 0.62.

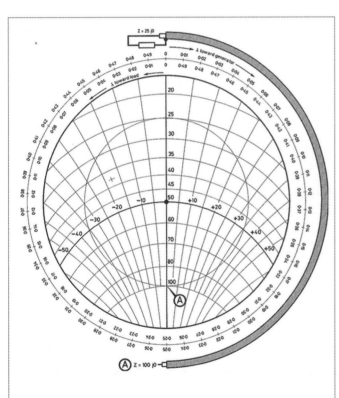

FIGURE 3: A restricted range Smith Chart showing the impedance transformation of a quarter wavelength of coax terminated with 25Ω resulting in 100Ω impedance at (A).

PHOTO 3: MFJ-259 being used to measuring the electrical quarter wavelength of a length of coax.

I realise the velocity factor figures in coax tables are nominal, nevertheless I was expecting 0.66.

REFERENCES

[1] Antennas, *RadCom* September 2012

[2] Controlled Feeder Radiation, G2HCG, *RadCom*, May 1990

[3] A linear loaded dipole described by Ray Cook, W4JOH, in *73 Amateur Radio Today*, June 1997 is also assigned the name COBRA (not an acronym that I am aware of)

[4] *Simple, Low Cost Wire Antennas for Radio Amateurs*, Radio Publications, Inc, 1972, William I Orr, W6SAI & Stuart D, Cowan, W2LX

[5] Resonant Feed-Line Dipoles, *QST*, August 1991, pp24-27

[6] The T2LT acronym is easily confused with the T2FD, a resistance loaded folded multiband dipole antenna

[7] TT *RadCom*, June 1997 (also Technical Topics 1995-1999)

[8] The HAK choked coaxial dipole, G8HAK, *RadCom* April 2013

[9] www.w8ji.com/building_a_current_meter.htm

# Antennas

## LF band noise reduction and fixing PL-259 plugs to coax

LF BAND NOISE. One of the most vexing problems of modern day amateur radio is the degree of noise on the lower frequency bands. An example of the problems faced due to this modern menace is described in an e-mail from John Totten, G7LWF. He says, "I am the ex chairman of Dorking & District ARC and 7 years ago moved to Devizes in Wiltshire. I have maintained contact with my old club, mainly by the Sunday 80m net on 3.770MHz between 8 and 9am BST, but have noticed a steady deterioration in the S/N ratio, on 80m, to the point where although they report 5/9s from me, I can barely hear them because of the atrocious noise level.

"One manifestation resembles the sound produced by an industrial band saw. Any ideas to seriously reduce this noise level would be most welcome. Something has to be done urgently."

PHOTO 1: A simple loop of coax cable supported on a wooden cross structure. An old wooden drawer acts as a temporary stand and as a receptacle for tools and test equipment.

COAX RECEIVING LOOP. I considered the magnetic loop as a candidate. I made a simple loop of coax cable supported on a wooden cross structure as shown in **Photo 1**. An old wooden drawer was used as a temporary stand and as a receptacle for tools and test equipment.

Because the loop is only being used for receive, the high voltage constructional considerations normally associated with these designs don't apply. A two-ganged receiver type 500pF air-spaced variable was used, as shown in **Photo 2**. The ends of the loop are connected to the fixed vanes of the capacitor so that when the capacitor is fully meshed the capacitance value across the loop is 250pF.

I wanted the loop to operate on both the 80 and 40m bands. To achieve this, additional fixed padding capacitors were added. You can see two 150pF fixed capacitors in parallel with the variable in Photo 2, which allows the loop to be resonated on 80m. The loop resonated on 40m using a 75pF padding capacitor. Loop resonance was measured simply by noting the lowest SWR on a length of coax linked to the loop.

PHOTO 2: A two-ganged receiver type 500pF air-spaced variable used to tune the loop. You will also note two 150pF fixed capacitors in parallel with the variable, see text.

MATCHING. Normally, a small loop of coax or a gamma match is used to couple and match the loop to the radio. In an article describing a two-metre diameter transmitting loop for 80m (reproduced in [1] [2] [3]) the author, PA2JBC, opted for a current transformer because the more conventional methods were not satisfactory. PA2JBC's loop was made of 22mm OD copper tubing. He calculated an impedance ratio of 940:1 with a transformer turns ratio of 30:1 to match the low impedance loop to 50Ω feed coax. In my case the impedance of the loop was unknown so I used an empirical approach and finished up with 25 turns on a T75 ferrite. The size of the ferrite ring will depend on the type of coax or conductor you are using for the loop. The matching transformer can be placed at any position around the loop.

Although this arrangement allowed the loop to work as a receiver antenna the matching was far from perfect, with a SWR of over 4:1 at resonance. The matching was improved by adding a series capacitance to the ferrite turns, as shown in **Photo 3**. The value of this capacitance was again determined empirically using a polyvaricon variable capacitor. When the optimum capacitance had been selected the value was measured and a fixed capacitance of the correct value substituted. As it turned out, 100pF was required for 40m and 545pF for 80m.

SELECTIVITY. Some idea of the selectivity of this loop can be gauged from the figures in **Table 1**, obtained using the test set up shown in **Photo 4**.

Unlike a transmitting loop, the receiving loop will work quite well a short distance off-resonance but at resonance the gain is greater. An improved match can be obtained by further optimising the value of the components on the matching transformer. I was surprised how sensitive the antenna was and found it unnecessary to switch in the receiver preamplifier on the IC-706.

OTHER CONSIDERATIONS. The most convenient place to have the loop is near to the operating position where the loop can be adjusted. In my case this turned out to be the worst place for electrical noise. In my situation the area of lowest noise is some distance from the shack and I would have to make some arrangement so the loop can be adjusted remotely. A low voltage spit motor and gearbox should do the trick. I have heard of varicap diodes being used to tune a receiver loop, although whether it would

PHOTO 3: The value of the coax feed series capacitance being measured for optimum matching using a polyvaricon variable capacitor.

PHOTO 4: Test setup for determining resonance and matching for the receiver loop antenna.

work in this case has not been tested.

The transceiver is connected to this low noise receiving loop only when receiving and switched to the main antenna during transmit. My FT-990 has a separate receive antenna socket that allows the use of a separate receiver antenna; otherwise you will have to make a relay box that automatically switches the main antenna connection to the receive antenna during the receive period.

**FITTING PL-259 PLUGS.** While sorting out lengths of coax for last month's Antennas, where I described measuring velocity factor, I came across one length that was faulty. Conductivity existed on the centre conductor but not on the braiding. This length of coax was terminated with PL-259 plugs. Both plugs looked well constructed with nicely flowing solder work around the plug, as shown in **Photo 5**.

I unsoldered the centre pin connection of one of the plugs and the coax came away from the plug before I had time to unsolder the braid, see **Photo 6**. As you can see, the braid has been appropriately tinned but the solder on PL-259 had not been heated enough to allow it to run through the solder holes to join up with the tinned braid.

It can be difficult to know if enough heat has been applied to make the solder run through the holes to make a good connection to the braid. If insufficient heat is used the result is no connection or a connection with a dry joint – too much heat and you can seriously cook the coax or the insulation on the plug. If you do favour the soldered approach it is probably a good idea to solder the braid to the plug first and do a mechanical test by tugging the coax from the plug before soldering the centre pin.

This subject was discussed in [4] and [5] with comments from G3JKV, G3EDD, G8JVM and GW8AWT on how to fix the braiding to the PL-259 without soldering. This discussion took place over 10 years ago so I have repeated the comments by GW8AWT. He remarked that he had never soldered the outer braid of any type of coax plug that he has ever used in the light of work done at around 1000MHz by EMI research in 1949. He advised that the braid needs to be clean and corrosion / tarnish free. The strands are gently combed out with something that is both sharp yet smooth, such as the test probe of an AVO. These strands are then stroked back along the outer of the PVC skin. The end is made up so that there is 1/8in (3mm) length of inner insulating material clear of the braid and that the bared inner conductor is plenty long enough to poke well clear of the PL-259 when the coax is fitted. The coax is screwed into the PL-259 plug until the shoulder of inner conductor has become visible through the solder holes in the plug and the folded back braid has just come into view.

Excess inner conductor is cropped and soldered to the PL-259 plug centre connector. The braid can then be cropped and grease or Vaseline worked into the solder holes and outer connection to make a water resistant joint.

This all assumes the coax and folded back outer braid forms a tight fit into the PL-259. RG-213, with a diameter of 10.5mm, plus the thickness of the braid makes for a very tight fit. Slightly thinner coax might require a layer of plastic tape to increase the diameter of the sheath in order to ensure a similarly tight fit, as shown in **Photo 7**.

PHOTO 5: Coax cable with an apparently well-made soldered joint.

PHOTO 6: Coax removed easily from the PL-259 indicating that the braid was not soldered correctly.

PHOTO 7: Coax braid folded back over the outer sheath for insertion into PL-259. In this case a layer of red plastic tape has been added to increase the cable diameter to ensure a tight fit.

TABLE 1: Loop selectivity test results.

| Frequency | SWR |
|---|---|
| 7099kHz | 3:1 |
| 7090kHz | 1.6:1 |
| 7077kHz | 3:1 |
| 3553kHz | 3:1 |
| 3548kHz | 2:1 |
| 3542kHz | 3:1 |

**REFERENCES**


[1] A two-metre diameter loop for 80m mobile, Lock d'Hunt, 'Eurotek', *RadCom* May 1993

[2] *Backyard Antennas*, Peter Dodd, G3LDO, RSGB bookshop

[3] *Building Successful HF Antennas*, Peter Dodd, G3LDO, RSGB bookshop

[4] Antennas, *RadCom* December 2002

[5] Antennas, *RadCom* March 2003

# Antennas

## In defence of the quad antenna

**EARLY DX ANTENNA.** My very first DX antenna was quad for the 15 and 10m bands. With this antenna I was able to work the world using a homebrew 60W AM transmitter. Mind you, this was in 1959, at the peak of the largest sunspot cycle the world has ever seen.

The choice of a quad was imposed because suitable aluminium tubing was not available for making a more conventional beam antenna and I had to settle for garden canes, insulated wire and insulation tape. I recall that it was a popular antenna at the time but I am unable to remember where the design that I used came from.

The basic design of the cubical quad comprises two full wavelength wire loops. One loop is used as the driven element and the second (with an added tuning stub to lower its resonant frequency) as a parasitic reflector. In the early days garden canes were used as element supports as shown in **Photo 1**.

**QUAD ANTENNA.** The quad can easily be configured as a multiband antenna simply by nesting the various band elements on the element supports. Furthermore, additional parasitic elements can be added to increase the gain and an example of this shown in **Photo 2**. This antenna arrangement was constructed by the late Al Slater, G3FXB and comprised four elements on 15 and 10m and three elements on 20m. This antenna formed part of a top grade station that helped Al achieve very high contest scores.

**G6XN QUAD ASSESSMENT.** I consulted G6XN's books **[1]** and **[2]** for additional information on the quad and found it discouraging. He notes, "Loop arrays such as the quad, which though satisfactory in terms of performance, are not advised for rotary beams since they are heavy, unsightly, expensive and, due to high wind loading, frequently blow down."

**PHOTO 1:** Basic single band cubical quad using plastic covered wire elements fixed to garden cane supports using plastic insulation tape. The canes are fixed to the boom using shelf brackets.

G6XN also puts the quad antenna in a category 'Antennas with Adverse Features' with the following comments: "Despite the popularity of the quad its use as a rotary beam is strongly deprecated for reasons that can be summed up by quoting remarks made to the author during the writing of this book. For much of the time he was using a fixed (reversible) quad and many of the stations contacted, after commenting on the excellence of this type of antenna, added that they used to have one themselves but it blew down. This in some cases has reduced them to using an inferior type of antenna such as a typical commercial trapped beam."

**THE G3LDO QUAD.** The quad in current use at my QTH was first described in 2007 **[3]** and 2008 **[4]** and is designed around a commercial boomless aluminium structure known as a 'spider', see **Photo 3**, plus second hand fibreglass spreaders. It covers the 20, 17 and 15m bands. The use of this spider causes the element supports to lean away from the hub at an angle of about 25° from the vertical. The result is that multi-band elements spacings are optimum for each band, see **Photo 4**.

**PHOTO 2:** The G3FXB quad comprising four elements on 15 and 10m and three elements on 20m.

One criticism often levied at the quad is that it unsightly, but I guess it depends on how it is built. The front cover of the latest *RSGB Antenna File* book **[5]** has been enhanced with a photo of my quad – so this antenna must have *some* aesthetic merit.

G6XN notes that the quad is heavy. Again, I suppose it depends on how it is built. I estimated the weight of my antenna by weighing various components. They add up as follows: four fibreglass poles, each 800g = 3.2kg; 1.5kg for the alloy spider and 1.4kg for the wire, making a total of just over 6kg. This compares favourably with commercial multiband beams, which start at around 10kg.

I do have a large steel multiband quad hub (described in [4]), which weighs around

**PHOTO 3:** Lightweight aluminium boomless 'spider' reputed to have been made by Labgear.

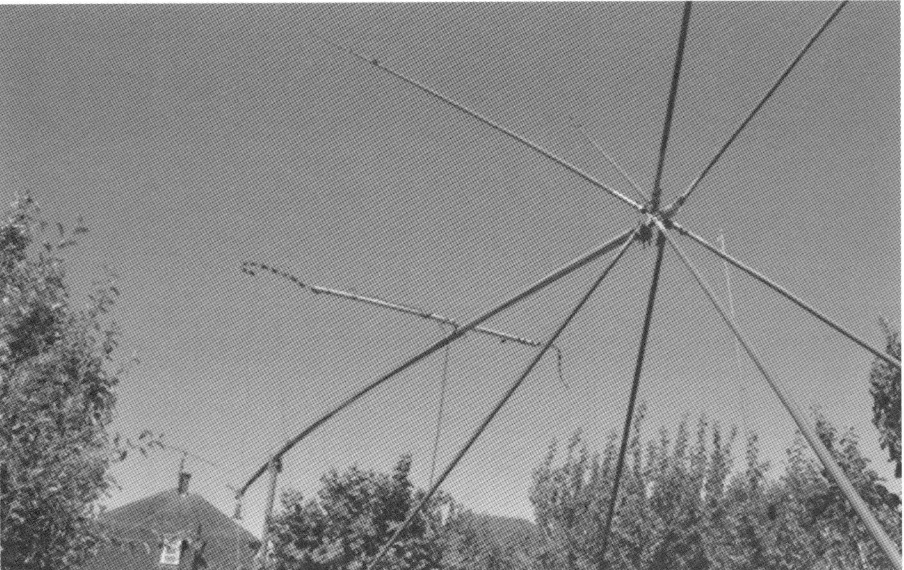

PHOTO 4: The G3LDO multiband boomless quad for 20, 17 and 15m, fixed to a counter-weighted fold over mast.

PHOTO 7: Improved method of fixing non-insulated wire elements to the element supports using jubilee clips (hose clamps) and strimmer cord.

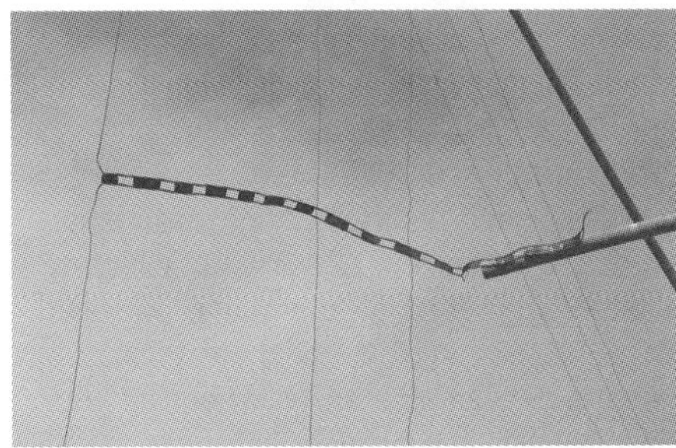

PHOTO 8: Method of tuning the 20m reflector using 450Ω ribbon line. It shows signs of the length being adjusted while tuning.

7.5kg. If I used this it would put up the weight of my antenna to 10.4kg. In my case, weight is an important consideration because it is fixed to a counter-weighted mast (seen in Photo 4) that can be raised or lowered in under a minute, all in the interests of experimenting and antenna adjusting.

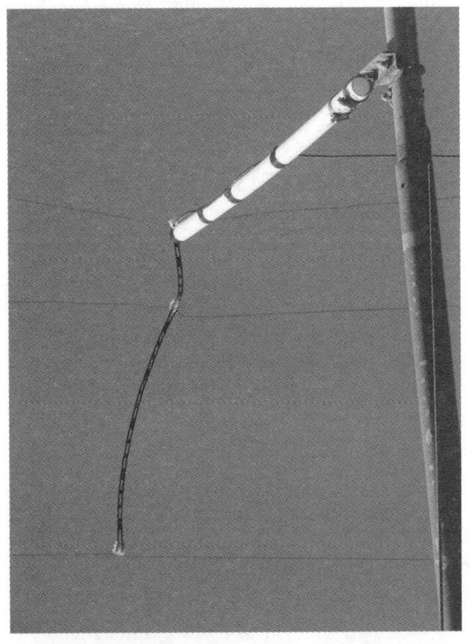

PHOTO 5: Multiband driven elements connected in parallel via 350Ω ladder line to the coax feed using connector blocks

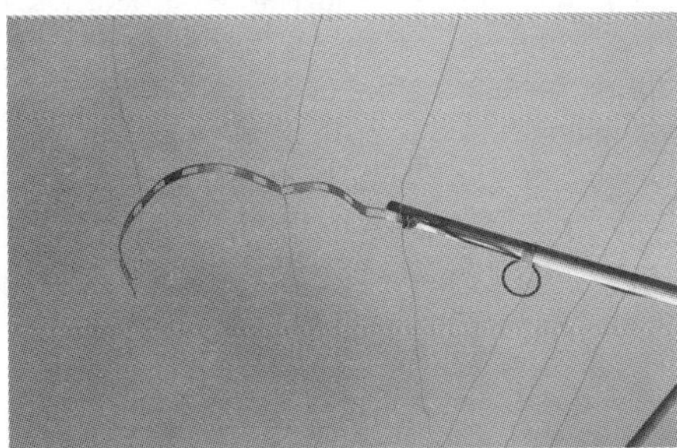

PHOTO 6: Improved method of connecting the coax to the multiband driven elements using 450Ω ladder line and soldering the connections.

This quad has now been up and in use for over 6 years and is located about 400m from the sea, which puts it in an exposed and corrosive environment. So how did it fare? In the early stages of development I found that I could circumvent some of the elaborate driven element feeding arrangements often seen in the literature simply by connecting the elements in parallel via ladder line as shown in **Photo 5**. Each element is connected to the ladder line using connector blocks. Earlier attempts to connect the various band elements directly in parallel were less successful.

Over the years this method of connecting the elements to 300Ω ladder line feeder turned out to be less than ideal. The connector block connections corroded and the elements tended to become disconnected. The fix was to use a stronger 450Ω ladder line and to solder all the connections, as shown in **Photo 6**.

The original method of connecting the elements to the element supports was to use tie wraps and jubilee clips (hose clamps). The sun and weather caused the tie wraps to weaken and break. The fix was to replace these tie wraps with nylon strimmer cord, see **Photo 7**, which is much tougher.

**TUNING AND PERFORMANCE.** The quad construction plan described in **[6]** uses the formula L (inches) = 250/f (MHz) for each side of the driven element and L = 258/f for the reflector. These lengths have to be multiplied by 4 to get the total element circumference. The element spacing is quoted as S = 118/f. You could make both elements L = 250/f and use a tuning stub to lower the frequency of the reflector, as shown in **Photo 8**. In fact most early quad designs used this approach.

The quad shown in Photo 4 uses large reflectors on the 17 and 15m bands and a tuning stub on 20m. I favour the non-stub approach because there is less material to flap around in the wind. However, my second hand fibreglass poles were too short for the non-stub design.

No matter how carefully you follow an antenna construction plans with regard to dimensions you will be lucky if you get it right first time. It is no surprise that top DXer stations perform well because their owners spend considerable amounts of time and effort honing their antennas for maximum performance. The method I used for tuning for performance and directivity was described in **[7]**.

As a measure of the performance of this quad I have worked over 100 countries on 14MHz CW using the vintage rig described in the July 2013 edition of *RadCom*. On other bands the performance is equal or better.

REFERENCES


[1] *HF Antennas for all Locations* 1st Edition, P91, P222, L A Moxon, G6XN, RSGB

[2] *HF Antennas for all Locations* 2nd Edition, P104, P313, L A Moxon, G6XN, RSGB

[3] Antennas, *RadCom,* October and November 2007

[4] *Building Successful HF Antennas*, Peter Dodd, G3LDO, RSGB

[5] *RSGB Antenna File,* RSGB

[6] *All about cubical quad antennas*, Bill Orr, W6SAI and Stuart Cowan, W2LX

[7] Antennas, *RadCom,* December 2007

# Antennas

## Measuring coax electrical length

**CORRECTION FROM OCTOBER.** My thanks to G3VLF for pointing out that the formula for the size of a quad given last month was incorrect. It should have been L (ft) = 250/f (MHz).

**ELECTRICAL LENGTH OF COAX.** It is very useful to be able to measure the resonant length (electrical length) of a length of coaxial cable. Sometimes we wish to avoid resonant lengths of transmission line to reduce the effects of common mode currents on the line. On the other hand we need resonant lengths to make a coaxial balun or a phasing network for a directional array or for circular polarised Yagi. The need for identical electrical lengths of coax also arises whenever you need to feed two or more antennas in phased arrays.

Usually you need a precise number of electrical half-wavelengths or quarter-wavelengths. You may also want to measure the electrical length of a section of cable that is already part of an antenna installation or a roll of cable on a drum.

Quarter wave and half wavelength piece of transmission lines have special properties. A line quarter wave in length acts like an impedance transformer. A short circuit at one end will appear as an open at the other. Likewise an open at one end will appear as a short at the other. This will happen only at the frequency where the line is 1/4, 3/4, 5/4 (etc) waves in length and is known as the 'dual', see **Figure 1**.

However, you can't just cut a physical length of coax that is half or a quarter wavelength long as you can an antenna element – there is the velocity factor to consider.

**VELOCITY FACTOR.** The dielectric material that separates the outer conductor of coax cable from its centre conductor performs two functions: 1) it determines the intensity of the electrostatic field that can exist between the two conductors, thus establishing the cable's electrical characteristics and 2) it ensures the inner conductor is physically centred relative to the outer conductor (braid).

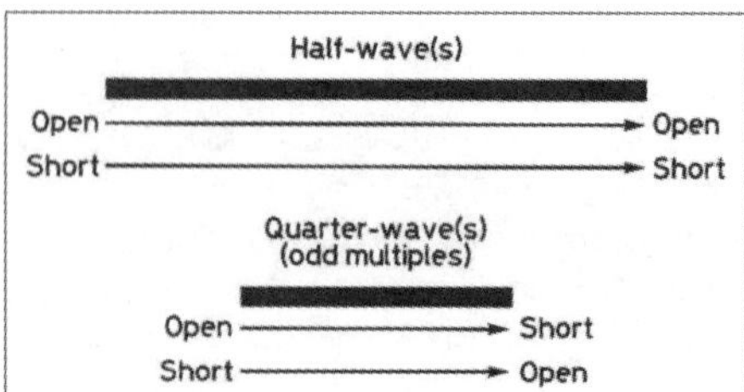


FIGURE 1: An electrical half-wave (or any multiple) shows the same impedance at its far end. An electrical quarter-wave (or any odd multiple) shows the 'dual' of impedance at its far end.

Common dielectric materials used in the manufacture of coax include polyethylene and polystyrene and many of the popular coax cables used In amateur radio use a solid polyethylene dielectric.

Electromagnetic waves travel at the speed of light in free space but are slowed down if they travel though a dielectric material. As already noted the two conductors of the transmission line are separated by a dielectric material. The RF energy is contained within these two conductors and is subjected to a delay caused by the dielectric constant of the insulating material. This delay is expressed in terms of the speed of light (either as a percentage or a decimal fraction) and is referred to as the velocity factor Vf.

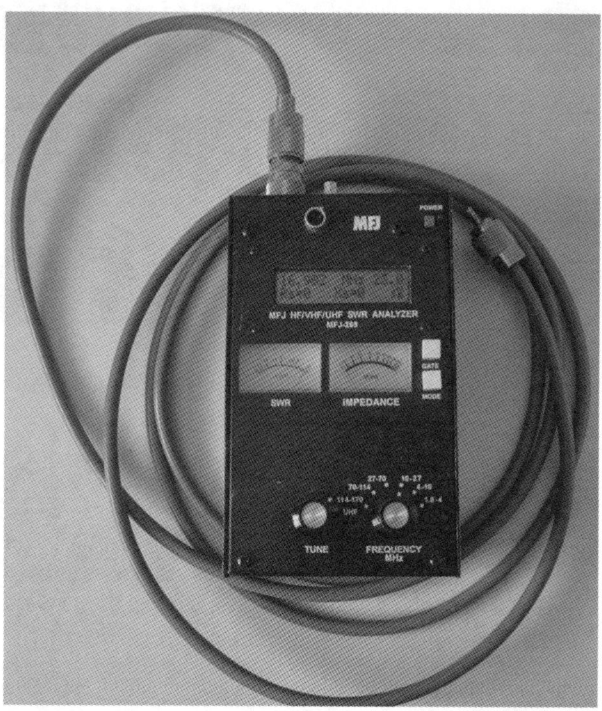


PHOTO 1: An MFJ-269 being used to measure the resonance of an open circuit length of coax. Originally an MFJ-259 was used, which can only measure the Rx component of impedance.

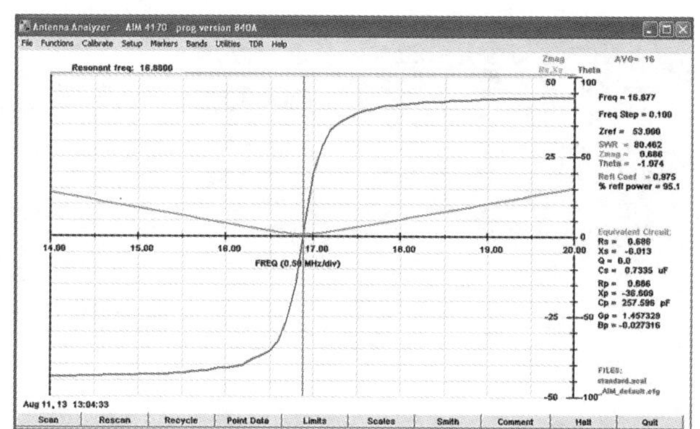


FIGURE 2: The impedances of a length of coax measured over a frequency range 14 to 20MHz plotted in polar coordinates. Note that the rate of change with frequency of theta (Xs) is much greater than Zmag (Rs).

Taking a length of RG-213 coax for example, from published data the dielectric type is polyethylene. This material has a velocity factor Vf of 0.66, which means the velocity of propagation within this coax is 0.66 x the velocity of light.

Other coax such as RG-58xx uses polyethylene with low-loss nitrogen (accomplished by bubbling nitrogen gas through molten polyethylene during the manufacturing process). This material, known as foam dielectric, offers half the dielectric losses at a modest increase in cost and its velocity factor is 0.82.

It follows that a quarter or half-wave of an electrical length of coax required to perform the functions described earlier will need to be 0.66 and 0.82 respectively for RG-213 and RG-58xx. A more elegant method of determining and electrical length is to actually measure it electronically.

The July edition of Antennas **[1]** partially addressed a question from Ron Bennett, G4DIY. He had a requirement for an electrical quarter wave of RG-213 for an antenna project and wanted to know how to measure it. I then described my efforts measuring the electrical quarter wavelength of a 9.25ft of open circuit Daiyu Denson SD-2V coax using an MFJ-269, as shown in **Photo 1**.

This method appeared to have accuracy issues. The problem arises when trying to determine the lowest value of Rx. As you can see from **Figure 2** (Zmag, the polar coordinate equivalent of Rx) varies slowly with changes of frequency. On the MFJ-259 the frequency could be swept over 400kHz (at 16MHz) with no

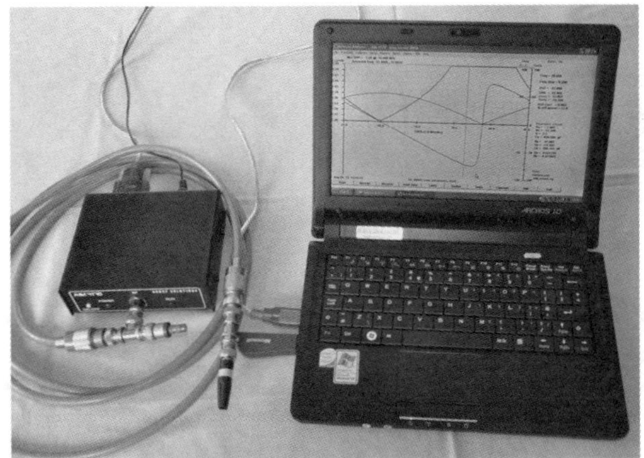

PHOTO 2: The AIM 4170 set up to measure SWR on a 'short' terminated line to see how it compares with Rx and Xs measurements.

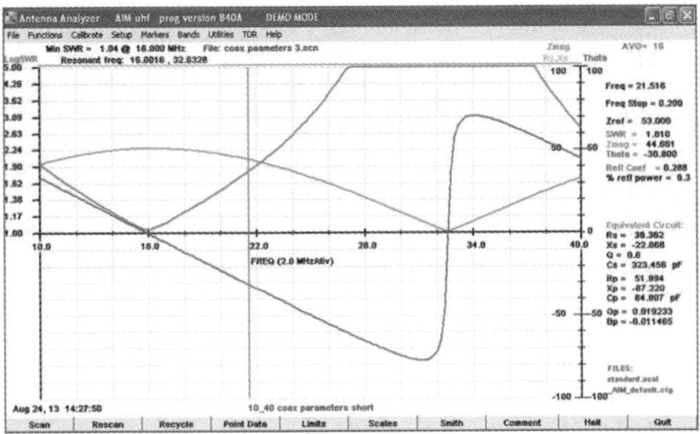

FIGURE 4: The rates of change in parameter values at the two resonant points with the AIM 4170 set up to measure Zmag=Rs (green), Theta=Xs(purple) and SWR (red).

perceptual variation around zero Rx. Accuracy was improved by sweeping the frequency either side of zero until the Rx reading was 10Ω and the average taken of the two readings.

On the other hand, from **Figure 2** you can see that the Xs rate of change with frequency is much greater than Rx so an instrument capable of measuring this parameter appears to be more suitable. The MFJ-269 displays Xs digitally. In practice the frequency could be varied from 16.26MHz to 17.04MHz before Xs moved from zero, which is an improvement compared with measuring Rx.

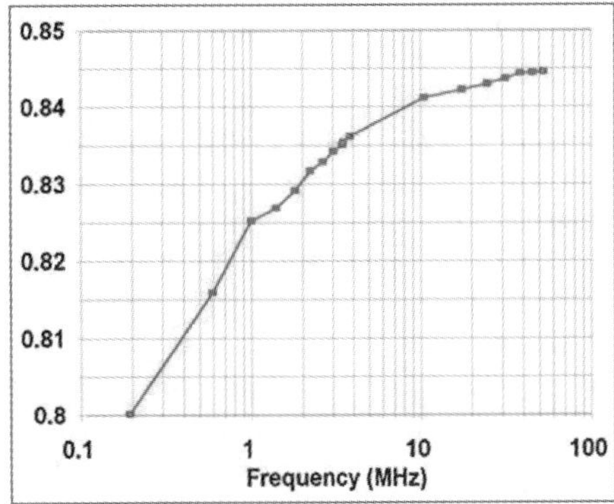


FIGURE 5: The variation in Vf with frequency of a high quality RG8 coaxial cable known as Commscope 3227. The published Vf for this cable is 0.84.

**MEASURING COAX LENGTH USING SWR.** Stewart Rolfe, GW0ETF, e-mailed me to say "You talk about the accuracy problem of determining zero impedance with an analyser. I've always used the method of having a 50Ω load in parallel with the coax, which is in this case shorted at the far end. When the frequency is correct for an electrical 90° (quarter wavelength) the coax presents 'infinite' impedance to the instrument and you're left with 50Ω pure resistance, which the instrument will indicate accurately. You just need a SO239 'T' piece and a dummy load with a very short lead on one branch and the lead under test on the other [1]". See **Figure 3**.

I did describe this method in **[2]** but it was never actually tried and I had forgotten about it. The method has the advantage that an impedance measuring instrument is not required and you can perform the measurement with standard items found in a ham radio shack.

The SWR test assembly is energised by a transmitter (with the power considerably reduced so that the PA is not damaged by any wild load impedances). In many cases the measurements using this method will be confined to within the amateur bands because of transmitter frequency limitations.

Variations in the values of Zmag and Theta (polar equivalents of Rx and Xs) have already been described and shown Figure 2. I then set the AIM 4170, shown in **Photo 2**, to additionally measure SWR so that results could be compared with previous measurements. The measurements shown in Figure 4 were performed using the same length and type of coax (terminated with a short) as used in previous measurements but measured over a frequency range of 10 to 40MHz. This clearly shows the rates of change in parameter values at the two resonant points.

There is another factor to be considered when terminating a coax length. Although I was using the 'short' termination (black-tipped in Photo 2) provided with the AIM 4170 I didn't have a suitable coax adapter and had to improvise with three stages of adaptors. This changed the resonant frequency down from 16.73MHz to 16.14MHz. When you use a termination with a connector or adapter consider that it may affect the length of the cable you are trying to measure.

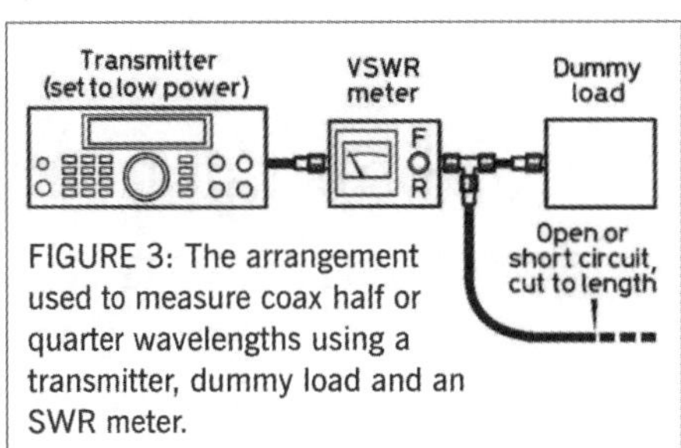


FIGURE 3: The arrangement used to measure coax half or quarter wavelengths using a transmitter, dummy load and an SWR meter.

**CALCULATING VELOCITY FACTOR.** If you have a length of coax with its pedigree stamped on the side then all you have to do is to look up the velocity factor in tables that can be found on the internet. Otherwise you can calculate velocity factor by comparing an electrically measured length with its physical length using the following formula:

Velocity factor Vf = physical length (ft) x frequency/246

For my 9.25ft length of SD-2V,

Vf = 9.25 x 16.49/246 = 0.62.

This wasn't the velocity factor figure I was expecting. It turned out that I had made an error in measuring the physical length of the coax. A new length measurement of 9.66ft resulting in a value of Vf = 0.6603

Vf = 9.66 x 16.82/246 = 0.6605 (measured 9ft 8in)

I can't say I like this length measurement in metric feet! It may have contributed to the physical measurement mistake; imperial rulers are not calibrated in decimal points. I now favour metric measurements and my length of cable was measured again giving a value of 2.94m. This requires a new formula for calculating Vf and I suggest the following:

Velocity factor Vf = Physical length (m) x frequency/74.88, so

2.94 x 16.82/74.88 = 0.6604

You can also measure the length of a large drum of coax to find its electrical length. If the coax type is printed of the cable or the drum then you should be able to find the physical length. However there's a bit more to the measurement than meets the eye. This is because the velocity factor Vf is not a constant – it varies with frequency, although this variation is small in the HF spectrum, as shown in **Figure 5**.

REFERENCES

[1] *Low Band DXing*, 4th edition, chapter 11 page 24, Phased Arrays, UN4UN

[2] *The Antenna Experimenter's Guide*, 2nd edition, P94, G3LDO

# Antennas

## More about quarter wavelengths of coax plus HF wire antennas in a suburban plot

**COAX RESONANT LENGTHS.** In last month's Antennas I noted reasons why it is useful to measure the electrical length of coax cable. In many cases resonant lengths are required to make up phasing units. On the other hand resonant lengths can be susceptible to common mode currents. These currents can cause unpredictable results to measurements when using some SWR analysers.

**DO IT IN SOFTWARE.** I thought you might be interested in a software product called *TLW*, Transmission Lines for Windows. It comes bundled with other software on the CD located on the rear inside cover of the *ARRL Antenna Handbook* and, when loaded, it presents the display shown in **Figure 1**.

The *TLW* program comes with a library of transmission line types and in Figure 1 you can see that I have selected RG-213. Rather than entering a physical length for the transmission line you can enter a quarter wavelength as 0.25w in the length box and the program will calculate the length from the frequency and the selected transmission line type.

The reflected impedance presented at one end of the coax is shown on the 'Input' line at the bottom of the display. This is the transform of whatever impedance is connected to the other end. For example in Figure 1 an impedance of 10000±j0 is reflected as 0.77 +j0 and an electrical quarter wavelength of RG-213 is 3.484m.

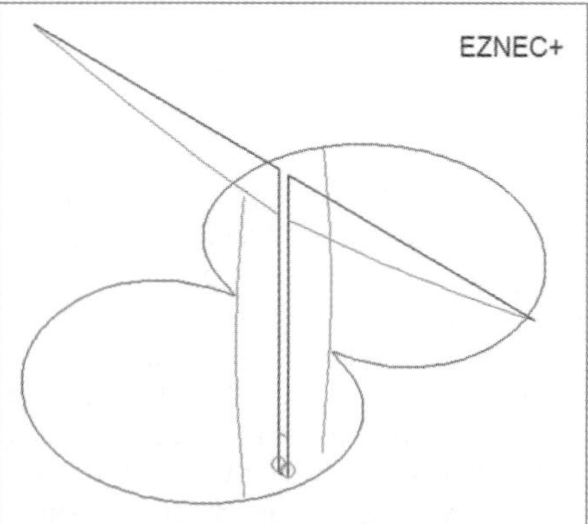


FIGURE 2: An idealised free-space doublet antenna, with equal antenna currents on each leg of the doublet and that the currents in the feeder are equal and opposite. Red lines = current distribution, blue lines = two dimensional signal distribution.

You can find the electrical quarter or half wavelength of coax for any given frequency without the need of test equipment or computer programs. To find a free space wavelength in metres L, divide c (speed of light in m/s, 300 x $10^6$) by frequency in Hz x $10^6$. This can be simplified to L = 300/f (MHz) A full wavelength of 14.2MHz is 300/14.2 = 21.126m For a quarter wavelength, it is 21.126/4 = 5.28m.

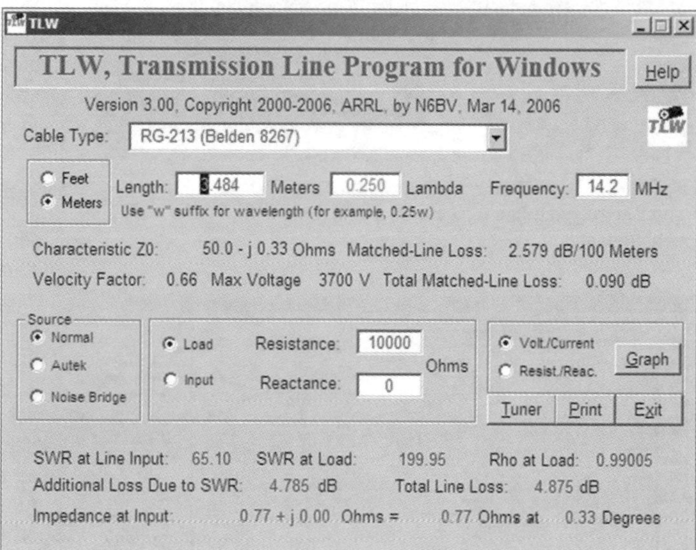


FIGURE 1: *TLW*, Transmission line program for windows showing the characteristics of a quarter wavelength of RG-213 terminated with a very high impedance (open circuit).

If we assume the coax to be RG-213 with a velocity factor of 0.66 then 5.28 x 0.66 = 3.483m, not very different from the length derived by *TLW*.

**THE BEST HF ANTENNA.** At times I am asked which is the best antenna for general HF operating in the normal restricted suburban environment. This can be a difficult question to answer because most of the time it is the antenna location that can be the main controlling factor. As I have said many times before, it is more important as to where the antenna is (located) than what it is.

So it is with interest that I heard from Roy Horton, G4GRM, who had been using a low profile 26m long, 8m high inverted-L antenna. This antenna had been in use for about 5 years now and gave a 'satisfactory' performance. He then erected a resonant (14.150MHz) delta loop for 20m, with an apex of 10m This loop was resonant in 14.15MHz orientated to at right angles to the inverted-L in an effort to try to work some east and west DX. The loop was fed at a lower corner nearest the shack via 50Ω coax and a 10 bifilar turn insulated 16SWG 1:4 balun wound on a piece of 35mm diameter plastic pipe. This loop was a disappointment with about 3-4 S-points of noise above that of the inverted-L and one S point down on signal strength compared with the inverted L (in all directions).

G4GRM tried various other antenna and configurations and finally settled on the simple arrangement described by G3GKG **[1]** and repeated in **[2]**. This antenna is a simple doublet fed with a slotted line feeder. Instead of using baluns a link coupled balanced tuner was constructed using parts available to hand.

Roy notes, "This antenna is a noticeable improvement in signal strength over the inverted-L regarding 14MHz DX stations. Not only that but the doublet is much quieter and also does not pick up bursts of static type QRN, which the inverted-L does. For 7MHz I had to insert an additional eighth wave of feeder to get the SWR down from 2:1 to 1:1. This is coiled up above the tuner in the shack so I can insert it as required".

**BALANCED ANTENNAS.** Some antenna articles and books describe a doublet as a balanced antenna. By 'balanced' I mean that the antenna currents on each leg of the doublet are equal and that the currents in the feeder are equal and opposite, as depicted in **Figure 2**. The currents in a balanced transmission line are equal and opposite and there is no radiation from the line on transmit; neither does the line pick up signals when the antenna is used for receive.

In the earlier days of amateur radio twin wire feeder was the only practical feeder

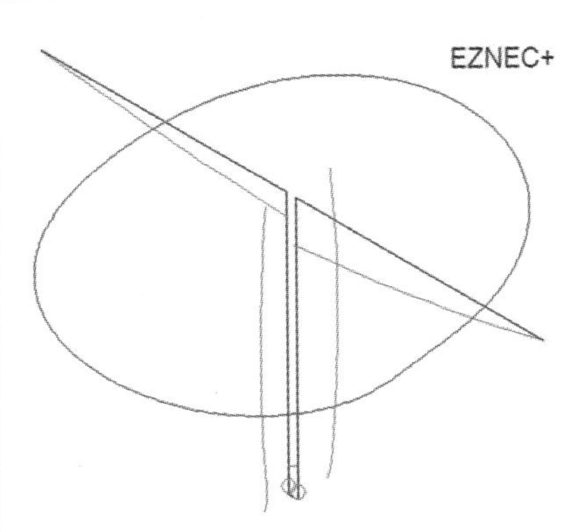


**FIGURE 3: Model of a 7MHz half wavelength high dipole fed with twin-wire feeder with the unequal currents in each conductor of the feeder.**

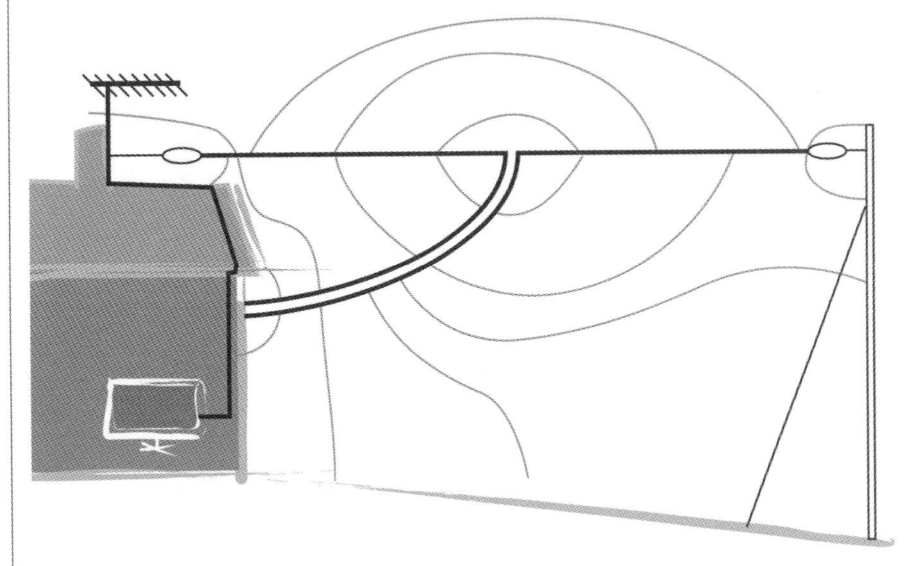

**FIGURE 4: The real world situation of most of our antenna arrangements showing vulnerability to electrical interference on receive and TVI on transmit.**

available and the design of the feed methods was influenced by commercial radio practice. The radio station at Rugby, for example, had a huge antenna farm of broadside arrays (later replaced by rhombics) on a several hundred acre site. Some of these lines had to be as long as 1.5km so they had to be efficient in transferring power without loss. Each twin wire line consisted of copper conductors, with one conductor placed 23cm from the other and supported 5m above ground.

With some 60 or 70 antennas the feedline system was somewhat complicated. On the main routes the feeders were arranged fairly close together. It can be appreciated that such an arrangement required that the feed lines should be well balanced (equal RF current in each conductor) to prevent radiation loss and crosstalk (mutual interference between sets of lines).

Unlike the idealised situation shown in Figure 2, in the real world the antenna is affected by ground reflection and interaction with nearby structures. Furthermore most ATUs use a balun to provide the balanced feed with no provision for adjusting the current in each conductor of the feeder for balance. In general the current distribution will be similar to that seen in **Figure 3**.

If the currents are not balanced then the feeders act as vertical antenna with consequent vertical antenna transmit and receive characteristics. Whether this is a good or a bad thing depends on the location of the antenna. For example if the antenna is located on an open space clear of electromagnetic obstructions then is might make a good DX antenna.

If, on the other hand, this antenna with its vertical characteristics is located close to the house then there are numerous possibilities of electrical interference, as shown in **Figure 4**. This is the situation in which most of our antennas are to be found. If you are using an antenna fed with ladder line or similar twin feeder and you have serious electrical interference then it might be a good idea to try a balanced feed ATU, as did G4GRM.

A very comprehensive balanced homebrew ATU by G0LMJ **[3] [4]** has provision for adjusting the currents in each conductor of the feeder. It uses plug-in coils rather than coil switching. It also incorporates a metering system for measuring these currents. This item could be built separately and used with any balance feed ATU to check just how balanced your antenna system is and whether balancing the transmission line reduced noise on receive.

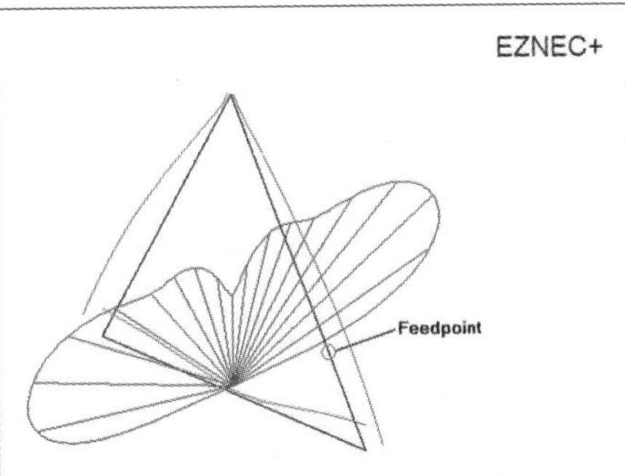


**FIGURE 5: Computer model of a 14MHz resonant delta loop with a 10m high apex. The model implies that it can be a good DX antenna provided it is fed one third of the way up one of the vertical sections.**

**COAX CABLE.** The same problem can also occur on coax fed antennas. In this case any difference between the current on the inner conductor and the inside if the braid will result in current flowing on the outside of the braid. Provided the conductor currents inside the coax are equal and opposite there will be no radiation from the line on transmit; neither does the coax pick up signals when the antenna is used for receive.

In the case of coax the solution is to suppress this outer braid current with a current choke. You may recall April edition of Antennas I tested a centre fed wire antenna that used a coax feed. There was no problem in transmitting but the noise level on receive was so high (S8.6 on 7MHz and S6.2 on 18MHz) that it only allowed contacts with very strong stations. This noise level seems to come from the telephone drop wire at this location, so I tried a couple of high impedance current chokes at each end of the coax section of the feeder. This reduced the noise to S6.5 on 7MHz and S4 on 18MHz, which allowed me to test the antenna with DX stations. If you have a receive noise problem at your QTH with a coax fed antenna then common mode chokes may be the answer.

**LARGE LOOP ANTENNAS.** Some further notes on the large loop antenna described by G4GRM earlier. I constructed a similar antenna for 7MHz some years ago and found it very good as a DX antenna for transmitting but it was very noisy receiving antenna – probably because it was located close to the house. Furthermore, no attempt was made to use balanced feeders. The large loop would appear to be reasonable DX antenna, see **Figure 5**, provided it is fed one third of the way up one of the vertical sections and that it is located some distance from the house.

**FINALLY.** I wish you all a pleasant Christmas and happy hours constructing antennas during the coming New Year.

**REFERENCES**

[1] 'The Doublet De-mystified', Brian Horsfall, G3GKG, *RadCom* January 2004

[2] 'The Doublet De-mystified', Brian Horsfall, G3GKG, *Antenna File* RSGB Books

[3] 'Balanced Line ASTU & Current Indicator, Ted Garrott, G0LMJ, *RadCom* July/August 1998

[4] *Backyard Antennas*, P54 – P63, RSGB Books

# Assessment of hf aerials using vhf aerials

by P. G. DODD, G3LDO

THE method normally used to assess the performance of a beam aerial at hf frequencies (14, 21 and 28MHz amateur bands) is to check on its front-to-back ratio (this is usually achieved by monitoring a transmission on the S-meter of a receiver while rotating the aerial), and a statistical check of two-way contacts, relying on experience with a previous aerial as a standard of comparison. If this experience is lacking, more reliance has to be placed on aerial performance figures given in aerial constructional articles in magazines and books.

Aerial performance figures are usually quoted as gain over a reference dipole, and some gain figures often quoted in books for various aerials are:

| 3-el beam | ZL special | 2-el quad | G4ZU birdcage |
|---|---|---|---|
| 7-8·3dB | 6-7dB | 5·6-9dB | 10dB |

With the exception of the three-element beam, angles of radiation of these aerials at different heights above ground are rarely quoted.

The author decided to make comparative tests on small rotatable beam aerials, capable of being accommodated in a small garden, for the 14, 21 and 28MHz bands, because the comparative aerial performance information available was inconsistent. The requirement was to record the horizontal and vertical polar diagrams and compare the forward gain figures. To achieve this, even at the highest frequency in the 28MHz band, would require a large range with a high tower at one end. As this was out of the question, the tests were carried out at 145MHz in the vhf band, so that the aerial models and the test range could be scaled down to a manageable size.

Initially the test range was 6m long with a tower at one end 6m high (see Fig 1). Consideration was given to conducting these tests at a much higher frequency (435MHz) but this was not done in case the behaviour of these very small aerials was different from that of the aerials with which they were being compared; considerations such as rf "skin effect" and length-to-diameter factor (K factor) could cause complications.

## Test range

Fig 1 shows the general layout of the test range. The transmitter was connected to the aerial under test and the signal strength measured on a diode field-strength meter. The tests were conducted over a rather wet lawn. The effect of the reflection coefficient of earth between, say, 14 and 145MHz was not known, so the vertical polar diagram of a horizontal dipole was measured at a quarter, half, three-quarter and one wavelength above ground (Fig 4). The half, three-quarter and one wavelength patterns were very close to the expected theoretical patterns; the effect of reflection coefficient between 14 and 145MHz was not regarded as significant enough to invalidate these tests.

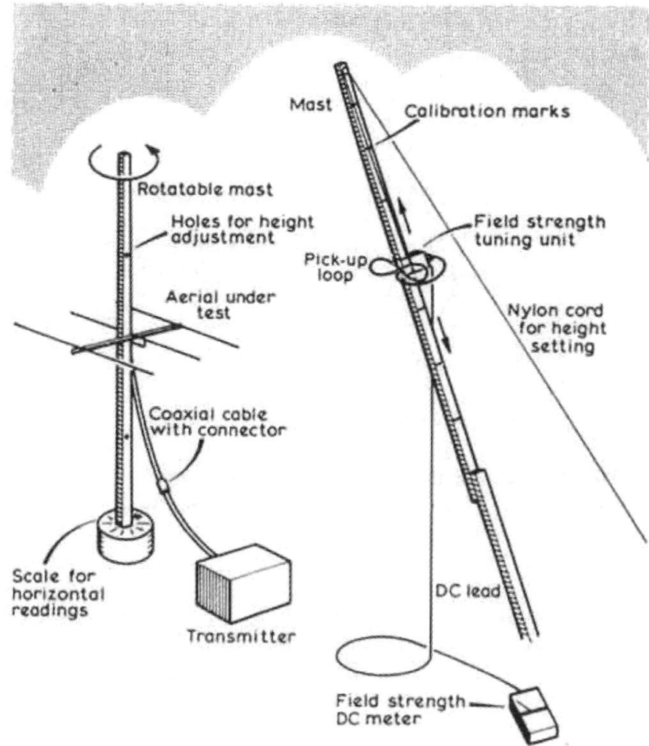


Fig 1. The test range

## Diode field-strength meter

The diode field-strength meter circuit diagram is shown in Fig 2. Special care was taken to filter the dc output leads because they were 9m (30ft) long. Because the overall test results are affected by the field-strength meter linearity an attempt was made to calibrate the linearity characteristics. The diode field-strength meter was not sensitive enough to be calibrated on a vhf signal generator [1], so in a further attempt to find the linearity characteristics, the diode field-strength meter was connected to a vertically-polarized dipole.

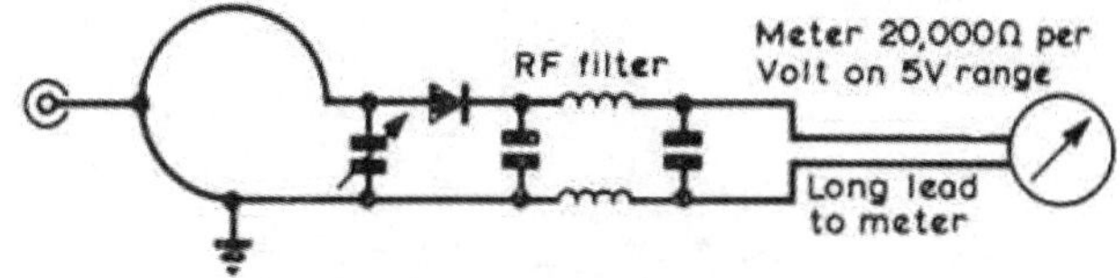


Fig 2. Field-strength meter

A further dipole, energized by a transmitter, was placed at various distances from the meter and the graph in Fig 3 was produced. This test was repeated several times and the results, each time, were roughly the same; at about 9m between the two dipoles the graph departed from the normal downward trend. This might have been caused by ground reflections or a change in characteristics of the field-strength meter diode at the lower rf field strengths. Consequently the readings taken during all the tests were kept between 0·5 and 5V whenever possible.

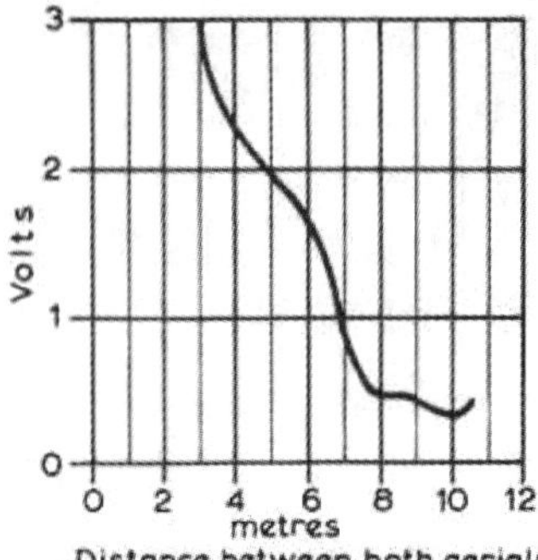


Fig 3. Field-strength meter linearity

## Horizontal polar diagram measurements

The horizontal polar diagram was measured by energizing the aerial under test and rotating it through 360°, all the time taking measurements at the field-strength meter. The field-strength dipole was tried at various angles but the horizontal pattern varied very little. The measurements were taken at the vertical angle of maximum radiation.

The dipole test gives a polar diagram similar to the therotetical pattern, see Fig 8. Comparative gains of the different aerials were not performed at this stage. Before commencing a test pattern on an aerial the field-strength meter was adjusted so that the maximum voltage was between 4 and 5V. This was to ensure that field-strength meter was operating over the linear section of its characteristic.

## Vertical polar diagram measurements

The vertical polar diagram was measured by energizing the aerial under test and plotting the field strength at various angles relative to the horizontal. This was carried out with a dipole and field-strength meter on a wooden mast situated at the opposite end of the test range to the aerial under test. The field-strength meter and dipole were attached to the mast in such a manner as to allow them to be moved up and down (see Fig 1) against calibration marks on the mast.

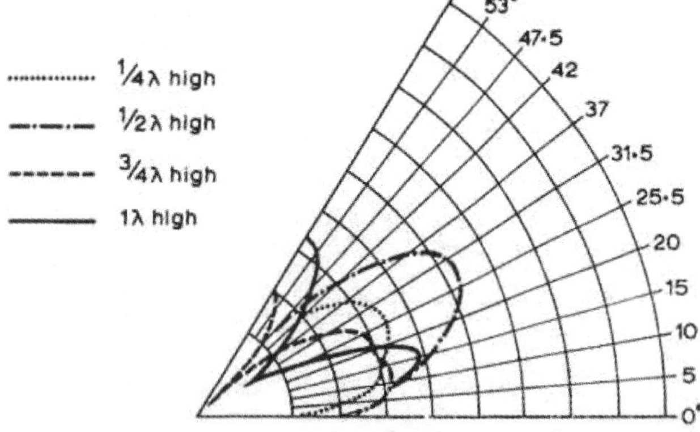


Fig 4. Vertical patterns for the dipole

The mast was 6m high, though only calibrated along 5m of its length. The lower half of the mast was adjustable so that the lowest calibration point was at the same height as the aerial under test when tested at various sub-multiples of a wavelength above ground. The mast was sloped at an angle of 59° (measured from the horizontal) towards the aerial under test. This was done to give the nearest approximation to a section of a circle required for the vertical polar diagram measurements, without making the test tower unduly complicated. Some disturbance of the vertical polar diagram was accepted, but the general effect of earth with the angles of propagation was clearly shown.

The first measurements were made using a dipole as a test aerial. This was tried at one quarter, one half, three quarter and one wavelength above ground. The results were close enough to the theoretical patterns to be encouraging, see Fig 4.

## Aerial models

The aerials tested were small practical beam types that could normally be accommodated in an average garden. The test aerials were cut for 144·95MHz and made of 11swg plain copper and 28swg tinned-copper wire. The aerials were constructed by stapling the elements to wooden battens.

### 3-element beam

This was to be the standard of comparison for the other aerials because more information existed for this type of beam than any other. It was constructed to design graphs in the ARRL handbook.

The aerial was easy to set up and adjustment of the gamma match for a low swr was straightforward. The vertical and horizontal polar diagrams showed expected results.

### Quad

This aerial was built to the conventional design using crossed wooden battens held to the boom by a spider. The driver element was fed direct with coaxial cable and the reflector tuned with a stub. The driven element length and reflection stub were adjusted for a compromise setting of swr, front-to-back ratio and forward gain. The vertical pattern showed a lower angle of radiation for a given height above ground and the horizontal pattern showed a broader pattern than the three-element beam. These results were as expected.

### Birdcage

This aerial was tried with the parasitic element, first as a reflector then as a director. A higher forward gain resulted with the parasitic element tuned as a director. The driven element was gamma matched and parasitic element length adjustments were carried out by making the elements larger than required and then pruning and re-soldering the wires. The excess wire was left on until after the correct length was found, then cut off. This was a mistake—the excess length had a loading effect and when cut off left the parasitic element too short. Wires were then soldered to the vertical sections of the director parasitic element and pruned for a compromise of front-to-back ratio and forward gain. The swr was taken care of by the gamma match. No amount of adjustment would reduce the two lobes radiated from the back, the horizontal polar diagram shows the best results that could be attained.

### ZL Special

The ZL Special was constructed of wire stretched out on an H-frame. The design was conventional and it was fed directly with 75Ω coaxial cable. On initial tests the swr was found to exceed 3:1; no amount of tuning or changing of length of the phasing lines made much difference although the horizontal pattern was good. It was suspected that the feed impedance was greater than 150Ω, in which case a coaxial balun should make some improvement. This was not done because most constructional articles state that the ZL Special can be connected directly to 75Ω coaxial cable.

**All-metal quad**

While working in Sierra Leone the author had to build an all-metal version of the cubical quad because materials to make a conventional quad were not available. A 14MHz aerial was constructed out of metal tubing which looked like two 28MHz two-element beams stacked at a half wavelength, with tips of the upper and lower bays joined together with copper wire. The resonant frequency of this aerial was found to be far too high, so, because it was impractical to increase the length of the horizontal tubular elements, the distance between the bays had to be increased. This distance was increased to 20ft before the beam became resonant within the 14MHz band.

An article by G. D. Weson, G3NUF/CX9AAN, [3], and another in *SWM* April 1968, make interesting reading and confirm the author's findings.

An aerial using the same construction technique was made for the test frequency, the ratio of dimensions being the same. The reflector was made larger by increasing the length of the horizontal tube elements because it was impractical to make the vertical wires longer. The driven element was fed directly with 75Ω coaxial cable. This aerial was easy to adjust and produced an excellent horizontal pattern.

## Results

**Vertical patterns (Fig 5)**

The aerials were measured at various heights above ground, the results showing that the gain of the dipole, element beam and ZL Special was greater at a half-wavelength high than at one wavelength. It was thought that this might be due to the test aerial and receiver aerial being too close together.

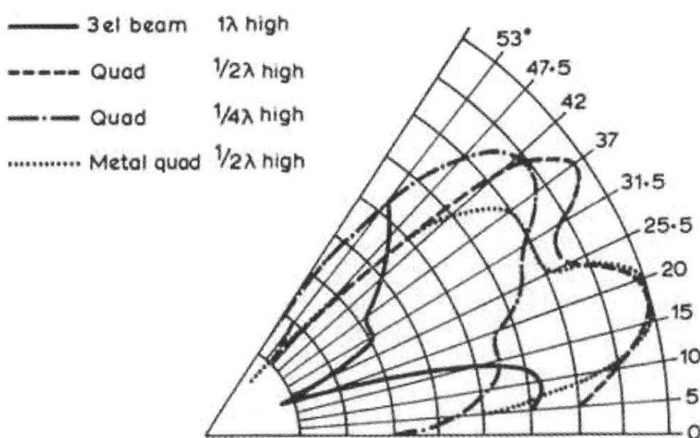


**Fig 5. Vertical pattern—3-element beam compared with quad**

The test was repeated at twice the distance, which showed the half and full-wave height patterns more equal (Fig 6), though the receiver mast was not high enough to look at the half-wave pattern properly. The angles of radiation seemed fairly close to the theoretical values available [4]. The kinks in the patterns cannot be explained, especially on the top lobe of the three-element beam full-wave pattern. It is possible that, though the aerial height is one wavelength, the electrical height is more, and a third lobe is emerging. The effect was more pronounced on the 12m range test where the lawn was known not to be as damp.

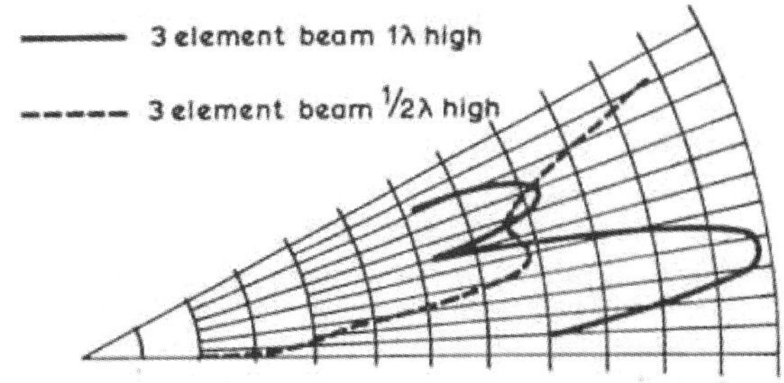


**Fig 6. Vertical pattern—3-element beam tested at 12m distance**

**Horizontal patterns (Figs 7 and 8)**

The dipole and three-element beam horizontal patterns were measured and compared against known patterns to check out the measurement technique, then the other patterns were completed.

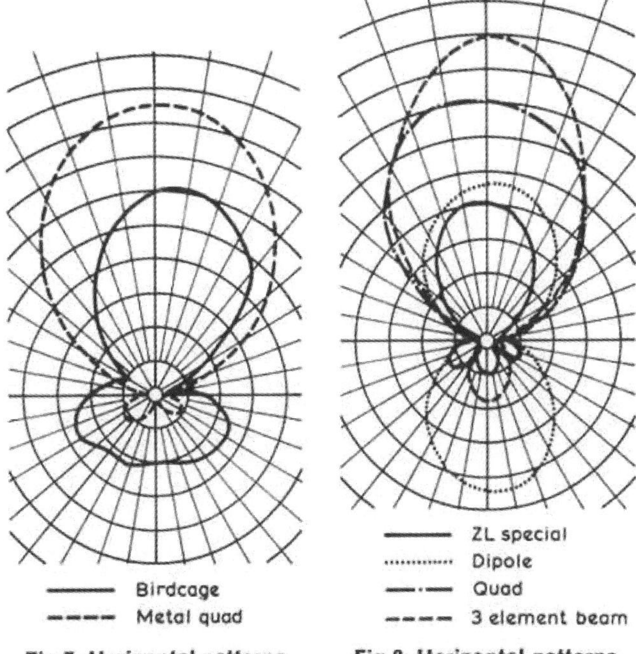


**Fig 7. Horizontal patterns** **Fig 8. Horizontal patterns**

**Relative gain measurements**

To obtain a gain comparison each aerial was connected to the transmitter in turn and the transmitter tuning and loading adjusted for the same rf output. It was important to maintain a constant transmitter output while comparing the gain of the different aerials. This was done by measuring the pa mode current and the rf current in the aerial lead (with an swr bridge) simultaneously. SWR readings on all aerials, with the exception of the ZL special, were less than 1·6:1.

A series of comparative readings was repeated at various distances and aerial heights and the average figures used to produce a factor. The aerial pattern figures were divided by the factor to produce the comparison polar diagrams. Gain figures have not been allotted to them as the characteristics of the field-strength meter were not known with sufficient precision.

The ZL Special proved to be a real problem. More time was spent trying to get it to perform properly than on all the other aerials put together. The transmitter could be loaded without difficulty but the swr was very high (3:1). This probably resulted in the poor comparative performance of this aerial.

## Conclusions

The polar diagrams in Figs 5, 7 and 8 indicate that a three-element beam, one wavelength high, gives the best performance. This means that a tri-band Yagi, 70ft high, would be the best all round hf aerial for amateur purposes. However, such an aerial is out of the question for most amateurs.

The quad works very well provided that the lower elements are a half-wavelength or more high (35ft on 14MHz). Although the all-metal quad gives the best performance, the conventional quad is more practical for three-band construction.

## Bibliography

[1] "Taming the diode field-strength meter", *CQ magazine*, February 1963.

[2] "Fold-over mast for beam support". *Short Wave Magazine*, August 1966.

[3] "Story of a cubical quad", *Short Wave Magazine*, June 1969.

[4] "Antennas and radio propagation", *US Army Manual.*

[5] "Ten-metre cubical quad", *Short Wave Magazine*, April 1968.

[6] *ARRL Handbook*, thirty seventh edition, pages 372 and 373.

# Wire beam antennas and the evolution of the G3LDO double-D

by P. DODD, G3LDO

## Introduction

During March 1979 the author needed a beam antenna to take advantage of the sudden improvement in conditions on 28MHz: it had to be lightweight because of the tall unguyed mast in use, and a quad was not feasible because of the obstructions encountered when the mast was tilted over. Its development is described below. The author went to some lengths to defend vhf modelling of hf antennas in a previous article [2], and it would seem that vhf modelling is a well established technique [3] and is used by many designers as a method of testing hf antenna design. Its use in the design of different types of antenna for amateur purposes would seem to be beneficial and has been used extensively in this project.

## First attempt

The first wire Yagi beam was constructed using graphs from the *ARRL Antenna Handbook* [1] as a guide, and the wire elements were laid on a crossed bamboo support as shown in Fig 1. The support was not quite large enough, and the driven element and the reflector were allowed to dangle over the edge of the support. The elements were pruned for a low swr and reasonable directivity, and the beam proved quite successful—giving two S-points improvement (on average) when compared with the previous dipole at the same height.

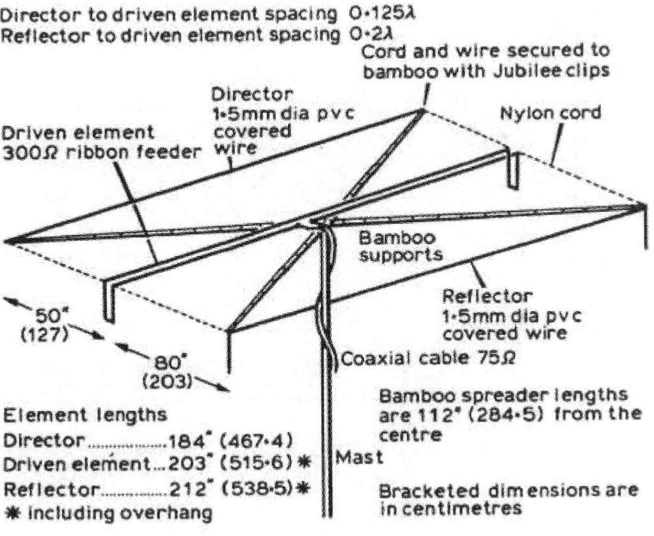


Fig. 1 Mk1 wire Yagi for 28·6MHz

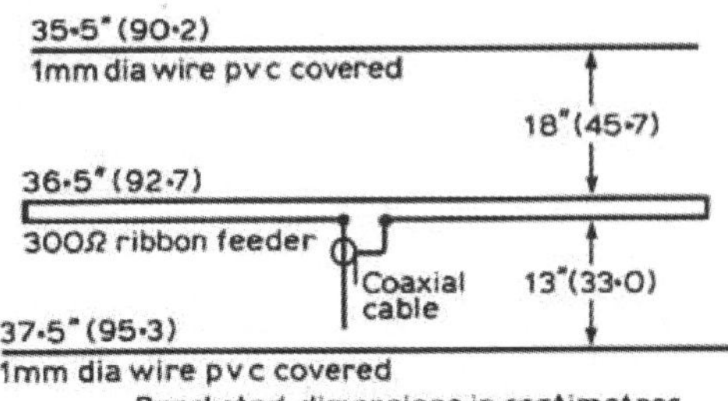


Fig 2. 145·6MHz Yagi dimensions for maximum gain

The only problems encountered were the dangling ends of the elements which in windy weather caused fluctuation in swr and, presumably, gain. Heavy rain caused an increase in swr from 1·4:1 to 1·8:1.

## Wire Yagi experiments

To obtain some insight into the performance of the wire Yagi a vhf model was constructed and measurements performed with test equipment used on previous tests (2). The elements were pruned for minimum swr and maximum forward gain, which fortunately occurred at the same element dimensions (Fig 2). The driven element of the Yagi was not located halfway between the director and the reflector because it would be too close to the metalwork of the support structure.

The field strength was compared with a reference dipole whose performance had been optimized. The model exhibited a performance equally as good as an all-metal beam at the centre of the band, with the directivity pattern shown in Fig 3.

The models were constructed from 1mm diameter wire, which gave a length to diameter ratio in the range $10^2$:1. When the model is scaled to the hf band the range will be in the $10^3$:1 region. The appropriate factor will have to be applied if the antenna is scaled directly from the vhf model, using the graph in Fig 4. When an attempt was made to calculate the factors for scaling up it was obvious something was wrong, and on checking the dimensions of the model it was noted that all the elements were nearly 2in (5cm) short compared with normal 144MHz antennas. The model was rebuilt using insulators at the end of the elements, and the tuning and testing procedure was performed again. The elements finished up slightly longer, but the increase was less than 0·25in (0·64cm).

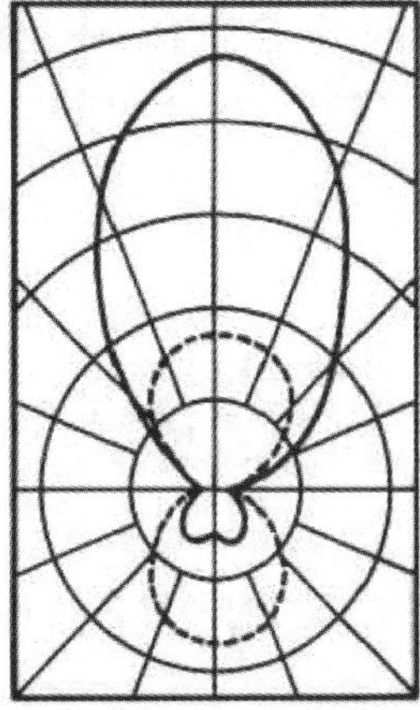

Fig 3. Wire Yagi and dipole polar diagrams compared

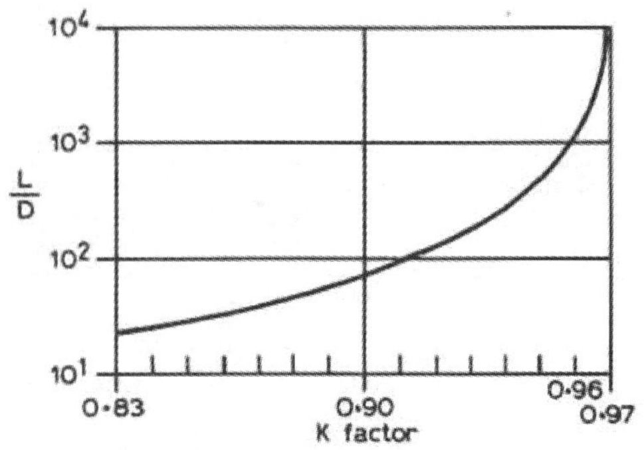


Fig 4. Length/diameter correction graph for element lengths

**Table 1. Design data**

| Freq | Reflector | | Drive: Elt: | | A | | B | | C | | D | |
|---|---|---|---|---|---|---|---|---|---|---|---|---|
| (MHz) | in | cm | in | cm | in | cm | in | cm | in | cm | in | cm |
| 14·2 | 452 | 1147 | 417 | 1060 | 245 | 622 | 263 | 668 | 180 | 457 | 33 | 84 |
| 21·25 | 302 | 767 | 279 | 708 | 154 | 390 | 166 | 420 | 113 | 287 | 22 | 56 |
| 28·5 | 225 | 572 | 208 | 528 | 114 | 290 | 122 | 310 | 85 | 216 | 15 | 38 |

The above figures are based on the following formula:

Driven element $\frac{5920}{f} = L(in)$ $\frac{15050}{f} = L(cm)$

Reflector $\frac{6413}{f} = L(in)$ $\frac{16288}{f} = L(cm)$

1. The above formula for pvc wire only, Multiply L by 1·04 if using uninsulated copper wire.
2. See Fig 10 for meaning of A, B, C and D dimensions.
3. Figures in C are only approximate and are an aid to construction.
4. A, B, C and D not critical and need not be altered if the elements are tuned to the band edge.

When the model was rèbuilt yet again but using uncovered wire for the parasitic elements, the difference in length measured returned to "normal" proportions and it was evident that the insulating material had a loading effect. To measure the loading effect of pvc insulation a 15ft (457cm) length of wire was measured for resonance using a gdo. The frequency measured was 31·1MHz. This is very close to the *ARRL Handbook* figure of $\frac{468}{f} = l\ (ft) \left(\frac{14213}{f} = l(cm)\right)$

Different thicknesses of a 15ft (457cm) length of pvc-covered wire were also measured, and were found to vary between 29·9 and 30MHz. It would seem that the velocity factor of pvc-covered wire is about 0·965.

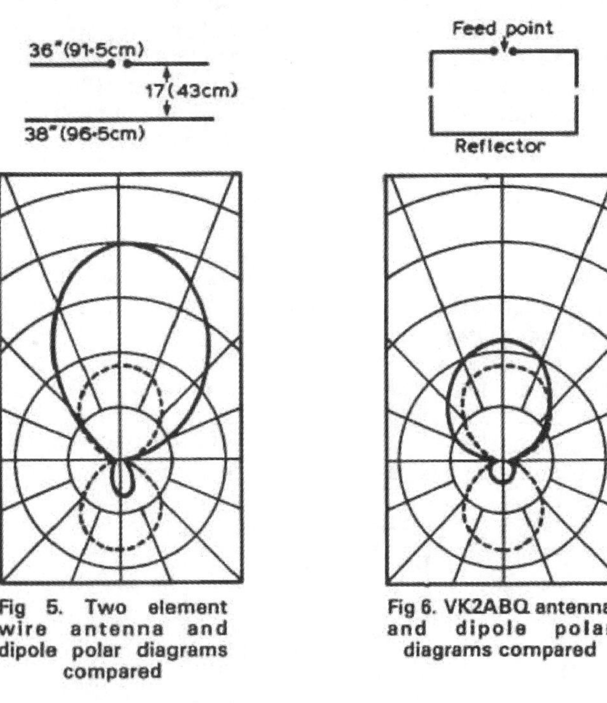


Fig 5. Two element wire antenna and dipole polar diagrams compared

Fig 6. VK2ABQ antenna and dipole polar diagrams compared

## Two-element wire beam

A two-element model was then constructed, and its dimensions and polar diagram are illustrated in Fig 5. A 28·6MHz antenna was scaled from this model and fed directly with 75Ω coaxial cable. The minimum swr of 1·5:1 probably results from a driven element centre impedance of 50Ω, and it would perform better if 50Ω cable were used.

The performance of this antenna over a period of three months is not detectably less than the three-element model previously used, but this could be accounted for by the difficulty in practice of adjusting three elements for optimum performance.

## Two-element wire beam derivatives

A number of experiments were performed to investigate methods of making the two-element beam more compact without compromising the gain. The approach used was to ignore all theoretical and previously published work on the subject and to perform numerous experiments using an empirical approach.

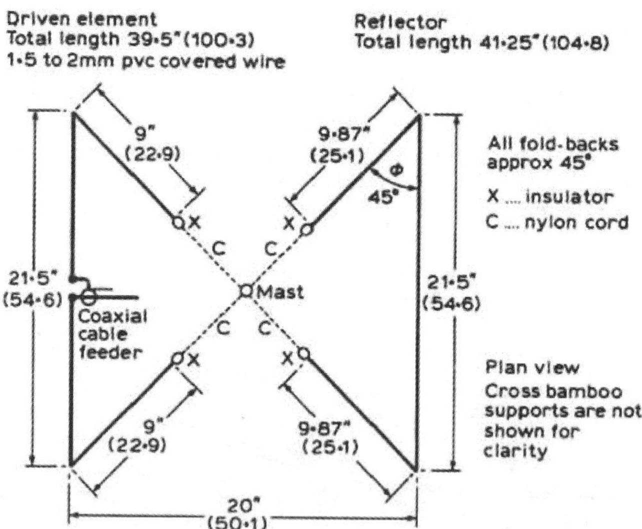


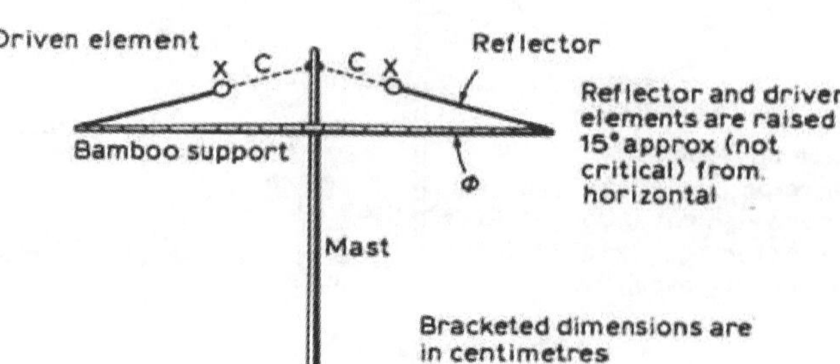


Fig 7. Double D, showing construction with dimensions for 145·6MHz

A further objective was simplicity. This is necessary because the more complex the array the more interacting parameters require adjusting. It is also more difficult to scale and build a complex array. Simplicity means ignoring traps and loading coils, which leaves element bending as the only solution to making a compact antenna. When an element is bent the resonant frequency appears to rise. A gdo is necessary to determine the exact frequency of a bent element.

What to do with the bent elements is a mechanical problem. One way out of this is to make a VK2ABQ configuration as shown in Fig 6. This has good directivity but poor gain compared with the two-element antenna. If the mechanical aspects are ignored and the elements allowed to droop (top half of a quad) the gain returns to that of the two-element antenna (Fig 5). As this seems to have the same gain as a quad there seems little point in making a full wavelength loop quad.

## The double-D configuration

The double-D was the final result of a number of experiments to overcome the problem of what to do with the folded parts of the elements. The construction is shown in Fig 7 and the polar diagram in Fig 8. The elements can be folded back in the horizontal plane with some loss of front-to-back ratio and a slightly higher swr. Dimensions are given in Table 1.

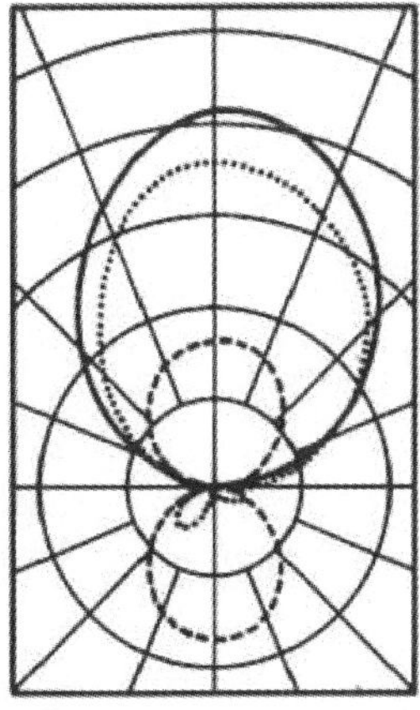

Fig 8. Double D monoband (solid line) and the effect of multiband elements (dotted line) compared with dipole

The length of the reflector of all the models was fairly critical. If any detuning of the element occurred, due to the proximity of an element for another band, the effect would be noticeable. Various lengths of wire, longer and shorter than the reflector element, were located close to the reflector. No observable effect on the polar diagram was apparent, so it was concluded that no detuning of any significance had occurred. When any wire elements were placed in close proximity to the driven element a dramatic change in swr resulted, with a consequent deterioration in gain but not directivity.

A driven element was made from 300Ω twin feeder. With careful adjustment a polar diagram as shown by the dotted line in Fig 8 resulted. Most of the adjustment was necessary because of the need to obtain an element spacing/maximum gain configuration/element coaxial matching compromise, with element coaxial matching being the most critical parameter. This could be overcome with a separate matching system (gamma match) for each driven element. From the experiments so far performed, a suggested form for a three-band array is given in Fig 9.

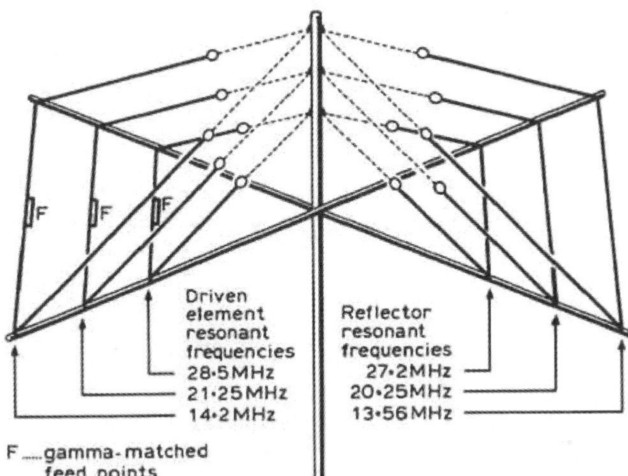


Fig 9. Suggested layout for multiband version of double D

## Construction details

The support is illustrated in Fig 10. The use of aluminium angle or dexion for the centre section will enable a 14MHz antenna with the gain of a quad to be constructed that would weigh around 10lb (4·5kg). The elements are fixed to the bamboo with pvc tape, and the ends of the element are tied to insulators. These insulators can be made out of rectangles of paxolin with holes drilled at either end. About 4in (10cm) should be added to the formula for element length for connection to

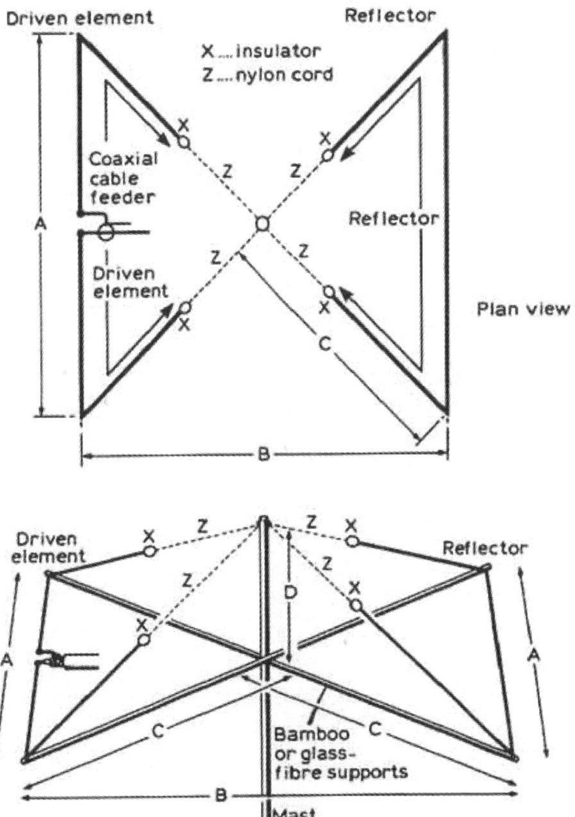


Fig 10. General construction details with dimension references (see Table 1)

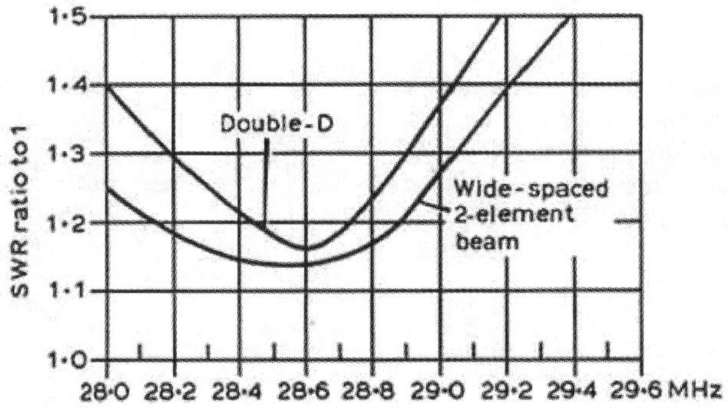


**Fig 11. SWR of double D and wide spaced 2-el beam compared**

the insulator. Nylon cord rather than wire should be used between the insulator and the mast if detuning effects are to be avoided.

## HF band performance

In practice, the performance of the double-D antenna on 28MHz appears as good as predicted by the vhf model. The front-to-back ratio, according to local reports, is about four or five S-points; when used with a QRP 3W homemade ssb transceiver, QSOs with all continents were made in less than a week of normal operating.

## References

[1] *ARRL Antenna Book* 13th edn p204.

[2] "Assessment of hf aerials using vhf aerials," P.G. Dodd. *Radio Communication* December 1972.

[3] "Aerial Gain and How it is Measured," M.F. Radford, MA. *Wireless World* October 1966. □

# Further Evolution of the G3LDO Double-D Antenna

**A decade of development has led Peter Dodd, G3LDO, to improve and expand upon the original design of his Double-D Antenna. Here he describes his experiments.**

## INTRODUCTION

In the June/July 1980 edition of *RadCom*[1] I described the evolution of a compact two element parasitic wire beam. The objective was to create a compact antenna without loading coils and traps. The solution was to bend the elements, and the configuration shown in **Fig 1** was the result. In essence, this antenna can best be described as a two element Yagi with folded elements. A number of VHF models were built and tested to find the best way to bend these elements; and it was found that they could be folded back to within 20 degrees from the horizontal before the gain started to deteriorate. The resulting configuration was named the "Double-D".

The wire Double-D was found to be amenable to multibanding. Three of these antennas, for 20, 15 and 10 metres were mounted on the same support. The simplest method of feeding turned out to be the best; paralleling the driven elements and feeding them with the one coaxial line as shown in **Fig 2.**

The rest of this article is devoted to my experiences in trying to make the single band antenna design more compact, but at the same time retaining the same efficiency as a full size two element Yagi. VHF modelling was used to explore these configurations. Two practical designs resulting from this work, together with outline constructional details, are given.

## DESIGN CONSIDERATIONS

To reduce the overall size of the antenna consideration has to be given to reducing both the element length and the boom length.

According to the diagrams in the ARRL Antenna Handbook, reproduced in **Figs 3** and **Figs 4,** whilst it is possible to reduce the boom length to 0.1 wavelength and to obtain a gain greater than 5dB the radiation resistance falls to around 10 ohms (and would probably be lower for bent elements). Any attempt to reduce the 'wingspan' of the Yagi elements using the bent element approach results in larger proportion of the ends of the elements in the vertical plane.

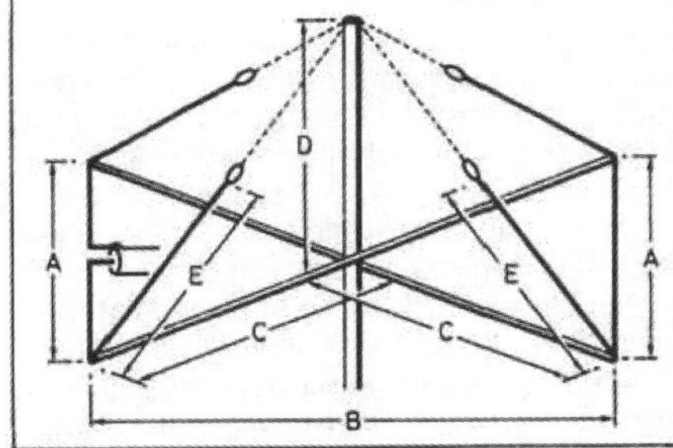


Fig 1. Standard wire Double-D antenna.

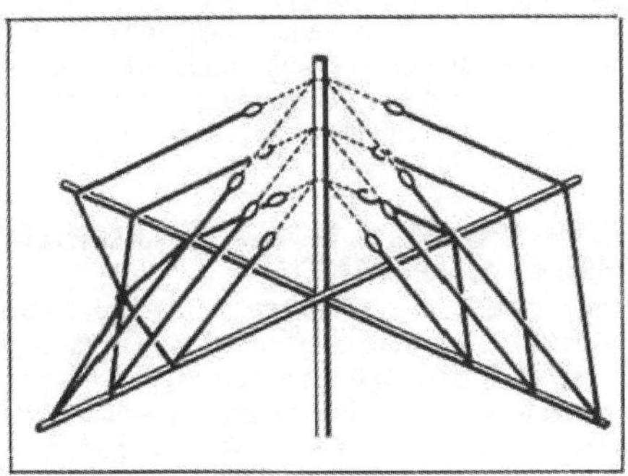

Fig 2. Multiband Double-D antenna.

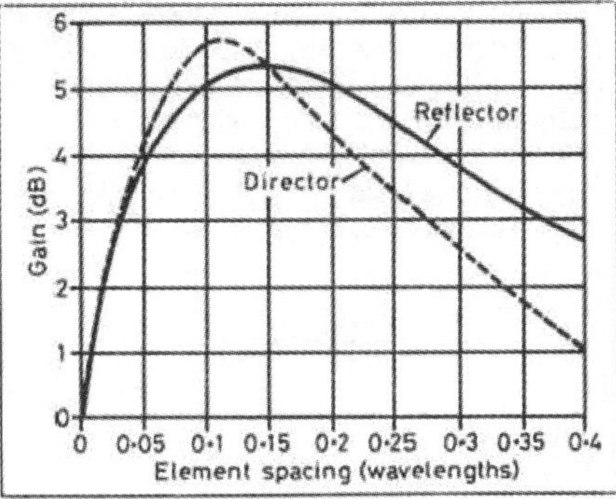


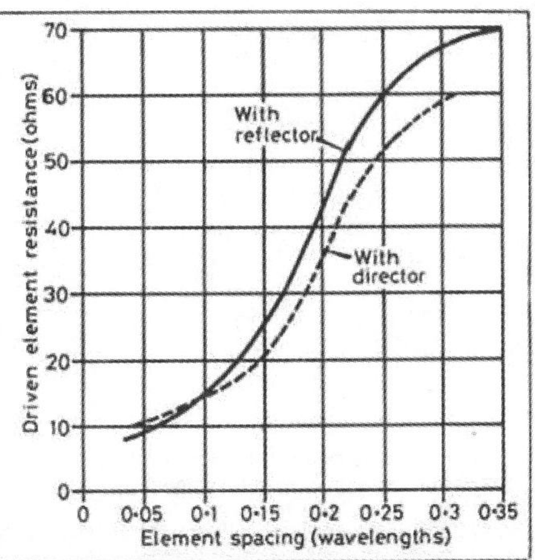


Figs 3 & 4. Graphs showing possibility of reducing boom length. Source *ARRL Antenna Handbook*© 1988 ARRL.

## EARLY EXPERIMENTAL WORK

A VHF model of a wire Double D single element was constructed and various configurations tried out. The element retained the gain of a dipole until the horizontal section was reduced to 0.16 wavelength.

I decided that it would be worthwhile trying to design a compact Double-D antenna using this element configuration; the implications of these initial experiments were that a 7MHz beam could be constructed having the same horizontal size as a three element beam for 15 metres. The actual construction would, however, depend on the radiation resistance. I measured the feed impedance of a dipole, a standard Double-D element and a compact Double-D element at approximately 1/4 wavelength above the ground, via a full wavelength of 50 ohm coaxial cable. These wire element models were measured at frequencies between 28 and 29MHz and the results are illustrated in **Fig 5.**

Because the measured input resistance was low I concluded that the use of all wire elements would result in reduced efficiency because the relatively high resistance of the wire would dissipate much of the input power. The addition of a parasitic element would reduce the radiation resistance (and hence the efficiency) still further.

## VHF DOUBLE-D MODEL

A VHF model of the Double-D element was constructed using 'plumbers delight' construction, with 18 AWG solid copper wire for the horizontal section and thin hook-up plastic covered wire for the end sections. The element was gamma matched and the element fed with 50 ohm coaxial cable. A parasitic element was then added using the same construction as the driven element. Initially I used an element spacing of 0.1 wavelength but it proved very difficult to set up. Any slight adjustment of the parasitic element, as either a director or reflector, or the slightest movement of the wire sections of the elements, caused large changes in feed impedance. The spacing was increased to 0.15 wavelengths and the model proved much more docile. The final model is illustrated in **Fig 6** and appeared to have a gain of 4 to 5dB relative to a reference dipole.

## 14MHz DOUBLE-D

The first large scale model was constructed for 20 metres. This decision was dictated mainly by the relatively small size of the garden at my previous QTH. This design used aluminium tubing for the horizontal section of the elements and plastic covered wire for the vertical end sections.

The only length of boom material available at the time was a 9 foot length of 2 inch aluminium tubing, so I decided on another attempt at the close spaced beam (element spacing about 0.13 wavelengths). The initial sizes chosen for the elements were 12 feet for the tubular horizontal section and 13'8" for the wire sections. The aspect ratio of these elements is slightly different to the VHF model, but as the model predicted good results for horizontal sections longer than 0.16

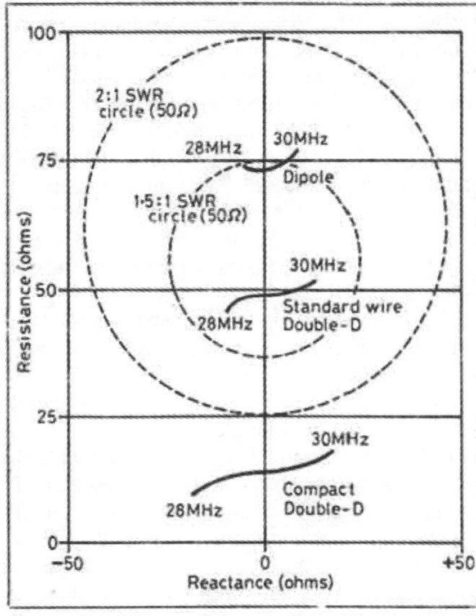


Fig 5. Impedance measurements of dipole and Double-D elements.

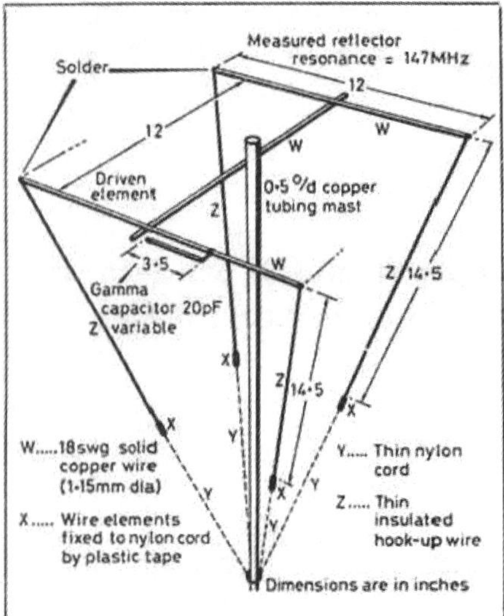


**Fig 6. VHF two-element Double-D.**

wavelength no problems were foreseen. The elements were then adjusted for resonance at 14.15 and 13.8MHz for the driven element and reflector respectively. The driven element was connected to the feeder via a gamma match.

All the tests were performed at a frequency of 14.15MHz. A receiver was connected to the antenna. A modulated signal generator, with an 18-inch short wire antenna, was placed at the apex of the roof inside the house, located about two wavelengths away from the antenna under test.

The receiver was tuned to the same frequency as the signal generator and the S-meter readings checked as the antenna was rotated. The length of the signal generator short wire antenna was adjusted to ensure the signal strength was within the range of the S meter. (This method had worked well for me in the past.)

The antenna exhibited poor directivity and the business of reflector adjustment commenced. Small adjustments to the reflector caused wild changes in feed impedance even before any improvement in directivity became apparent; in fact an action replay of trying to set up the VHF model. The lessons of the VHF model were being relearned. The boom was extended to 12 feet (0.17 wavelengths) with odd sections of tubing. This tamed the beast and the gamma match was adjusted without any difficulty. The front to back ratio continued to be very poor in spite of many adjustments of the reflector. Reflector resonances between 13.9 and 13.1MHz were tried with no improvement in antenna performance.

Because the VHF model predicted that the configuration would work I did not give up hope, although it was in a mood of desperation that I shortened the parasitic element to try it as a director. At 14.0MHz the element commenced to work as a reflector! At 14.1MHz the front to back ratio improved. The element continued to operate as a reflector, with a reduced front to back ratio, up to 14.45MHz. The final reflector resonance chosen was 14.1MHz because it appeared to give the greatest front to back ratio.

The final dimensions are shown in **Fig 7.** A table of design data was derived from these dimensions and is also shown in **Fig 7.**

The performance of the 14MHz band was quite encouraging even though the top section of the antenna was only 32 feet high. The antenna exhibited 'beam quality and a number of 6,000 miles plus DX contacts were made in the DX doldrums of December and January 1984.

So why were the front to back ratio adjustment difficulties encountered with the 14MHz beam not foreseen with the VHF model? The problem arose because no method of measuring element resonance accurately at VHF was at hand, although this situation changed later; see test equipment below. The VHF model, at this stage, was only capable of modelling the general configuration. Maybe I could have been more careful in extrapolating the physical dimensions, although I have not found this method very successful in the past.

In the spring of 1985 I moved QTH. At this new QTH I did not have an antenna mast so I looked into the possibility of fixing a 21MHz beam to the chimney of the house. The largest 'wingspan' practicable was around 12ft because the house is not very big. The design I came up with is shown in **Fig 8** and is halfway between the original wire version shown in **Fig 1** and the compact derivative shown in **Fig 7.** The vertical support for the ends of the elements has been used as a 2 metre J type vertical, and was also tried as a 28MHz ground plane. The former was very successful and the latter impractical due to interaction with the Double-D elements.

The main difference between this Double-D configuration and the compact model is that the reflector resonance has to be lower than the operating frequency. This antenna can be adjusted relatively close to ground level because the ends of the elements point upwards.

Groundwave tests with G3FXB, 20 miles away, showed a front-to-back ratio of about 2.5 S points measured on the S meter of a Drake R4C. (1 S point = 6dB).

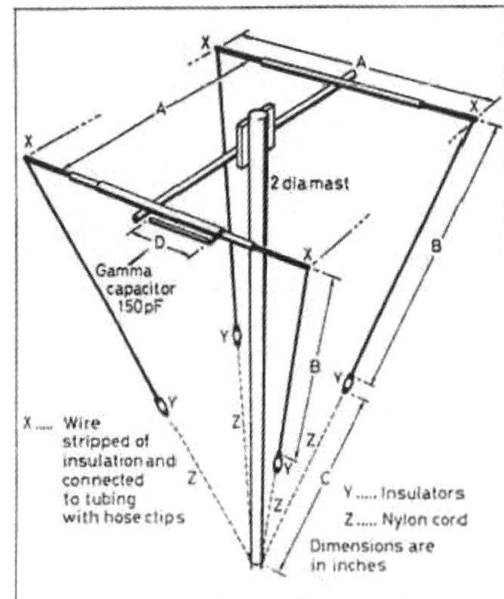


**Fig 7. Perspective diagram showing constructional details of a compact Double-D antenna.**

$A = l = \frac{1870}{f(MHz)}$ $B = l = \frac{2226}{f(MHz)}$ $C = l = \frac{1176}{f(MHz)}$ $D = l = \frac{620}{f(MHz)}$

l = length in inches

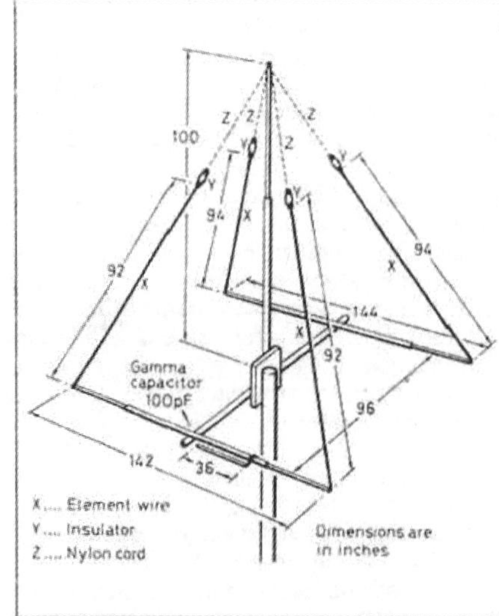


**Fig 8. 21MHz Double-D.**

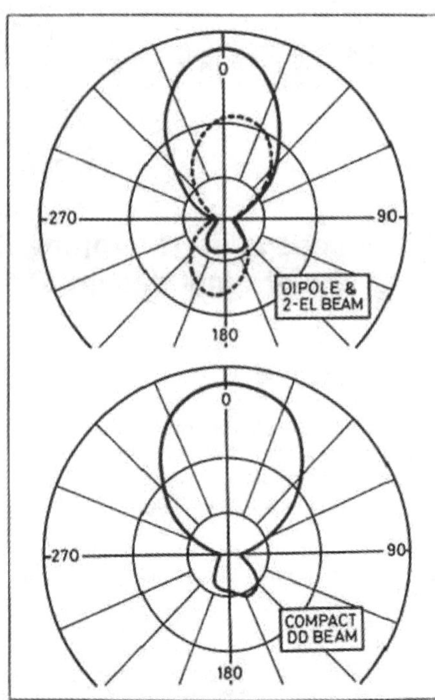


**Fig 9. Reference dipole and two-element beam polar diagrams.**

## TEST EQUIPMENT

As a result of difficulties in modelling the early designs accurately I decided that further progress could only be made if I possessed better test equipment. As a result I acquired the following:

1. A FET dipper and a frequency counter so that I could measure the resonance of the elements of the VHF models more accurately. The original VHF model of the compact Double-D was measured and the resonance is shown in **Fig 6.**

The VHF Double-D element shows a good dip when resonance is measured. When I first used this test equipment to measure resonance of the elements the driven element was 4.5MHz lower than expected. The cause was found to be the two metres of 50ohm feeder attached to the element. The feeder should be removed when measuring driven element resonance. If removal of the feeder is not possible or impractical its effect can be minimised by terminating the transmitter end with a 50ohm resistor.

2. A professional VHF field strength meter; the one I use was acquired at a flea market at a radio rally. One of the disadvantages of the diode field strength meter is that the device is inherently non-linear particularly at low field strengths. The effect of this is to give inflated front-to-back ratio readings when making polar diagrams.

Because manual plotting of polar diagrams is difficult and tedious I have automated the process. I use a BBC computer, which has an analogue port accessible via the BASIC language. This, together with suitable software and a fast rotator, make a fairly usable automated system.

The outer, middle and inner rings on the printouts represent 0, -4 and -10dB respectively in these tests which indicated that the two element beam and the Double-D both have an average gain of approximately 4dB over a dipole.

## VHF MODELS, POLAR DIAGRAM MEASUREMENTS

VHF models of a reference dipole and a two element beam were constructed. All the models used 'plumbers delight' construction and employed gamma matching. The polar diagrams of the reference antennas and Double-D are compared in **Fig 9.**

**Fig 12 (left). The compset Double-D antenna in its upright position.**

**Fig 13 (above). The original standard Double-D mounted on the roof of the author's QTH.**

The compact Double-D could not be made to operate with the parasitic element as a director. As the frequency was lowered the front-to-back ratio of the polar diagram did show a tendency to reverse before it collapsed.

## 10MHz DOUBLE-D

In the summer of 1988 I became interested in 10MHz mainly because I now had a rig (Drake TX4C/R4C) that would operate on that band. I decided to try a compact Double-D for 10MHz. I used the 14MHz design data as a starting point but modified it slightly by increasing the horizontal section and reducing the vertical sections of the elements to fit the existing mast. The final dimensions are shown in **Fig 7**.

Checking the front-to-back ratio on this band using the methods used on the 14MHz model was a problem because of the strong commercial stations, so I tried a different approach. I borrowed a professional HF field strength meter from G3PVH which had the advantage of having a very large signal strength meter calibrated in decibels. I placed this on the flat roof of the house extension about two wavelengths from the antenna. The transmitter was connected to the Double-D and a few watts fed to it. I then viewed the meter on the field strength meter, through binoculars, while rotating the antenna. The front-to-back ratio, measured this way, was about 14dB. (This antenna measurement procedure has cast doubts among my nearest neighbours regarding my mental stability).

## CONSTRUCTION AND ADJUSTMENT

The construction of the 10, 14 and 21MHz antennas is very similar so I will describe only the construction here. The detail of each antenna is given in **Figs 7 and 8**. The boom was fixed to the tubular mast with a metal plate and car exhaust U clamps. The elements were constructed from $^3/_4$ inch diameter tubing and connected to the boom in the same manner. Half an inch of the plastic insulation was stripped from the wire element extensions and fixed with hose clamps to the end of the metal elements. The other end of the wire was terminated at an insulator and nylon cord. The nylon cord was then attached to the mast.

All metal surfaces forming a joint should be given a protective layer of grease. This is particularly important where copper wire is fixed to the aluminium on the elements. The effect of clamping dissimilar metals can result in a film of oxide on the joints within a few weeks of construction resulting in antenna inefficiency and the danger of TVI, if this protection is not carried out.

To tune the reflector on the prototype I used the traditional method of adjusting element lengths by using elements made from two different diameter tubes clamped with jubilee clips. Another method is to make the elements slightly longer than the design figure states and prune the ends of the elements for maximum gain or front-to-back ratio; this method has advantages when the antenna is mounted on a non-tiltable mast because the tips of the elements can be reached by climbing a ladder if the antenna is not too high.

In the initial stages of adjustment the best place to measure resonance by dipping is the point where the wire part of the element joins the tubular part. I find it very difficult to see any sort of a dip at the centre of the element because of the problem of coupling the dipper to the element.

Note that, although dimensions are shown for the Double-D, it is almost impossible to get complete reproducibility of any design. All installations are in different situations, made of slightly different materials and at different heights. For example, if you use bare copper wire instead of plastic insulated wire for the ends of the elements it will be necessary to multiply the wire dimension figures by 1.04 (plastic covered wire appears to have a velocity factor of about 0.96. Try dipping two identical lengths of wire, one with insulation and the other without to check this). The design data does not include extra wire that may be needed to fix it to the insulator. All installations benefit from some tuning and most well known DX operators have spent a considerable amount of time adjusting their antennas for maximum efficiency. However, having said that, I have found the Double-D not a critical antenna to tune and the 10MHz model worked first time using design data obtained from the 14MHz model. The Double-D has an excellent bandwidth for a compact beam and SWR plots are shown in **Figs 10 and 11.**

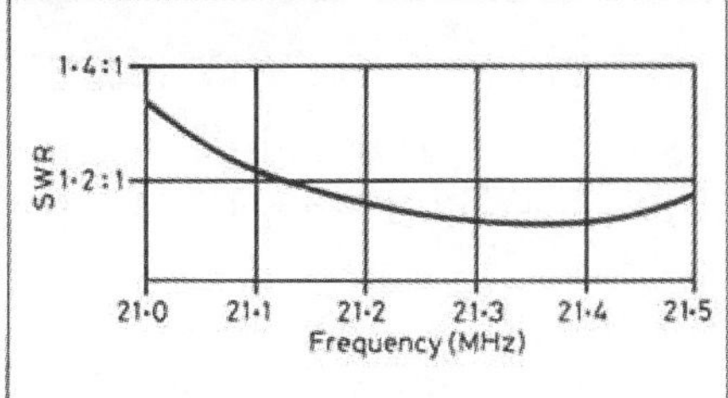


**Fig 10. 21MHz beam SWR curve.**

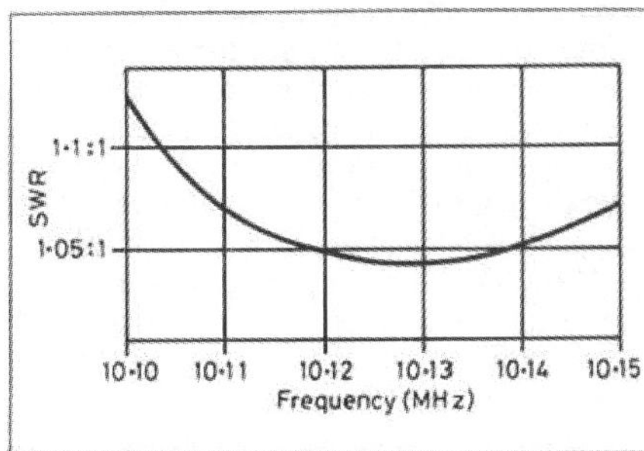


**Fig 11. 10MHz beam SWR curve.**

One point should be made regarding the Double-D antenna; it is horizontally polarised and requires the same height above ground as full size beam to get the equivalent performance. However, it is considerably easier to support an antenna with an element span of 16ft than a span of 40ft.

There is a further consideration; if a large Double-D is mounted on a tilt-over mast that bends like mine, the wire elements need to be slackened off to prevent the top element from being strained when the mast is lowered.

There is no reason why the Double-D should not be mounted on a more traditional non-rotatable mast, provided the element wire ends and the nylon cord supports are slack enough to allow the antenna to be rotated. I have not devised a way of guying my antenna system because I find it easier to just tilt the whole structure over if high winds are forecast. The antenna is shown in the upright position in **Fig 12.**

## COMPACT DOUBLE-D PERFORMANCE

I now have had some operating experience with a 14MHz model at 32ft and a 10MHz model at 42ft. On 14MHz the antenna exhibited reasonable directivity and a lot of DX was worked but my signal was rather outclassed by the three or more element beams at more than one wavelength in height.

On 10MHz it was a different matter. Most operators on 10MHz use 100 watts to either a dipole or a vertical. It was surprising what one (theoretical) S point difference made on transmit; also the improvement in signal to noise (and QRM) ratio was well worthwhile.

## REFERENCE

[1]P. Dodd, G3LDO, "Wire beam antennas and the evolution of the G3LDO Double-D", *Radio Communication*, June/July 1980. □

# Evaluation of the G2AJV Toroidal Antenna

**By *RadCom* Technical Editor, Peter Dodd, G3LDO**

THE TOROID ANTENNA, proposed by Roger Jennison, G2AJV, seemed so radical that a model was built to examine its viability before the article [1] was published. Since then there has been much interest (and scepticism) regarding these antennas so the tests were extended. This article is a description of construction and tests on the first prototype and subsequent models of these toroid antennas.

The theory of how toroid antennas work is discussed further in [1] and on this month's *The Last Word* pages.

You may question the emphasis on mobile versions of this antenna, considering the complex structure of the toroid. The reason is that I have a mobile HF rig in the car and I work away from home during the week. Additionally my bedsitting room is an eminently impractical place for experimenting with these HF antennas (small as they are).

Although this mobile experimental work has been very successful it does not imply that I consider that the antenna configurations described are necessarily the best solution for amateur mobile operation.

Initially I made a single loop toroid for 14MHz band, as shown in part one of [1]. This model was unsuccessful, possibly due to poor construction [see Note 1]. I discussed the problem with Roger Jennison, and he suggested that an end-fed double toroid, similar to the one he had proposed for mobile VHF operation, would be less critical.

I then tried the double toroid VHF antenna as described in [1]. It was fixed to my car using a mag-mount but the SWR was too high to be of any use. I then tried several models and at the third attempt found one with an acceptable SWR. This tiny antenna did work and bandwidth was relatively wide. Signal strength readings from repeaters in range of Potters Bar varied between 0.5 and 2 S points down on a quarter wave vertical. I had difficulty defining why the final model had a greater measure of success than the two previous ones.

I felt that an HF double toroid would allow me to investigate the matching problem because the physical parameters of a larger structure could be measured more easily.

In all, I made three HF versions of the Double Toroid Antenna.

- The Mk1 (14MHz) was used to investigate the double toroid feasibility.
- The Mk2 (14MHz) was built specifically for obtaining data on the original design.

- The Mk3 (21MHz) was built to investigate construction methods different from the Mk1 and Mk2.

## THE MARK 1 TOROID

A DIAGRAM OF the Mk1 14MHz toroid mobile antenna is shown in **Fig 1**. It was constructed from hard-drawn 16SWG antenna wire, supported in a cylindrical cage made from *white* plastic garden fencing, using plastic tie-wraps. The construction of the complete antenna is shown in **Photo 1**. The structure was mounted on a metal plate, which in turn was fixed to a four footed mag-mount (see 'Antenna Mounting' later).

The toroids were constructed separately and joined together when installed in the plastic support. Each toroid was constructed by winding approximately a quarter wavelength of wire on a two-inch diameter plastic former, then removing it from the former and looping the coil into a toroid. The ends of the toroid were held together with ceramic insulators made from old air-spaced capacitors with most of the metal parts removed. Each toroid was adjusted so that it was 8in (200mm) in diameter, by tensioning it to the plastic frame using the plastic tie-wraps. Note that the direction of winding for the top toriod is opposite to the bottom one.

Initially, the lowest SWR at resonance was around 5:1 and no amount of playing around with its physical dimensions made much difference to this SWR figure. Preliminary impedance measurements indicated a feed impedance of around 5Ω at resonance. Additionally, I had not put enough turns on the toroids (28 turns) and the resonant frequency was about 500kHz too high.

I built capacitors from tin lids and fixed them to the ceramic insulators across the toroids, to bring the antenna into resonance into the 14MHz amateur band. I later found that only one capacitor was required, across the lower toroid as shown in **Fig 1**.

To match the antenna to the feeder I used a well tried technique for matching low impedance antennas; I built a shunt feed arrangement and aimed for the correct impedance by tapping up the coil. The inductive reactance of the shunt feed was neutralised with a series 100pF capacitor.

Now, at last, things started happening and strong signals where heard on the mobile transceiver when this antenna was connected to it. The antenna proved easy to load and the first short skip QSO reports ranged from 5/5 to 5/9. My first SSB DX contact was a reply to my CQ, from VK6ADP in Perth. Although

**I stayed with Bert Weller, WD8KBW, during a visit to the USA. It transpired that Bert had worked with James Corum, K1AON, the holder of a the patent on the toroid antenna. We arranged a meeting at the Dayton Hamvention and talked antennas for a couple of hours. From left to right: K1AON, G3LDO, WD8KBW.**

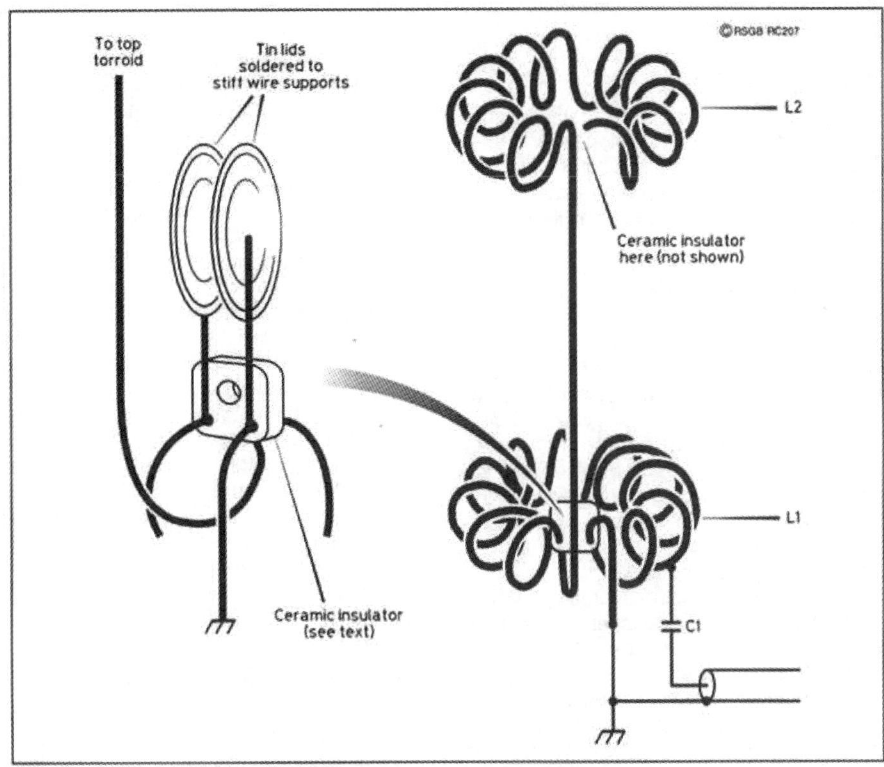


Fig 1: Mk 1 double toroid antenna using shunt feed and parallel capacitor tuning.

Photo 1: Mk 1 shunt fed antenna (14MHz) fixed to a four-footed mag-mount.

my signal report was only 5/1 the band was quiet and we were able to chat for around ten minutes.

The measured SWR bandwidth of this antenna was found to be rather narrow (see **Fig 2**) and I felt that this was due to the capacity across the lower toroid. In a further conversation with G2AJV he suggested the capacity would reduce the efficiency of the antenna and that I should persevere with the series fed arrangement. He also said that matching could be improved by going for a lower resonant frequency of the antenna by adding a couple of turns to each of the toroids and end feeding via a variable series capacitor. On the question of coarse tuning the resonance of the double toroid, G2AJV suggested scraping some of the insulation off the outside loop of two adjacent turns of the toroids and tinning with solder. A shorting link could then be added to increase the resonant frequency without, apparently, affecting the performance of the antenna.

## THE MARK 2 TOROID

I THEN BUILT the Mk2 double toroid antenna as shown in **Photo 2**. Because this antenna was designed for obtaining data it was constructed so that most parameters, such as the distance between the toroids and the inductance of the toroids were variable. Each toroid was constructed from 30 turns of 16SWG enamelled insulated wire [Note 2] and the construction of the antenna was almost the same as for the Mk 1. The diameter of the Mk2 toroids was 6in (150mm), smaller than the Mk1. The reason was that the Mk 1 elements were made from uninsulated copper wire and it was important that the adjacent coil loops did not touch. Two sections of a plastic terminal block were used to support the ends of the toroids.

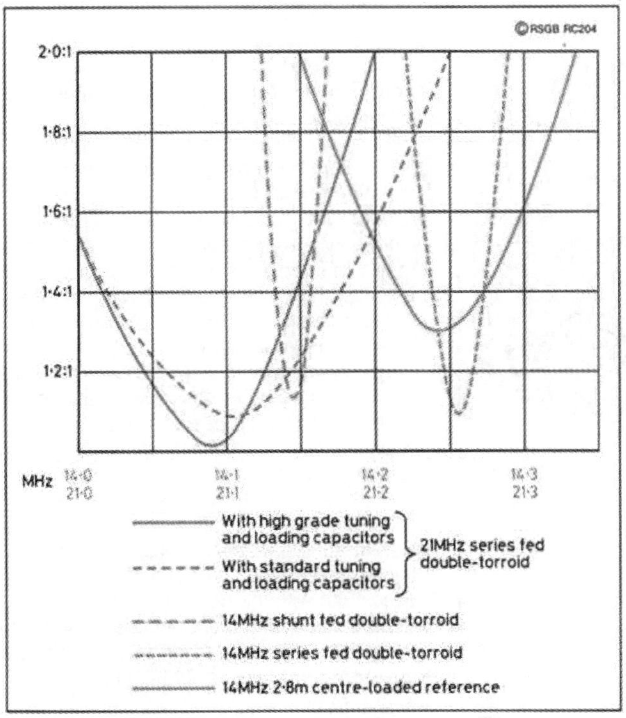

Fig 2: SWR curves of the Mks 1, 2 and 3 antennas together with a 14MHz reference antenna.

I connected the antenna to the coax exactly as shown in [1]. As with the Mk1 version it would not load. The reason for the high SWR at resonance became plain when I made an impedance plot. The feed impedance was found to be around 5Ω at resonance as shown in **Fig 3**.

A series variable capacitance was added as suggested by G2AJV. This did alter loading slightly although it affected the resonant frequency far more.

I decided to try a shunt capacitor – a method sometimes used to match a conventional loaded mobile whip antenna. With this

Photo 2: Mk 2 series fed antenna (14MHz) using home made mobile roof mount. The clamping magnets not shown.

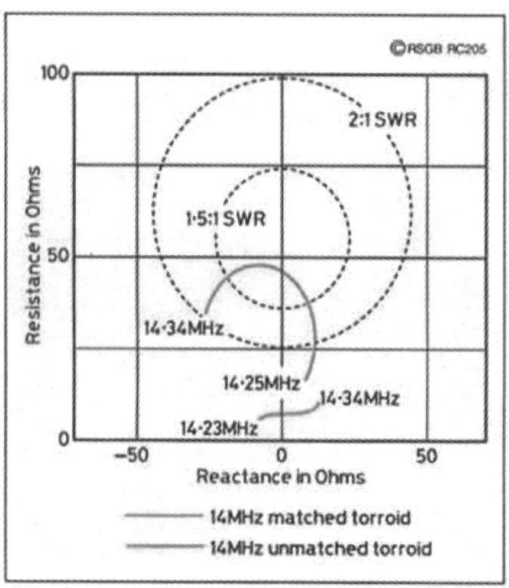


**Fig 3: Impedance signatures of the series fed double toroid, with and without capacitor matching and tuning capacitors.**

matching arrangement the antenna is made than an electrical quarter wavelength to increase the radiation resistance.

With the series 50pf variable capacitor C1 the impedance is around 5 + J24Ω. A shunt 1000pf varible capacitor C2 can then be used to bring the impedance close to 50 J0Ω.

The final matching and tuning arrangement is shown in **Fig 4**. The series capacitor (fine tuning) and parallel loading capacitors are variable, enabling the antenna resonance and the matching to be adjusted and set quite easily. The impedance plot of the matched 14MHz double toroid antenna is shown in Fig 3 [see Note 3]. This is confirmed by the SWR plot of the series tuned double toroid shown in Fig 2.

The base of this antenna and the method of connecting it to the car is described under 'Antenna Mounting'.

**Fig 4: Mk 2 double toroid antenna using series feed, shunt capacitor matching and series tuning.**

## MK 3 TOROID

THE Mk3 WAS USED to investigate construction using different materials and conductor diameters and to see what effect this would have on antenna performance. At the local scrap yard I searched for suitable copper tubing but was out of luck. However, I found among the scrap electrical cable some material called Pyro, mineral insulated electrical wire. This material has an outer copper tubing sheath with inner conductor wire(s) in magnesium oxide. It is easy to bend and shape and seemed a promising material for the toroid antenna. It comes in various diameters and I used 3mm for the Mk3 double toroid for 21MHz. Pyro turned out to be excellent material for winding coils. Because the copper tube sheath is filled with oxide material it can be bent into shapes having a small radius without the tube kinking.

The Mk 3 toroid was constructed for 21MHz, rather than 14MHz, by accident rather than design. I only had enough pyro material to make a 21MHz model!

This antenna is shown in **Photo 3**. The coils of the toroid are self-supporting with a resonant frequency of around 20MHz. Fixed silver mica capacitors were used for the series tuning and parallel loading capacitors; their values, 18pF and a 150pF respectively. These values were extrapolated from the experimental work on the Mk2 antenna. This 21MHz antenna worked straight away; it was resonant at 21.2MHz and the SWR was less than 1.7:1.

**Photo 3: Mk 3 self-supporting structure (21MHz) fixed to a gutter mount.**

As can be seen in Fig 2 the bandwidth of this tiny antenna seemed suspiciously wide, implying losses. I assumed that it was being caused by the relatively lossy tuning and matching fixed capacitors. These were replaced by higher grade capacitors. I used an air spaced 50pF variable as the series tuning capacitor and a fixed 180pF Steafix fixed capacitor for parallel loading.

This allowed the SWR to be adjusted to a lower value at resonance and produced a slightly narrower bandwidth, see Fig 2. There was no real noticeable improvement in the antenna performance. The conclusion is that the wider bandwidth is the result of using a larger gauge material in the construction of the toroid, although more experimental work is required to verify this.

## ANTENNA MOUNTING

THE WAY IN WHICH these antennas were mounted on the car had a profound effect on their tuning and loading. G2AJV's HF models used magmounts. A magmount introduces capacitance between the earth point of the antenna (and the coax screen) and the body of the car. This capacitance may not be significant at VHF but with a low impedance feedpoint HF antenna the results will be unpredictable. One of these unpredictable effects is that there are antenna currents on the feedline. Even with the Mk1 antenna, with its large four-footed magmount, performance was improved with a direct earth connection.

The 21MHz antenna was fixed to the car using a antenna gutter clamp. To get the best antenna/earth connection to the car I scraped away the paint down to bare metal under the clamp and coated the area with grease to prevent corrosion. This earth point then served as a low resistance point for all other antennas tested and proved useful for testing the effectiveness of magnetic base clamps for HF antennas.

Those of you who may be horrified that I should have treated my Vauxhall car in such a cavalier fashion [how else – *Ed*] can rest assured that I have developed a much more car friendly antenna mounting system. This is made of a sheet of aluminium – theoretically the larger the better. My Mk 2 antenna uses one of these mounts and it is shown in Photo 2. Construction is as follows:

Eight holes are drilled in the base plate in groups of two. The metal between the holes is lifted so that tie-wraps can be inserted to fix the plastic cage to the base without touching the roof of the car.

A hole is drilled for the earth point, which should be close to the antenna feedpoint when the antenna is assembled. The hole is countersunk so that the head of the earthing bolt is flush with the bottom of the base.

The outside edges of the base, facing the roof of the car, is faced with strips of plastic tape to prevent the base scratching the roof of the car. Magnets, with plastic sheet protec-

# EVALUATION OF THE G2AJV TOROIDAL ANTENNA

tion, can be used to hold the base in place and reduce the base/car roof capacity.

As I have already said the base has some effect on the antenna tuning. I tried the Mk2 antenna fixed and earthed to the aluminium frame of a greenhouse. The antenna resonant frequency had shifted from 14.2 (when fixed to the car) to 14.8 MHz, although its performance was good when the antenna was retuned.

## ANTENNA PERFORMANCE COMPARISONS

I MADE SOME COMPARISON signal strength tests of the 14MHz toroid antenna using an 8ft (2.5m) home made centre loaded vertical as a reference. This antenna has a lower section constructed from 22mm copper tubing and the air-spaced loading coil 3in (760mm) in diameter. This reference antenna was fixed to the rear of the car, level with the bumper, with a good earth connection to the car chassis for the coax braiding.

The Mk 2 toroid was fixed to the roof, as already described, and both antennas remained in place during the tests. I reasoned there would be little interaction because the unused antenna is detuned as the feeder is disconnected from the transceiver (load) when the antennas are changed over. (the feeder was not a multiple of a quarter of a wavelength at the test frequency).

Short skip contacts to Europe were inconclusive; sometimes the vertical antenna outperformed the toroid and other times toroid was the better performer.

I then tried ground wave tests with GB3RS, the RSGB HQ station. At distances of between quarter and half a mile away from RSGB I transmitted a carrier, carefully monitored on a power meter. John Crabb, G3WFM, the senior station operator made measurements using the S-meter on the IC781.

Most of the measurements gave the vertical a 0.5 to 1 S-point advantage. The exception was when the car was facing the HQ station, when the toroid antenna had the 1 S-point advantage.

Some DX contacts worked using these toroid antennas are shown in extracts from my mobile log book, see **Fig 5**

## CONCLUSIONS

THE DOUBLE TOROID design appears to work very well once the problems of matching are overcome. The implications are that the G2AJV design is particularly useful for low band HF, particularly where space is at a premium.

Because the antenna works so well, and has a reasonable bandwidth, there is a suspicion that it violates the principles established by H A Wheeler [2] and L J Chu [3] [see Note 4]. This principle states that the bandwidth as a fraction of the frequency of interest cannot exceed a constant times the volume of the sphere (expressed in units of wavelength cubed) in which the antenna can be contained, no matter what shape the antenna is or what material it is made from.

However, it is highly unlikely that the double toroid does violate these principles. In a European Patent Application EP 0 043 591 AI on a toroidal antenna, [see Note 5] made by James Corum, K1AON, of West Virginia, USA (brought to my notice by Pat Hawker, G3VA,[4]) it was claimed that the basic principle of toroid antennas "by virtue of their construction possess a greater radiation resistance than known antennas of similar electrical size not having the slow-wave winding features possess greater radiation resistance and radiation efficiency than loop antennas of similar size".

## AREAS FOR EXPERIMENTATION

THERE ARE A NUMBER of areas where the additional experimenting would be useful and interesting. An analysis of toroid antennas, using the MFJ-249 antenna analyser, indicates that there are higher order resonances. The third resonance looks promising because of its wide bandwidth, although the performance as an antenna in this mode is so far unknown.

Other unknowns regarding toroidal antenna performance are: the ratio of series capacitor to inductor, capacity of the base to earth, spacing of top and bottom toroids and the diameter of the toroids. The effect of earth on an end fed double toroid also requires more investigation.

## NOTES

1. G2AJV, in further correspondence regarding my experiments using toroids wound on ferrite rings, comments that a toroid wound on a ferrite ring will only be one hundredth as effective as an air spaced toroid.
2. Various sizes of large gauge enamelled copper wire can be obtained from AA&A Ltd, Sycamore House, Northwood, Wem, Shropshire SY4 5NN.
3. The method of producing these impedance plots using a computer, plus experimenting with, and measurements of, antennas generally is described in *The Antenna Experimenter's Guide,* available from the RSGB, see page 94.
4. Copies of these documents are available at RSGB HQ for viewing only. We are unable to provide photocopies because of copyright restrictions.
5. The James Corum patent on the toroid antenna is available from The British Library, Science Reference and Information Service, 25 Southampton Buildings, London WC2A 1AW; enclosing a cheque for £10 and quoting Patent Application EP 0 043 591.

## ACKNOWLEDGEMENTS

TO BERT WELLER, WD8KBW, for arranging the meetings with the Batelle Radio Club and James Corum, K1AON, and for locating the original papers by Harold A Wheeler and L J Chu, see [2] and [3] below.

To James Corum K1AON, for supplying additional information on his toroid antennas.

To Batelle (industrial research company), Columbus, Ohio, USA, for access to their comprehensive technical library.

## REFERENCES

[1] 'The G2AJV Toroidal Antenna', Roger Jennison, G2AJV, *Radio Communication,* April and May 1994.

[2] 'Fundamental Limitations of Small Antennas', Harold A Wheeler, *Proceedings of the IRE,* December 1947 (see Note 4).

[3] 'Physical Limitations of Omni-Directional Antennas', L J Chu, *Journal of Applied Physics,* Volume 19, December 1948 (see Note 4)

[4] 'Toroidal Helix Antennas', Pat Hawker, G3VA, *Technical Topics, Radio Communication,* June 1994.

| | | | | | | | | | | | |
|---|---|---|---|---|---|---|---|---|---|---|---|
| 21/4 | 1745 | PP5AUM | 21016 | 559 | 559 | 90W | A1 | SM | San Francisco Island | QSL via PP5LL | T2 |
| " | 1755 | PY2NFE | 21034 | 569 | 579 | " | " | SM | Sao Paulo | Ron | T2 |
| " | 1948 | PZ1DY | 21026 | 539 | 579 | " | " | SM | | | T2 |
| " | 2000 | VP2MCO | 21016 | 579 | 559 | " | " | SM | | Larry QSL via AA6WL | T2 |
| 22/4 | 0635 | VK3ARC | 14062 | 539 | 539 | " | " | SM | Melbourne | Rob | T1 |
| | 0700 | VK1FF | 14033 | 449 | 549 | " | " | SM | Dipole Ant Canberra | Jim | T1 |
| | 0725 | VK2ALH | 14055 | 519 | 529 | " | " | SM | | Les | T1 |
| 15/6 | 2055 | LU9ELU | 21045 | 559 | 579 | " | " | PB | BA | Ric | T |
| " | 2110 | LW3DGE | 21019 | 529 | 529 | " | " | PB | | | T2 |
| 16/6 | 2045 | 9Y4VU | 21012 | 559 | 579 | " | " | PB | | | T2 |

**Fig 5: Extract from the mobile log during the period of tests on the double toroid antenna.**

# The User Friendly Smith Chart

By *RadCom* Technical Editor Peter Dodd, G3LDO

NEARLY EVERY MAJOR book on antennas has a description of a complicated circular graph known as a Smith chart, with instructions on how to use it. The Smith chart is very useful and is used by the professionals to design antennas and impedance matching networks. In spite of this I have never, in 37 years of amateur radio, met anyone who uses the Smith chart to solve a practical antenna problem. So why should this be? And what's wrong with the good old SWR meter for solving antenna matching problems?

## THE SWR METER

THERE DOES NOT SEEM to be any problem with a general understanding of standing wave ratio (SWR). Even the most non-technical radio amateur is aware that the coaxial transmission line connecting the rig to the antenna has a characteristic impedance, which is around 50Ω; and that an SWR meter can be used to measure any 'standing waves' on the coaxial line caused by the antenna impedance having a different value to that of the coaxial line. In nearly every ham shack there is usually a SWR meter connected permanently into the coaxial between the transmitter and the antenna or antenna system.

The method of antenna adjustment using an SWR meter is well known. You connect up your antenna system then make a number of adjustments to the antenna and then see which one improves the SWR. This approach is fine with simple antennas such as dipoles. However, things don't always go smoothly. It is not unusual to hear: "I've tried everything but I can't get the SWR down". The setting up and adjustment of a gamma match on a beam, or matching network on a compact antenna can be quite frustrating if the only indication that you have is an SWR meter.

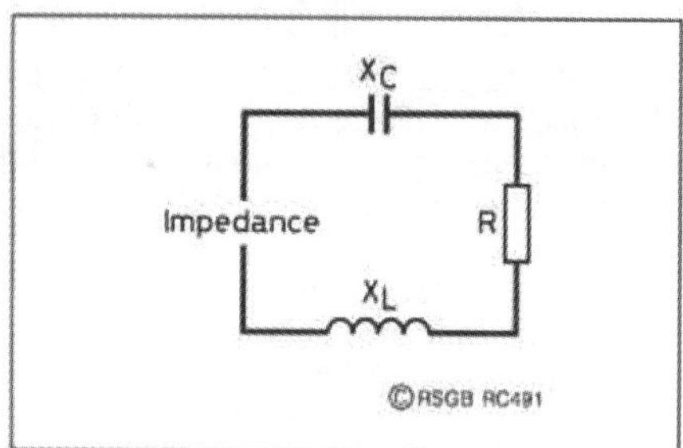


Fig 1: Equivalent antenna circuit

## WHAT IS IMPEDANCE?

THE BEST WAY TO TELL what is happening at the feedpoint of an antenna is to measure its impedance directly.

Impedance (whose symbol is Z) is a general term, which can be applied to any electrical circuit that impedes the flow of AC current. An antenna is a tuned circuit having inductance, capacitance and resistance and an equivalent circuit is shown in **Fig 1.**

When transmitter power is fed to the antenna the current in the resistive part is in phase with the applied voltage; while the current in the inductive or capacitive part (reactance) is 90 degrees out of phase with the applied voltage. Thus the phase relationship between current and voltage in a tuned circuit or antenna element can be anything between zero and plus or minus 90 degrees, depending on the ratio of resistance and reactance.

Because of this, impedance is always expressed in two parts; resistive and reactive. An impedance having an resistance of 75Ω and a inductive reactance 50Ω is conventionally written as:

75 +j50

The j symbol bothers a lot of people. This is probably due to the way it is described in literature as "the square root of minus one" or "imaginary". Furthermore, impedance is described as "complex". All these terms are derived from the mathematics used in impedance calculations. For our consideration of impedance, j can simply be regarded as a convention for reactance. The '+j' indicates inductive reactance and a '-j' indicates capacitive reactance. When the antenna is at its resonant frequency the +j and -j parts are equal and opposite so only the resistive part remains.

An impedance value can be plotted as co-ordinates on a rectangular chart or map in just the same way that a QTH longitude and latitude is plotted on a map. A position of, say, 52°N 3°E would be plotted on a map as shown in **Fig 2.** Our impedance value of 75 +j50 would be plotted on an impedance map or chart as shown in **Fig 3**. On the impedance chart we use + or -j instead of E or W longitude.

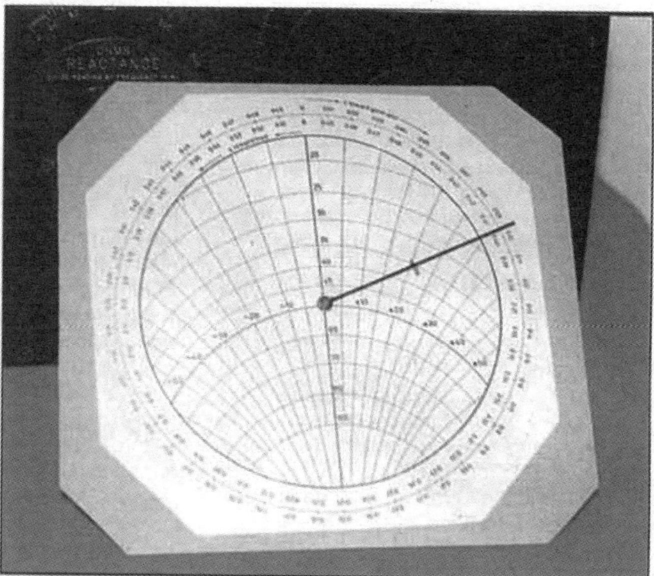

General construction of the Smith chart calculator.

## IMPEDANCE MEASUREMENT

BEFORE WE CAN MAKE full use an impedance chart we need an instrument for determining a position on the chart. A simple instrument for measuring impedance was described by Ed Chicken G3BIK [1]. A even simpler and more accurate impedance measuring technique, known as the 3-Meter

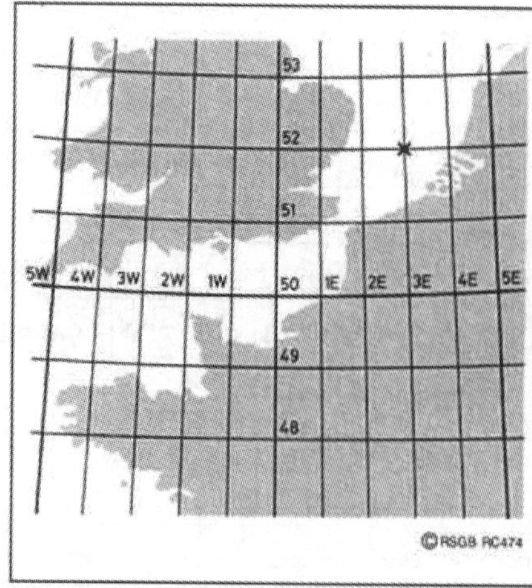


Fig 2: Map showing co-ordinates of latitude and longitude.

General Radio 1606 impedance bridge, showing the resistance and reactance scales.

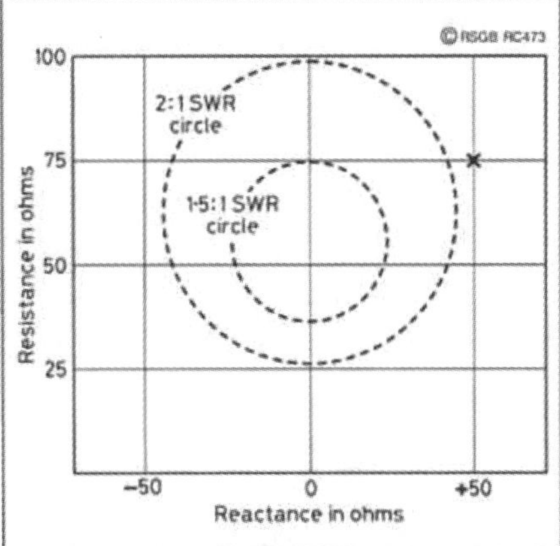


Fig 3: Impedance map showing co-ordinates of resistance and reactance.

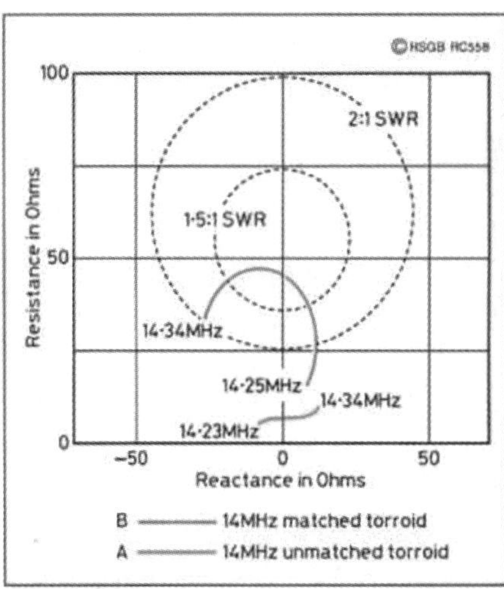


Fig 4: Impedance 'signatures' of a double toroid antenna.

method, is described in *The Antenna Experimenters Guide*, available from the RSGB, see page 90.

A professional impedance bridge is shown in the above photo. As you can see there are two calibrated controls, one for R and the other for j. Information from the calibrated dials on the instrument can be used to establish the impedance position on the chart.

The chart in **Fig 3** also illustrates the limitations of SWR as a means of determining the characteristics of the feedpoint of an antenna. The two circles shown in Fig 3 are circles of constant SWR, one for 2:1 and the other for 1.5:1. Using our map analogy they can be regarded as SWR contours. When you measure SWR to try to find out what is going on at the antenna you are measuring the effect of the antenna not having the same value of impedance as the antenna. However, an impedance of 100 +j0 would give the same SWR as an impedance of 25 +j0. You will see that there is a large number of impedance values that can give an SWR of 2:1. If you measure an SWR value of 2:1 then all you know is that you are somewhere on the 2:1 circle. This explains why an SWR meter is not necessarily the best instrument for adjusting an antenna with a matching network such as a Gamma match.

If you make several impedance measurements of an antenna over a range of frequencies they can be used to produce an impedance 'signature' of the antenna. **Fig 4** shows two of these signatures, which were obtained when evaluating the G2AJV double toroid antenna [2]. Plot A shows that the resistance is around 8Ω at resonance, and explains why no amount of antenna pruning would bring the SWR value to usable proportions. With a suitable matching circuit, the impedance is very close to 50Ω at resonance as shown in plot B.

(Resonance is where the inductive and capacitive reactances in a tuned circuit or antenna element are equal and opposite, and this condition exists only on the 0 reactance vertical line of Figs 3 and 4)

To obtain the results shown in Fig 4 it is necessary to measure the antenna feedpoint impedance at the point where the coaxial is connected to it. There are many practical difficulties in doing this and it is much more convenient if impedances could be measured via a length of coaxial cable. Now while SWR is the same anywhere along a transmission line (neglecting any losses) the measured impedance at one end depends on the transmission line electrical length. This is where the Smith chart comes in.

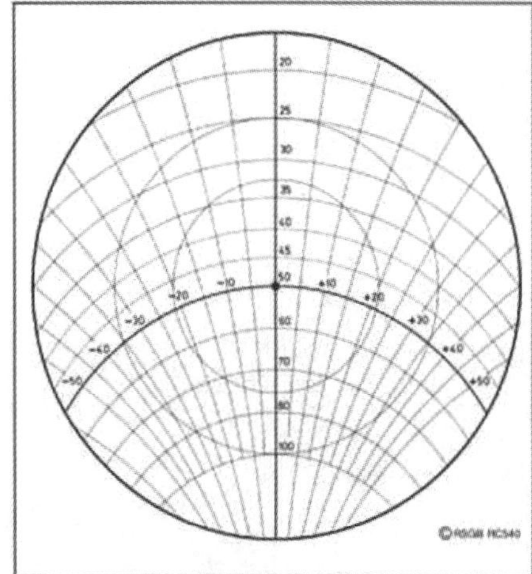

Fig 5: Basic simplified Smith chart.

The Smith chart, shown in **Fig 5** is an impedance map similar to the ones shown in Figs 3 and 4. It can be considered as just a different projection, just as maps have different projections, such as the Mercator Projection or the Great Circle projection. The most obvious difference with the Smith chart is that all the co-ordinate lines are sections of a circle instead of being straight.

The Smith chart, by convention, has the resistance scale decreasing towards the top. With this projection the SWR circles are concentric, centred on the 50Ω point, which is known as the prime centre.

If you are familiar with a normal Smith chart you will recognise that the one shown in Fig 5 is simplified. The differences and the reasons for simplification are described later.

One advantage of the Smith projection is that it can be used for calculating impedance transforms over a length of coaxial feeder. Because the reflected impedance varies along the feeder it follows that you need to know the electrical length of your coaxial feeder to the antenna. You can then calculate the transform of impedance measured at the shack end of the feeder using the noise bridge.

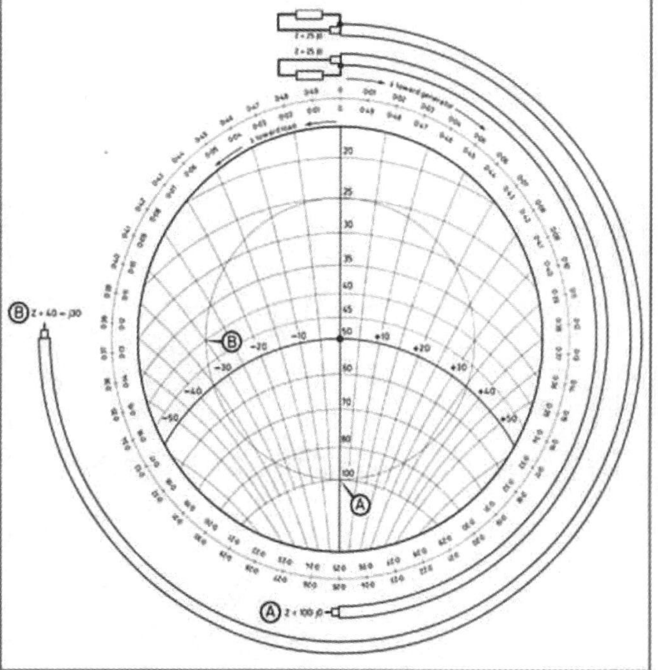

Fig 6: Smith chart, with transmission line electrical length scale, superimposed on two lengths of coaxial cable.

The impedance transformation Smith chart is illustrated in **Fig 6**. An additional scale is added around the circumference, calibrated in electrical wavelength. Halfway round the chart equals 0.25 or quarter wavelength, while a full rotation equals 0.5 or half wavelength.

Two lengths of 50Ω coaxial feeder are shown superimposed around the circumfer-

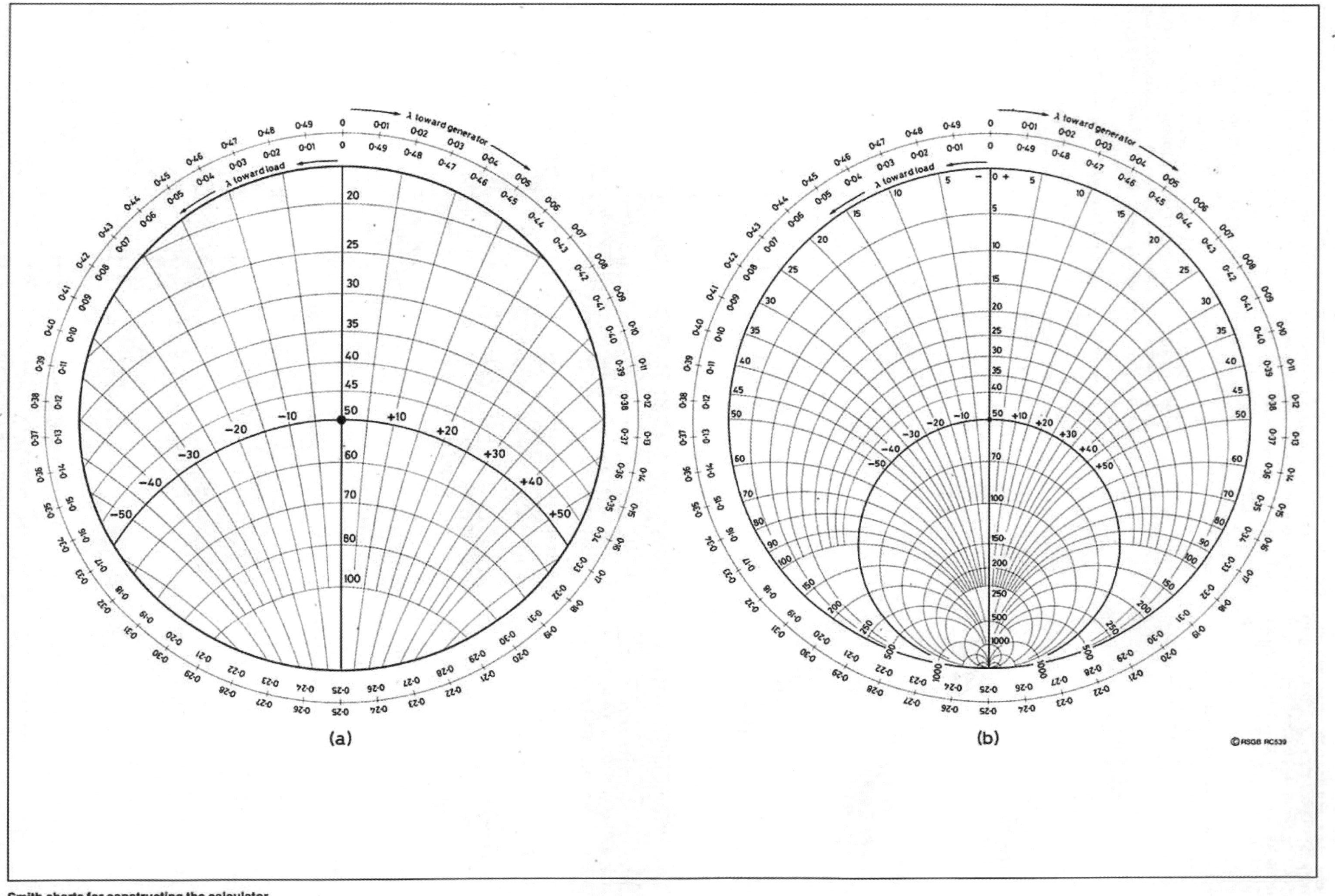


Smith charts for constructing the calculator.

ence of a Smith chart in Fig 6; one length quarter wave long and the other 3/8 wavelength). Both lengths are connected to a load having an impedance of 25 +j0. The quarter wave length of line (0.25) gives a measured impedance of 100 +j0 at the other end while the 3/8 section (0.375) gives an impedance of 40 +j30. It can also be seen from Fig 6 that a halfwave length of coaxial cable would transform the impedance back to 25 +j0.

## A PRACTICAL SMITH CHART CALCULATOR

YOU CAN USE EITHER of the charts on Page 42 to construct a Smith chart calculator.

Chart (a) has a restricted impedance range but is easier to use. It is used where the impedance excursions are limited and do not cause an SWR much greater than 2.5:1.

Chart (b) is the standard chart which covers impedances from (theoretically) zero to infinity.

For this exercise we will make an impedance calculator using the restricted range chart, which is easier read and use, see the photograph on page 40.

Make a photocopy of the chart enlarging it to bring it to a usable size. I suggest an enlargement from A4 to A3; a single chart will then fit on a single piece of A4 paper. The chart is then glued to a circular sheet of stiff cardboard or thin aluminium. A small hole is drilled in the chart and backing material at the 50 +j0 point.

From a piece of very thin perspex or transparent plastic or celluloid cut a circle the same size as the chart to make an overlay. A hole is then drilled exactly at the overlay centre. Identifying the centre point should be no problem if a pair of compasses is used to mark the overlay before cutting.

Make a cursor by drawing a line along the radius of the overlay, using a fine tipped marker pen. Cover the line with a strip of cellotape to prevent the line rubbing out. Trim off the excess tape.

Fix the transparent overlay to the chart with a nut and bolt with the tape covered line against the chart. Adjust the nut and bolt so that the overlay can be easily rotated, as shown in the photograph.

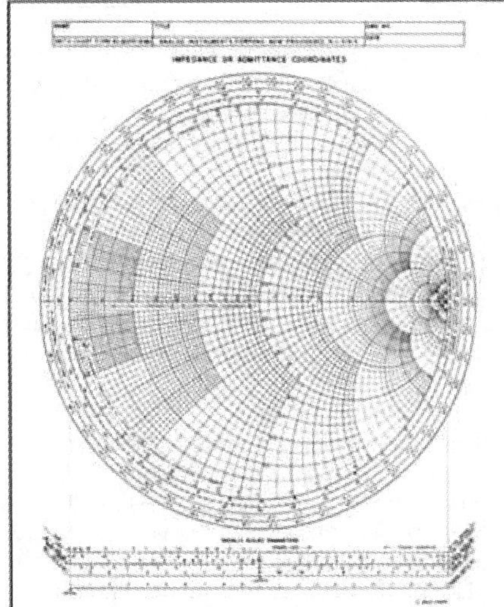

**Fig 7: View of a normalized standard Smith chart.**

## USING THE CALCULATOR

THE USES TO WHICH this calculator can be put are too numerous to be included in this article. But here are three examples.

## MEASURING COAXIAL CABLE ELECTRICAL LENGTH

YOU CAN FIND THE electrical length of coaxial cable by physically measuring its length and multiplying it by the cable velocity factor.

A more accurate method is to measure the electrical length directly using an RF impedance measuring instrument (eg a noise bridge). It also assumes there are no cable losses; in practice this means that the procedure will only work with relatively short lengths of fairly good quality coaxial cable. You should be using reasonable grade coaxial anyway to measure antenna characteristics - even SWR.

1 Terminate the load (antenna) end of the cable with a 22Ω resistor.
2 Measure the impedance at the other end of the feeder.
3 Move the cursor so that it intersects the measured impedance point. The cursor will now point to the electrical wavelength of the feeder marked on the outer scale marked 'wavelengths towards generator'.

The cable may be several half wavelengths and part of a half wavelength long. The Smith chart will only register the 'part of a half wavelength', which is all we are interested in regarding the impedance transform effect.

## CALCULATING ANTENNA IMPEDANCE

THIS IS A METHOD of calculating antenna impedance from a measured impedance value, using coaxial cable whose electrical length has already been determined.

1 Connect the cable to the antenna.
2 Measure the impedance at the other end of the coaxial.
3 Move the cursor over the measured impedance point and mark the point on the overlay with a wax pencil.
5 Follow the cursor radially outwards to the scale marked 'wavelengths towards load'. Write this number down.
6 Add the length of cable in wavelengths to this number.
7 If the number is larger than 0.5, subtract 0.5.
8 Rotate the overlay until the cursor points to this number on the 'wavelengths towards load' scale.
9 The antenna impedance will be found on the cursor directly under the wax pencil mark.

### EXAMPLE

The measured impedance is 35 +j20Ω and the cursor points to 0.407 on the 'wavelengths towards load' scale.

The cable electrical length was measured as 0.13 wavelengths.

Then 0.407 + 0.13 = 0.537 wavelengths. Off scale - too big! So subtract 0.5 wavelengths = 0.037 wavelengths.

Rotate the overlay until the cursor points to 0.037 on the 'wavelengths towards load' scale.

The antenna impedance is shown as 28 -j8Ω under the cursor at the same radius as the measured impedance.

## MEASUREMENT OF SWR

CALCULATION OF SWR is very simple using the Smith chart. The result is useful for correlating impedance measurements with SWR measurements. To measure SWR:

1 Move the cursor over the measured impedance point.
2 Mark the point on the overlay with a wax pencil.
3 Move the cursor to the 0 point on the outside scales.
4 The SWR can be read off as 50 divided by the mark on the cursor. The impedance measured above gives a reading of 27 +j0. 50 divided by 27 equals 1.85; the SWR in this case is 1.85:1.

You can, of course, calibrate the cursor in SWR. Just place the cursor in the vertical zero position and place marks on the cursor at the 33.3, 25 and 20 resistance points to give SWR marks at 1.5:1, 2:1 and 2.5:1 respectively.

## CONCLUSION

USING THE SMITH CHART, as described above, doesn't seem so complicated, so why is it not more widely used?

It is probably because the Smith chart is designed for professional use and is required to have high resolution to give accuracy to the results. Like any graphic aid, the higher the line density the greater is its resolution but the harder it is to read as you can see in **Fig 7**.

In addition most Smith charts are 'normalized' so that they can be used at any impedance and not restricted to 50Ω, as are the ones described in this article. This is achieved by assigning 1 to the prime centre; other values, for example, are 0.5 for 25Ω and 2 for 100Ω in a 50Ω system.

## NOTE

YOU COULD OBVIOUSLY measure the impedance of the antenna using a halfwave, or a multiple of a half wavelength, of coaxial cable and dispense with the Smith chart altogether. In fact this is often done but there are a couple of disadvantages. Because the cable is resonant it can result in antenna currents on the cable, which can give inconsistent impedance measurement results. Also if you make several impedance measurements over a range of frequencies remember that the cable is a half wavelength long on one frequency only.


## ACKNOWLEDGEMENT

TO PETER SWALLOW, G8EZE, for checking the manuscript and help on a procedure for using the Smith chart.


## REFERENCES


[1] 'Tone Modulated HF Impedance Bridge', E Chicken, G3BIK, *Radio Communication*, June/July 1994.

[2] 'Evaluation of the G2AJV Toroidal Antenna', Peter Dodd, G3LDO, *Radio Communication*, August 1994. ♦

# The Helikite Virtual Mast

**By *Radcom* Technical Editor, Peter Dodd, G3LDO**

A HELIKITE IS a combination of a specially designed kite and a helium-filled mylar balloon; first described in *Product News, Radcom*, June 1995. The kite section is made from rip-stop nylon, which wraps around and protects the silver mylar balloon, see the photograph above. It is claimed to be able to fly in wind speeds from 0 to 10 on the Beaufort wind scale. Although designed primarily for agriculture as a hovering birdscarer it appeared to practical solution to providing temporary support to a long-wire vertical antenna.

This review describes my experiences of using the Helikite as a support for a low-band long-wire vertical antenna. The manufacturer suggested that the best method of using the Helikite as a lifting support was to use two kites in tandem. This doubles the lifting power and provides a more stable lifting platform.

## MOBILE OPERATION

IT SEEMED SENSIBLE to try using the kites away from obstructions such as buildings and trees. In order to carry the kites and radio equipment to such a site required a car and suggested mobile operation, particularly as my vehicle was already fitted with mobile radio equipment (FT-707).

As a start I decided to try 80 metres using a half wavelength of 0.6mm plastic covered wire. I reasoned that a voltage fed half-wave would be the best DX antenna under the circumstances because it would reduce the ground losses normally associated with mobile operation. I constructed a simple ATSU arrangement, which was fixed to the rear of the car on the mobile mount bracket, see the photograph bottom left. The antenna and kite cord were connected at the kite end and run together. At the car the cord was tethered to the one of the door hinges and the antenna connected to the ASTU.

**Top right: The kite section, made from rip-stop nylon, wraps around and protects the silver mylar balloon.**
**Left: The ASTU comprised a tapped parallel tuned circuit fixed to the mobile antenna mount.**

| | | | | | | | | | |
|---|---|---|---|---|---|---|---|---|---|
| 15/4 | 0500 | VE3YJ | 3772 | 5/6 | 5/9 | 100 | SSB | High down | HK Guelph, SW Toronto Rocco |
| | 0530 | KV7S | 3779 | 3/3 | 5/7 | " | " | " | [illegible] Dan |
| | 0540 | TI2CF | 3799 | 5/9 | 5/9 | " | " | " | |
| | 0544 | ZL1HY | 3799 | 5/7 | 5/7 | " | " | " | Walton Mike |
| | 0600 | ZL4AS | 3799 | 5/5 | 5/6 | " | " | " | Cliff |

**Fig 1: Log book extract for the first hour of Helikite operation on 14 April 1995.**

The QTH for the first tests was a car park on South-downs Way, an area of the South Downs overlooking West Worthing.

Because I feel that the only real test of an antenna is working DX it was necessary for me to be operational at around daybreak for any chance of a DX contact on 80 metres. It was dark and there was quite a strong wind blowing. I managed to launch the two kites in tandem but the antenna wire got into an awful tangle. This took quite a lot of sorting out in the dark because the wire was covered in black plastic insulation. By the time the antenna wire was sorted out, the kites flying properly and the antenna connected to the ASTU it was just getting light.

I took a listen around but there was no real DX. At this point the wind started to decrease and change direction. The kites lost some altitude and were in danger of being entangled in some nearby trees, not at first noticed in the darkness. I drove the car, with the antenna system still connected, to another area of the car park, clear of trees, and started operating again listening for SSB signals at the top end of the band. The first DX contact was with VE3YJ who gave me a 5/6 report. This was followed by other DX contacts shown in a sample of the logbook in **Fig 1**.

During the period of operation the wind dropped to zero but the kites kept flying, although the height was reduced. However the top quarter-wavelength of the antenna was substantially vertical and there was no noticeable reduction in performance. At the time I was operating in the down-wind side of the hill so there was probably a downdraft in the airflow that reduced the height of Helikites. They certainly flew in what appeared to be zero wind.

## FIXED SITE

NEXT, THE HELIKITE system was tried from the top of the RSGB HQ building. Initially the kites were without the antenna attached and they seemed to fly quite well. As a result of this test flight I then decided to use the Helikit system to support an 80-metre halfwave antenna to give a good 3.5MHz signal for the special event station GB100IMD. However, on the night, it proved impossible to launch the kites in the dark, with a turbulent wind and the ajacent RSGB antenna structures.

## WHAT ABOUT THE HELIUM?

THE HELIUM IS supplied by Lindgas and must be paid for separately. It comes in the form of balloon gas which is about 98% helium and 2% air. The helium comes in a hired 65cm tall cylinder which is not heavy and is easy to move. The cylinder and gas can be obtained from regional depots listed in the information that comes with the Helikites. A cylinder will fill about 12 balloons although in practice you only need to fill two, and top them up weekly with a small amount of gas.

## GENERAL NOTES

WIND SPEED INCREASES with height; weather forecasts give wind speeds as measured at 33ft (10m) above the ground where it will be about one third faster than at ground level. Even when there appears to be no wind at all there will often be some wind once clear of ground level.

Helikites can be stacked. The first kite is launched and the line is then attached to a second kite, so that the two kites fly about 60ft (20m) apart. This allows the first kite to find, and fly in, the stronger and more stable air stream that occurs at some distance above the ground.

Air Traffic Control Regulations state that the maximum height a kite or balloon can be flown, without notification, is 60m. The Helikite has quite a lot of drag so it tends to fly at around 45 degrees from the vertical. In practice this means that you can use a use a 130ft (40m) antenna without any problem.

## SAFETY

IN COMMON WITH any other kite flying activity Helikites should *not* be flown anywhere near overhead power lines, over buildings or roads.

Never fly the Helikite during electrical storms. If an electrical storm brews up while the kite is aloft disconnect the rig and try to get the kite down. If the storm comes upon you very quickly then just disconnect the rig and don't go near the kite antenna until the storm has finished.

## CONCLUSIONS

THE TWO KITES as described certainly flew in what appeared to be zero wind, a condition that no other kite would have flown in. However, they did have a struggle carrying the 80m half-wave of 0.6mm plastic covered wire in low wind conditions. Enamelled covered 18 or 20SWG wire would be much lighter. The nylon control line takes all the strain. Even when the antenna wire sagged, a halfwave vertical end fed antenna performed very well.

The Helikite becomes rather unstable in high winds. This instability can be minimised by using a drogue or tail.

Helikites have to be transported in an inflated condition. They float around inside the car unless fixed to the floor or seat of the vehicle with a weight. When not in use I leave them parked on the ceiling of the garage. A Helikite must always be tethered otherwise it is gone forever.

Using a Helikite as a method of circumventing antenna planning restrictions seemed attractive. I tried launching the kites from my back garden. They rose above the houses and trees but were buffeted about by wind turbulence until well clear of obstructions. I felt that this was not a solution for supporting an antenna from a suburban site.

A Helikite lifting kit can be obtained from Allsopp Helikites, Cheshunt Lodge, Chalford, Stroud, Glos, GL6 8NW, tel: 01453 886515. It comprises two kites, balloons, drogues, several rolls of line and four spare balloons. The cost is £210.32 plus £5 P&P. Helium is available as described above at £30 per cylinder, with a cylinder rental of £26 for 12 months. Additionally you will need an inflator at £19.50. Helium prices are exclusive of VAT. ♦

# 80m DXing From a Vehicle

**by RadCom *Technical Editor, Peter Dodd, G3LDO***

WORKING DX DURING the low sunspot cycle on 80m and topband is most interesting. If you live in an area where there is hostility to large low-band antennas, operation from a vehicle at a remote site is an option.

The antenna can be a long wire fixed to a tall tree or supported by a kite or balloon. You can use your existing mobile equipment if you have it; in my case the vehicle is already fitted with a mobile HF transceiver (Yaesu FT-707).

This article describes some of the considerations for operating DX on 80 metres; some of which could also apply to topband.

Most DX openings on these bands are early in the morning or after dark. Fixing antennas to trees in the dark is not my idea of fun so this article concentrates on using kites and balloons as a support for a wire antenna.

## KITES

PROVIDED THE WIND strength is in the range of light breeze (4-6 knots) to fresh breeze (17-21 knots), a kite is a good way of supporting a long wire antenna.

The essential requirements for a kite used for this purpose is that it is simple, easy to launch, provides a good lift at low windspeeds and is rugged. When it is flown it should be stable; by this I mean that it should remain stationary in the sky even in turbulent wind.

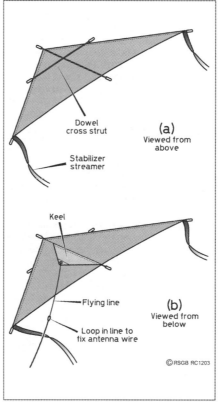

**Fig 1: Construction of a Delta kite.**

A kite with these characteristics is the Delta shown in **Fig 1**. It is constructed from a tough lightweight material called 'ripstop nylon' and uses fibre glass spreaders. The side and centre spreaders are fixed into the kite when it is constructed. The cross spreader is fixed to the kite when it is prepared for flying and removed so that the kite can be folded for transportation. When the kite is flying the cross spreader flexes, increasing the dihedral; this reduces lift and increases stability in strong gusts of wind.

Details of how to construct such a kite is given in [1] although suitable kites can also be purchased (see Availability).

The only experiments carried out so far have been on 80 metres. The antenna comprised a half wavelength of 0.6mm plastic covered wire wound around the thin nylon kite flying line as shown in **Fig 2**.

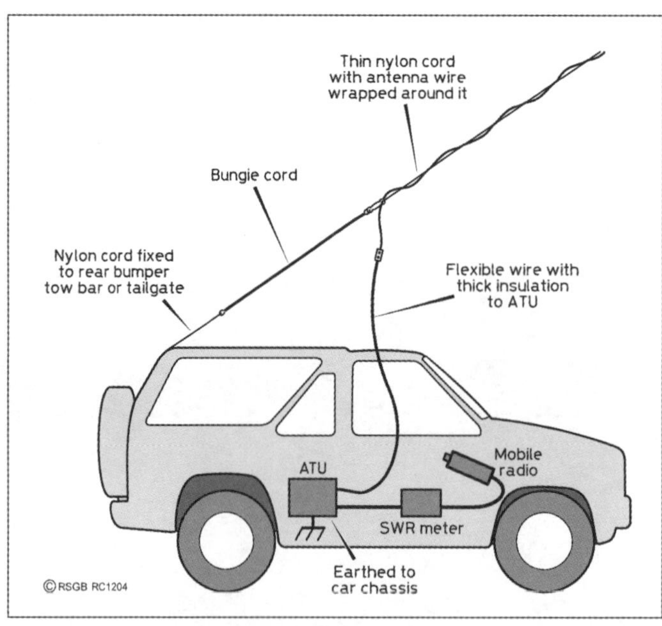


**Fig 2: Method of connecting a kite or balloon antenna to a vehicle. The bungie cord is not required for balloons and is only of use with kites in blustery winds.**

I find that an essential item of equipment for launching and recovering kites is a winder, shown in **Fig 3**. This allows the antenna and the line to be played out and recovered in a tidy fashion; a major consideration when launching a kite in darkness or half light.

The flying line is fixed to the vehicle as shown in Fig 2. I fix my kite flying line to a roofrack, which is very convenient. A length of bungie cord can be used to reduce the strain on the line and kite in strong gusty winds. The wire end of the antenna is brought through a wind-down rear window. When the wire is in position the window is wound up, making an effective insulated clamp. The wire is connected to the ASTU as shown in **Fig 4.** The wire must be positioned so that it is always slack, whatever the position of the kite; the nylon flying line takes all the strain.

## BALLOONS

THE WIND OFTEN disappears in the early dawn or after sunset, when the DX is at its best; just when you needed a breeze to keep the kite antenna flying. A solution to this problem is to use a balloon. Mylar balloons are often obtainable from flower shops. The largest I was able to obtain was one metre in diameter and was referred to as a 'jumbo' balloon. They have to be transported in an inflated condition (balloon gas is expensive).

At least three of these balloons (preferably four) are required to lift a halfwave 80 metre wire. An anchor point to the balloon is made using brown plastic tape as shown in **Fig 5**. Balloons can be harnessed together via the plastic tape loops with a nylon cord and the antenna wire tied to the harness.

In no wind conditions when a balloon can be flown the pull is very much less than a kite. The main disadvantage of using a number of relatively small balloons linked together is that the lifting system has a lot of drag. The effect of drag is that even a very light breeze will blow the balloons sideways so that the antenna is anything but vertical. This defeats the object of using a balloon to make a large vertical DX

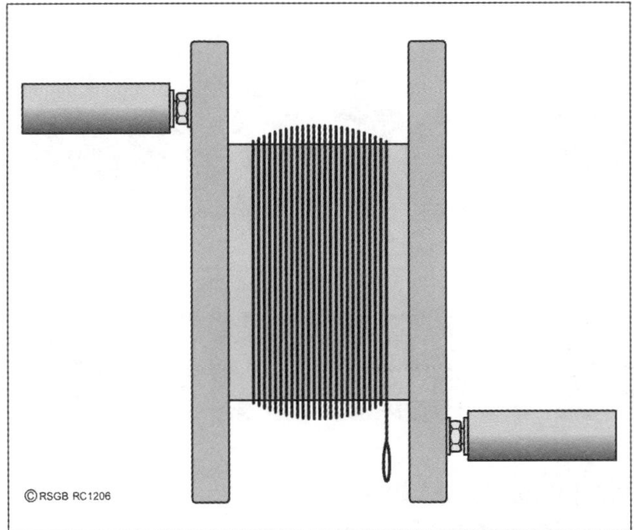


Fig 3: Flat wooden winder for launching and recovering kites or balloons.

antenna. Ideally, a balloon should be streamlined, like a barrage or advertising balloon, to increase the lift to drag ratio. Nevertheless, a cluster of balloons is useful when the wind is 0 on the Beaufort wind scale (wind speed 0 - 1 knots). The antenna must be as light as possible so a thin wire (0.6mm plastic covered), without the nylon flying line, can be used. I am looking into other types of suitable light weight wire for this purpose. Fine aluminium welding wire in parallel with fishing line can been used.

The method of connecting the antenna to the ASTU is the same as described for the kite. The antenna can be clamped into the rear window as previously described, but cushioned with a piece of plastic or rubber.

Balloon gas is about 98% helium and 2% air. This gas comes in a hired 65cm tall cylinders which are not heavy and are easy to move. The cylinder and gas can be obtained from regional depots: see the *Yellow Pages* for information of a gas supplier near you. A cylinder will fill about 12 balloons although in practice you only need to fill two, and top them up weekly with a small amount of gas.

## KITE OR BALLOON?

WINDSPEEDS OF 1 to 3 knots (1 on the Beaufort wind scale) poses the greatest problem of supporting an antenna using the methods so far described. As already stated this is often the wind condition when the DX is at its best.

One method is to use the Allsop Helikite, which is a combination of kite and balloon and was reviewed in *Radcom*, July 1995. (see Availability). Since the review the Helikite has been improved so that only one is required to lift an 80 metre halfwave antenna. This effectively halves its original price of £210, although at this stage I have not tried one.

## OPERATION

THE TRANSCEIVER is mounted in the normal operating position as used for mobile operation. The antenna cable is connected to the ASTU, which lies on the back seat of the car. The ASTU comprises a simple parallel tuned circuit using good transmitting type components.

The ASTU tuning, which can be adjusted from the driver's seat, is set for minimum SWR.

A voltage fed half wave vertical antenna is good for DX under such circumstances because it reduces the ground losses normally associated with mobile operation. While it is excellent for transmitting, it does suffer from the disadvantage of static noise on receive. The solution is to either use a very high selectivity preselector or a separate high Q receiving antenna.

The antenna could be modified for Topband operation. The maximum permitted length of a vertical antenna is 60m so the antenna would be around 5/8 wavelengths. This would give a useful increase in feed impedance (and reduction in losses) compared with a quarter wave antenna. The same type of antenna tuner can be used, as shown in Fig 4, but an extra 15 or 20 turns would be required on the coil (assuming the same coil former diameter).

## CHOOSING A SITE

A GOOD LOCATION for flying a kite is dictated by interaction of the ground with the wind. The best location is a flat open space with no buildings or trees. Regardless of which way the wind blows there will be the minimum of wind turbulence. Flat seaside shores are good particularly with an onshore breeze. This type of location should also theoretically provide a good radio QTH.

Hill tops, while being fine for VHF operation, are not ideal for flying a kite. This is because there is a lot of turbulence and down drafts on the down wind side of the hill.

I normally operate from an area near Worthing in Sussex called Southdown because it is conveniently close to home. It has a public car park about one third up the Southdown hills facing the sea. If there is a southerly on-shore breeze then I'm in luck as air moving towards a gentle slope gives good lift - to a kite or balloon. If the wind is blowing from the north or north east then operation is difficult or impossible.

Keep kites and balloons away from obstructions such as buildings and trees. These obstructions create a lot of air turbulence as well as providing a trap for the kite or balloon.

I use a separate antenna and winder for the balloon antenna system. If the wind speed increases I then wind in the balloon antenna and launch the kite antenna.

Air Traffic Control regulations state that the maximum height a kite or balloon can be flown, without notification, is 60m. In practice this means that you can use a use a 130ft (40m) antenna without any problem.

## SAFETY

IN COMMON WITH any other kite or balloon flying activity, they should not be flown anywhere near overhead power lines, over buildings or roads.

Never fly a kite during electrical storms or if the weather is severe in any way.

## AVAILABILITY

KITES CAN BE obtained from any good kite shop. Two kites used in the tests described above were from 'Kite Corner', 675 Watford Way, London NW7 3JR, tel: 0181 959 0619.

The Delta Supreme, 200x110cm with glass fibre frame, costs £29.95 including line on halo reel.

The Delta Magnum, 270x138cm with wooden frame, costs £39.95 including line on halo reel. This kite pulls like a train and is really too big for using with antennas.

Note the change of address of Allsopp, who make the Helikite. It is now South End Farm, Damerham, Fordingbridge, Hants FP6 3HW; tel: 01725 518750.

## REFERENCE

[1] *Kite Cookery*, Squadron Leader Don Dunford, MBE. Published by Cochranes of Oxford OX8 5NT (obtainable from Kite Corner, see above). ♦

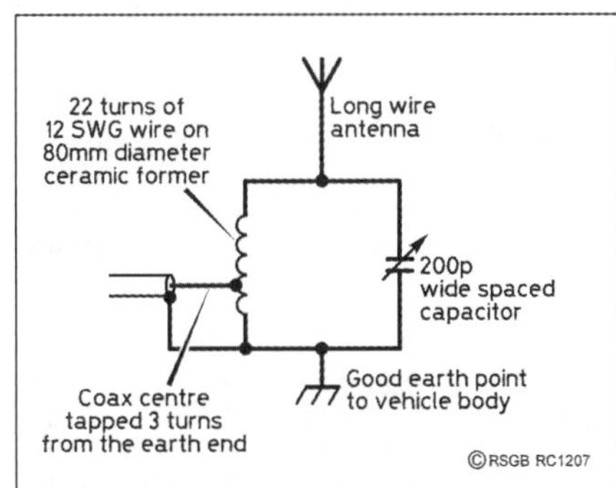


Fig 4: Circuit diagram of the Antenna System Tuning Unit. The values of the inductor and capacitor are not critical. The prototype was built on a flat piece of aluminium.

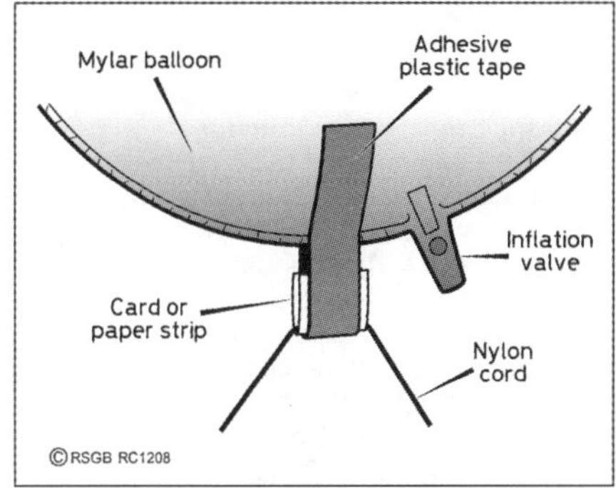


Fig 5: Method of connecting an antenna to a balloon. The nylon cord is used for tethering two or more balloons together and the antenna is connected to the cord.

# Evolution of the Beam Antenna

**PART 1 With the 90th anniversary of the RSGB being celebrated this month, it is an appropriate time to look back at the history of that most ubiquitous of radio antenna – the Yagi beam. *RadCom* 'Antennas' columnist Peter Dodd, G3LDO, takes an affectionate look at the development of the beam antenna over the last nine decades.**

When someone describes their antenna to you during an HF QSO it might be described as a "beam" having, say, four elements. At VHF or UHF it could be a "Yagi" with, say, 15 elements. From my office/shack window I can see around 10 or 11 houses all, without exception, sprouting TV and/or VHF radio Yagi antennas. This antenna, which is described in most literature as the 'Parasitic Array', has become the most familiar in our daily lives and the three-element beam has become an icon for HF amateur radio.

While the origins of many popular antennas are well known, the same cannot be said for the Yagi antenna. The purpose of this article is to explore how this antenna came into being and its development by radio amateurs.

## EARLY DAYS

The parasitic beam antenna was the result of research carried out at Tohoku Imperial University in Japan in the early 1920s. The research team was headed by Professor Hidetsugu Yagi, who by that time had considerable experience of radio engineering, gained in Europe and the USA. Professor Yagi selected several students and co-researchers. Two of these were Kinjiro Okabe, who was to carry out research on the magnetron, and Shintaro Uda, who was to investigate the properties of antennas.

From the beginning of radio technology the frequencies of electromagnetic waves were defined in wavelengths and it is from these early days that classifications such as Long Wave (LW), Medium Wave (MW) and Short Wave (SW) were defined. Wavelengths shorter that 10m (frequencies higher than 30MHz) were classified as Ultra Short Waves. Although these frequencies had no practical use at the time they proved useful for investigating antennas because the small physical size of resonant lengths was convenient to handle.

Much of the work carried out Tohoku University concerned the generation of continuous electromagnetic waves, which followed on from Yagi's earlier research work with Flemming [1].

Shintaro Uda's early antenna work concerned the measurement of the single-wire resonant loop radiation pattern and he observed and recorded the effect of ground. He also noted that nearby unconnected resonant loops caused changes in directivity, and from this a directional antenna was created. Improved directivity was obtained when the loops were replaced with rods, then the driven element itself was replaced with a half-wave dipole [2]. The antenna design went from a loop to a dipole configuration, and the now familiar 'Yagi' antenna, with the dipole and parasitic rods vertically polarised emerged. Uda produced an in-depth analysis of the variables that controlled directivity such as parasitic element lengths, spacing and geometric arrangement of parasitic elements, and the effects of receiving antenna height and transmitting antenna height. All this research work appeared in a series of papers, first published in early 1926 [3]. This work was, of course, published in Japanese.

## BEAM TRANSMISSION OF ULTRA SHORT WAVES IRE PAPER

In 1928, Professor Hidetsugu Yagi visited the USA, giving speeches to IRE members in New York City. He also contributed to the IRE a paper in English called *Beam Transmission of Ultra Short Waves* [4]. This two-part paper, which is now regarded as a classic, described the development of the beam antenna and the generation of ultra-short waves using the split anode magnetron. In summarising Shintaro Uda's work he said: "Suppose that a vertical antenna is radiating electromagnetic waves in all directions. If a straight oscillating system, whether it be a metal rod of finite length or an antenna with capacities at both ends and an inductance at the middle, is erected vertically in the field, the effect of this oscillator upon the wave will be as follows. If its natural frequency is equal to or lower than that of the incident wave, it will act as a 'wave reflector.' If, on the other hand, its natural frequency is higher than that of the incident wave, it will act as a 'wave director.' The field will converge upon this antenna, and radiation in a plane normal to it will be augmented. By utilising this wave-directing quality, a sharp beam may be produced.

"A triangle formed of three or five antennas erected behind the main or radiating antenna will act as a reflector. This system is called a 'trigonal reflector'. In front of the radiating antenna, a number of wave-directors may be arranged along the line of propagation. By properly adjusting the distance between the wave-directors and their natural frequencies, it is possible to transmit a larger part of the energy in the wave along the row of directors. Adjustment of the natural frequency of the directors is made by simply changing their length or by adjusting the inductance inserted at the middle of these antennas. The number of wave-directors has a very marked effect on the sharpness of the beam, the larger number of directors producing the sharper beam. It has been found convenient to designate such a row of directors as a 'wave canal... In general the effect of increasing the forming the canal is shown in **Fig 1**. The length of the directors must be accurately adjusted otherwise successful directing action will not be obtained. It has been found that the interval between the adjacent directors must be adjusted to a suitable value. The most advantageous value for this interval seems

***Fig 1: The effect of varying the number and length of directors in wave canals on received current.***

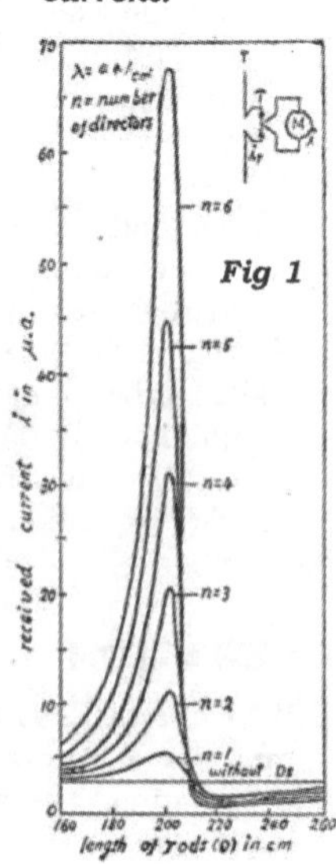

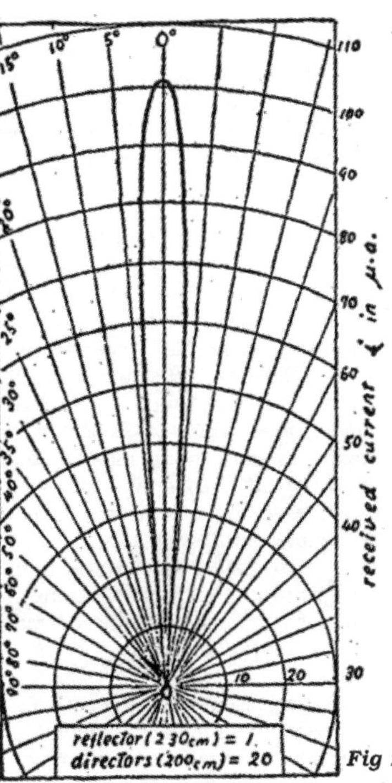


*Fig 2: The beam radiation from a radiator utilising a wave canal.*

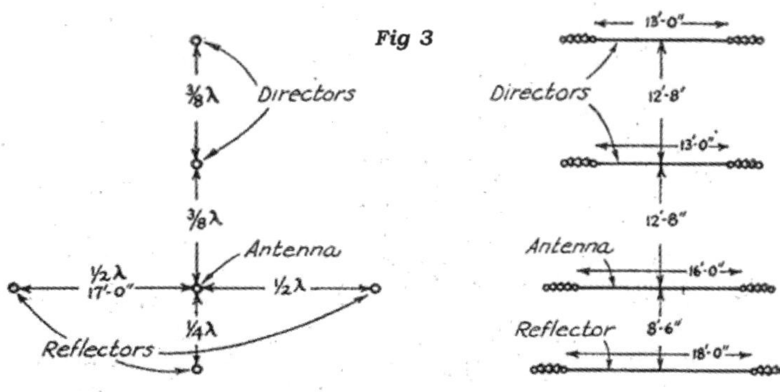


*Fig 3: The 1CCZ 28MHz antenna using a driven element, three reflector wires and two director wires.*

*Fig 4: Construction of the 1CCZ 28MHz antenna, showing the complexity required to support the wires (shown in Fig 3) and alter the elevation angle of the antenna.*

to be approximately 3/8 wavelength.

"A typical polar curve showing the beam radiation from such a projector is shown in is given in **Fig 2**. The measurements were taken on a horizontal plane near the earth's surface. It has been found that the power received increases nearly proportional to the square of the number of directors forming the canal".

## FIRST AMATEUR YAGI ANTENNA, 1CCZ, 1928

In 1902 it was independently suggested by Heaviside and Kennelly [5] that a conducting layer existed in the upper atmosphere, which would allow radio waves to follow the earth's curvature. This layer was postulated to explain why Marconi's transmissions from Poldhu in Cornwall were received in Newfoundland.

The existence of a conductive, or ionised, layer was proved by Sir Edward Appleton in 1924 using the Bournemouth transmitter of the BBC. Radio pulses were transmitted vertically and by measuring the delay of the received pulses a layer, 60 miles high, was detected. By 1925, after many more experiments, it was found that the structure of this ionised layer was not as simple as might have been supposed. There were several ionised layers, which showed daily and seasonal variations and interacted differently at different frequencies.

This information would have been available at the time Uda was performing his experiments with antennas. It may have been the reason why he used a 'wave canal', described in [4], as follows: "A canal was arranged parallel to the surface of the earth in the first case and along the line inclined 30 deg to the horizontal in the second case... Thus, by the use of wave canals, high angle radiation may be propagated at various angles to the surface of the earth. This may find some practical application in long distance work".

In October 1928 the first documented amateur use of a parasitic beam appeared in *QST* [6]. It described the work of Mr E C Crossett, 1CCZ [note 1], who built a beam antenna for 28MHz [note 2] and operated from his summer home at Cape Cod. It was undertaken under the auspices of the ARRL Technical Development Program to explore the possibilities of long distance communication using the reflected signals from the ionosphere.

The antenna was built primarily to permit variable high angle radiation in somewhat the same manner as that described by Meissner in 1927 [6]. Because the presence of the ionosphere was detected using a vertically projected signal it was assumed, at the time, that communications using the ionosphere would require the signal to be projected at a high angle.

Meissner conducted experimental transmissions on 27.27MHz from Nauen in Germany to Buenos Aires. He used a beam antenna, which was

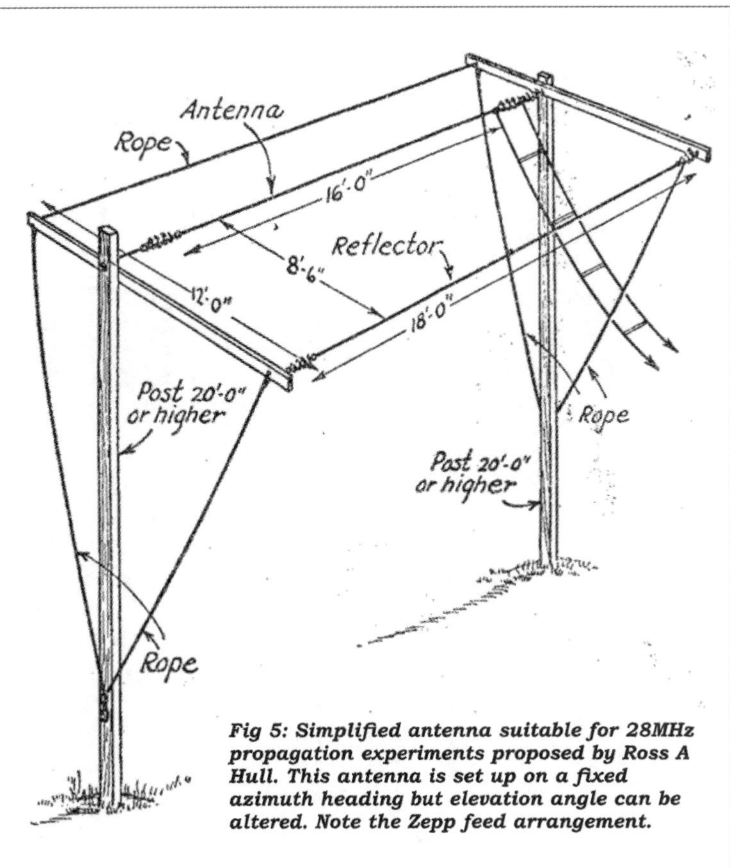


*Fig 5: Simplified antenna suitable for 28MHz propagation experiments proposed by Ross A Hull. This antenna is set up on a fixed azimuth heading but elevation angle can be altered. Note the Zepp feed arrangement.*

aligned on a fixed azimuth great circle path to Buenos Aires, although the elevation angle was adjustable. He noted, "Contrary to computations and theories, the 27,270kc [kHz] frequency was found to be highly effective in daylight between these two points providing the angle of the beam was adjusted to approximately 38 degrees or 80 degrees from the horizontal. With a simple vertical antenna in place of the beam, signals were rarely heard and then only at very low signal strength".

The experiments undertaken by 1CCZ were more ambitious. The objective was "...to endeavour to find the beam angle which would permit satisfactory contact with Australia – a distance over which one might expect 28,000kc to exhibit some of its useful characteristics". The antenna system, located at 1CCZ's QTH in Cape Cod, was arranged at a fixed azimuth angle 14 degrees north of west, on the great circle path to eastern Australia. The antenna could be tilted in the vertical plane by means of ropes. The antenna system consisted of a Yagi with a driven element, three reflector wires and two director wires, and described as: "...arranged in the manner suggested by Uda and Yagi [4]. The placing and dimensions of these wires is shown in **Fig 3**. The system is seen to be both complex and cumbersome and not particularly suited for the average amateur. The idea, however, was not to attempt to build a truly practical antenna for general amateur work on 28,000kc, but to put up a system strictly in accordance with the present understanding of the requirements. In this way, it was hoped, the work of developing a practical antenna would be, to some extent, facilitated".

The complexity of the structure can be seen in **Fig 4**. The method of feeding this antenna is neither illustrated nor described.

During the month of September the transmitter was operated on schedule with listeners in Australia but during the first two transmissions no reports from Australia were received. The signals, however, were reported R6 by 7ACS at Tacoma, Washington, on the West Coast of the USA.

A report of experimental work done by amateurs in the 28MHz band appeared in January 1929, written by Ross A Hull [8], the Associate Technical Editor of *QST*, who was also in charge of the ARRL Technical Development Program. It outlined the USA coast to coast and transatlantic contacts that had been made to that date, plus other results from other parts of the world. The antenna and equipment used by 1CCZ, by now W1CCZ [see note 3], was made available for a week of experimental work by other members of the ARRL Technical Development Program. Hull describes the antenna experiments: "Experiments, with different beam angles and with the director and some or all of the reflectors removed, was made, extending over almost the entire hours when communication was possible. Code letters were sent to designate the different settings of the beam and in this way W6UF selected the most effective setting without knowledge of the angle. Many splendid checks were obtained of the improved signal intensity and greatly reduced fading at beam angles within a few degrees of 30 degrees. In contrast to Meissner's results no particularly effective angles above this were evidenced. The removal of the director made it clear that it was of very slight benefit. Also, experimental removal of the side reflectors made it appear that they were not of appreciable importance. The rear reflector, it seemed, was performing most of the work by itself. When it also was removed, leaving the antenna system as a simple horizontal fundamental Hertz approximately one wavelength above ground, the signal strength immediately dropped from the normal R5–R9 to R4–R5 and fading became pronounced.

"The experiences with the W1CCZ beam antenna have made it evident that any such system can be made much simpler than was first thought. In its most practical form the system would consist of a half-wave antenna mounted centrally between two reflector wires one wavelength apart. A quarter wave behind the antenna the third reflector would be mounted, the four wires being supported in some wooden structure which would permit the angle to be var-

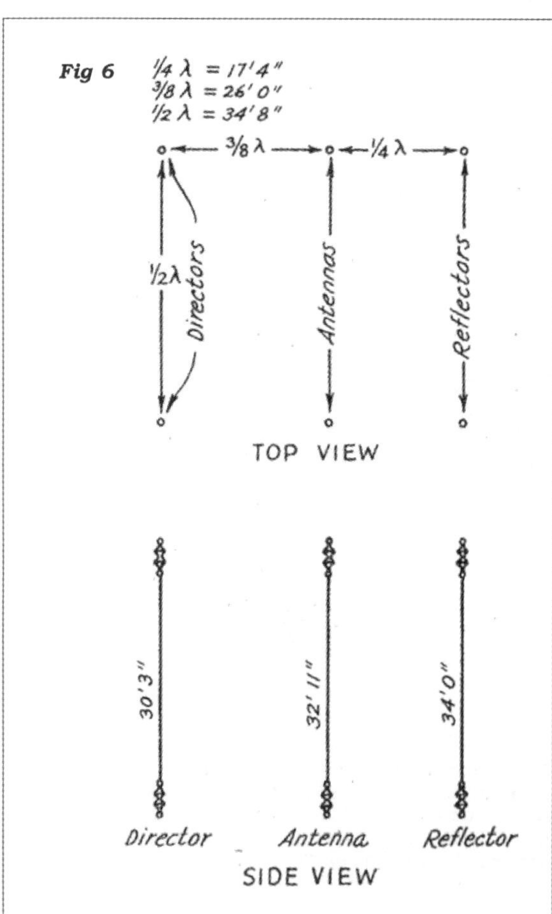


**Fig 6: Dimensions of element lengths and spacings for 14.2MHz.**

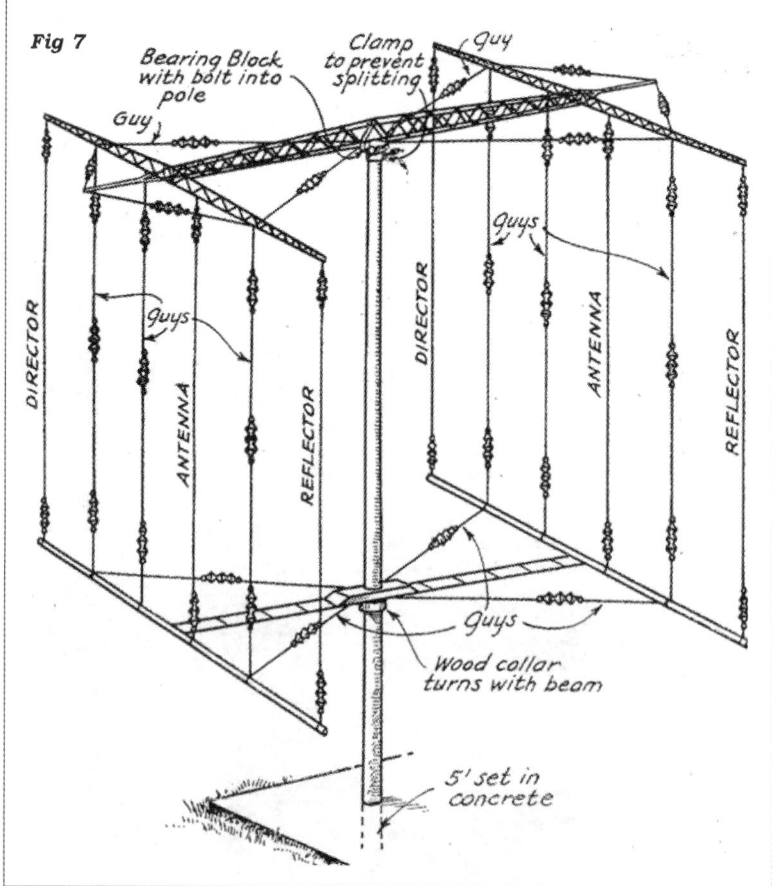


**Fig 7: Three dimensional view of the W3CIJ antenna. It is rotated by ropes fixed to the top main girder.**

ied. The exact form of the supporting frame is not of particular importance and the amateur can be depended upon to design some assembly which is most suited to his facilities. Another highly satisfactory and still simpler system would consist of a horizontal half-wave antenna with a single reflector wire behind it. The reflector could be tied into place with ropes and made adjustable in the manner shown in **Fig 5**."

The simplified 28MHz antenna shown in Fig 5 is the first time that details were given of how the driven element was fed. This 'Zepp' feed arrangement was very popular with radio amateurs at the time and was used in larger antenna systems, to be described later.

## THE W3CIJ 6-ELEMENT 14MHZ ROTARY BEAM

One of the earliest designs of an amateur DX beam was built by John P Shanklin, W3CIJ, and described in *QST* in July 1934 [9]. This antenna comprised two three-element vertical Yagis fed in phase. This is an excellent article and describes the antenna in detail. The dimensional arrangement of these elements is shown in **Fig 6**. The spacing between the elements are shown in fractions of a wavelength and in actual dimensions for a frequency of 14.2MHz. The complete beam assembly is shown in **Fig 7**.

W3CIJ describes the construction of the support structure in detail. The individual components are shown in **Fig 8**: "A good husky wooden pole of about 50-foot height carries the whole load. This is set in concrete, to ensure its remaining rigidly vertical. Pine flooring and plaster lath are the materials from which the main girder and end supports are made, the cost of the wood being about $115 and the whole works weighing only about 300 pounds. The tongue and groove were removed from the 1-inch by 3-inch pieces of flooring to make the 3-inch pieces, and those serving as the 1-inch by 2-inch pieces were cut down further to the latter dimension.

"With the bearing block on top and the collar at the bottom properly fitted, the beam is readily turned in any direction in a few minutes by means of a couple of rope stays. Once set at the desired position the ropes are pegged down to keep the beam from turning with the wind. To keep the feeders from becoming tangled up when the beam is turned, the line from the shack is anchored to the pole below the lower bearing point and flexible jumpers of sufficient length are connected between the line terminals and the quarter-wave coupling section of the beam. A pulley and weight arrangement keeps the line running to the shack taut under varying conditions of weather and temperature".

The Zepp method of feeding the driven elements is shown in **Fig 9.** Transposition of the feed line half way between the two radiators is necessary to excite the two antennas in phase. The feeders are extended a quarter-wave from one of the antennas; this quarter-wave section being shorted at its outer end to allow the antenna to be matched to the 520Ω feed line.

W3CIJ also describes a method of measuring the antenna's performance shown in **Fig 10**: "The intensity meter used in getting the experimental curve consisted of a Type 33 tube used as a diode rectifier, with both grids and the plate tied together, a 0 - 1 milliammeter connected in the output circuit giving the indications. Before taking the measurements it was calibrated on 60-cycle AC. In taking the measurements the intensity meter was set up 10 wavelengths from the beam and the beam was then revolved through 180 degrees, measurements being taken at a sufficient number of settings. The dotted portion of curve 'B' is approximate, the reading being too small in this region to be determined accurately.

"Theoretically the beam should boost the signal approximately 6dB over a non-directional antenna or, in other words, should give a power increase of four times, which means that the 50 watts here is effectively made equal to some several hundred watts with a non-directional antenna."

## THE ZS1H 4-ELEMENT 14MHZ ROTARY BEAM

The antenna shown in **Fig 11** was constructed by ZS1H and a brief description of it appeared in the *T&R Bulletin* [10]. The antenna comprises two half-wave vertical driven elements, spaced a half-wavelength apart and fed in phase with 500Ω feeder (presumably using the Zepp end-fed arrangement). The two reflectors are half-waves, spaced a half-wavelength from the driven elements. The design appears to be a simplification of the W6CIJ beam.

The antenna support and mast were constructed of wood. The lattice mast was 54ft high and the top structure was 36ft long and 18ft wide and the whole support structure rotated on roller bearings. The antenna and construction is obviously influenced by earlier articles in *QST*.

## THE G6CJ REVERSIBLE DIRECTION BEAM

By the early 1930s the Radio Society of Great Britain had a 'Research and Experimental Section' to the *T&R Bulletin*. Various individuals had specialised subjects and 'Aerial Design' was written by F ('Dud') Charman, G6CJ. In December 1935, G6CJ [11] described what appears to be a two-element reversible beam set up on a fixed (unquoted) azimuth angle. His edited description is as follows: "Some experiments recently carried out with a reflector system have shown that a considerable improvement in long-distance performance can be obtained fairly cheaply. Consider for a moment a horizontal half-wave aerial. This normally radiates in a broad direction at right angles to the wire with an angle to the horizon, which is determined by its height.

"...Now suppose that behind our horizontal dipole we can place a wire,

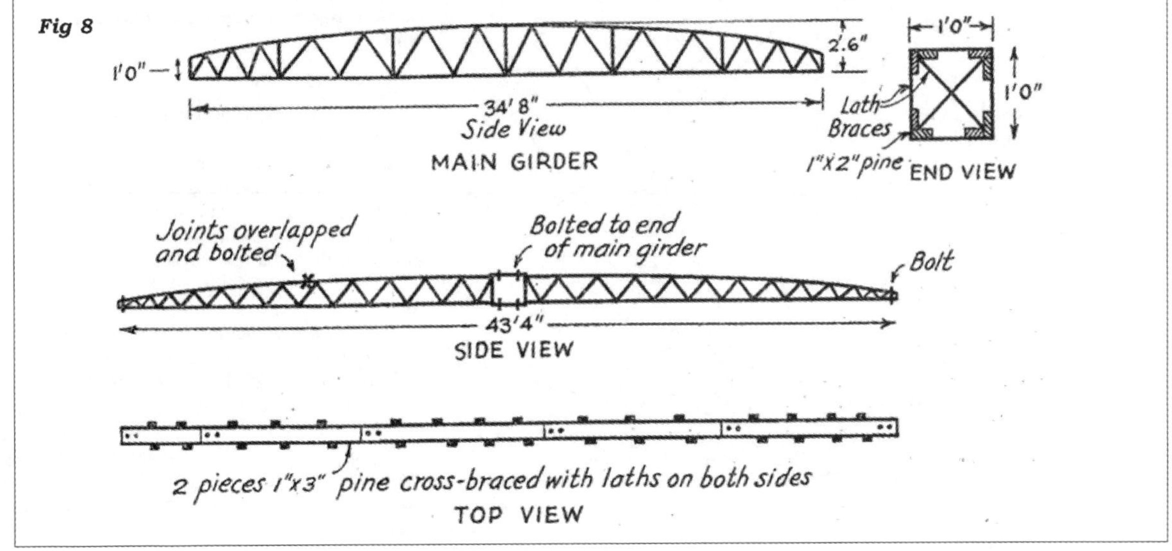


**Fig 8: Construction details of the support structure of the W3CIJ antenna.**

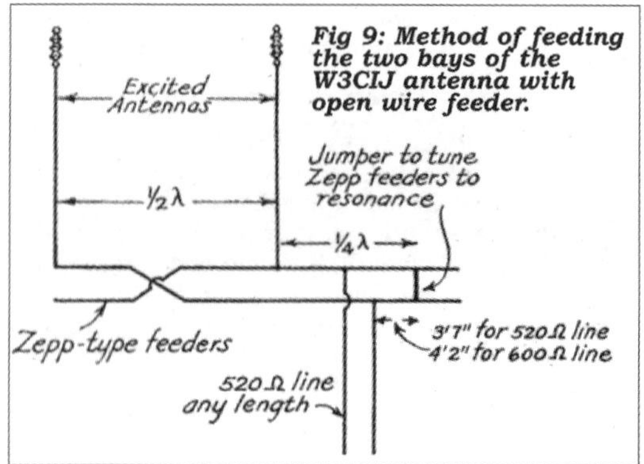


**Fig 9: Method of feeding the two bays of the W3CIJ antenna with open wire feeder.**

which is in resonance. At a quarter-wave spacing it will be seen, allowing a phase reversal for reflection, that the wave reflected back towards the dipole will be in phase with the next radiated cycle and will add in this direction; also in the opposite direction the two waves, the direct and the re-radiated, will be in opposition and tend to cancel. The system has become more directive and will, in addition to sending twice as much energy one way, also give lower angle propagation.

"The extra signal strength to be expected from doubled power is only 1.4, and is hardly perceptible, but the lower angle will allow of a long journey with less reflections between earth and F layer, and this will result in a reduction of attenuation which may be worth a hundredfold increase in power, and probably also a reduction in fading.

"...The experimental reflector was first tried on 14mc [MHz]. Theory showed that as there was a reactive coupling as well as resistive, the reflector might have to be longer than the usual 33ft, and 35ft was found to give best results. The radiation resistance of the radiator was increased somewhat by its presence, which means bringing the feeder tap or taps nearer the centre. The system was first faced west. Results were frankly astonishing. Signals in W6 rose from one to two points, and instead of getting through occasionally, stations were worked every time, and G6CJ became one of the best European signals over there. In Australia in the mornings signals went up two points and lasted out longer than any others.

"This was very encouraging, and the next thing was to make it easy to reverse direction. This was done by shortening the free wire to 31ft. This has the effect of trying to advance the phase of the re-radiated wave and so 'leading' the wave that way. Results were as before.

"...Turning to the practical side, the systems have so far been supported from one pair of poles by using 16ft spreaders. It is necessary to find the correct suspension point to allow for the weight of the feeders on one side, and the corners can be held back by cords to give stability. One and a quarter inch square pine will hold up a pair of 33ft wires, but it should be suspended from the middle as well as the ends in a sort of triangle. If full height is desired, 2 in x 1in may be used without the end triangle, but a rather stout halyard is necessary.

"A word of warning must be given regarding field strength measurements made with directive systems. In the horizontal system field strength measurements made locally mean practically nothing. The reflections from the ground at angles widely different from the direct ray completely spoil any attempts to find the directive properties of the system. If it is desired to carry out tests of this nature to determine the correct adjustment of the free wire, then the whole system must be made vertical and free from local reflecting objects. For convenience the design may be carried out on a scale model on 28 or 56mc, but the wire diameter should also be scaled down.

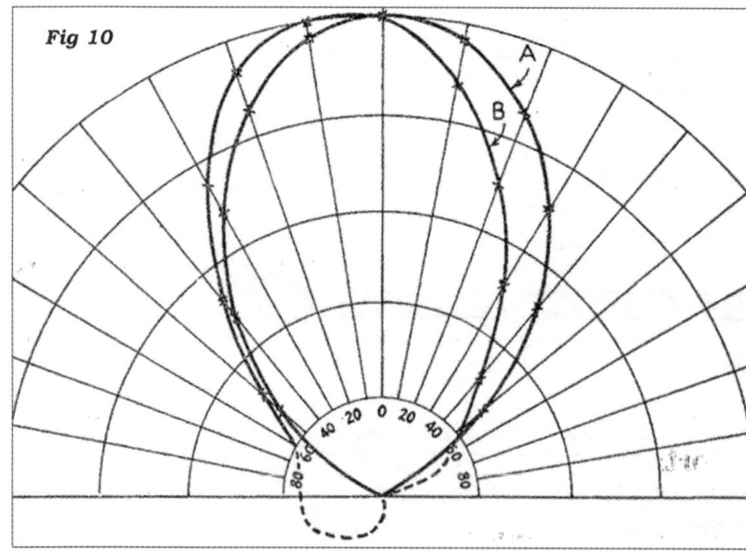


"...The writer wishes to register thanks to his fellow experimenter, 2ASP, for his enthusiastic assistance in connection with this experimental work".

There are no illustrations and the method of feeding is unclear. Furthermore there are no references so it has not been possible to ascertain if this was the first time a parasitic array had been used in the UK. The construction appears to be similar to that shown in Fig 5.

**Fig 11: The ZS1H 14MHz four-element beam. A method for supporting the bottom ends of the vertical elements is not visible so it was probably done with ropes.**

## REFERENCES

[1] 'Pioneers', W A Atherton, *Electronics and Wireless World*, January 1989.
[2] 'Yagi: The Man and his Antenna', Robert H Welsh, N3RW, *QST*, October 1993.
[3] 'On the Wireless Beam of Short Electric Waves', S Uda. A series of 11 papers published by *Journal of the IEE (Japan)* from March 1926 until July 1929.
[4] 'Beam Transmission of Ultra Short Waves', Prof Hidetsugu Yagi, *Proc: IRE* Vol 16, No: 6, June 1926.
[5] *Short Wave Radio and the Ionosphere*, T W Bennington.
[6] 'High Angle Radiation', Paul S Hendricks, 1CCZ, *QST*, October 1928.
[7] 'Directional Radiation with Horizontal Antennas', A Meissner, *Proc: IRE*, November, 1927.
[8] 'The Status of 28,000-kc Communication', Ross A Hull, *QST*, January 1929.
[9] 'A 14-Mc Rotary Beam Antenna for Transmitting and Receiving', John P Shanklin, W3CIJ, *QST*, July 1934.
[10] 'A 14-Mc Beam Aerial'. G A Shoyer, ZS6H, *The T & R Bulletin*, June 1935.
[11] 'Reflectors and Directors', F Charman G6CJ, *The T & R Bulletin*, December 1935.

***In the concluding part next month, Peter Dodd looks at such interesting designs as the W5BDB 'Signal Squirter', GM6RG's massive 28MHz beam from the late 1930s, and the modern, all-metal, beam similar to those used today.***

## NOTES

[Note 1] Although prefixes had been assigned to countries, amateur stations did not originally qualify for international callsigns. The USA was divided into nine call areas and amateurs were granted calls consisting of the call area number, followed by two or three letters, such as 1CCZ or 6MN. W and K prefixes started to be assigned to USA amateurs on 1 October 1928. [From http://www.ac6v.com/history.htm]

[Note 2] The 28MHz band become available to radio amateurs in March 1928.

[Note 3] The 28MHz experiments performed by 1CCZ ceased when he moved to his Chicago home in September. ◆

***Fig. 10: (A) Calculated horizontal field pattern. (B) Measured field pattern.***

# Evolution of the Beam Antenna

## PART 2 Peter Dodd, G3LDO, concludes his investigation into the development of the beam antenna, starting with the W5BDB 14MHz 'Signal Squirter' design of 1935.

W5BDB described details of his compact directional antenna in QST [12]. This antenna was, like G6CJ's design described in Part 1 last month, also a two-element 14MHz antenna that could be rotated, using a mechanical arrangement, from the shack. It was a lightweight design with a mixture of wood and aluminium tube used in the construction. The article is a clear unambiguous construction description with good diagrams, one of which is shown in Fig 12. It appears to be the first rotatable beam antenna design that could be reproduced by any radio amateur with the space to erect an antenna with a spread of 35 x 18ft.

W5BDB describes the construction: "The material used in the antenna in the final version is aluminium alloy tube 7/8in in diameter. Each side of the antenna consists of a 14ft section of this material with a 3 1/2ft section of a smaller tube that just telescopes inside the larger, providing the means of varying antenna length to the desired transmitting frequency. A small clamp is provided which allows a set screw to extend through a hole in the outer tubing, thus placing pressure against the inner tube and giving good contact between the two sections. The antenna is fed with EO1 transmission cable because of its extreme flexibility and ease with which it may be coupled to any final amplifier."

The reflector was mounted in a manner that space variations between the antenna and reflector might be made by moving the insulators supporting the reflector closer to or further away from the antenna. It was expected that the reflector would be further back from the centre than the antenna, which was desirable to provide a balance of weight since the antenna has the EO1 cable to support over a short distance. The reflector is of the same material as the antenna. W5BDB then describes how the performance was measured. It was the first time standing waves on a transmission line is mentioned: "Finally, after using the Signal Squirter on the air for some little time and becoming thoroughly convinced that the thing really did do the work, we went to work with the field-strength measuring equipment and started making final adjustments. There were several factors to be taken into consideration in doing this. First, the spacing between the two halves of the antenna; next, the exact length of the antenna; then, the spacing between the antenna and reflector; and finally, the length of the reflector.

". . . Element length change was easily made by sliding each end section of the antenna into or out of the larger section of tubing, the final adjustment being fastened firmly in place. A very critical point was the proper spacing between the two halves of the antenna itself, this adjustment being quite necessary to give the best match to the EO1 cable. This adjustment brought considerable improvement and eliminated a tendency for standing waves to appear on the feeder system. Final adjustment finally settled down at about 22in separation between the adjacent ends of the two halves of the antenna.

"Next came the location of the reflector back from the antenna. This spacing had been set arbitrarily at 17ft so that the reflector might be moved back further or up closer. The checks with the field-strength meter indicated very definitely that the spacing between the elements was important but not so critical as the actual length of the antenna and reflector. It was also found that the spacing between the two elements could be varied over a couple or three inches with little or no effect.

"After having found that the reflector seemed to do its best job when at about 16ft 10in instead of the usually recommended spacing of 17ft 4in, we started pruning the reflector length as the final step in adjustment. . . The final selection was 33ft 10.5in for our frequency of 14,215kc. The adjustments of reflector length were found to be quite effective and produced a noticeable difference as each change was made. In fact, it seemed at this stage of the game that the length of the reflector was fully as important as the antenna length, and that both of these were more important than the actual adjustment of space between the two elements in so far as critical and close adjustments were concerned".

### G5PP 56MHz TWO-ELEMENT BEAM

Surprisingly, this is the first reference I can find of a parasitic antenna used for VHF, considering that the Yagi was designed for VHF in the first place. This two-element beam for 56MHz by G5PP [13] used a driven element and a reflector fixed to a wooden frame, which rotated within an outer supporting frame as shown in Fig 13. The elements were made

***Fig 12: The W5BDB 14MHz two-element 'Signal Squirter'. This lightweight design uses a mixture of wood and aluminium tube in the construction. Note that the driven element is fed in the centre rather that the Zepp method in previous designs.***

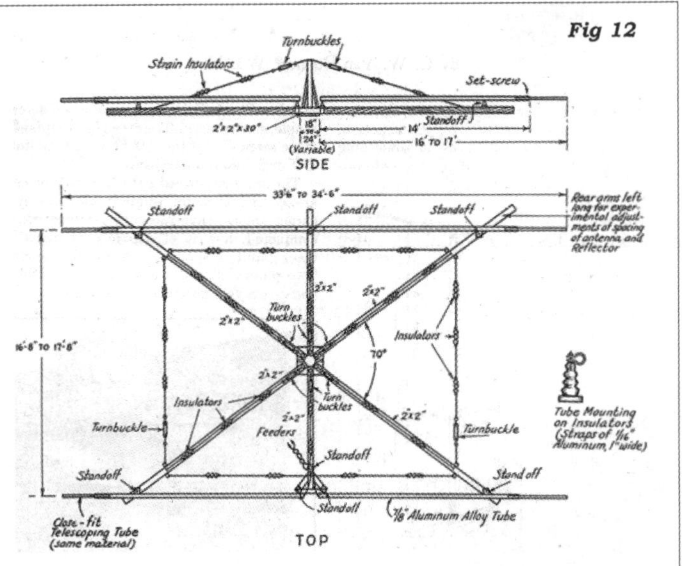

*Fig 14. The W8CPC two-element 14MHz 'signal squirter'. (a) Antenna configuration showing the bent elements. (b) Construction details showing method of using supported thin copper elements and method of tuning.*

from 5/16in (8mm) copper tubing, which were fixed to the inner frame with 'midget stand-off insulators'.

The driven element was fed using a Zepp type feed. However, G5PP notes: ". . . but the single or double wire matched impedance type antennas can be used equally successfully, particularly as the feeder lines of the matched impedance aerial gives less trouble than the Zepp type during rotation." I am not sure what this alternative feed method is but I assume it is a centre fed arrangement. The antenna was rotated from the shack by a cord and pulley arrangement.

## W1QP / W8CPC COMPACT BEAM

This compact version of a two-element beam was first suggested by John Reinartz, W1QP, and looks as though it was inspired by the W5BDB 14MHz as shown in Fig 12, where the strengthening wire could perhaps be the antenna element. A model was constructed for 14MHz by Burton Simson, W8CPC, and described in QST, October 1937[14].

This configuration is the same as the later VK2ABQ wire beam antenna and predates it by many years. A wooden frame was used to support the elements, which allows the element ends to be folded towards each other. The configuration and construction is shown in Fig 14. The elements were constructed from 1/4in copper tubing with brass tuning rods that fitted snugly into the ends of the elements. An additional brass rod was used as a shorting bar for the centre of the reflector.

The tuning procedure was interesting. The only test equipment available appeared to be an RF meter (0 - 5 amps), the transmitter PA current meter and the receiver S-meter. An RF meter was connected by short leads to the gap in the reflector and the driven element connected to the link coil of the transmitter by low-impedance twin transmission line. The brass rods at the ends of the driven element were adjusted for maximum transmitter PA current. The rods at the tips of the reflector were then adjusted for maximum RF current. These adjustments were interactive and would have had to be repeated. When the adjustments were complete the RF meter was removed and the gap closed with the brass rod. This tune-up procedure tunes the reflector to transmitter frequency.

*Fig 13: The two element beam for 56MHz by G5PP used a driven element and a reflector fixed to a wooden frame, fixed inside a support frame.*

## A 14MHz CLOSE-SPACED ARRAY

By 1938 parasitic antenna designs were becoming more practical and efficient. A description of a two-element beam in the RSGB Handbook [15] is an example. It consists of a radiator and director spaced one-tenth wave with the radiator fed in the centre by means of a double Q matching section and an untuned line. The input Q consists of 72 ohm cable whilst the lower Q has a pair of No 14 SWG wires spaced 1.5in. The Zepp type of feeding is now regarded as not very satisfactory for these frequencies, as it is difficult to balance, and feeder radiation may be considerable.

The antenna is designed for 14.1MHz. The driven element is cut to 16ft 7in either side of the centre and the director slightly shorter, approximately 16ft 3in on either side with a small tuning stub in the centre. An inch gap is left between the two sections of the radiator (driven element).

Several construction methods are described for the centre arm of the rotating framework. The antenna elements are insulated from the wooden framework with ribbed type insulators with brass inserts.

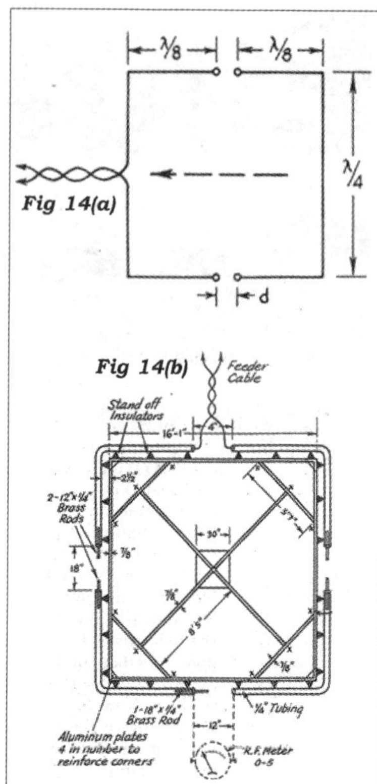


## A 28MHz ROTARY BEAM

For some years GM6RG had operated DX using wire beams. He wanted a rotatable beam and embarked on an ambitious project [16] to meet the following specifications: "The problem was to design an aerial having a gain of over 12dB which would give an angle of radiation not higher than 16 degrees. It had to be rotatable to cover all the world; further, remote operation was required with means provided to indicate at the remote controlling position the exact direction in which it was aiming. Finally it had to be strong enough to stand any gale up to 80mph, and yet be as light as reasonably possible".

GM6RG calculated that he would need two vertical phased parasitic antennas, each comprising a driven element, reflector and three directors to meet the above specification. A fairly large structure would be required to support these wire antennas and lattice beams. The construction method he chose was the same as used by W3CIJ, described earlier.

The large H centre of the top support structure was massive, with the centre section of the H being 45ft long and a local building contractor was employed to build it. He specified that the main supporting beam would have to be able to stand a steady weight of one ton!

The whole rotating aerial was supported on a Post Office pole, 50ft long and about 16in thick. This is set into the ground for about 8ft and is also stayed at a height of 20ft. The antenna is shown in Fig 15. The antenna had a couple of modern features. For a start the whole antenna was rotated using an electric motor and gearbox that weighed 360lb! It also had an azimuth position indicator described: "On top of the gearbox, but insulated from it, is a 16-contact commutator, with 15 of the contacts in use. Fixed to the drive shaft is a wiper, wide enough to touch two contacts at a time. A 16-core lead-covered cable runs from this point down to the controlling position, and is there suitably connected to 15 lamps, so arranged that as the beam is rotated the correct lamp is brought into circuit. The lamps are arranged to illuminate that part of a great-circle map at which the beam is aiming".

This large antenna did not live up to its expectations. GM6RG says, ". . . although the original design had been adopted with the intention of obtaining a very narrow angle of radiation, this condition had not quite been met. Results were very good, but

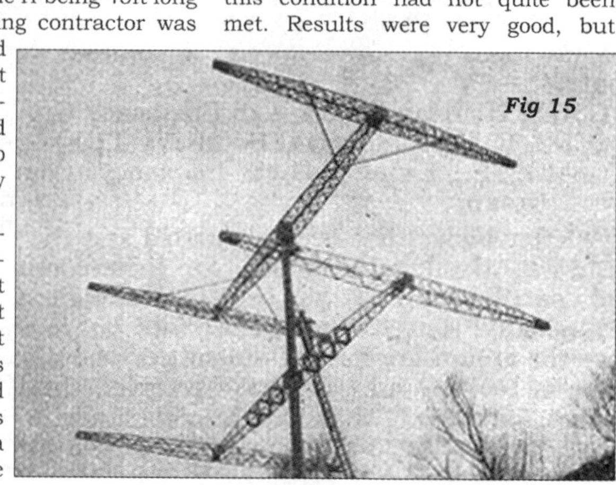


*Fig 15: The GM6RG twin vertical phased parasitic antennas, each comprising a driven element, reflector and three directors. Some idea of the size of the structure can be seen compared with the figure at the top of the ladder.*

since one of the (requirements was) to investigate the effect on fading of a restricted vertical coverage, such tests were not possible. Added to this, there was a severe storm in Galashiels, and although the rotary [beam] was not damaged, it offered such a large surface area to the gale that it was tossed about in the most violent manner. As a consequence it was decided forthwith to make alterations".

The new design [17] used the original heavy top central lattice structure as a boom to support a nine-element parasitic array using self-supporting tubular elements instead of wire elements, see Fig 16. It comprised one driven element, six directors, and two reflectors, all at a height above ground of 48ft. GM6RG describes it: "The lengths of the various elements for a working frequency of 28,460kc are as follows. Directors, 15ft 4in; driven element 16ft 6in; nearer reflector 17ft; further reflector 17ft 1in. The spacing is 3ft 6in between all directors and between the driven element and the first director, 7ft between driven element and nearer reflector, and 5ft between the near and more distant reflectors. The feed to the aerial is made by open 470 ohm line, and Y match, with a rather complicated system of wooden arms and insulators, which do, however, keep the line absolutely matched in whatever position the beam may be. It has been found much more satisfactory with very high-Q arrays, such as this one, to feed with a Y match and open line rather than by the more usual method of breaking the centre of the aerial. With the latter method it is impossible to keep the feed system clear of standing waves during tuning. . ."

I checked this antenna using EZNEC3 and found it had over 10dBi gain, which must have been very impressive for those days. It is difficult to know why GM6RG chose to use two reflectors - the second reflector contributes no improvement. If he had used one reflector and the director spacings (without changing his director lengths or numbers) closer to that recommended by Yagi [4] and 1CCZ [6] he could have increased the gain to over 13dBi with the long boom that he had at his disposal.

***Fig 16: The new GM6RG design used the original heavy top central lattice structure as a boom to support a nine element parasitic array using self-supporting tubular elements instead of wire elements.***

## THE MODERN ALL-METAL BEAM

I spent some time trying to find the first instance of the all-metal construction that characterises the modern form of the parasitic beam antenna and was surprised at how late it made its appearance. The first instance of all metal constructed beams appears in the ARRL Handbook of 1947 [18]. The 'Antenna Systems' chapter has descriptions of parasitic beam support systems all constructed from wood, with stand-off insulators to hold the metal antenna elements in place. One design even uses a ladder for a parasitic antenna boom.

However, buried in a page of suggested antenna construction methods is the example shown in Fig 17. There is no description of it in the text but the caption reads "Pipe assembly three-element beam, 'Plumber's Delight' [note 4] with a folded-dipole driven element. Because all three elements are at the same RF potential at their centres it is possible to join them electrically as well as mechanically with no effect on the performance".

In the 'VHF Antennas' chapter of the same publication [18] there is a description of collapsible 50MHz two-element beam for portable use, which also uses this 'Plumber's Delight' construction and is illustrated in Fig 18. It comprises a radiator, which is fed with coaxial line by means of a T-match, and a reflector, which is spaced 0.15-wavelength behind the driven element. It is made entirely of 3/4in dural tubing, except for the vertical support, which is 1in tubing of the same material.

The fed section of the T-matching device is composed of two pieces of 3/4in dural tubing about 14in long. The two sections are held together mechanically, but insulated electrically by a piece of polystyrene rod, which is turned down just enough to make a tight fit in the tubing. The inner and outer conductors of the coaxial line are fastened to the two inside ends of the matching section. The positions of clips, which connect the T-match sections to the driven element, are adjusted for minimum standing wave ratio on the feeder. The idea for this antenna was suggested by W7OWX [19].

The W6SAI Beam Antenna Book [20], [1955], was one of the most comprehensive books on parasitic beam antenna construction and design ever published. I have an old well-thumbed copy, given to me by the late Eric Knowles, G2XK, who used it to design a six-element 10m Yagi on a 37ft long boom. This book helped me with many beam antenna construction projects and probably helped fashion the commercial and home-made designs of Yagi antenna that prevail today.

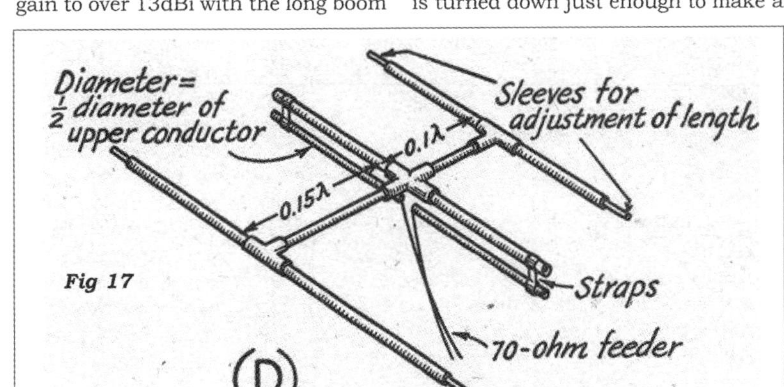


***Fig 17: Pipe assembly three-element beam ('Plumber's Delight') with a folded-dipole driven element. The construction implies that it possibly came from the television industry.***

## ACKNOWLEDGMENTS

I wish to thank John Crabbe, G3WFM, curator of the RSGB Museum and Library, for all the effort he put into searches for relevant articles, papers and books; to Laurie Mayhead, G3AQC, for the Yagi IEE paper [4] and to Robert H Welsh, N3RW, for information via e-mail.

## NOTES

[Note 4] 'Plumber's Delight' is a generally-accepted name for all-metal construction parasitic beams, where the antenna elements are fixed to a metal boom without insulators.

## REFERENCES

[12] 'The All-Around 14-Mc Signal Squirter'. M P Mimms, W5BDB, QST, December 1935.

[13] 'A 56 Mc Rotating Beam Antenna', R Palmer, G5PP, The T & R Bulletin, December 1936.

[14] 'Concentrated Directional Antennas for Transmission and

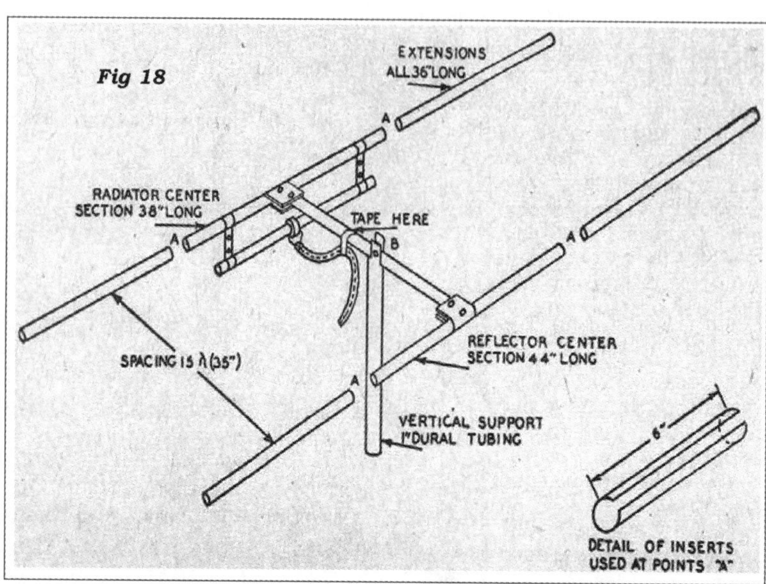


***Fig. 18: Detail drawing of the collapsible 50MHz beam. For carrying purposes, it is taken apart at Points A and B, inserts of slotted dural tubing being used at Point A to hold the sections together. All extensions are the same length, the difference in element length being provided by the length of the centre sections.***

Reception', John Reinartz, W1QP, and Burton Simson, W8CPC, QST October 1937.

[15] The Radio Amateur Handbook, RSGB, 1938.

[16] 'A 28 Mc Rotary Beam', Bryan Groom, GM6RG, The T & R Bulletin, June 1938.

[17] 'Rotatable Array Design', Bryan Groom, GM6RG, The T & R Bulletin, December 1938.

[18] The Radio Amateur's Handbook, 1947 edition, ARRL.

[19] 'Hints and Kinks', W7OWX, QST, April 1946, page 148.

[20] The Beam Antenna Handbook, William I Orr, W6SAI, and Stuart D Cowan, W2LX (1955). This book is now in its sixth reprint.

*The drawings and photographs in both parts of this article are reproduced from the original publications dating from the 1920s to 1940s.* ◆

# Vine Antennas LFA Yagis

## Does this new loop feed give better performance?

PHOTO 1: The assembled 6m antenna 6M4LFA, plus cat for scale. The antenna is shown upside down; all the elements are fixed below the boom instead of the more conventional above the boom.

TWO TO TRY. This review covers two antennas, a 6m 4-element Yagi and a 2m 9-element Yagi. The reason that the two antennas are reviewed together is that they both use an unusual loop driven element.

These antennas, designed by Justin Johnson, G0KSC [1], are described as Loop Fed Array Yagis and are made and distributed by Vine Antennas [2]. The assembled 6m antenna (6M4LFA) and 2m antenna (2M9LFA) are shown in **Photo 1** and **Photo 2** respectively.

CONSTRUCTION. The most obvious constructional characteristic of these antennas is the use of square section tubular booms. The antennas were easy to assemble and the instructions were clear and easy to follow.

The construction of the 6M4LFA is shown in **Photo 3**. The boom is 2.75m (9ft) long and the antenna elements are simply fixed to the boom using square plates and insulators. The loop driven element is also insulated from the mounting plate and fed directly via a coax choke balun. Note that all the elements of this antenna are fixed below the boom rather than the more conventional method of fixing them above the boom.

The most noticeable feature of the antenna is the very close spacing (0.043 wavelengths) of rear section of the driven element loop to the reflector; the characteristics of this arrangement are discussed later.

The construction of the 2M9LFA is shown in **Photo 4**. The boom is 5.2m (17ft) long. The method of fixing the driven element to the boom is slightly different from the 6M4LFA in that the feed point is below the boom the front part is above the boom. The parasitic elements are fixed to the boom using through boom construction and 'top hat' nylon insulators.

SETTING UP. With both antennas the driven elements are assembled using preformed U sections, which fit inside the ends of straight sections of the driven elements and held in place using jubilee clips (hose clamps) as shown in **Photo 5**. I found it helpful to give these clips a coat of oil or grease and ensure that the threads 'run' before assembly. The exact position of the end sections determine the feed impedance of the antenna and hence the SWR.

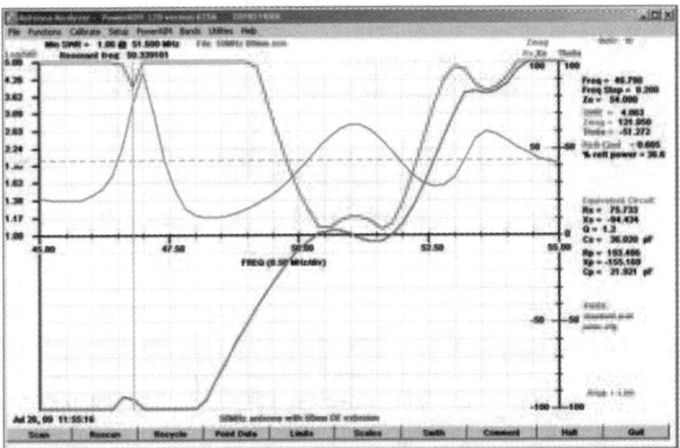

FIGURE 1: The 6M4LFA characteristics measured with the AIM-4170 antenna analyser and a calibrated feeder. It shows a 'band pass' characteristic SWR with a very low SWR (in red). The AIM-4170 has been set to show R±j with R shown in green and ±j shown in blue.

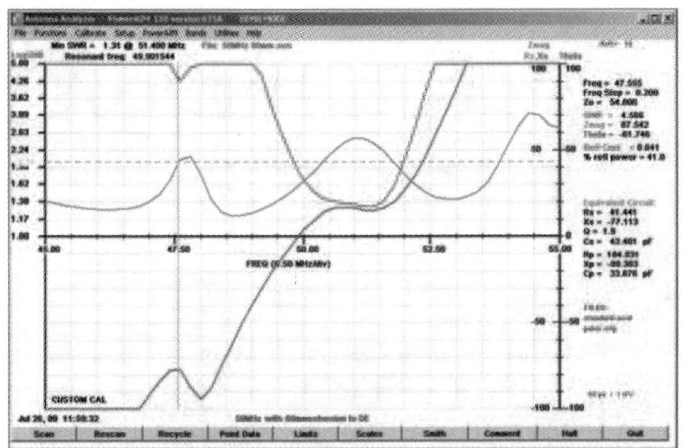

FIGURE 2: Increasing the size of the driven element loop increased the SWR and changed the reflector & director resonant frequencies but did not move the bandpass characteristic.

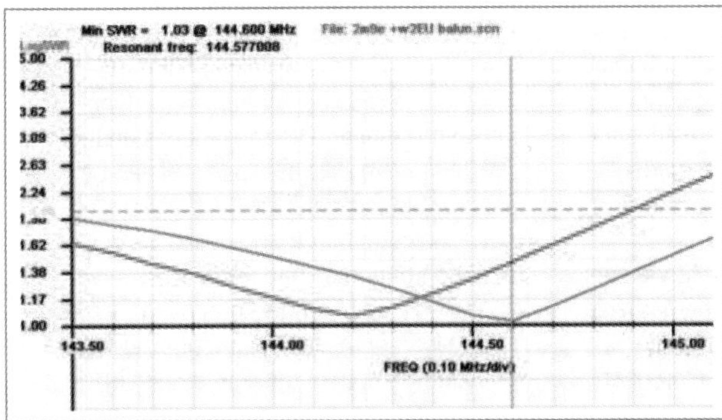


FIGURE 3: The 2M9LFA driven element adjusted for the lowest SWR (red) when using the supplied coax balun. Using a ferrite loaded coax balun caused the SWR characteristic to shift upwards (shown in green).

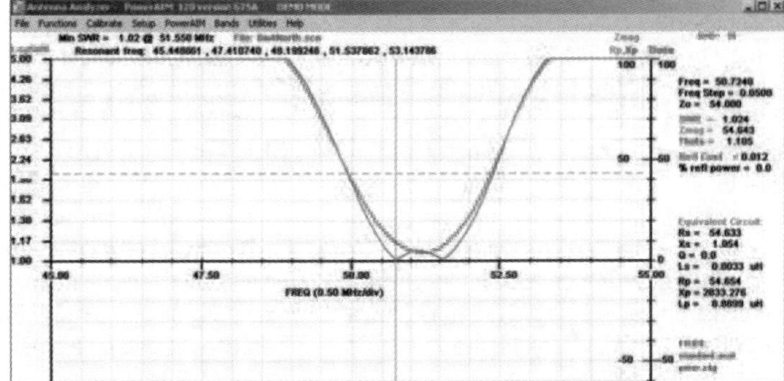

FIGURE 4: SWR normal characteristics of the 6M4LFA when mounted on the roof and beamed north, shown in green. The SWR when the antenna is beamed south is shown in red; the difference is probably due to the nearby TV antenna.

PHOTO 2: The assembled 2m antenna, 2M9LFA.

PHOTO 5: Hose clamps fix the U-shaped movable section inside the ends of the driven elements. The exact position of these end sections determine the feed impedance of the antenna and hence the SWR.

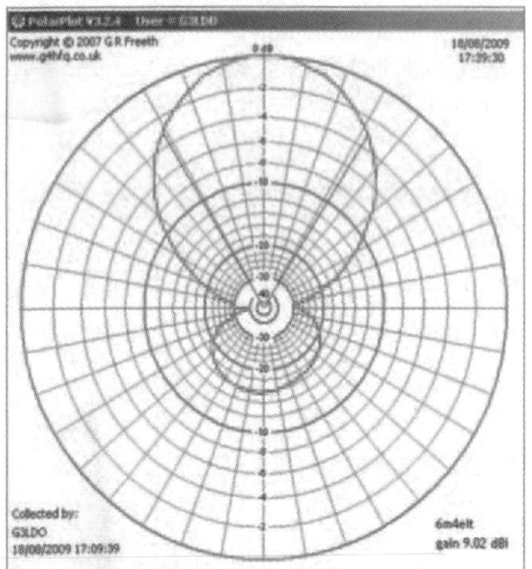

FIGURE 5: Radiation pattern of the 6M4LFA using PolarPlot, giving a calculated gain of just over 9dBi.

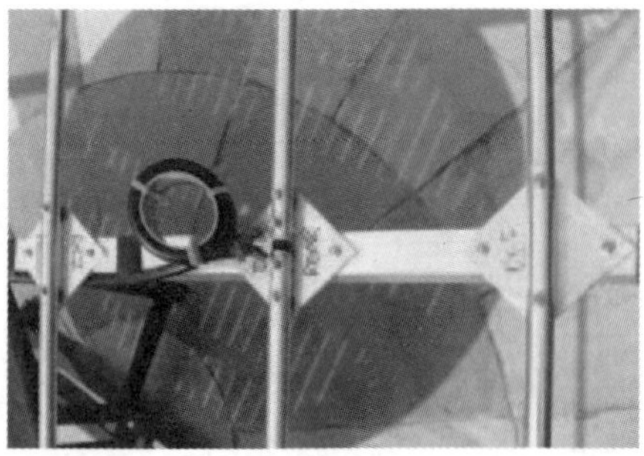

PHOTO 3: The 6M4LFA driven element is fed via a coaxial balun. Note how the elements are fixed to the boom.

PHOTO 6: The 6M4LFA antenna installed on the chimney of my house.

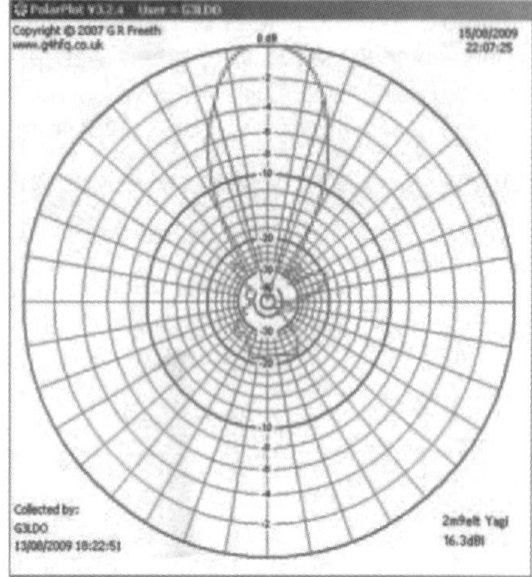

FIGURE 6: Radiation pattern of the 2M9LFA using PolarPlot, showing a gain of just over 16dBi.

PHOTO 4: The 2M9LFA driven element is mounted across the boom. Parasitic elements are fixed through the boom using 'top hat' nylon insulators.

The 6M4LFA exhibited some interesting feed point characteristics. The best position for the end sections turned out to be 60mm. This was measured from the end of the straight section by the hose clamp to the furthest extremity of the end section. As you can see from **Figure 1** the SWR has a band pass characteristic with a very low SWR. Additionally the resonance points of the reflector and the first director can be seen at 46.7MHz and 54.5MHz respectively.

When the end sections were increased to 80mm the SWR increased although the bandpass characteristic did not move down the band as expected, see **Figure 2**. The reflector and director frequencies moved up to 57.55MHz and 56.0MHz respectively.

The 2M9LFA driven element was adjusted for the lowest SWR by altering the length of the driven element loop. The results, plotted in red, are shown in **Figure 3** and show a very low SWR with a good SWR bandwidth characteristic. At a later stage I tried different baluns in an unsuccessful attempt to reduce the minor lobes on the measured radiation pattern. The green graph shows an increase in the frequency of the SWR characteristic when I used a W2DU type ferrite-loaded coax balun. Other baluns caused frequency shift in the SWR characteristic.

On the 2m aerial my AIM-4170 was not able to detect the resonance of the parasitic elements, as in the 6M4LFA, probably because the greater element spacing near to the driven element.

PERFORMANCE. The SWR results shown in Figures 1 and 2 were obtained with the antenna mounted on a pole around 5m high. The 6M4LFA was then installed on the chimney as shown in **Photo 6**. The same results were obtained with the antenna in its new location when the antenna was beamed north as shown Photo 6. At other headings the SWR characteristic changed, probably due to the nearby TV antenna, see **Figure 4**.

IN USE. The antenna was installed on 26 July. I have no previous experience of 6m operating, except for a short spell of transatlantic 10m/6m crossband operation in the 1970s, so I didn't know what to expect. The band was quite lively and within half an hour I had worked 5 countries. In the next few days the propagation switched to the south and my total of countries increased to 11, the best being EA8BLL on CW. I probably just caught the end of the summer season Sporadic-E – I haven't heard much since.

A radiation pattern plot of the 6M4LFA was made using PolarPlot, as described in 'Antennas' this month. This gave a calculated gain of just over 9dBi (see **Figure 5**), very close to that predicted by G0KSC. This and other tests indicated a front to back ratio of around 13dB.

On air tests were not performed on the 2M9LFA, however I did improved my garden antenna range so that the radiation pattern could be checked using PolarPlot. One of the many plots performed is shown in **Figure 6**. This shows a nice clean main lobe with a greater gain than that predicted by G0KSC, although this might be partly due to the ground gain effect.

FINAL COMMENTS. I liked these antennas. The construction is simple and the main lobes of the radiation patterns are clean and symmetrical. The minor lobes on the 2M9LFA were not small as predicted by the G0KSC computer model but were nevertheless better than any real long Yagi radiation patterns I had seen.

I wish to thank Vine Antenna Products for the loan of these two antennas. The retail price for the both of these antennas is the same: £169.

**WEBSEARCH**

[1] www.g0ksc.co.uk
[2] www.vinecom.co.uk

# Notes

1: Feb 2002. Fig 3. In the caption the wires are described as being colour coded for clarity. These wires are also marked B, Y and R for blue, yellow and red respectively, so there is no confusion or ambiguity.

2: Aug 2002. Fig 2. The original is in colour and the polar diagram for each frequency is easy to see. 21.0MHz has the lowest F/B ratio. The greatest F/B ratio occurs at 21.14MHz. There is not much difference in forward gain through this frequency range so adjusting for maximum F/B ratio at a centre frequency appears to be the most practical method of optimising a two-element quad.

3: Oct 2002. Fig 2. The ragged impedance plot is the result of measurements using the VA1 SWR analyser. The perfect circle is ideally what it theoretically should be and the remaining plot was obtained using an HP4085A vector impedance meter.

4: Feb 2003. In this column Peter Cole, G3JFS, offers the sound advice on the best antenna to use in a restricted suburban location.

5: June 2004. Referenced G3LDO web pages as originally published are now mostly invalid. At the time of writing the website is at www.g3ldo.co.uk

6: July 2004. GWM Radio has regretably ceased trading.

7: Dec 2006. Additional material regarding Yagi antennas following on from 'Evolution of the Beam Antenna'.

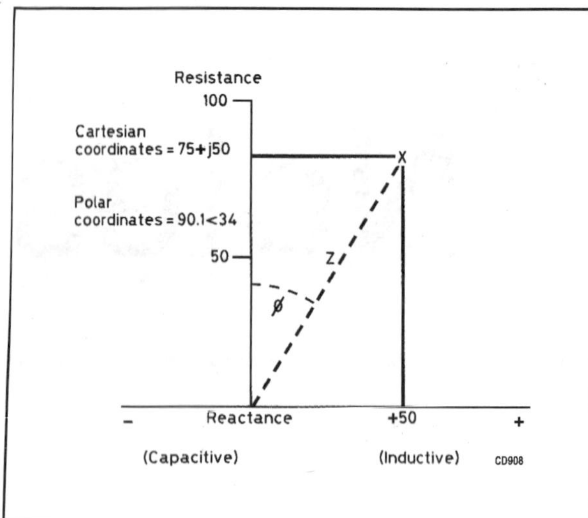


Figure T1: The relationship between the more familiar R ± j Cartesian coordinates and Polar coordinates.

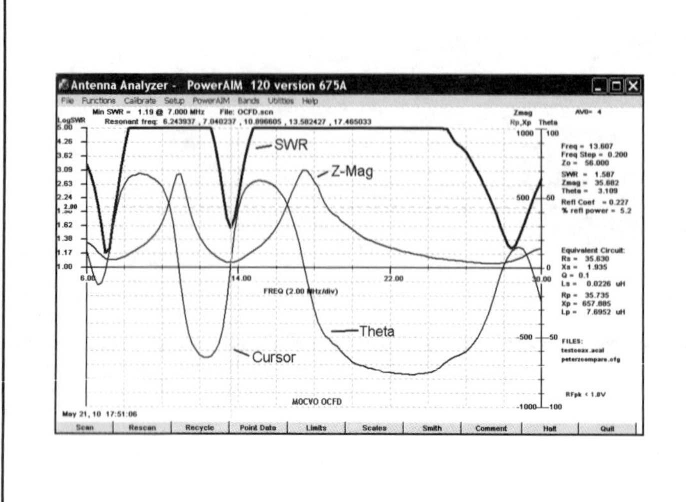


Figure T2: Example display page of the AIM4170 being used to plot the characteristics of a commercial multiband antenna. The SWR plot dips at points of resonance and the theta plot crosses the zero degree line at resonance. The remaining graph plots Z magnitude at these resonant points. A mouse controlled cursor can be placed over any measurement of interest which in turn displays data, such as equivalent R ±j (Rs and Xs).

8: Oct 2007. The AIM4170 is an antenna analyser used to plot complex impedance in terms of magnitude and phase where impedance is described as the vector sum of resistance and reactance as shown in **Figure T1**. This instrument can perform these measurements at each frequency of interest in the range 0.1MHz to 170MHz. A program on a connected PC can be used to calculate SWR, Rho, R ±j and other parameters vs frequency on a graph or a Smith Chart. The original display is in colour and **Figure T2** is provided to give an example of the parameter characteristics in monochrome.

9: April 2010. Peter Martinez, G3PLX, had this to say about my comments on small transmitting loop antennas. "If I read your column correctly, you are puzzled by an apparent contradiction between (a) the statement that the current round a small loop is fairly constant and (b) the presence of high voltages across the capacitor. You seemed to be trying to find ways to make one of these conditions vanish in order to resolve the contradiction.

"The answer lies in Ohm's Law. Not the V = IR version but V = I*(2*pi*F*L). That is, the voltage is the product of the current and the reactance of the loop inductance. From your Fig 2 the loop reactance is 335 ohms and the circulating current is 10 amps. The product of these two is 3.3kV. This will be the voltage across the capacitor. Since the loop is small, this analysis is sufficient. I think you may have been trying to think of the loop in the same terms as much larger antennas with standing wave patterns, which always have currents *or* voltages but not both!"

Brian Austin, G0GSF, makes very similar comments. Additionally he says: "Your *EZNEC* model using two closely-spaced wires to model a capacitor is in fact a short, open-circuit transmission line which is, of course, capacitive at its input terminals. So it's valid to tune the loop this way though it may present breakdown issues at high(ish) powers but you can ignore them in this theoretical case. Since the far end of that line is an open circuit the current has to be zero there (and, equally, the voltage must be a maximum), but both will change along the length of the line in an approximately linear manner. Thus the current distribution is as shown by *EZNEC*."

# Index

# E



# F



# G



# H



# I



# K



# L



# M



# N